MACHINE TOOL PRACTICES

MACHINE TOOL PRACTICES

SECOND EDITION

Richard R. Kibbe
Director, RRK General Machining and Manufacturing
Oxnard, California

John E. Neely
Instructor, Machine Technology
Lane Community College, Eugene, Oregon

CONTRIBUTING CO-AUTHORS

Roland O. Meyer
Lane Community College

Warren T. White

175 YEARS OF PUBLISHING
1807 1982

John Wiley & Sons
New York ☐ Chichester ☐ Brisbane ☐ Toronto ☐ Singapore

Cover design: Ann Clementino
Editors: Judy Green and Al Lesure
Manuscript editor: Dex Ott
Manuscript supervisor: Rosemary Wellner
Production supervisor: Linda Sadovnick
Text design: Laura C. Ierardi

Library of Congress Cataloging in Publication Data:

Kibbe, Richard R.
  Machine tool practices.

  Previous ed. cataloged under title:
  Includes index.
  1. Machine-tools.   2. Machine-shop practice.
I. Neely, John, 1920–   II. Title.
TJ1185.K458 1982   621.9′02   81-7606
ISBN 0-471-05788-6   AACR2

Printed in the United States of America

10 9 8 7 6 5 4

PREFACE

This book is intended for students training to become machinists, either through apprenticeship training, vocational schools, or community college programs. The content deals with topics usually presented in a combined lecture and laboratory program. To better meet the needs of users of this book, the authors made a careful study of the entire text; they consulted with many users of the first edition to tailor the second edition more closely to the needs of students and instructors and industry training standards.

As in the first edition, each section begins with an overview introductory component, followed by instructional units with clearly stated objectives. Many units are designed around specific projects that provide much of the performance experience for the student. Also, the structure of the text allows an instructor to easily insert projects more applicable to his or her specific program.

Self-tests have been retained with answers to questions appearing in the appendixes. Post-test questions for instructional units appear in the Instructor's Manual.

Material in the Instructor's Manual may be freely reproduced. A new Student Workbook is also available, containing worksheets with projects and exercises, alternative projects, and a number of tables for student use.

Additions to the second edition include:

1. A unit on fits, tolerances, and geometric dimensions.
2. Basic coverage on reading drawings.
3. Additional tables in the appendixes.
4. A section on vertical milling machines that reflects a more logical order of topic development.
5. Informational material on advanced machining processes.
6. A glossary of terms pertaining to the entire text.

Richard R. Kibbe
John E. Neely
Roland O. Meyer
Warren T. White

ACKNOWLEDGMENTS

The authors wish to thank the following for their contributions to this textbook.

American Society for Metals, Metals Park, Ohio
American Society of Mechanical Engineers, New York, New York
California State University at Fresno, Department of Industrial Arts and Technology, Fresno, California
DeAnza College, Engineering and Technology, Cupertino, California
Epsilon Pi Tau Fraternity, Alpha Lambda Chapter, California State University at Fresno, Fresno, California
Foothill College District, Office of Technical Education, Individualized Machinist's Curriculum Project, Los Altos Hills, California
Lane Community College, Mechanics Department, Eugene, Oregon
National Machine Tool Builders Association, McLean, Virginia
National Screw Machine Products Association, Cleveland, Ohio
North County Technical School, St. Louis County, Missouri
Yuba College, Applied Arts Department, Marysville, California

Our special thanks go to the following firms and their employees with whom we corresponded and visited and who supplied us with invaluable technical information and illustrations.

Accurate Diamond Tool Corporation, Hackensack, New Jersey
Aloris Tool Company, Inc., Clifton, New Jersey
American Chain & Cable Company, Inc., Wilson Instrument Division, Bridgeport, Connecticut
American Iron & Steel Institute, Washington, D.C.
American SIP Corporation, Elmsford, New York
Ameropean Industries, Inc., Hamden, Connecticut
Ames Research Center, National Aeronautics and Space Administration (NASA), Mountain View, California
Barber-Colman Company, Rockford, Illinois
Barnes Drill Company, Rockford, Illinois
Barret Centrifugals, Worcester, Massachusetts
Bay State Abrasives, Division of Dresser Industries, Westborough, Massachusetts
Bendix Corporation, South Bend, Indiana
Bethlehem Steel Corporation, Bethlehem, Pennsylvania
Boyer-Schultz Corporation, Broadview, Illinois
Bridgeport Milling Machine Division, Textron, Inc., Bridgeport, Connecticut
Brown & Sharpe Manufacturing Company, North Kingstown, Rhode Island
Bryant Grinder Corporation, Springfield, Vermont
Buck Tool, Kalamazoo, Michigan
The Carborundum Company, Niagara Falls, New York
Cincinnati Incorporated, Cincinnati, Ohio
Cincinnati Milacron, Inc., Cincinnati, Ohio

Clausing Corp., Kalamazoo, Michigan
Cleveland Twist Drill Company, Cleveland, Ohio
Cone-Blanchard Machine Company, Windsor, Vermont
Dake Corporation Grand Haven, Michigan
Desmond-Stephan Manufacturing Company, Urbana, Ohio
Diamond Abrasive Corporation, New York, New York
DoAll Company, Des Plaines, Illinois
Dover Publications Inc., New York, New York
The du Mont Corporation, Greenfield, Massachusetts
El-Jay Inc., Eugene, Oregon
Elm Systems, Inc., Arlington Heights, Illinois
Enco Manufacturing Company, Chicago, Illinois
Engis Corporation, Morton Grove, Illinois
Ex-Cell-O Corporation, Troy, Michigan
Exolon Company, Tonawanda, New York
Federal Products Corporation, Providence, Rhode Island
Fellows Corporation, Springfield, Vermont
Floturn, Inc., Division of Lodge & Shipley Company, Cincinnati, Ohio
Gaertner Scientific Corporation, Chicago, Illinois
General Electric Company, Detriot, Michigan, and Specialty Materials Department, Worthington, Ohio
Geometric Tool, New Haven, Connecticut
Giddings & Lewis, Fond Du Lac, Wisconsin
Gleason Works, Rochester, New York
Great Lakes Screw, Chicago, Illinois
Hammond Machinery Builders, Kalamazoo, Michigan
Hardinge Brothers, Inc., Elmira, New York
Harig Products, Inc., Elgin, Illinois
Heald Machine Division, Cincinnati Milacron Company, Worcester, Massachusetts
Hewlett-Packard Company, Palo Alto and Santa Clara, California
Hitachi Magna-Lock Corporation, Big Rapids, Michigan
Illinois/Eclipse, Division of Illinois Tool Works, Inc., Chicago, Illinois
Industrial Plastics Products, Inc., Forest Grove, Oregon
Industrial Press, New York, New York
Ingersoll Milling Machine Company, Rockford, Illinois
Japax Inc., Kawasaki City, Japan
Jarvis Products Corporation, Middletown, Connecticut
K & M Tool, Inc., Eugene, Oregon
Kasto-Racine, Inc., Monroeville, Pennsylvania
Kennametal, Latrobe, Pennsylvania
Landis Tool Company, Division of Litton Industries, Waynesboro, Pennsylvania
Lapmaster Division, Crane Packing Company, Morton Grove, Illinois
LeBlond, Inc., Cincinnati, Ohio
Louis Levin & Son, Inc., Culver City, California
Lodge & Shipley Company, Cincinnati, Ohio
M & M Tool Manufacturing Company, Dayton, Ohio
Madison Industries, Division of Amtel, Inc., Providence, Rhode Island
Mahr Gage Company, New York, New York
Mattison Machine Works, Rockford, Illinois
Megadiamond Industries, New York, New York
Minnesota Mining and Manufacturing Company (3M), St. Paul, Minnesota
The MIT Press, Cambridge, Massachusetts
Monarch Machine Tool Company, Sidney, Ohio

Moog, Inc., Hydra Point Division, Buffalo, New York
Moore Special Tool Company, Bridgeport, Connecticut
MTI Corporation, New York, New York
National Broach & Machine Division, Lear Siegler, Inc., Detroit, Michigan
National Twist Drill & Tool Division, Lear Siegler, Inc., Rochester, Michigan
Newcomer Products, Inc., Latrobe, Pennsylvania
Norton Company, Worcester, Massachusetts
PMC Industries, Wickliffe, Ohio
Pratt & Whitney Machine Tool Division of The Colt Industries Operating Corporation, West Hartford, Connecticut
Precision Diamond Tool Company, Elgin, Illinois
Ralmike's Tool-A-Rama, South Plainfield, New Jersey
Rank Scherr-Tumico Inc., Des Plaines, Illinois
Rockford Machine Tool Company, Rockford, Illinois
Sipco Machine Company, Marion, Massachusetts
Harry M. Smith & Associates, Santa Clara, California
Snap-On Tools Corporation, Kenosha, Wisconsin
Southwestern Industries, Inc., Los Angeles, California
Speedfam Corporation, Des Plaines, Illinois
Standard Gage Company, Poughkeepsie, New York
L. S. Starret Company, Athol, Massachusetts
Sunnen Products Company, St. Louis, Missouri
Superior Electric Company, Bristol, Connecticut
Surface Finishes, Inc., Addision, Illinois
Syclone Products, Inc., Ranchita, California
Taft-Pierce Manufacturing Company, Woonsocket, Rhode Island
Taper Micrometer Corporation, Worcester, Massachusetts
Tinius Olsen Testing Machine Company, Inc., Willow Grove, Pennsylvania
TRW Inc., Greenfield, Massachusetts, Plymouth, Michigan, Buffalo, New York
Ultramatic Equipment Company, Addison, Illinois
Unison Corporation, Madison Heights, Michigan
Waldes Kohinoor, Inc., Long Island City, New York
Walton Company, Hartford, Connecticut
Warner & Swasey Company, Cleveland, Ohio, and King of Prussia, Pennsylvania
Weldon Tool Company, Cleveland, Ohio
Whitnon Spindle Division, Mite Corporation, Farmington, Connecticut
Wilton Tool Division, Wilton Corporation, Des Plaines, Illinois

The authors would also like to thank the following for their contributions to the second edition.

Mr. Michael J. Buckland, State Technical Institute; Mr. Alan Stephan, Mid-Florida Technical Institute; Mr. John Waters, Orange Coast College; Mr. A. Douglas Morley, Honolulu Community College; Mr. Ken DeGrasse, Otero Junior College; Mr. Gary Nelson, North Hennepin Technical College; Mr. Nino Valmassoi, Pasadena City College; Mr. Jerry L. Frana, Sauk Valley College; Mr. E. L. Brenner, Los Angeles Trade & Technical College.

R.R.K.
J.E.N.
R.O.M.
W.T.W

CONTENTS

CONTENTS

MACHINE TOOL PRACTICES

SECTION A
INTRODUCTION

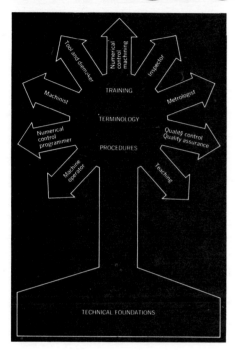

In our highly industrialized and mechanized society, we are indeed surrounded by many mechanical marvels. These devices are so common we tend to take them for granted. Technical advances have come so fast in recent years that in less than a century humankind has learned to fly, explored the deepest oceans, and begun the exploration of space.

Such technical achievements would not have been possible had human beings not learned to extract metals from the planet on which they live and then shape these metals into useful products. Furthermore, metalworking is essential to the extraction or creation of many other nonmetallic materials that are equally important to the building of technical hardware. Although metalworking has been done since ancient times, only in quite recent history has it developed into a scientifically based technology.

The most important aspect of metalworking is that of shaping metals into useful products. Many methods have been and are used today to shape metals. However, few of these methods produce the wide variety of items as do the processes of **machining.** In fact, machining is probably the most important method by which metals and other materials are transformed into the many products enjoyed by so many. Machining technology is at the very base of our way of life in an industrialized society.

Machining is basically a process of shaping materials using a variety of cutting tools. The material is shaved away in small pieces or chips uncovering the final size and shape of the workpiece. This may be done by direct contact of a cutting tool material that is harder than the workpiece material. Machining may be accomplished by other means as well. Large pieces may be removed by various sawing processes. Material may also be removed by using electric spark, electrochemical, or ultrasonic sound processes. However, most machining is accomplished by direct contact of a cutting tool. These cutting tools are frequently motor driven. Thus, machining is done with a motor driven tool or **machine tool.** There are many types of machine tools. and they are generally grouped together in a **machine shop.**

Machine shops vary greatly in size and types of work. A machine shop may have many types of machine tools and produce many different products. Almost every mechanical marvel that is enjoyed today began as a model built in a machine shop. In this book, you will learn about many machine tools, and you will see the great potential of these tools for making the hardware of technology.

PART 1 MACHINING AND YOU

You might be asking yourself if a career as a machinist, machine operator, or other related trade might be for you. Whether or not a career in machining is for you will of course depend on your personal goals. Machining is probably one of the most interesting of all the skilled trades; furthermore, it is essential to the support of a modern industrial technology. However, like most technologies, machining has become a highly specialized business. It can be safely said that the **general machinist** will always be in demand for new development and prototype building. On the other hand, production manufacturing makes extensive use of **machine operators** who have specialized skills in operating sophisticated machine tools. These individuals must have a thorough knowledge of tooling and measurement, but need not have the much broader range of skills and knowledge required of the general machinist.

If your skills and interest in machining develop keenly, the field of **tool and die making** is open to you. Tool and die makers are individuals with a broad and usually extensive background in general machining and who have developed a talent for detail and measurement. The tool and die maker often commands excellent pay for his abilities, and tool makers are found behind the scenes in almost every manufacturing business.

Beyond the realms of the machine operator, general machinist and tool maker are several other professions closely related to machining. Today, much machining is done by machine tools operated by automatic control systems and computers. Machine control by **direct numerical control (D N/C)** and by **computer numerical control (C N/C)** is in widespread use. Although these advances in machining technology are indeed marvelous, they require highly skilled technicians behind the scenes to make these systems function efficiently. These individuals include **programmers, jig and fixture designers,** and **cutting tool engineers,** to name a few. Many individuals in these professional positions have a broad background in fundamentals of machine tools and machining practices, and by supplementing their practical machine shop training and education they have branched off into these related areas. These professional careers are available to you as well, and as you progress through your machine shop training you will find the knowledge you gain to be invaluable no matter what area of machining technology you might choose to follow in your career. The purpose of this textbook is to both introduce and broaden your knowledge of this fascinating subject and help you in achieving your desired goals.

PART 2 TECHNICAL FOUNDATIONS

If you are like most people when presented with something new and interesting, you probably are anxious to begin operating machine tools and machining parts. Before you can begin, however, it is necessary you have some basic instruction so you can operate an expensive and precision machine tool safely without injury to yourself or damage to the equipment. You must also be familiar with the hardware that provides adjustment and

maintenance to the machine and you must be able to read and interpret a drawing of the part you will be making so your efforts will turn out satisfactorily. These **technical foundations** of **safety, mechanical hardware,** and **reading drawings** comprise the introductory section of this book. In the section immediately following you will study the selection and use of hand tools that supplement all machine tool operations, adjustment, and main-

tenance. All of this information is extremely important and even though you are anxious to begin operating the machine, it will be of great benefit to you to take the time to study the technical foundations discussed in the following pages.

PART 3 SHOP SAFETY

Safety is not often thought about as you proceed through your daily tasks. Often you expose yourself to needless risk because you have experienced no harmful effects in the past. Unsafe habits become almost automatic. You may drive your automobile without wearing a seat belt. You know this to be unsafe, but you have done it before and so far no harm has resulted. None of us really likes to think about the possible consequences of an unsafe act. However, safety can and does have an important effect on anyone who makes a living in a potentially dangerous environment such as a machine shop. An accident can reduce or end your career as a machinist. You may spend several years learning the trade and more years gaining experience. Experience is a particularly valuable asset. It can only be gained through time spent on the job. This becomes economically valuable to you and to your employer. Years spent in training and gaining experience can be wasted in an instant if you should have an accident, not to mention a possible permanent physical handicap for you and hardship on your family. Safety is an attitude that should extend far beyond the machine shop and into every facet of your life. You must constantly think about safety in everything you do.

PERSONAL SAFETY

Eye Protection
Eye protection is a primary safety consideration around the machine shop. Machine tools produce metal chips, and there is always a possibility that these may be ejected from a machine at high velocity. Sometimes they can fly many feet. Furthermore, most cutting tools are made from hard materials. They can occasionally break or shatter from the stress applied to them during a cut. The result can be more flying metal particles.

Eye protection must be worn **at all times** in the machine shop. There are several types of eye protection available. Plain safety glasses are all that are required in most shops. These have shatterproof lenses that may be changed if they become scratched. The lenses have a high resistance to impact. Common types include fixed bow safety glasses (Figure 1) and the flexible bow safety

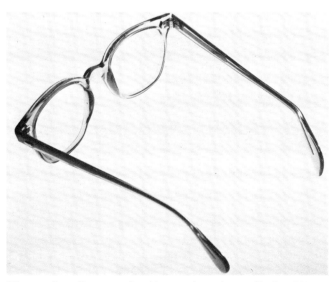

Figure 1. Common fixed bow safety glasses (Epsilon Pi Tau Fraternity, CSU, Fresno).

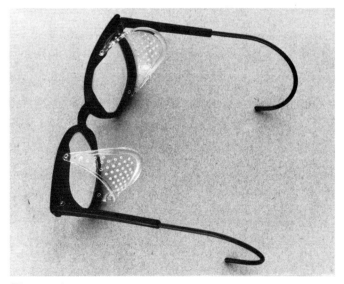

Figure 2. Perforated side shield safety glasses (Epsilon Pi Tau Fraternity, CSU, Fresno).

Figure 3. Safety face shield.

glasses. The flexible bow may be adjusted to the most comfortable position for the wearer.

Side shield safety glasses must be worn around any grinding operation. The side shield protects the side of the eye from flying particles. Side shield safety glasses may be of the solid or perforated type (Figure 2). The perforated side shield fits closer to the eye. Bows may wrap around the ear. This prevents the safety glasses from falling off.

If you wear prescription glasses, you may want to cover them with a safety goggle. The full face shield may also be used (Figure 3). Prescription glasses can be made as safety glasses. In industry, prescription safety glasses are sometimes provided free to employees.

Foot Protection
Generally, the machine shop does not present too great a hazard to the feet. However, there is always a possibility that you could drop something on your foot. A safety shoe is available. This will have a steel toe shield designed to resist impacts. Some safety shoes also have an instep guard. Shoes must be worn at all times in the machine shop. A solid leather shoe is recommended. Tennis shoes and sandals should not be worn. You must never even enter a machine shop with bare feet. **Remember that the floor is often covered with razor sharp metal chips.**

Ear Protection
The instructional machine shop usually does not present a noise problem. However, an industrial machine shop may be adjacent to a fabrication or punch press facility. New safety regulations are quite strict regarding exposure to noise. Several types of sound suppressors and noise reducing ear plugs may be worn. Excess noise can cause a permanent hearing loss. Usually this occurs over a period of time, depending on the intensity of the exposure. Noise is considered an industrial hazard if it is continuously above 85 *decibels,* the units used in mea-

suring sound waves. If it is over 115 decibels for short periods of time, ear protection must be worn (Figure 4). Ear muffs or plugs should be used wherever high intensity noise occurs. A considerate workman will not create excessive noise when it is not necessary. Table 1 shows the decibel level of various sounds; sudden sharp or high intensity noises are the most harmful to your eardrums.

Grinding Dust and Hazardous Fumes
Grinding dust is produced by abrasive wheels and consists of extremely fine metal particles and abrasive wheel particles. These should not be inhaled. In the machine shop, most grinding machines have a vacuum dust collector (Figure 5). Grinding may be done with coolants that aid in dust control. A machinist may be involved in portable grinding operations. This is common in such industries as shipbuilding. You should wear an approved respirator if you are exposed to grinding dust. Change the respirator filter at regular intervals. Grinding dust can present a great danger to health. Examples include the dust of such metals as beryllium, or the presence of radioactivity in nuclear systems. In these situations, the spread of grinding dust must be carefully controlled.

Some metals such as zinc give off toxic fumes when heated above their boiling point. Some of these fumes when inhaled cause temporary sickness, but other fumes can be severe or even fatal. The fumes of mercury and lead are especially dangerous, as their effect is cumulative in your body and can cause irreversible damage. Cadmium and beryllium compounds are also very poisonous. Therefore, when welding, burning, or heat treating metals, adequate ventilation is an absolute necessity. This is also true when parts are being carburized with compounds containing potassium cyanide. These *cyanogen compounds* are deadly poisonous and every precaution should be taken when using them. Kasenite, a trade name for a carburizing compound that is not toxic, is often found in school shops and in machine shops. Uranium salts are toxic and all radioactive materials are extremely dangerous.

Clothing, Hair, and Jewelry
Wear a short sleeve shirt or roll up long sleeves above the elbow. Keep your shirt tucked in and remove your necktie. It is recommended that you wear a shop apron. If you do, keep it tied behind you. If apron strings become entangled in the machine, you may be reeled in as well. A shop coat may be worn as long as you roll up long sleeves. Do not wear fuzzy sweaters around machine tools.

If you have long hair, keep it secured properly. In industry, you may be required to wear a hair net so that your hair cannot become entangled in a moving machine. The result of this can be disastrous (Figure 6).

Remove your wristwatch and rings before operat-

Figure 4. Sound suppressors are designed to protect the ears from damage caused by loud noises.

Table 1
The Decibel Level of Various Sounds

130 — Painful sounds: jet engine on ground
120 — Airplane on ground: Reciprocating engine
110 — Boiler factory
      — Pneumatic riveter
100 —
      — Maximum street noise
      — Roaring lion
90 —
      — Loud shout
80 — Diesel truck
      — Piano practice
      — Average city street
70 —
      — Dog barking
      — Average conversation
60 —
      — Average city office
50 —
      — Average city residence
40 — One typewriter
      — Average country residence
30 — Turning page of newspaper
      — Purring cat
20 —
      — Rustle of leaves in breeze
      — Human heartbeat
10 —
 0 — Faintest audible sound

Figure 5. Vacuum dust collector on grinders (California State University at Fresno).

Figure 6. Long hair may be caught and reeled into the machine (Courtesy of John Allan, Jr.).

Figure 7. Use a brush to clear chips (Courtesy of California Community Colleges IMC Project).

6

ing any machine tool. These can cause serious injury if they should be caught in a moving machine part.

Hand Protection

There is really no device that will totally protect your hands from injury. Next to your eyes, your hands are the most important tools that you have. It is up to you to keep them out of danger. Use a brush to remove chips from a machine (Figure 7). Do not use your hands. Chips are not only razor sharp, they are often extremely hot. Resist the temptation to grab chips as they come from a cut. Long chips are extremely dangerous. These can often be eliminated by properly sharpening your cutting tools. Chips should *not* be removed with a rag. The metal particles become imbedded in the cloth and they may cut you. Furthermore, the rag may be caught in a moving machine. Gloves must not be worn around most machine tools, although they are acceptable when working with a band saw blade. If a glove should be caught in a moving part, it will be pulled in, along with the hand inside it.

Various cutting oils, coolants, and solvents may affect your skin. The result may be a rash or possible infection. Avoid direct contact with these products as much as possible and wash your hands as soon as possible after contact.

Lifting

Improper lifting can result in a permanent back injury that can limit or even end your career. Back injury can be avoided if you lift properly at all times. If you must lift a large or heavy object, get some help or make use of a hoist or forklift. Don't try to be a ''superman'' and lift something that you know is too heavy. It is not worth the risk.

Objects within your lifting capability can be lifted safely by the following procedure (Figures 8a and 8b):

1. Keep your back straight.
2. Squat down, bending your knees.
3. Lift smoothly using the muscles in your legs to do the work. Keep your back straight. Bending over the load puts an excessive stress on your spine.
4. Position the load so that it is comfortable to carry. Watch where you are walking when carrying a load.
5. If you are placing the load back to floor level, lower it in the same manner you picked it up.

Scuffling and Horseplay

The machine shop is no place for scuffling and horseplay. This activity can result in a serious injury to you, a fellow student, or worker. Practical joking is also very hazardous. What might appear to be a comical situation to you could result in a disastrous accident to someone else. In industry, horseplay and practical joking are often grounds for dismissal of an employee.

Injuries

If you should be injured, report it immediately to your instructor.

Figure 8a. The wrong way to lift, placing excessive strain on the back (Lane Community College).

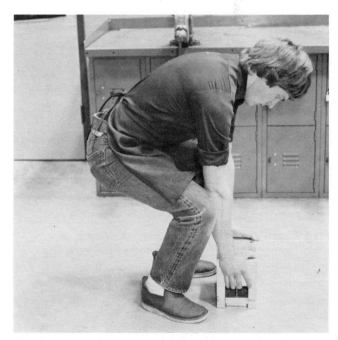

Figure 8b. The right way to lift with knees bent, using leg muscle to do the work (Lane Community College).

IDENTIFYING SHOP HAZARDS

A machine shop is not so much a dangerous place as a potentially dangerous place. One of the best ways to be safe is to be able to identify shop hazards before they involve you in an accident. By being aware of potential danger, you can better make safety part of your work in the machine shop.

Compressed Air

Most machine shops have compressed air. This is needed to operate certain machine tools. Often flexible air hoses are hanging about the shop. Few people realize the large amount of energy that can be stored in a compressed gas such as air. When this energy is released, extreme danger may be present. You may be tempted to blow chips from a machine tool using compressed air. This is not good practice. The air will propel metal particles at high velocity. They can injure you or someone on the other side of the shop. Use a brush to clean chips from the machine. Do not blow compressed air on your clothing or skin. The air can be dirty and the force can implant dirt and germs into your skin. Air can be a hazard to ears as well. An eardrum can be ruptured.

Should an air hose break, or the nozzle on the end come unscrewed, the hose will whip wildly. This can result in an injury if you happen to be standing nearby. When an air hose is not in use, it is good practice to shut off the supply valve. The air trapped in the hose should be vented. When removing an air hose from its supply valve, be sure that the supply is turned off and the hose has been vented. Removing a charged air hose will result in a sudden venting of air. This can surprise you and an accident might result.

Housekeeping

Keep floor and aisles clear of stock and tools. This will insure that all exits are clear if the building should have to be evacuated. Material on the floor, especially round bars, can cause falls. Clean oils or coolants that may spill on the floor. Several preparations designed to absorb oil are available. These may be used from time to time in the shop. Keep oily rags in an approved safety can (Figure 9). This will prevent possible fire from spontaneous combustion.

Fire Extinguishers

It is an important safety consideration to know the correct fire extinguisher to use for a particular fire. For example, if you should use a water-based extinguisher on an electrical fire, you could receive a severe or fatal electrical shock. Fires are classed according to types as given in Table 2.

There are four basic types of fire extinguishers used other than the use of tap water.

Figure 9. Store oil soaked rags in an approved safety can (De Anza College).

1. The dry chemical type is effective on Classes B and C fires.
2. The pressurized water and loaded stream types are safe only on Class A fires. This type may actually spread an oil or gasoline fire.
3. The dry chemical multi-purpose extinguisher may be safely used on Classes A, B, and C fires.
4. Pressurized carbon dioxide (CO_2) can be used on Classes B and C fires.

You should always make yourself aware of the locations of fire extinguishers in your working area. Take time to look at them closely and note their types and capabilities. This way, if there should ever be an oil-based or electrical fire in your area, you will know how to safely put it out.

Electrical

Electricity is another potential danger in a machine shop. Your exposure to electrical hazard will be minimal unless you become involved with machine maintenance. A machinist is mainly concerned with the on and off switch on a machine tool. However, if your are adjusting the machine or accomplishing maintenance, you should

Table 2
Types of Extinguishers Used on the Classes of Fire. (Brodhead-Garrett Company)

	Pressurized Water	Loaded Stream	CO_2	Regular Dry Chemical	All Use Dry Chemical
CLASS A FIRES Paper, wood, cloth, etc. Where quenching by water or insulating by general purpose dry chemical is effective.	Yes Excellent	Yes Excellent	Small surface fires only	Small surface fires only	Yes Excellent Forms smothering film, prevents reflash
CLASS B FIRES Burning liquids (Gasoline, oils, cooking fats, etc.) where smothering action is required.	No Water will spread fire	Yes Has limited capability	Yes Carbon Dioxide has no residual effects on food or equipment	Yes Excellent Chemical Smothers fire	Yes Excellent Smothers fire prevents reflash
CLASS C FIRES Fire in live electrical equipment (Motors, switches, appliances, etc.) Where a non-conductive extinguishing agent is required.	No Water is a conductor of electricity	No Water is a conductor of electricity	Yes Excellent CO_2 is a non-conductor leaves no residue	Yes Excellent Non-conducting smothering film. Screens operator from heat	Yes Excellent Non-conducting smothering film. Screens operator from heat

unplug it from the electrical service. If it is permanently wired, the circuit breaker may be switched off and tagged with an appropriate warning. In industry, this procedure often means that the operator must sign a clearance stating that electrical service has been secured. Service cannot be restored until the operator signs a restoration order. Normally you will not disconnect the electrical service for routine adjustments such as changing speeds. However, when a speed change involves a belt change, you must insure that no other person is likely to turn on the machine while your hands are in contact with belts and pulleys.

Carrying Objects
Carry long stock in the vertical position. Be careful of light fixtures and ceilings. A better way is to have someone carry each end of a long piece of material. Do not carry sharp tools in your pockets. They can injure you or someone else.

MACHINE HAZARDS
There are many machine hazards. Each section of this book will discuss the specific dangers applicable to that type of machine tool. Remember that a machine has no intelligence of its own. It cannot distinguish between cutting metal and cutting fingers. Do not think that you are strong enough to stop a machine should you become tangled in moving parts. You are not. When operating a machine, think about what you are going to do before

you do it. Go over a safety checklist.

1. Do I know how to operate this machine?
2. What are the potential hazards involved?
3. Are all guards in place?
4. Are my procedures safe?
5. Am I doing something that I probably should not do?
6. Have I made all the proper adjustments and tightened all locking bolts and clamps?
7. Is the workpiece secured properly?
8. Do I have proper safety equipment?
9. Do I know where the stop switch is?
10. Do I think about safety in everything that I do?

INDUSTRIAL SAFETY AND FEDERAL LAW
In 1970, Congress passed the **Williams-Steiger Occupational Safety and Health Act.** This act took effect on April 28, 1971. The purpose and policy of the act are "to assure so far as possible every working man and woman in the Nation safe and healthful working conditions and to preserve our human resources."

The **Occupational Safety and Health Act** is commonly known as **OSHA.** Prior to its passage, industrial safety was the individual responsibility of each state. The establishment of OSHA added a degree of standardization to industrial safety throughout the nation. OSHA encourages states to assume full responsibility in admin-

istration and enforcement of federal occupational safety and health regulations.

Duties of Employers and Employees
Each employer under OSHA has the general duty to furnish employment and places of employment free from recognized hazards causing or likely to cause death or serious physical harm. The employer has the specific duty of complying with safety and health standards as defined under OSHA. Each employee has the duty to comply with safety and health standards and all rules and regulations established by OSHA.

Occupational Safety and Health Standards
Job safety and health standards consist of rules for avoiding hazards that have been proven by research and experience to be harmful to personal safety and health. These rules may apply to all employees as in the case of fire protection standards. Many standards apply only to workers engaged in specific types of work. A typical standard states that aisles and passageways shall be kept clear and in good repair, with no obstruction across or in aisles that could create a hazard.

Complaints of Violations
Any employee who believes that a violation of job safety or health standard exists may request an inspection by sending a signed written notice to OSHA. This includes anything that threatens physical harm or represents an imminent danger. A copy must also be provided to the employer. However, the name of the person complaining need not be revealed to the employer.

Enforcement of OSHA Standards
OSHA inspectors may enter a plant or school at any rea-sonable time and conduct an inspection. They are not permitted to give prior notice for this. They may question any employer, owner, operator, agent, or employee in regard to any safety violation. The employer and a representative of the employees have the right to accompany the inspector during the inspection.

If a violation is discovered, a written citation is issued to the employer. A reasonable time is permitted to correct the condition. The citation must be posted at or near the place of the violation. If, after a reasonable time, the condition has not been corrected, a fine may be imposed on the employer. If the employer has made an attempt to correct the unsafe condition but has exceeded the time limit, a hearing may be held to determine progress.

Penalties
Willful or repeated violations may incur penalties up to $10,000. Citations issued for serious violations incur mandatory penalties of $1,000. A serious violation where extreme danger exists may be penalized up to $1,000 for each day the violation exists.

OSHA Education and Training Programs
The Occupational Safety and Health Act provides for programs to be conducted by the Department of Labor. These programs provide for education and training of employers and employees in recognizing, avoiding, and preventing unsafe and unhealthful working conditions. The act also provides for training an adequate supply of qualified personnel to carry out OSHA's purpose.

SELF-TEST

1. What is the primary piece of safety equipment in the machine shop?
2. What can you do if you wear prescription glasses?
3. Describe proper dress for the machine shop.
4. What can be done to control grinding dust?
5. What hazards exist from coolants, oils, and solvents?
6. Describe proper lifting procedure.
7. Describe at least two compressed air hazards.
8. Describe good housekeeping procedures.
9. How should long pieces of material be carried?
10. List at least five points from the safety checklist for a machine tool.

PART 4 MECHANICAL HARDWARE

Many precision machined products produced in the machine shop would be useless until assembled into a machine, tool, or other mechanism. This assembly requires many types of fasteners and other mechanical hardware. In this unit, you will be introduced to many of these important hardware items.

THREADS

The **thread** is an extremely important mechanical device. It derives its usefulness from the inclined plane, one of the six simple machines. Almost every mechanical device is assembled with threaded fasteners. A thread is a helical groove that is formed on the outside or inside diameter of a cylinder (Figure 10). These helical grooves take several forms. Furthermore, they have specific and even spacing. One of the fundamental tasks of a machinist is to produce both external and internal threads using several machine tools and hand tools. The majority of threads appear on **threaded fasteners.** These include many types of **bolts, screws,** and **nuts.** However, threads are used for a number of other applications aside from fasteners. These include threads for adjustment purposes, measuring tool applications, and the transmission of power. A close relative to the thread, the helical auger, is used to transport material.

THREAD FORMS

There are a number of thread forms. In later units, you will examine these in detail, and you will have the opportunity to make several of them on a machine tool. As far as the study of machined hardware is concerned, you will be most concerned with the **unified thread form** (Figure 11). The unified thread form was an outgrowth of the American National Standard form. In order to help standardize manufacturing in the United States, Canada, and Great Britain, the unified form was developed. Unified threads are a combination of the American National and the British Standard Whitworth forms. Unified threads are divided into the following series:

> UNC – National Coarse
> UNF – National Fine
> UNS – National Special

IDENTIFYING THREADED FASTENERS

Unified coarse and unified fine refers to the number of threads per inch of length on standard threaded fasteners. A specific diameter of bolt or nut will have a specific number of threads per inch of length. For example, a $\frac{1}{2}$ in. diameter Unified National Coarse bolt will have 13 threads per inch of length. This bolt will be identified by the following marking:

$$\frac{1}{2}\text{ in.}-13\text{ UNC}$$

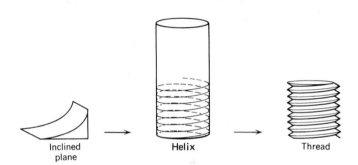

Figure 10. Thread helix.

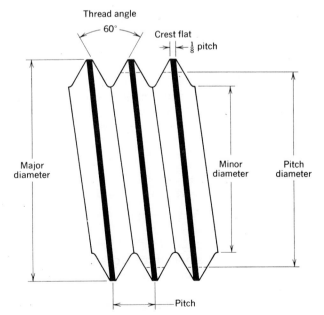

Figure 11. Unified thread form.

One half is the **major diameter** and **13** is the **number of threads per inch of length.** A $\frac{1}{2}$ in. diameter Unified National Fine bolt will be identified by the following marking:

$$\frac{1}{2} \text{ in.} - 20 \text{ UNF}$$

One-half is the major diameter and 20 is the number of threads per inch.

The Unified National Special Threads are identified in the same manner. A $\frac{1}{2}$ in. diameter UNS bolt may have 12, 14, or 18 threads per inch. These are less common than the standard UNC and UNF. However, you may see them in machining technology. There are many other series of threads used for different applications. Information and data on these can be found in machinist's handbooks. You might wonder why there needs to be a UNC and UNF series. This has to do with thread applications. For example, an adjusting screw might require a fine thread, while a common bolt may require only a coarse thread.

CLASSES OF THREAD FITS

The preceding information was necessary for an understanding of **thread fit classes.** Some thread applications can tolerate loose threads, while other applications require tight threads. For example, the head of your car's engine is held down by a threaded fastener called a stud bolt, or simply a stud. A stud is threaded on both ends. One end is threaded into the engine block. The other end receives a nut that bears against the cylinder head. When the head is removed, it is desirable to have the stud remain screwed into the engine block. This end requires a tighter thread fit than the end of the stud accepting the nut. If the fit on the nut end is too tight, the stud may unscrew as the nut is removed.

Unified **thread fits** are classified as **1A, 2A, 3A,** or **1B, 2B, 3B.** The **A symbol** indicates an **external** thread. The **B symbol** indicates an **internal** thread. This notation is added to the thread size and number of threads per inch. Let us consider the $\frac{1}{2}$ in. diameter bolt discussed previously. The complete notation reads:

$$\frac{1}{2} - 13 \text{ UNC 2A}$$

On this particular bolt, the class of fit is 2. The symbol A indicates an external thread. If the notation had read:

$$\frac{1}{2} - 13 \text{ UNC 3B}$$

this would indicate an internal thread with a class 3 fit. This could be a nut or a hole threaded with a tap. Taps are a very common tool for producing an internal thread.

Class 1A and 1B have the greatest manufacturing tolerance. They are used where ease of assembly is desired and a loose thread is not objectionable. Class 2 fits are used on the largest percentage of threaded fasteners. Class 3 fits will be tight when assembled. Each class of fit has a specific tolerance on major diameter and pitch diameter. These data may be found in machinist's handbooks and are required for the manufacture of threaded fasteners.

STANDARD SERIES OF THREADED FASTENERS

Threaded fasteners, including all common bolts and nuts, range from quite small machine screws through quite large bolts. Below a diameter of $\frac{1}{4}$ in. threaded fasteners are given a number. Common UNC and UNF series threaded fasteners are listed in the following tables.

UNC and UNF Threaded Fasteners

UNC		UNF	
Size	Threads/Inch	Size	Threads/Inch
		0	80
1	64	1	72
2	56	2	64
3	48	3	56
4	40	4	48
5	40	5	44
6	32	6	40
8	32	8	36
10	24	10	32
12	24	12	28

From here, the major diameter is expressed in fractional form.

$\frac{1}{4}$ in.	20	$\frac{1}{4}$ in.	28
$\frac{5}{16}$ in.	18	$\frac{5}{16}$ in.	24
$\frac{3}{8}$ in.	16	$\frac{3}{8}$ in.	24
$\frac{7}{16}$ in.	14	$\frac{7}{16}$ in.	20
$\frac{1}{2}$ in.	13	$\frac{1}{2}$ in.	20
$\frac{9}{16}$ in.	12	$\frac{9}{16}$ in.	18
$\frac{5}{8}$ in.	11	$\frac{5}{8}$ in.	18
$\frac{3}{4}$ in.	10	$\frac{3}{4}$ in.	16
$\frac{7}{8}$ in.	9	$\frac{7}{8}$ in.	14
1 inch	8	1 inch	12

Both series continue up to about 4 inches.

All of the sizes listed in the table are very common fasteners in all types of machines, automobiles, and other mechanisms. Your contact with these common sizes will be so frequent that you will soon begin to recall them from memory.

COMMON EXTERNALLY THREADED FASTENERS

Common mechanical hardware includes threaded fasteners such as bolts, screws, nuts, and thread inserts. All of these are used in a variety of ways to hold parts and assemblies together. Complex assemblies such as an airplane, ship, or automobile may have many thousands of fasteners taking many forms.

Bolts and Screws

A general definition of a **bolt** is an externally threaded fastener that is inserted through holes in an assembly. A bolt is tightened with a **nut** (Figure 12 right). A **screw** is an externally threaded fastener that is inserted into a threaded hole and tightened or released by turning the head (Figure 12 left). From these definitions, it is apparent that a bolt can become a screw or the reverse can be true. This depends on the application of the hardware. Bolts and screws are the most common of the threaded fasteners. These fasteners are used to assemble parts quickly and they make disassembly possible.

The strength of an assembly of parts depends to a large extent on the diameter of the screws or bolts used. In the case of screws, strength depends on the amount of **thread engagement.** Thread engagement is the distance that a screw extends into a threaded hole. The minimum thread engagement should be a distance equal to the diameter of the screw used; preferably it would be $1\frac{1}{2}$ times the screw diameter. Should an assembly fail, it is better that the screw break than to have the internal thread stripped from the hole. It is generally easier to remove a broken screw than to drill and tap for a larger screw size. With a screw engagement of $1\frac{1}{2}$ times its diameter, the screw will usually break rather than strip the thread in the hole.

Machine bolts (Figure 13) are made with **hexagonal** or **square** heads. These bolts are often used in the assembly of parts that do not require a precision bolt. The body diameter of machine bolts is usually slightly larger than the nominal or standard size of the bolt. Body diameter is the diameter of the unthreaded portion of a bolt below the head. A hole that is to accept a common bolt must be slightly larger than the body diameter. When machine bolts are purchased, nuts are frequently included. Common bolts are made with a class 2A unified thread and come in both UNC and UNF series. Sizes in hexagonal head machine bolts range from a $\frac{1}{4}$ in. diameter to a 4 in. diameter. Square head machine bolts are standard to $1\frac{1}{2}$ in. diameter.

Stud bolts (Figure 14) have threads on both ends. Stud bolts are used where one end is semipermanently screwed into a threaded hole. A good example of the use of stud bolts is an automobile engine. The stud bolts are tightly held in the cylinder block and easily changed

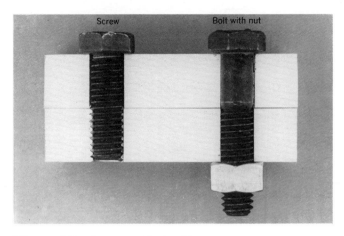

Figure 12. Screw and bolt with nut.

Figure 13. Square head bolt and hex head bolt. Square nut and hex nut.

Figure 14. Stud bolt.

nuts hold the cylinder heads in place. The end of the stud bolt screwed into the tapped hole has a class 3A thread, while the nut end is a class 2A thread.

Carriage bolts (Figure 15) are used to fasten wood and metal parts together. Carriage bolts have round heads with a square body under the head. The square part of the carriage bolt, when pulled into the wood, keeps the bolt from turning while the nut is being tightened. Carriage bolts are manufactured with class 2A coarse threads.

Machine screws are made with either coarse or fine thread and are used for general assembly work. The heads of most machine screws are slotted to be driven by screw drivers. Machine screws are available in many sizes and lengths (Figure 16). Several head styles are also available (Figure 17). Machine screw sizes fall into two categories. Fraction sizes range from diameters of $\frac{1}{4}$ to $\frac{3}{4}$ in. Below $\frac{1}{4}$ in. diameter, screws are identified by num-

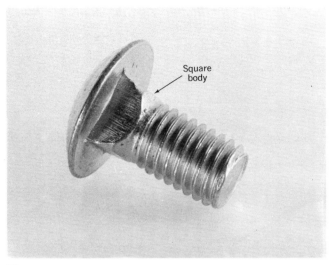

Figure 15.　Carriage bolt.

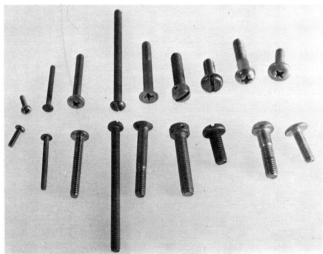

Figure 16.　Machine screws.

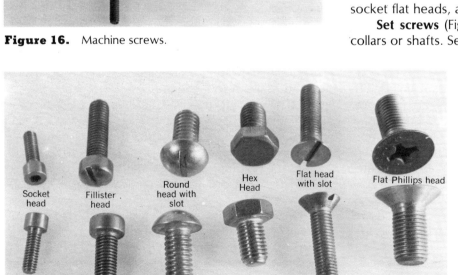

Figure 17.　(Opposite page) Machine screw head styles (Courtesy of Great Lakes Screw).

bers from 0 to 12. A number 0 machine screw has a diameter of .060 in. (sixty thousandths of an inch). For each number above zero add .013 in. to the diameter.

EXAMPLE

Find the diameter of a number 6 machine screw:

$$\# \ 0 \ \text{diameter} = .060 \ \text{in.}$$
$$\# \ 6 \ \text{diameter} = .060 \ \text{in.} + (6 \times .013 \ \text{in.})$$
$$= .060 \ \text{in.} + .078 \ \text{in.}$$
$$= .138 \ \text{in.}$$

Machine screws 2 in. long or shorter have threads extending all the way to the head. Longer machine screws have a $1\frac{3}{4}$ in. thread length.

Cap screws (Figure 18) are made with a variety of different head shapes and are used where precision bolts or screws are needed. Capscrews are manufactured with close tolerances and have a finished appearance. Capscrews are made with coarse, fine, or special threads. Capscrews with a 1 in. diameter have a class 3A thread. Those greater than a 1 in. diameter have a class 2A thread. The strength of screws depends mainly on the kind of material used to make the screw. Different screw materials are aluminum, brass, bronze, low carbon steel, medium carbon steel, alloy steel, stainless steel, and titanium. Steel hex head cap screws come in diameters from $\frac{1}{4}$ to 3 in., and their strength is indicated by symbols on the hex head (Figure 19). Slotted head capscrews can have flat heads, round heads, or fillister heads. Socket head capscrews are also made with socket flat heads, and socket button heads.

Set screws (Figure 20) are used to lock pulleys or collars or shafts. Set screws can have square heads with

Figure 18.　Cap screws.

PAN
Low large diameter with high outer edges for maximum driving power. With slotted or Phillips recess for machine screws. Available plain for driving screws.

FLAT UNDERCUT
Standard 82° flat head with lower 1/3 of countersink removed for production of short screws. Permits flush assemblies in thin stock.

TRUSS
Similar to round head, except with shallower head. Has a larger diameter. Good for covering large diameter clearance holes in sheet metal. For machine screws and tapping screws.

FLAT, 100°
Has larger head than 82° design. Use with thin metals, soft plastics, etc. Slotted or Phillips driving recess.

BINDER
Undercut binds and eliminates fraying of wire in electrical work. For machine screws, slotted or Phillips driving recess.

FLAT TRIM
Same as 82° flat head except depth of countersink has been reduced. Phillips driving recess only.

ROUND
Used for general-purpose service. Used for bolts, machine screws, tapping screws and drive screws. With slotted or Phillips driving recess.

OVAL
Like standard flat head. Has outer surface rounded for added attractiveness. Slotted, Phillips or clutch driving recess.

ROUND WASHER
Has integral washer for bearing surface. Covers larger bearing area than round or truss head. For tapping screws only; with slotted or Phillips driving recess.

OVAL UNDERCUT
Similar to flat undercut. Has outer surface rounded for appearance. With slotted or Phillips driving recess.

FLAT FILLISTER
Same as standard fillister but without oval top. Used in counter bored holes that require a flush screw. With slot only for machine screws.

OVAL TRIM
Same as oval head except depth of countersink is less. Phillips driving recess only.

FILLISTER
Smaller diameter than round head, higher, deeper slot. Used in counterbored holes. Slotted or Phillips driving recess. Machine screws and tapping screws.

ROUND COUNTERSUNK
For bolts only. Similar to 82° flat head but with no driving recess.

HEXAGON
Head with square, sharp corners, and ample bearing surface for wrench tightening. Used for machine screws and bolts.

SQUARE (SET-SCREW)
Square, sharp corners can be tightened to higher torque with wrench than any other set-screw head.

HEXAGON WASHER
Same as Hexagon except with added washer section at base to protect work surface against wrench disfigurement. For machine screws and tapping screws.

SQUARE (BOLT)
Square, sharp corners, generous bearing surface for wrench tightening.

FLAT, 82°
Use where flush surface is desired. Slotted, clutch, Phillips, or hexagon-socket driving recess.

SQUARE COUNTERSUNK
For use on plow bolts, which are used on farm machinery and heavy construction equipment.

the head extending above the surface or, more often, the set screws are slotted or have socket heads. **Slotted or socket head set screws** usually disappear below the surface of the part to be fastened. A pulley or collar where the set screws are below the surface is much safer for persons working around them. Socket head set screws may have hex socket heads or spline socket heads. Set screws are manufactured in number sizes from 0 to 10 and in fractional sizes from $\frac{1}{4}$ to 2 in. Set screws are usually made from carbon or alloy steel and hardened.

Square head set screws are often used on tool holders (Figure 21) or as jackscrews in leveling machine tools (Figure 22). Set screws have several different points (Fig-

Bolt head marking	SAE — Society of Automotive Engineers ASTM — American Society for Testing and Materials SAE — ASTM Definitions	Material	Minimum tensile strength in pounds per square inch (PSI)
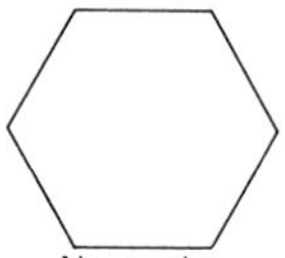 No marks	SAE grade 1 SAE grade 2 Indeterminate quality	Low carbon steel Low carbon steel	65,000 PSI
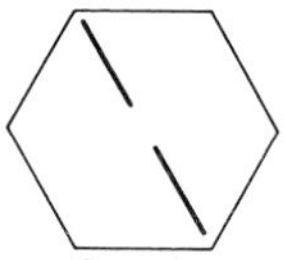 2 marks	SAE grade 3	Medium carbon steel, cold worked	110,000 PSI
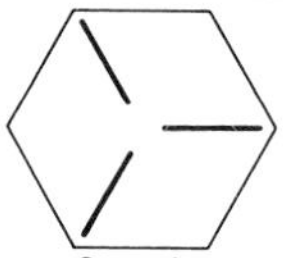 3 marks	SAE grade 5 ASTM — A 325 Common commercial quality	Medium carbon steel, quenched and tempered	120,000 PSI
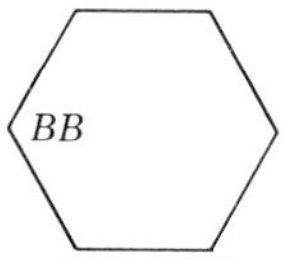 Letters BB	ASTM — A 354	Low alloy steel or medium carbon steel, quenched and tempered	105.000 PSI
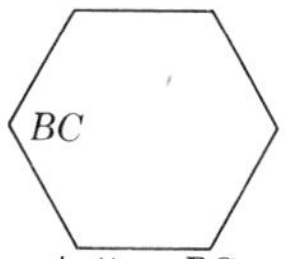 Letters BC	ASTM — A 354	Low alloy steel or medium carbon steel, quenched and tempered	125,000 PSI
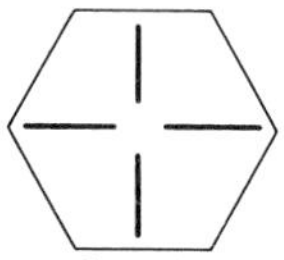 4 marks	SAE grade 6 Better commercial quality	Medium carbon steel, quenched and tempered	140,000 PSI
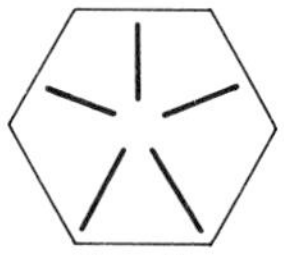 5 marks	SAE grade 7	Medium carbon alloy steel, quenched and tempered, roll threaded after heat treatment	133,000 PSI
 6 marks	SAE grade 8 ASTM — A 345 Best commercial quality	Medium carbon alloy steel, quenched and tempered	150,000 PSI

Figure 19. Grade markings for bolts.

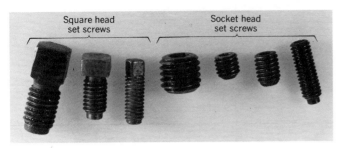

Figure 20.　Socket and square head set screws.

Figure 21.　Square head set screws are found in tool holders (Lane Community College).

Figure 22.　Square head jack screw (Lane Community College).

Figure 24.　Thumb screw and wingscrew.

ure 23). The flat point set screw will make the least amount of indentation on a shaft and is used where frequent adjustments are made. A flat point set screw is also used to provide a jam screw action when a second set screw is tightened on another set screw to prevent its release through vibration. The oval point set screw will make a slight indentation as compared with the cone point. With a half dog or full dog point set screw holding a collar to a shaft, alignment between shaft and collar will be maintained even when the parts are disassembled and reassembled. This is because the shaft is drilled with a hole of the same diameter as the dog point. Cup pointed set screws will make a ring-shaped depression in the shaft and will give a very slip-resistant connection. Square head set screws have a class 2A thread and are usually supplied with a coarse thread. Slotted and socket head set screws have a class 3A UNC or UNF thread.

Thumbscrews and wingscrews (Figure 24) are used where parts are to be fastened or adjusted rapidly without the use of tools.

Thread forming screws (Figure 25) form their own threads and eliminate the need for tapping. These screws are used in the assembly of sheet metal parts, plastics, and nonferrous material. Thread forming screws form threads by displacing material with no cutting action. These screws require an existing hole of the correct size.

Figure 23.　Set screw points.

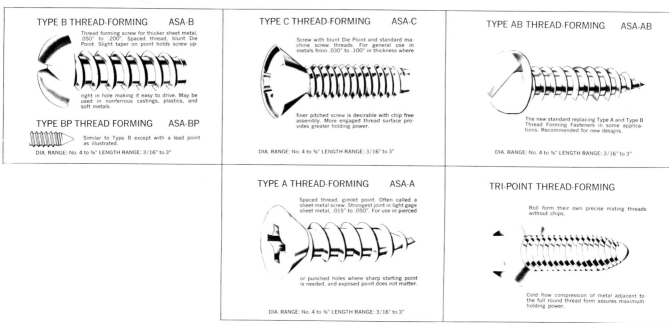

Figure 25. Self-tapping screws (Courtesy of Great Lakes Screw).

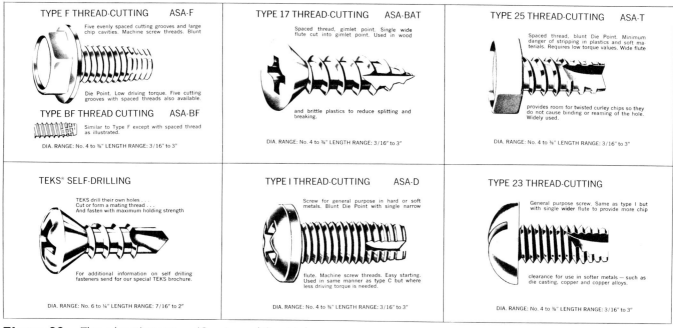

Figure 26. Thread cutting screws (Courtesy of Great Lakes Screw).

Thread cutting screws (Figure 26) make threads by cutting and producing chips. Because of the cutting action these screws need less driving torque than thread forming screws. Applications are similar as those for thread forming screws. These include fastening sheet metal, aluminum brass, diecastings, and plastics.

Drive screws (Figure 27) are forced into the correct size hole by hammering or with a press. Drive screws make permanent connections and are often used to fasten name plates or identification plates on machine tools.

Figure 27. Drive screw.

18

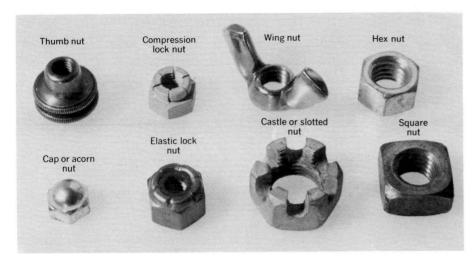

Figure 28. Common nuts.

COMMON INTERNALLY THREADED FASTENERS

Nuts

Common nuts (Figure 28) are manufactured in as many sizes as there are bolts. Most nuts are either hex or square in shape. Nuts are identified by the size of the bolt they fit and not by their outside size. Common hex nuts are made in different thicknesses. A **thin hex nut** is called a **jam nut.** They are used where space is limited or where the strength of a regular nut is not required. Jam nuts are often used to lock other nuts (Figure 29). Regular hex nuts are slightly thinner than their size designation. A $\frac{1}{2}$ in. regular hex nut is $\frac{7}{16}$ in. thick. A $\frac{1}{2}$ in. heavy hex nut is $\frac{31}{64}$ in. thick. A $\frac{1}{2}$ in. high hex nut measures $\frac{11}{16}$ in. thick. Other common nuts include various stop or lock nuts. Two common types are the **elastic stop nut** and the **compression stop nut.** They are used in applications where the nut might vibrate off the bolt. Wing nut and thumb nuts are used where quick assembly or disassembly by hand is desired. Other hex nuts are slotted and castle nuts. These nuts have slots cut into them. When the slots are aligned with holes in a bolt, a cotter pin may be used to prevent the nut from turning. Axles and spindles on vehicles have slotted nuts to prevent wheel bearing adjustments from slipping.

Cap or acorn nuts are often used where decorative nuts are needed. These nuts also protect projecting threads from accidental damage. Nuts are made from many different materials, depending on their application and strength requirements.

INTERNAL THREAD INSERTS

Internal thread inserts may be used where an internal thread is damaged or stripped and it is not possible to drill and tap for a larger size. A thread insert retains the original thread size. However, it is necessary to drill and

Figure 29. Jam nuts (CSU, Fresno).

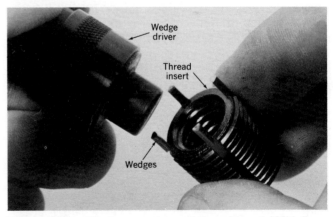

Figure 30. Wedge-type internal thread insert (CSU, Fresno).

tap a somewhat larger hole to accept the thread insert.

One common type of internal thread insert is the wedge type. The thread insert has both external and internal threads. This type of thread insert is screwed into a hole tapped to the same size as the thread on the outside of the insert. The four wedges are driven in using a special driver (Figure 30). This holds the insert in place. The internal thread in the insert is the same as the original hole.

Figure 31. Stainless steel thread insert used in an aluminum valve housing (CSU, Fresno).

A second type of internal thread insert is also used in repair applications as well as in new installations. Threaded holes are often required in products made from soft metals such as aluminum. If bolts, screws, or studs were to be screwed directly into the softer material, excessive wear could result, especially if the bolt is taken in and out a number of times. To overcome this problem, a thread insert made from a more durable material may be used. Stainless steel inserts are frequently used in aluminum (Figure 31). This type of thread insert requires an insert tap, an insert driver, and a thread insert (Figure 32). After the hole for the thread insert is tapped, the insert driver is used to screw the insert into the hole (Figure 33). The end of the insert coil must be broken off and removed after the insert is screwed into place. The insert in the illustration is used to repair sparkplug threads in engine blocks.

WASHERS, PINS, RETAINING RINGS, AND KEYS

Washers

Flat washers (Figure 34) are used under nuts and bolt heads to distribute the pressure over a larger area. Washers also prevent the marring of a finished surface when nuts or screws are tightened. Washers can be manufactured of many different materials. The nominal size of a washer is intended to be used with the same nominal size bolt or screw. Standard series of washers are narrow, regular, and wide. For example, the outside diameter of a $\frac{1}{4}$ in. narrow washer is $\frac{1}{2}$ in., the outside diameter of a $\frac{1}{4}$ in. regular washer is almost $\frac{3}{4}$ in., and the diameter of a wide $\frac{1}{4}$ in. washer measures 1 in.

Lock washers (Figure 35) are manufactured in many styles. The helical spring lock washer provides hardened

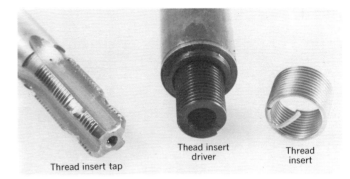

Figure 32. Thread insert tap, driver, and repair insert for sparkplug holes (CSU, Fresno).

Figure 33. Thread insert driver (CSU, Fresno).

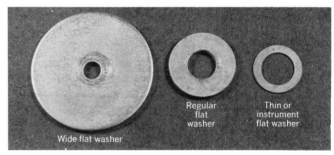

Figure 34. Wide, regular, and thin (or instrument) flat washers.

bearing surfaces between a nut or bolt head and the components of an assembly. The spring-type construction of this lock washer will hold the tension between a nut and bolt assembly even if a small amount of looseness should develop. Helical spring lock washers are manufactured in series: light, regular, heavy, extra duty, and hi-collar. The hi-collar lock washer has an outside diameter equal to the same nominal size socket head cap screw. This makes the use of these lock washers in a counterbored bolt hole possible. Counterbored holes have the end enlarged to accept the bolt head. A variety of standard tooth lock washers are produced, the exter-

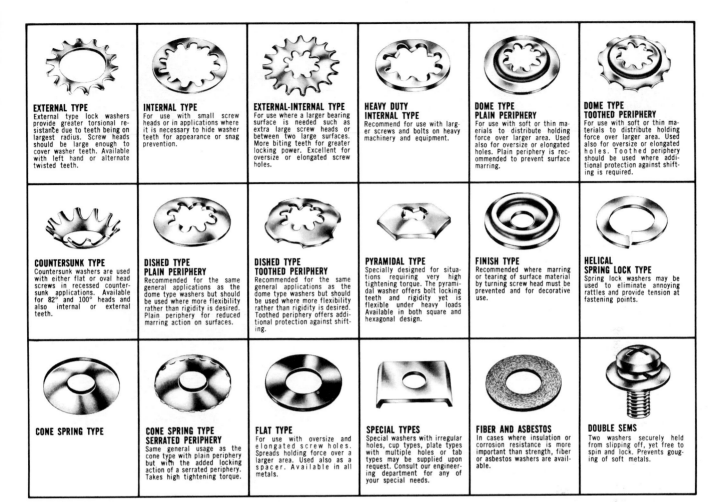

EXTERNAL TYPE
External type lock washers provide greater torsional resistance due to teeth being on largest radius. Screw heads should be large enough to cover washer teeth. Available with left hand or alternate twisted teeth.

INTERNAL TYPE
For use with small screw heads or in applications where it is necessary to hide washer teeth for appearance or snag prevention.

EXTERNAL-INTERNAL TYPE
For use where a larger bearing surface is needed such as extra large screw heads or between two large surfaces. More biting teeth for greater locking power. Excellent for oversize or elongated screw holes.

HEAVY DUTY INTERNAL TYPE
Recommend for use with larger screws and bolts on heavy machinery and equipment.

DOME TYPE PLAIN PERIPHERY
For use with soft or thin materials to distribute holding force over larger area. Used also for oversize or elongated holes. Plain periphery is recommended to prevent surface marring.

DOME TYPE TOOTHED PERIPHERY
For use with soft or thin materials to distribute holding force over larger area. Used also for oversize or elongated holes. Toothed periphery should be used where additional protection against shifting is required.

COUNTERSUNK TYPE
Countersunk washers are used with either flat or oval head screws in recessed countersunk applications. Available for 82° and 100° heads and also internal or external teeth.

DISHED TYPE PLAIN PERIPHERY
Recommended for the same general applications as the dome type washers but should be used where more flexibility rather than rigidity is desired. Plain periphery for reduced marring action on surfaces.

DISHED TYPE TOOTHED PERIPHERY
Recommended for the same general applications as the dome type washers but should be used where more flexibility rather than rigidity is desired. Toothed periphery offers additional protection against shifting.

PYRAMIDAL TYPE
Specially designed for situations requiring very high tightening torque. The pyramidal washer offers bolt locking teeth and rigidity yet is flexible under heavy loads Available in both square and hexagonal design.

FINISH TYPE
Recommended where marring or tearing of surface material by turning screw head must be prevented and for decorative use.

HELICAL SPRING LOCK TYPE
Spring lock washers may be used to eliminate annoying rattles and provide tension at fastening points.

CONE SPRING TYPE

CONE SPRING TYPE SERRATED PERIPHERY
Same general usage as the cone type with plain periphery but with the added locking action of a serrated periphery. Takes high tightening torque.

FLAT TYPE
For use with oversize and elongated screw holes. Spreads holding force over a larger area. Used also as a spacer. Available in all metals.

SPECIAL TYPES
Special washers with irregular holes, cup types, plate types with multiple holes or tab types may be supplied upon request. Consult our engineering department for any of your special needs.

FIBER AND ASBESTOS
In cases where insulation or corrosion resistance is more important than strength, fiber or asbestos washers are available.

DOUBLE SEMS
Two washers securely held from slipping off, yet free to spin and lock. Prevents gouging of soft metals.

Figure 35. Lock washers (Courtesy of Great Lakes Screw).

nal type providing the greatest amount of friction or locking effect between fastener and assembly. For use with small head screws and where a smooth appearance is desired, an internal tooth lock washer is used. When large bearing area is desired or where the assembly holes are oversized, an internal-external tooth lock washer is available. A countersunk tooth lock washer is used for a locking action with flat head screws.

Pins

Pins (Figure 36) find many applications in the assembly of parts. **Dowel pins** are heat treated and precision ground. Their diameter varies from the nominal dimension by only plus or minus .0001 in. ($\frac{1}{10,000}$ of an inch). Dowel pins are used where very accurate alignments must be maintained between two or more parts. Holes for dowel pins are reamed to provide a slight press fit. Reaming is a machining process during which a drilled hole is slightly enlarged to provide a smooth finish and accurate diameter. Dowel pins only locate. Clamping pressure is supplied by the screws. Dowel pins may be driven into a

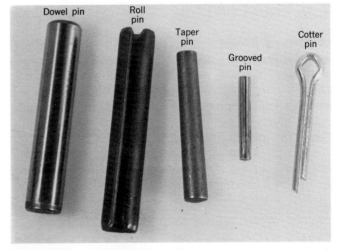

Figure 36. Pins (CSU, Fresno).

blind hole. A blind hole is closed at one end. When this kind of hole is used, provision must be made to let the air that is displaced by the pin escape. This can be done by drilling a small through hole or by grinding a narrow

flat the full length of the pin. Always use the correct lubricant when screw and pin assemblies are made.

One disadvantage of dowel pins is that they tend to enlarge the hole in an unhardened workpiece if they are driven in and out several times. When parts are intended to be disassembled frequently, **taper pins** will give accurate alignment. Taper pins have a taper of $\frac{1}{4}$ in. per foot of length and are fitted into reamed taper holes. If a taper pin hole wears larger because of frequent disassembly, the hole can be reamed larger to receive the next larger size of taper pin. Diameters of taper pins range in size from $\frac{1}{16}$ in. to $\frac{11}{16}$ in. measured at the large end. Taper pins are identified by a number from 7/0 (small diameter) to number 10 (large diameter) as well as by their length. The large end diameter is constant for a given size pin, but the small diameter changes with the length of the pin.

Some taper pins have a threaded portion on the large end. A nut can be threaded on the pin and used to pull the pin from the hole much like a screw jack. This facilitates removal of the pin.

A **grooved pin** is either a cylindrical or tapered pin with longitudinal grooves pressed into the pin body. This causes the pin to deform. A groove pin will hold securely in a drilled hole even after repeated removal.

Roll pins can also be used in drilled holes with no reaming required. These pins are manufactured from flat steel bands and rolled into cylindrical shape. Roll pins, because of their spring action, will stay tight in a hole even after repeated disassemblies.

Cotter pins are used to retain parts on a shaft or to lock a nut or a bolt as a safety precaution. Cotter pins make a quick assembly and disassembly possible.

Retaining Rings

Retaining rings are fasteners used in many assemblies. Retaining rings can easily be installed in machined grooves, internally in housings, or externally on shafts or pins (Figure 37). Some types of retaining rings do not require grooves but have a self-locking spring-type action. The most common application of a retaining ring is to provide a shoulder to hold and retain a bearing or other part on an otherwise smooth shaft. They may also be used in a bearing housing (Figure 38). Special pliers are used to install and remove retaining rings.

Keys

Keys (Figure 39) are used to prevent the rotation of gears or pulleys on a shaft. Keys are fitted into key seats in both the shaft and the external part. Keys should fit the key seats rather snugly. **Square keys,** where the width and the height are equal, are preferred on shaft sizes up to a $6\frac{1}{2}$ in. diameter. Above a $6\frac{1}{2}$ in. diameter rec-

Figure 37.   External retaining ring used on a shaft (Courtesy of Waldes Kohinoor, Inc.).

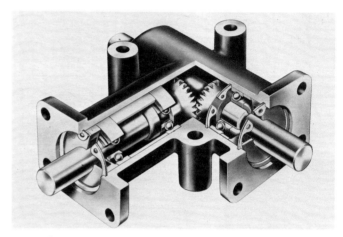

Figure 38.   Internal retaining rings used to retain bearings (Courtesy of Waldes Kohinoor, Inc.).

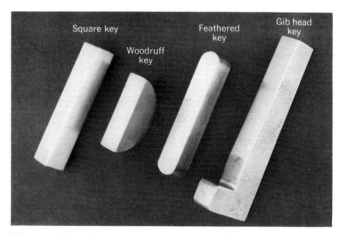

Figure 39.   Keys (Lane Community College).

tangular keys are recommended. **Woodruff keys,** which are almost in the shape of a half circle, are used where relatively light loads are transmitted. One advantage of woodruff keys is that they cannot change their axial

location on a shaft because they are retained in a pocket. A key fitted into an endmilled pocket will also retain its axial position on the shaft. Most of these keys are held under tension with one or more set screws threaded through the hub of the pulley or gear. Where extremely heavy shock loads or high torques are encountered, a **taper key** is used. Taper keys have a taper of $\frac{1}{8}$ in. per foot. Where a tapered key is used, the key seat in the shaft is parallel to the shaft axis and a

taper to match the key is in the hub. Where only one side of an assembly is accessible, a **gib head taper key** is used instead of a plain taper key. When a gib head taper key is driven into the key seat as far as possible, a gap remains between the gib and the hub of the pulley or gear. The key is removed for disassembly by driving a wedge into the gap to push the key out. A **feathered key** is a key that is secured in a key seat with screws. A feathered key is often a part of a sliding gear or sliding pulley.

SELF-TEST

1. What is the difference between a bolt and a screw?
2. How much thread engagement is recommended when a screw is used in an assembly?
3. When are class 3 threads used?
4. What is the difference between a machine bolt and a cap screw?
5. What is the outside diameter of a No. 8 machine screw?
6. Where are set screws used?
7. When are stud bolts used?
8. Explain the difference between thread forming and thread cutting screws.
9. Where are castle nuts used?
10. Where are cap nuts used?
11. Explain two reasons why flat washers are used.
12. What is the purpose of a helical spring lock washer?
13. When is an internal-external tooth lock washer used?
14. When are dowel pins used?
15. When are taper pins used?
16. When are roll pins used?
17. What are retaining rings?
18. What is the purpose of a key?
19. When is a woodruff key used?
20. When is gib head key used?

PART 5 READING DRAWINGS

From earliest times, man has communicated his thoughts through drawings. The pictorial representation of an idea is a vital line of communication between the designer and the people who produce the final product. Technological design would be impossible were it not for the several different ways an idea may be represented by a drawing. The drawing also provides an important testing phase for an idea. Many times an idea may be rejected at the drawing board stage before a large investment is made to equip a manufacturing facility and risk production of an item that does not meet the design requirements.

This does not mean that all design problems can be solved in the drafting room. Almost anything can be represented by a drawing, even to the extent that some designs can be quite impossible to manufacture. It is important that the designer be aware of the problems that confront the machinist. On the other hand, you

must fully understand all of the symbols and terminology on the designer's drawing. You must then interpret these terms and symbols in order to transform the ideas of the designer into useful products.

ISOMETRIC DRAWING
An isometric drawing (Figure 40) is one method used to represent an object in three dimensions. In the isometric format, the lines of the object remain parallel and the object is drawn about the three isometric axes that are 120 degrees apart.

OBLIQUE DRAWING
Object lines in the oblique drawing (Figure 41) also remain parallel. The oblique differs from the isometric in that one axis of the object is parallel to the plane of the

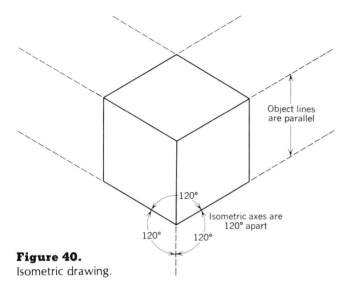

Figure 40.
Isometric drawing.

Figure 41.
Oblique drawing.

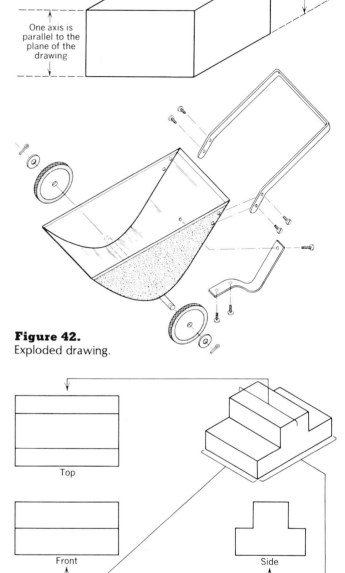

drawing. Isometric and oblique are also not generally used as working drawings for the machinist. However, you may occasionally see them in the machine shop.

EXPLODED DRAWINGS

The exploded drawing (Figure 42) is a type of pictorial drawing designed to show several parts in their proper location prior to assembly. Although the exploded view is not used as the working drawing for the machinist, it has an important place in mechanical technology. Exploded views appear extensively in manuals and handbooks that are used for repair and assembly of machines and other mechanisms.

Figure 42.
Exploded drawing.

ORTHOGRAPHIC DRAWINGS

The Orthographic Projection Drawing

In almost every case, the working drawing for the machinist will be in the form of the **three view** or **orthographic drawing.** The typical orthographic format always shows an object in the three view combination of side, end, and top (Figure 43). In some cases, an object can be completely shown by a combination of only two orthographic views. However, any orthographic drawing must have a minimum of two views in order to show an object completely. The top view is referred to as the **plan** view. The front or side views are referred to as **elevation** views. The terms plan and elevation may appear on some drawings, especially those of large complex parts or assemblies.

Figure 43.   Standard orthographic drawings.

Hidden Lines for Part Features Not Visible

Features that are not visible are indicated by dotted lines. These are called **hidden lines** as they indicate the locations of part features hidden from view. The plain

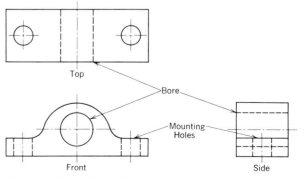

Figure 44.   Hidden lines for part features not visible.

bearing (Figure 44) is shown in a typical orthographic drawing. The front view is the only one in which the hole through the bearing, or bore, can be observed. In the side and top views, the bore is not visible. Therefore, it is indicated by dotted or hidden lines. The mounting holes through the base are visible only in the top view. They appear as hidden lines in the front and side views.

Sectioned Views

When internal features are complex to the extent that indicating them as hidden lines would be confusing, a **sectioned drawing** may be employed. Two common styles of sections are used. In the **full section** (Figure 45*a*), the object has been cut completely through. In the **half section** (Figure 45*b*), one quarter of the object is removed. The section indicator line shows the plane at which the section is taken. For example (Figure 45*a*), the end view of the object shows the section line marked by the symbol "AA." The section line "BB" (Figure 45*b*) indicates the portion removed in the half section. An object may be sectioned at any plane as long as the section plane is indicated on the drawing.

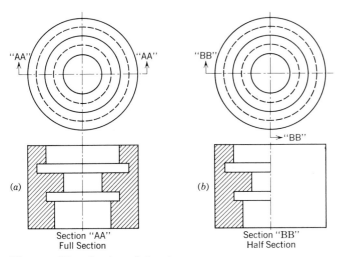

Figure 45. Sectioned drawings.

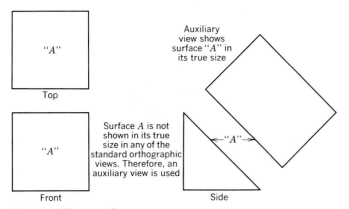

Figure 46. Auxiliary view.

Auxiliary Views

One of the reasons for adopting the orthographic drawings is to represent an object in its true size and shape. This is not possible with the pictorial drawings discussed earlier. Generally, the orthographic drawing meets this requirement. However, the shape of certain objects is such that their actual size and shape are not truly represented. An **auxiliary view** may be required (Figure 46). On the object shown in the figure, surface "A" does not appear in its true size in any of the standard orthographic views. Therefore, surface "A" is projected to the auxiliary view, thus revealing its true size.

READING AND INTERPRETING DRAWINGS

Scale

In some cases, an object may be represented by a drawing that is the same size as the object. In other cases, an object may be too large to draw full size, or a very small part may be better represented by a drawing that is larger. Therefore, all drawings are drawn to a specific **scale.** For example, when the drawing is the same size as the object, the scale is said to be full, or 1 = 1. If the drawing is one-half size, the scale is one-half, or $\frac{1}{2}$ = 1. A drawing twice actual size would be double scale, or 2 = 1. The scale used is generally indicated on the drawing.

Dimensioning of Detail and Assembly Drawings

You will primarily come in contact with the **detail drawing.** This is a drawing of an individual part and, in almost all cases, will appear in orthographic form. Depending on the type of work a machinist may be doing, he may also see an **assembly drawing.** The assembly drawing is a drawing of subassemblies or several individual parts assembled into a complete unit. For example, a drawing of a complete automobile engine would be an assembly drawing. In addition, a detail drawing of each engine component would also exist.

A detail drawing contains all the essential information needed by you in order to make the part. Most important are the **dimensions.** Dimensioning refers generally to the sizes specified for the part and the locations of its features. Furthermore, dimensions reflect many design considerations, such as the fit of mating parts, that will affect the operating characteristics of all machines. Much of the effort you expend performing the various machining operations will be directed toward controlling the dimensions specified on the drawing.

Several styles of dimensioning appear on drawings. The most common of these is the standard **fractional inch** notation (Figure 47). The outline of the part along

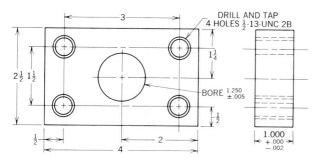

Figure 47. Fractional inch dimensioning.

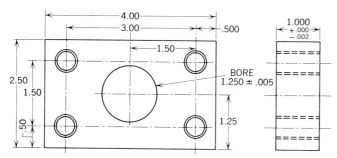

Figure 48. Decimal inch dimensioning.

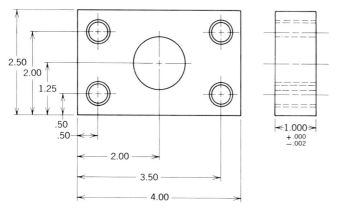

Figure 49. Absolute or coordinate dimensioning.

with the several holes are dimensioned according to size and location. Generally, the units of the dimensions are not shown. Note that certain dimensions are specified to come within certain ranges. This is known as **tolerance.**

Tolerance refers to an acceptable range of part size or feature location and is generally expressed in the form of a minimum and maximum limit. The bore (Figure 47) is shown to be 1.250 in. ± .005 in. This notation is called a **bilateral tolerance** because the acceptable size range is both above and below the nominal (normal) size of 1.250 in. The bored hole could be any size from 1.245 to 1255 in diameter. The thickness of the part is specified as 1000 + .000 and − .002. This tolerance is **unilateral** as all the range is on one side of nominal. Thus, the thick-

ness could range from .998 in. to 1000 in.

No tolerance is specified for the outside dimensions of the part or the locations of the various features. Since these dimensions are indicated in standard fractional form, the tolerance is taken to be plus or minus $\frac{1}{64}$ of an inch unless otherwise specified on the drawing. This range is known as **standard tolerance** and applies only to dimensions expressed in standard fractional form.

Another system of dimensioning used in certain industries is that of **decimal fraction** notation (Figure 48). In this case, tolerance is determined by the number of places indicated in the decimal notation:

2 places	.00 tolerance is	± .010
3 places	.000 tolerance is	± .005
4 places	.0000 tolerance is	± .0005

Always remember that standard tolerances apply only when no other tolerance is specified on the drawing.

The **coordinate** or **absolute** system of dimensioning (Figure 49) may be found in special applications such as numerically controlled machining. In this system, all dimensions are specified from the same zero point. The figure shows the dimensions expressed in decimal form. Standard fraction notation may also be used. Standard tolerances apply unless otherwise specified.

With the increase in metrification in recent years, some industries have adopted a system of dual dimensioning of drawings with both metric and inch notation (Figure 50). Dual dimensioning has, in some cases, created a degree of confusion for the machinist. Hence industry is constantly devising improved methods by which to differentiate metric and inch drawing dimensions. You must use caution when reading a dual-dimensioned drawing to insure that you are conforming your work to the proper system of measurement for your tools. In the figure, metric dimensions appear above the line and inch dimensions appear below the line.

Abbreviations for Machine Operations (Figure 51)

Working drawings contain several symbols and abbreviations that convey important information to the machinist. For example, certain machining operations may be abbreviated. **Countersinking** is a machining operation in which the end of a hole is shaped to accept a flat head screw. On a drawing, countersinking may be abbreviated as C.S. The desired angle will also be specified. In **counterboring,** the end of a hole is enlarged in diameter so that a bolt head may be recessed. Counterboring may be abbreviated C'BORE. **Spotfacing** is usually spelled out. This operation is similar to counterboring except that the spotfacing depth is only sufficient to provide a smooth and flat surface around a hole.

Figure 50. Dual dimensioning: metric and inch.

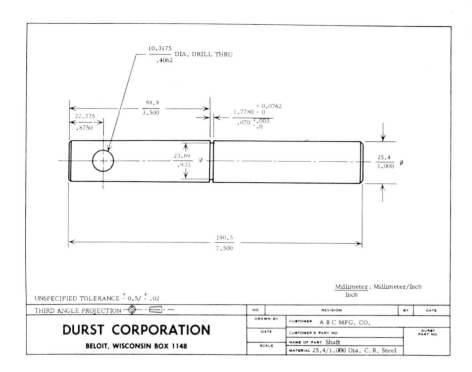

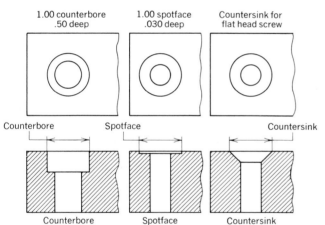

Figure 51. Countersinking, counterboring, and spotfacing symbols.

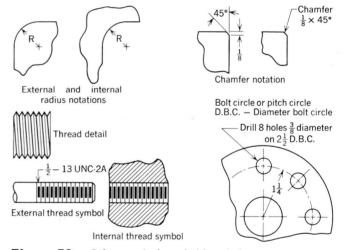

Figure 53. Other symbols and abbreviations.

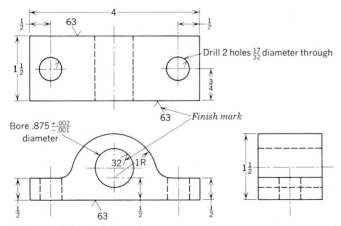

Figure 52. Finish marks.

Finish Marks (Figure 52)

Very often you will perform work on a part that has already been partially shaped. An example of this might be a casting or forging. The **finish mark** is used to indicate which surfaces are to be machined. Furthermore, the finish mark may also indicate a required degree of surface finish. For example, a finish mark notation of 4, 32, or 64 refers to a specific surface finish.

Other Common Symbols and Abbreviations (Figure 53)

External and internal radii are generally indicated by the abbreviation *R* and the specified size. **Chamfers** may be indicated by size and angle as shown in the figure.

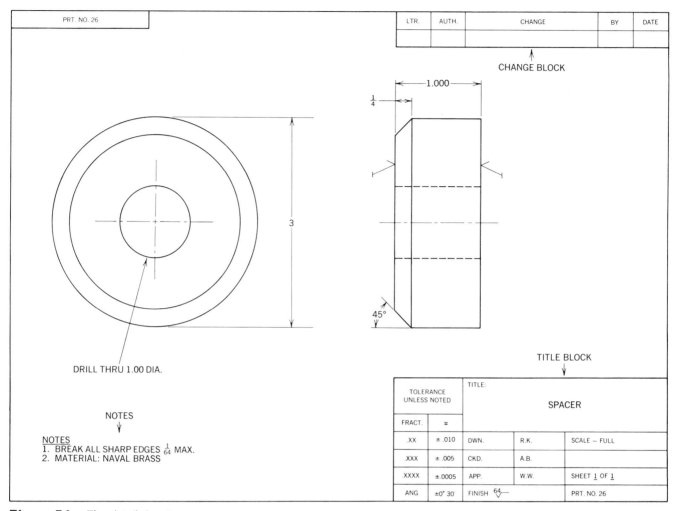

Figure 54. The detail drawing.

Threads are generally represented by symbols or they may be drawn in detail. Threads will also have a notation that indicates type, size, and fit. Consider the notation $\frac{1}{2}$-13 UNC 2A. This thread notation indicates the following:

$\frac{1}{2}$ — Major thread diameter

13 — Number of threads per inch

UNC — Shape and series of thread

2 — Class of fit

A — External thread (internal is denoted B)

A specific bolt circle or pitch circle is often indicated by the abbreviation **D.B.C.** meaning **Diameter of Bolt Circle.** The size of the diameter is indicated by normal dimensioning or with an abbreviation such as $1\frac{1}{2}$ D.B.C.

BLUEPRINT FORMATS

A designer's idea may at first appear as a freehand sketch perhaps in one of the pictorial forms discussed previously. After further discussion and examination, the decision may be made to have a part or an assembly manufactured. This necessitates suitable orthographic drawings that can be supplied to the machine shop. The original drawings produced by the drafting department are not used directly by the machine shop. These original drawings must be carefully preserved, as a great deal of time and money has been invested in them. Were they to be sent directly to the machine shop, they would soon be destroyed by constant handling. Therefore, a copy of the original drawing is made.

Several methods are employed to obtain copies of original drawings. One of the most common is **blueprinting.** Any number of blueprints may be made and distributed to the various departments of a manufacturing facility. For example, assembly blueprints are needed in the assembly area while blueprints of individual parts are required at the machine tool stations and in the inspection department.

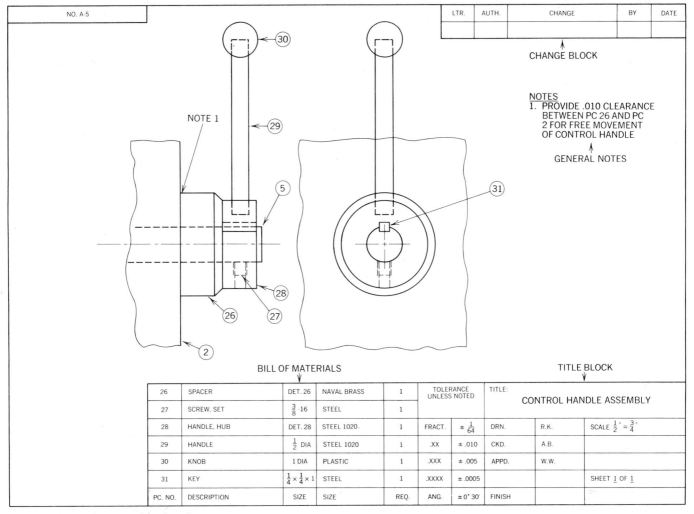

LTR.	AUTH.	CHANGE	BY	DATE

CHANGE BLOCK

NOTES
1. PROVIDE .010 CLEARANCE BETWEEN PC 26 AND PC 2 FOR FREE MOVEMENT OF CONTROL HANDLE

GENERAL NOTES

NO. A-5

NOTE 1

BILL OF MATERIALS

TITLE BLOCK

PC. NO.	DESCRIPTION	SIZE	SIZE	REQ.				
26	SPACER	DET. 26	NAVAL BRASS	1	TOLERANCE UNLESS NOTED		TITLE: CONTROL HANDLE ASSEMBLY	
27	SCREW, SET	$\frac{3}{8}$ -16	STEEL	1				
28	HANDLE, HUB	DET. 28	STEEL 1020.	1	FRACT.	$\pm \frac{1}{64}$	DRN. R.K.	SCALE $\frac{1}{2}$" = $\frac{3}{4}$"
29	HANDLE	$\frac{1}{2}$ DIA	STEEL 1020	1	.XX	$\pm$ .010	CKD. A.B.	
30	KNOB	1 DIA	PLASTIC	1	.XXX	$\pm$ .005	APPD. W.W.	
31	KEY	$\frac{1}{4} \times \frac{1}{4} \times 1$	STEEL	1	.XXXX	$\pm$ .0005		SHEET 1 OF 1
PC. NO.	DESCRIPTION	SIZE	SIZE	REQ.	ANG.	$\pm 0° 30'$	FINISH	

Figure 55. The assembly drawing.

The typical detail blueprint format (Figure 54) contains a suitable title block. In many cases, the name of the firm appears in the title block (Figure 50). The block also contains the name of the part, specified tolerance, scale, and the initials of the draftsman. A finish mark notation may also appear. The blueprint may also contain a change block. Often designs may be modified after an original drawing is made. Subsequent drawings will reflect any changes. A blueprint may also contain one or more general notes. The notes contain important information for the machinist. Therefore, you should always find and read any general notes appearing on a blueprint.

A typical assembly blueprint format contains essentially the same information as found on the detail plan (Figure 55). However, assembly blueprints generally show only those dimensions that pertain to the assembly. Dimensions of the individual parts are found on the detail plans. In addition to the normal information, a **bill of materials** appears on the assembly plan. This bill contains the part number, description, size, material, and required quantity of each piece in the assembly. Often, the source of a specific item not manufactured by the assembler will be specified in the bill of material. An assembly blueprint may also include a list of references to detail blueprints of the parts in the assembly. Any general notes containing information regarding the assembly will also be included.

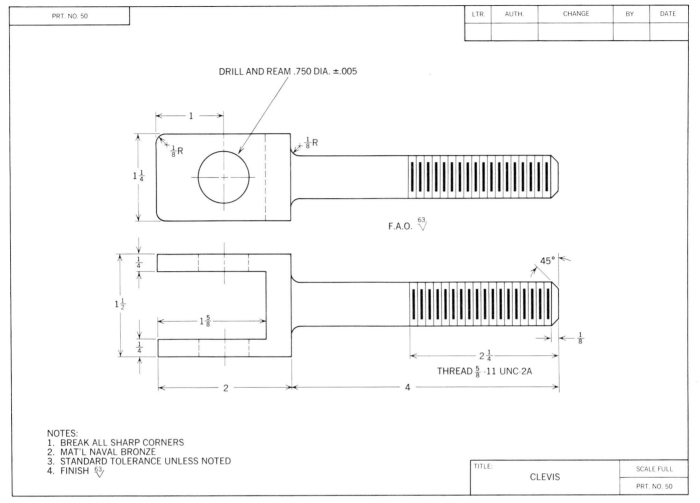

Figure 56.

SELF-TEST

1. Sketch the object (Figure 56) as it would appear in correct orthographic form.
   (For problems 2 to 10, refer to Figure 57.)
2. What is the minimum size of the hole through the clevis head?
3. What length of thread is indicated on the drawing?
4. What is the tolerance of the slot in the clevis head?
5. What radius is specified where the shank and clevis head meet?
6. What is the total length of the part?
7. What is the width of the slot in the clevis head?
8. Name two machining operations specified on the drawing.

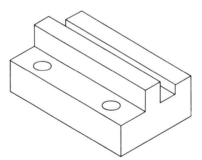

Figure 57.

9. What is the size and angle of the chamfer on the thread end?
10. What does note 1 mean?

SECTION B HAND TOOLS

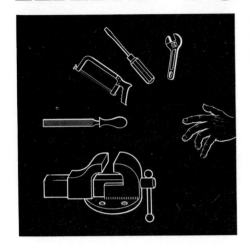

Our ability to make and use tools has been directly responsible for all technical advance. Prior to the development of advanced metalworking, natural materials such as stone, flint, and wood provided the only tool materials. When metals and metalworking techniques became better established, tool development was advanced greatly, which led to the many fine tools of today. A study of tools must logically begin with those used by hand for hand operations. In this section you will be introduced to the basic complement of hand tools used in all branches of mechanical technology.

Workholding devices were not developed in early times. Craftsmen in many Middle East and Asian countries still preferred to use their feet instead of a vise to hold the workpiece. Machinists today tend to take the bench vise for granted, seldom realizing that they could hardly get along without it.

Arbor presses and hydraulic shop presses are very useful and powerful shop tools. If they are used incorrectly, however, they can be very hazardous to the operator, and workpieces can be ruined.

Noncutting tools such as screwdrivers, pliers, and wrenches should be properly identified. It is impossible to request a particular tool from the toolroom without knowing its correct name.

Cutting hand tools such as hacksaws, files, hand reamers, taps, and dies are very important to a machinist. In this section you will also be introduced to the pedestal grinder and its important functions in the machine shop.

The units that follow in this section will instruct you in the identification, selection, use, and safety of these important hand tools and hand operated machines.

UNIT 1 WORKHOLDING FOR HAND OPERATIONS

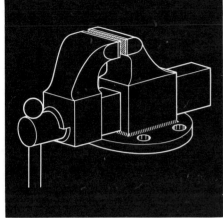

The bench vise is a basic but very necessary tool in the shop. With proper care and use, this workholding tool will give many years of faithful service.

OBJECTIVES

After completing this unit, you should be able to:
1. Identify various types of vises and their uses.
2. Explain the procedures used for the care and maintenance of vises.

TYPES OF VISES

Vises of various types are used by machinists when doing hand or bench work. They should be mounted in such a way that a long workpiece can be held in a vertical position extending alongside the bench (Figure 1). Some bench vises have a solid base (Figure 2), and others have a swivel base (Figure 3). The machinist's bench vise is measured by the width of the jaws (Figure 4).

Toolmakers often use small vises that pivot on a ball and socket for holding delicate work. Hand-held vises, called pin vises, are made for holding very small or delicate parts.

Most bench vises have hardened insert jaws that are serrated for greater gripping power (Figure 5). These criss-cross serrations are sharp and will dig into finished workpieces enough to mar them beyond repair. Soft jaws (Figure 6) made of copper, other soft metals, or wood, are used to protect a finished surface on a workpiece. These soft jaws are made to slip over the vise jaws. Some vises used for sheet metal work have smooth, deep jaws (Figure 7).

Figure 1. When long work is clamped in the vise vertically, it should clear the workbench (Lane Community College).

Figure 2. A solid base bench vise (Lane Community College).

Figure 3. A swivel base bench vise (Lane Community College).

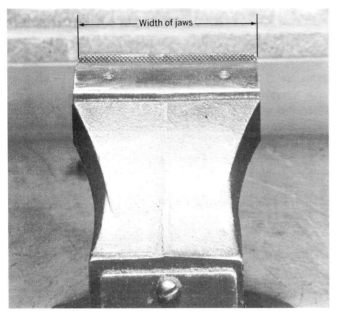

Figure 4. How to measure a vise (Lane Community College).

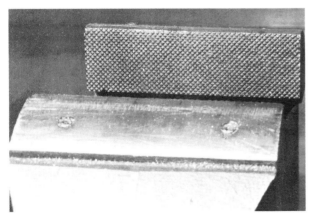

Figure 5. View of the hardened, serrated insert jaws on the vise (Lane Community College).

Figure 6. View of the soft jaws placed on the vise (Lane Community College).

Figure 7. Smooth-jawed vise for working with sheet metal (Lane Community College).

USES OF VISES

Vises are used to hold work for filing, hacksawing, chiseling, and bending light metal. They are also used for holding work when assembling and disassembling parts.

Vises should be placed on the workbench at the correct working height for the individual. The top of the vise jaws should be at elbow height. Poor work is produced when the vise is mounted too high or too low. A variety of vise heights should be provided in the shop or skids made available to stand on.

CARE OF VISES

Like any other tool, vises have limitations. "Cheater" bars or pipes should not be used on the handle to tighten the vise. Heat from a torch should not be applied to work held in the jaws as the hardened insert jaws will then become softened. There is usually one vise in a shop reserved for heating and bending.

Heavy hammering should not be done on a bench

Figure 8. Hammering on the slide bar should never be done to a vise. This may crack or distort it (Lane Community College).

vise. The force of bending or pounding should be against the fixed jaw rather than the movable jaw of the vise. Bending light, flat stock or small round stock in the jaws is permissible if a light hammer is used. The movable jaw slide bar (Figure 8) **should never be hammered upon** as it is usually made of thin cast iron and can be cracked quite easily. An anvil is often provided behind the solid jaw for the purpose of light hammering.

Bench vises should occasionally be taken apart so that the screw, nut, and thrust collars may be cleaned and lubricated. The screw and nut should be cleaned in solvent. A heavy grease should be packed on the screw and thrust collars before reassembly.

SELF-TEST

1. What clamping position should be considered when mounting a vise on a workbench?
2. Name two types of bench vises.
3. How is the machinist's bench vise measured for size?
4. Small, delicate work may be held in a _____ or a _____ vise.
5. Explain two characteristics of the insert jaws on vises.
6. How can a finished surface be protected?
7. In what way are vises that are used for sheet metal work different from a machinist's vise?
8. What are vises usually used for?
9. Name three things that should never be done to a vise.
10. How should a vise be lubricated?

This unit has no post-test.

UNIT 2 ARBOR AND SHOP PRESSES

The arbor press and the small shop press are very common sights in most machine shops. It would be difficult indeed to get along without them. You will find these tools extremely useful when you know how to use them, but if you are not instructed in their use, they can be dangerous to you and destructive to the workpiece.

OBJECTIVES

After completing this unit, you should be able to:
1. Install and remove a bronze bushing using an arbor press.
2. Press on and remove a ball bearing from a shaft on an arbor press using the correct tools.
3. Press on and remove a ball bearing from a housing using an arbor press and correct tooling.
4. Install and remove a mandrel using an arbor press.
5. Install and remove a shaft with key in a hub using the arbor press.

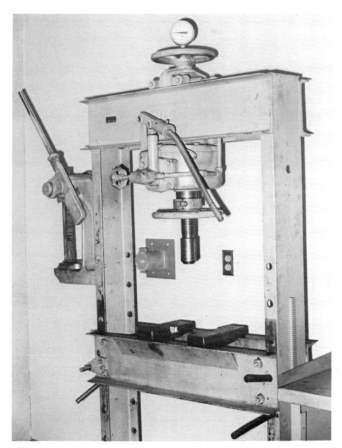

Figure 1. Fifty-ton capacity hydraulic shop presses (Lane Community College).

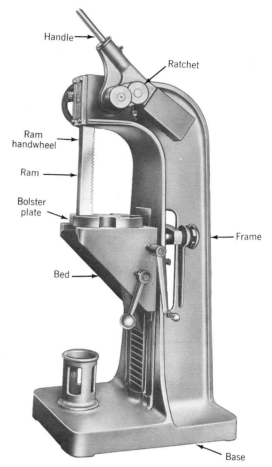

Figure 2. Simple rachet floor type arbor press (Courtesy of Dake Corporation).

TYPES

The arbor press is an essential piece of equipment in the small machine shop. Without it a machinist would be forced to resort to the use of a hammer or sledge to make any forced fit, a process that could easily damage the part.

Two basic types of arbor presses are manufactured and used: the hydraulic (Figure 1) and the mechanical (Figure 2). Both types are handpowered with a lever. The lever gives a "feel" or a sense of pressure applied, which is not possible with power-driven presses. This pressure sensitivity is needed when small delicate parts are being pressed so that a workman will know where to stop before collapsing the piece.

USES

The major uses of the arbor press are bushing installation and removal, ball and roller bearing installation and removal (Figure 3), pressing shafts into hubs (Figure 4), pressing mandrels into workpieces, broaching keyways (Figure 5), and straightening and bending (Figure 6).

PROCEDURES

Installing Bushings

A bushing is a short metal tube, machined inside and out to precision dimensions, and usually made to fit into a bore, or accurately machined hole. Many kinds of bushings are used for various purposes and are usually installed with an **interference fit** or press fit. This means that the bushing is slightly larger than the hole into which it is pressed. The amount of interference will be considered in greater detail in a later unit. There are many bushings made of many materials including bronze and hardened steel, but they all have one thing in common: they must be lubricated with high pressure lube before they are pressed into the bore. Oil is not used as it will simply wipe off and cause the bushing to seize the bore. Seizing is the condition where two unlubricated metals tend to weld together under pressure. In this case it may cause the bushing to be damaged beyond repair.

The bore should always have a strong chamfer, that is, an angled or beveled edge, since a sharp edge would cut into the bushing and damage it (Figures 7a and 7b).

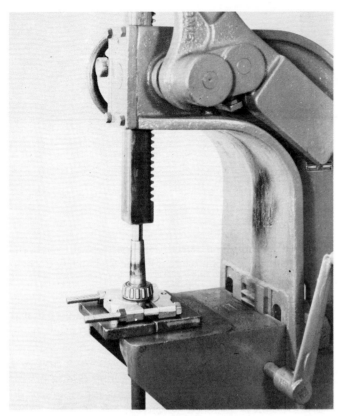

Figure 3. Roller bearing being removed from axle (Lane Community College).

Figure 5. Keyway being broached in gear hub with a mechanical arbor press (Courtesy of The duMont Corporation).

Figure 4. Shaft being pressed into hub (Lane Community College).

Figure 6. Shaft being straightened in hydraulic shop press (Lane Community College).

The bushing should also have a long tapered chamfer or **start** so it will not **dig in** and enter misaligned. Bushings are prone to go in crooked if there is a sharp edge, especially if it is a hardened steel bushing. Care should

be taken to see that the bushing is straight entering the bore, and that it continues into the bore in proper alignment. This should not be a problem if the tooling is right; that is, if the end of the press ram is square and if it is

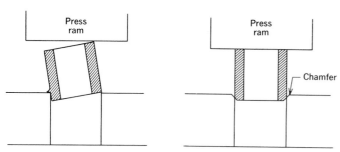

Figure 7a. Bushing being pressed where bore is not chamfered and bushing is misaligned. **Figure 7b.** Bushing being pressed into correctly chamfered hole in correct alignment.

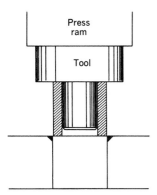

Figure 8. Special tool to keep bushing square to press ram.

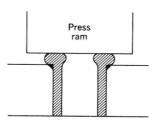

Figure 9. Effect of excessive pressure on bushing that exceeds bore length.

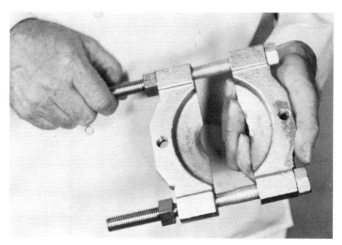

Figure 10. Bearing puller, a special tool for supporting inner bearing race. (See Figure 3.) (Lane Community College).

not loose and worn. The proper bolster plate should also be used under the part so that it cannot tilt out of alignment. Sometimes special tooling is used to guide the bushing (Figure 8). Only the pressure needed to force the bushing into place should be applied, especially if the bushing is longer than the bore length. Excessive pressure might distort the bushing and cause it to be undersized (Figure 9).

Ball and Roller Bearings

Ball and roller bearings pose special problems when they are installed and removed by pressing. This is because the pressure must be applied directly against the race and not through the balls or rollers since this could destroy the bearing. Frequently, when removing ball bearings from a shaft, the inner race is hidden by a shoulder and cannot be supported in the normal way. In this case, a special tool called a **bearing puller** is used (Figure 10). On the inner and outer races, bearings may be installed by pressing on the race with a steel tube of the proper diameter. As with bushings, high pressure lubricant should be used.

Sometimes there is no other way to remove an old ball bearing except by exerting pressure through the balls. When this is done, there is a real danger that the race may be violently shattered. In this case a scatter shield must be used. A scatter shield is a heavy steel tube about 8 to 12 in. long and is set up to cover the work. The shield is placed around the bearing during pressing to keep shattered parts from injuring the operator. It is a good safety practice to always use a scatter shield when ball bearings are removed from a shaft by pressing. Safety glasses should be worn during all pressing operations.

Bores and Shafts

Holes in the hubs of gears, sprockets, and other machine parts are also frequently designed for a force fit. In these instances, there is usually a keyway that needs to be aligned. A keyway is a groove in which a key is placed. This key, in turn, also fits into a slot in the hub of a gear or pulley, and secures the part against the shaft, keeping it from rotating. When pressing shafts with keys into hubs with keyways, it is sometimes helpful to chamfer the leading edge of the key so it will align itself properly (Figure 11). Seizing will occur in this operation, as with the installation of bushings, if high pressure lubricant is not used.

Mandrels

Mandrels, cylindrical pieces of steel with a slight taper, are pressed into bores in much the same way that shafts are pressed into hubs. There is one important difference, however; since the mandrel is tapered about .006 of an inch per foot, it can be installed only with the small end in first.

The large end of the mandrel may have a flat on which the lathe dog screw can rest. The large end may also be determined by measuring with a micrometer, or

Figure 11. Chamfer on key helps in alignment of parts being pressed together (Lane Community College).

Figure 13. Hexagonal shape being push broached (Courtesy of The duMont Corporation).

Figure 12. Mandrel being lubricated and pressed into part for further machining (Lane Community College).

Figure 14. A typical set of keyway broaches (Courtesy of The duMont Corporation).

by trying the mandrel in the bore. The small end should start into the hole, but the large end should not. Apply lubricant and press the mandrel in until definite resistance is felt (Figure 12).

Keyway Broaching

The process of broaching is just one of the machining processes. Broaching can be done on both internal and external surfaces. In keyway broaching a slot or groove is cut inside the bore through a hub or pulley so that a key can be retained.

Although many types of keyseating machines are in use in many machine shops, keyway broaching is often done on arbor presses. Broaching is the process of cutting out shapes on the interior of a metal part. Keyways are only one type of cutting that can be done by the push-type procedure. Such internal shapes as a square or hexagon can also be cut by this method (Figure 13). All that is needed for these procedures is the proper size of arbor press and a set of keyway broaches (Figure 14),

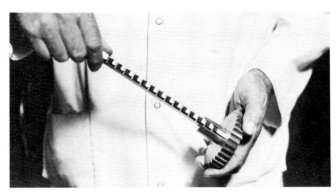

Figure 15. Broach with guide bushing inserted into gear (Lane Community College).

Figure 16. Broach, guide bushing placed in arbor press that is ready to lubricate and to perform first pass (Lane Community College).

Figure 17. Shims in place behind broach that is ready to lubricate and make final cut on part (Lane Community College).

3. Place this assembly in the arbor press (Figure 16).
4. Lubricate.
5. Push the broach through.
6. Clean the broach.
7. Place second-pass shim in place.
8. Insert broach.
9. Lubricate.
10. Push the broach through.
11. If more than one shim is needed to obtain the correct depth, repeat the procedure (Figure 17).

The tools should be cleaned and returned to their box and the finished keyway should be deburred and cleaned.

Production or single-pass broaching requires no shims or second-pass cuts, and with some types no bushings need be used (Figure 18).

Two important things to remember when push broaching are alignment and lubrication. Misalignment, caused by a worn or loose ram, can cause the broach to hog (dig in) or break. Sometimes this can be avoided by facing the teeth of the broach toward the back of the press and permitting the bushing to protrude above the work to provide more support for the broach. After

which are hardened cutters with stepped teeth so that each tooth cuts only a definite amount as pushed or pulled through a part. These are available in inch and metric dimensions.

Broaching keyways (multiple pass method) is done as follows:

1. Choose the bushing that fits the bore and the broach, and put it in place in the bore.
2. Insert the correct size broach into the bushing slot (Figure 15).

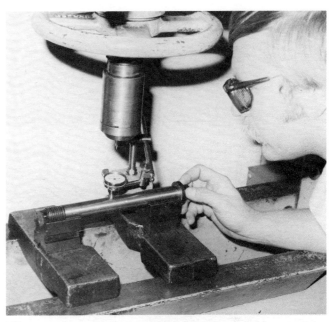

Figure 19. Part being indicated for runout prior to straightening (Lane Community College).

Figure 18. Production push broaching without bushings on shims (Courtesy of The duMont Corporation).

starting the cut, relieve the pressure to allow the broach to center itself. Repeat this procedure during each cut.

At least two or three teeth should be in contact with the work. If needed, stack two or more workpieces to lengthen the cut. The cut should never exceed the length of the standard bushing used with the broach. Never use a broach on material harder than Rockwell C35, one of many grades of a hardness test you will meet later in this book. If it is suspected that a part is harder than mild steel, its hardness should be determined before any broaching is attempted.

Use a good high pressure lubricant. Also apply a sulfur base cutting oil to the teeth of the broach. Always lubricate the back of the keyway broach to reduce friction, regardless of the material to be cut. Brass is usually broached dry, but bronzes cut better with oil or soluble oil. Cast iron is broached dry, and kerosene or cutting oil is recommended for aluminum.

Bending and Straightening
Bending and straightening are frequently done on hydraulic shop presses. Mechnical arbor presses are not usually used for this purpose. There is a definite safety hazard in this type of operation as a poor setup can allow pieces under pressure to suddenly fly out of the press. Brittle materials such as cast iron or hardened steel bearing races can suddenly break under pressure and explode into fragments.

A shaft to be straightened is placed between two nonprecision vee blocks — steel blocks with a vee-shaped groove running the length of the blocks that support a round workpiece. In the vee blocks, the shaft is rotated to detect runout, or the amount of bend in the shaft. The rotation is measured on a dial indicator, which is a device capable of detecting very small mechanical movements, and read from a calibrated dial. The high point is found and marked on the shaft (Figure 19). After removing the indicator, a soft metal pad such as copper is placed between the shaft and the ram and pressure is applied (Figure 20). The shaft should be bent back to a straight position and then very slightly beyond that point. The pressure is then removed and the dial indicator is again put in position. The shaft is rotated as before, and the position of the mark noted, as well as the amount of runout. If improvement has been found, continue the process; but if the first mark is not opposite the high point, too much pressure has been applied. Repeat the same steps, applying less pressure on opposite side.

Other straightening jobs on flat stock and other shapes are done in a similar fashion. Frequently, two or more bends will be found that may be opposite or are not in the same direction. This condition is best corrected by straightening one bend at a time and checking with a straight-edge and feeler gage. Special shop press tooling is sometimes used for simple bending jobs in the shop.

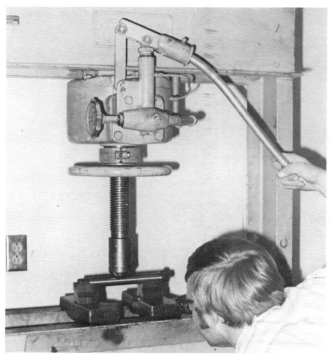

Figure 20. Pressure being applied to straighten shaft (Lane Community College).

SELF-TEST

1. Is it important to know how to use the arbor press properly and how to correctly set up pressing operations? Why?
2. What kinds of arbor presses are made? What makes them different from large commercial presses?
3. List several uses of the arbor press.
4. A newly machined steel shaft with an interference fit is pressed into the bore of a steel gear. The result is a shaft ruined beyond repair; the bore of the gear is also badly damaged. What has happened? What caused this failure?
5. The ram of an arbor press is loose in its guide and the pushing end is rounded off. What kind of problems could be caused by this?
6. A $\frac{1}{2}$ in. diameter bronze bushing is $\frac{1}{8}$ in. longer than the bore. Should you apply 30 tons of pressure to make sure it has seated on the press plate? If your answer is no, how much pressure should you apply?
7. If the inner race on a ball bearing is pressed onto a shaft, why should you not support the outer race while pushing the shaft off?
8. What difference is there in the way a press fit is obtained between mandrels and ordinary shafts?
9. Prior to installing a bushing with the arbor press, what two important steps must be taken?
10. Name five ways to avoid tool breakage and other problems when using push broaches for making keyways in the arbor press.

UNIT 3 NONCUTTING HAND TOOLS

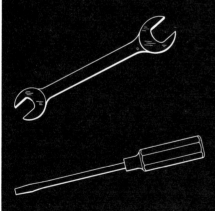

Hand tools are essential in all of the mechanical trades. This unit will help you learn the names and uses of most of the noncutting tools used by machinists.

OBJECTIVES

After completing this unit, you should be able to:
1. Identify the proper tool for a given job.
2. Determine the correct use of a selected tool.

CLAMPS

C-clamps (Figure 1) are used to hold workpieces on machines such as drill presses, and are also used for clamping parts together. The size of the clamp is determined by the largest opening of its jaws. The clamp shown in the top view (Figure 1) has a shielded screw.

The clamp screw is protected by a sheet metal cover. Thus, the screw is protected from dirt and damage. Parallel clamps (Figure 2) are used to hold small parts. Since they do not have as much holding power as C-clamps, this usually limits the use of parallel clamps to delicate work. Precision measuring setups are usually held in place with parallel clamps.

PLIERS

Pliers come in several shapes and with several types of jaw action. Simple combination or slip joint pliers (Figure 3) will do most jobs for which you need pliers. The slip joint allows the jaws to expand to grasp a larger size work. They are measured by overall length and are made in 5, 6, 8, and 10 in. sizes.

Interlocking joint pliers (Figure 4), or water pump pliers, were made to tighten packing gland nuts on water pumps on cars and trucks, but are useful for a variety of jobs. Pliers should never be used as a substitute for a wrench, as the nut or bolt head will be permanently deformed by the serrations in the plier jaws and the wrench will no longer fit properly. Round nose pliers (Figure 5) are used to make loops in wire and shape light

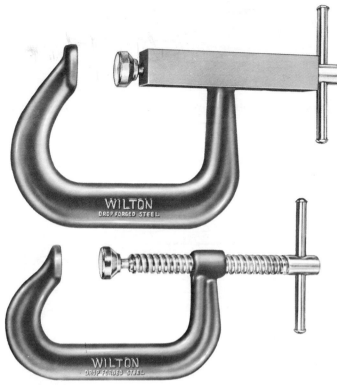

Figure 1. Two types of C-clamps (Courtesy of Wilton Corporation).

Figure 2. Single size parallel clamps (DeAnza College).

Figure 3. Slip joint or combination pliers (Courtesy of Snap-on Tools Corporation).

Figure 4. Interlocking joint or water pump pliers (Courtesy of Snap-on Tools Corporation).

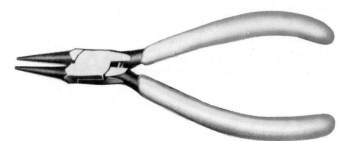

Figure 5. Round nose or wire looper pliers (Courtesy of Snap-on Tools Corporation).

Figure 6.   Needlenose pliers, straight (Courtesy of Snap-on Tools Corporation).

Figure 7.   Needlenose pliers, bent (Courtesy of Snap-on Tools Corporation).

Figure 8.   Side cutting pliers (Courtesy of Snap-on Tools Corporation).

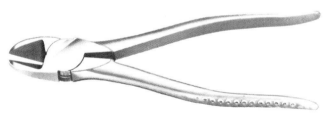

Figure 9.   Diagonal cutters (Courtesy of Snap-on Tools Corporation).

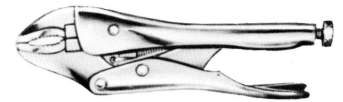

Figure 10.   Vise grip wrench (Courtesy of Snap-on Tools Corporation).

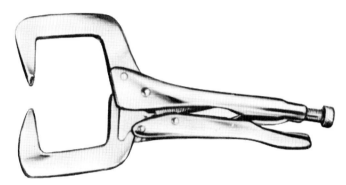

Figure 11.   Vise grip C-clamp (Courtesy of Snap-on Tools Corporation).

Figure 12.   Mall.

Figure 13.   Ball peen hammer.

metal. Needle nose pliers are used for holding small delicate workpieces in tight spots. They are available in both straight (Figure 6) and bent nose (Figure 7) types. Linemen's pliers (Figure 8) can be used for wire cutting and bending. Some types have wire stripping grooves and insulated handles. Diagonal cutters (Figure 9) are only used for wire cutting.

The lever-jawed locking wrench has an unusually high gripping power. The screw in the handle adjusts the lever action to the work size (Figure 10). They are made with special jaws for various uses such as the C-clamp type used in welding (Figure 11).

HAMMERS

Hammers are classified as either hard or soft. Hard hammers have steel heads such as blacksmith types or mauls made for heavy hammering (Figure 12). The ball peen hammer (Figure 13) is the one most frequently used by machinists. It has a rounded surface on one end of the head, which is used for upsetting or riveting metal and a hardened striking surface on the other. Two hammers should never be struck together on the face, as pieces could break off. Hammers are specified according to the weight of the head. Ball peen hammers range from two ounces to three pounds. Those under 10 ounces are

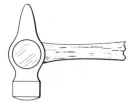

Figure 14. Straight peen hammer.

Figure 15. Cross peen hammer.

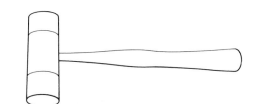

Figure 16. Plastic hammer.

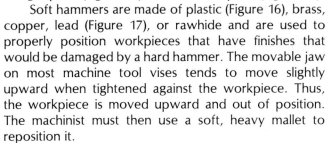

Figure 17. Lead hammer.

Figure 18. Adjustable wrench showing the correct direction of pull. Movable jaw should always face the direction of rotation (Courtesy of Snap-on Tools Corporation).

Figure 19. Open end wrench (Courtesy of Snap-on Tools Corporation).

Figure 20. Box wrench (Courtesy of Snap-on Tools Corporation).

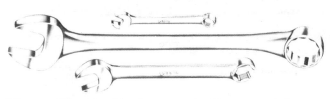

Figure 21. Combination wrench (Courtesy of Snap-on Tools Corporation).

used for layout work. Two other shop hammers are the straight peen (Figure 14) and the cross peen (Figure 15).

Soft hammers are made of plastic (Figure 16), brass, copper, lead (Figure 17), or rawhide and are used to properly position workpieces that have finishes that would be damaged by a hard hammer. The movable jaw on most machine tool vises tends to move slightly upward when tightened against the workpiece. Thus, the workpiece is moved upward and out of position. The machinist must then use a soft, heavy mallet to reposition it.

WRENCHES

A large variety of wrenches is made for different uses such as turning cap screws, bolts, and nuts. The adjustable wrench (Figure 18) is a general purpose tool and will not suit every job, especially those requiring work in close quarters. The wrench should be rotated toward the movable jaw and should fit the nut or bolt tightly. The size of the wrench is determined by its overall length in inches.

Open end wrenches (Figure 19) are best suited to square-headed bolts, and usually fit two sizes, one on each end. The ends on this type of wrench are also angled so they can be used in close quarters. Box wrenches (Figure 20) are also double ended and offset to clear the user's hand. The box completely surrounds the nut or bolt and usually has 12 points so that the wrench can be reset after rotating only a partial turn. Mostly used on hex-headed bolts, these wrenches have the advantage of precise fit. Combination and open end wrenches are made with a box at one end and an open end at the other (Figure 21).

Socket wrenches are similar to box wrenches in that they also surround the bolt or nut and usually are made with 12 points contacting the six-sided nut. Sockets are made to be detached from various types of drive handles (Figure 22).

Pipe wrenches, as the name implies, are used for holding and turning pipe. These wrenches have sharp serrated teeth and will damage any finished part on which they are used (Figure 23). Strap wrenches (Figure

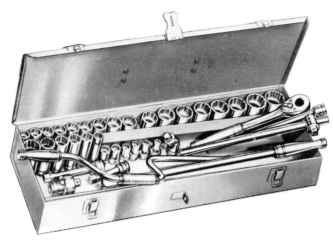

Figure 22. Socket wrench set (Courtesy of Snap-on Tools Corporation).

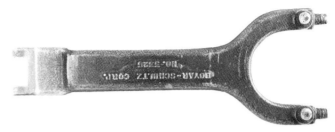

Figure 25. Fixed face spanner.

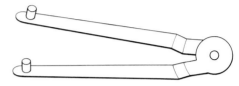

Figure 26. Adjustable face spanner.

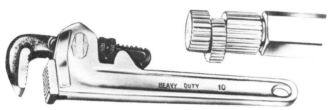

Figure 23. Pipe wrenches, external and internal (Courtesy of Snap-on Tools Corporation).

Figure 27. Hook spanner.

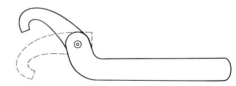

Figure 28. Adjustable hook spanner.

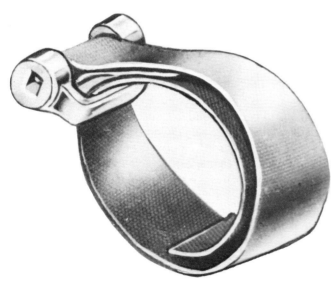

Figure 24. Strap wrench (Courtesy of Snap-on Tools Corporation).

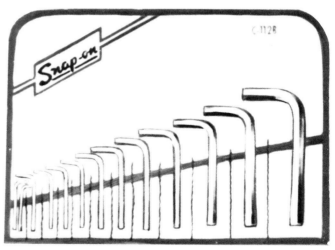

Figure 29. Socket head wrench set (Courtesy of Snap-on Tools Corporation).

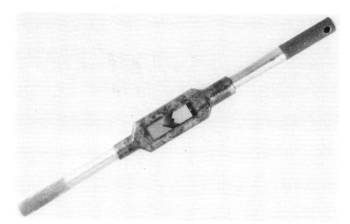

Figure 30.   Hand tap wrench.

Figure 31.   T-handle tap wrench.

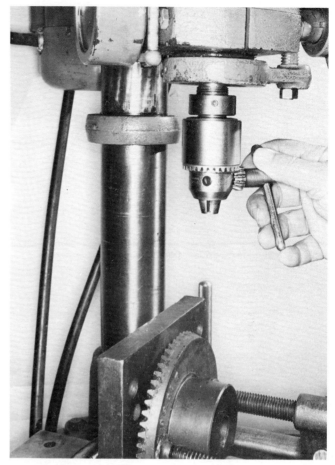

Figure 32.   Chuck key and drill chuck in use (Lane Community College).

24) are used for extremely large parts or to avoid marring the surface of tubular parts.

Spanner wrenches come in several basic types including face and hook. Face types are sometimes called pin spanners (Figure 25). Spanners are made in fixed sizes or adjustable types (Figures 26, 27, and 28).

Socket head wrenches (Figure 29) are six-sided bars having a 90-degree bend near one end. They are used with socket head cap screws and socket set screws.

The hand tap wrench (Figure 30) is used for medium and large size taps. The T-handle tap wrench (Figure 31) is used for small taps $\frac{1}{4}$ inch and under, as its more sensitive ''feel'' results in less tap breakage.

Here are safety hints for using wrenches:

1. Make sure the wrench you select fits properly. If it is a loose fit, it may round off the corners of the nut or bolt head.
2. Pull on a wrench instead of pushing to avoid injury.
3. Never use a wrench on moving machinery.
4. Do not hammer on a wrench or extend the handle for additional leverage. Use a larger wrench.

Chuck keys (Figure 32) are used to open and close chucks on drill presses and electric hand drills. Their size is determined by the size of the chuck. They should never be left in a chuck, as they can become a dangerous missile as soon as the machine is turned on. Some keys are designed with a spring mechanism so they will slip out of the chuck when released. These are called **safety keys.**

SCREWDRIVERS
The two types of screwdrivers that are most used are

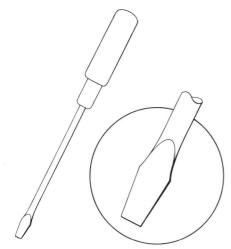

Figure 33. Screwdriver, standard.

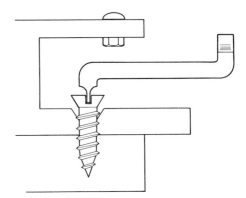

Figure 35. Offset screwdriver in use.

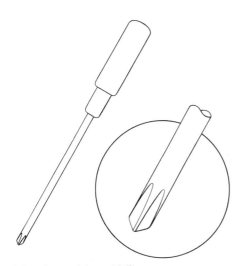

Figure 34. Screwdriver, Phillips.

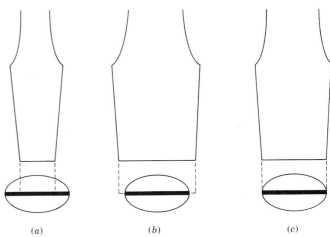

(a)   (b)   (c)

Figure 36. The proper width of a screwdriver blade: (a) Too narrow, (b) too wide, and (c) correct width.

the standard (Figure 33) and Phillips (Figure 34). Both types are made in various sizes and in several styles, straight, shank, and offset (Figure 35). It is important to use the right width blade when installing or removing screws (Figure 36). The shape of the tip is important also. If the tip is badly worn or incorrectly ground, it will tend to jump out of the slot. The correct method of grinding a standard screwdriver is shown in Figure 37. Be careful not to overheat the tip when grinding, as it will become soft. Never use a screwdriver for a chisel or pry bar. Keep a screwdriver in proper shape by using it only on the screws for which it was meant.

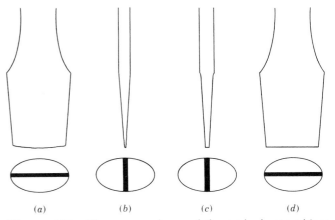

(a)   (b)   (c)   (d)

Figure 37. The proper shape of the end of screwdriver blade. Blades (a) and (b) are badly worn; blades (c) and (d) are ground correctly.

SELF-TEST

1. A four-inch machinist bench vise has jaws four inches on each side. True _____ False _____
2. What is the purpose of false jaws or jaw caps?
3. Parallel clamps are used for heavy duty clamping work, and C-clamps are used for holding precision setups. True _____ False _____
4. In order to remove a nut or bolt, slip joint or water pump pliers make a good substitute for a wrench when a wrench is not handy. True _____ False _____
5. What advantage does the lever jawed wrench offer over other similar tools such as pliers?
6. Would you use a three-pound ball peen hammer for lay-out work? If not, what size do you think is right?
7. Some objects should never be struck with a hard hammer, a finished machine surface or the end of a shaft, for instance. What could you use to avoid damage?
8. A machine has a capscrew that needs to be tightened and released quite often. Which wrench would be best to use in this case; the adjustable or box-type wrench? Why?
9. Why should pipe wrenches never be used on bolts, nuts, or shafts?
10. What are two important things to remember about standard screwdrivers that will help you avoid problems in their use?

UNIT 4 HACKSAWS

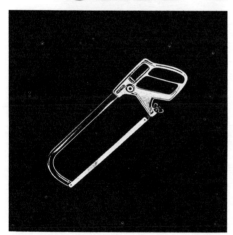

Hacksaws are one of the more frequently used hand tools. The hand hacksaw is a relatively simple tool to use, but the facts and rules contained in this unit will help you improve your use of the hacksaw.

OBJECTIVE

After completing this unit, you should be able to: Identify, select, and use hand hacksaws.

The hacksaw consists of three parts: the frame, the handle, and the saw blade (Figure 1). Frames are either the solid or adjustable type. The solid frame can only be used with one length of saw blade. The adjustable frame can be used with hacksaw blades from 8 to 12 in. in length. The blade can be mounted to cut in line with the frame or at a right angle to the frame. (Figures 2a and 2b). By turning the blade at right angles to the frame, you can continue a cut that is deeper than the capacity of the frame. If the blade is left in line with the frame, the frame will eventually hit the workpiece and limit the depth of cut.

Most hacksaw blades are made from high speed steel, and in standard lenghts of 8, 10, and 12 in. Blade length is the distance between the centers of the holes at each end. Hand hacksaw blades are generally $\frac{1}{2}$ in. wide and .025 inch thick. The kerf or cut produced by the hacksaw is wider than the .025 inch thickness of the blade because of the set of the teeth (Figure 3).

The set refers to the bending of teeth outward from the blade itself. Two kinds of set are found on hand hacksaw blades. The first is the straight or alternate set (Figure 4) where one tooth is bent to the right and the

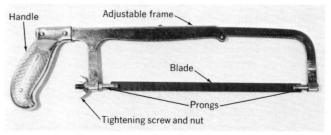

Figure 1. The parts of a hacksaw.

Figure 2a. Straight sawing with a hacksaw (Lane Community College).

Figure 2b. Sawing with the blade set at 90 degrees to the frame (Lane Community College).

next tooth to the left for the length of the blade. The second kind of set is the wavy set in which a number of teeth are gradually bent to the right and then to the left (Figure 5). A wavy set is found on most fine tooth hacksaw blades.

The spacing of the teeth on a hand hacksaw blade is called the pitch and is expressed in teeth per inch of length (Figure 6). Standard pitches are 14, 18, 24, and 32 teeth per inch, with the 18 pitch blade used as a general purpose blade.

The hardness and size or thickness of a workpiece determine to a great extent which pitch blade to use. As a rule, you should use a coarse tooth blade on soft materials, to have sufficient clearance for the chips, and a fine tooth blade on harder materials. But you also should have at least three teeth cutting at any time, which may require a fine tooth blade on soft materials with thin cross sections.

Hand hacksaw blades fall into two categories: soft-backed or flexible blades and all-hard blades. On the flexible blades only the teeth are hardened, the back being tough and flexible. The flexible blade is less likely to break when used in places difficult to get at such as in cutting off bolts on machinery. The all-hard blade is, as

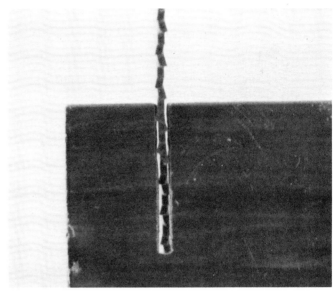

Figure 3. The kerf is wider than the blade because of the set of the teeth (Lane Community College).

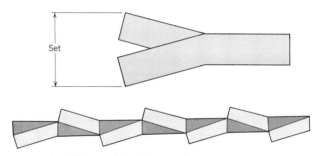

Figure 4. The straight (alternate) set.

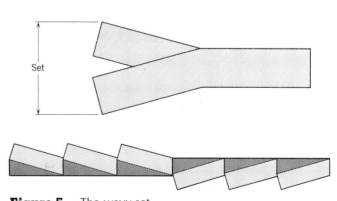

Figure 5. The wavy set.

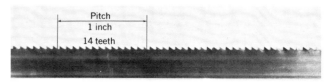

Figure 6. The pitch of the blade is expressed as the number of teeth per inch (Lane Community College).

Figure 7. A new blade must be started on the opposite side of the work, not in the same kerf as the old blade (Lane Community College).

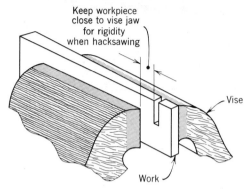

Figure 8. The workpiece is being sawed close to the vise to avoid vibration and chatter (Lane Community College).

the name implies, hard and very brittle and should be used only where the workpiece can be rigidly supported, as in a vise. On an all-hard blade even a slight twisting motion may break the blade. All-hard blades, in the hands of a skilled person, will cut true straight lines and give long service.

The blades are mounted in the frame with the teeth pointing away from the handle so that the hacksaw cuts only on the forward stroke. No cutting pressure should be applied to the blade on the return stroke as this tends to dull the teeth. The sawing speed with a hacksaw should be from 40 to 60 strokes per minute. To get the maximum performance from a blade, make long, slow, and steady strokes using the full length of the blade. Sufficient pressure should be maintained on the forward stroke to keep the teeth cutting. Teeth on a saw blade will dull rapidly if too little or too much pressure is put on the saw. The teeth will dull also if too fast a cutting stroke is used; a speed in excess of 60 strokes a minute will dull the blade because friction will overheat the teeth.

The saw blade may break if it is too loose in the frame or if the workpiece slips in the vise while sawing. Too much pressure may also cause the blade to break. A badly worn blade where the set has been worn down,

will cut a too narrow kerf, which will cause binding and perhaps breakage of the blade. When this happens and a new blade is used to finish the cut, turn the workpiece over and start with the new blade from the opposite side and make a cut to meet the first one (Figure 7). The set on the new blade is wider than the old kerf. Forcing the new blade into an old cut will immediately ruin it by wearing the set down.

A cut on a workpiece should be started with only light cutting pressure, with the thumb or fingers on one hand acting as a guide for the blade. Sometimes it helps to start a blade when a small vee-notch is filed in the workpiece. When a workpiece is supported in a vise, make sure that the cutting is done close to the vise jaws for a rigid setup free of chatter (Figure 8). Work should be positioned in a vise so that the saw cut is vertical. This makes it easier for the saw to follow a straight line. At the end of a saw cut, just before the pieces are completely parted, reduce the cutting pressure or you may be caught off balance when the pieces come apart and cut your hands on the sharp edges of the workpiece. To saw thin material, sandwich it between two pieces of wood for a straight cut. Avoid bending the saw blades because they are likely to break, and when they do, they usually shatter in all directions and could injure you or others nearby.

SELF-TEST

1. What is the kerf?
2. What is the set on a saw blade?
3. What is the pitch of the hacksaw blade?
4. What determines the selection of a saw blade for a job?
5. Hand hacksaw blades fall into two basic categories. What are they?
6. What speed should be used in hand hacksawing?

7. Give four causes that make saw blades dull.
8. Give two reasons why hacksaw blades break.
9. A new hacksaw blade should not be used in a cut started with a blade that has been used. Why?
10. What dangers exist when a hacksaw blade breaks while it is being used?

UNIT 5 FILES AND OFF-HAND GRINDING

Files are often used to put the finishing touches on a machined workpiece, either to remove burrs or sharp edges or as a final fitting operation. Intricate parts or shapes are often entirely produced by skilled craftsmen using files. In this unit you are introduced to the types and uses of files in metalworking.

Although really a machine tool, the pedestal grinder is used for many hand grinding operations, especially in sharpening and shaping tool bits. In this unit you will study the setup, use, and safety aspects of this important machine.

OBJECTIVES

After completing this unit, you should be able to:
1. Identify eight common files and some of their uses.
2. Describe setup, use, and safety on the pedestal grinder.

TYPES OF FILES

Files are tools that anyone in metalwork will use. Often, through lack of knowledge, these tools are misused. Files are made in many different lengths ranging from 4 to 18 in. (Figure 1). Files are manufactured in many different **shapes** and are used for many specific purposes. Figure 2 shows the parts of a file. When a file is measured, the length is taken from the heel to the point, with the tang excluded. Most files are made from high carbon steel and are heat-treated to the correct hardness range. They are manufactured in four different cuts: single, double, curved tooth, and rasp. The single cut, double cut, and curved tooth are commonly encountered in machine shops (Figure 3). Rasps are usually used with wood. Curved tooth files will give excellent results with soft materials such as aluminum, brass, plastic, or lead.

Files also vary in their **coarseness: rough, coarse, bastard, second cut, smooth,** and **dead smooth.** The files most often used are the bastard, second cut, and smooth grades. Different sizes of files within the same coarseness designation will have varying sizes of teeth (Figure 4): the longer the file, the coarser the teeth. For maximum metal removal a double cut file is used. If the emphasis is on a smooth finish, a single cut file is recommended.

The face of most files is slightly convex (Figure 5) because they are made thicker in the middle than on the ends. Through this curvature only some teeth are cutting at any one time, which makes them penetrate better. If the face were flat, it would be difficult to obtain an even

surface because of the tendency to rock a file while filing. Some of this curvature is also offset by the pressure applied to make the file cut. New files do not cut as well as slightly used ones, since on new files some teeth are longer than most others and leave scratches on a workpiece.

Files are either blunt or tapered (Figure 6). A blunt file has the same cross-sectional area from heel to point, where a tapered file narrows toward the point.

Files fall into five basic categories: **mill** and **saw** files,

Figure 1. Files are made in several different lengths (Lane Community College).

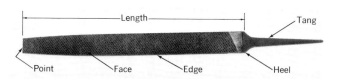

Figure 2. The parts of a file.

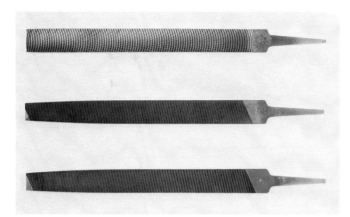

Figure 3. Three files that are frequently found in machine shops are the curved tooth, double cut, and single cut files (De Anza College).

Figure 4. These two files are both bastard cut, but since they are of different lengths, they have different coarsenesses (Lane Community College).

Figure 5. The edge of this file shows the convex face (Lane Community College).

machinists' files, **Swiss pattern files, curved tooth** files, and **rasps.** Machinists' and mill and saw files are classified as American pattern files. Mill files (Figure 7) were originally designed to sharpen large saws in lumber mills, but now they are used for draw filing, filing on a lathe (Figure 8), or filing a finish on a workpiece. Mill files are single cut and work well on brass and bronze. Mill files are slightly thinner than an equal-sized flat file, a machinist's file (Figure 9) that is usually double cut. Double cut files are used when fast cutting is needed. The finish produced is relatively rough.

Figure 6. Blunt and tapered file shapes (DeAnza College).

Figure 7. A mill file (DeAnza College).

Figure 8. The lathe file has a longer angle on the teeth to clear the chips when filing on the lathe (DeAnza College).

Figure 9. The flat file is usually a double cut file (DeAnza College).

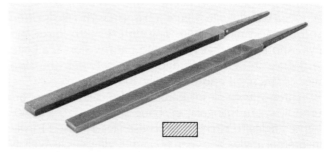

Figure 10. Two pillar files (Lane Community College).

Pillar files (Figure 10) have a narrower but thicker cross section than flat files. Pillar files are parallel in width and taper slightly in thickness. They also have one or two safe edges that allow filing into a corner without

Figure 11. The square file (Lane Community College).

Figure 12. Warding file (Lane Community College).

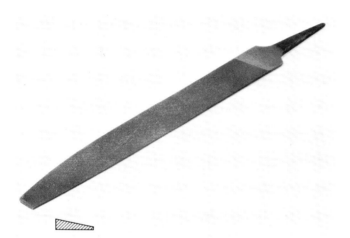

Figure 13. Knife file (Lane Community College).

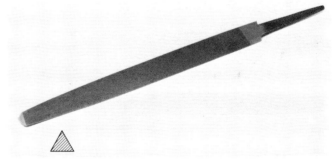

Figure 14. Three-square files are used for filing angles between 60 and 90 degrees (Lane Community College).

Figure 15. Half-round files are used for internal curves (Lane Community College).

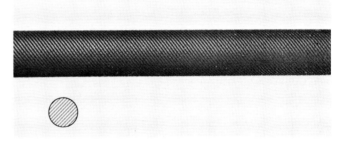

Figure 16. Round files are used to file a small radius or to enlarge a hole (DeAnza College).

damaging the shoulder. **Square** files (Figure 11) usually are double cut and are used to file in keyways, slots, or holes.

If a very thin file is needed with a rectangular cross section, a **warding** file (Figure 12) is used. This file is often used by locksmiths when filing notches into locks and keys. Another file that will fit into narrow slots is a knife file (Figure 13). The included angle between the two faces of this file is approximately 10 degrees.

Three-square files (Figure 14), also called three-cornered files, are triangular in shape with the faces at 60-degree angles to each other. These files are used for filing internal angles between 60 and 90 degrees as well as to make sharp corners in square holes. Half-round files (Figure 15) are available to file large internal curves. Half-round files, because of their tapered construction, can be used to file many different radii. Round files (Figure 16) are used to file small radii or to enlarge holes. These files are available in many diameter sizes.

Swiss pattern files (Figure 17) are manufactured to much closer tolerances than American pattern files, but are made in the same shapes. Swiss pattern files are more slender as they taper to finer points and their teeth extend to the extreme edges. Swiss pattern files range in length from 3 to 10 in. and their coarseness is indicated by numbers from 00 (coarse) to 6 (fine). Swiss pattern files are made with tangs to be used with file handles or as needle files with round or square handles that are part of the files. Another type of Swiss pattern files are **die sinkers' rifflers** (Figure 18). These files are double-ended with cutting surfaces on either end. Swiss pattern files are used primarily by tool and die makers, mold makers, and other craftsmen engaged in precision filing on delicate instruments.

Curved tooth files (Figure 19) cut very freely and remove material rapidly. The teeth on curved tooth files

Figure 17. A set of Swiss pattern files. Since these small files are very delicate and can be broken quite easily, great care must be exercised in their use (DeAnza College).

Figure 18. Die sinker's rifflers.

Figure 19. Curved tooth files are used on soft metals (DeAnza College).

Figure 20. A file with a safe edge will not cut into shoulders or corners when filing is being done (DeAnza College).

Figure 21. Thread files (Lane Community College).

are all of equal height and the gullets or valleys between teeth are deep and provide sufficient room for the filings to curl and drop free. Curved tooth files are manufactured in three grades of cut — standard, fine, and smooth — and in lengths from 8 to 14 inches. These files are made as rigid tang types for use with a file handle, or as rigid or flexible blade types used with special handles. Curved tooth file shapes are flat, half-round, pillar, and square.

The **bastard cut** file (Figure 20) has a safe edge that is smooth. Flat filing may be done up to the shoulders of the workpiece without fear of damage. Files of other cuts and coarseness are also available with safe edges on one or both sides.

Thread files (Figure 21) are used to clean up and reshape damaged threads. They are square in cross section and have eight different thread pitches on each file. The thread file of the correct pitch is most effectively used when held or stroked against the thread while it is rotating in a lathe. A thread can be repaired, however, even when it cannot be turned in a lathe.

CARE AND USE OF FILES

Files do an efficient job of cutting only while they are sharp. Files and their teeth are very hard and brittle. Do not use a file as a hammer or as a pry bar. When a file breaks, particles will fly quite a distance at high speed and may cause an injury. Files should be stored so that they are not in contact with any other file. The same applies to files on a workbench. Do not let files lie on top of each other because one file will break teeth on the other file (Figure 22). Teeth on files will also break if

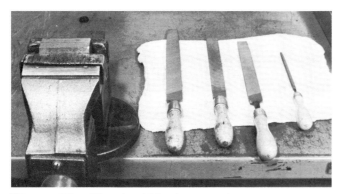

Figure 22. Files should be kept neatly arranged so that they will not strike each other and damage the cutting edges (Lane Community College).

Figure 23. Using a file card to clean a file (DeAnza College).

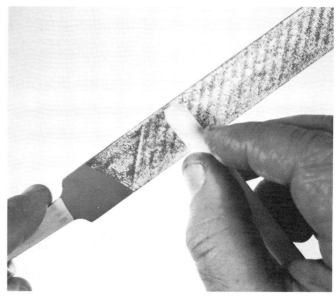

Figure 24. Using chalk on the file to help reduce pinning (DeAnza College).

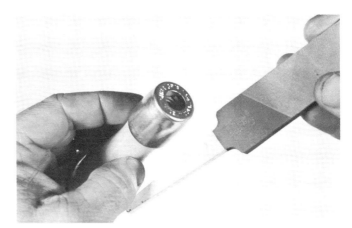

Figure 25 a. A file should never be used without a file handle (DeAnza College).

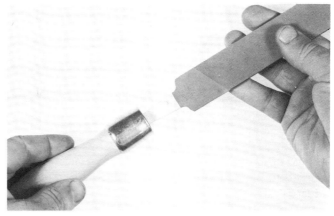

Figure 25 b. This style of handle is designed to screw on rather than be driven on the tang (DeAnza College).

too much pressure is put on them while filing. On the other hand, if not enough pressure is applied while filing, the file only rubs the workpiece and dulls the teeth. A dull file can be identified by its shiny, smooth teeth and by the way it slides over the work without cutting. Dulling of teeth is also caused by the filing of hard materials or when filing too fast. A good filing speed is 40 to 50 strokes per minute, but remember that the harder the material, the slower the strokes should be; the softer the material, the coarser the file should be.

Too much pressure on a new file may cause **pinning,** that is, filings wedged in the teeth; the result is deep scratches on the work surface. If the pins cannot be removed with a file card, try a piece of brass, copper, or mild steel and push it through the teeth (Figure 23). Do not use a scriber or other hard object for this operation. A file will not pin as much if some blackboard chalk is applied to the face (Figure 24). *Never use a file without a file handle or the pointed tang may cause serious hand or wrist injury* (Figures 25 a and 25 b).

Figure 26. Workpiece in vise with protective jaws. The work extends only $\frac{1}{4}$ in. from the vise jaws for better rigidity (Lane Community College).

Figure 27. The cross-hatch pattern shows that this piece has been filed from two directions thus producing a flatter surface (Lane Community College).

Figure 28. Proper filing position (Lane Community College).

Figure 29. Draw filing (Lane Community College).

Many filing operations are performed with the workpiece held in a vise. Clamp the workpiece securely, but remember to protect it from the serrated vise jaws with some soft piece of material such as copper, brass, wood, or paper (Figure 26). The workpiece should extend out of the vise so that the file clears the vise jaws by $\frac{1}{8}$ to $\frac{1}{4}$ in. Since a file cuts only on the forward stroke, no pressure should be applied on the return stroke. Letting the file drag over the workpiece on the return stroke helps release the small chips so that they can fall from the file. However, this can also dull the file and scratch the part, so do it cautiously.

Use a stroke as long as possible; this will make the file wear out evenly instead of just in the middle. To file a flat surface, change the direction of the strokes fre-

quently to produce a cross-hatch pattern (Figure 27). By using a straightedge steel rule to test for flatness, we can easily determine where the high spots are that have to be filed away. It is best to make flatness checks often because, if any part is filed below a given layout line, the rest of the workpiece may have to be brought down just as far.

Figure 28 shows how a file should be held to file a flat surface. A smooth finish is usually obtained by draw filing (Figure 29), where a single cut file is held with both hands and drawn back and forth on a workpiece. The file should not be pushed over the ends of the workpiece as this would leave rounded edges. To get a smooth finish it sometimes helps to hold the file as shown in Figure 30, making only short strokes. The pres-

Figure 30. Use this procedure to correct high spots on curvatures on the workpiece. Apply pressure with short strokes only where cutting is needed (Lane Community College).

Figure 31. Using a piece of wood to hold the wheel while removing the spindle nut (Lane Community College).

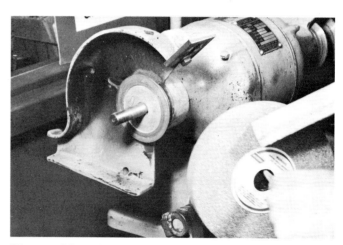

Figure 32. The ring test is made before mounting the wheel (Lane Community College).

sure is applied by a few fingers and does not extend over the ends of the workpiece. When a round file or half-round file is used, the forward stroke should also include a clockwise rotation for deeper cuts and a smoother finish. A tendency of people who are filing is to run their hands or fingers over a newly filed surface. This deposits a thin coat of skin oil on the surface. When filing is resumed, the file will not cut for several strokes, but will only slip over the surface causing the file to dull more quickly.

OFF-HAND GRINDING ON PEDESTAL GRINDERS

The **pedestal grinder** is really a machine tool. However, since the workpiece is hand held, it is more logical to discuss this machine in conjunction with cutting hand tools. Furthermore, you must be familiar with the pedestal grinder, as you will be using it very early in your study of machine tool practices.

The pedestal grinder gets its name from the floor stand or pedestal that supports the motor and abrasive wheels. The pedestal grinder is a common machine tool that you will use almost daily in the machine shop. This grinding machine is used for general purpose, **off-hand grinding** where the workpiece is hand held and applied to the rapidly rotating abrasive wheel. One of the primary functions of the pedestal grinder is the shaping and sharpening of tool bits and drills in machine shop work. Pedestal grinders are often modified for use with rotary wire brushes or buffing wheels.

Setup of the Pedestal Grinder

The pedestal grinder in your shop stands ready for use most of the time. If it becomes necessary to replace a worn wheel, the side of the guard must be removed and the tool rest moved out of the way. A piece of wood may be used to prevent the wheel from rotating so that the spindle nut can be turned and removed (Figure 31). Remember that the **left side** of the spindle has **left-handed** threads, while those on the **right side** are **right-handed.**

A new wheel should be **ring tested** to determine if there are any cracks or imperfections (Figure 32). Gently tap the wheel near its rim with a screwdriver handle or a piece of wood and listen for a clear ringing sound like a bell. A clear ring indicates a sound wheel that is safe to use, but if a dull thud is heard, the wheel may be cracked and **should not be used.** The flanges and the spindle should be clean before mounting the wheel. Be sure that

Figure 33. The wheel is mounted with the proper bushing in place (Lane Community College).

Figure 35. The spark guard is adjusted (Lane Community College).

Figure 34. The tool rest is adjusted (Lane Community College).

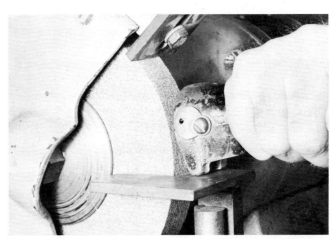

Figure 36. The wheel is being dressed (Lane Community College).

the center hole in the wheel is the correct size for the grinder spindle. If a bushing must be used, be sure that it is the correct size and properly installed (Figure 33). Place a clean, undamaged blotter on each side between wheel and flanges. The spindle nut should be tightened just enough to hold the wheel firmly. **Excessive tightening will break the wheel.**

After the guard and cover plate have been replaced, the tool rest should be brought up to the wheel so that between $\frac{1}{16}$ and $\frac{1}{8}$ **inch clearance** exists between the rest and wheel (Figure 34). If there is excessive space between the tool rest and the wheel, a small workpiece, such as a tool bit that is being ground, may flip up and catch between the wheel and tool rest. Your finger may be caught between workpiece and grinding wheel resulting in a serious injury. The **clearance** between the tool rest and wheel should **never exceed $\frac{1}{8}$ inch.** The **spark guard,** located on the upper side of the

wheel guard (Figure 35), should be adjusted to **within $\frac{1}{16}$ inch** of the wheel. This protects the operator if the wheel should shatter.

Using the Pedestal Grinder

Stand aside out of line with the rotation of the grinding wheel and turn on the grinder. **Let the wheel run idle for one full minute.** A new wheel does not always run exactly true and therefore must be dressed (Figure 36). A Desmond **dresser** may be used to true the face of the wheel. Pedestal grinder wheels often become grooved, out of round, glazed, or misshapen, and must be frequently dressed to obtain proper grinding results.

The grinding wheel dresser (Figure 36) should be used so that the notch on the lower side is hooked behind the work rest. Many times you will see the dresser used as shown in the figure. If possible it should be hooked behind the work rest.

Bring the workpiece into contact with the wheel gently without bumping. Grind only **on the face** of the wheel. The workpiece will heat from friction during the grinding operation. It may become too hot to hold in just a few seconds. To prevent this, cool the workpiece in the water pot attached to the grinder. Be especially careful when grinding drills and tool bits so that they do not become overheated. Excessive heat may permanently affect tool steel metallurgical properties.

Safety Checkpoints on the Pedestal Grinder

Always wear appropriate **eye protection** when dressing wheels or grinding on the pedestal grinder. Be sure that grinding wheels are rated at the proper speed for the grinder that you are using. The safety shields, wheel guards, and spark guard must be kept in place at all times while grinding. The tool rest must be adjusted and the setting corrected as the diameter of the wheel decreases from use. Grinding wheels and rotary wire brushes **may catch loose clothing or long hair** (Figure 37). Long hair should be contained in an industrial type hair net. Wire wheels **often throw out** small pieces of wire at high velocities.

Nonferrous metals such as aluminum and brass should never be ground on the **aluminum oxide** wheels found on most pedestal grinders. These metals fill the voids or spaces between the abrasive particles in the grinding wheel so that more pressure is needed to accomplish the desired grinding. This additional **pressure** sometimes causes the **wheel to break or shatter.** Pieces of grinding wheel may be thrown out of the machine at extreme velocities. Always use **silicon carbide** abrasive wheels **for grinding nonferrous metals.** Excessive pressure should **never** be used in any grinding operation. If this seems to be necessary, the improper grit or grade of abrasive is being used, or the wheel is glazed and

Figure 37. The force and speed of this action was such that the operator's head was jerked suddenly into the guard. Note that the cast aluminum guard was shattered as a result of the impact.

needs to be dressed. Always use the **correct** abrasive **grit** and **grade** for the particular grinding that you are doing.

Grinding wheel **grit** refers to the size of the abrasive used in the wheel. Coarse grit will remove metal from the workpiece faster than fine grit. Grinding wheel **grade** refers to the strength of the bond holding the abrasive particles in the wheel. A hard grade would have a strong bond and a soft grade would have a weaker bond.

SELF-TEST

1. How is a file identified?
2. What are the four different cuts found on files?
3. Name four coarseness designations for files.
4. Which of the two kinds of files — single cut or double cut — is designed to remove more material?
5. Why are the faces of most files slightly convex?
6. What difference is there between a blunt and a tapered file?
7. What difference exists between a mill file and an equal-sized flat file?
8. What is a warding file?
9. An American pattern file differs in what way from a Swiss pattern file?
10. What are the coarseness designations for needle files?
11. Why should files be stored so they do not touch each other?
12. What happens if too much pressure is applied when filing?
13. What causes a file to get dull?
14. Why should a handle be used on a file?
15. Why should workpieces be measured often?
16. What happens when a surface being filed is touched with the hand or fingers?
17. How does the hardness of a workpiece affect the selection of a file?
18. How can rounded edges be avoided when a workpiece is drawfiled?
19. Should pressure be applied to a file on the return stroke?
20. Why is a round file rotated while it is being used?
21. Describe safety factors on the pedestal grinder.

UNIT 6 HAND REAMERS

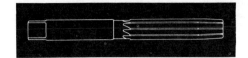

Holes produced by drilling are seldom accurate in size and often have rough surfaces. A reamer is used to finish a hole to an exact dimension with a smooth finish. This unit will describe some commonly used hand reamers and how they are used.

OBJECTIVES

After completing this unit, you should be able to:
1. Identify at least five types of hand reamers.
2. Hand ream a hole to a specified size.

Hand reamers are often used to finish a previously drilled hole to an exact dimension and a smooth surface. When parts of machine tools are aligned and fastened with cap screws or bolts, the final operation is often the hand reaming of a hole in which a dowel pin is placed to maintain the alignment. Hand reamers are designed to remove only a small amount of material from a hole — usually from .001 to .005 in. These tools are made from high carbon or high speed steel.

FEATURES OF HAND REAMERS

Figure 1 shows the major features of the most common design of hand reamer. Another design is available with a pilot ahead of the starting taper (see *Machinery's Handbook* for details). The square on the end of the shank permits the clamping of a tap wrench or T-handle wrench to provide the driving torque for reaming. The diameter of this square is between .004 and .008 in. smaller than the reamer size, and the shank of the reamer is between .001 and .006 in. smaller, to guide the reamer and permit it to pass through a reamed hole without marring it. It is very important that these tools **not** be put into a drill chuck, because a burred shank can ruin a reamed hole as the shank is passed through it.

Hand reamers have a long starting taper that is usually as long as the diameter of the reamer, but may be as long as one third of the fluted body. This starting taper is usually very slight and may not be apparent at a casual glance. Hand reamers do their cutting on this tapered portion. The gentle taper and length of the taper help to start the reamer straight and keep it aligned in the hole.

Details of the cutting end of the hand reamer are shown in Figure 2. The full diameter or actual size of the hand reamer is measured where the starting taper ends and the margin of the land appears. The diameter of the reamer should only be measured at this junction, as the

hand reamer is generally back tapered or reduced in outside diameter by about .0005 to .001 in. per inch of length toward the shank. This back tapering is done to reduce tool contact with the workpiece. When hand reamers become dull, they are resharpened at the starting taper, using a tool and cutter grinder.

The function of the hand reamer is like that of a scraper, rather than an aggressive cutting tool like most drills and machine reamers. For this reason hand reamers typically have zero or negative radial rake on the cutting

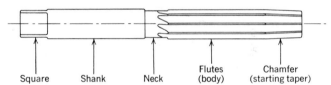

Figure 1. Major features of the hand reamer.

Square   Shank   Neck   Flutes (body)   Chamfer (starting taper)

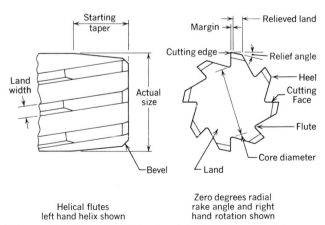

Figure 2. Functional details of the hand reamer (Courtesy of Bendix Industrial Tools Division).

face, rather than the positive radial rake characteristic of most machine reamers. (See Section G, Unit 7, ''Reaming in the Drill Press''.) The right-hand cut with a left hand helix is considered standard for hand reamers. The left-hand helix produces a negative axial rake for the tool, which contributes to a smooth cutting action.

Most reamers, hand or machine types have staggered spacing on teeth, which means that the flutes or body channels are not precisely of uniform spacing. The difference is very small, only a degree or two, but it tends to reduce chatter by reducing harmonic effects between cutting edges. Harmonic chatter is especially a problem with adjustable hand reamers which often leave a tooth pattern in the work.

Hand reamers are made with straight flutes (Figure 3) or with helical flutes (Figure 4). Most hand reamers are manufactured with a right-hand cut, which means they will cut when rotated in a clockwise direction. Helical or spiral fluted reamers are available with a right-hand helix or a left-hand helix. Helical flute reamers are especially useful when reaming a hole having keyways or grooves cut into it, as the helical flutes tend to bridge the gaps and reduce binding or chattering.

Hand reamers for cylindrical holes are made as solid (Figures 3 and 4) or as expansion types (Figure 5). Expansion reamers are designed for use where it is necessary to enlarge a hole slightly for proper fit such as in maintenance applications. These reamers have an adjusting screw that allows limited expansion to an exact size. The maximum expansion of these reamers is approximately .006 in. for diameters up to $\frac{1}{2}$ in., .010 in. for diameters between $\frac{1}{2}$ and 1 in., and .012 in. for diameters between 1 and $1\frac{1}{2}$ in. These tools are frequently broken by attempts to expand them beyond these limits.

Helical flute expansion reamers are especially adapted for the reaming of bushings or holes having a keyway or straight grooves because of their bridging and shearing cutting action. Expansion reamers have a slightly undersized pilot on the end that guides the reamer and helps to keep it in alignment.

The adjustable hand reamer (Figure 6) is different from the expansion reamer in that it has inserted blades. These cutting blades fit into tapered slots in the body of the reamer and are held in place by two locking nuts. The blades have a taper corresponding to the taper of the slots that keeps them parallel at any setting. Adjustments in reamer size are made by loosening one nut while tightening the other. Adjustable hand reamers are available in diameters from $\frac{1}{4}$ to 3 in. The adjustment range varies from $\frac{1}{32}$ in. on the smaller diameter reamers to $\frac{5}{16}$ in. on the larger size reamers. Only a small amount of material should be removed at one time, as too large a cut will usually cause chatter.

Taper pin reamers (Figures 7 and 8) are used for

reaming holes for standard taper pins used in the assembly of machine tools and other parts. Taper pin reamers have a taper of $\frac{1}{4}$ in. per foot of length, and are manufacturer in 18 different sizes numbered from 8/0 to 0 and on up to size 10. The smallest size, number 8/0, has a large end diameter of .0514 in. and the largest reamer, a number 10, has a large end diameter of .7216 in. The

Figure 3. Straight flute hand reamer (Courtesy of TRW, Inc.).

Figure 4. Helical flute hand reamer (Courtesy of TRW, Inc.).

Figure 5. Straight flute expansion hand reamer (Courtesy of TRW, Inc.).

Figure 6. Adjustable hand reamers. The lower reamer is equipped with a pilot and tapered guide bushing for reaming in alignment with a second hole (Lane Community College).

Figure 7. Straight flute taper pin hand reamer (Courtesy of TRW, Inc.).

Figure 8. Spiral flute taper pin hand reamer (Courtesy of TRW, Inc.).

sizes of these reamers are designed to allow the small end of each reamer to enter a hole reamed by the next smaller size reamer. As with other hand reamers, the helical flute reamer will cut with more shearing action and less chattering, especially on interrupted cuts.

Morse taper socket reamers are designed to produce holes for American Standard Morse taper shank tools. These reamers are available as roughing reamers (Figure 9) and as finishing reamers (Figure 10). The roughing reamer has notches ground at intervals along the cutting edges. These notches act as chip-breakers and make the tool more efficient at the expense of fine finish. The finishing reamer is used to impart the final size and finish to the socket. Morse taper socket reamers are made in sizes from number 0, with a large end diameter of .356 in., to number 5, with a large end diameter of 1.8005 in. There are two larger Morse tapers, but they are typically sized by boring rather than reaming.

USING HAND REAMERS

A hand reamer should be turned with a tap wrench or T-handle wrench rather than with an adjustable wrench. The use of a single end wrench makes it almost impossible to apply torque without disturbing the alignment of the reamer with the hole. A hand reamer should be rotated slowly and evenly, allowing the reamer to align itself with the hole to be reamed. Use a tap wrench large enough to give a steady torque and to prevent vibration and chatter. Use a steady and large feed; feeds up to one-quarter of the reamer diameter per revolution can be used. Small and lightweight workpieces can be reamed by fastening the reamer vertically in a bench vise and rotating the work over the reamer by hand (Figure 11).

In all hand reaming with solid, expansion, or adjustable reamers, never rotate the reamer backwards to remove it from the hole, as this will dull it rapidly. If possible, pass the reamer through the hole and remove it from the far side without stopping the forward rotation. If this is not possible, it should be withdrawn while maintaining the forward rotation.

The preferred stock allowance for hand reaming is between .001 and .005 in. Reaming more material than this would make it very difficult to force the reamer through the workpiece. Reaming too little, on the other hand, results in excessive tool wear because it forces the reamer to work in the zone of material work-hardened during the drilling operation. This stock allowance does not apply to taper reamers, for which a hole has to be drilled at least as large as the small diameter of the reamer. The hole size for a taper pin is determined by the taper pin number and its length. These data can be found in machinist's handbooks.

Figure 9. Morse taper socket roughing reamer (Courtesy of TRW, Inc.).

Figure 10. Morse taper socket finishing reamer (Courtesy of TRW, Inc.).

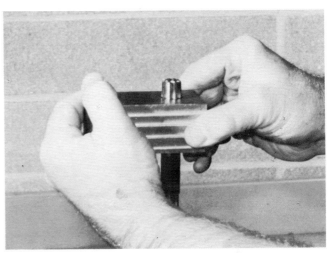

Figure 11. Hand reaming a small workpiece with the reamer held in a vise (Lane Community College).

Since cylindrical hand reaming is restricted to small stock allowances, it is most important that you be able to drill a hole of predictable size and of a surface finish that will assure a finished cleanup cut by the reamer. It is a good idea to drill a test hole in a piece of scrap of similar composition and carefully measure both for size and for an enlarged or bell-mouth entrance. You may find it necessary to drill a slightly smaller hole before drilling the correct reaming size to assure a more accurate hole size. Carefully spot drill the location before drilling the hole in your actual workpiece. The hole should then be lightly **chamfered** with a countersinking tool to remove burrs and to promote better reamer alignment.

The use of a cutting oil also improves the cutting action and the surface finish when reaming most metals. Exceptions are cast iron and brass, which should be reamed dry.

When a hand reamer is started it should be checked for squareness on two sides of the reamer, 90 degrees

apart. Another way to assure alignment of the reamer with the drilled hole is to use the drill press as a reaming fixture. Put a piece of cylindrical stock with a 60 degree center in the drill chuck (Figure 12) and use it to guide and follow the squared end of the reamer as you turn the tool with the tap wrench. Be sure to plan ahead so that you can drill, countersink, and ream the hole without moving the table or head of the drill press between operations.

On deep holes, or especially on holes reamed with taper reamers, it becomes necessary to remove the chips frequently from the reamer flutes to prevent clogging. Remove these chips with a brush to avoid cutting your hands.

Reamers should be stored so they do not contact one another to avoid burrs on the tools that can damage a hole being reamed. They should be kept in their original shipping tubes or set up in a tool stand. Always check reamers for burrs or for pickup of previous material before you use them. Otherwise the reamed hole can be oversized or marred with a rough finish.

Figure 12. Using the drill press as a reaming fixture (Lane Community College).

SELF-TEST

1. How is a hand reamer identified?
2. What is the purpose of a starting taper on a reamer?
3. What is the advantage of a spiral flute reamer over a straight flute reamer?
4. How does the shank diameter of a hand reamer compare with the diameter measured over the margins?

5. When are expansion reamers used?
6. What is the difference between an expansion and an adjustable reamer?
7. What is the purpose of coolant used while reaming?
8. Why should reamers not be rotated backwards?
9. How much reaming allowance is left for hand reaming?

UNIT 7 IDENTIFICATION AND USES OF TAPS

Most internal threads produced today are made with taps. These taps are available in a variety of styles, each one designed to perform a specific type of tapping operation efficiently. This unit will help you identify and select taps for threading operations.

OBJECTIVES

After completing this unit, you should be able to:
1. Identify common taps.
2. Select taps for specific applications.

IDENTIFYING COMMON TAP FEATURES

Taps are used to cut internal threads in holes. This process is called tapping. Tap features are illustrated in Figures 1 and 2. The active cutting part of the tap is the chamfer, which is produced by grinding away the tooth form at an angle, with relief back of the cutting edge, so that the cutting action is distributed progressively over a number of teeth. The fluted portion of the tap provides space for chips to accumulate and for the passage of cutting fluids. Two, three, and four flute taps are common.

The major diameter (Figure 2) is the outside diameter of the tool as measured over the thread crests at the first full thread behind the chamfer. This is the largest diameter of the cutting portion of the tap, as most taps are back tapered or reduced slightly in thread diameter toward the shank. This back taper reduces the amount of tool contact with the thread during the tapping process, hence making the tap easier to turn.

The pitch diameter (Figure 2) is the diameter of an imaginary cylinder where the width of the spaces and the width of the threads are equal. The pitch of the thread is the distance between a point on one thread and the same point on the next thread.

Taps are made from either high carbon steel or high speed steel and have a hardness of about Rockwell C63. High speed steel taps are far more common in manufacturing plants than carbon steel taps. High speed steel taps typically are ground after heat treatment to ensure accurate thread geometry.

Another identifying characteristic of taps is the amount of chamfer at the cutting end of a tap (Figure 3). A set consists of three taps, taper, plug, and bottoming taps, which are identical except for the number of chamfered threads. The taper tap is useful in starting a tapped thread square with the part. The most commonly used tap, both in hand and machine tapping, is a plug tap. Bottoming taps are used to produce threads that extend almost to the bottom of a blind hole. A blind hole is one that is not drilled clear through a part.

Serial taps (Figure 4) are also made in sets of three taps for any given size of tap. Each of these taps has one, two, or three rings cut on the shank near the square. The number 1 tap has smaller major and pitch diameters and is used for rough cutting the thread. The number 2 tap cuts the thread slightly deeper, and the number 3 tap finishes it to size. Serial taps are used when tough metals are to be tapped by hand. Another tap used for tough

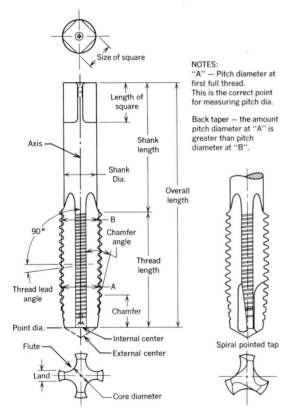

Figure 1. General tap terms (Courtesy of Bendix Industrial Tools Division).

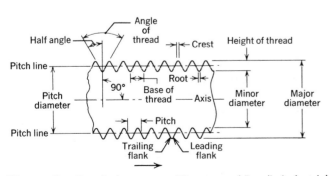

Figure 2. Detailed tap terms (Courtesy of Bendix Industrial Tools Division).

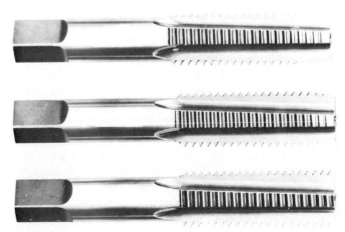

Figure 3. Chamfer designations for cutting taps (Courtesy of TRW, Inc.).

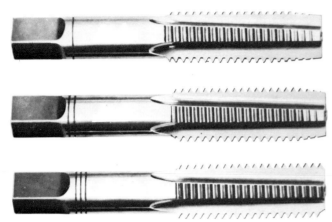

Figure 4.   Set of serial taps (Courtesy of TRW, Inc.).

Figure 5.   Interrupted thread tap (DeAnza College).

Figure 6.   Identifying marking on a tap.

Figure 7.   Hand tap.

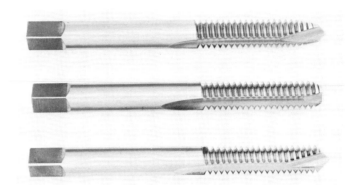

Figure 8.   Set of spiral pointed (or gun) taps (DeAnza College).

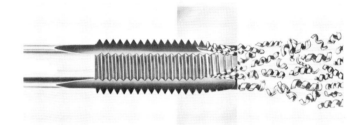

Figure 9.   Cutting action of spiral pointed taps (Courtesy of TRW, Inc.).

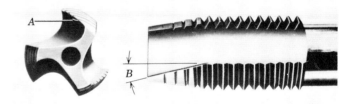

Figure 10.   Detail of spiral pointed tap (Courtesy of TRW, Inc.).

metal such as stainless steel is the interrupted thread tap (Figure 5). This tap has alternate teeth removed to reduce tapping friction.

Figure 6 shows the identifying markings of a tap, where $\frac{5}{8}$ in. is the nominal size, 11 is the number of threads per inch, and NC refers to the standardized National Coarse thread series. G is the symbol used for ground taps. H3 identifies the tolerance range of the tap. HS means that the tap material is high speed steel. Left-handed taps will also be identified by an LH or left-hand marking on the shank.

OTHER KINDS AND USES OF TAPS

Figure 7 illustrates the most commonly used kind of tap — the hand tap. The hand tap is manufactured to produce threads in both machine screw sizes and fractional sizes. Hand taps were originally intended for hand tapping of threads, but are now commonly used in machine production jobs as well.

Spiral pointed taps (Figure 8), often called gun taps, are especially useful for machine tapping of through holes or blind holes with sufficient chip room below the threads. When turning the spiral point, the chips are forced ahead of the tap (Figure 9). Since the chips are pushed ahead of the tap, the problems caused by

clogged flutes, especially breakage and dulling of taps, are eliminated. Also, since they are not needed for chip disposal, the flutes of gun taps can be made shallower, thus increasing the strength of the tap.

Spiral pointed taps can be operated at higher speeds and require less torque to drive than ordinary hand taps. Figure 10 shows the design of the cutting edges. The cutting edges (*A*) at the point of the tap are ground at an angle (*B*) to the axis. Fluteless spiral pointed taps (Figure 11) are recommended for production tap-

Figure 11. Fluteless spiral pointed tap for thin materials (DeAnza College).

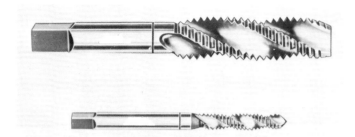

Figure 12. Spiral fluted taps—regular spiral (Courtesy of TRW, Inc.).

Figure 13. Spiral fluted tap—fast spiral. The action of the tap lifts the chips out of hole to prevent binding (Courtesy of TRW, Inc.).

Figure 14. Fluteless thread forming tap (DeAnza College).

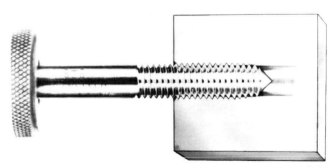

Figure 15. The thread forming action of a fluteless thread forming tap (Courtesy of TRW, Inc.).

ping of through holes in sections no thicker than the tap diameter. This type of tap is very strong and rigid, which reduces tap breakage caused by misalignment. Fluteless spiral point taps give excellent results when tapping soft and stringy materials or sheet metal.

Spiral fluted taps are made with helical instead of straight flutes (Figure 12), which draw the chips out of the hole. This kind of tap is also used when tapping a hole that has a keyway or spline as the helical lands of the tap will bridge the interruptions. Spiral fluted taps are recommended for tapping deep blind holes in ductile materials such as aluminum, magnesium, brass, copper, and die-cast metals. Fast spiral fluted taps (Figure 13) are similar to regular spiral fluted taps, but the faster spiral flutes increase the chip lifting action and permit the spanning of comparably wider spaces.

Thread forming taps (Figure 14) are fluteless and do not cut threads in the same manner as conventional taps. They are forming tools and their action can be compared with external thread rolling. On ductile materials such as aluminum, brass, copper, die castings, lead, and leaded steels these taps give excellent results. Thread forming taps are held and driven just as are conventional taps, but because they do not cut the threads no chips are produced. Problems of chip congestion and removal often associated with the tapping of blind holes are eliminated. Figure 15 shows how the forming tap displaces metal. The crests of the thread that are at the minor diameter may not be flat but will be slightly concave because of the flow of the displaced metal. Threads produced in this manner have improved surface finish and increased strength because of the cold working of the metal. The size of the hole to be tapped must be closely controlled, since too large a hole will result in a poor thread form and too small a hole will result in the breaking of the tap.

A tapered pipe tap (Figure 16) is used to tap holes with a $\frac{3}{4}$ in. per foot taper for pipes with a matching

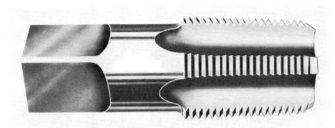

Figure 16.   Taper pipe tap (Courtesy of TRW, Inc.).

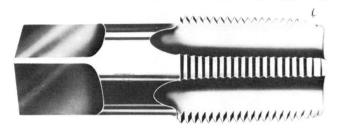

Figure 17.   Straight pipe tap (Courtesy of TRW, Inc.).

Figure 18.   Pulley tap (Courtesy of TRW, Inc.).

Figure 19.   Nut tap (Courtesy of TRW, Inc.).

Figure 20.   Bent shank tapper tap (Courtesy of TRW, Inc.).

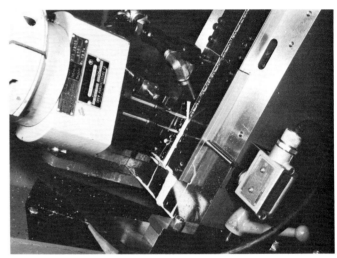

Figure 21.   Automatic tapping machine for tapping nuts and irregularly shaped small parts.

thread and to produce a leakproof fit. The nominal size of a pipe tap is that of the pipe fitting and not the actual size of the tap. When tapping taper pipe threads, every tooth of the tap engaged with the work is cutting until the rotation is stopped. This takes much more torque than does the tapping of a straight thread in which only the chamfered end and the first full thread are actually cutting. Straight pipe taps (Figure 17) are used for tapping holes or couplings to fit taper threaded pipe and to secure a tight joint when a sealer is used.

A pulley tap (Figure 18) is used to tap set-screw and oilcup holes in the hubs of pulleys. The long shank also permits tapping in places that might be inaccessible for regular hand taps. When used for tapping pulleys, these taps are inserted through holes in the rims, which are slightly larger than the shanks of the taps. These holes serve to guide the taps and assure proper alignment with the holes to be tapped.

Nut taps (Figure 19) differ from pulley taps in that their shank diameters are smaller than the root diameter of the thread. The smaller shank diameter makes the tapping of deep holes possible. Nut taps are used when small quantities of nuts are made or when nuts have to be made from tough materials such as some stainless steels or similar alloys. Bent shank tapper taps (Figure 20) are designed for the mass production of nuts in automatic tapping machines. Tapping in these machines is continuous; nuts are automatically fed to the tap by a hopper and after the nut has been tapped it passes on over the shank and is automatically ejected. Automatic nut tapping and tapping of irregularly shaped small parts is also done in machines, as the one shown in Figure 21. In this type of machine the tap reverses to clear the workpiece.

The Acme thread form will be discussed in more detail later in the text. If you are curious about the Acme thread, check Unit 15 in Section H.

Figure 22 shows Acme taps for roughing and finishing. Acme threads are used to provide accurate movement such as lead screws on machine tools and for applying pressure in various mechanisms. On some Acme taps the roughing and finishing operation is performed with one tap (Figure 23). The length of this tap usually requires a through hole.

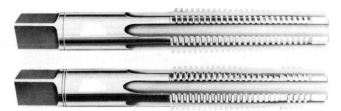

Figure 22. Set of Acme thread taps. The upper tap is used for roughing, the lower tap for finishing (Courtesy of TRW, Inc.).

Figure 23. A tandem Acme tap designed to rough and finish cut the thread in one pass (Lane Community College).

Table 1
Recommended Tap Rake Angles

0–5 Degrees	8–12 Degrees	16–20 Degrees
Bakelite	Bronze	Aluminum and alloys
Plastics	Hard rubber	Zinc die castings
Cast iron	Cast steel	Copper
Brass	Carbon steel	Magnesium
Hard rubber	Alloy steel	
	Stainless steel	

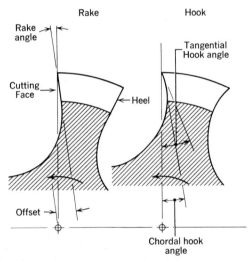

Figure 24. Rake and hook angles on cutting taps (Courtesy of Bendix Industrial Tools Division).

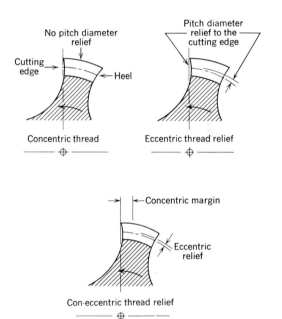

Figure 25. Pitch diameter relief forms on taps (Courtesy of Bendix Industrial Tools Division).

RAKE AND HOOK ANGLES ON CUTTING EDGES

When selecting a tap for the most efficient cutting, the cutting face geometry will be an important factor. It should vary depending on the material to be tapped. Cutting face geometry is expressed in terms of rake and hook (Figure 24). The rake of a tap is the angle between a line through the flat cutting face and a radial line from the center of the tool to the tooth tip. The rake can be negative, neutral, or positive. Hook angle, on the other hand, relates to the concavity of the cutting face. It is defined by the intersection of the radial line with the tangent line through the tooth tip (tangential hook) or by the average angle of the tooth face from crest to root (chordal). Unlike the rake angle, hook angle cannot be negative. Table 1 gives the rake angle recommendations for some workpiece materials. In general, the softer or more ductile the material, the greater the rake angle. Harder and more brittle materials call for reduced rake angles.

REDUCING FRICTION IN TAPPING

As discussed earlier in this unit, a tap is usually back tapered along the thread to relieve the friction between the tool and the workpiece. There is another form of relief often applied to taps with the same results. When the fully threaded portion of the tap is cylindrical (other than back taper), it is called a concentric thread (Figure 25). If the pitch diameter of the fully threaded portion of the tap is brought uniformly closer to the axis of the tap as measured from face to back (heel), it has eccentric relief. This means less tool contact with the workpiece and less friction. A third form of friction relief combines the concentric thread and the eccentric thread relief,

and is termed con-eccentric. The concentric margin gives substantial guidance and the relief following the margin reduces friction. Relief is also provided behind the chamfer of the tap to provide radial clearance for the cutting edge. Relief may also be provided in the form of a channel that runs lengthwise down the center of the land (Figure 26), termed a concave groove land relief.

Other steps may also be taken to reduce friction and to increase tap life. Surface treatment of taps is often an answer if poor thread forming or tap breakage is caused by chips adhering to the flutes or welding to the cutting faces. These treatments generally improve the wear life of taps by increasing their abrasion resistance.

Three different kinds of surface treatments are used by tap manufacturers. Liquid nitride produces a very hard shallow surface on high speed steel tools when these tools are immersed in cyanide salts at closely controlled temperatures. Oxide finishes are usually applied

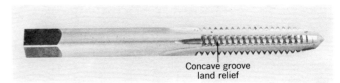

Figure 26. Tap with concave groove land relief (DeAnza College).

in steam tempering furnaces and can be identified by their bluish-black color. The oxide acts as a solid lubricant. It also holds liquid lubricant at the cutting edges during a tapping operation. Oxide treatments prevent welding of the chips to the tool and reduce friction between the tool and the work. Chrome plating is a very effective treatment for taps used on nonferrous metals and some soft steels. The chromium deposit is very shallow and often referred to as flash chrome plating.

SELF-TEST

1. What difference exists between a set of taps and serial taps?
2. Where is a spiral pointed tap used?
3. When is a fluteless spiral pointed tap used?
4. When is a spiral fluted tap used?
5. How are thread forming taps different from conventional taps?
6. How are taper pipe taps identified?
7. What is the difference between a pulley tap and a nut tap?
8. Why are finishing and roughing Acme taps used?
9. Why are the rake angles varied on taps for different materials?
10. Name at least three methods used by tap manufacturers to reduce friction between the tap and the workpiece material.

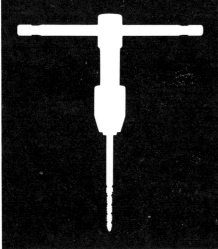

UNIT 8 TAPPING PROCEDURES

Today's mass production of consumer goods depends to a large extent on the efficient and secure assembly of parts using threaded fasteners. It takes skill to produce usable tapped holes, so a craftsman in the metal trades must have an understanding of the factors that affect the tapping of a hole, such as the work material and its cutting speed, the proper coolant, and the size and condition of the hole. A good machinist can analyze a tapping operation, determine whether or not it is satisfactory, and usually find a solution if it is not. In this unit, you will learn about common tapping procedures.

OBJECTIVES

After completing this unit, you should be able to:
1. Select the correct tap drill for a specific percentage of thread.

2. Determine the cutting speed for a given work material-tool combination.
3. Select the correct coolant for tapping.
4. Tap holes by hand or with a drill press.
5. Identify and correct common tapping problems.

Taps are used to cut internal threads in holes. The actual cutting process is called tapping and can be performed by hand or with a machine. A tap wrench (Figure 1) or a T-handle tap wrench (Figure 2) attached to the tap is used to provide driving torque while hand tapping. To obtain a greater accuracy in hand tapping, a hand tapper (Figure 3) is used. This fixture acts as a guide for the tap to insure that it stays in alignment and cuts concentric threads.

Holes can also be tapped in a drill press that has a spindle reverse switch, which is often foot operated for convenience. Drill presses without reversing switches can be used for tapping with a tapping attachment (Figure 4). Some of these tapping attachments have an internal friction clutch where downward pressure on the tap turns the tap forward and feeds it into the work. Releasing downward pressure will automatically reverse the tap and back it out of the workpiece. Some tapping attachments have lead screws that provide tap feed rates equal to the lead of the tap. Most of these attachments also have an adjustment to limit the torque to match the size of tap, which eliminates most tap breakage.

THREAD PERCENTAGE AND HOLE STRENGTH

The strength of a tapped hole depends largely on the workpiece material, the percentage of full thread used, and the length of the thread. The workpiece material is usually selected by the designer, but the machinist can often control the percentage of thread produced and the depth of the thread. The percentage of thread produced is dependent on the diameter of the drilled hole. Tap drill charts generally give tap drill sizes to produce 75 percent thread.

An example will illustrate the relationships between the percentage of thread, torque required to drive the tap, and resulting thread strength. An increase in thread depth from 60 to 72 percent in AISI 1020 steel required twice the torque to drive the tap, but it increased the strength of the thread by only 5 percent. The practical limit seems to be 75 percent of full thread, since greater

Figure 1. Tap wrench.

Figure 2. T-handle tap wrench.

Figure 3. Hand tapper (Courtesy of Ralmike's Tool-A-Rama).

Figure 4. Drill press tapping attachment (Lane Community College).

percentage of thread does not increase the strength of the threaded hole in most materials.

In some difficult-to-machine materials such as titanium alloys, high tensile steels, and some stainless steels, 50 to 60 percent thread depth will give sufficient strength to the tapped hole. Threaded assemblies are usually designed so that the bolt breaks before the threaded hole strips. Common practice is to have a bolt engage a tapped hole by 1 to $1\frac{1}{2}$ times its diameter.

DRILLING THE RIGHT HOLE SIZE

The condition of the drilled hole affects the quality of the thread produced, as an out-of-round hole leads to an out-of-round thread. Bell-mouthed holes will produce bell-mouthed threads. When an exact hole size is needed, the hole should be reamed before tapping. This is especially important for large diameter taps and when fine pitch threads are used. The size of the hole to be drilled is usually obtained from tap drill charts, which usually show a 75 percent thread depth. If a thread depth other than 75 percent is wanted, use the following formula to determine the proper hole size:

$$\text{Outside diameter of thread} - \frac{.01299 \times \text{percentage of thread}}{\text{Number of threads per inch}}$$
$$= \text{Hole size}$$

For example, calculate the hole size for a 1 in. — 12 thread fastener with a 70 percent thread depth:

$$1 - \frac{.01299 \times 70}{12} = .924 \text{ in.}$$

SPEEDS FOR TAPPING

The quality of the thread produced also depends on the speed at which a tap is operated. The selection of the best speed for tapping is limited, unlike the varying speeds and feeds possible with other cutting tools, because the feed per revolution is fixed by the lead of the thread. Excessive speed develops high temperatures that cause rapid wear of the tap's cutting edge. Dull taps produce rough or torn and off-size threads. High cutting speeds prevent adequate lubrication at the cutting edges and often create a problem of chip disposal.

When selecting the best speed for tapping, you should consider not only the material being tapped, but also the size of the hole, the kind of tap holder being used, and the lubricant being used. Table 1 gives some guidelines in selecting a speed and a lubricant for some materials when using high speed steel taps.

These cutting speeds in feet per minute have to be translated into RPM to be useful. For example, calculate the RPM when tapping a $\frac{3}{8}$ — 24 UNF hole in free machining steel. The cutting speed chart gives a cutting speed between 60 and 80 feet per minute. Use the lower figure; you can increase the speed once you see how the material taps. The formula for calculating RPM is:

$$\frac{\text{Cutting Speed} \times 4}{\text{Diameter}} \quad \text{or} \quad \frac{60 \times 4}{\frac{3}{8}} = 640 \text{ RPM}$$

Lubrication is one of the most important factors in a tapping operation. Cutting fluids used when tapping serve as coolants, but are more important as lubricants. It is important to select the correct lubricant because the use of a wrong lubricant may give results that are worse than if no lubricant was used. For lubricants to be effective, they should be applied in sufficient quantity to the actual cutting area in the hole.

Table 1
Recommended Cutting Speeds and Lubricants for Machine Tapping

Material	Speeds (ft/min)	Lubricant
Aluminum	90–100	Kerosene and light base oil
Brass	90–100	Soluble oil or light base oil
Cast iron	70– 80	Dry or soluble oil
Magnesium	20– 50	Light base oil diluted with kerosene
Phosphor bronze	30– 60	Mineral oil or light base oil
Plastics	50– 70	Dry or air jet
Steels		
Low carbon	40– 60	Sulphur base oil
High carbon	25– 35	Sulphur base oil
Free machining	60– 80	Soluble oil
Molybdenum	10– 35	Sulphur base oil
Stainless	10– 35	Sulphur base oil

SOLVING TAP PROBLEMS

In Table 2, common tapping problems are presented with some possible solutions.

Occasionally it becomes necessary to remove a broken tap from a hole. If a part of the broken tap extends out of the workpiece, removal is relatively easy with a pair of pliers. If the tap breaks flush with or below the surface of the workpiece, a tap extractor can be used (Figure 5). Before trying to remove a broken tap, the chips in the flutes should be removed. A jet of compressed air or cutting fluid can be used for this. **Always stand aside when cleaning out holes with compressed air as chips and particles tend to fly out at high velocity.**

When the chips are packed so tightly in the flutes or

Table 2

Common Tapping Problems and Possible Solutions

Causes of Tap Breakage	Solutions
Tap hitting bottom of hole or bottoming on packed chips	Drill hole deeper. Eject chips with air pressure. (*Caution:* Stand aside when you do this and always wear safety glasses.) Use spiral fluted taps to pull chips out of hole. Use a thread forming tap.
Chips are packing in flutes	Use tap style with more flute space. Tap to a lesser depth or use a smaller percentage of threads. Select a tap that will eject chips foward (spiral point) or backward (spiral fluted).
Hard materials or hard spots	Anneal the workpiece. Reduce cutting speed. Use longer chamfers on tap. Use taps with more flutes.
Inadequate lubricant	Use the correct lubricant and apply a sufficient amount of it under pressure at the cutting zone.
Tapping too fast	Reduce cutting speed.
Excessive wear:	
Abrasive materials	Improve lubrication. Use surface treated taps. Check the alignment of tap and hole to be tapped.
Chips clogging flutes:	
Insufficient lubrication	Use better lubricant and apply it with pressure at the cutting zone.
Excessive speed	Reduce cutting speed.
Wrong-style tap	Use a more free cutting tap such as spiral pointed tap, spiral fluted tap, interrupted thread tap, or surface treated taps.
Torn or rough threads:	
Dull tap	Resharpen.
Chip congestion	Use tap with more chip room. Use lesser percentage of thread.
	Drill deeper hole. Use a tap that will eject chips.
Inadequate lubrication and chips clogging flutes	Correct as previously suggested.
Hole improperly prepared	Torn areas on the surface of the drilled, bored, or cast hole will be shown in the minor diameter of the tapped thread.
Undersize threads:	
Pitch diameter of tap too small	Use tap with a larger pitch diameter
Excessive speed	Reduce tapping speed.
Thin wall material	Use a tap that cuts as freely as possible. Improve lubrication. Hold the workpiece so that it cannot expand while it is being tapped. Use an oversize tap.
Dull tap	Resharpen.
Oversize or bellmouth threads:	
Loose spindle or worn holder	Replace or repair spindle or holder.
Misalignment	Align spindle, fixture, and work.
Tap oversize	Use smaller pitch diameter tap.
Dull tap	Resharpen.
Chips packed in flutes	Use tap with deeper flutes, spiral flutes, or spiral points.
Buildup on cutting edges of tap	Use correct lubricant and tapping speed.

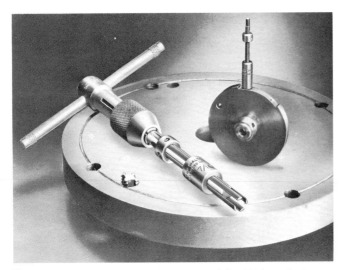

Figure 5.   Tap extractor (Courtesy of the Walton Co.).

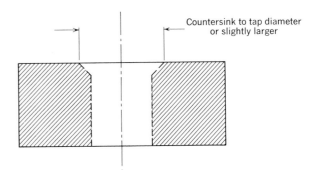

Countersink to tap diameter
or slightly larger

Figure 6.   Preparing the workpiece.

the tap is jammed in the work so that a tap extractor cannot be used, the tap may be broken up with a pin punch and removed piece by piece. If the tap is made from carbon steel and cannot be pin punched, the tap can be annealed so it becomes possible to drill out.

On high speed steel taps it may be necessary to use an electrical discharge machine (EDM) to remove the broken tap. These machines erode away material from extremely hard workpieces while they are immersed in a fluid. The shape of the hole conforms precisely to that of the electrode.

TAPPING PROCEDURE, HAND TAPPING

1. Determine the size of the thread to be tapped and select the tap.
2. Select the proper tap drill with the aid of a tap drill chart. A taper tap should be selected for hand tapping; or if a drill press or tapping machine is to be used for alignment, use a plug tap.
3. Fasten the workpiece securely in a drill press vise. Calculate the correct RPM for the drill used:

$$RPM = \frac{CS \times 4}{D}$$

Drill the hole using the recommended coolant. Check the hole size.

4. Countersink the hole entrance to a diameter slightly larger than the major diameter of the threads (Figure 6). This allows the tap to be started more easily, and it protects the start of the threads from damage.
5. Mount the workpiece in a bench vise so that the hole is in a vertical position.
6. Tighten the tap in the tap wrench.

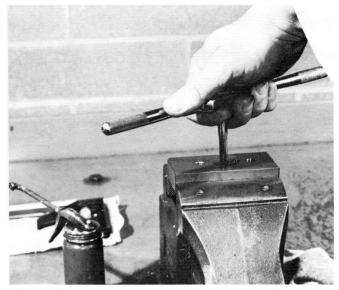

Figure 7.   Starting the tap (Lane Community College).

7. Cup your hand over the center of the wrench (Figure 7) and place the tap in the hole in a vertical position. Start the tap by turning two or three turns in a clockwise direction for a right-hand thread. At the same time keep a steady pressure downward on the tap. When the tap is started, it may be turned as shown in Figure 8.
8. After the tap is started for several turns, remove the tap wrench without disturbing the tap. Place the blade of a square against the solid shank of the tap to check for squareness (Figure 9). Check from two positions 90 degrees apart. If the tap is not square with the work, it will ruin the thread and possibly break in the hole if you continue tapping. Back the tap out of the hole and restart.
9. Use the correct cutting oil on the tap when cutting threads.
10. Turn the tap clockwise one-quarter to one-half turn and then turn it back a three-quarter turn to break

Figure 8. Tapping a thread by hand (Lane Community College).

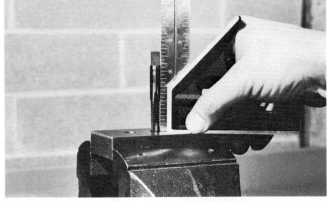

Figure 9. Checking the tap for squareness (Lane Community College).

the chip. This is done with a steady motion to avoid breaking the tap.

11. When tapping a blind hole, use the taps in the order of starting, plug, and then bottoming. Remove the chips from the hole before using the bottoming tap and be careful not to hit the bottom of the hole with the tap.

12. Figure 10 shows a 60 degree point center chucked in a drill press to align a tap squarely with the previously drilled hole. Only very slight follow-up pressure should be applied to the tap. Too much downward pressure will cut a loose, oversize thread.

Figure 10. Using the drill press as a tapping fixture (Lane Community College).

SELF-TEST

1. What kind of tools are used to drive taps when hand tapping?
2. What is a hand tapper?
3. What is a tapping attachment?
4. Which three factors affect the strength of a tapped hole?
5. How deep should the usable threads be in a tapped hole?
6. When should tap drill holes be reamed?
7. What causes taps to break while tapping?
8. What causes rough and torn threads?
9. What causes oversize threads in a hole?
10. Give three methods of removing broken taps from holes.

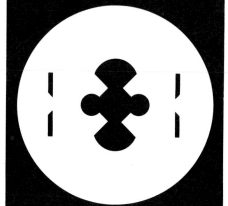

UNIT 9 THREAD CUTTING DIES AND THEIR USES

A **die** is used to cut external threads on the surface of a bolt or rod. Many machine parts and mechanical assemblies are held together with threaded fasteners, most of which are mass produced. Occasionally, however, a machinist has to make a bolt or extend the threads on a bolt for which he uses a die. In this unit you will be introduced to some dies and their hand threading uses.

OBJECTIVES

After completing this unit, you should be able to:
1. Identify dies used for hand threading.
2. Select and prepare a rod for threading.
3. Cut threads with a die.

Dies are used to cut external threads on round materials. Some dies are made from carbon steel, but most are made from high speed steel. Dies are identified by the markings on the face as to the size of thread, number of threads per inch, and form of thread, such as NC, UNF, or other standard designations (Figure 1).

COMMON TYPES OF HAND THREADING DIES

The die shown in Figure 1 is an example of a **round split adjustable die,** also called a **button** die. These dies are made in all standardized thread sizes up to $1\frac{1}{2}$ in. thread diameters and $\frac{1}{2}$ in. pipe threads. The outside diameters of these dies vary from $\frac{5}{8}$ to 3 in.

Adjustments on these dies are made by turning a fine pitch screw that forces the sides of the die apart or allows them to spring together. The range of adjustment of round split adjustable dies is very small, allowing only for a loose or tight fit on a threaded part. Adjustments made to obtain threads several thousandths of an inch oversize will result in poor die performance because the heel of the cutting edge will drag on the threads. Excessive expansion may cause the die to break.

Some round split adjustable dies do not have the built-in adjusting screw. Adjustments are then made with the three screws in the die stock (Figure 2). Two of these screws on opposite sides of the die stock hold the die in

the die stock and also provide closing pressure. The third screw engages the split in the die and provides opening pressure. These dies are used in a die stock for hand threading or in a machine holder for machine threading.

Another type of threading die is the **two piece die,** whose halves (Figure 3) are called blanks. These blanks

Figure 1. Markings on a die. (Example shown is a round split adjustable die.)

Figure 2. Diestock for round split adjustable dies (Courtesy of TRW, Inc.).

Figure 3. Die halves for two piece die (Courtesy of TRW, Inc.).

Cap   Guide   Collet

Figure 4. Components of a split adjustable die collet (Courtesy of TRW, Inc.).

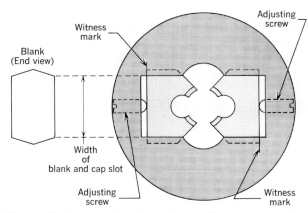

Figure 5. Setting the die position to the witness marks on the die and collet assembly (Courtesy of TRW, Inc.).

Figure 6. Diestock for adjustable die and collet assembly (Courtesy of TRW, Inc.).

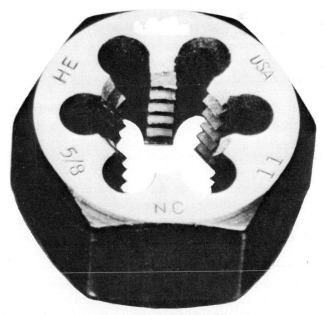

Figure 7. Hexagon rethreading die (Courtesy of TRW, Inc.).

are assembled in a **collet** consisting of a **cap** and the **guide** (Figure 4). The normal position of the blanks in the collet is indicated by witness marks (Figure 5). The adjusting screws allow for precise control of the cut thread size. The blanks are inserted in the cap with the tapered threads toward the guide. Each of the two die halves is stamped with a serial number. Make sure the halves you select have the same numbers. The guide used in the collet serves as an aid in starting and holding the dies square with the work being threaded. Each thread size uses a guide of the same nominal or indicated size. Collets are held securely in die stocks (Figure 6) by a knurled setscrew that seats in a dimple in the cap.

Hexagon rethreading dies (Figure 7) are used to

Figure 8. Solid square die (Courtesy of TRW, Inc.).

Figure 9. Threading a rod with a hand die in a lathe (Lane Community College).

recut slightly damaged or rusty threads. Rethreading dies are driven with a wrench large enough to fit the die. Solid square dies (Figure 8) have the same uses and limitations as hexagon rethreading dies. All of the previously discussed die types are also available in bolt and pipe sizes. Square dies are used to cut new threads and have sufficient chip clearance for this purpose.

HAND THREADING PROCEDURES

Threading of a rod should always be started with the leading or throat side of the die. This side is identified by the chamfer on the first two or three threads and also by the size markings. The chamfer distributes the cutting load over a number of threads, which produces better threads and less chance of chipping the cutting edges of the die. Cutting oil or other threading fluids are very important in obtaining quality threads and maintaining long die life. Once a cut is started with a die, it will tend to follow its own lead, but uneven pressure on the die stock will make the die cut variable helix angle or "drunken" threads.

Threads cut by hand often show a considerable accumulated lead error. The lead of a screw thread is the distance a nut will move on the screw if it is turned one full revolution. This problem is caused by the dies being relatively thin when compared to the diameter of thread that they cut. Only a few threads in the die can act as a guide on the already cut threads. This error usually does not cause problems when standard or thin nuts are used on the threaded part. However, when an item with a long internal thread is assembled with a threaded rod, it usually gets tight and then locks, not because the thread depth is insufficient, but because there is a lead error. This lead error can be as much as one-fourth of a

thread in one inch of length.

The outside diameter of the material to be threaded should not be over the nominal size of the thread and preferably a few thousandths of an inch (.002 to .005 in.) undersize. After a few full threads are cut, the die should be removed so that the thread can be tested with a nut or thread ring gage. A thread ring gage set usually consists of two gages, a go and a no go gage. As the names imply, a go gage should screw on the thread, while the no go gage will not go more than $1\frac{1}{2}$ turns on a thread of the correct size. Do not assume that the die will cut the correct size thread; always check by gaging or assembling. Adjustable dies should be spread open for the first cut and set progressively smaller for each pass after checking the thread size.

It is very important that a die is started squarely on the rod to be threaded. A lathe can be used as a fixture for cutting threads with a die (Figure 9). The rod is fastened in a lathe chuck for rotation, while the die is held square because it is supported by the face of the tailstock spindle. The carriage or the compound rest prevents the die stock from turning while the chuck is rotated *by hand*. As the die advances, the tailstock spindle is also advanced to stay in contact with the die. Do not force the die with the tailstock spindle, or a loose thread may result. A die may be used to finish to size a long thread that has been rough threaded on the lathe.

Occasionally, a die is used to extend the thread on a bolt. Make certain that the bolt is not hardened or the die will be ruined. To cut full, usable threads close to a shoulder, first cut the thread normally until the die touches the shoulder, then reverse the die and use the unchamfered side to finish the last few threads.

It is always good practice to chamfer the end of a workpiece before starting a die (Figure 10). The chamfer

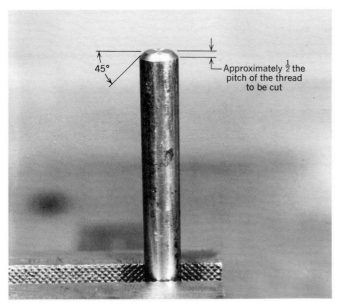

Figure 10. Chamfer workpiece before using die (Lane Community College).

Figure 11. Start the die with one hand (Lane Community College).

Figure 12. Use both hands to turn the threading die (Lane Community College).

on the end of a rod can be made by grinding on a pedestal grinder, by filing or with a lathe. This will help in starting the cut and it will also leave a finished thread end. While cutting threads with a hand die, the die rotation should be reversed after each full turn forward to break the chips into short pieces that will fall out of the die. Chips jammed in the clearance holes will tear the thread.

THREADING PROCEDURE, THREADING DIES

1. Select the workpiece to be threaded and measure its diameter. Then chamfer the end. This may be done on a grinder or with a file. The chamfer should be at least as deep as the thread to be cut.
2. Select the correct die and mount it in a die stock.
3. Mount the workpiece in a bench vise. Short workpieces are mounted vertically and the long pieces usually are held horizontally.
4. To start the thread, place the die over the workpiece. Holding the die stock with one hand (Figure 11), apply downward pressure and turn the die.
5. When the cut has started, apply cutting oil to the workpiece and die and start turning the die stock with both hands (Figure 12). After each complete revolution forward, reverse the die one-half turn to break the chips.
6. Check to see that the thread is started square, using a machinist's square. Corrections can be made by applying slight downward pressure on the high side while turning.
7. When several turns of the thread have been completed, you should check the fit of the thread with a nut, thread ring gage, thread micrometer, or the mating part. If the thread fit is incorrect, adjust the die with the adjustment screws and take another cut with the adjusted die. Continue making adjustments until the proper fit is achieved.
8. Continue threading to the required thread length. To cut threads close to a shoulder, invert the die after the normal threading operation and cut the last two or three threads with the side of the die that has no chamfer.

SELF-TEST

1. What is a die?
2. What tool is used to drive a die?
3. How much adjustment is possible with a round split adjustable die?

4. What is the purpose of the guide in a two-piece adjustable die collet?
5. What are important points to watch when assembling two-piece dies in a collet?
6. Where are hexagon rethreading dies used?
7. Why do dies have a chamfer on the cutting end?
8. Why are cutting fluids used?
9. What diameter should a rod be before being threaded?
10. Why should a rod be chamfered before being threaded?

SECTION C DIMENSIONAL MEASUREMENT

> *When you can measure what you are speaking about and express it in numbers, you know something about it, but when you cannot measure it, when you cannot express it in numbers, your knowledge is of a meager and unsatisfactory kind . . . . .*
>
> *Lord Kelvin*
> *1883*

All of us, no matter what we may be doing, are totally surrounded by measurement. Measurement can be generally defined as: the assignment of a value to time, length, and mass. We cannot escape measurement. Our daily lives are greatly influenced by the clock, a device that measures time. Mass or weight is measured in almost every product we buy, and the measure of length is incorporated in every creation of man, ranging from the minute components of a watch to many thousands of miles of superhighways extending across a continent.

Measurement, in the modern age, has been developed to an exact science known as metrology. As the hardware of technology has become more complex, a machinist is ever more concerned with that branch of the science called dimensional metrology. Furthermore, mass production of goods has made necessary very complex systems of metrology to check and control the critical dimensions that control standardization and interchangeability of parts. Components of an automobile, for example, may be manufactured at locations far removed from each other and then brought to a central assembly point, with the assurance that all parts will fit as intended by the designer. In addition, the development and maintenance of a vast system of carefully controlled measurement has permitted manufacturers to locate their factories close to raw materials and available labor. Because of the standardization of measurement, industry has been able to diversify its products, Thus, manufacturers can do what they do best, and manufacturing effort can be directed toward the quality of a product and its production at a competitive price. As a result, metrology not only affects the technical aspects of production but also the economic aspects. Metrology is a common thread woven through the entire fabric of manufacturing from the drafting room to the shipping dock.

MEASUREMENT NEEDS OF THE MACHINIST

A machinist is mainly concerned with the measurement of **length;** that is, the distance along a line between two points (Figure 1). It is length that defines the **size** of most objects. **Width** and **depth** are simply other names for length. A machinist measures length in the basic units of linear measure such as **inches, millimeters,** and, in advanced metrology, wavelengths of light. In addition, the machinist sometimes needs to measure the relationship of one surface to another, which is commonly called **angularity** (Figure 2). **Squareness,** which is closely related to angularity, is the measure of deviation from true perpendicularity. A machinist will measure angularity in the basic units of angular measure, **degrees, minutes,** and **seconds of arc.**

In addition to the measure of length and angularity, a machinist also needs to measure such things as **surface finish, concentricity, straightness,** and **flatness.** He or she also occasionally comes in contact with measurements

Figure 1. The measurement of length may appear under several different names.

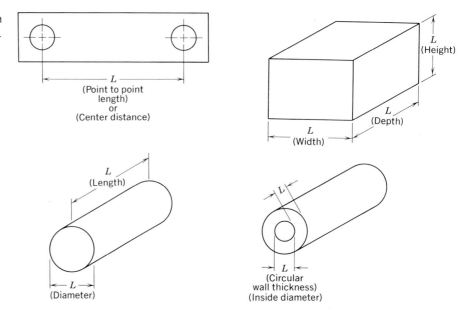

Figure 2. Measurement of surface relationships or angularity.

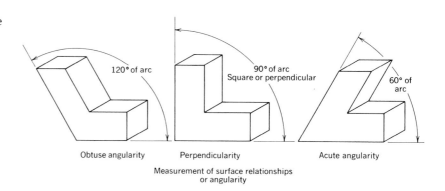

Figure 3. Other measurements encountered by the machinist.

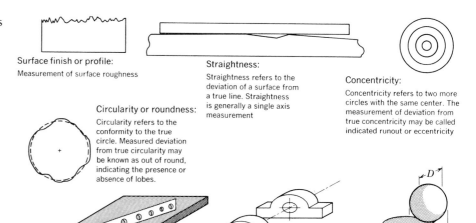

that involve circularity, sphericity, and alignment (Figure 3). However, many of these more specialized measurement techniques are in the realm of the inspector or laboratory metrologist and appear infrequently in general machine shop work.

GENERAL PRINCIPLES OF METROLOGY

A machinist has available a large number of measuring tools designed for use in many different applications. However, not every tool is equally suited for a specific measurement. As with all the tools of a machinist, selecting the proper measuring tool for the specific application at hand is a primary skill. The successful outcome of a machinist's work may indeed depend upon the choice of measuring tools. In this regard, a machinist must be familiar with several important terms and principles of metrology.

Accuracy

Accuracy in metrology has a twofold meaning. First, accuracy can refer to whether or not a specific measurement is actually within its stated size. For example, a certain drill has its size stamped on its shank. A doubtful machinist decides to verify the drill size using a properly adjusted micrometer. The size is found to be as stated. Therefore, the size stamped on the drill is accurate. Second, accuracy refers to the act of measurement itself with regard to whether or not the specific measurement taken is within the capability of the measuring tool selected. A machinist obtains a drill with the size marked on the shank and decides to verify it using a steel rule. The edge of this rule with the finest graduations is selected; the machinist then lays the drill over the marks. Sighting along the drill, he discovers that it is really three graduations, on his rule, smaller than the size stamped on the shank. He then reasons that the size marked on the drill must be in error. In this example, the act of measurement is not accurate because the inappropriate measuring tool was selected and the improper procedure was used. **User accuracy** is also an important consideration. If, when the machinist measured the drill with his micrometer, as described in the first example, he did not bother to confirm the accuracy of the instrument prior to making the measurement, an inaccuracy that can be attributed to the user, may have resulted.

Precision

The term **precision** is relative to the specific measurement being made, with regard to the degree of exactness required. For example, the distance from the earth to the moon, measured to within one mile, would indeed be a precise measurement. Likewise, a clearance of five-thousandths of an inch between a certain bearing and journal might be precise for that specific application. However, five-thousandths of an inch clearance between ball and race on a ball bearing would not be considered precise, as this clearance would be only a very few millionths of an inch. **There are many degrees of precision dependent on application and design requirements.** For a machinist, any measurement made to a degree finer than one sixty-fourth of an inch or one-half millimeter, can be considered a **precision measurement** and must be made with the appropriate precision measuring instrument.

Reliability

Reliability in measurement refers to the ability to obtain the desired result to the degree of precision required. Reliability is most important in the selection of the proper measuring tool. A certain tool may be reliable for a certain measurement, but totally unreliable in another application. For example, if it were desired to measure the distance to the next town, the odometer on an automobile speedometer would yield quite a reliable result, provided a

degree of precision of less than one-tenth mile is not required. On the other hand, to measure the length of a city lot with an odometer is much less likely to yield a reliable result. This is explained by examining another important principle of metrology, that of the discrimination of a measuring instrument.

Discrimination

Discrimination refers to the degree to which a measuring instrument divides the basic unit of length it is using for measurement. The automobile odometer divides the mile into 10 parts; therefore, it discriminates to the nearest tenth of a mile. A micrometer, one of the most common measuring instruments of a machinist, subdivides an inch into 1000 or, in some cases, 10,000 parts. Therefore, the micrometer discriminates to .001 or .0001 of an inch. If a measuring instrument is used beyond its discrimination, a loss of reliability will result. Consider the example cited previously regarding the measurement of a city lot. Most lots are less than one-tenth of a mile in length; therefore, the discrimination of the auto odometer for this measurement is not sufficient for reliability.

The 10:1 Ratio for Discrimination

In general, a measuring instrument should **discriminate 10 times finer** than the smallest unit that it will be asked to measure. The odometer, which discriminates to a tenth of a mile, is most reliable for measuring whole miles. To measure the length of a city lot in feet requires an instrument that discriminates at least to one-tenth of a foot. Since most surveyors' measuring tapes used for this application discriminate to tenths and in some cases to hundredths of a foot, they are an appropriate tool for the measurement.

The Position of a Linear Measuring Instrument with Regard to the Axis of Measurement

A large portion of the measurements made by a machinist is linear in nature. These measurements attempt to determine the shortest distance between two points. In order to obtain an accurate and reliable linear measurement, **the measuring instrument must be exactly in line with the axis of that measurement.** If this condition is not met, reliability will be in question. The alignment of the measuring instrument with the axis of measurement applies to all linear measurements (Figure 4). The figure illustrates the alignment of the instrument with the axis of measurement using a simple graduated measuring device. Only under the reliable condition can the measurement approach accuracy. Misalignment of the instrument, as illustrated in the unreliable situation, will result in inaccurate measurements.

Responsibility of the Machinist in Measurement

The following units in this section discuss most of the common measuring tools available to a machinist. The capabilities, discrimination, and reliability as well as procedures for use are examined. It is, of course, the responsibility of a machinist to select the proper measuring instrument for the job at hand. When faced with a need to measure, a machinist should ask the following questions:

1. What degree of accuracy and precision must this measurement meet?
2. What degree of measuring tool discrimination does this required accuracy and precision demand?
3. What is the most reliable tool for this application?

Calibration.   Accurate and reliable measurement places a considerable amount of responsibility on a machinist. He is responsible for the conformity of his measuring tools to the appropriate standards. This is the process known

Figure 4. The axis of a linear measuring instrument must be in line with the axis of measurement.

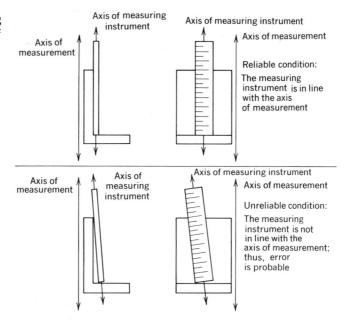

as **calibration.** In a large industrial facility, all measuring tools are periodically cycled through the metrology laboratory where they are calibrated against appropriate standards. Any adjustments are then made to bring the tools into conformity to the standards. Only through this process can standardized measure within an individual plant or within an entire industrial nation be maintained. Most of the common measuring instruments provide a factory standard. Even though calibration cannot be carried out under laboratory conditions, the instruments should at least be checked periodically against available standards.

Variables in Measuring. A machinist should be further aware that any measurement is **relative to the conditions under which it is taken.** A common expression that is often used around the machine shop is: "the measurement is right on." There is, of course, little probability of obtaining a measurement that is truly exact. Each measurement has a certain degree of deviation from the theoretical exact size. This degree of error is dependent on many variables including the measuring tool selected, the procedure used, the temperature of the part, the temperature of the room, the cleanliness of the room air, and the cleanliness of the part at the time of measurement. The deviation of a measurement from exact size is taken into consideration by the designer. Every measurement has a tolerance, meaning that the measurement is acceptable within a specific range. Tolerance can be quite small depending on design requirements. When this condition exists, reliable measurement becomes more difficult because it is more heavily influenced by the many variables present. Therefore, before a machinist makes any measurement, he should stop for a moment and consider the possible variables involved. He should then consider what might be done to control as many of these variables as possible.

If you understand these basic principles of dimensional metrology and you assume the proper responsibility in the selection, calibration, and application of measuring instruments, you will experience little difficulty in performing the many measurements encountered in the science of machine tools and machining practices.

TOOLS FOR DIMENSIONAL MEASUREMENT

There are many hundreds of measuring instruments available to a machinist. In this modern age there is a measuring instrument that can be applied to almost any conceivable measurement. Many instruments are simply variations and combinations of a few common precision measuring tools. As you begin your study of machine tool practices, you will be initially concerned with the use, care, and applications of the common measuring instruments found in the machine shop. These will be discussed in detail within this section.

In addition to these, there is a large variety of instruments that are designed for many specialized uses. Some of these are rarely seen in the school or general purpose machine shop. Others are intended for use in the tool room or metrology laboratory where they are used in the calibration process. Your contact with these instruments will depend on the particular path you take while learning the trade.

Many measuring instruments have undergone modernization in recent years. Even though the function of these tools is basically the same, many have been redesigned and equipped with mechanical or electronic digital displays. These features make the instruments easier to read and improve accuracy. As a machinist, you must be skilled in the use of all the common measuring instruments. In addition, you should be familiar with the many important instruments used in production machining, inspection, and calibration. In the following pages many of these tools will be briefly described so that you may become familiar with the wide selection of measuring instruments available to the machinist.

Fixed Gages and Air Gages

Fixed Gages. In production machining, where large numbers of duplicate parts are produced, it may only be necessary to determine if the part is within acceptable tolerance. Many types of fixed gages are used. The **adjustable limit snap gage** (Figure 5) is used to check outside diameter. One anvil is set to the minimum limit of the tolerance to be measured. The other anvil is set to the maximum limit of the tolerance. If both anvils slip over the part, an undersized condition is indicated. If neither anvil slips over the part, an oversized condition is indicated. The gage is set initially to a known standard such as gage blocks.

Threaded products are often checked with fixed gages. The **thread plug gage** (Figure 6) is used to check internal threads. The **thread ring gage** (Figure 7) is used to check external threads. These are frequently called **go** and **no-go** or **not-go** gages. One end of the plug gage is at the low limit of the tolerance, while the other end is at the high limit of the tolerance. The thread gage functions in the same manner. Thread gages appear in many different forms (Figure 8).

Fixed gages are also used to check internal and external tapers (Figure 9). Plug gages are used for internal holes (Figure 10). A ring gage is used for external diameters (Figure 11).

Air Gages. **Air gages** are also known as **pneumatic comparators.** Two types of air gages are used in comparison measuring applications. In the pressure-type air gage (Figure 12), filtered air flows through a reference and measuring channel. A sensitive differential pressure meter is connected across the channels (Figure 13). The gage head is adjusted to a master setting gage. Air gage heads may be ring, snap (Figure 14), or plug types (Figure 15). Air flowing through the reference and measuring channel is adjusted until the differential pressure meter reads zero with the setting master in place. A difference in workpiece size above or below the master size will cause more or less air

Figure 5. Adjustable limit snap gage (Courtesy of Rank Scherr-Tumico, Inc.).

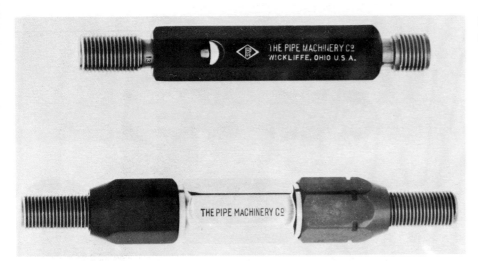

Figure 6. Thread plug gage (Courtesy of PMC Industries).

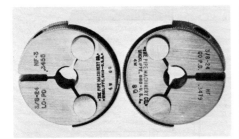

Figure 7. Thread ring gage (Courtesy of PMC Industries).

Figure 9. Taper plug and taper ring gage (Courtesy of PMC Industries).

Figure 10. Using the cylindrical plug gage (Courtesy of PMC Industries).

Figure 8. Fixed thread gages appear in many different forms (Courtesy of PMC Industries).

Figure 11. Cylindrical ring gages (Courtesy of PMC Industries).

Figure 12. Pressure-type air gage. (Courtesy of Federal Products Corporation—Dimensionair is a registered trademark of Federal Products Corp.).

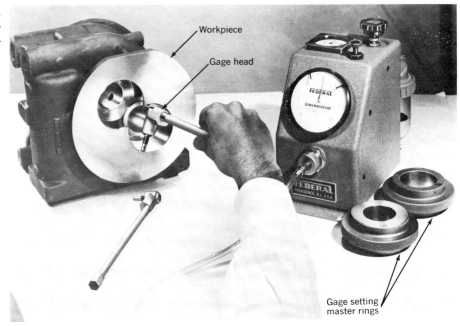

Figure 13. Pressure-type air gage system (Courtesy of Federal Products Corporation—Dimensionair is a registered trademark of Federal Products Corp.).

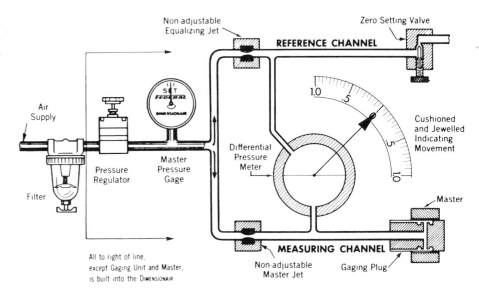

to excape from the gage head. This, in turn, will change the pressure on the reference channel. The pressure change will be indicated on the differential pressure meter. The meter scale is graduated in suitable linear units. Thus, workpiece size above or below the master can be directly determined.

In the column or flow-type air gage (Figure 16) air flow from the gage head is indicated on a flow meter or rotameter (Figure 17). This type of air gage is also set to master gages. In the case of the plug gage shown, if the workpiece is oversized, more air will flow from the gage head. An undersized condition will permit less air to flow. Differences in flow are indicated on a suitably graduated flowmeter scale. Workpiece size deviation can be read directly.

Air gages have several advantages. The gage head does not touch the

Figure 14. Pressure-type air snap gage (Courtesy of Federal Products Corporation—Dimensionair is a registered trademark of Federal Products Corp.).

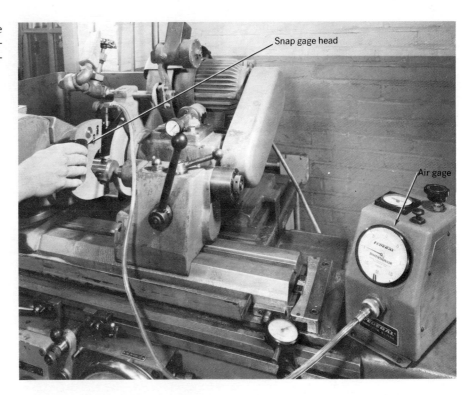

Figure 15. Air plug gage (Courtesy of Federal Products Corporation).

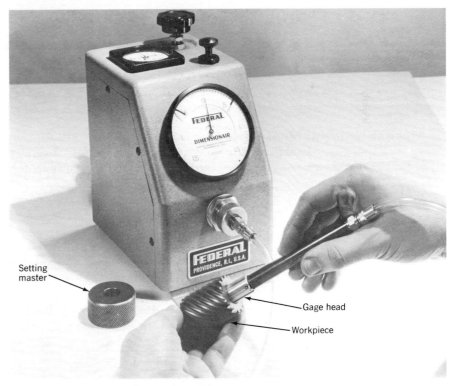

workpiece. Consequently there is no wear on the gage head and no damage to the finish of the workpiece. Variations in workpiece geometry that would be difficult to measure by mechanical means can be detected by air gaging (Figure 18).

Figure 16. Column or flow-type air gage (Courtesy of the Automation and Measurement Divison — Bendix Corporation).

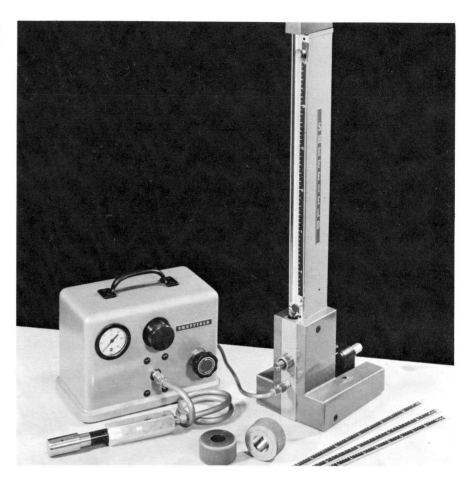

Mechanical Dial Measuring Instruments

Measuring instruments that show a measurement on a dial have become very popular in recent years. Several of the common dial instruments are outgrowths from vernier instruments of the same type. Dial instruments have an advantage over their vernier counterparts in that they are easier to read. Dial measuring equipment is frequently found in the inspection department where many types of measurements must be made quickly and accurately.

Dial Thickness Gage. The **dial thickness gage** (Figure 19) is used to measure the thickness of paper, leather, sheet metal, and rubber. Discrimination is .0005 in.

Dial Indicating Snap Gages. Dial indicating snap gages (Figure 20) are used for determining whether workpieces are within acceptable limits. They are first set to a gage block standard. Part size deviation is noted on the dial indicator.

Dial Bore Gage. The **dial bore gage** (Figure 21) uses a three point measuring contact. This more accurately measures the true shape of a bore (Figure 22). The dial bore gage is useful for checking engine block cylinders for size, taper, bell mouth, ovality, barrel shape, and hour glass shape (Figure 23). Dial bore gages are set to a master ring and then compared to a bore diameter. Discrimination ranges from .001 to .0001 in.

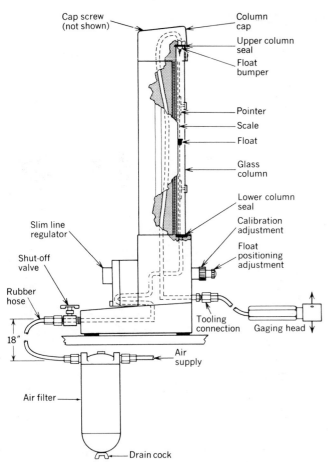

Figure 17. Column-type air gage system (Courtesy of the Automation and Measurement Division — Bendix Corporation).

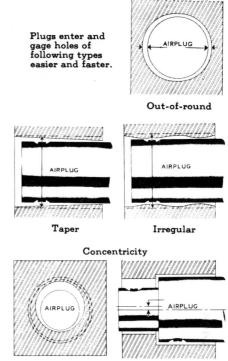

Plugs enter and gage holes of following types easier and faster.

Out-of-round

Taper   Irregular

Concentricity

Figure 18. Hole geometry detectable by air gaging (Courtesy of Federal Products Corporation).

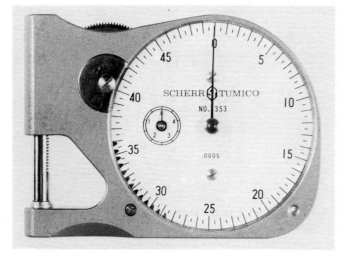

Figure 19. Dial thickness gage (Courtesy of Rank Scherr-Tumico, Inc.).

Figure 20. Using the indicating snap gage (Courtesy of Federal Products Corporation).

Figure 21. Dial bore gage (Courtesy of Rank Scherr-Tumico, Inc.).

Figure 22. Using the dial bore gage (Courtesy of the L. S. Starrett Company).

Figure 23. Hole geometry detectable with the dial bore gage.

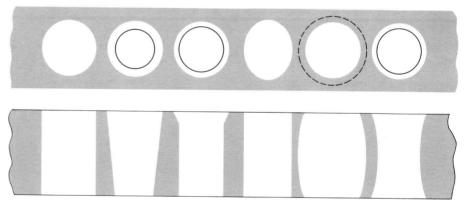

Dial Indicating Expansion Plug Bore Gage. The **indicating expansion plug gage** (Figure 24) is used to measure the inside diameter of a hole or bore. This type gage is built to check a single dimension. It can detect ovality, bell-mouth, barrel shape, and taper. The expanding plug is retracted and the instrument inserted into the hole to be measured (Figure 25).

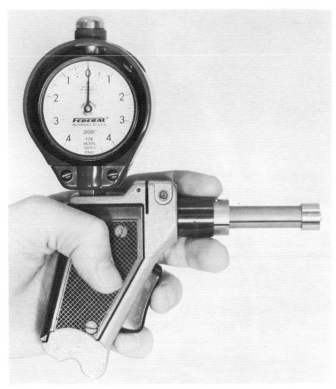

Figure 24. Dial indicating expansion plug bore gage (Courtesy of Federal Products Corporation).

Figure 25. Using the expansion plug bore gage (Courtesy of Federal Products Corporation).

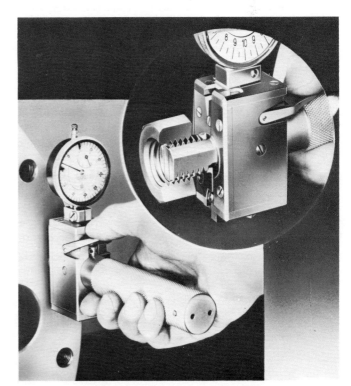

Figure 26. Using the indicating thread plug gage (Courtesy of the Mahr Gage Company).

Dial Indicating Thread Plug Gage. The **indicating thread plug gage** (Figure 26) is used to measure internal threads. This type of gage need not be screwed into the thread. The measuring anvils retract so that the gage may be inserted into a threaded hole.

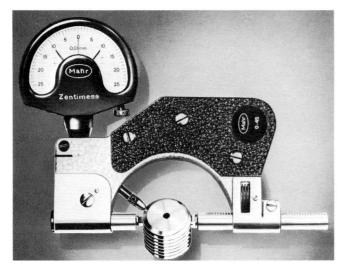

Figure 27. Dial indicating thread snap gage (Courtesy of the Mahr Gage Company).

Figure 28. Dial indicator-inprocess grinding gage, in retracted position (Courtesy of Federal Products Corporation).

Dial Indicating Screw Thread Snap Gage. The **dial indicating screw thread snap gage** (Figure 27) is used to measure an external thread. The instrument may be fitted with suitable anvils for measuring the major, minor, or pitch diameter of screw threads. Discrimination is .0005 or .00005 in. depending on the dial indicator used.

Dial Indicating Inprocess Grinding Gage. Gages can be built into machining processes. The **indicating inprocess grinding gage** is used to measure the workpiece while it is still running in the machine tool (Figure 28). The instrument swings down over the part to be measured (Figure 29). The machine can remain running. These instruments are used in such applications as cylindrical grinding. Discrimination can be .0005 or .00005 in., depending on the dial indicator used.

Mechanical Dial Indicating Travel Indicators. **Mechanical dial indicators** can be used to indicate the travel of machine tool components. This is very valuable to the machinist in controlling machine movement that in turn controls the dimensions of the parts produced. Mechanical dial travel indicators are used in many applications such as indicating table and saddle travel on a milling machine (Figure 30). They may also be used to indicate vertical travel of quills and spindles. Mechanical dial travel indicators are also useful for indicating travel in metric dimensions. Discrimination is .001 in., .005 in., and .01 mm.

Inspection and Calibration Through Mechanical Measurement

All measuring instruments must be periodically checked against accepted standards if the control that permits interchangeability of parts is to be maintained. Without control of measurement there could be no diverse mass production of parts that will later fit together to form the many products that we now enjoy.

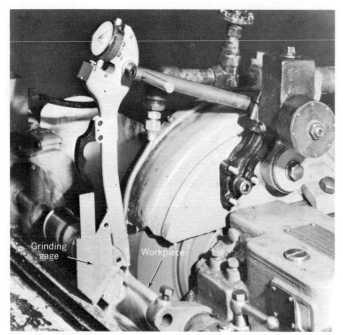

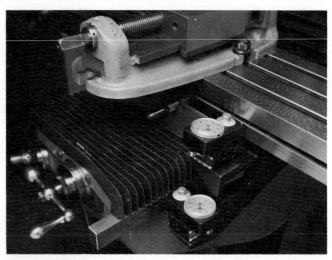

Figure 30. Mechanical dial travel indicators installed on a milling machine (Courtesy of Southwestern Industries, Inc., Trav-A-Dial®).

Figure 29. Inprocess grinding gage measuring the workpiece (Courtesy of Federal Products Corporation).

Figure 31. Indicating bench micrometer or supermicrometer (Courtesy of Colt Industries, Pratt and Whitney Cutting Tool and Gage Division).

Parts produced on a machine tool must be inspected to determine if their size meets design requirements. Parts produced out of tolerance can greatly increase the dollar cost of production. These must be kept to a minimum, and this is the purpose of part inspection and calibration of measuring instruments.

Indicating Bench Micrometer. The **indicating bench micrometer,** commonly called a **supermicrometer** (Figure 31), is used to inspect tools,

Figure 32. Visual surface roughness comparator gage (Courtesy of the DoAll Company).

Figure 33. Coordinate measuring machine (Courtesy of the Automation and Measurement Division, Bendix Corporation).

parts, and gages. This instrument has a discrimination of .00002 in. (20 millionths).

Surface Finish Visual Comparator. Surface finish may be approximated by visual inspection using the **surface roughness gage** (Figure 32). Samples of finishes produced by various machining operations are indicated on the gage. These can be visually compared to a machined surface to determine the approximate degree of surface finish.

Coordinate Measuring Machines. The **coordinate measuring machine** (Figure 33) is an extremely accurate instrument that can measure the workpiece in three dimensions. Coordinate measuring machines are very useful for determining the location of a part feature relative to a reference plane, line, or point.

Measurement with Electronics

Remote Gaging. Electronic technology has come into wide use in measurement. Electronic equipment can be designed with greater sensitivity than mechanical equipment. Thus, higher discrimination can be achieved. Electronics can be applied in **remote gaging** applications (Figure 34). In this application, there is no direct connection to the gage head. The head is free to

Figure 34. Remote electronic gaging system (Courtesy of Federal Products Corporation).

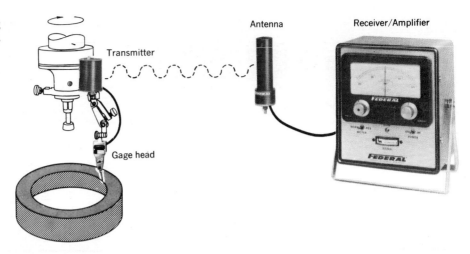

Figure 35. Surface finish indicator being calibrated (DeAnza College).

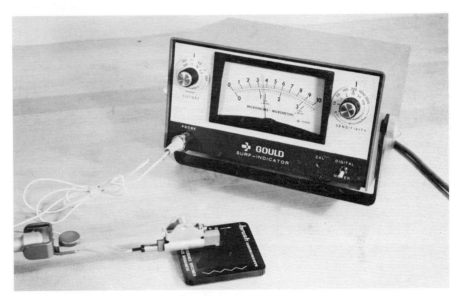

move with the machine tool since there are no attached wires. This facilitates use of the gaging instruments.

Surface Finish Indicators.   Surface finish is critical on many parts such as bearings, gears, and hydraulic cylinders. Surface finish is a measure of **surface roughness** or **profile**. The measurement is in **microinches**. A **microinch** is **one millionth of an inch.** A surface finish indicator (Figure 35) consists of a diamond stylus connected to a suitably graduated dial (meter). The stylus records surface deviations, which are indicated on the dial.

Electronic Digital Travel Indicators.   **Electronic digital travel indicators** use a sensor attached to the machine tool. These systems will discriminate to .0001 in. and can be switched to read in metric dimensions. The travel of the machine component is indicated on a digital display (Figure 36). They are very useful for the accurate positioning of machine tables on such tools as milling machines and jig borers (Figure 37). A sensor on the machine tool detects movement of the machine components. The amount of travel is displayed on an electronic digital display. Discrimination may be as close as .0001 in.

Figure 36. Electronic digital travel indicator display (Courtesy of Elm Systems, Inc.).

Figure 37. Electronic digital travel indicator system installed on a jib borer (Courtesy of Elm Systems, Inc.).

Figure 38. Electronic comparator (Courtesy of the DoAll Company).

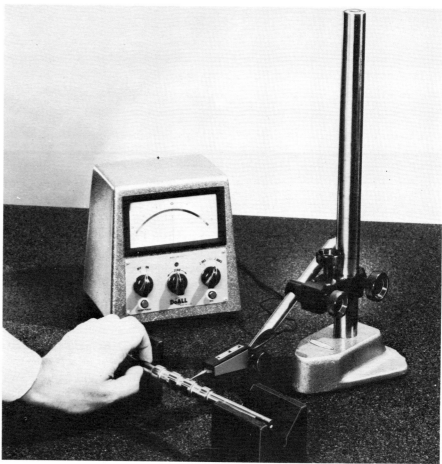

Figure 39. Toolmaker's microscope (Courtesy of Gaertner Scientific Corporation).

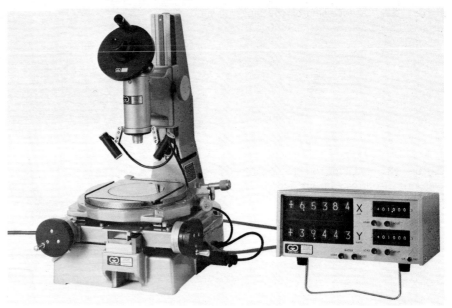

Figure 40. Optical comparator (Courtesy of Rank Scherr-Tumico, Inc.).

Measurement with Light

Figure 41. Using optical flats to check micrometer measuring faces (Courtesy of the DoAll Company).

Electronic Comparators. Electronic comparators (Figure 38) take advantage of the sensitivity of electronic equipment. They are used to make comparison measurements of parts and other measuring tools. For example, gage blocks may be calibrated using a suitable electronic comparator.

Toolmaker's Microscope. The **toolmaker's microscope** (Figure 39) is used to inspect parts, cutting tools, and measuring tools. The microscope has a stage that can be precisely rotated and moved in two perpendicular axes. The instrument may be equipped with an electronic accessory measuring system that discriminates to .0001 in. Thus, stage movement can be recorded permitting measurements of a workpiece to be made.

Optical Comparators. The **optical comparator** (Figure 40) is used in the inspection of parts, cutting tools, and other measuring instruments. Optical comparators project a greatly magnified shadow of the object on a screen. The surface of the workpiece may also be illuminated. Shape patterns or graduated patterns can be placed on the screen and used to make measurements on the workpiece projection.

Optical Flat. **Optical flats** are used in the inspection of other measuring instruments and for the measurement of flatness. They can be used, for example, to reveal the surface geometry of a gage block or measuring faces of a micrometer (Figure 41). Optical flats take advantage of the principles of light interferometry to make extremely small measurements in millionths of an inch.

Autocollimators. The **autocollimator** in Figure 42 is being used to check the flatness of a surface plate. The mirror on the left is moved along the straightedge in small increments. Deviations from flatness are shown by angular changes of the mirror. This change is recorded by the instrument.

Alignment Telescope. A machinist may accomplish alignment tasks by optical means. Optical alignment may be used on such applications as ship

Figure 42. Autocollimator checking a surface plate for flatness (DeAnza College).

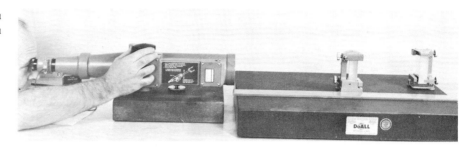

Figure 43. Dual micrometer alignment telescope (Courtesy of the DoAll Company).

Figure 44. Laser interferometer being used for straightness determination (Courtesy of the Hewlett-Packard Company).

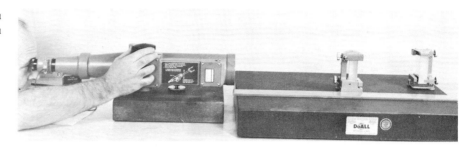

Figure 45. Laser interferometer checking the measuring system on a jig boring machine (DeAnza College).

propeller shaft bearings. Portable machine tools such as boring bars may be positioned by optical alignment. The **dual micrometer alignment telescope** (Figure 43) is a very useful alignment instrument. The micrometers permit the deviation of the workpiece from the line of sight to be determined.

Laser Interferometer. The term laser is an acronym for **light activated stimulation of radiation**. A laser light beam is a coherent beam. This means that each ray of light follows the same path. Thus, it does not disperse over long distances. This property makes the laser beam very useful in many measurement and alignment applications. For example, the laser beam may be used to determine how straight a machine tool table travels (Figure 44). Other uses include the checking of machine tool measuring systems (Figure 45).

UNIT 1 SYSTEMS OF MEASUREMENT

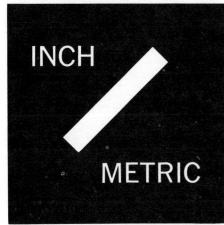

INCH / METRIC

Throughout history there have been many systems of measurement. Prior to the era of national and international industrial operations, an individual craftsman was often responsible for the manufacture of a complete product. Since he made all the necessary parts and did the required assembly, he needed to conform only to his particular system of measurement. However, as machines replaced men and diversified mass production was established on a national and international basis, the need for standardization of measurement became readily apparent. Total standardization of measurement throughout the world still has not been fully realized. Most measurement in the modern world does, however, conform to either the English (inch-pound-second) or the metric (meter-kilogram-second) system. Metric measurement is now predominant in most of the industrialized nations of the world. The inch system is still used to a great extent in the United States. However, because of the interdependence of the world's industrial community, even the United States is turning more and more toward the use of metric measurement.

Today's machinist must now begin to think in terms of metric measurement. During his career he will come in contact with more and more metric specifications. However, for the present and the near future he will also be using inch measurement. Until a full transition to metrics takes place, you, as a machinist, may have to convert from one system to the other. Since you are primarily concerned with length measurement, this unit will review the basic length standards of both systems, examine mathematical and other methods of converting from system to system, and look at techniques by which a machine tool can be converted to work in metrics.

OBJECTIVES

After completing this unit, you should be able to:
1. Identify common methods of measurement conversion.
2. Convert inch dimensions to metric equivalents and convert metric dimensions to inch equivalents.

THE ENGLISH SYSTEM OF MEASUREMENT

The English system of measurement uses the units of inches, pounds, and seconds to represent the measurement of time, length, and mass. Since we are primarily concerned with the measurement of length in the machine shop, we will simply refer to the English system as the **inch** system. Most of us are thoroughly familiar with inch measurement.

Subdivisions and Multiples of the Inch

The following table shows the common subdivisions and multiples of the inch that are used by the machinist.

Common Subdivisions

.000001	millionth
.00001	hundred thousandth
.0001	ten thousandth
.001	thousandth
.01	hundredth
.1	tenth
1.00	*Unit inch*

Common Multiples

12.00	1 foot
36.00	1 yard

Other common subdivisions of the inch are:

$\frac{1}{128}$	.007810 (decimal equivalent)
$\frac{1}{64}$	.015625
$\frac{1}{32}$	.031250
$\frac{1}{20}$	.050000
$\frac{1}{16}$	.062500
$\frac{1}{8}$	.125000
$\frac{1}{4}$	.250000
$\frac{1}{2}$	.500000

Multiples of Feet
3 feet = 1 yard
5280 feet = 1 mile
Multiples of Yards
1760 yards = 1 mile

THE METRIC SYSTEM AND THE INTERNATIONAL SYSTEM OF UNITS—SI

The basic unit of length in the metric system is the **meter.** Originally the length of the meter was defined by a natural standard, specifically a portion of the earth's circumference. Later, more convenient metal standards were constructed. In 1886, the metric system was legalized in the United States, but its use was not made mandatory. Since 1893 the yard has been defined in terms of the metric meter by the ratio

$$1 \text{ yard} = \frac{3600}{3937} \text{ meter}$$

Although the metric system has been in use for many years in many different countries, it still lacked complete standardization among its users. Therefore, an attempt was made to modernize and standardize the metric system. From this effort has come the **Systeme International d'Unites,** known as **SI** or the **International Metric System.**

The basic unit of length in SI is the meter, or metre (in the common international spelling). The SI meter is defined by a physical standard that can be reproduced anywhere with unvarying accuracy.

1 meter = 1,650,763.73 wavelengths in a vacuum of the orange-red light spectrum of the Krypton-86 atom

Probably the primary advantage of the metric system is that of convenience in computation. All subdivisions and multiples use 10 as a divisor or multiplier. This can be seen in the following table.

.000001	(one-millionth meter or micrometer)
.001	(one-thousandth meter or millimeter)
.01	(one-hundredth meter or centimeter)
.1	(one-tenth meter or decimeter)
1.00	*Unit meter*
10	(ten meters or one dekameter)
100	(100 meters or one hectometer)
1000	(1000 meters or one kilometer)
1,000,000	(one million meters or one megameter)

METRIC SYSTEM EXAMPLES
1. One meter (m) = _____ millimeters (mm).
   Since a mm is $\frac{1}{1000}$ part of an m, there are 1000 mm in a meter.
2. 50 mm = _____ centimeters (cm).
   Since 1 cm = 10 mm, $\frac{50}{10}$ = 5 cm in 50 mm.
3. Four kilometers (km) = _____ m.
   Since 1 km = 1000 m then 4 km = 4000 m.
4. 582 mm = _____ cm.
   Since 10 mm = 1 cm, $\frac{582}{10}$ = 58.2 cm.

CONVERSION BETWEEN SYSTEMS

Much of the difficulty with working in a two-system environment is experienced in converting from one system to the other. This can be of particular concern to the machinist as he must exercise due caution in making conversions. Arithmetic errors can be easily made. Therefore, the use of a calculator is recommended.

Conversion Factors and Mathematical Conversion

Since the historical evolution of the inch and metric systems is quite different, there are no obvious relationships between length units of the two systems. You simply have to memorize the basic conversion factors. We know from the preceding discussion that the yard has been defined in terms of the meter. Knowing this relationship, you can derive mathematically any length unit in either system. However, the conversion factor

$$1 \text{ yard} = \frac{3600}{3937} \text{ meter}$$

is a less common factor for the machinist. A more common factor can be determined by the following:

$$1 \text{ yard} = \frac{3600}{3937} \text{ meter}$$

Therefore,

$$1 \text{ yard} = .91440 \text{ meter}$$
$$\left(\frac{3600}{3937} \text{ expressed in decimal form} \right)$$

Then

$$1 \text{ inch} = \tfrac{1}{36} \text{ of } .91440 \text{ meter}$$

So

$$\frac{.91440}{36} = .025400$$

We know that

$$1 \text{ m} = 1000 \text{ mm}$$

Therefore,

$$1 \text{ inch} = .025400 \times 1000$$

Or

1 inch = 25.4000 mm

The conversion factor 1 in. = 25.4 mm is very common and should be memorized. From the example shown it should be clear that in order to find inches knowing millimeters, you must divide inches by 25.4.

$$1000 \text{ mm} = \underline{\quad} \text{ inches}$$
$$\frac{1000}{25.4} = 39.37 \text{ inches}$$

In order to simplify the arithmetic, any conversion can always take the form of a multiplication problem.

EXAMPLE

Instead of $\frac{1000}{25.4}$, multiply by the reciprocal of 25.4, which is $\frac{1}{25.4}$ or .03937.

Therefore, $1000 \times .03937 = 39.37$ inches

EXAMPLES OF CONVERSIONS [INCH TO METRIC]
1. 17 in. = _____ cm.
   Knowing inches, to find centimeters multiply inches by 2.54: 2.54 × 17 in. = 43.18 cm.
2. .807 in. = _____ mm.
   Knowing inches, to find millimeters multiply inches by 25.4: 25.4 × .807 in. = 20.49 mm

EXAMPLES OF CONVERSIONS [METRIC TO INCH]
1. .05 mm = _____ in.
   Knowing millimeters, to find inches multiply millimeters by .03937: .05 × .03937 = .00196 inches.
2. 1.63 m = _____ in.
   Knowing meters, to find inches, multiply meters by 39.37: 1.63 × 39.37 m = 64.173 in.

Conversion Factors to Memorize

1 in. = 25.4 mm or 2.54 cm
1 mm = .03937 in.

Other Methods of Conversion

The **conversion chart** (Figure 1) is a popular device for making conversions between systems. Conversion charts are readily available from many manufacturers. However, most conversion charts give equivalents for whole millimeters or standard fractional inches. If you must find an equivalent for a factor that does not appear on the chart, you must interpolate. In this instance, knowing the common conversion factors and determining the equivalent mathematically is more efficient.

Several electronic calculators designed to convert directly from system to system are available. Of course, any calculator can and should be used to do a conversion problem. The direct converting calculator does not require that any conversion constant be remembered. These constants are permanently programmed into the calculator memory.

Converting Machine Tools

With the increase in metric measurement in industry, which predominantly uses the inch system, several devices have been developed that permit a machine tool to function in either system. These conversion devices eliminate the need to convert all dimensions prior to beginning a job.

Conversion equipment includes **conversion dials** (Figure 2) that can be attached to lathe cross slide screws as well as milling machine saddle and table screws. The dials are equipped with gear ratios that permit a direct

MILLIMETERS TO INCHES
(Basis: 1 inch = 25.4 millimeters)

Millimeters	Inches	Millimeters	Inches	Millimeters	Inches	Millimeters	Inches
1	0.039370	26	1.023622	51	2.007874	76	2.992126
2	.078740	27	1.062992	52	2.047244	77	3.031496
3	.118110	28	1.102362	53	2.086614	78	3.070866
4	.157480	29	1.141732	54	2.125984	79	3.110236
5	.196850	30	1.181102	55	2.165354	80	3.149606
6	.236220	31	1.220472	56	2.204724	81	3.188976
7	.275591	32	1.259843	57	2.244094	82	3.228346
8	.314961	33	1.299213	58	2.283465	83	3.267717
9	.354331	34	1.338583	59	2.322835	84	3.307087
10	.393701	35	1.377953	60	2.362205	85	3.346457
11	.433071	36	1.417323	61	2.401575	86	3.385827
12	.472441	37	1.456693	62	2.440945	87	3.425197
13	.511811	38	1.496063	63	2.480315	88	3.464567
14	.551181	39	1.535433	64	2.519685	89	3.503937
15	.590551	40	1.574803	65	2.559055	90	3.543307
16	.629921	41	1.614173	66	2.598425	91	3.582677
17	.669291	42	1.653543	67	2.637795	92	3.622047
18	.708661	43	1.692913	68	2.677165	93	3.661417
19	.748031	44	1.732283	69	2.716535	94	3.700787
20	.787402	45	1.771654	70	2.755906	95	3.740157
21	.826772	46	1.811024	71	2.795276	96	3.779528
22	.866142	47	1.850394	72	2.834646	97	3.818898
23	.905512	48	1.889764	73	2.874016	98	3.858268
24	.944882	49	1.929134	74	2.913386	99	3.897638
25	.984252	50	1.968504	75	2.952756	100	3.937008

Note: The above table is approximate: 1/25.4 0.039370078740

Figure 1. Metric conversion chart (Courtesy of the MTI Corporation).

Figure 2. Inch/metric conversion dials for machine tools (Courtesy of the Sipco Machine Co.).

Figure 3. Metric mechanical dial travel indicator (Courtesy of Southwestern Industries, Inc., Trav-A-Dial®).

Figure 4. Metric mechanical dial travel indicators reading milling machine saddle and table movement (Courtesy of Southwestern Industries, Inc., Trav-A-Dial®).

metric reading to appear on the dial.

Metric mechanical and electronic travel indicators can also be used. The mechanical dial travel indicator (Figure 3) uses a roller that contacts a moving part of a machine tool. Travel of the machine component is indicated on the dial. This type of travel indicator discriminates to .01 millimeter. Whole millimeters are counted on the one millimeter counting wheel. Mechanical dial travel indicators are used in many applications such as reading the travel of a milling machine saddle and table (Figure 4).

The electronic travel indicator (Figure 5) uses a sensor that is attached to the machine tool. Machine tool component travel is indicated on an electronic digital display. The equipment can be switched to read travel in inch or metric dimensions.

Metric conversion devices can be fitted to existing machine tools for a moderate expense. Many new machine tools, especially those built abroad, have dual system capability built into them.

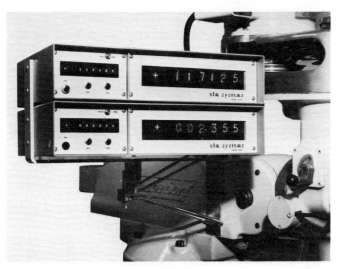

Figure 5. Inch/metric electronic travel indicator with digital display (Courtesy of Elm Systems, Inc.).

SELF-TEST

Perform the following conversions:

1. 35 mm =
2. 125 in. =
3. 6.273 in. =
4. Express the tolerance ± .050 in metric terms to the nearest mm.
5. To find cm knowing mm, _____ (multiply/divide) by 10.
6. Express the tolerance ± .02 mm in terms of inches to the nearest $\frac{1}{10,000}$ in.
7. What is meant by SI?
8. Describe methods by which conversions between metric and inch measurement systems may be accomplished.
9. How is the yard presently defined?
10. Can an inch machine tool be converted to work in metric units?

UNIT 2 USING STEEL RULES

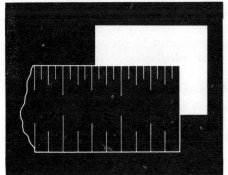

One of the most practical and common measuring tools available in the machining and inspection of parts is the steel rule. It is a tool that the machinist uses daily in different ways. It is important that anyone engaged in machining be able to select and use steel rules.

OBJECTIVES

After completing this unit, you should be able to:
1. Identify various kinds of rules and their applications.
2. Apply rules in typical machine shop measurements.

SCALES AND RULES

The terms **scale** and **rule** are often used interchangeably and often incorrectly. A rule is a linear measuring instrument whose graduations represent **real units** of lengths and their subdivisions. In contrast, a **scale** is graduated into **imaginary** units that are either smaller or larger than the real units they represent. This is done for convenience where proportional measurements are needed. For example, an architect uses a scale that has graduations representing feet and inches. However, the actual length of the graduations on the architect's scale are quite different from full-sized dimensions.

DISCRIMINATION OF STEEL RULES

The general concept of **discrimination** was discussed in the introduction to this section. Discrimination refers to the extent to which a unit of length has been divided. If the smallest graduation on a specific rule is $\frac{1}{32}$ in., then the rule has a discrimination of, or discriminates to $\frac{1}{32}$ in. Likewise, if the smallest graduation of the rule is $\frac{1}{64}$ in., then this rule discriminates to $\frac{1}{64}$ in.

The maximum discrimination of a steel rule is generally $\frac{1}{64}$ in. or in the case of the decimal inch rule, $\frac{1}{100}$ in. The metric rule has a discrimination of $\frac{1}{2}$ mm (millimeter). Remembering that a measuring tool should never be

used beyond its discrimination, the steel rule will not be reliable in trying to ascertain a measurement increment smaller than $\frac{1}{64}$ or $\frac{1}{100}$ in. If a specific measurement falls between the markings on the rule, only this can be said of this reading: it is more or less than the amount of the nearest mark. No further data as to how much more or less can be reliably determined. It is not recommended practice to attempt to read between the graduations on a steel rule with the intent of obtaining reliable readings.

RELIABILITY AND EXPECTATION OF ACCURACY IN STEEL RULES

For reliability, great care must be taken if the steel rule is to be used at its maximum discrimination. Remember that the markings on the rule occupy a certain width. A good quality steel rule has engraved graduations. This means that the markings are actually fine cut in the metal from which the rule is made. Of all types of graduations, engraved ones occupy the least width along the rule. Other rules, graduated by other processes, may have markings that occupy greater width. These rules are not necessarily any less accurate, but they may require more care in reading. Generally, the reliability of the rule will diminish as its maximum discrimination is approached. The smaller graduations are more difficult to see without the aid of a magnifier. Of particular importance is the point from which the measurement is taken. This is the **reference point** and must be carefully aligned at the point where the length being measured begins.

From a practical standpoint, the steel rule finds widest application for measurements no smaller than $\frac{1}{32}$ in. on a fractional rule or $\frac{1}{50}$ in. on a decimal rule. This does not mean that the rule cannot measure to its maximum discrimination, because under the proper conditions it certainly can. However, at or very near maximum discrimination, the time consumed to insure reliable measurement is really not justified. You will be more productive if you make use of a type of measuring instrument with considerably finer discrimination for measurements below the nearest $\frac{1}{32}$ or $\frac{1}{50}$ in. It is good practice to take more than one reading when using a steel rule. After determining the desired measurement, apply the rule once again to see if the same result is obtained. By this procedure, the reliability factor is increased.

TYPES OF RULES

Rules may be selected in many different shapes and sizes, depending on the need. The common **rigid steel rule** is six inches long, $\frac{3}{4}$ in. wide, and $\frac{3}{64}$ in. thick. It is engraved with number 4 standard rule graduations. A

number 4 graduation consists of $\frac{1}{8}$ and $\frac{1}{16}$ in. on one side (Figure 1) and $\frac{1}{32}$ and $\frac{1}{64}$ in. divisions on the reverse side (Figure 2). Other common graduations are summarized in the following table.

Graduation number	Front Side	Back Side
Number 3	32nds / 64th	10ths / 50ths
Number 16	50ths / 100ths	32nds / 64ths

The number 16 graduated rule is often found in the aircraft industry where dimensions are specified in decimal fraction notations, based on 10 or a multiple of 10 divisions of an inch rather than 32 or 64 divisions as found on common rules. Many rigid rules are one inch wide.

Another common rule is the **flexible type** (Figure 3). This rule is six inches long, $\frac{1}{2}$ in. wide, and $\frac{1}{64}$ in. thick. Flexible rules are made from hardened and tempered spring steel. One advantage of a flexible rule is that it will bend, permitting measurements to be made in a space shorter than the length of the rule. Most flexible rules are 6 or 12 inches long.

The **narrow rule** (Figure 4) is very convenient when measuring in small openings, slots, or holes. Most narrow rules have only one set of graduations on each side. These can be number 10, which is 32nds and 64ths, or number 11, which is 64ths and 100ths.

The **standard hook rule** (Figure 5) makes it possible to reach through an opening; the rule is hooked on the far side in order to measure a thickness or the depth of a slot (Figure 6). When a workpiece has a chamfered edge, a hook rule will be advantageous over a common rule. If the hook is not loose or excessively worn, it will provide an easy to locate reference point.

The **short rule set** (Figure 7) consists of a set of rules with a holder. Short rule sets have a range of $\frac{1}{4}$ to 1 in. They can be used to measure shoulders in holes or steps in slots, where space is extremely limited. The holder will attach to the rules at any angle, making these very versatile tools.

The **slide caliper rule** (Figure 8) is a versatile tool used to measure round bars, tubing, and other objects where it is difficult to measure at the ends and difficult to estimate the diameter with a rigid steel rule. The small slide caliper rule can also be used to measure internal dimensions from $\frac{1}{4}$ in. up to the capacity of the tool.

The **rule depth gage** (Figure 9) consists of a slotted steel head in which a narrow rule slides. For depth measurements the head is held securely against the surface with the rule extended into the cavity or hole to be measured (Figure 10). The locking nut is tightened and the

Figure 1. Six inch rigid steel rule (front side).

Figure 2. Six-inch rigid steel rule (back side).

Figure 3. Flexible steel rule (metric).

Figure 4. Narrow rule (decimal inch).

Figure 5. Standard hook rule.

Figure 6. Standard hook rule in use.

rule depth gage can then be removed and the dimension determined.

CARE OF RULES

Rules are precision tools, and only those that are properly cared for will provide the kind of service they are designed to give. A rule should not be used as a screw-

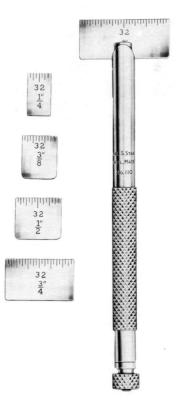

Figure 7. Short rule set with holder (Courtesy of the L. S. Starrett Co.).

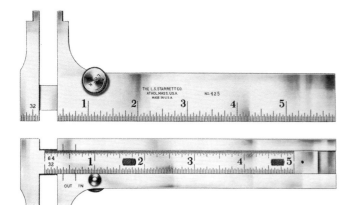

Figure 8. Slide caliper rule (Courtesy of the L. S. Starrett Co.).

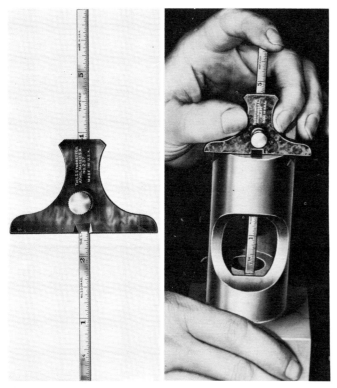

Figure 9. *(left)* Rule depth gage (Courtesy of the L. S. Starrett Co.).
Figure 10. *(right)* Rule depth gage in use (Courtesy of the L. S. Starrett Co.).

driver. Rules should be kept separate from hammers, wrenches, files, and other hand tools to protect them from possible damage. An occasional wiping of a rule with a lightly oiled shop towel will keep it clean and free from rust.

APPLYING STEEL RULES

When using a steel rule in close proximity to a machine tool, **always keep safety in mind.** Stop the machine before attempting to make any measurements of the workpiece. Attempting to measure with the machine running may result in the rule being caught by a moving part. This may damage the rule, but worse, may result in serious injury to the operator.

One of the problems associated with the use of rules is that of **parallax error.** Parallax error results when the observer making the measurement is not in line with the workpiece and the rule. You may see the graduation either too far left or too far right of its real position (Figure 11). Parallax error occurs when the rule is read from a point other than one directly above the point of measurement. The **point of measurement** is the point at which the measurement is read. It may or may not be the true reading of the size depending on what location was used as the reference point on the rule. Parallax can be controlled by always observing the point of measurement from **directly above.** Furthermore, the graduations on a rule should be placed as close as possible to the surface being measured. In this regard, a thin rule is preferred over a thick rule.

As a rule is used it becomes worn, usually on the ends. The outside inch markings on a worn rule are less than one inch from the end. This has to be considered when measurements are made. A reliable way to measure (Figure 12) is to **use the one inch mark on the rule as the reference point.** In the figure, the measured point is at $2\frac{1}{32}$. Subtracting one inch results in a size of $1\frac{1}{32}$ for the part.

Round bars and tubing should be measured with the rule applied on the end of the tube or bar (Figure 13). Select a reference point and set it carefully at a point on the circumference of the round part to be measured. Using the reference point as a pivot, move the rule back and forth slightly to find the largest distance across the diameter. When the largest distance is determined, read the measurement at that point.

Rules are also used for transfer measurements with calipers. The caliper is set to the part, and the reading is obtained by use of the rule. Both inside and outside calipers can be used in this manner (Figures 14 and 15).

READING FRACTIONAL INCH RULES

Most dimensions are expressed in inches and fractions of inches. These dimensions are measured with fractional inch rules. The typical machinist's rule is broken down into 1, $\frac{1}{2}$, $\frac{1}{4}$, $\frac{1}{8}$, $\frac{1}{16}$, $\frac{1}{32}$, and $\frac{1}{64}$ in. graduations. In order to facilitate reading, the 1, $\frac{1}{2}$, $\frac{1}{4}$, $\frac{1}{8}$, and $\frac{1}{16}$ in. graduations appear on one side of the rule (Figure 16). The reverse side of the rule has one edge graduated in $\frac{1}{32}$ in. incre-

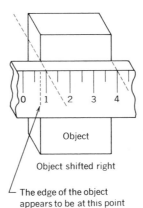

Figure 11. Parallax error.

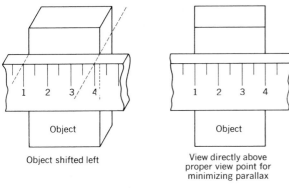

Object shifted left

View directly above proper view point for minimizing parallax

Object shifted right

The edge of the object appears to be at this point on the rule

When viewed from directly above, the rule graduations are exactly in line with the edge of the object being measured. However, when the object is shifted right or left of a point directly above the point of measurement, the alignment of the object edge and the rule graduations appears to no longer coincide

Figure 12. Using the one inch mark as the reference point.

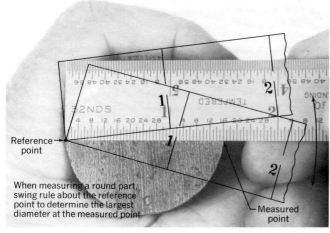

Figure 13. Measuring round objects.

When measuring a round part, swing rule about the reference point to determine the largest diameter at the measured point

Reference point

Measured point

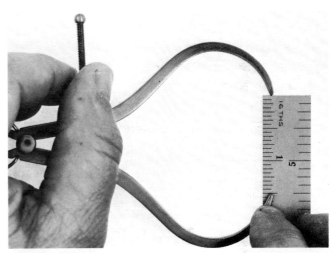

Figure 14. Using a rule to set an outside caliper.

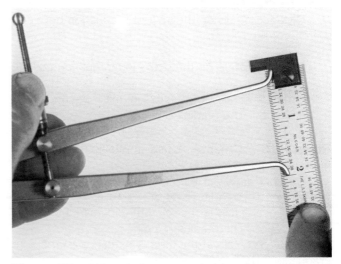

Figure 15. Using a rule to set an inside caliper.

ments and the other edge graduated in $\frac{1}{64}$ in. increments. On the $\frac{1}{32}$ in. side, every fourth mark is numbered and on the $\frac{1}{64}$ in. side, every eighth mark is numbered (Figure 17). This eliminates the need to count graduations from the nearest whole inch mark. On these rules, the length of the graduation line varies with the one inch line being the longest, the $\frac{1}{2}$ in. line being next in length, the $\frac{1}{4}$, $\frac{1}{8}$, and $\frac{1}{16}$ in. lines each being consecutively shorter. The difference in line lengths is an important aid in reading a rule.

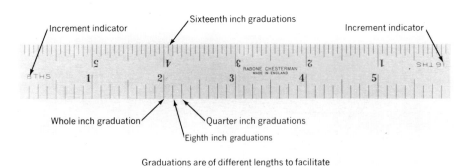

Figure 16. Front side graduations of the typical machinist's rule.

Graduations are of different lengths to facilitate reading of the rule

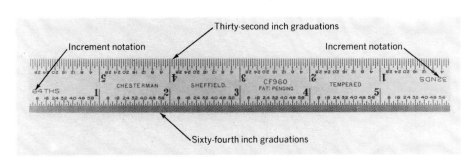

Figure 17. Back side graduations of the typical machinist's rule.

The smallest graduations on any edge of a rule is marked by small numbers on the end. Note that the words 8THS and 16THS appear at the ends of the rule. The numbers 32NDS and 64THS appear on the reverse side of the rule, thus indicating thirty-seconds and sixty-fourths of an inch.

Examples of Fractional Inch Readings

Figure 18. Distance A falls on the third $\frac{1}{8}$ in. graduation. This reading would be $\frac{3}{8}$ in.

Distance B falls on the longest graduation between the end of the rule and the first full inch mark. The reading is $\frac{1}{2}$ in.

Distance C falls on the sixth $\frac{1}{8}$ in. graduation making it $\frac{6}{8}$ or $\frac{3}{4}$ in.

Distance D falls at the fifth $\frac{1}{8}$ in. mark beyond the 2 in. graduation. The reading is $2\frac{5}{8}$ in.

Figure 19. Distance A falls at the thirteenth $\frac{1}{16}$ in. mark making the reading $\frac{13}{16}$ in.

Distance B falls at the first $\frac{1}{16}$ in. mark past the 1 in. graduation. The reading is $1\frac{1}{16}$ in.

Distance C falls at the seventh $\frac{1}{16}$ in. mark past the 1 in. graduation. The reading is $1\frac{7}{16}$ in.

Distance D falls at the third $\frac{1}{16}$ in. mark past the 2 in. graduation. The reading is $2\frac{3}{16}$ in.

Figure 20. Distance A falls at the third $\frac{1}{32}$ in. mark. The reading is $\frac{3}{32}$ in.

Distance B falls at the ninth $\frac{1}{32}$ in. mark. The reading is $\frac{9}{32}$ in.

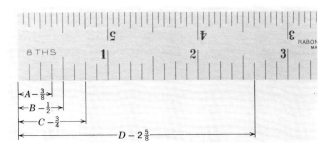

Figure 18. Examples of readings on the $\frac{1}{8}$ in. discrimination edge.

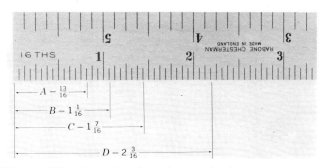

Figure 19. Examples of readings on the $\frac{1}{16}$ in. discrimination edge.

Distance C falls at the eleventh $\frac{1}{32}$ in. mark past the 1 in. graduation. The reading is $1\frac{11}{32}$ in.

Distance D falls at the fourth $\frac{1}{32}$ in. mark past the 2 in. graduation. The reading is $2\frac{4}{32}$ in., which reduced to lowest terms becomes $2\frac{1}{8}$ in.

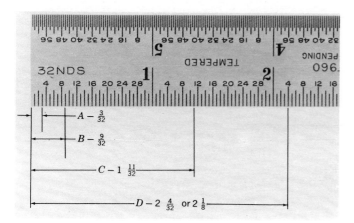

Figure 20. Examples of readings on the $\frac{1}{32}$ in. discrimination edge.

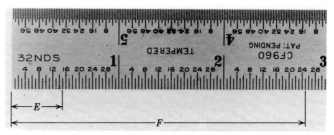

Figure 21. Examples of readings on the $\frac{1}{64}$ in. discrimination edge.

Figure 21. Distance A falls at the ninth $\frac{1}{64}$ in. mark making the reading $\frac{9}{64}$ in.

Distance B falls at the fifty-seventh $\frac{1}{64}$ in. mark making the reading $\frac{57}{64}$ in.

Distance C falls at the thirty-third $\frac{1}{64}$ in. mark past the 1 in. graduation. The reading is $1\frac{33}{64}$ in.

Distance D falls at the first $\frac{1}{64}$ in. mark past the 2 in. graduation, making the reading $2\frac{1}{64}$ in.

SELF-TEST

Read and record the dimensions indicated by the letters A to H in Figures 22.

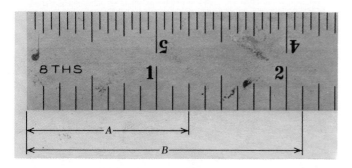

Figure 22. A and B.

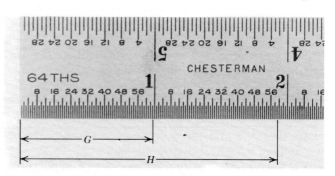

Figure 22. E and F.

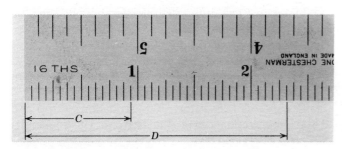

Figure 22. C and D.

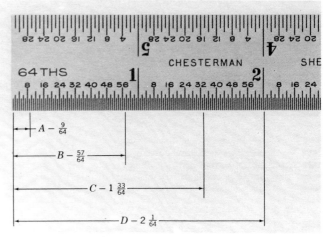

Figure 22. G and H.

On the 50th scale, each inch is divided into
50 equal parts with each part equal to $\frac{1}{50}$
or .020 (twenty thousandths of an inch). The
scale is also marked at each $\frac{1}{10}$ increment for
easier reading ($\frac{1}{10}$ = 100 thousandths or .100)

Figure 23.   Six inch decimal rule.

On the 100th scale, each inch is divided into
100 equal parts with each part equal to $\frac{1}{100}$
or .010 (ten thousandths). The scale is also
marked at each $\frac{1}{10}$ increment for easier reading.

READING DECIMAL INCH RULES

Many dimensions in the auto, aircraft, and missile indus-tries are specified in **decimal notations,** which refers to the division of the inch into 10 parts or a multiple of 10 parts, such as 50 or 100 parts. In this case, a **decimal rule** would be used. Decimal inch dimensions are specified and read as thousandths of an inch. Decimal rules, how-ever, do not discriminate to the individual thousandth because the width of an engraved or etched division on the rule is approximately .003 in. (three thousandths of an inch). Decimal rules are commonly graduated in incre-ments of $\frac{1}{10}$ in., $\frac{1}{50}$ in., or $\frac{1}{100}$ in.

A typical decimal rule may have $\frac{1}{50}$ in. divisions on the top edge and $\frac{1}{100}$ in. divisions on the bottom edge (Figure 23). The inch is divided into 10 equal parts, mak-ing each numbered division $\frac{1}{10}$ in. or .100 in. (100 thou-sandths of an inch). On the top scale each $\frac{1}{10}$ increment is further subdivided into five equal parts, which makes the value of each of these divisions .020 in. (20 thou-sandths of an inch).

Examples of Decimal Inch Readings

Figure 24.   Distance *A* falls on the first marked grad-uation. The reading is $\frac{1}{10}$ or .100 thousandths in. This can also be read on the 50ths in. scale, as seen in the figure.

Distance *B* can only be read on the 100th in. scale, as it falls at the seventh graduation beyond the .10 in. mark. The reading is .100 in. plus .070 in., or .170 in. This distance cannot be read on the 50th in. scale because discrimination of the 50th in. scale is not sufficient.

Distance *C* falls at the second mark beyond the .400 in. line. This reading is .400 in. plus .020 in., or .420 in. Since .020 in. is equal to $\frac{1}{50}$ in., this can also be read on the 50th in. scale as shown in the figure.

Distance *D* falls at the sixth increment beyond the .400 in. line. The reading is .400 in. plus .060 in., or .460 in. This can also be read on the 50th in. scale, as seen in the figure.

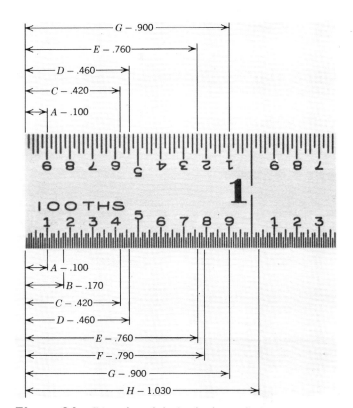

Figure 24.   Examples of decimal rule readings.

Distance *E* falls at the sixth division beyond the .700 in. mark. The reading is .700 in. plus .060 in., or .760 in. This can also be read on the 50th in. scale.

Distance *F* falls at the ninth mark beyond the .700 in. line. The reading is .700 in. plus .090 in., or .790 in. This cannot be read on the 50th in. scale.

Distance *G* falls at the .100 graduation on top and at the .900 graduation on the bottom. The reading is .900 or $\frac{9}{10}$ of an inch.

Distance *H* falls three marks past the first full inch mark. The reading is 1.00 in. plus .030 in., or 1.030 in. This cannot be read on the 50th in. scale.

SELF-TEST

Read and record the dimensions indicated by the letters *A* to *E* in Figures 25.

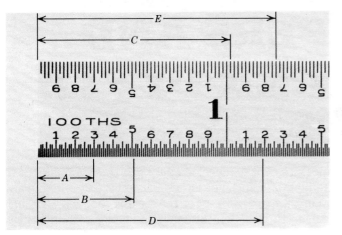

Figure 25. Decimal inch rule.

READING METRIC RULES

Many products are made in metric dimensions requiring a machinist to use a **metric rule.** The typical metric rule has millimeter (mm) and half millimeter graduations (Figure 26).

Examples of Reading Metric Rules

Figure 27. Distance *A* falls at the 53rd graduation on the mm scale. The reading is 53 mm.

Distance *B* falls at the 22nd graduation on the mm scale. The reading is 22 mm.

Distance *C* falls at the sixth graduation on the mm scale. The reading is 6 mm.

Distance *D* falls at the 18th half mm mark. The reading is 8 mm plus an additional half mm, giving a total of 8.5 mm.

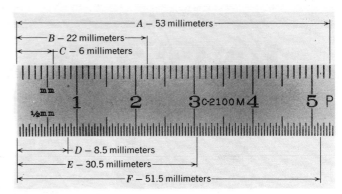

Figure 27. Examples of metric rule readings.

Distance *E* falls one-half mm beyond the 3 centimeter (cm) graduation. Since 3 cm is equal to 30 mm, the reading is 30.5 mm.

Distance *F* falls one-half mm beyond the 51 mm graduation. The reading is 51.5 mm. In machine design, all dimensions are specified in mm. Hence, 1.5 meters (m) would be 1500 mm.

SELF-TEST

Read and record the dimensions indicated by the letters *A* to *F* in Figure 28.

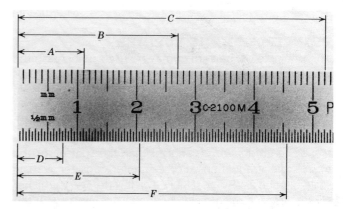

Figure 28. *A* to *F*.

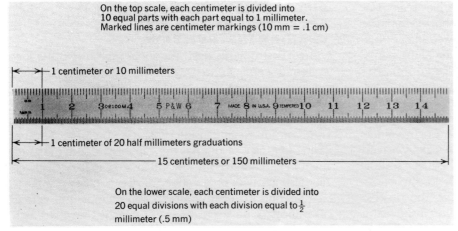

Figure 26. 150 millimeter metric rule.

UNIT 3 USING VERNIER CALIPERS AND VERNIER DEPTH GAGES

The inspection and measurement of machined parts requires various kinds of measuring tools. Often the discrimination of a rule is sufficient, but, in many cases the discrimination of a rule with a vernier scale is required. This unit explains the types, use, and applications of common vernier instruments.

OBJECTIVES

After completing this unit, you should be able to:
1. Measure and record dimensions to an accuracy of plus or minus .001 in. with a vernier caliper.
2. Measure and record dimensions to an accuracy of plus or minus .02 mm using a metric vernier caliper.
3. Measure and record dimensions using a vernier depth gage.

PRINCIPLE OF THE VERNIER

The principle of the **vernier** may be used to increase the discrimination of all graduated scale measuring tools used by a machinist. A vernier system consists of a **main scale** and a **vernier scale.** The vernier scale is placed adjacent to the main scale so that graduations on both scales can be observed together. The spacing of the vernier scale graduations is shorter than the spacing of the main scale graduations. For example, consider a main scale divided as shown (Figure 1a). It is desired to further subdivide each main scale division into 10 parts with the use of a vernier. The spacing of each vernier scale division is made $\frac{1}{10}$ of a main scale division shorter than the spacing of a main scale division. This may sound confusing, but, think of it as 10 vernier scale divisions corresponding to nine main scale divisions (Figure 1a). The vernier now permits the main scale to discriminate to $\frac{1}{10}$ of its major divisions. Therefore, $\frac{1}{10}$ is known as the **least count** of the vernier.

The vernier functions in the following manner. Assume that the zero line on the vernier scale is placed as shown (Figure 1b). The reading on the main scale is two, plus a fraction of a division. It is desired to know the amount of the fraction over two, to the nearest tenth or least count of the vernier. As you inspect the

alignment of the vernier scale and the main scale lines, you will note that they move closer together until one line on the vernier scale **coincides** with a line on the main scale. This is the **coincident line** of the vernier and indicates the fraction in tenths that must be added to the main scale reading. The vernier is coincident at the sixth line. Since the least count of the vernier is $\frac{1}{10}$, the zero vernier line is six-tenths past two on the main scale. Therefore, the main scale reading is 2.6 (Figure 1b).

DISCRIMINATION AND APPLICATIONS OF VERNIER INSTRUMENTS

Vernier instruments used for linear measure in the inch system discriminate to .001 in. ($\frac{1}{1000}$). Metric verniers generally discriminate to .02 ($\frac{1}{50}$) of a millimeter.

The most common vernier instruments include several styles of **calipers.** The common vernier caliper is used for outside and inside linear measurement. Another style of vernier caliper has the capability depth measurement in addition to outside and inside capacity. The vernier also appears on a variety of depth gages.

Beyond its most common applications, the vernier also appears on a height gage, which is an extremely

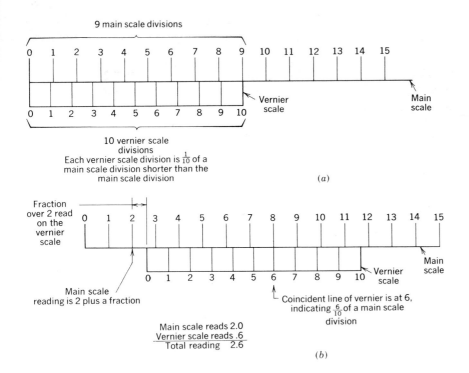

Figure 1. (a) and (b) Principle of the vernier.

important layout tool for a machinist. The vernier is also used on the gear tooth caliper, a special vernier caliper used in gear measurement. As the principle of the vernier can be used to subdivide a unit of angular measure as well as linear measure, it appears on various types of protractors used for angular measurement.

RELIABILITY AND EXPECTATION OF ACCURACY IN VERNIER INSTRUMENTS

Reliability in vernier calipers and depth gages is highly dependent on proper use of the tool. The simple fact that the caliper or depth gage has increased discrimination over a rule does not necessarily provide increased reliability. The improved degree of discrimination in vernier instruments requires more than the mere visual alignment of a rule graduation against the edge of the object to be measured. The zero reference point of a vernier caliper is the positively placed contact of the solid saw with the part to be measured. On the depth gage, the base is the zero reference point. Positive contact of the zero reference is an important consideration in vernier reliability.

The vernier scale must be read carefully if a reliable measurement is to be determined. On many vernier instruments the vernier scale should be read with the aid of a magnifier. Without this aid, the coincident line of the vernier is difficult to determine. Therefore, the reliability of the vernier readings can be in question. The typical vernier caliper has very narrow jaws and thus must be carefully aligned with the axis of measurement. On the

plain slide vernier caliper, no provision is made for the "feel" of the measuring pressure. Some calipers and the depth gage are equipped with a screw thread fine adjustment that gives them a slight advantage in determining the pressure applied during the measurement.

Generally, the overall reliability of vernier instruments for measurement at maximum discrimination of .001 is fairly low. The vernier should never be used in an attempt to discriminate below .001. The instrument does not have that capability. Vernier instruments are a popular tool on the inspection bench, and they can serve very well for measurement in the range of plus or minus .005 of an inch. With proper use and an understanding of the limitations of a vernier instrument, this tool can be a valuable addition to the many measuring tools available to you.

VERNIER CALIPERS

With a rule, measurements can be made to the nearest $\frac{1}{64}$ or $\frac{1}{100}$ in., but often this is not sufficiently accurate. A measuring tool based on a rule but with much greater discrimination is the **vernier caliper** (Figure 2). Vernier calipers have a discrimination of .001 in. The **beam** or **bar** is engraved with the **main scale**. This is also called the **true scale,** as each inch marking is exactly one inch apart. The beam and the solid jaw are square, or at 90 degrees to each other.

The movable jaw contains the **vernier scale.** This scale is located on the sliding jaw of a vernier caliper or it is part of the base on the vernier depth gage. The func-

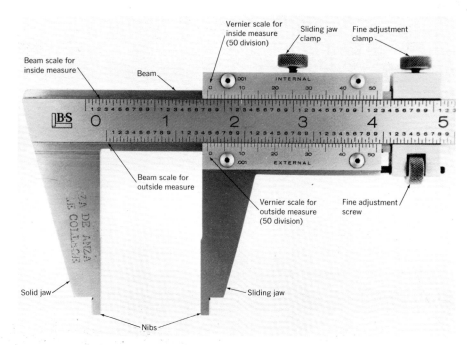

Figure 2. Typical inside-outside, 50 division vernier caliper (DeAnza College).

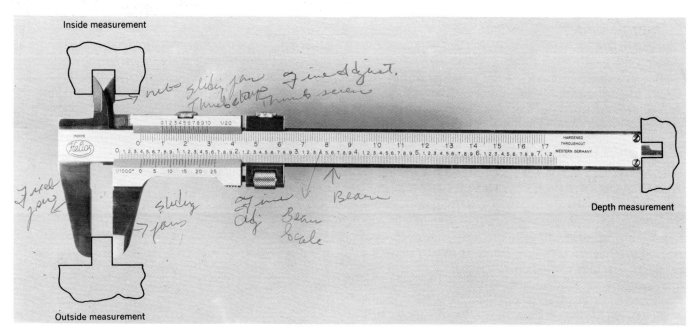

Figure 3. Common vernier caliper.

tion of the vernier scale is to subdivide the minor divisions on the beam scale into the smallest increments that the vernier instrument is capable of measuring. For example, a 25 division vernier subdivides the minor divisions of the beam scale into 25 parts. Since the minor division are equal to .025 thousandths of an inch, the vernier divides them into increments of .001 of an inch. This is the finest discrimination of the instrument.

Most of the longer vernier calipers have a fine adjustment clamp for precise adjustments of the mova-

ble jaw. Inside measurements are made over the **nibs** on the jaw and are read on the top scale of the vernier caliper (Figure 2). The top scale is a duplicate of the lower scale, with the exception that it is offset to compensate for the size of the nibs.

The standard vernier caliper is very common (Figure 3). This is a versatile tool because of its capacity to make outside, inside, and depth measurements. Many different measuring applications are made with this particular design of vernier caliper (Figure 4).

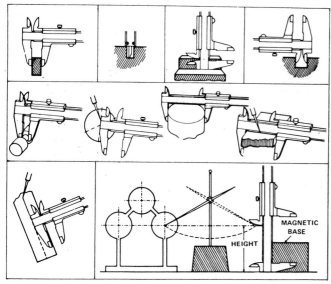

Figure 4. This design of vernier caliper has many applications (Courtesy of the M.T.I. Corporation).

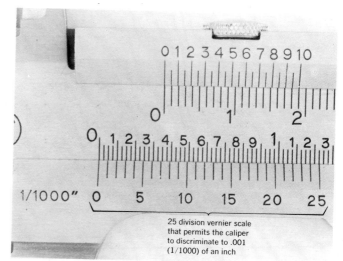

Figure 5. Lower scale is a 25 division vernier.

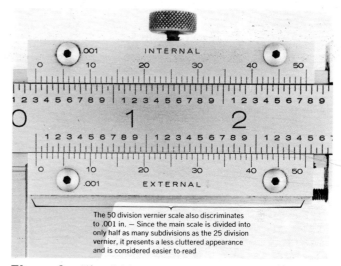

Figure 6. Fifty division vernier caliper.

VERNIER CALIPER PROCEDURES

To test a vernier caliper for accuracy, clean the contact surfaces of the two jaws. Bring the movable jaw with normal gaging pressure into contact with the solid jaw. Hold the caliper against a light source and examine the alignment of the solid and movable jaws. If wear exists, a line of light will be visible between the jaw faces. A gap as small as .0001 ($\frac{1}{10,000}$) of an inch can be seen against a light. If the contact between the jaws is satisfactory, check the vernier scale alignment. The vernier scale zero mark should be in alignment with the zero on the main scale. Realignment of the vernier scale to adjust it to zero can be accomplished on some vernier calipers.

A vernier caliper is a delicate precision tool and should be treated as such. It is very important that the correct amount of pressure or feel is developed while taking a measurement. The measuring jaws should contact the workpiece firmly. However, excessive pressure will spring the jaws and give inaccurate readings. When measuring an object, use the solid jaw as the reference point. Then move the sliding jaw until contact is made. When measuring with the vernier caliper make certain that the beam of the caliper is in line with the surfaces being measured. Whenever possible, read the vernier caliper while it is still in contact with the workpiece. Moving the instrument may change the reading. Any measurement should be taken at least twice to assure reliability.

READING INCH VERNIER CALIPERS

Vernier scales are engraved with 25 or 50 divisions (Figures 5 and 6). On a 25 division vernier caliper, each inch on the main scale is divided into 10 major divisions numbered from 1 to 9. Each major division is .100 (one hundred thousandth). Each major division has four subdivisions with a spacing of .025 (twenty-five thousandths). The vernier scale has 25 divisions with the zero line being the index.

To read the vernier caliper, count all of the graduations to the left of the index line. This would be 1 whole inch plus $\frac{2}{10}$ or .200, plus 1 subdivision valued at .025, plus part of one subdivision (Figure 7). The value of this partial subdivision is determined by the coincidence of one line on the vernier scale with one line of the true scale. For this example, the coincidence is on line 13 of the vernier scale. This is the value in thousandths of an inch that has to be added to the value read on the beam. Therefore, 1 + .100 + .100 + .025 + .013 equals the total reading of 1.238. An aid in determining the coincidental

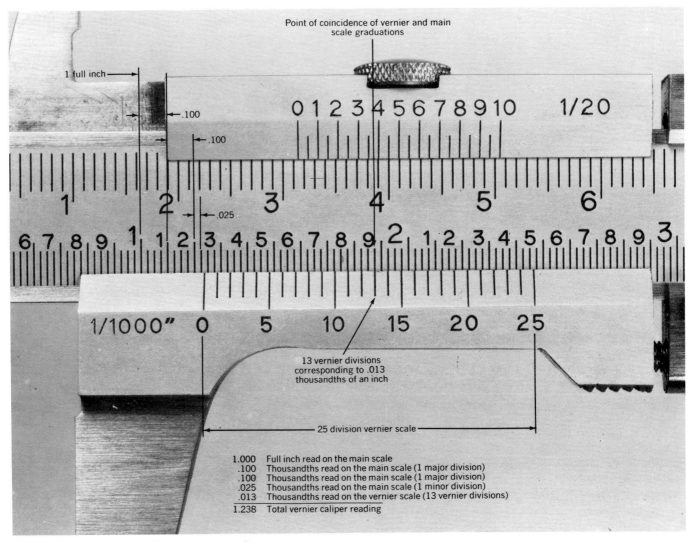

Figure 7. Reading a 25 division vernier caliper.

1.000	Full inch read on the main scale
.100	Thousandths read on the main scale (1 major division)
.100	Thousandths read on the main scale (1 major division)
.025	Thousandths read on the main scale (1 minor division)
.013	Thousandths read on the vernier scale (13 vernier divisions)
1.238	Total vernier caliper reading

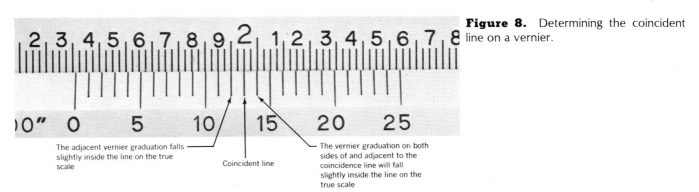

Figure 8. Determining the coincident line on a vernier.

line is the **lines adjacent to the coincidental line fall inside the lines on the true scale** (Figure 8).

The 50 division vernier caliper is read as follows (Figure 9). The true scale has each inch divided into 10 major divisions of .100 in. each, with each major division subdivided in half, thus being .050 in. The vernier scale has 50 divisions. The 50 division vernier caliper reading shown is read as follows:

Figure 9.   Reading a 50 division vernier.

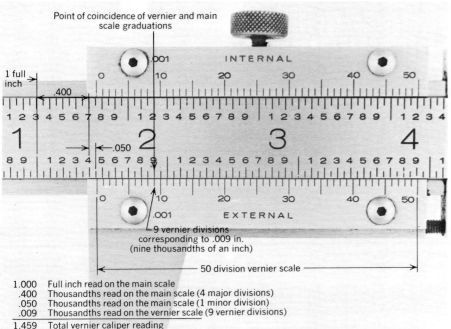

1.000   Full inch read on the main scale
 .400   Thousandths read on the main scale (4 major divisions)
 .050   Thousandths read on the main scale (1 minor division)
 .009   Thousandths read on the vernier scale (9 vernier divisions)
1.459   Total vernier caliper reading

Beam whole inch reading	1.000
Additional major divisions	.400
Additional minor divisions	.050
Vernier scale reading	.009
Total caliper reading	1.459

DIAL CALIPER

An outgrowth from the vernier caliper is the dial caliper (Figure 10). However, this instrument does not employ the principle of the vernier. The beam scale on the dial caliper is graduated only into .10 in. increments. The caliper dial is either graduated into 100 or 200 divisions. The dial hand is operated by a pinion gear that engages a rack on the caliper beam. On the 100 division dial, the hand makes one complete revolution for each .10 in. movement of the sliding jaw along the beam. Therefore, each dial graduation represents $\frac{1}{100}$ of .10 in., or .001 in. maximum discrimination. On the 200 division dial the hand makes only one-half a revolution for each .10 in. of movement along the beam. Discrimination is also .001 in.

Since the dial caliper is direct reading, the need to

Figure 10.   Dial caliper (Harry Smith & Associates).

determine the coincident line of a vernier scale is eliminated. This greatly facilitates reading of the instruments and, for this reason, the dial caliper has all but replaced its vernier counterpart in many applications. When using the dial caliper, remember what you have learned about the expectation of accuracy in caliper instruments.

SELF-TEST—READING INCH VERNIER CALIPERS

Determine the dimensions in the vernier caliper illustrations (Figures 11a to 11d).

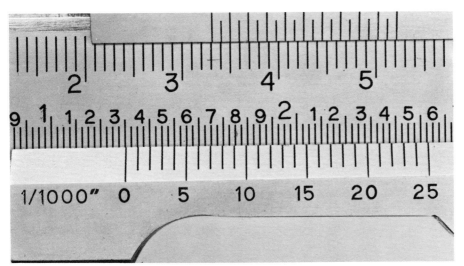

Figure 11*a.*

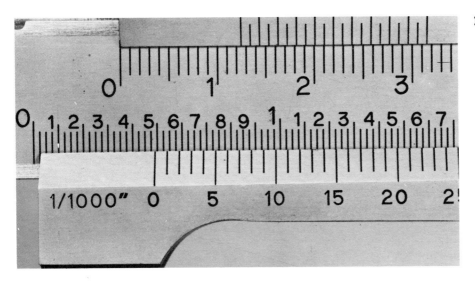

Figure 11*b.*

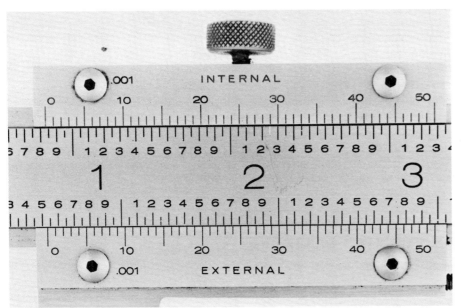

Figure 11*c.*

Figure 11*d.*

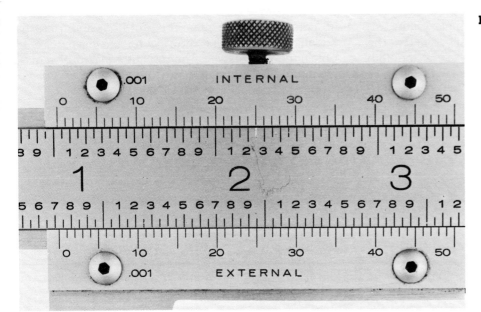

READING METRIC VERNIER CALIPERS

The applications for a metric vernier caliper are exactly the same as those described for an inch system vernier caliper. The discrimination of metric vernier caliper models varies from .02 millimeter, .05 mm, or .1 mm. The most commonly used type discriminates to .02 mm. The main scale on a metric vernier caliper is divided into millimeters with every tenth millimeter mark numbered. The 10 millimeter line is numbered 1, the 20 millimeter line is numbered 2 and so on, up to the capacity of the tool (Figure 12). The vernier scale on the sliding jaw is divided into 50 equal spaces with every 5th space numbered. Each numbered division on the vernier represents one tenth of a millimeter. The five smaller divisions between the numbered lines represent two hundredths (.02 mm) of a millimeter.

To determine the caliper reading, read, on the main scale, whole millimeters to the left of the zero or the

Figure 12. Reading a metric vernier caliper with .02 millimeter discrimination.

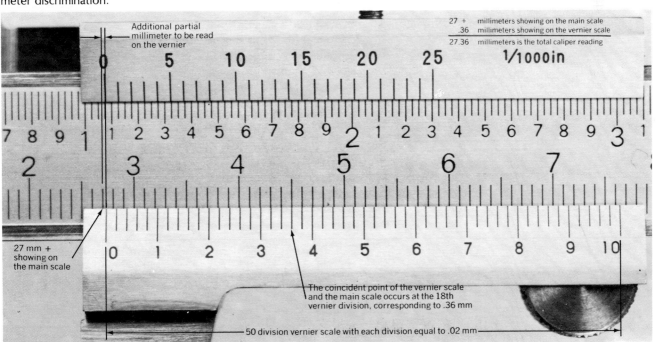

27 +   millimeters showing on the main scale
.36   millimeters showing on the vernier scale
27.36   millimeters is the total caliper reading

1/1000in

Additional partial millimeter to be read on the vernier

27 mm + showing on the main scale

The coincident point of the vernier scale and the main scale occurs at the 18th vernier division, corresponding to .36 mm

50 division vernier scale with each division equal to .02 mm

index line of the sliding jaw. The example (Figure 11) shows 27 mm plus part of an additional millimeter. The vernier scale coincides with the main scale at the 18th vernier division. Since each vernier scale spacing is equal to .02 mm. the reading on the vernier scale is equal to 18 times .02, or .36 mm. Therefore, .36 mm must be added to the amount showing on the main scale to obtain the final reading. The result is equal to 27 mm + .36 mm or 27.36 mm. (Figure 11).

SELF-TEST—READING METRIC VERNIER CALIPERS

Determine the metric vernier caliper dimensions illustrated in Figures 13a to 13d.

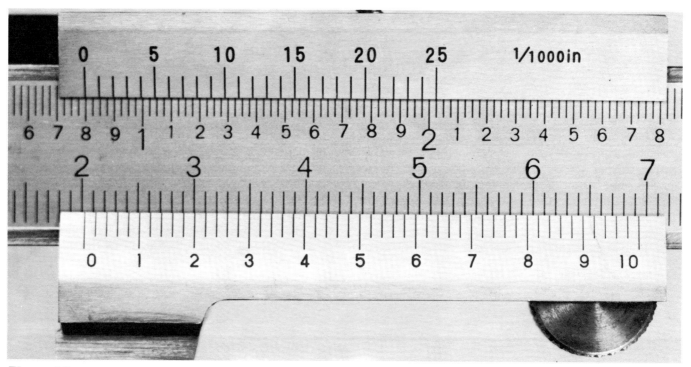

Figure 13a.

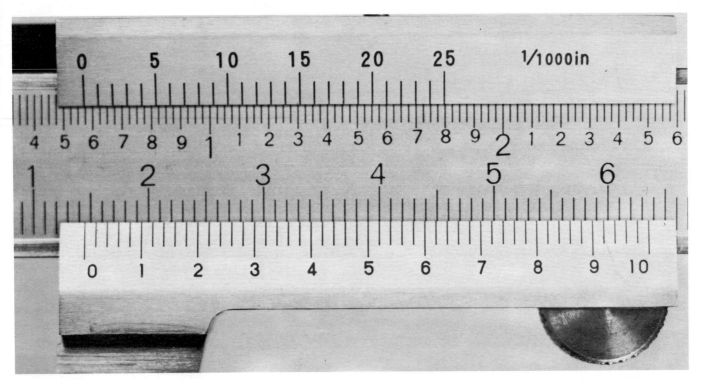

Figure 13*b*.

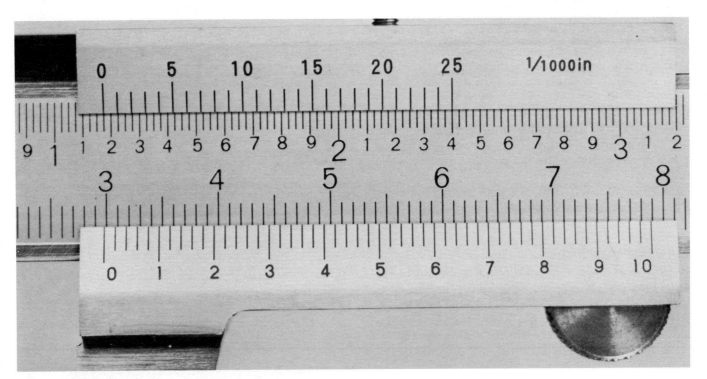

Figure 13*c*.

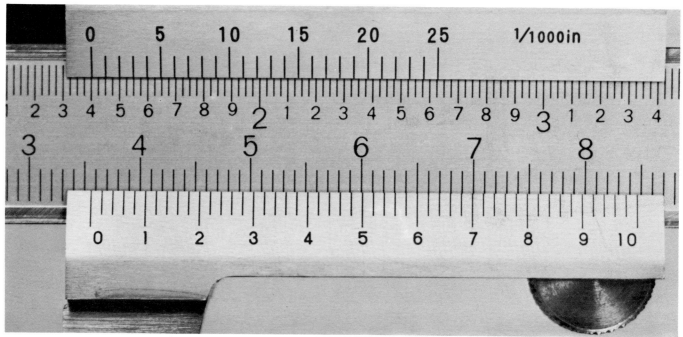

Figure 13*d.*

READING VERNIER DEPTH GAGES

These measuring tools are designed to measure the depth of holes, recesses, steps, and slots. Basic parts of a vernier depth gage include the base or anvil with the vernier scale and the fine adjustment screw (Figure 14). Also shown is the graduated beam or bar that contains the true scale. To make accurate measurements the reference surface needs to be flat and free from nicks and burrs. The base should be held firmly against the reference surface while the beam is brought in contact with the surface being measured. The measuring pressure should approximately equal the pressure exerted when making a light dot on a piece of paper with a pencil. On a vernier depth gage, dimensions are read in the same manner as on a vernier caliper.

DIAL DEPTH GAGES

As with vernier calipers, vernier depth gages have their dial counterparts (Figure 15). The dial depth gage functions in the same manner as the dial caliper. Readings are direct without the need to use a vernier scale. The dial depth gage has the capacity to measure over several inches of range, depending on the length of the beam. Discrimination is .001 in.

Another type of dial depth gage uses a dial indicator (Figure 16). However, the capacity and discrimination of this instrument is dependent on the range and discrimination of the dial indicator used. The tool is primarily used in comparison measuring applications.

Figure 14. Vernier depth gage with .001 in. discrimination.

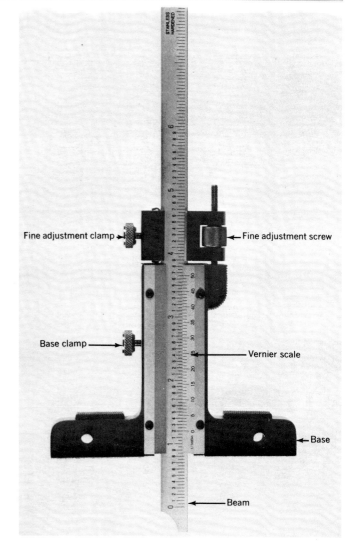

Figure 15. Dial depth gage (Harry Smith & Associates).

Figure 16. Dial indicator depth gage (Courtesy of the L. S. Starrett Company).

SELF-TEST—READING VERNIER DEPTH GAGES

Determine the depth measurements illustrated in Figures 17 a to 17 d.

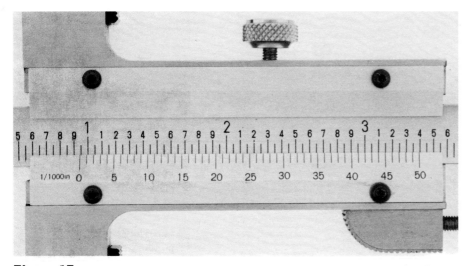

Figure 17 a.

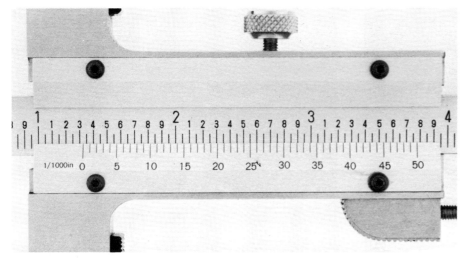

Figure 17*b.*

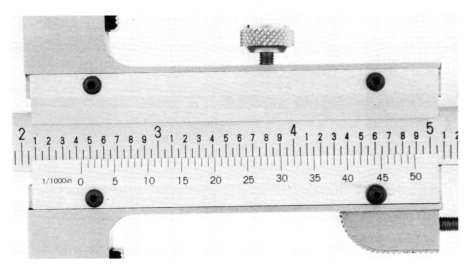

Figure 17*c.*

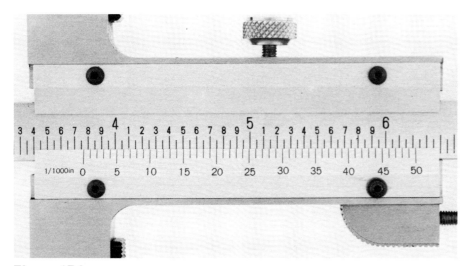

Figure 17*d.*

UNIT 4 USING MICROMETER INSTRUMENTS

Micrometer measuring instruments are the most commonly used precision measuring tools found in industry. Correct use of them is essential to anyone engaged in making or inspecting machined parts.

OBJECTIVES

After completing this unit and with the use of appropriate measuring kits, you should be able to:

1. Measure and record dimensions using outside micrometers to an accuracy of plus or minus .001 of an inch.
2. Measure and record diameters to an accuracy of plus or minus .001 in. using an inside micrometer.
3. Measure and record depth measurements using a depth micrometer to an accuracy of plus or minus .001 in.
4. Measure and record dimensions using a metric micrometer to an accuracy of plus or minus .01 mm.
5. Measure and record dimensions using a vernier micrometer to an accuracy of plus or minus .0001 in. (assuming proper measuring conditions).

TYPES OF MICROMETER INSTRUMENTS

The common types of micrometer instruments, **outside, inside,** and **depth,** are discussed in detail within this unit. The micrometer appears in many other forms in addition to these common types.

Blade Micrometer

The blade micrometer (Figure 1), so-called because of its thin spindle and anvil, is used to measure narrow slots and grooves (Figure 2) where the standard micrometer spindle and anvil could not be accommodated because of their diameter.

Combination Metric/Inch or Inch/Metric Micrometer

The combination micrometer (Figure 3) is designed for dual system use in metric and inch measurement. The tool has a digital reading scale for one system while the other system is read from the sleeve and thimble.

Point Micrometer and Comparator Micrometer

The point micrometer (Figure 4) is used in applications where limited space is available or where it might be desired to take a measurement at an exact location. Several point angles are available. The 60 degree comparator micrometer (Figure 5) is usually called a screw thread comparator micrometer. It is most often used to compare screw threads to some known standard like a thread plug gage (Figure 6).

Disc Micrometer

The disc micrometer (Figure 7) finds application in measuring thin materials such as paper where a measuring face with a large area is needed. It is also useful for such measurements as the one shown in the figure where the distance from the slot to the edge is to be determined.

Direct Reading Micrometer

The direct reading micrometer, which may also be known as a high precision micrometer, reads directly to .0001 ($\frac{1}{10,000}$) of an inch (Figure 8).

Hub Micrometer

The frame of the hub micrometer (Figure 9) is designed

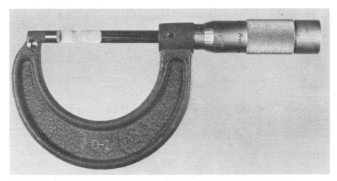

Figure 1. Blade micrometer (DeAnza College).

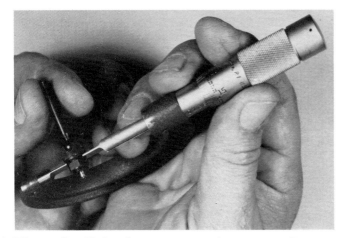

Figure 2. Blade micrometer measuring a groove (DeAnza College).

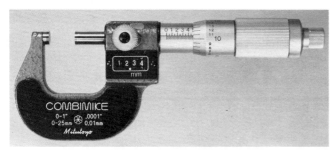

Figure 3. Combination inch/metric micrometer.

Figure 4. Thirty degree point comparator micrometer.

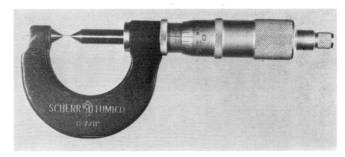

Figure 5. Screw thread comparison micrometer (DeAnza College).

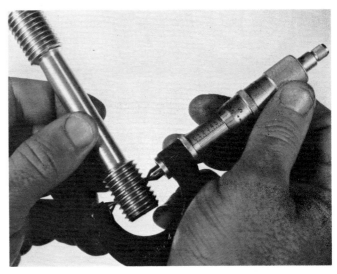

Figure 6. Screw thread comparison micrometer measuring a screw thread (DeAnza College).

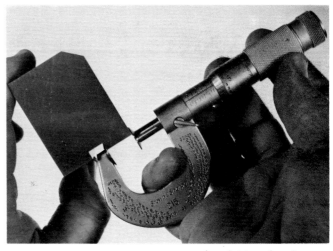

Figure 7. Disc micrometer measuring slot to edge distance (DeAnza College).

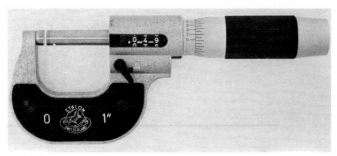

Figure 8.   Direct reading digit micrometer (Harry Smith & Associates).

Figure 9.   Hub micrometer (DeAnza College).

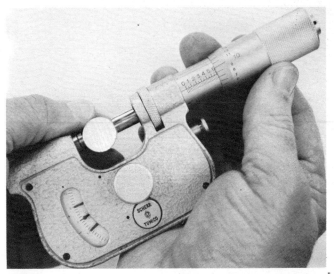

Figure 11.   Indicating micrometer (Harry Smith & Associates).

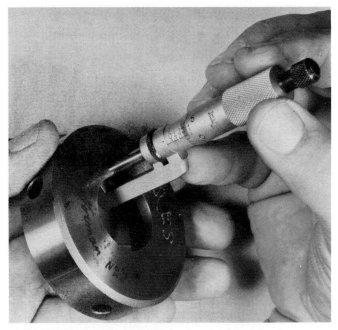

Figure 10.   Hub micrometer measuring through a bore (DeAnza College).

Figure 12.   Inside micrometer caliper

ing discriminating to .0001 of an inch. When an object is measured, the size deviation above or below the micrometer setting will be indicated on the dial. The indicating dial usually has a range of plus or minus .001 of an inch.

Inside Micrometer Caliper
The inside micrometer caliper (Figure 12) has jaws that resemble those on a vernier caliper. This instrument is designed for inside measurement. Thus, the versatility of the caliper and the reliability of the micrometer are combined.

Internal Micrometer
The internal micrometer (Figure 13) uses a three point measuring contact system to determine the size of a bore or hole. The instrument is direct reading and is

such that the instrument may be put through a hole or bore in order to measure the hub thickness of a gear or sprocket (Figure 10).

Indicating Micrometer
The indicating micrometer (Figure 11) is useful in inspection applications where a determination of acceptable tolerance is to be made. The instrument has an indicating mechanism built into the frame that permits a dial read-

Figure 13. Internal micrometer (Harry Smith & Associates).

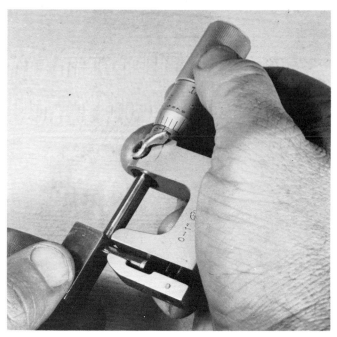

Figure 15. Interchangeable anvil micrometer with pin anvil (DeAnza College).

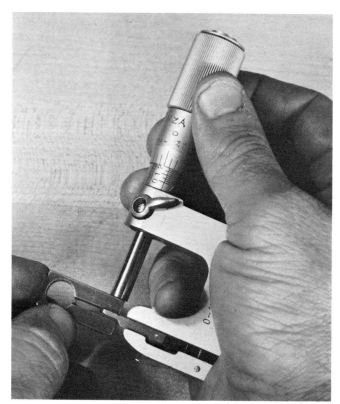

Figure 14. Interchangeable anvil micrometer with flat anvil (DeAnza College).

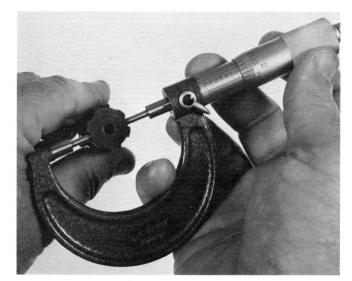

Figure 16. Spline micrometer.

more likely to yield a reliable reading because its three point measuring contacts make the instrument self-centering as compared to a tool making use of only two contacts.

Interchangeable Anvil Type Micrometer

The interchangeable anvil type micrometer is often called a multi-anvil micrometer. It can be used in a variety of applications. A straight anvil is used to measure

into a slot (Figure 14). A cylindrical anvil may be used for measuring into a hole (Figure 15). Various shaped anvils may be clamped into position to meet special measuring requirements.

Spline Micrometer

The spline micrometer (Figure 16) has a small diameter spindle and anvil. The length of the anvil is also considerably longer than that of the standard micrometer. The

frame of the instrument is also larger. This type of micrometer is well suited to measuring the minor diameter of a spline.

Screw Thread Micrometer

The screw thread micrometer (Figure 17) is specifically

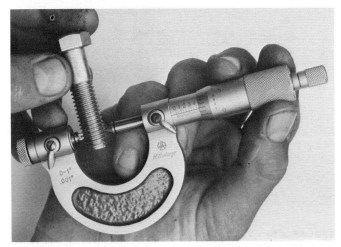

Figure 17. Screw thread micrometer (Yuba College).

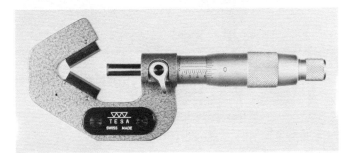

Figure 18. V-anvil micrometer (Yuba College).

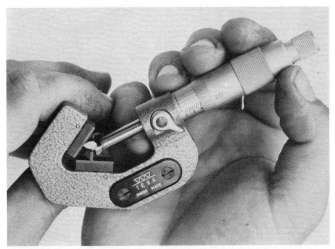

Figure 19. V-anvil micrometer measuring a three fluted end mill (Yuba College).

designed to measure the pitch diameter of a screw thread. The anvil and spindle tips are shaped to match the form of the thread to be measured.

V-Anvil Micrometer

The V-anvil micrometer (Figure 18) is used to measure the diameter of an object with odd-numbered symmetrical or evenly spaced features. They are designed for specific numbers of these features. The type shown is for three-sided objects like the three fluted end mill being measured (Figure 19). This design is also very useful in checking out-of-round conditions in centerless grinding that cannot be determined with a conventional outside micrometer caliper. The next most common type of V-anvil micrometer is for five fluted tools.

Tubing Micrometer

One type of tubing micrometer has a vertical anvil with a cylindrically shaped tip. Another design is like the ordinary micrometer caliper except that the anvil is a half sphere instead of a flat surface. This instrument is designed to measure the wall thickness of tubing (Figure 20). The tubing micrometer can also be applied in other applications such as determining the distance of a hole from an edge (Figure 21).

A standard outside micrometer may also be used to determine the wall thickness of tube or pipe (Figure 22). In this application, a ball adaptor is placed on the anvil. The diameter of the ball must be subtracted from the micrometer reading in order to determine the actual reading.

Caliper-Type Outside Micrometer

The caliper-type outside micrometer is used where mea-

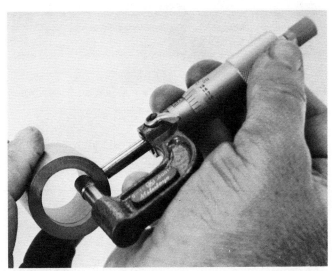

Figure 20. Tubing micrometer measuring a tubewall (DeAnza College).

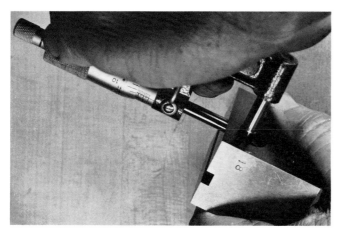

Figure 21. Tubing micrometer measuring hole to edge distance (DeAnza College).

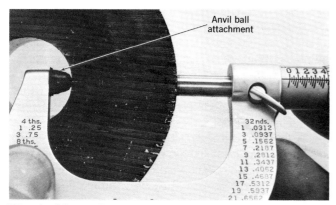

Figure 22. Ball attachment for tubing measurement (Harry Smith & Associates).

Figure 23. Caliper-type outside micrometer (Harry Smith & Associates).

surements to be taken are inaccessible to a regular micrometer (Figure 23).

Taper Micrometer
The taper micrometer can measure inside tapers (Figure 24) or outside tapers (Figure 25).

Groove Micrometer
The groove micrometer (Figure 26) is well-suited to measuring grooves and slots, especially in inaccessible places.

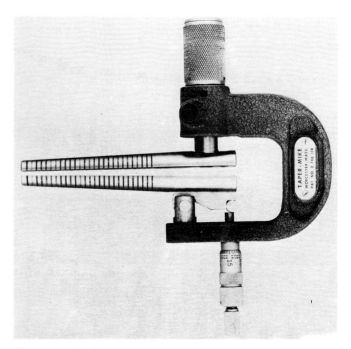

Figure 24. Inside taper micrometer (Courtesy of Taper Micrometer Corp.).

Figure 25. Outside taper micrometer in use (Courtesy of Taper Micrometer Corp.).

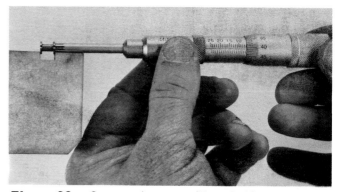

Figure 26. Groove micrometer (Harry Smith & Associates).

DISCRIMINATION OF MICROMETER INSTRUMENTS

The standard micrometer will discriminate to .001 ($\frac{1}{1000}$) of an inch. In its vernier form, the discrimination is increased to .0001 ($\frac{1}{10,000}$) of an inch. The common metric micrometer discriminates to .01 ($\frac{1}{100}$) of a millimeter. The same rules apply to micrometers as apply to all measuring instruments. The tool should not be used beyond its discrimination. A standard micrometer with .001 discrimination should not be used in an attempt to ascertain measurements beyond that point. In order to measure to a discrimination of .0001 with the vernier micrometer, certain special conditions must be met. These will be discussed in more detail within this unit.

RELIABILITY AND EXPECTATION OF ACCURACY IN MICROMETER INSTRUMENTS

The micrometer has increased reliability over the vernier. One reason for this is readability of the instruments. The .001 graduations that dictate the maximum discrimination of the micrometer are placed on the circumference of the thimble. The distance between the marks is therefore increased, making them easier to see.

The micrometer will yield very reliable results to .001 discrimination if the instrument is properly cared for, properly calibrated, and correct procedure for use is followed. Care and procedure will be discussed in detail within this unit. **Calibration** is the process by which any measuring instrument is compared to a known standard. If the tool deviates from the standard, it may then be adjusted to conformity. This is an additional advantage of the micrometer over the vernier. The micrometer must be periodically calibrated if reliable results are to be obtained.

Can a micrometer measure reliably to within .001?

The answer is "no" for the standard micrometer, as this violates the 10 to 1 rule for discrimination. The answer is "yes" for the vernier micrometer, but only under controlled conditions. What then, is an acceptable expectation of accuracy that will yield maximum reliability? This is dependent to some degree on the tolerance specified and can be summarized in the following table.

Tolerance Specified		Acceptability of the Standard Micrometer	Acceptability of the Vernier Micrometer
−.000 or +.001	−.001 +.000	No	Yes (under controlled conditions)
±.001		Yes	Yes (vernier will not be required)

For a specified tolerance within .001 in., the vernier micrometer should be used. Plus or minus .001 in. is a total range of .002 in. or within the capability of the standard micrometers.

The micrometer is indeed a marvelous example of precision manufacturing. These rugged tools are produced in quantity with each one conforming to equally high standards. Micrometer instruments, in all their many forms, constitute one of the fundamental measuring instruments for the machinist.

CARE OF OUTSIDE MICROMETERS

You should be familiar with the names of the major parts of the typical outside micrometer (Figure 27). The micrometer uses the movement of a precisely threaded rod turning in a nut for precision measurements. The accuracy of micrometer measurements is dependent on the quality of its construction, the care the tool receives, and the skill of the user. Consider some of the important factors in the care of the micrometer. A micrometer should be wiped clean of dust and oil before and after it is used. A micrometer should not be opened or closed by holding it by the thimble and spinning the frame around the axis of the spindle. Make sure that the micrometer is not dropped. Even a fall of a short distance can spring the frame. This will cause misalignment between the anvil and spindle faces and destroy the accuracy of this precision tool. A micrometer should be kept away from chips on a machine tool. The instrument should be placed on a clean tool board (Figure 28) or on a clean shop towel (Figure 29) close to where it is needed.

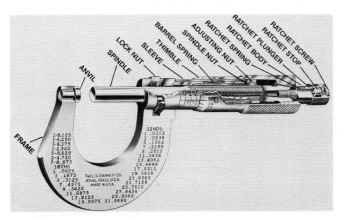

Figure 27. Parts of the outside micrometer (Courtesy of the L. S. Starrett Co.).

Figure 28. Micrometers should always be kept on a tool board when used near a machine tool (Lane Community College).

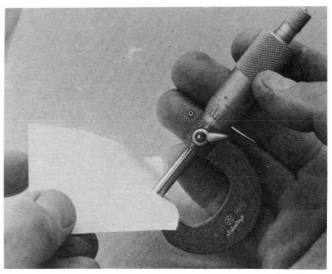

Figure 30. Cleaning the measuring faces (Lane Community College).

Figure 29. Micrometers should be kept on a clean shop towel when used on the bench (Lane Community College).

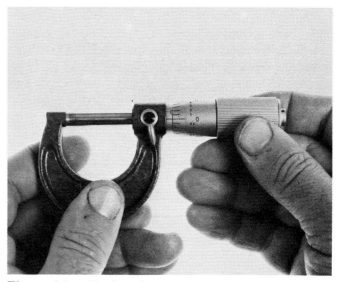

Figure 31. Checking the zero reading.

Always remember that the machinist is responsible for any measurements that he may make. To excuse an inaccurate measurement on the grounds that a micrometer was not properly adjusted or cared for would be less than professional. When a micrometer is stored after use, make sure that the spindle face does not touch the anvil. Perspiration, moisture from the air, or even oils promote corrosion between the measuring faces with a corresponding reduction in accuracy.

Prior to using a micrometer, clean the measuring faces. The measuring faces of many newer micrometers are made from an extremely hard metal called tungsten carbide. These instruments are often known as carbide-

tipped micrometers. If you examine the measuring faces of a carbide-tipped micrometer, you will see where the carbide has been attached to the face of the anvil and spindle. Carbide-tipped micrometers have very durable and long-wearing measuring faces. Screw the spindle down lightly against a piece of paper held between it and the anvil (Figure 30). Slide the paper out from between the measuring faces and blow away any fuzz that clings to the spindle or anvil. At this time, you should test the zero reading of the micrometer by bringing the spindle slowly into contact with the anvil (Figure 31). Use the ratchet stop or friction thimble to perform this operation. The ratchet stop or friction thimble found on most

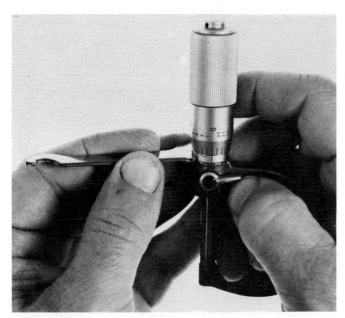

Figure 32.   Adjusting the index line to zero.

micrometers is designed to equalize the gaging force. When the spindle and anvil contact the workpiece, the ratchet stop or friction thimble will slip as a predetermined amount of torque is applied to the micrometer thimble. If the micrometer does not have a ratchet device, use your thumb and index finger to provide a slip clutch effect on the thimble. Never use more pressure when checking the zero reading than when making actual measurements on the workpiece. If there is a small error, it may be corrected by adjusting the index line to the zero point (Figure 32). The manufacturer's instructions provided with the micrometer should be followed when making this adjustment. Also, follow the manufacturer's instructions for correcting a loose thimble to spindle connection or incorrect friction thimble or ratchet stop action. One drop of instrument oil applied to the micrometer thread at monthly intervals will help it to provide many years of reliable service. A machinist is often judged by his associates on the way he handles and cares for his tools. Therefore, if he cares for his tools properly, he will more likely be held in higher professional regard than if he is careless.

READING INCH MICROMETERS

Dimensions requiring the use of micrometers will generally be expressed in decimal form to three decimal places. In the case of an inch instrument, this would be the thousandths place. You should think in terms of thousandths whenever reading decimal fractions. For example, the decimal .156 of an inch would be read as one hundred and fifty-six thousandths of an inch. Like-

wise, .062 would be read as sixty-two thousandths.

On the **sleeve** of the micrometer is a graduated scale with 10 numbered divisions, each one being $\frac{1}{10}$ of one inch or .100 (100 thousandths) apart. Each of these major divisions is further subdivided into four equal parts, which makes the distance between these graduations $\frac{1}{4}$ of .100 of .025 (25 thousandths) (Figure 33). The **spindle screw** of a micrometer has 40 threads per inch. When the spindle is turned one complete revolution, it has moved $\frac{1}{40}$ of one inch, or expressed as a decimal, .025 (25 thousandths).

When you examine the **thimble,** you will find 25 evenly spaced divisions around its circumference (Figure 33). Because each complete revolution of the thimble causes it to move a distance of .025 in., each thimble graduation must be equal to $\frac{1}{25}$ of .025, or .001 in. (one thousandth). On most micrometers, each thimble graduation is numbered to facilitate reading the instrument. On older micrometers only every fifth line may be numbered.

When reading the micrometer (Figure 34), first determine the value indicated by the lines exposed on the sleeve. The edge of the thimble exposes 3 major divisions. This represents .300 in. (three hundred thousandths). However, there are also 2 minor divisions showing on the sleeve. The value of these is .025, for a total of .050 in. (fifty thousandths). The reading on the thimble is 9, which indicates .009 in. (nine thousandths). The final micrometer reading is determined by adding the total of the sleeve and thimble readings. In the example shown (Figure 34), the sleeve shows a total of .350 in. Adding this to the thimble, the final reading becomes .350 in. + .009 in., or .359 in..

USING THE MICROMETER

A micrometer should be gripped by the **frame** (Figure 35) leaving the thumb and forefinger free to operate the thimble. When possible, take micrometer readings while the instrument is in contact with the workpiece (Figure 36). Use only enough pressure on the **spindle** and **anvil** to yield a reliable result. This is what the machinist refers to as **feel.** The proper feel of a micrometer will come only from experience. Obviously, excessive pressure will not only result in an inaccurate measurement, it will also distort the frame of the micrometer and possibly damage it permanently. You should also remember that too light a pressure on the part by the measuring faces can yield an unreliable result.

The micrometer should be held in both hands whenever possible. This is especially true when measuring cylindrical workpieces (Figure 37). Holding the instrument in one hand does not permit sufficient control for reliable readings. Furthermore, cylindrical workpieces

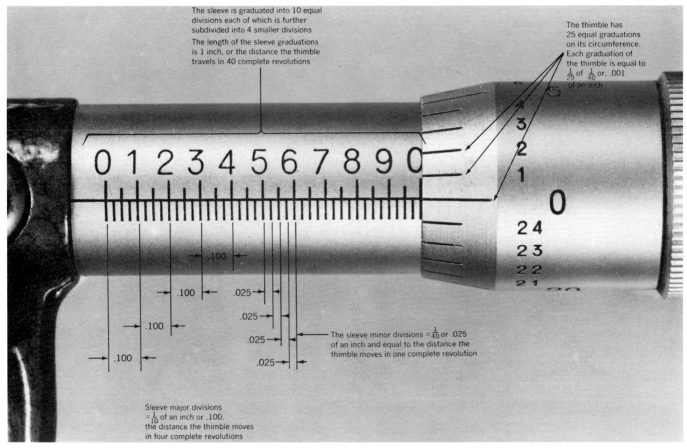

Figure 33. Graduations on the inch micrometer.

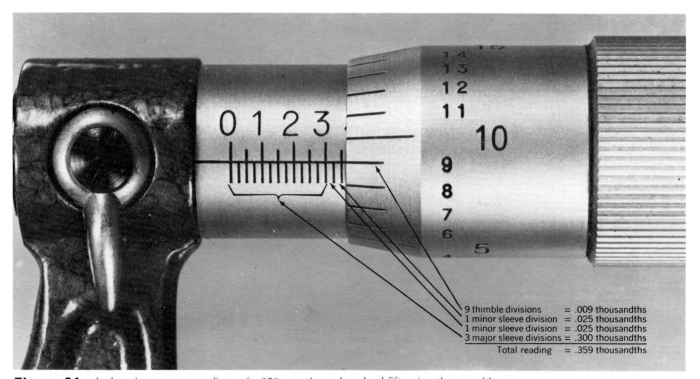

9 thimble divisions	= .009 thousandths
1 minor sleeve division	= .025 thousandths
1 minor sleeve division	= .025 thousandths
3 major sleeve divisions	= .300 thousandths
Total reading	= .359 thousandths

Figure 34. Inch micrometer reading of .359 or three hundred fifty-nine thousandths.

Figure 35. Proper way to hold a micrometer (Lane Community College).

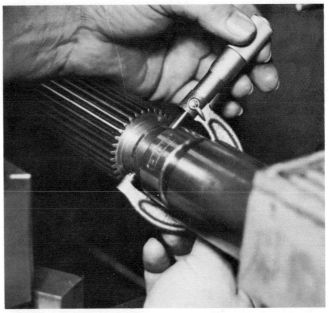

Figure 37. Hold a micrometer in both hands when measuring a round part (Lane Community College).

Figure 36. Read a micrometer while still in contact with the workpiece (Lane Community College).

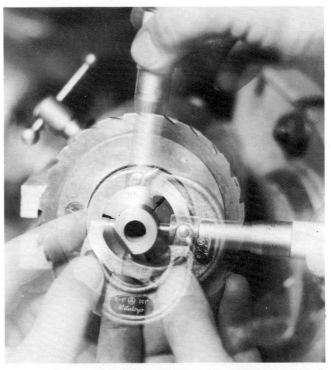

Figure 38. When measuring round parts, take two readings 90 degrees apart (Lane Community College).

should be checked at least twice with **measurements made 90 degrees apart.** This is to check for an out-of-round condition (Figure 38). When critical dimensions are measured, that is, any dimension where a very small amount of tolerance is acceptable, make at least two consecutive measurements. Both readings should indicate identical results. If two identical readings cannot be determined, then the actual size of the part cannot be stated reliably. **All critical measurements should be made at a temperature of 68° Fahrenheit (20° Celsius or Centigrade).** A workpiece warmer than this temperature will be larger because of heat expansion.

Outside micrometers usually have a measuring range of one inch. They are identified by size as to the largest dimensions they measure. A two inch micrometer will measure from one to two inches. A three inch

micrometer will measure from two to three inches. The capacity of the tool is increased by increasing the size of the frame. Typical outside micrometers range in capacity from 0 to 168 inches. It requires a great deal more skill to get consistent measurements with large capacity micrometers.

SELF-TEST

1. Why should a micrometer be kept clean and protected?
2. Why should a micrometer be stored with the spindle out of contact with the anvil?
3. Why are the measuring faces of the micrometer cleaned before measuring?
4. How precise is the standard micrometer?
5. What affects the accuracy of a micrometer?
6. What is the difference between the sleeve and thimble?
7. Why should a micrometer be read while it is still in contact with the object to be measured?
8. How often should an object be measured to verify its actual size?
9. What effect has an increase in temperature on the size of a part?
10. What is the purpose of the friction thimble or ratchet stop on the micrometer?
11. Read and record the five outside micrometer readings in Figures 39a to 39e.

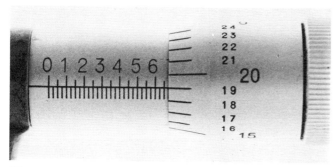

Figure 39a.

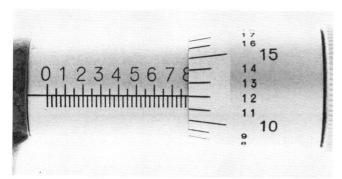

Figure 39b.

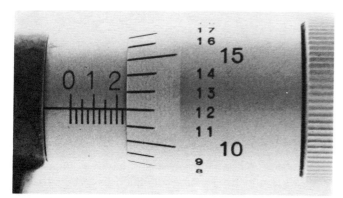

Figure 39c.

Figure 39d.

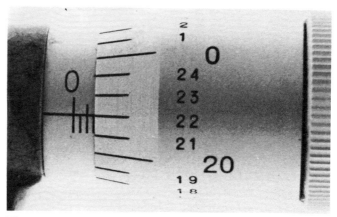

Figure 39e.

USING INSIDE MICROMETERS

Inside micrometers are equipped with the same graduations as outside micrometers. Inside micrometers discriminate to .001 in. and have a measuring capacity ranging from 1.5 to 20 in. or more. A typical **tubular type** inside micrometer set (Figure 40) consists of the **micrometer head** with detachable **hardened anvils** and several **tubular measuring rods** with **hardened contact tips**. The lengths of these rods differ in increments of .5 in. to match the measuring capacity of the micrometer head,

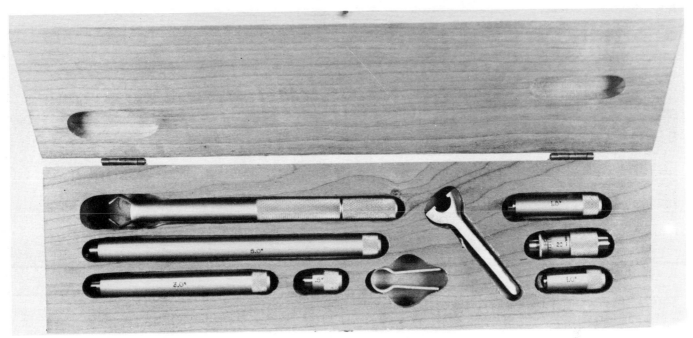

Figure 40. Tubular type inside micrometer set (Harry Smith & Associates).

which in this case is .5 in. A handle is provided to hold the instrument in places where holding the instrument directly would be difficult. Another common type of inside micrometer comes equipped with relatively small diameter solid rods that differ in inch increments, even though the head movement is .5 in. In this case, a .5 in. spacing collar is provided. This can be slipped over the base of the rod before it is inserted into the measuring head.

Inside micrometer heads have a range of .250, .500, 1.000, or 2.000 in. depending on the total capacity of the set. For example, an inside micrometer set with a head range of .500 in. will be able to measure from 1.500 to 12.500 in.

The measuring range of the inside micrometer is changed by attaching the extension rods. Extension rods may be solid or tubular. Tubular rods are lighter in weight and are often found in large range inside micrometer sets. Tubular rods are also more rigid. It is very important that all parts be **extremely clean** when changing extension rods (Figure 41). Even small dust particles can affect the accuracy of the instrument.

When making internal measurements, set one end of the inside micrometer against one side of the hole to be measured (Figure 42). An inside micrometer should not be held in the hands for extended periods, as the resultant heat may affect the accuracy of the instrument. A handle is usually provided, which eliminates the need to hold the instrument and also facilitates insertion of the micrometer into a bore or hole (Figure 43). One end of the micrometer will become the center of the arcing

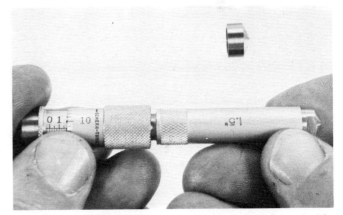

Figure 41. Attaching 1.5 in. extension rod to inside micrometer head (Harry Smith & Associates).

movement used when finding the centerline of the hole to be measured. The micrometer should then be adjusted to the size of the hole. When the correct hole size is reached, there should be a very light drag between the measuring tip and the work when the tip is moved through the centerline of the hole. The size of the hole is determined by adding the reading of the micrometer head, the length of the extension rod, and the length of the spacing collar, if one was used. Read the micrometer **while it is still in place if possible.** If the instrument must be removed to be read, the correct range can be determined by checking with a rule (Figure 44). A skilled craftsman will usually use an **accurate outside micrometer to verify** a reading taken with an inside micrometer. In this case, the inside micrometer becomes an easily adjustable transfer measuring tool (Figure 45).

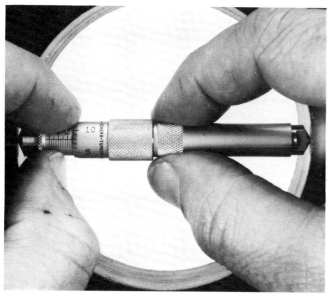

Figure 42. Placing the inside micrometer in the bore to be measured (Harry Smith & Associates).

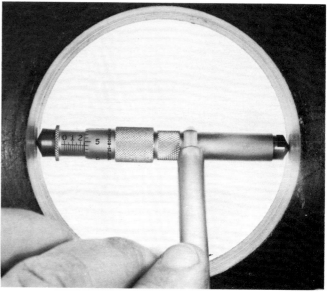

Figure 43. The inside micrometer head used with a handle (Harry Smith & Associates).

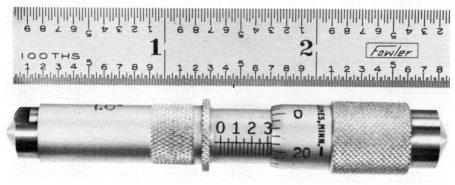

Figure 44. Confirming inside micrometer range using a rule (Harry Smith & Associates).

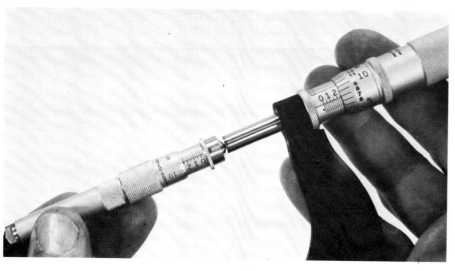

Figure 45. Checking the inside micrometer with an outside micrometer (Harry Smith & Associates).

Take at least two readings 90 degrees apart to obtain the size of a hole or bore. The readings should be identical. Inside micrometers do not have a spindle lock. Therefore, to prevent the spindle from turning while establishing the correct feel, the adjusting nut should be maintained slightly tighter than normal.

SELF-TEST

Read and record the five inside micrometer readings (Figures 46a to 46e). Micrometer head is 1.500 in. when zeroed.

Obtain an inside micrometer set from your instructor and practice using the instrument on objects around your laboratory. Measure examples such as lathe spindle holes, bushings, bores of roller bearings, hydraulic cylinders, and tubing.

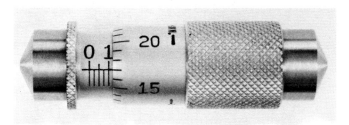

Figure 46a

Figure 46b

Figure 46c *(.5 in. extension)*

Figure 46d *(1.0 in. extension)*

Figure 46e *(1.0 in. extension)*

USING DEPTH MICROMETERS

A **depth micrometer** is a tool that is used to measure precisely depths of holes, grooves, shoulders, and recesses. As other micrometer instruments, it will discriminate to .001 in. Depth micrometers usually come as a set with interchangeable rods to accommodate different depth measurements (Figure 47). The basic parts of the depth micrometer are the **base, sleeve, thimble, extension rod, thimble cap,** and frequently a **ratchet stop.** The bases of a depth micrometer can be of various widths. Generally the wider bases are more stable, but in many instances, space limitations dictate the use of narrower bases. Some depth micrometers are made with only a half base for measurements in confined spaces.

The extension rods are installed or removed by holding the thimble and unscrewing the thimble cap. Make sure that the seat between the thimble cap and rod adjusting nuts is clean before reassembling the micrometer. Do not overtighten when replacing the thimble cap. Furthermore, **do not attempt to adjust the rod length by turning the adjusting nuts.** These rods are factory adjusted and matched as a set. **The measuring rods from a specific depth micrometer set should always be kept with that set.** Since these rods are factory adjusted and matched to a specific instrument, **transposing measuring rods** from set to set **will** usually **result in incorrect measurements.**

When making depth measurements, it is very important that the micrometer base has a smooth and flat surface on which to rest. Furthermore, sufficient pressure must be applied to keep the base in contact

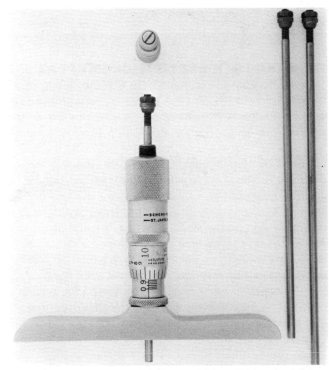

Figure 47. Depth micrometer set (DeAnza College).

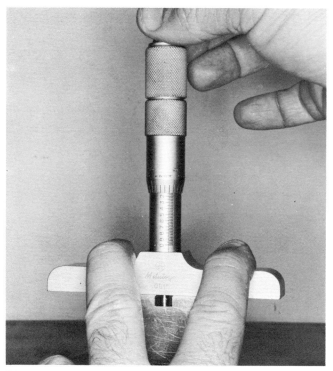

Figure 48. Proper way to hold the depth micrometer (DeAnza College).

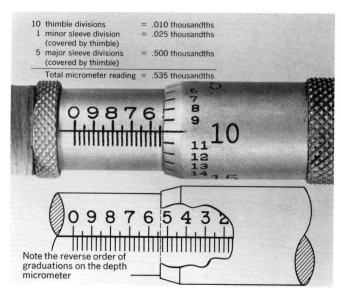

10 thimble divisions	= .010 thousandths
1 minor sleeve division (covered by thimble)	= .025 thousandths
5 major sleeve divisions (covered by thimble)	= .500 thousandths
Total micrometer reading	= .535 thousandths

Note the reverse order of graduations on the depth micrometer

Figure 49. Sleeve graduations on the depth micrometer are numbered in the opposite direction as compared to the outside micrometer.

with the reference surface. When a depth micrometer is used without a ratchet, a slip clutch effect can be produced by letting the thimble slip while turning it between the thumb and index finger (Figure 48).

READING INCH DEPTH MICROMETERS

When a comparison is made between the sleeve of an outside micrometer and the sleeve of a depth micrometer, note that the graduations are numbered in the opposite direction (Figure 49). When reading a depth micrometer, the distance to be measured is the value covered by the thimble. Consider the reading shown (Figure 49). The thimble edge is between the number 5 and 6. This indicates a value of at least .500 in. on the sleeve major divisions. The thimble also covers the first minor division on the sleeve. This has a value of .025 in. The value on the thimble circumference indicates .010 in. Adding these three values results in a total of .535 in., or the amount of extension of the rod from the base.

A depth micrometer **should be tested for accuracy** before it is used. When the 0 to 1 in. rod is used, retract the measuring rod into the base. Clean the base and contact surface of the rod. Hold the micrometer base firmly against a flat highly finished surface, such as a surface plate, and advance the rod until it contacts the reference surface (Figure 50). If the micrometer is properly

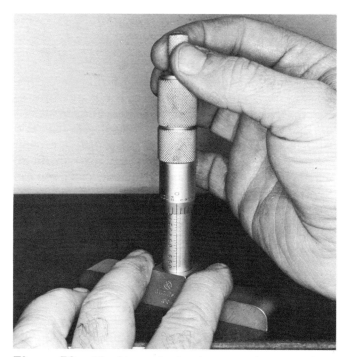

Figure 50. Checking a depth micrometer for zero adjustment using the surface plate as a reference surface (DeAnza College).

adjusted, it should read zero. When **testing for accuracy** with the **one inch extension rod,** set the base of the micrometer on a **one inch gage block** and measure to the reference surface (Figure 51). Other extension rods can be tested in a like manner.

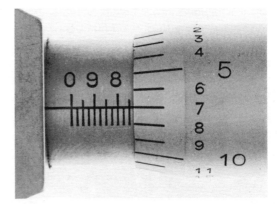

Figure 51. Checking the depth micrometer calibration at the 1.000 in. position in the 0-1 in. rod and a 1 in. square or **Hoke-type** gage block (DeAnza College).

SELF-TEST

Read and record the five depth micrometer readings in Figures 52a to 52e.

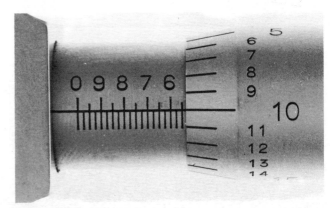

Figure 52c

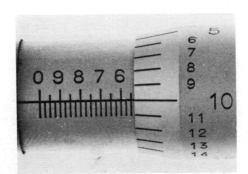

Figure 52a

Figure 52d

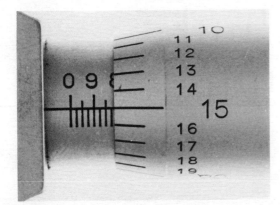

Figure 52b

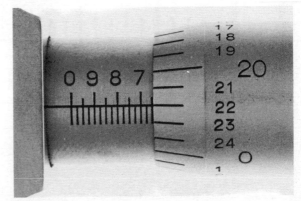

Figure 52e

READING METRIC MICROMETERS

The **metric micrometer** (Figure 53) has a spindle thread with a .5 mm lead. This means that the spindle will move .5 mm when the thimble is turned one complete revolution. Two revolutions of the thimble will advance the spindle one millimeter. In precision machining, metric dimensions are usually expressed in terms of .01 ($\frac{1}{100}$) of a millimeter. On the metric micrometer the thimble is graduated into 50 equal divisions with every fifth division numbered (Figure 54). If one revolution of the thimble is .5 mm, then each division on the thimble is equal to .5 mm divided by 50 or .01 mm. The sleeve of the metric micrometer is divided into 25 main divisions above the index line with every fifth division numbered. These are whole millimeter graduations. Below the index line are graduations that fall halfway between the divisions above the line. The lower graduations represent half or .5 mm values. The thimble edge (Figure 55) leaves the 12 mm line exposed with no .5 mm line showing. The thimble reading is 32, which is .32 mm. Adding the two figures results in a total of 12.32 mm.

The 15 mm mark (Figure 56) is exposed on the sleeve plus a .5 mm graduation below the index line. The thimble reads 20 or .20 mm. Adding these three values, 15.00 + .50 + .20, results in a total of 15.70 mm.

Any metric micrometer should receive the same care discussed in the section on outside micrometers.

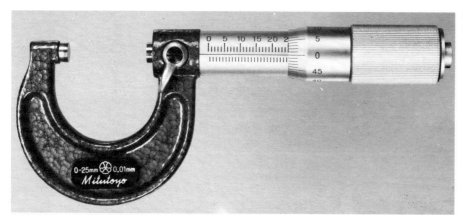

Figure 53. Metric micrometer (Lane Community College).

Figure 54. Graduations on the metric micrometer.

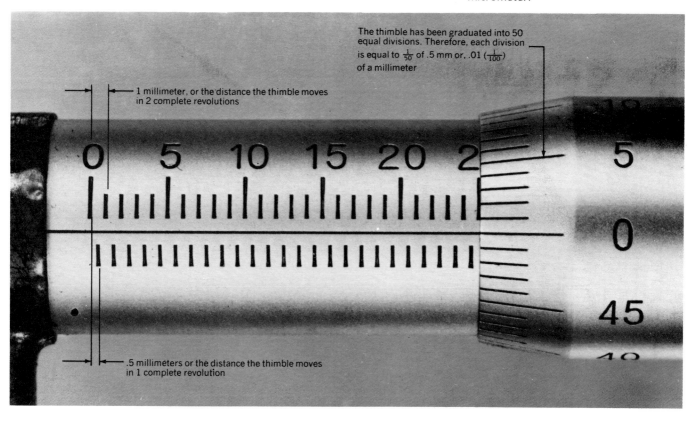

The thimble has been graduated into 50 equal divisions. Therefore, each division is equal to $\frac{1}{50}$ of .5 mm or, .01 ($\frac{1}{100}$) of a millimeter

1 millimeter, or the distance the thimble moves in 2 complete revolutions

.5 millimeters or the distance the thimble moves in 1 complete revolution

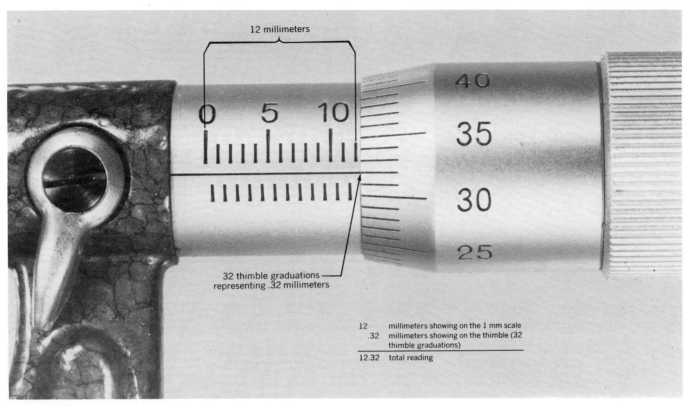

12 millimeters

32 thimble graduations
representing .32 millimeters

12	millimeters showing on the 1 mm scale
.32	millimeters showing on the thimble (32 thimble graduations)
12.32	total reading

Figure 55. Metric micrometer reading of 12.32 millimeters.

Figure 56. Metric micrometer reading of 15.70 millimeters.

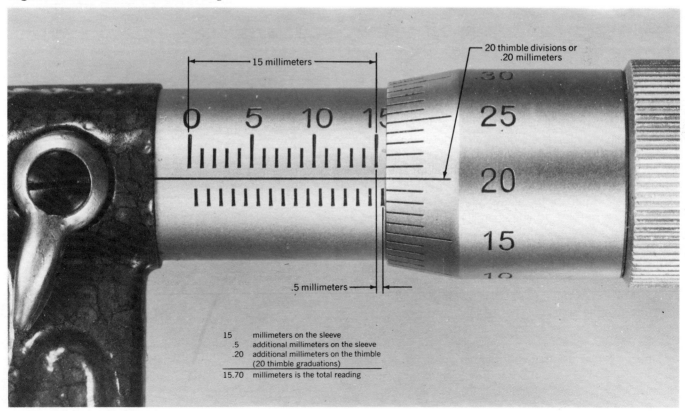

15 millimeters

20 thimble divisions or
.20 millimeters

.5 millimeters

15	millimeters on the sleeve
.5	additional millimeters on the sleeve
.20	additional millimeters on the thimble (20 thimble graduations)
15.70	millimeters is the total reading

SELF-TEST

Read and record the five metric micrometer readings in Figures 57a to 57e.

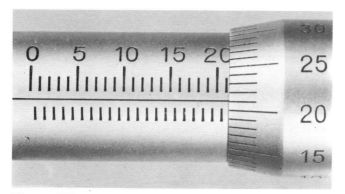

Figure 57a

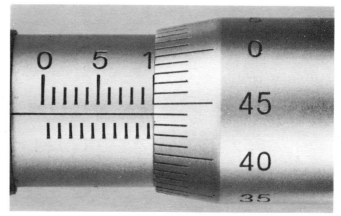

Figure 57c

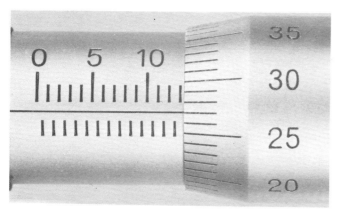

Figure 57b

Figure 57d

READING VERNIER MICROMETERS

When measurements must be made to a discrimination greater than .001 in., a standard micrometer is not sufficient. With a **vernier micrometer,** readings can be made to a **ten-thousandth part of an inch** (.0001 in.). This kind of micrometer is commonly known as a "tenth mike." A vernier scale is part of the sleeve graduations. The vernier scale consists of 10 lines parallel to the index line and located above it (Figure 58).

If the 10 spaces on the vernier scale were compared to the spacing of the thimble graduations, the 10 vernier spacings would correspond to 9 spacings on the thimble. Therefore, the vernier scale spacing must be smaller than the thimble spacing. That is, in fact, precisely the case. Since 10 vernier spacings compare to 9 thimble spacings, the vernier spacing is $\frac{1}{10}$ smaller than the thimble space. We know that the thimble graduations correspond to .001 in. (one thousandth). Each vernier spacing must then be equal to $\frac{1}{10}$ of .001 in., or .0001 in. (one

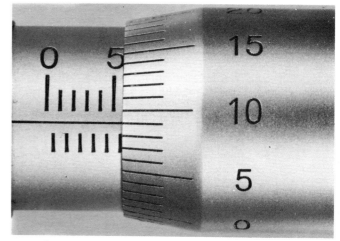

Figure 57e

ten-thousandth). Thus, according to the principle of the vernier, each thousandth of the thimble is subdivided into 10 parts. This permits the vernier micrometer to discriminate to .0001 in.

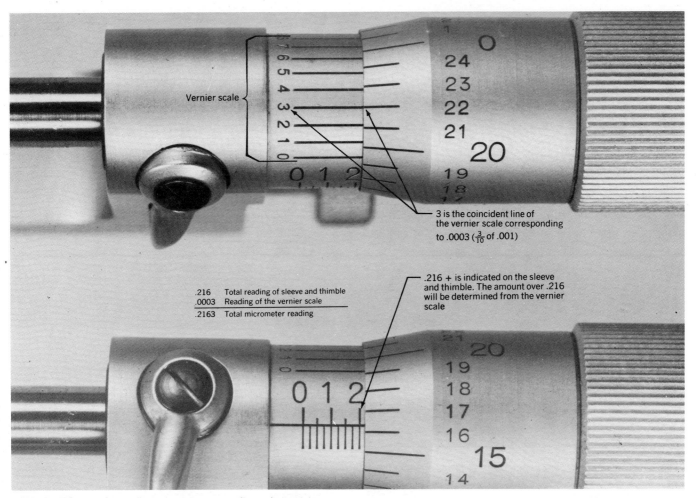

3 is the coincident line of the vernier scale corresponding to .0003 ($\frac{3}{10}$ of .001)

.216 + is indicated on the sleeve and thimble. The amount over .216 will be determined from the vernier scale

.216	Total reading of sleeve and thimble
.0003	Reading of the vernier scale
.2163	Total micrometer reading

Figure 58.   Inch vernier micrometer reading of .2163 in.

To read a vernier micrometer, first read to the nearest thousandth as on a standard micrometer. Then, find the line on the vernier scale that coincides with a graduation on the thimble. The value of this coincident vernier scale line is the value in ten thousandths, which must be added to the thousandths reading thus making up the total reading. **Remember to add the value of the vernier scale line and not the number of the matching thimble line.**

In the lower view (Figure 58), a micrometer reading of slightly more than .216 in. is indicated. In the top view, on the vernier scale, the line numbered 3 is in alignment with the line on the thimble. This indicated that .0003 (three ten-thousandths) must be added to the .216 in. for a total reading of .2163. This number is read "two hundred sixteen thousandths and three tenths."

You must exercise cautious judgment when attempting to measure to a tenth of a thousandth using a vernier micrometer. There are many conditions that can influence the reliability of such measurements. The 10 to 1 rule discussed in the section introduction states that for maximum reliability, a measuring instrument must be able to discriminate 10 times finer than the smallest measurement that it will be asked to make. A vernier micrometer meets this requirement for measurement to the nearest thousandth. However, the instrument does not have the capability to discriminate to a one-hundred thousandth, which it should have if it is to be applied in tenth of a thousandth measurement. This does not mean that a vernier micrometer should not be used for tenth measurement. The modern micrometer is manufactured with this potential in mind. It does mean that tenth measure should be carried out under **controlled conditions** if truly reliable results are to be obtained. The finish of the workpiece must be extremely smooth. Contact pressure of the measuring faces must be very consistent. The workpiece and instrument must be temperature stabilized. Heat transferred to the micrometer by handling can cause it to deviate considerably. Furthermore, the micrometer must be carefully calibrated against a known standard. Only under these conditions can true reliability be realized.

SELF-TEST

Read and record the five vernier micrometer readings in Figures 59a to 59e.

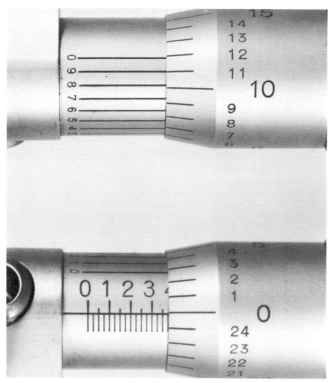

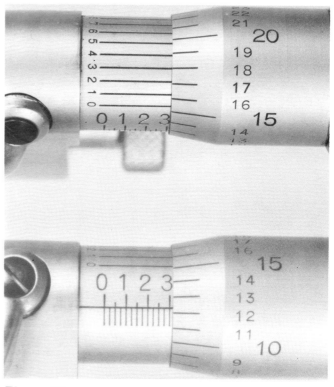

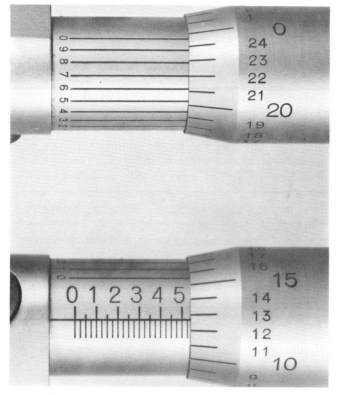

Figure 59a

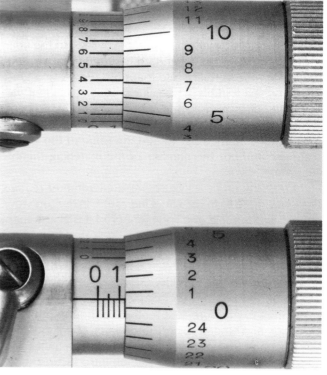

Figure 59c

Figure 59b

Figure 59d

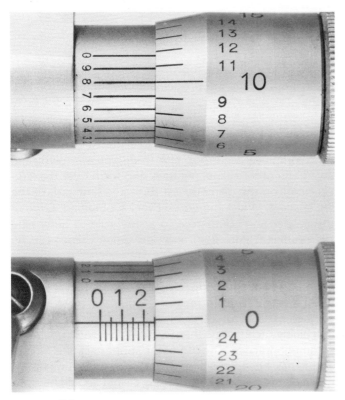

Figure 59*e*

UNIT 5 USING COMPARISON MEASURING INSTRUMENTS

As a machinist, you will use a large number of measuring instruments that have no capacity within themselves to show a measurement. These tools will be used in comparison measurement applications where they are compared to a known standard, or used in conjunction with an instrument that has the capability of showing a measurement. In this unit you are introduced to the principles of comparison measurement, the common tools of comparison measurement, and their applications.

OBJECTIVES

After completing this unit, you should be able to:

1. Define comparison measurement.
2. Identify common comparison measuring tools.
3. Given a measuring situation, select the proper comparison tool for the measuring requirement.

MEASUREMENT BY COMPARISON

All of us, at some time, were probably involved in constructing something in which we used no measuring instruments of any kind. For example, suppose that you had to build some wooden shelves. You have the required lumber available with all boards longer than the shelf spaces. You hold a board to the shelf space and mark the required length for cutting. By this procedure, you have **compared** the length of the board **(the unknown length)** to the shelf space **(the known length or standard).** After cutting the first board to the marked length, it is then used to determine the lengths of the remaining shelves. The board, in itself, has no capacity to show a measurement. However, in this case, it became a measuring instrument.

A great deal of comparison measurement often involves the following steps.

1. A device that has no capacity to show measurement is used to establish and represent an unknown distance.
2. This representation of the unknown is then **transferred** to an instrument that has the capability to show a measurement.

This is commonly known as **transfer measurement.** In the example of cutting shelf boards, the shelf space was transferred to the first board and then the length of the first board was transferred to the remaining boards.

Transfer of measurements may involve some reduction in reliability. This factor must be kept in mind when using comparison tools requiring that a transfer be made. Remember that an instrument with the capability to show measurement directly is always best. **Direct reading instruments should be used whenever possible** in any situation. Measurements requiring a transfer must be accomplished with proper caution if reliability is to be maintained.

COMMON COMPARISON MEASURING TOOLS AND THEIR APPLICATIONS

Spring Calipers

The spring caliper is a very common comparison measuring tool for rough measurements of inside and outside dimensions. To use a spring caliper, set one jaw on the workpiece (Figure 1). Use this point as a pivot and swing the other caliper leg back and forth over the largest point on the diameter. At the same time, adjust the leg spacing. When the correct feel is obtained, remove the caliper and compare it to a steel rule to determine the reading (Figure 2). The inside spring caliper can be used in a similar manner (Figure 3).

The use of spring calipers is limited. It has been stated by some in the machining business that they can use a spring caliper to measure to .002 or even .001 of an inch. This is of questionable reliability. In modern machining technology, there is little room for crude measurement practice. The use of the spring caliper is fading, and it has been replaced by measuring instruments of much higher reliability. The spring caliper should be used only for the roughest of measurements.

Telescoping Gage

The telescoping gage is also a very common comparison measuring instrument. Telescoping gages are widely used in the machine shop, and they can accomplish a variety of measuring requirements. The telescoping gage is sometimes called a snap gage. This, however, is incorrect. A snap gage is another type of comparison measuring tool and was discussed in the introduction to this section.

Telescoping gages generally come in a set of six gages (Figure 4). The range of the set is usually $\frac{5}{16}$ to 6 in. (8 to 150 mm). The gage consists of two telescoping plungers with a handle and locking screw. The gage is inserted into a bore or slot, and the plungers are permitted to extend, thus conforming to the size of the feature. The gage is then removed and transferred to a micrometer where the reading is determined. The telescoping gage can be a reliable and versatile tool if proper procedure is used in its application.

Procedure for Using the Telescoping Gage

1. Select the proper gage for the desired measurement range.
2. Insert the gage into the bore to be measured and release the handle lock screw (Figure 5). Rock the gage sideways to insure that you are measuring at the full diameter (Figure 6). This is especially important in large diameter bores.

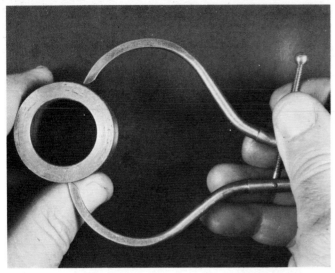

Figure 1. Set one leg of the caliper against the workpiece.

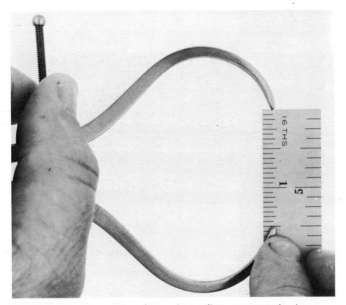

Figure 2. Comparing the spring caliper to a steel rule.

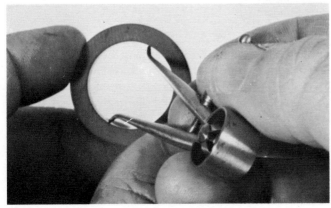

Figure 3. Using an inside spring caliper.

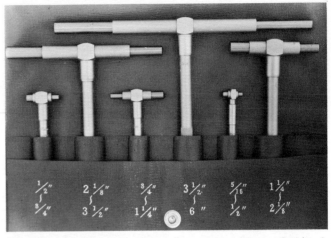

Figure 4. Set of telescoping gages (Harry Smith & Associates).

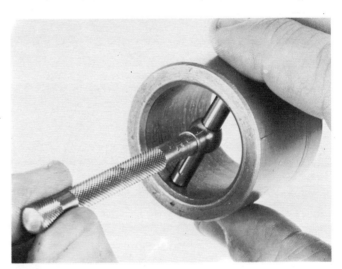

Figure 5. Inserting the telescoping gage into the bore (DeAnza College).

3. Lightly tighten the locking screw.

4. Use a downward or upward motion and roll the gage through the bore. The plungers will be pushed in, thus conforming to the bore diameter (Figure 7). Tighten the locking screw firmly and roll the gage back through the bore. Feel for a light drag.

5. Remove the gage and measure with an outside micrometer (Figure 8). Place the gage between micrometer spindle and anvil. Try to determine the same feel on the gage with the micrometer as you felt while the gage was in the bore. Excessive pressure with the micrometer will depress the gage plungers and cause an incorrect reading.

6. Take at least two readings or more with the telescoping gage in order to verify reliability. If the readings do not agree, repeat procedure steps 2 to 6.

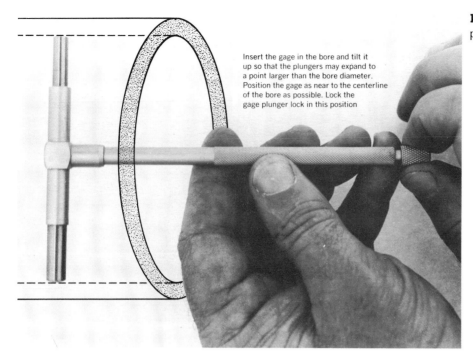

Insert the gage in the bore and tilt it up so that the plungers may expand to a point larger than the bore diameter. Position the gage as near to the centerline of the bore as possible. Lock the gage plunger lock in this position

Figure 6. Release the lock and let the plungers expand larger than the bore.

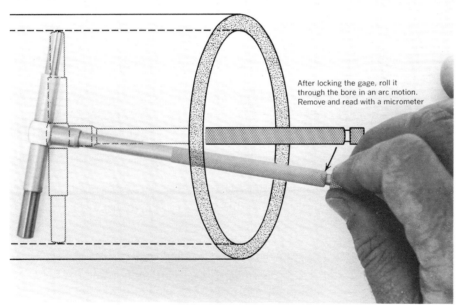

After locking the gage, roll it through the bore in an arc motion. Remove and read with a micrometer

Figure 7. Tighten the lock and roll the gage through the bore.

Small Hole Gages

Small hole gages, like telescoping gages, come in sets with a range of $\frac{1}{8}$ to $\frac{1}{2}$ in. (4 to 12 mm). One type of small hole gage consists of a split ball that is connected to a handle (Figure 9). A tapered rod is drawn between the split ball halves causing them to extend and contact the surface to be measured (Figure 10). The split ball small hole gage has a flattened end so that a shallow hole or slot may be measured. After the gage has been expanded in the feature to be measured, it should be moved back and forth to determine the proper feel. The gage is then removed and measured with an outside micrometer (Figure 11).

A second type of small hole gage consists of two small balls that can be moved out to contact the surface to be measured. This type of gage is available in a set ranging from $\frac{1}{16}$ to $\frac{1}{2}$ in. (1.5 to 12 mm). Once again, the proper feel must be obtained when using this type of small hole gage (Figure 12). After the gage is set, it is removed and measured with a micrometer.

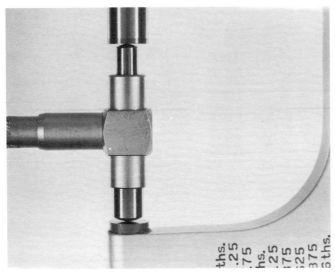

Figure 8. Checking the telescoping gage with an outside micrometer (Harry Smith & Associates).

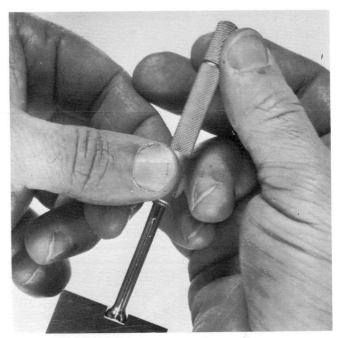

Figure 10. Insert the small hole gage in the slot to be measured (Harry Smith & Associates).

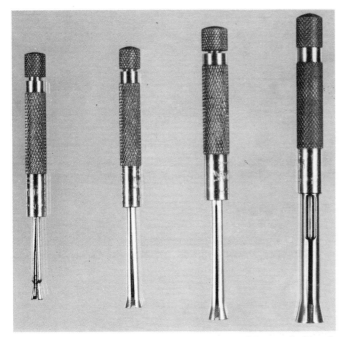

Figure 9. Set of small hole gages (Harry Smith & Associates).

Adjustable Parallels

For the purpose of measuring slots, grooves, and keyways, the adjustable parallel may be used. Adjustable parallels are available in sets ranging from about $\frac{3}{8}$ to $1\frac{1}{2}$ in. (10 to 38 mm). They are precision ground for accuracy. The typical adjustable parallel consists of two parts that slide together on an angle. Adjusting screws are provided so that clearance in the slide may be adjusted or the parallel locked after setting for a measurement.

Figure 11. Withdraw the gage and measure with an outside micrometer (Harry Smith & Associates).

As the halves of the parallel slide, the width increases or decreases depending on direction. The parallel is placed in the groove or slot to be measured and expanded until the parallel edges conform to the width to be measured. The parallel is then locked with a small screwdriver and

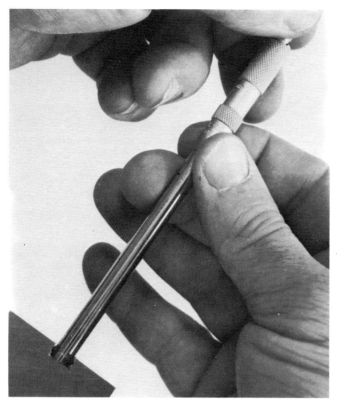

Figure 12. Using the twin ball small hole gage (Harry Smith & Associates).

Figure 14. Using an individual radius gage.

Figure 15. Radius gage set.

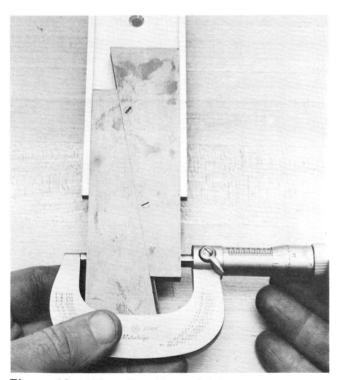

Figure 13. Using adjustable parallels (DeAnza College).

measured with a micrometer (Figure 13). If possible, an adjustable parallel should be left in place while being measured.

Radius Gages

The typical radius gage set ranges in size from $\frac{1}{32}$ to $\frac{1}{2}$ in. (.8 to 12 mm). Larger radius gages are also available. The gage can be used to measure the radii of grooves and external or internal fillets (rounded corners). Radius gages may be separate (Figure 14) or the full set may be contained in a convenient holder (Figure 15).

Thickness Gages

The thickness gage (Figure 16) is often called a feeler gage. It is probably best known for its various automotive applications. However, a machinist may use a thickness gage for such measurements as the thickness of a shim, setting a grinding wheel above a workpiece, or determining the height difference of two parts. The thickness gage is not a true comparison measuring instrument, as each leaf is marked as to size. However, it is good practice to check a thickness gage with a micrometer, especially when a number of leaves are stacked together.

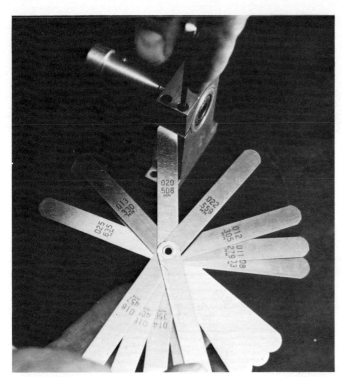

Figure 16. Using a feeler or thickness gage.

Figure 17. Setting the planer gage with an outside micrometer (DeAnza College).

Figure 18. Setting the dial test indicator to a gage block (DeAnza College).

Planer Gage

The planer gage functions much like an adjustable parallel. Planer gages were originally used to set tool heights on shapers and planers. They can also be used as a comparison measuring tool.

The planer gage may be equipped with a scriber and used in layout. The gage may be set with a microm-

eter (Figure 17) or in combination with a dial test indicator and gage blocks. In this application, the planer gage is set by using a test indicator set to zero on a gage block (Figure 18). This dimension is then transferred to the planer gage (Figure 19). After the gage has been set, the scriber is attached and the instrument used in a layout application (Figure 20).

Figure 19. Transferring the measurement to the planer gage (DeAnza College).

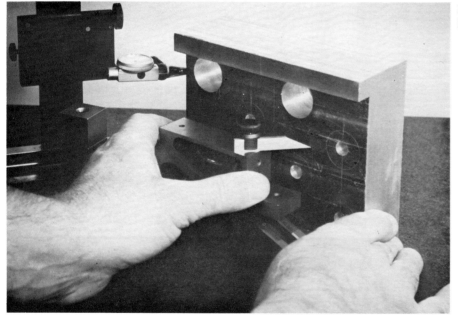

Figure 20. Using the planer gage in layout (DeAnza College).

Squares

The square is an important and useful tool for the machinist. A square is a comparative measuring instrument in that it compares its own degree of perpendicularity with an unknown degree of perpendicularity on the workpiece. You will use several common types of squares.

Machinist's Combination Square. The combination square (Figure 21) is part of the combination set (Figure 22). The combination set consists of a graduated rule, square head, bevel protractor, and center head.

Figure 21. Combination square head with scriber.

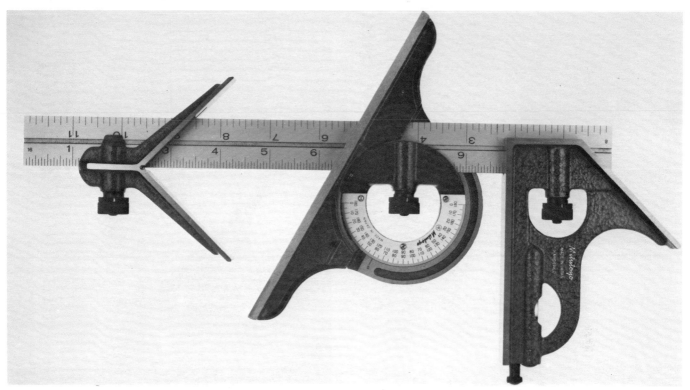

Figure 22. Machinist's combination set.

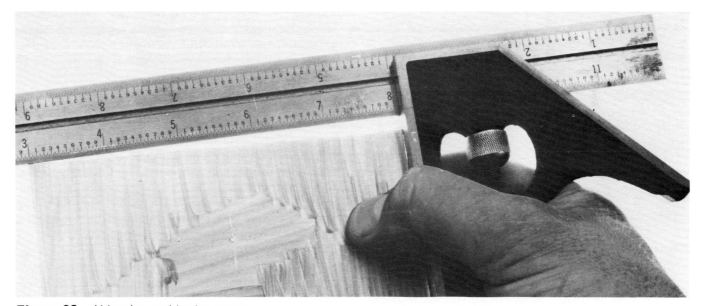

Figure 23. Using the combination square.

The square head slides on the graduated rule and can be locked at any position (Figure 23). This feature makes the tool useful for layout as the square head can be set according to the rule graduations. The combination square head also has a 45 degree angle along with a spirit level and layout scriber. The combination set is one of the most versatile tools of the machinist.

Solid Beam Square. On the solid beam square, the beam and blade are fixed. Solid beam squares range in size from 2 to 72 in. (Figure 24).

Precision Beveled Edge Square. The precision beveled edge square is an extremely accurate square used in the toolroom and in inspection applications. The

Figure 24. Solid beam square (CSU, Fresno).

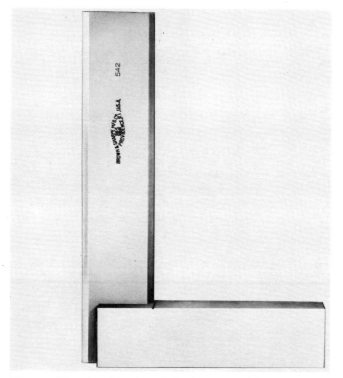

Figure 25. Precision beveled edge square (Courtesy of the Brown and Sharpe Manufacturing Company).

beveled edge permits a single line of contact with the part to be checked. Precision squares range in size from 2 to 14 in. (Figure 25).

The squares discussed up to this point do not have any capacity to directly indicate the amount of deviation from perpendicularity. The only determination that can be made is that the workpiece is: as perpendicular or not as perpendicular as the square. The actual amount of deviation from perpendicularity on the workpiece must be determined by other measurements. With the follow-

Figure 26. Cylindrical square (Yuba College).

ing group of squares, the deviation from perpendicularity can be measured directly. In this respect, the following instruments are not true comparison tools, since they have capacity to show a measurement directly.

Cylindrical Square. The direct reading cylindrical square (Figure 26) consists of an accurate cylinder with one end square to the axis of the cylinder. The other end is made slightly out of square with the cylindrical axis. When the nonsquare end is placed on a clean surface plate, the instrument is actually tilted slightly. As the square is rotated (Figure 27), one point on the circumference of the cylinder will eventually come into true perpendicularity with the surface plate. On a cylindrical square, this point is marked by a vertical line running the full length of the tool. The cylindrical square has a set of curved lines marked on the cylinder that permits deviation from squareness of the workpiece to be determined. Each curved line represents a deviation of .0002 of an inch over the length of the instruments.

Cylindrical squares are applied in the following manner. The square is placed on a clean surface plate and brought into contact with the part to be checked. The square is then rotated until contact is made over the entire length of the instrument. The deviation from squareness is determined by reading the amount corresponding to the line on the square that is in contact with the workpiece. Cylindrical squares are often used to

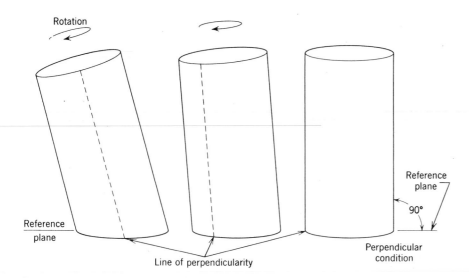

Rotation

Reference plane

Line of perpendicularity

Reference plane

90°

Perpendicular condition

Principle of the spherical square

Figure 27. Principle of the cylindrical square.

Figure 28. Diemaker's square (Courtesy of the L. S. Starrett Company).

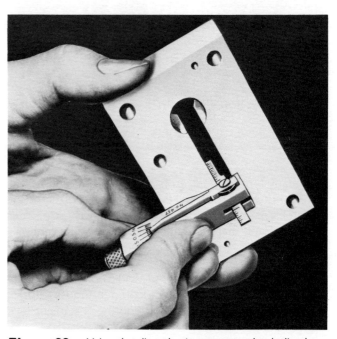

Figure 29. Using the diemaker's square to check die clearance (Courtesy of the L. S. Starrett Company).

check the accuracy of another square (Figure 26). When the instrument is used on its square end, it may be applied as a plain square. Cylindrical squares range in size from 4 to 12 in.

Diemaker's Square. The diemaker's square (Figure 28) is used in such applications as checking clearance on a die (Figure 29). The instrument can be used with a straight or offset blade. A diemaker's square can be used to measure a deviation of 10 degrees on either side of the perpendicular.

Micrometer Square. The micrometer square (Figure 30) is another type of adjustable square. The blade is tilted by means of a micrometer adjustment to determine the deviation of the part being checked.

The square is one of the few tools used in measurement that is essentially self-checking. If you have a workpiece with accurately parallel sides, as measured with a micrometer, one end can be observed under the beam of the square and the error observed. Now the part can be rotated under the beam 180 degrees and rechecked. If the error is identical but reversed, the square is accurate. If there is a difference, except for simple reversal, the square should be considered inaccurate. It should then be checked against a standard, such as a cylindrical square.

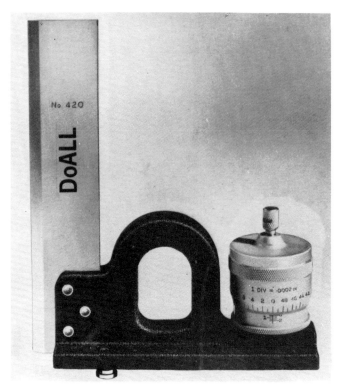

Figure 30. Micrometer square (Courtesy of the DoAll Company).

Indicators

The many types of indicators are some of the most valuable and useful tools for the machinist. There are two general types of indicators in general use. These are **dial indicators** and **dial test indicators.** Both types generally take the form of a spring loaded spindle that, when depressed, actuates the hand of an indicating dial. At the initial examination of a dial or test indicator, you will note that the dial face is usually graduated in thousandths of an inch or subdivisions of thousandths. This might lead you to the conclusion that the indicator spindle movement corresponds directly to the amount shown on the indicator face. However, this conclusion is to be arrived at only with the most cautious judgment. **Dial test indicators should not be used to make direct linear measurements.** Reasons for this will be developed in the information to follow. Dial indicators can be used to make linear measurements, but only if they are specifically designed to do so and under proper conditions.

As a machinist, you will use dial and test indicators almost daily in the machine shop. Indicators are very essential to the accurate completion of your job. However, do not ask that an indicator do what it was not designed to do. Dial and test indicators when properly used are an invaluable member of the machinist's many tools.

Dial Indicators. Dial indicators have discriminations that typically range from .00005 to .001 of an inch. In metric dial indicators, the discriminations typically range from .002 to .01 mm. Indicator ranges or the total reading capacity of the instrument may commonly range from .003 to 2.000 in., or .2 to 50 mm for metric instruments. On the **balanced** indicator (Figure 31), the face numbering goes both clockwise and counterclockwise from zero. This is convenient for comparator applications where readings above and below zero need to be indicated. The indicator shown has a lever actuated stem. This permits the stem to be retracted away from the workpiece if desired.

The continuous reading indicator (Figure 32) is numbered from zero in one direction. This indicator has a discrimination of .0005 and a total range of one inch. The small center hand counts revolutions of the large hand. Note that the center dial counts each .100 in. of spindle travel. This indicator is also equipped with **tolerance hands** that can be set to mark a desired limit. Many dial indicators are designed for high discrimination and short range (Figure 33). This indicator has a .0001 discrimination and a range of .025 in.

The **back plunger** indicator (Figure 34) has the spindle in the back or at right angles to the face. This type of indicator usually has a range of about .200 in. with .001 in. discrimination. It is a very popular model for use on a machine tool. The indicator usually comes with a number of mounting accessories (Figure 34).

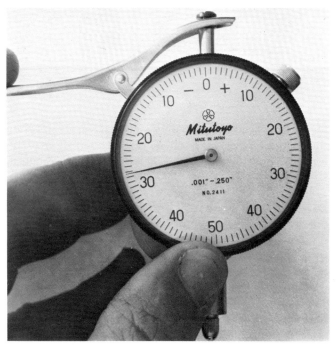

Figure 31. Balanced dial indicator (Harry Smith & Associates).

Figure 32. Dial indicator with one inch travel (Harry Smith & Associates).

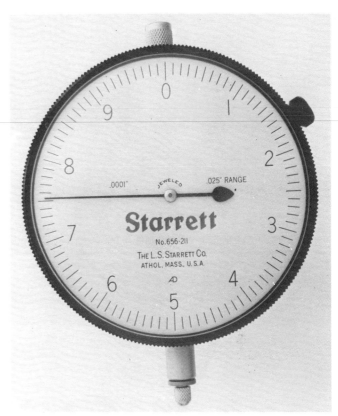

Figure 33. Dial indicator with .025 in. range and .0001 in. discrimination (Harry Smith & Associates).

Indicators are equipped with a **rotating face or bezel.** This feature permits the instrument to be set to zero at any desired place. Many indicators also have a **bezel lock.** Dial indicators may have removable spindle tips, thus permitting use of different shaped tips as required by the specific application (Figure 35).

Care and Use of Indicators. Dial indicators are precision instruments and should be treated accordingly. They **must not be dropped** and should **not be exposed to severe shocks.** Dropping an indicator may bend the spindle and render the instrument useless. Shocks, such as hammering on a workpiece while an indicator is still in contact, may damage the delicate operating mechanism. The spindle should be kept free from dirt and grit. This can cause binding that results in damage and false readings. It is important to **check** indicators **for free travel** before using. When an indicator is not in use, it should be stored carefully with a protective device around the spindle.

One of the problems encountered by indicator users is **indicator mounting.** All indicators must be **mounted solidly** if they are to be reliable. Indicators

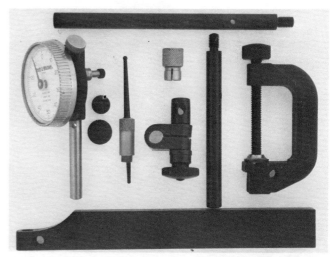

Figure 34. Back plunger indicator with mounting accessories (Harry Smith & Associates).

must be clamped or mounted securely when used on a machine tool. A number of mounting devices are in common use. Some of these have magnetic bases that permit an indicator to be attached at any convenient place on a machine tool. The permanent magnet indi-

Figure 35. Dial indicator tips with holder (Courtesy of Rank Scherr-Tumico, Inc.).

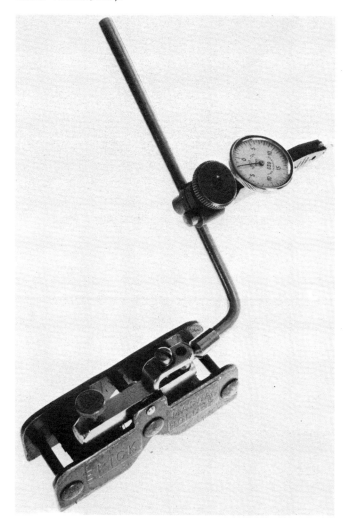

Figure 36. Permanent magnetic indicator base.

cator base (Figure 36) is a useful accessory. This type of indicator base is equipped with an adjusting screw that can be used to set the instrument to zero. Another useful magnetic base has a provision for turning off the mag-

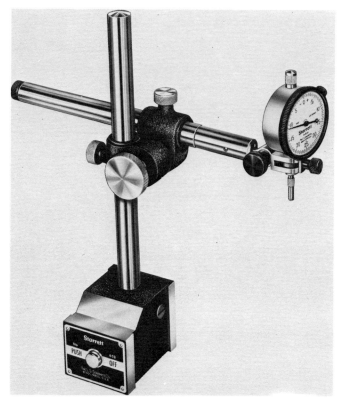

Figure 37. Magnetic base indicator holder with on/off magnet (Courtesy of the L. S. Starrett Company).

net by mechanical means (Figure 37). This feature makes for easy locating of the base prior to turning on the magnet. A number of bases making use of flexible link indicator holding arms are also in general use. Often they are not adequately rigid for reliability. In addition to holding an indicator on a magnetic base, it may be clamped to a machine setup by the use of any suitable clamps.

Dial Test Indicators. Dial test indicators frequently have a discrimination of .0005 in. and a range of about .030 in. The test indicator is frequently quite small (Figure 38) so that it can be used to indicate in locations inaccessible to other indicators. The spindle or tip of the test indicator can be swiveled to any desired position. Test indicators are usually equipped with a **movement reversing lever.** This means that the indicator can be actuated by pressure from either side of the tip. The instrument need not be turned around. Test indicators, like dial indicators, have a rotating bezel for zero setting. Dial faces are generally of the balanced design. The same care given to dial indicators should be extended to test indicators.

Potential for Error in Using Dial Indicators. Indicators must be used with appropriate caution if reliable results are to be obtained. The spindle of a dial

Figure 38.   Dial test indicator (Harry Smith & Associates).

indicator usually consists of a gear rack that engages a pinion and other gears that drive the indicating hand. In any mechanical device, there is always some clearance between the moving parts. There are also minute errors in the machining of the indicator parts. Because of these, small errors may creep into an indicator reading. This is especially true in long travel indicators. For example, if a one-inch travel indicator with .001 discrimination had plus or minus one percent error at full travel, the following condition could exist if the instrument were to be used for a direct measurement.   You wish to determine if a certain part is within the tolerance of .750 ± .003 in. The one-inch travel indicator has the capacity for this,

but remember: it is only accurate to plus or minus one percent of full travel. Therefore, .01 × 1.000 in. is equal to ± .010 in. or the total possible error. To calculate the error per thousandth of indicator travel, divide .010 in. by 1000. This is equal to .00001 in., which is the average error per thousandth of indicator travel. This means that at a travel amount of .750 in., the indicator error could be as much as .00001 in. × 750, or ± .0075 in. In a direct measurement of the part, the indicator could read anywhere from .7425 to .7575. As you can see, this is well outside the part tolerance and would hardly be reliable (Figure 39).

The indicator should be used as a comparison measuring instrument by the following procedure (Figure 39). The indicator is set to zero on a .750 in. gage block. The part to be measured is then placed under the indicator spindle. In this case, the error caused by a large amount of indicator travel is greatly reduced, because the travel is never greater than the greatest deviation of a part from the basic size. The total part tolerance is .006 in. (± .003 in.). Therefore, 6 × .00001 in. error per thousandth is equal to only ± .00006 in. This is well within the part tolerance and, in fact, cannot even be read on a .001 in. discrimination indicator.

Of course, you will not know what the error amounts to on any specific indicator. This can only be determined by a calibration procedure. Furthermore, you would probably not use a long travel indicator in this particular application. A moderate to short travel indicator would be more appropriate. Keep in mind that any indicator may contain some **travel error** and that by using a fraction of that travel, this error can be reduced considerably.

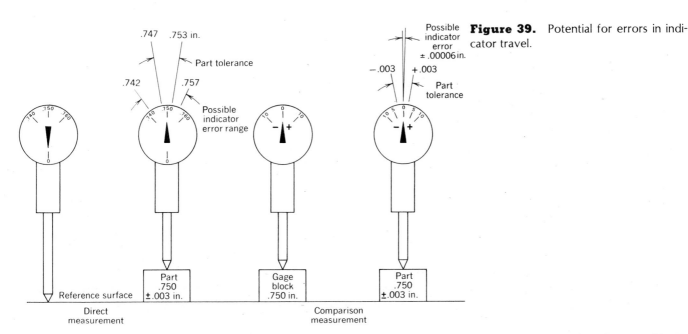

Figure 39.   Potential for errors in indicator travel.

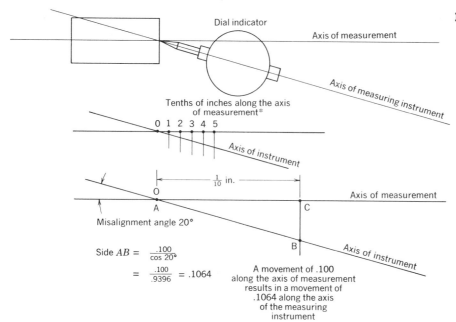

Figure 40. Cosine error.

In the introduction to this section you learned that the axis of a linear measurement instrument must be in line with the axis of measurement. If a dial indicator is misaligned with the axis of measurement, the following condition will exist.

Line AC represents the axis of measurement, while line AB represents the axis of the dial indicator (Figure 40). If the distance from A to C is .100 in., then the distance from A to B is obviously larger, since it is the hypotenuse of triangle ABC. The angle of misalignment, angle A, is equal to 20 degrees. The distance from A to B can then be calculated by the following:

$$AB = \frac{.100}{\cos A}$$
$$AB = \frac{.100}{.9396}$$
$$AB = .1064 \text{ in.}$$

This shows that a movement along the axis of measurement results in a much larger movement along the instrument axis. This **error** is known as **cosine error** and must be kept in mind when using dial indicators. Cosine error is increased as the angle of misalignment is increased.

When using dial test indicators, watch for **arc versus chord length errors** (Figure 41). The tip of the test indicator moves through an arc. This distance may be considerably greater than the chord distance of the measurement axis. Dial test indicators should **not** be used to make direct measurements. They should only be applied in comparison applications.

Using Dial Test Indicators in Comparison Measurements. The dial test indicator is very useful

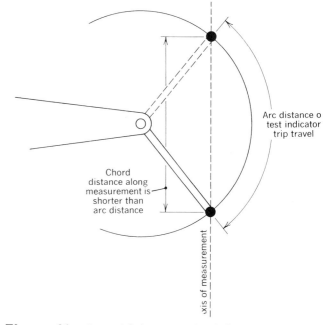

Figure 41. Potential for error in dial test indicator tip movement.

in making comparison measurements in conjunction with the height gage and height transfer micrometer. Comparison measurement using a vernier height gage is accomplished by the following procedure.

1. Set the height gage to zero and adjust the test indicator until it also reads zero when in contact with the surface plate (Figure 42). It is very important to use a test indicator for this procedure. Using a scriber tip

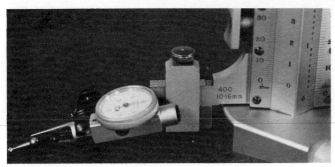

Figure 42.   Setting the dial test indicator to zero on the reference surface (DeAnza College).

Figure 43.   Using the dial test indicator and vernier height gage to measure the workpiece (DeAnza College).

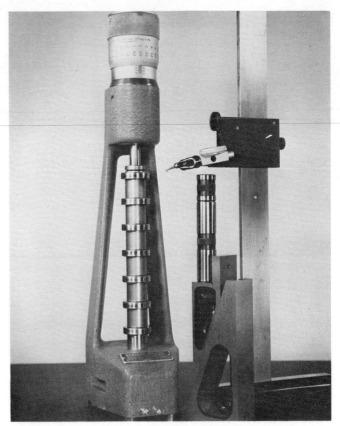

Figure 44.   Precision height gage (DeAnza College).

Figure 45.   Reading the precision height gage (DeAnza College).

on a height gage is an inferior way to attempt measurements and can lead to substantial error.

2. Raise the indicator and adjust the height gage vernier until the indicator reads zero on the workpiece (Figure 43). Read the dimension from the height scale.

Comparison measurement can also be accomplished using a precision height gage (Figure 44). The precision height gage shown consists of a series of rings that are moved by the micrometer spindle. The ring spacing is a very accurate one inch and the micrometer head has a one inch travel. Other designs use projecting gage blocks at inch intervals, or other types of measuring steps. Discrimination of the typical height micrometer is .0001 in. (Figure 45). Precision height gages come in various height capacities and sometimes have riser

blocks as accessories. In Figure 47, a planer gage is being set using the test indicator and height micrometer. The following procedure is used.

1. The height transfer micrometer is adjusted to the desired height setting. The test indicator is zeroed on the appropriate ring (Figure 46). A height transfer

Figure 46. Setting the dial test indicator to the precision height gage (DeAnza College).

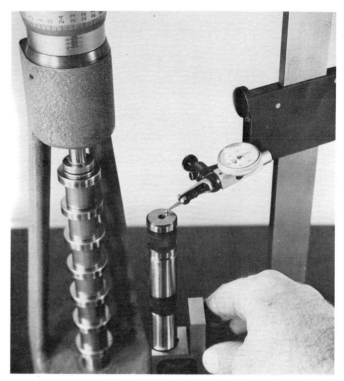

Figure 47. Transferring the measurement to the planer gage (DeAnza College).

gage, vernier height gage, or other suitable means can be used to hold the indicator.

2. The indicator is then moved over to the planer gage. The planer gage is then adjusted until the test indicator reads zero (Figure 47).

Test indicators can also be used to accomplish comparison measurement in conjunction with an optical height gage (Figure 48).

Comparators

Comparators are exactly what their name implies. They are instruments that are used to compare the size or shape of the workpiece to a known standard. Types include dial indicator comparators, optical, electrical, and electronic comparators. Comparators are used where parts must be checked to determine acceptable tolerance. They may also be used to check the geometry of such things as threads, gears, and formed machine tool cutters. The electronic comparator may be found in the inspection area, toolroom, or gage laboratory and used in routine inspection and calibration of measuring tools and gages.

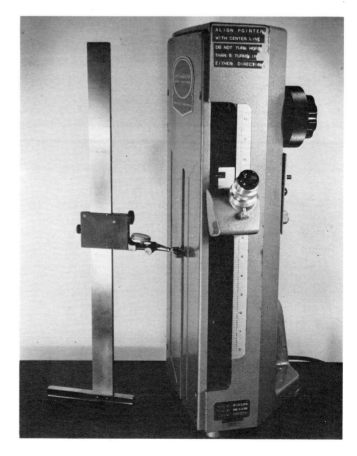

Figure 48. Setting the dial test indicator using the optical height gage (DeAnza College).

Figure 49. Dial indicator comparator (DeAnza College).

Figure 51. Using the dial indicator comparator (DeAnza College).

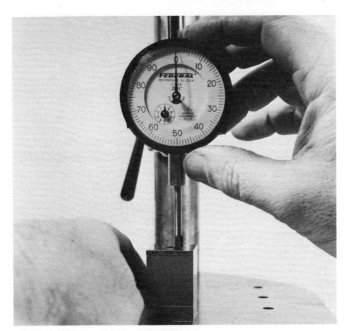

Figure 50. Setting the dial indicator to zero using gage blocks (DeAnza College).

Figure 52. Dial comparator indicator with cable lift (Harry Smith & Associates).

Dial Indicator Comparators. The dial indicator comparator is no more than a dial indicator attached to a rigid stand (Figure 49). These are dial indicator instruments such as the ones previously discussed. However, in their application as comparator instruments, as many errors as possible have been eliminated by the fixed design of the instrument's components. The indicator is set to zero at the desired dimension by use of gage blocks (Figure 50). When using a dial indicator comparator, keep in mind the **potential for error** in indicator travel and instrument alignment along the axis of measurement. Once the indicator has been set to zero, parts can be checked for acceptable tolerance (Figure 51). A particularly useful comparator indicator for this is one equipped with tolerance hands (Figure 52). The tolerance hands can be set to establish an upper and lower limit for part size. On this type of comparator indicator, the spindle can be lifted clear of the workpiece by using

Figure 53. Optical comparator checking a screw thread (Courtesy of Rank Scherr-Tumico, Inc.).

Figure 54. Shadow of the screw thread as seen on the optical comparator screen (DeAnza College).

the cable mechanism. This permits the indicator to always travel downward as it comes into contact with the work. This is an additional compensation for any mechanical error in the indicator mechanism.

Optical Comparators. The optical comparator (Figure 53) projects onto a screen a greatly magnified profile of the object being measured. Various templates or patterns in addition to graduated scales can be placed on the screen and compared to the projected shadow of the part. The optical comparator is particularly useful for inspecting the geometry of screw threads, gears, and formed cutting tools.

For example, to check a screw thread, the part is mounted on the comparator stage and dusted to provide a clearly defined shadow. The stage of the comparator is adjusted for the helix angle of the thread and the magnified shadow of the part is viewed on the comparator screen (Figure 54). The surface of the workpiece may also be inspected by use of a surface illuminator.

Electromechanical and Electronic Comparators. Electromechanical and electronic comparators convert dimensional change into changes of electric current or voltage. These changes are read on a suitably graduated scale (meter). Economical mass production of high precision parts requires that fast and reliable measurements be made so that over- and under-sized parts can be sorted from those within tolerance. Electromechanical comparators can be used in this application (Figure 55). The comparator shown is used to check a camshaft.

The electronic comparator (Figure 56) is a very sensitive instrument. It is used in a variety of comparison measuring applications in inspection and calibration. The comparator is set to a gage block by first adjusting the coarse adjustment. This mechanically moves the measuring probe. Final adjustment to zero is accomplished electronically. This is one of the unique advantages of such instruments. The electronic comparator shown has three scales. The first scale reads ±.003 in. at full range, with a discrimination of .0001 in. The second scale reads ±.001 in. at full range, with a discrimination of .00005 in. The third scale reads ±.0003 at full range, with a discrimination of .00001 in.

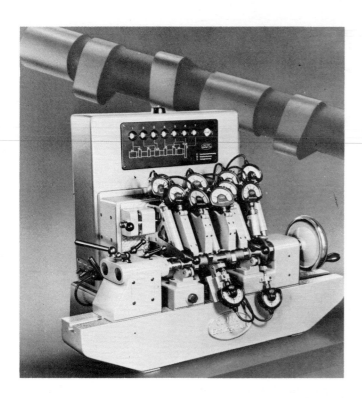

Figure 55. Electromechanical comparator inspecting a camshaft (Courtesy of the Mahr Gage Company).

Figure 56. Electronic comparator with maximum discrimination of .00001 in. (Courtesy of the DoAll Company).

SELF-TEST

1. Define comparison measurement.
2. What can be said of most comparison measuring instruments?
3. Define cosine error.
4. How can cosine error be reduced?

   Match the following measuring situations with the following list of comparison measuring tools. Answers may be used more than once.

5. A milled slot two inches wide with a tolerance of ± .002 in.
6. A height transfer measurement.
7. The shape of a form lathe cutter.
8. Checking a combination square to determine its accuracy.
9. The diameter of a $1\frac{1}{2}$ in. hole.
10. Measuring a shim under a piece of machinery.

a. Spring caliper
b. Telescope gage
c. Adjustable parallel
d. Radius gage
e. Thickness gage
f. Planer gage
g. Combination square
h. Solid beam square
i. Beveled edge square
j. Cylindrical square
k. Diemaker's square
l. Micrometer square
m. Dial indicator
n. Dial test indicator
o. Dial indicator comparator
p. Optical comparator
q. Electronic comparator

UNIT 6 USING GAGE BLOCKS

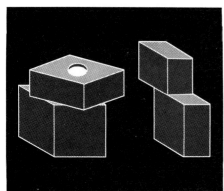

In the introduction to this section, we discussed the need for standardization of measurement. Today's widespread manufacturing can function only if machinists everywhere are able to check and adjust their measuring instruments to the same standards. Gage blocks permit a comparison between the working measurement instruments of manufacturing and recognized international standards of measurement. They are one of the most important measuring tools you will encounter. The practical use of gage blocks in the metrology laboratory, toolroom, and machine shop include the calibration of precision measuring instruments, establishing precise angles, and often measurements involved in the positioning of machine tool components and cutting tools.

OBJECTIVES

After completing this unit, you should be able to:
1. Describe the care required to maintain gage block accuracy.
2. Wring gage blocks together correctly.
3. Disassemble gage block combinations and properly prepare the blocks for storage.
4. Calculate combinations of gage block stacks with and without wear blocks.
5. Describe gage blocks applications.

GAGE BLOCK TYPES AND GRADES

Gage blocks are commonly available individually or in sets. A common gage block set will contain 81 to 88 blocks ranging in thickness from .050 to 4.000 in. The total measuring range of the set is over 25 in. (Figure 1). Also available are 121 block sets that permit measurement from .010 to 18 in. Sets with 4, 6, 9, 12, and 34 blocks are also used depending on measuring requirements. Sets of extra long blocks are available permitting measurements to 84 in. Metric gage block sets contain blocks ranging from .5 to 100 millimeters. **Angular gage blocks** can measure from 0 to 30 degrees. Gage blocks for linear measurement are either rectangular or square.

The three grades of gage blocks are **grade AA (laboratory), grade A+ (inspection),** and **grade B (shop).** Grades AA and A+ are manufactured grades, while grade B blocks are usually out-of-tolerance AA or A+ sets that are no longer used by the inspection or metrology laboratory (Table 1).

THE VALUE OF GAGE BLOCKS

As you know, a truly exact size cannot be obtained.

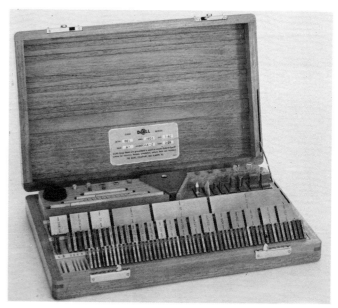

Figure 1. Gage block set with accessories (Courtesy of the DoAll Company).

Table 1
Gage Block Tolerances

| Block Size | Length | Grade AA | | Surface Finish in Microinches (Micro-millionth) |
		Flatness	Parallelism	
.100 to 2.00 in.	±.000002 in.	±.000002 in.	±.000002 in.	0-.4
Over 2.00	±.000002 in.	±.000002 in.	±.000004 in.	0-.4
		Grade A+		
.100 to 2.00 in.	+.000004 in. −.000002 in.	±.000002 in.	±.000002 in.	0-.4
Over 2.00 in.	+.000004 in. −.000002 in.	±.000005 in.	±.000005 in.	0-.4

However, it can be quite closely approached. Gage blocks are one of the physical standards that can closely approach exact dimensions. This makes them useful as measuring instruments with which to check other measuring tools. From the table on gage block tolerances, you can see that the length tolerance on a grade AA block is ±.000002 in. This is only four millionths of an inch total tolerance. Such a small amount is hard to visualize. Consider that the thickness of a page of this book is about .003 in. Compare this amount with total gage block tolerance and you will note that the page is 750 times thicker than the tolerance. This should indicate that a gage block would be very useful for checking a measuring instrument with .001 or even .0001 in. discrimination.

As a further demonstration of gage block value, consider the following example. It is desired to establish a distance of 20 inches as accurately as possible. Using a typical gage block set, imagine a hypothetical situation where each block has been made to the plus tolerance of .000002 in. over the actual size. This situation would not exist in an actual gage block set, as the tolerance of each block is most likely bilateral. If it required 30 blocks to make up a 20 in. stack, the cumulative tolerance would amount to .000060 in. (sixty millionths). As you can see, the 20 in. length is still extremely close to actual size. In a real situation, because of the bilateral tolerance of the gage blocks, the 20 in. stack will actually be much closer to 20.000000 than 20.000060 in. Because the gage block is so close to actual size, cumulative tolerance has little effect even over a long distance.

PREPARING GAGE BLOCKS FOR USE
Gage blocks are, at the same time, **rugged** and **delicate.** During their manufacture, they are put through many heating and cooling cycles that stabilize their dimensions.

In order for a gage block to function, its **surface** must be **extremely smooth** and **flat.**

Gage blocks are almost always used in combination with each other. This is known as the gage block stack. The secret of gage block use lies in the ability to place two or more blocks together in such a way that most of the air between them is displaced. The space or interface between wrung gage blocks is known as the wringing interval. This is the process of **wringing.** Once this is accomplished, atmospheric pressure will hold the stack together. Properly wrung gage block stacks are essential if cumulative error is to be avoided. Two gage blocks simply placed against each other will have an air layer between them. The thickness of the air layer will greatly affect the accuracy of the stack.

Before gage blocks can be wrung, they must be properly prepared. Burrs, foreign material, lint, grit, and even dust from the air can prevent proper wringing and permanently damage a gage block. The main cause of gage block wear is the wringing of poorly cleaned blocks. Preparation of gage blocks should conform to the following procedure.

1. Remove the desired blocks from the box and place them on a lintfree tissue. It is recommended that the blocks be handled with an **insulated forceps.** This will minimize heat transfer from the hands that can temporarily affect the size of the block.

2. The gage block must be cleaned thoroughly before wringing. This can be done with an appropriate cleaning solvent or commercial gage block cleaner (Figure 2). Use the solvent sparingly, especially if an aerosol is applied. The evaporation of a volatile solvent can cool the block and cause it to temporarily shrink out of tolerance.

3. Dry the block immediately with a lintfree tissue.

4. Any burrs on a gage block can prevent a proper

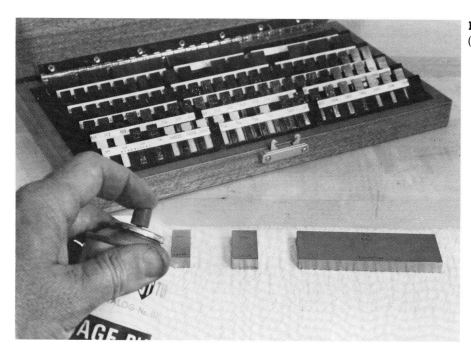

Figure 2. Applying gage block cleaner (DeAnza College).

Figure 3. Using the conditioning stone (CSU, Fresno).

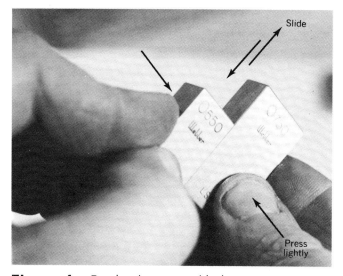

Figure 4. Overlapping gage blocks prior to wringing (DeAnza College).

wring and possibly damage the highly polished surface. Deburring is accomplished with a special deburring stone or dressing plate (Figure 3). The block should be lightly moved over the stone using a single back and forth motion. After deburring, the block must be cleaned again.

WRINGING GAGE BLOCKS

Gage blocks should be wrung immediately after clean-ing. If more than a few seconds elapses, dust from the air will settle on the wringing surface. The block may require dusting with a camel's hair brush. To wring rectangular gage blocks, the following procedure should be used.

1. Place the freshly cleaned and deburred mating surfaces together and overlap them about $\frac{1}{8}$ in. (Figure 4).

2. Slide the blocks together while lightly pressing together. During the sliding process, you should feel an increasing resistance. This resistance should then level off.

Figure 5.   Wrung gage blocks in line (DeAnza College).

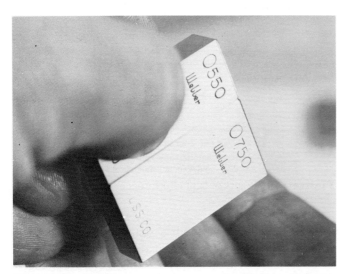

Figure 6.   Making sure of a proper wring (DeAnza College).

3. Position the blocks so that they are in line (Figure 5).
4. Make sure that the blocks are wrung by holding one block and releasing the other. Hold your hand under the stack in case the block should fall (Figure 6).

Square gage blocks require the same cleaning and deburring as rectangular blocks. Square gage blocks are wrung by a slightly different technique. Since they are square, they should be placed together at a 45 degree angle. The upper block is then slid over the lower block while at the same time twisting the blocks and applying a light pressure.

During the wringing process, heat from the hands may cause the block stack to expand often well out of tolerance. The stack should be placed on a heat sink in order to normalize the temperature. Generally, gage blocks should be handled as little as possible to minimize heat problems.

If, during the wring, the blocks tend to slide freely, slip them apart immediately and recheck cleaning and deburring. If the blocks fail to wring after proper preparation has been followed, they may be warped or have a surface imperfection. A gage block may be inspected for these conditions by the use of an optical flat.

CHECKING GAGE BLOCKS WITH OPTICAL FLATS

An **optical flat** is an extremely flat piece of quartz (Figure 7). Like gage blocks, there are various grades of flats. First grade or reference optical flats are flat within .000001 in. (one millionth). Round optical flats range from 1 to 10 in. in diameter. Square flats range from 1 × 1 in. to 4 × 4 in.

The optical flat uses the principles of **light interferometry** to make measurements and reveal surface geometry that could not be detected by other means. The working surface of the flat is placed on the gage block (Figure 8). The block and flat are then placed under a single color or **monochromatic** light source. Since it is not possible to produce a truly flat surface, some surface deviation will exist even on the most perfect of gage blocks. Therefore, a portion of the block will be in direct contact with the optical flat. Other portions will not be in contact.

In the areas of no contact, a small space exists between the optical flat and the gage block. Monochromatic light passing through the optical flat is reflected by both the lower surface of the flat and the surface of the gage block. Under certain conditions, dependent on the distance existing between block and flat, light reflected from the block surface will cancel light reflected from the lower surface of the optical flat. This cancellation effect, called **interference,** is directly related to the distance between block and flat. If this distance is the same

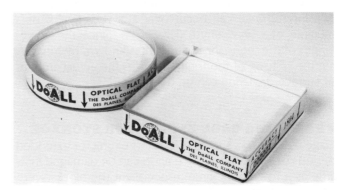

Figure 7.   Round and square optical flats (Courtesy of the DoAll Company).

Figure 8. Inspecting a gage block under monochromatic light (DeAnza College).

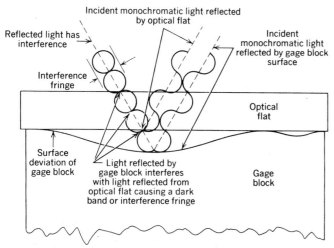

Figure 9. The optical flat in light interference.

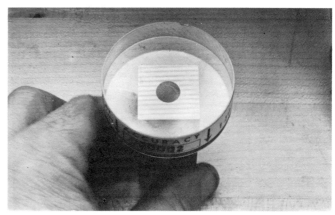

Figure 10. Interference fringe patterns (DeAnza College).

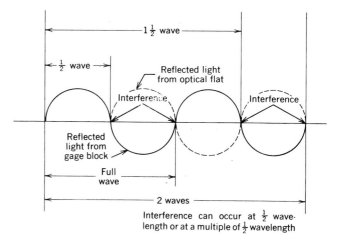

Figure 11. Points of light interference.

as or proportional to the wavelength of the light used, interference can occur (Figure 9). The result of interference produces a dark band or **interference fringe** (Figure 10). Interference can occur only at $\frac{1}{2}$ wavelength or a multiple of $\frac{1}{2}$ wavelength (Figure 11). Since the wavelength of the monochromatic light is known, by measuring the spacing of the fringe patterns the actual amount of surface deviation can be determined.

PREPARING GAGE BLOCKS FOR STORAGE
Gage block stacks should not be left wrung for extended periods of time. The surface finish can be damaged in as little as a few hours' time, especially if the blocks were not exceedingly clean at the time of wringing. After use, the stack should be unwrung and the blocks cleaned once again. Blocks should be handled with tissue (Figure

12). Spray each block with a suitable gage block preservative and replace them in the box. The entire set should then be lightly sprayed with gage block preservative (Figure 13).

CALCULATING GAGE BLOCK COMBINATIONS
In making a gage block stack, a minimum number of blocks should be used, each surface or wringing interval between blocks can increase the opportunity for error. Poor wringing can make this error relatively large. In order to check your wringing ability, assemble a combination of blocks totaling 4.000 in. Compare this to the 4.000 in. block under a sensitive comparator. Make the comparison immediately after wringing to observe the effect of heat on the stack length. Place the wrung stack on a special heat sink or on the surface plate for about 15 minutes and then check the length again. This will provide some reasonable estimate of the wringing interval. Two millionths of an inch per interval is considered good wringing.

Figure 12. Handle gage blocks only with tissue (DeAnza College).

Figure 13. Applying gage block preservative (DeAnza College).

Table 2 gives the specifications of a typical set of 83 gage blocks. Note that they are in four series.

In the following example, it is desired to construct a gage block stack to a dimension of 3.5752 in. Wear blocks will be used on each end of the stack.

3.5762	
.100	First, eliminate the two .050 in. wear blocks
3.4762	

3.4762	Then eliminate the last figure right, by subtracting the .1002 block
.1002	
3.3760	

	Once again, eliminate the last figure right, by subtracting the .126 block
.126	
3.250	

	Eliminate the last figure right, using the .250 block
.250	
3.000	

	Eliminate the 3.000 in. with the 3.000 in. block
3.000	
0.000	

Therefore, the blocks required to construct this stack are:

Quantity	Size
2	.050 in. wear blocks
1	.1002 block
1	.126 in. block
1	.350 in. block
1	3.000 in. block

As a second example, we shall construct a gage block stack of 4.2125 without wear blocks.

4.2125
.1005
4.1120
.112
4.0000
4.0000
0.0000

Blocks for this stack are:

Quantity	Size
1	.1005
1	.112
1	4.000

USING WEAR BLOCKS

When gage blocks are used in applications where direct contact is made, it is advisable to use **wear blocks.** For example, if you were using a gage block stack to calibrate a large number of micrometers, wear blocks would be recommended to reduce the wear on the gage blocks. Wear blocks are usually included in typical gage block sets. They are made from a particularly hard material known as tungsten carbide. A wear block is placed on one or both ends of a gage block stack to protect it from possible damage by direct contact. Wear blocks are usually .050 or .100 in. thick.

GAGE BLOCK APPLICATIONS

Gage blocks are used in setting sine bars for establishing precise angles. The use of the sine bar is discussed in the

Table 2
Typical 83 Piece Gage Block Set

First: .0001 Series — 9 blocks								
.1001	.1002	.1003	.1004	.1005	.1006	.1007	.1008	.1009

Second: .001 Series — 49 Blocks								
.101	.102	.103	.104	.105	.106	.107	.108	.109
.110	.111	.112	.113	.114	.115	.116	.117	.118
.119	.120	.121	.122	.123	.124	.125	.126	.127
.128	.129	.130	.131	.132	.133	.134	.135	.136
.137	.138	.139	.140	.141	.142	.143	.144	.145
.146	.147	.148	.149					

Third: .050 Series — 19 Blocks										
.050	.100	.150	.200	.150	.300	.350	.400	.450	.500	.550
.600	.650	.700	.750	.800	.850	.900	.950			

Fourth: 1.000 Series — 4 Blocks
1.000   2.000   3.000   4.000
Two .050 wear blocks

Figure 14. Gage and wear blocks for setting a snap gage (DeAnza College).

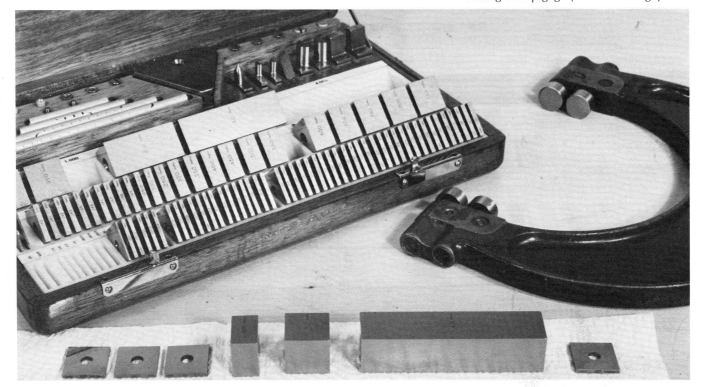

unit on angular measure. Gage blocks are used to set other measuring instruments such as a snap gage (Figure 14). The proper blocks are selected for the desired dimension and the stack assembled (Figure 15). Since this is a direct contact application, wear blocks should be used. The stack is then used to set the gage (Figure 16).

Gage block measurement is facilitated by various accessories (Figure 17). Accessories include scribers, bases, gage pins, and screw sets for holding the stack together. In any application where screws are employed to secure gage block stacks, a torque screwdriver must be used. This will apply the correct amount of pressure on the gage block stack. Gage block and accessories can be assembled into precision height gages for layout (Figure 18). With gage pins (Figure 19), gage blocks may be used for direct gaging or for checking other measuring instruments. Machine tool applications include the use of gage blocks as auxiliary measuring systems on milling machines, setting cutter heights, and spacing straddle milling cutters.

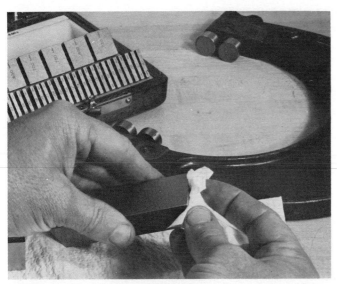

Figure 15. Cleaning blocks prior to wringing (DeAnza College).

Figure 16. Setting a snap gage using gage blocks (DeAnza College).

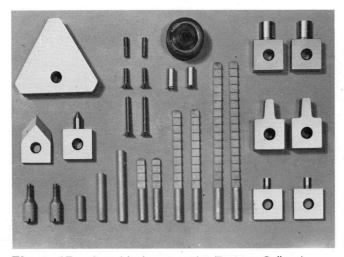

Figure 17. Gage block accessories (DeAnza College).

Figure 18. Precision height gage assembled from gage blocks (Courtesy of the DoAll Company).

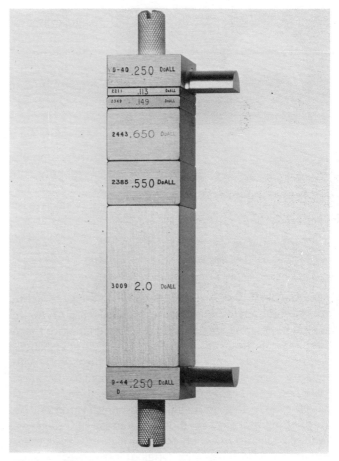

Figure 19. Gage block stack with accessory gage pins (Courtesy of the DoAll Company).

177

SELF-TEST

1. What is a wringing interval?
2. Why are wear blocks frequently used in combination with gage blocks?
3. As related to gage blocks usage, what is meant by the term normalize?
4. What length tolerances are allowed for the following grades of gage blocks (under 2.000 in. sizes)? AA, A+, B.
5. What is a conditioning stone and how is it used?
6. What does the term microinch regarding surface finish of a gage block mean?
7. Describe the handling precautions necessary for the preservation of gage block accuracy.
8. What gage blocks are necessary in order to assemble a stack equal to 3.0213, without using wear blocks?
9. List gage blocks necessary for a stack equal to 1.9643 with wear blocks.
10. Describe at least two gage block applications.

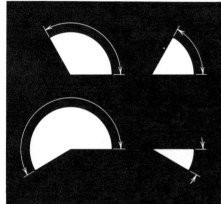

UNIT 7 USING ANGULAR MEASURING INSTRUMENTS

Angular measurement is as important as linear measurement. The same principles of metrology apply to angular measure as apply to linear measure. Angular measuring instruments have various degrees of discrimination. They must not be used beyond their discrimination. Angular measuring instruments require the same care and handling as any of your precision tools.

OBJECTIVES

After completing this unit, you should be able to:
1. Identify common angular measuring tools.
2. Read and record angular measurements using a vernier protractor.
3. Calculate sine bar elevations and measure angles using a sine bar and adjustable parallels.
4. Calculate sine bar elevations and establish angles using a sine bar and gage blocks.

As a machinist, you will find the need to measure **acute angles, right angles,** and **obtuse angles** (Figure 1). Acute angles are less than 90 degrees. Obtuse angles are more than 90 degrees but less than 180 degrees. Ninety degree or right angles are generally measured with squares. However, the amount of angular deviation from perpendicularity may have to be determined. This would require that an angular measuring instrument be used. Straight angles, or those containing 180 degrees, generally fall into the category of straightness or flatness and are measured by other types of instruments.

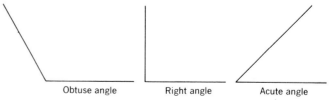

Obtuse angle   Right angle   Acute angle

Figure 1.   Acute, right, and obtuse angles.

UNITS OF ANGULAR MEASURE

In the inch system, the unit of angular measure is the **degree.**

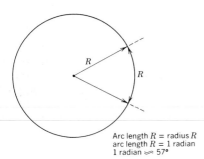

Arc length R = radius R
arc length R = 1 radian
1 radian ⇌ 57°

Figure 2. Radian measure.

Full circle = 360 degrees
1 degree = 60 minutes of arc (1° = 60′)
1 minute = 60 seconds of arc (1′ = 60″)

In the metric system, the unit of angular measure is the **radian**. A radian is the length of an arc on the circle circumference that is equal in length to the radius of the circle (Figure 2). Since the circumference of a circle is equal to 2 pi r (radius), there are 2 pi radians in a circle. Converting radians to degrees gives the equivalent:

$$1 \text{ radian} = \frac{360}{2 \text{ pi } r}$$

Assuming a radius of 1 unit:

$$1 \text{ radian} = \frac{360}{2 \text{ pi}}$$
$$= 57° \ 17′ \ 44″ \text{ (approximately)}$$

It is unlikely that you will come in contact with much radian measure. All of the common comparison measuring tools you will use read in degrees and fractions of degrees. Metric angles expressed in radian measure can be converted to degrees by the equivalent shown.

REVIEWING ANGLE ARITHMETIC

You may find it necessary to perform angle arithmetic. Use your calculator, if you have one available.

Adding Angles

Angles are added just like any other quantity. One degree contains 60 minutes. One minute contains 60 seconds. Any minute total of 60 or larger must be converted to degrees. Any second total of 60 or larger must be converted to minutes.

EXAMPLES

$$35° + 27° = 62°$$
$$3° \ 15′ + 7° \ 49′ = 10° \ 64′$$

Since 64′ = 1° 4′, the final result is 11° 4′
265° 15′ 52″ + 10° 55′ 17″ = 275° 70′ 69′

Since 69″ = 1′ 9″ and 70′ = 1° 10′, the final result is 276° 11′ 9″

Subtracting Angles

When subtracting angles where borrowing is necessary, degrees must be converted to minutes and minutes must be converted to seconds.

EXAMPLE
$$15° - 8° = 7°$$

EXAMPLE
15° 3′ − 6° 8′ becomes
14° 63′ − 6° 8′ = 8° 55′

EXAMPLE
39° 18′ 13″ − 17° 27′ 52″ becomes
38° 77′ 73″ − 17° 27′ 52″ = 21° 50′ 51″

ANGULAR MEASURING INSTRUMENTS

Plate Protractors

Plate protractors have a discrimination of one degree and are useful in such applications as layout and checking the point angle of a drill (Figure 3).

Bevel Protractors

The bevel protractor is part of the machinist's combi-

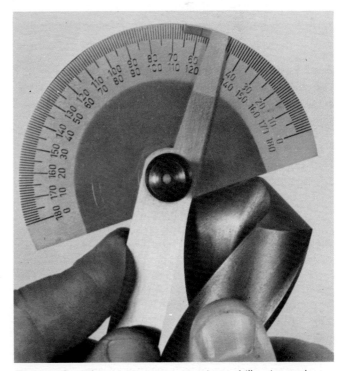

Figure 3. Plate protractor measuring a drill point angle.

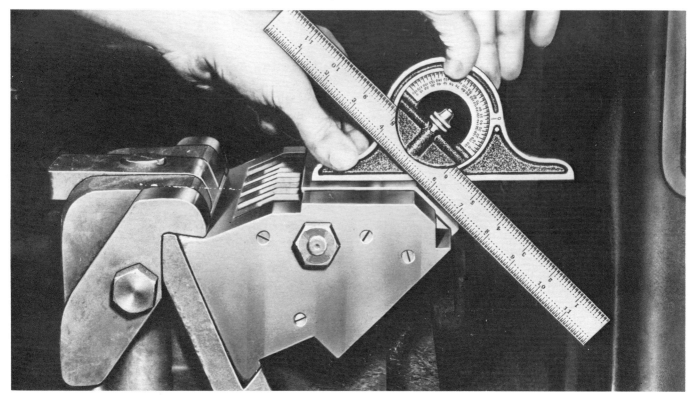

Figure 4. Using the combination set bevel protractor (Courtesy of the L. S. Starrett Company).

nation set. This protractor can be moved along the rule and locked in any position. The protractor has a flat base permitting it to rest squarely on the workpiece (Figure 4). The combination set protractor has a discrimination of one degree.

Dial Indicating Sinometer Angle Gage

The indicating sinometer (Figure 5) permits fast and accurate measurement of all angles. Discrimination is 30 seconds of arc per dial division.

Universal Bevel Vernier Protractor

The universal bevel vernier protractor (Figure 6) is equipped with a vernier that permits discrimination to $\frac{1}{12}$ of a degree or 5 minutes of arc.

The instrument can measure an obtuse angle (Figure 7). The acute attachment facilitates the measurement of angles less than 90 degrees (Figure 8). When used in conjunction with a vernier height gage, angle measurements can be made that would be difficult by other means (Figure 9).

Vernier protractors are read like any other instrument employing the vernier. The main scale is divided into whole degrees. These are marked in four quarters each 0 to 90 degrees. The vernier divides each degree into 12 parts each equal to 5 minutes of arc.

Figure 5. Dial indicating sinometer angle gage (Courtesy of Rank Scherr-Tumico, Inc.).

To read the protractor, determine the nearest full degree mark between zero on the main scale and zero on the vernier scale. **Always read the vernier in the same direction as you read the main scale.** Determine the number of the vernier coincident line. Since each vernier line is equal to 5 minutes, multiply the number of the coincident line by 5. Add this to the main scale reading.

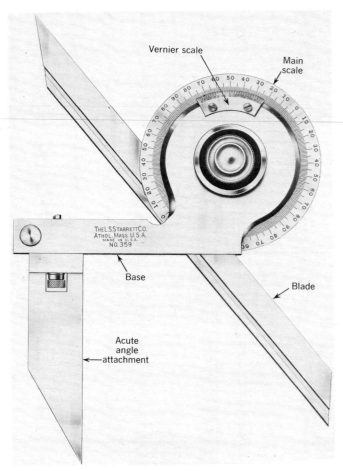

Vernier scale

Main scale

Base

Blade

Acute angle attachment

Figure 6. Parts of the universal bevel vernier protractor (Courtesy of the L. S. Starrett Company).

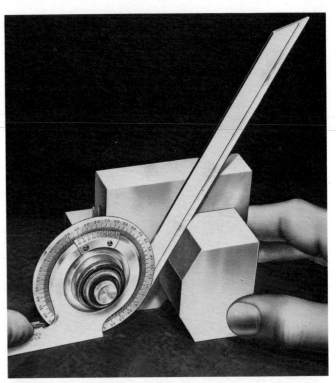

Figure 7. Measuring an obtuse angle with the vernier protractor (Courtesy of the L. S. Starrett Company).

Example Reading (Figure 10). The protractor shown has a magnifier so that the vernier may be seen more easily.

> Main scale 56°
> Vernier coincident at line 6
> 6 × 5 minutes = 30 minutes
> Total reading is 56° 30′

For convenience, the vernier scale is marked at 0, 30, and 60, indicating minutes.

The vernier bevel protractor can be applied in a variety of angular measuring applications (Figure 11).

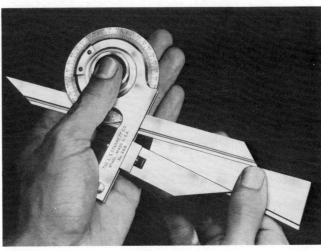

Figure 8. Using the acute angle attachment (Courtesy of the L. S. Starrett Company).

USING THE SINE BAR

Precise angles can be measured using the **sine bar** (Figure 12). A sine bar is a precision bar that has been hardened and then ground and lapped to very precise dimensions. The sine bar has a precise cylinder attached to each end. The center spacing of the cylinders is either 5 or 10 in. and is precisely established.

When in use, the sine bar becomes the hypotenuse of a right triangle. Angles are measured or established by elevating one end of the bar a specified amount. The amount of sine bar elevation for any desired angle is determined by the following formula.

Bar elevation = bar length × sine of the desired angle.

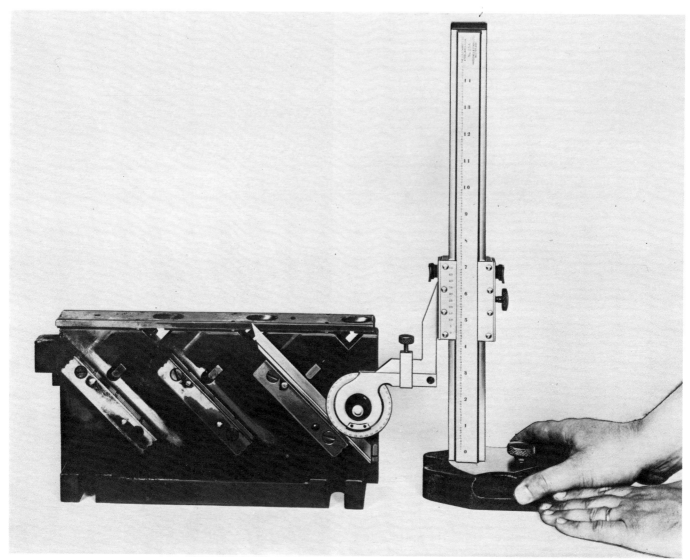

Figure 9. Using the vernier protractor in conjunction with the vernier height gage (Courtesy of the L. S. Starrett Company).

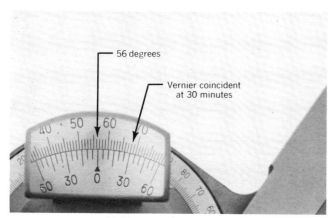

Figure 10. Vernier protractor reading of 56 degrees and 30 minutes.

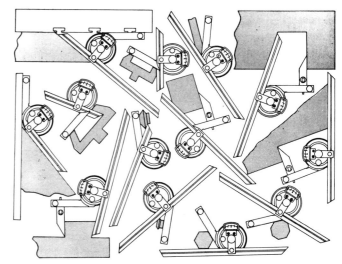

Figure 11. Applications of the vernier bevel protractor (Courtesy of MTI Corporation).

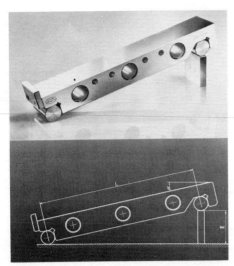

Figure 12.   Sine bar (Courtesy of Mahr Gage Company).

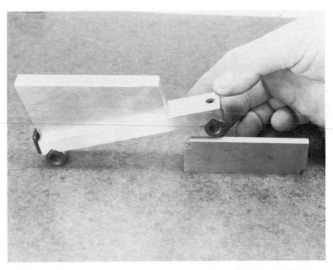

Figure 13.   Placing the adjustable parallel under the sine bar (DeAnza College).

EXAMPLE

Determine the elevation for 30 degrees using a 5 in. sine bar.

$$\text{Bar elevation} = 5 \text{ in.} \times \sin 30°$$
$$= 5 \times .5$$
$$= 2.500 \text{ in.}$$

This means that if the bar were elevated 2.500 in., an angle of 30 degrees would be established.

EXAMPLE

Determine the elevation for 42 degrees using a 5 in. sine bar.

$$\text{Bar elevation} = 5 \text{ in.} \times \sin 42°$$
$$= 5 \times .6691$$
$$= 3.3456 \text{ in.}$$

Determining Workpiece Angle Using the Sine Bar and Measuring Workpiece Angle Using the Sine Bar and Adjustable Parallel

An angle may be measured using the sine bar and adjustable parallel. The adjustable parallel is used to elevate the sine bar (Figure 13). The workpiece is placed on the sine bar and a dial test indicator is set to zero on one end of the part (Figure 14). The parallel is adjusted until the dial indicator reads zero at each end of the workpiece (Figure 15). The parallel is then removed and measured with a micrometer (Figure 16). To determine the angle of the workpiece, simply transpose the sine bar elevation formula and solve for the angle.

Bar elevation = bar length × sine of the angle desired
Sine of the angle desired = elevation/bar length

Sin of angle	= 1.9935 (micrometer reading/5)
Sin	= .3987
Angle	= 23° 29′ 48″

Figure 14.   Setting the test indicator to zero at the end of the workpiece (DeAnza College).

Figure 15.   Checking the zero reading at the opposite end of the workpiece (DeAnza College).

Figure 16.   Measuring the adjustable parallel with an out-side micrometer.

Figure 17.   Wringing the gage block stack for the sine bar elevation (DeAnza College).

Figure 18.   Placing the gage block stack under the sine bar (DeAnza College).

Establishing Angles Using the Sine Bar and Gage Blocks

Extremely precise angles can be measured or established by using gage blocks to elevate the sine bar. Bar elevation is calculated in the same manner. The required gage blocks are properly prepared and the stack is wrung (Figure 17). The gage block stack totalling 1.9940 in. is placed under the bar (Figure 18). This will establish an

angle of 23° 30′ 11″ using a 5 in. sine bar. The angle of the workpiece is checked using a dial test indicator (Figure 19).

Sine Bar Constant Tables

The elevations for angles up to about 55 degrees can be obtained directly from a **table of sine bar constants.** Such tables can be found in machinist's handbooks. The sine

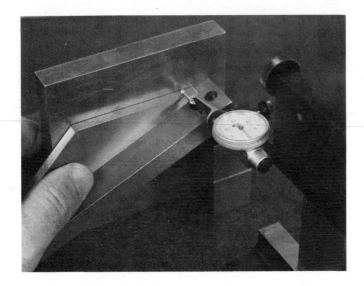

bar constant table eliminates the need to perform a trigonometric calculation. The sine bar table may only discriminate to minutes of arc. If discrimination to seconds of arc is required, it is better to calculate the amount of sine bar elevation required.

Figure 19.   Checking the workpiece using the dial test indicator (DeAnza College).

SELF-TEST

1. Name two angular measuring instruments with one degree of discrimination.
2. What is the discrimination of the universal bevel protractor?
3. Describe the use of the sine bar.

4.–8. Read and record the following vernier protractor readings (Figures 20 to 24).

4.
5.
6.
7.
8.
9. Calculate the required sine bar elevation for an angle of 37 degrees. (Assume a 5 in. sine bar.)
10. A 10 in. sine bar is elevated 2.750 in. Calculate the angle established to the nearest minute.

Figure 22

Figure 20

Figure 21

Figure 23

Figure 24

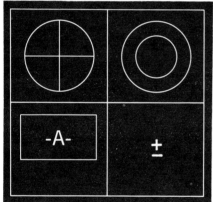

UNIT 8 TOLERANCES AND FITS

Almost no product today is totally manufactured by a single maker. Although you might think that a complex product like an automobile or aircraft is made by a single manufacturer, if you look behind the scenes you would discover that the manufacturer uses many suppliers that make components for the final assembly.

In order to make all the component parts fit together, or **interface,** to form a complex assembly, you have already learned that a standardized system of measurement is essential. You have further learned that the measurement instruments must be compared to known standards in the process of **calibration** in order to maintain their accuracy.

Although standardized measurement is essential to modern industry, perhaps even more important are the design specifications that indicate the **dimensions** of a part. These dimensions control the **size** of a part, its features, and/or their location on the part or relative to other parts. Through this, parts are able to be interchanged and mated to each other to form complete assemblies. The purpose of this unit is to introduce the basic terminology of tolerances and fits.

OBJECTIVES

After completing this unit, you should be able to:
1. Describe basic reasons for tolerance specifications.
2. Recognize common geometric dimension and tolerance call outs on drawings.
3. Describe the reasons for press fits and know where to find press fit allowance information.

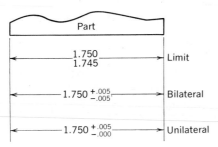

Figure 1. Tolerance notations.

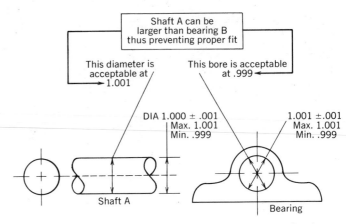

Figure 2. Tolerance overlap can prevent proper fit of mating parts.

LIMIT AND TOLERANCE

Since it is impossible to machine a part to an exact size, a designer must specify an acceptable range of sizes that will still permit the part to fit and function as intended. The maximum and minimum sizes in part dimensions that are acceptable are **limits** between which the actual part dimension must fall. The difference between the maximum and minimum limits is **tolerance,** or the total amount by which a part dimension may vary. Tolerances on drawings are often indicated by specifying a limit, or by **plus** and **minus** notations (Figure 1). With plus and minus tolerancing, when the tolerance is both above and below the nominal (true theoretical) size, it is said to be **bilateral** (two sides). When the tolerance is indicated all on one side of nominal, it is said to be **unilateral** (one sided).

HOW TOLERANCE AFFECTS MATING PARTS

When two parts mate or are interchanged in an assembly, tolerance becomes vitally important. Consider the following example (Figure 2): The shaft must fit the bearing and be able to turn freely. The diameter of the shaft is specified as $1.000 \pm .001$. This means that the maximum limit of the shaft is 1.001 and the minimum is .999. The tolerance is then .002 and bilateral.

The maximum limit of the bearing bore is also 1.001 and the minimum limit is .999. The tolerance is once again .002. Will the shaft made by one machine shop fit the bearing made by another machine shop using the tolerances specified? If the shaft is turned to the maximum limit of 1.001 and the bearing is bored to its minimum limit of .999, both parts would be within acceptable tolerance, but would not fit to each other since the shaft is .002 larger than the bearing. However, if the bearing bore was specified in limit form or unilateral tolerance of $1.002 \, {}^{+.002}_{-.000}$, the parts would fit as intended. Even if the shaft was turned to the high limit of 1.001, it would still fit the bearing even though the bore was machined to the low limit of 1.002. Although a machinist is not usually concerned with establishing tolerance and limit specifications, you can easily see how fit problems can be created by overlapping tolerances discussed in this example.

STANDARD TOLERANCES

On many drawings you will use in the machine shop, tolerances will be specified at the dimensions. If no particular tolerances are specified at the dimension, accepted standard tolerances may be applied. These are often listed in part of the title block on the drawing and generally conform to the following.

Fractional dimensions $\pm 1/64$
Two place decimal fractions $\pm .010$
Three place decimal fractions $\pm .005$
Four place decimal fractions $\pm .0005$
Angles $\pm \frac{1}{2}$ degree

Always check any drawing carefully to determine if standard tolerances apply and what they might be for the particular job you are doing.

FITS

Fit refers to the amount or lack of clearance between two mating parts. Fits can range from free running or sliding, where a certain amount of clearance exists between mating parts, to **press** or **interference** fits where parts are forced together under pressure. Clearance fits can range from a few millionths of an inch, such as would be the case in the component parts of a ball or roller bearing, to a clearance of several thousandths of an inch for a very low speed drive or control lever application.

Many times a machinist is concerned with press or

interference fits. In this case two parts are forced together usually by mechanical or hydraulic pressing. The frictional forces involved then hold the parts together without any additional hardware such as keys or set screws. Tolerances for press fits can become very critical because parts can be easily damaged by attempting to press fit them if there is an excessive difference in their mating dimensions. In addition, press fitting physically deforms the parts to some extent. This can result in damage, mechanical binding, or require a secondary resizing operation such as hand reaming or honing after the parts are pressed together.

A very typical example of press fit is when a ball bearing inner race is pressed onto a shaft or an outer race is pressed into a bore. Thus, the bearing is retained by friction and the free running feature is obtained within the bearing itself. Ball to race clearance is only a few millionths of an inch in precision bearings. If a bearing is pressed into a bore or onto a shaft with excessive force because pressing allowances are incorrect, the bearing may be physically deformed to the extent that mechanical binding is present. This will often cause excess friction and heat while in operation resulting in rapid failure of the part. On the other hand, insufficient frictional retention of the part resulting from a press fit that is not sufficient, can result in the wrong part turning under load or some of the mechanism falling apart while operating.

Press Fit Allowances

Press fit allowances depend on a number of factors including: length of engagements, diameter, material, particular components being pressed, need for later disassembly of parts.

Soft materials such as aluminum can be pressed very successfully. However, soft materials may experience considerable deformation and these parts may not stand up to repeated pressings. Like metal parts pressed without the benefits of lubrication may gall, making them very difficult if not impossible to press apart. Very thin parts such as tubing may bend or deform to such a degree that the press retention is not sufficient to hold the parts together under design loads. The following general rule can be applied when determining the press allowance for cylindrical parts.

Allowance $= .0015 \times$ Diameter of part in inches

EXAMPLES:
Determine the press allowance for a pin with a .250 in. diameter.

$.0015 \times .250 =$

.000375 (slightly more than 3/10,000 of an inch)

Determine the press allowance for 4.250 dia.

$.0015 \times 4.250 =$

.006375 (slightly more than 6/1000 of an inch)

Generally, pressing tolerances range from a few tenths to a few thousandths of an inch depending on the diameter of the parts and the other factors previously discussed. Proper measurement tools and techniques must be employed to make accurate determinations of the dimensions involved. For further specific dimensions on pressing allowances, consult a machinist's handbook.

Shrink and Expansion Fits

Parts can be fitted by making use of the natural tendency of metals to expand or contract when heated and cooled. By heating a part, it will expand and can be then slipped on a mating part. Upon cooling, the heated part will contract and grip the mating part often with tremendous force. Parts may also be mated by cooling one or the other so that it contracts, thus making it smaller. Upon warming to ambient temperature, it will expand to meet the mating part.

Shrink and expansion fits can have superior holding power over press fits although special heating and cooling equipment may be necessary. Like press fits, however, allowances are extremely important. Consult a machinist's handbook for proper allowance specifications.

GEOMETRIC DIMENSIONING AND TOLERANCING

Equally important and in many cases more important than controlling the size of a particular individual part, is controlling the **form** and **position** of a part or assembly feature. This relates directly to the ability to interchange individualized parts and assemblies. For example, you have undoubtedly purchased standard replacement parts for your auto from many different sources. In many cases, these may be made by manufacturers other than the original maker of your auto. However, they fit and function exactly as the original equipment. To make this kind of interface possible, the manufacturing and engineering community has developed a system of geometric dimensioning and tolerancing that helps a manufacturer control form and position of parts and assemblies. **Geometric dimensioning** and **tolerancing** is a complex subject and would require a great deal of time and space to cover completely. You will learn more about this as you go further into your training. For the present, the following discussion is intended to cover the basic concepts only.

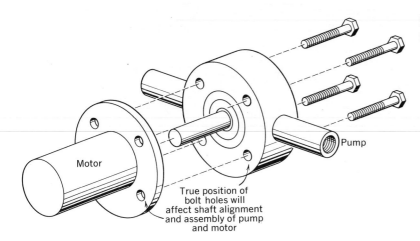

True position of bolt holes will affect shaft alignment and assembly of pump and motor

Motor

Pump

Controlling Feature Location

You can obviously see that to bolt the pump to the motor (Figure 3) it is necessary to insure that the pattern of bolt holes in the pump matches the pattern of bolt holes in the motor. Also, the bore in the pump housing must match the boss on the motor such that, the shaft will engage the motor with proper alignment. If the respective assemblies are made by different manufacturers, you can see that if either bolt pattern position deviates very far from the specified dimensions, the assemblies would be difficult or impossible to interface. As long as the two manufacturers work closely together, the assemblies will interface. However, if the pump manufacturer wants to start using a motor made by another manufacturer, the bolt hole pattern on the new pump motor will also have to interface with the pattern on the pump. This is an example where the **location** or the **true position** of the holes could be more critical than the size of the holes themselves. On drawings the following symbols are used to indicate location control:

⊕ True position
◎ Concentricity
⹀ Symmetry

Controlling Form

Controlling **form** is equally important. Consider the pump and motor assembly in the previous example. The pump drive shaft must be perpendicular to the impeller case so that it can engage the motor without mechanical binding. Therefore, **perpendicularity** is one example of form that must be controlled during manufacturing. On drawings the following symbols are used to indicate form control:

⊥ Perpendicularity (squareness)
— Straightness
▱ Flatness

∠ Angularity
∥ Parallelism
○ Roundness
⌭ Cylindricity
⌒ Profile of any line
⌓ Profile of any surface
↗ Runout (circular or total)

Datums and Basic Dimensions

Datums are reference points, lines, and planes taken to be exact for the purpose of calculations and measurements. An initially machined surface on a casting, for example, may be selected as a datum surface and used as a reference from which to measure and locate other part features. Datums are usually not changed by subsequent machining operations and are identified by single or sometimes double letters except I, O, and Q inside a rectangular frame. For example,

| - A - | | - B - |

The term **basic** on a drawing represents a true theoretically exact dimension describing location or shape of a part feature. Basic dimensions in theory have no tolerance. They are taken to be exact. Basic dimensions are shown on drawings by the following notations:

1.375 Basic
1.375 BSC
1.375
BSC
| 1.375 |

Drawing Formats

The following format is used to express some of the common geometric dimensions and tolerances on working drawings.

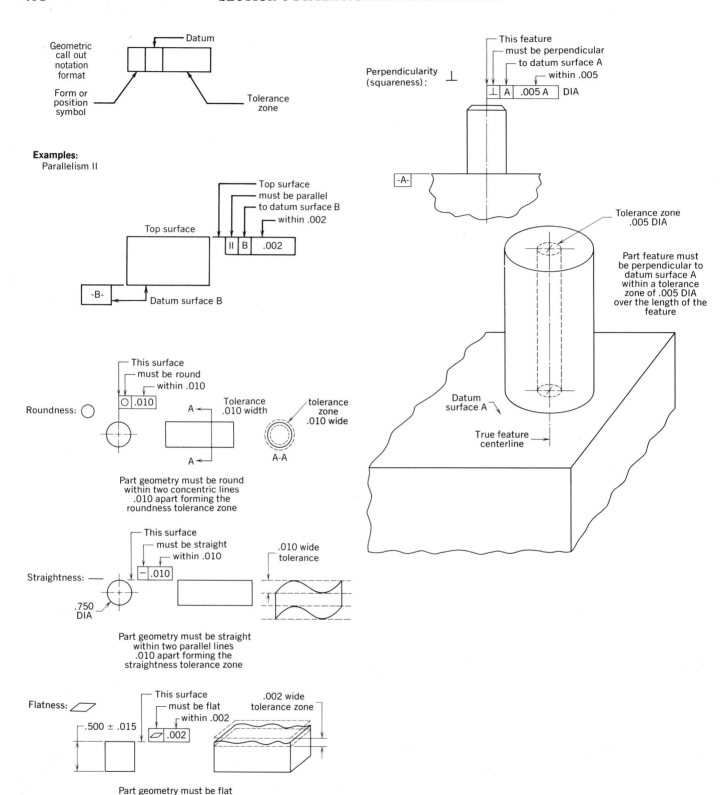

Geometric call out notation format

Datum

Form or position symbol

Tolerance zone

Examples:

Parallelism ∥

Top surface must be parallel to datum surface B within .002

Top surface

∥ | B | .002

-B- Datum surface B

Roundness: ○

This surface must be round within .010

○ | .010

Tolerance .010 width

tolerance zone .010 wide

A-A

Part geometry must be round within two concentric lines .010 apart forming the roundness tolerance zone

Straightness: ─

This surface must be straight within .010

─ | .010

.750 DIA

.010 wide tolerance

Part geometry must be straight within two parallel lines .010 apart forming the straightness tolerance zone

Flatness: ▱

This surface must be flat within .002

▱ | .002

.500 ± .015

.002 wide tolerance zone

Part geometry must be flat within two parallel planes .002 apart forming the flatness tolerance zone

Perpendicularity (squareness): ⊥

This feature must be perpendicular to datum surface A within .005

⊥ | A | .005 A DIA

-A-

Tolerance zone .005 DIA

Part feature must be perpendicular to datum surface A within a tolerance zone of .005 DIA over the length of the feature

Datum surface A

True feature centerline

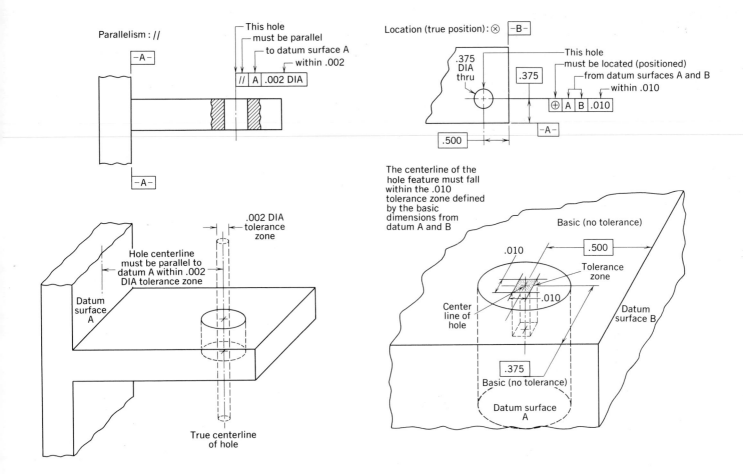

MMC and RFS

Two other symbols you will encounter on working drawings are **MMC,** or **maximum material condition,** and **RFS,** or **regardless of feature size.** These specifications are identified by the following symbols:

> or **MMC for maximum material condition.**
> or **RFS for regardless of feature size.**

MMC refers to the maximum amount of material remaining. On an external cylindrical feature this would be the **high limit** of the feature tolerance. For example,

a shaft with a diameter of .750 ± .010 would have an MMC diameter of .760 since this would leave maximum material remaining on the part. For an internal cylindrical feature such as a hole, the MMC diameter would be the **low limit** of the tolerance since this would leave maximum material remaining.

RFS, or regardless of feature size, means that the form or position tolerance of a feature must be met no matter what the feature size is. An example of RFS would be a hole located to a true position tolerance call out, but where the size of hole itself is not important or not as important as the location.

SELF-TEST

1. Why are tolerances important in manufacturing?
2. What are typical standard tolerances?
3. Name three geometric specifications called out on drawings?
4. What is the general rule for press fit allowances?
5. Describe shrink and expansion fits.

This unit has no post test.

SECTION D MATERIALS

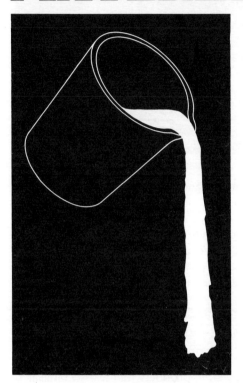

If there were a single thing to which we could attribute the progress of man, it would have to be his ability to make and use tools. The discovery and use of metals would follow close behind, for without metal man still would be fashioning tools of bone and stone.

Nearly everything we need for our present civilization depends upon metals. Vast amounts of iron and steel are used for automobiles, ships, bridges, buildings, machines, and a host of other products (Figure 1). Almost everything that uses electricity depends on copper and many other metals. Some metals that were impossible to smelt or extract from ores a few years ago are now being used in large quantities. These are usually called **space age** metals. There are also hundreds of combinations of metals, called alloys.

We have come a long way since the first iron was smelted, as some believe, by the Hittites about 3500 years ago. Their new iron tools, however, were not much better than those of the softer metals, copper and bronze, that were already in use at the time. This was because iron, as iron wire or wrought iron bars, would bend and not hold an edge. The steel making process, which uses iron to make a strong and hard material by heat treatment, was still a long way from being discovered.

Metallic ores are first smelted into metals, and these metals are then formed into the many different products needed in our society. Many metallic ores exist in nature as oxides, in which metals are chemically combined with oxygen. Most iron is removed from the ore by a process called oxidation reduction. Metallic ores are also found as carbonates and silicates.

Figure 1. Large scale production of metal products is performed in modern steel mills (Courtesy of Bethlehem Steel Corporation).

Figure 2. Just prior to the Industrial Revolution, iron working had become a highly skilled craft (Courtesy of Dover Publications, Inc.).

Modern metallurgy stems from man's ancient desire to fully understand the behavior of metals. Long ago, the art of the metal worker was enshrouded in mystery and folklore. Crude methods of making and heat treating small amounts of steel were discovered by trial and error only to be lost and discovered again by others (Figure 2). We have come a long way, indeed, from those early open forges that produced the soft wrought iron in amounts of 20 or 30 pounds a day to our modern production marvels that produce more than 100 million tons yearly in the United States.

The modern story of iron and steel begins with the raw materials: iron ore, coal, and limestone. From these ingredients pig iron is produced. Pig iron is the source of almost all our ferrous metals. The steel mill refines it in furnaces, after which it is cast into ingot molds to solidify. The ingot is then formed in various ways into the many steel products that are so familiar to us.

In this section, you will investigate the many materials you will work with in the machine shop. You should learn the characteristics of many metals, and become familiar with hardening and tempering processes that strengthen and harden by heating and cooling. Different metals often have different properties; for example, cast iron is brittle while soft iron is easily bent, and the difference is due to how they are made. Some steels can be made as hard as needed by heat treatment. You will learn several tests by which you can measure the hardness and resistance of a metal to penetration.

All metals are classified for industrial use by their specific working qualities; you will have to be able to select and identify materials using tables in your handbook or by testing processes in the shop. Some systems are numbers used to classify metals, others use color codes, which consist of a brand painted on the end of a piece of the material. Spark testing is one popular shop method for identifying metals that you will meet in this book.

It is important to be able to recognize and identify these materials of the trade in order to do a job according to its specifications. This section has been developed to help you achieve this goal.

SAFETY IN MATERIAL HANDLING

Safety must be observed when handling material just as it is when using hand and machine tools.

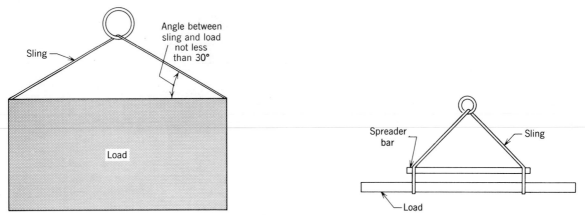

Figure 3. Load sling.

Figure 4. Sling for lifting long bars.

Lifting and Hoisting

Machinists were once expected to lift pieces of steel weighing a hundred pounds or more into awkward positions. This is a dangerous practice, however, that results in too many injuries. Hoists and cranes are used to lift all but the smaller parts. Steel weighs about 487 pounds per cubic foot; water weighs 62.5 pounds per cubic foot, so it is evident that steel is a very heavy material for its size. You can easily be misled into thinking that a small piece of steel does not weigh much. Follow these two rules in all lifting that you do: don't lift more than you can easily handle, and bend your knees and keep your back straight. If a material is too heavy or awkward for you to position it on a machine such as a lathe, use a hoist. Once the workpiece has been hoisted to the required level, it can hang in that position until the clamps or chuck jaws on the machine have been secured.

When lifting heavy metal parts with a mechanical or electric hoist, always stand in a safe position, no matter how secure the slings and hooks seem to be. They don't often break, but it can and does happen, and if your foot is under the edge, a painful or crippling experience is sure to follow. Slings should not have less than a 30 degree angle with the load (Figure 3). When hoisting long bars or shafts, a spreader bar (Figure 4) should be used so the slings cannot slide together and unbalance the load. When operating a crane, be careful that someone else is not standing in the way of the load or hook. If you are using a block, chain hoist, or electric winch, be sure that the lift capacity rating of the equipment and its support structure is proper for the load.

Carrying Objects

Carry long stock in the horizontal position. If you must carry it in the vertical position, be careful of light fixtures and ceilings. A better way is to have someone carry each end of a long piece of material. Do not carry sharp tools in your pockets. They can injure you or someone else.

Hot Metal Safety

Oxy-acetylene torches are often used for cutting shapes, circles, and plates in machine shops. Safety when burning them requires proper clothing, gloves, and eye protection. It is also very important that any metal that has been heated by burning or welding be plainly marked, especially if it is left unattended. The common practice is to write the word *HOT* with soapstone on such items. Whenever arc welding is performed in a shop, the arc flash should be shielded from the other workers. *Never* look toward the arc because if the arc light enters your eye even from the side, the eye can be burned.

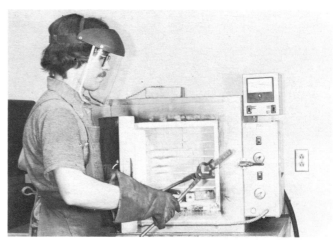

Figure 5. Face shield and gloves are worn for protection while heat treating and grinding (Lane Community College).

When handling and pouring molten metals such as babbitt, aluminum, or bronze, wear a face shield and gloves. Do not pour molten metals where there is a concrete floor unless it is covered with sand.

When heat treating, always wear a face shield and heavy gloves (Figure 5). There is a definite hazard to the face and eyes when cooling tool steel by oil quenching, that is, submerging it in oil. The oil, hot from the steel, tends to fly upward, so you should stand to one side of the oil tank.

Certain metals, when finely divided as a powder or even as coarse as machining chips, can ignite with a spark or just by the heat of machining. Magnesium and zirconium are two such metals. The fire, once started, is difficult to extinguish, and if water or a water-based fire extinguisher is used, the fire will only increase in intensity. Chloride-based power fire extinguishers are commercially available. These are effective for such fires as they prevent water absorption and form an air-excluding crust over the burning metal. Sand is also used to smother fires in magnesium.

UNIT 1 SELECTION AND IDENTIFICATION OF STEELS

When the village smithy plied his trade, there were only wrought iron and carbon steel for making tools, implements, and horseshoes, so the task of separating metals was relatively simple. As industry began to need more alloy steels and special metals, they were gradually developed, so today there are many hundreds of these metals in use. Without some means of reference or identification, work in the machine shop would be chaotic. Therefore, this unit introduces you to several systems used for marking steels and some ways to choose between them.

OBJECTIVE

After completing this unit, you should be able to:
Identify different types of metals by various means of shop testing.

STEEL IDENTIFICATION SYSTEMS

Color coding is used as one means of identifying a particular type of steel. Its main disadvantage is that there is no universal color coding system. Each manufacturer has his own system. The two identification systems most used in the United States are numerical: Society of Automotive Engineers (SAE) and American Iron and Steel Institute (AISI). See Table 1.

The first two numbers denote the alloy. Carbon, for instance, is denoted by the number 10. The third and fourth digits, represented by x, always denote the percentage of carbon in hundredths of one percent. For carbon steel, it could be anywhere from .08 to 1.70 percent. For alloys the second digit designates the approximate percentage of the major alloying element. Steels having over one percent carbon require a five digit number; also certain corrosion and heat resisting alloys use a five digit number to identify the approximate alloy composition of the metal.

The AISI numerical system is basically the same as the SAE system with certain capital letter prefixes. These prefixes designate the process used to make the steel. The lowercase letters from a to i as a suffix denote special conditions in the steel.

AISI prefixes:

B — Acid Bessemer, carbon steel

C — Basic open hearth carbon steel

CB — Either acid Bessemer or basic open hearth carbon steel at the option of the manufacturer

D — Acid open hearth carbon steel

E — Electric furnace alloy steel

STAINLESS STEEL

It is the element chromium (Cr) that makes stainless steels stainless. Steel must contain a minimum of about 11 percent chromium in order to gain resistance to atmospheric **corrosion.** Higher percentages of chromium make steel even more resistant to corrosion and high temperatures. Nickel is added to improve **ductility,** corrosion resistance, and other properties. (Undefined words may be found in the glossary.)

Excluding the **precipitation hardening** types that harden over a period of time after **solution heat treatment,** there are three basic types of stainless steels: the **martensitic** and **ferritic** types of the 400 series, and the **austenitic** types of the 300 series.

The martensitic, hardenable type has carbon content up to 1 percent or more, so it can be hardened by heating to a high temperature, and then quenching (cooling) in oil or air. The cutlery grades of stainless are to be found in this group. The ferritic type contains little or no carbon. It is essentially soft iron that has 11 percent or more chromium content. It is the least expensive of

Table 1
SAE-AISI Numerical Designation of Alloy Steels (x Represents Percent of Carbon in hundredths)

Carbon steels:	
Plain carbon	10xx
Free-cutting, resulfurized	11xx
Manganese steels	13xx
Nickel steels	
.50% nickel	20xx
1.50% nickel	21xx
3.50% nickel	23xx
5.00% nickel	25xx
Nickel-chromium steels	
1.25% nickel, .65% chromium	31xx
1.75% nickel, 1.00% chromium	32xx
3.50% nickel, 1.57% chromium	33xx
3.00% nickel, .80% chromium	34xx
Corrosion and heat-resisting steels	303xx
Molybdenum steels	
Chromium	41xx
Chromium-nickel	43xx
Nickel	46xx and 48xx
Chromium steels	
Low-chromium	50xx
Medium-chromium	511xx
High-chromium	521xx
Chromium-vanadium steels	6xxx
Tungsten steels	7xxx and 7xxxx
Triple alloy steels	8xxx
Silicon-manganese steels	9xxx
Leaded steels	11Lxx (Example)

the stainless steels and is used for such things as building trim, pots, and pans. Both ferritic and martensitic types are magnetic.

Austenitic stainless steel contains chromium and nickel, little or no carbon, and cannot be hardened by quenching, but it readily **work hardens** while retaining much of its ductility. For this reason it can be work hardened until it is almost as hard as a hardened martensitic steel. Austenitic stainless steel is somewhat magnetic in its work hardened condition, but nonmagnetic when **annealed** or soft.

Table 2 illustrates the method of classifying the stainless steels. Only a very few of the basic types are given here. You should consult a manufacturer's catalog for further information.

TOOL STEELS
Special carbon and alloy steels called tool steels have their own classification. There are six major tool steels for which one or more letter symbols have been assigned:

1. Water hardening tool steels
   W — high carbon steels
2. Shock resisting tool steels
   S — Medium carbon, low alloy
3. Cold work tool steels
   O — Oil hardening types
   A — Medium alloy air hardening types
   D — High carbon, high-chromium types

Table 2
Classification of Stainless Steels

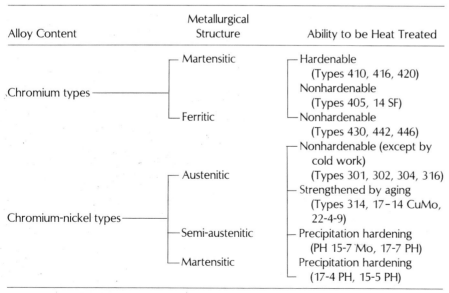

Alloy Content	Metallurgical Structure	Ability to be Heat Treated
Chromium types	Martensitic	Hardenable (Types 410, 416, 420)
		Nonhardenable (Types 405, 14 SF)
	Ferritic	Nonhardenable (Types 430, 442, 446)
Chromium-nickel types	Austenitic	Nonhardenable (except by cold work) (Types 301, 302, 304, 316)
		Strengthened by aging (Types 314, 17-14 CuMo, 22-4-9)
	Semi-austenitic	Precipitation hardening (PH 15-7 Mo, 17-7 PH)
	Martensitic	Precipitation hardening (17-4 PH, 15-5 PH)

Source. Armco Steel Corporation, Middletown, Ohio, *Armco Stainless Steels*, 1966. The following are registered trademarks of Armco Steel Corporation: 17-4 PH, 15-5 PH, 17-7 PH, and PH 15-7 Mo.

4. Hot work tool steels
   H — H1 to H19, chromium base types
       H20 to H39, tungsten base types
       H40 to H59, molybdenum base types
5. High speed tool steels
   T — Tungsten base types
   M — Molybdenum base types
6. Special purpose tool steels
   L — Low alloy types
   F — Carbon tungsten types
   P — Mold steels P1 to P19, low carbon types
       P20 to P39, other types

Several metals can be classified under each group, so that an individual type of tool steel will also have a suffix number that follows the letter symbol of its alloy group. The carbon content is given only in those cases where it is considered an identifying element of that steel.

Type of Steel	Examples
Water hardening: straight carbon tool steel	W1, W2, W4
Manganese, chromium, tungsten: oil hardening tool steel	01, 02, 06
Chromium (5.0%): airhardening die steel	A2, A5, A10
Silicon, manganese, molybdenum: punch steel	S1, S5
High speed tool steel	M2, M3, M30 T1, T5, T15

SHOP TESTS FOR IDENTIFYING STEELS

One of the disadvantages of steel identification systems is that the marking is often lost. The end of a shaft is usually marked. If the marking is obliterated or cut off and the piece is separated from its proper storage rack, it is very difficult to ascertain its carbon content and alloy group. This shows the necessity of returning stock material to its proper rack. It is also good practice to leave the identifying mark on one end of the stock material and always cut off the other end.

Unfortunately, there are always some short ends and otherwise useful pieces in most shops that have become unidentified. Also, when repairing or replacing parts for old or nonstandard machinery, there is usually no record available for material selection. There are many shop methods a machinist may use to identify the basic type of steel in an unknown sample. By process of elimination, the machinist can then determine which of the several steels of that type in the shop is most comparable to the sample. The following are several methods of shop testing that you can use.

Visual

Some metals can be identified by visual observation of their surface finishes. Heat scale or black **mill scale** is found on all hot rolled (HR) steels. These can be either low carbon (.05 to .30 percent), medium carbon (.30 to .60 percent), high carbon (.60 to 1.70 percent), or alloy steels. Other surface coatings that might be detected are the **sherardized, plated, case hardened,** or **nitrided** surfaces. *Sherardizing* is a process in which zinc vapor is inoculated into the surface of iron or steel.

Cold finish (CF) steel usually has a metallic luster. Ground and polished (G and P) steel has a bright, shiny finish with closer dimensional tolerances than CF. Also cold drawn **ebonized,** or black, finishes are sometimes found on alloy and **resulfurized** (free machining) shafting.

Chromium nickel stainless steel, which is austenitic and nonmagnetic, usually has a white appearance. Straight 12 to 13 percent chromium is ferritic and magnetic with a bluish-white color. Manganese steel is blue when polished, but copper colored when **oxidized.** White cast iron fractures will appear silvery or white. Gray cast iron fractures appear dark gray and will smear a finger with a gray graphite smudge when touched.

Magnet Test

All **ferrous** metals such as iron and steel are magnetic; that is, they are attracted to a magnet. Nickel, which is **nonferrous** (metals other than iron or steel), is also magnetic. United States "nickel" coins contain about 25 percent nickel and 75 percent copper, so they do not respond to the magnet test, but Canadian "nickel" coins are attracted to a magnet. Ferritic and martensitic (400 series) stainless steels are also attracted to a magnet and so cannot be separated from other steels by this method. Austenitic (300 series) stainless steel is not magnetic unless it is work hardened.

Hardness Test

Wrought iron is very soft since it contains almost no carbon or any other alloying element. Generally speaking, the more carbon (up to 2 percent) and other elements that steel contains, the harder, stronger, and less ductile it becomes, even if in an annealed state. Thus, the **hardness** of a sample can help us to separate low carbon steel from an alloy steel or a high carbon steel. Of course, the best way to check for hardness is with a hardness tester. The Rockwell, Brinell, and other types of hardness testing will be studied in another unit. Not all machine shops have hardness testers available, in which case the following shop methods can prove useful.

Scratch Test

Geologists and "rock hounds" scratch rocks against items of known hardness for identification purposes. The same method can be used to check metals for relative hardness. Simply scratch one sample with another and the softer sample will be marked. Be sure all scale or other surface impurities have been removed before scratch testing. A variation of this method is to strike two similar edges of two samples together. The one receiving the deepest indentation is the softer of the two.

File Tests

Files can be used to establish the relative hardness between two samples, as in the scratch test, or they can determine an approximate hardness of a piece on a scale of many steels. Table 3 gives the Rockwell and Brinell hardness numbers for this file test when using new files. This method, however, can only be as accurate as the skill that the user has acquired through practice.

Care must be taken not to damage the file, since filing on hard materials may ruin the file. Testing should be done on the tip or near the edge.

Spark Testing

Spark testing is a useful way to test for carbon content in many steels. The metal tested, when held against a grinding wheel, will display a particular spark pattern depending on its content. Spark testing provides a convenient means of distinguishing between tool steel (of medium or high carbon) and low carbon steel. High carbon steel (Figure 1) shows many more bursts than low carbon steel (Figure 2).

Almost all tool steel contains some alloying elements besides the carbon, which affects the carbon burst. Chromium, molybdenum, silicon, aluminum, and tungsten suppress the carbon burst. For this reason spark testing is not very useful in determining the content of an unknown sample of steel. It is useful, however, as a comparison test. Comparing the spark of a known sample to that of an unknown sample can be an effective method of identification for the trained observer. Cast iron may be distinguished from steel by the characteristic spark stream (Figure 3). High speed steel can also be readily identified by spark testing (Figure 4).

When spark testing always wear safety glasses or a face shield. Adjust the wheel guard so the spark will fly outward and downward, and away from you. A coarse grit wheel that has been freshly dressed to remove contaminants should be used.

Machinability

Machinability can be used in a simple comparison test to determine a specific type of steel. For example, two unknown samples identical in appearance and size can

Table 3

File Test and Hardness Table

Type Steel	Rockwell		Brinell	File Reaction
	B	C		
Mild steel	65		100	File bites easily into metal. (Machines well but makes built up edge on tool.)
Medium carbon steel		16	212	File bites into metal with pressure. (Easily machined with high speed tools.)
High alloy steel				File does not bite into metal except with
High carbon steel		31	294	difficulty. (Readily machinable with carbide tools.)
Tool steel		42	390	Metal can only be filed with extreme pressure. (Difficult to machine even with carbide tools.)
Hardened tool steel		50	481	File will mark metal but metal is nearly as hard as the file, and machining is impractical; should be ground.
Case hardened parts and hardened tool steel		64	739	Metal is as hard as the file; should be ground.

Note: Rockwell and Brinell hardness numbers are only approximations since file testing is not an accurate method of hardness testing

Source. J. E. Neely. *Practical Metallurgy and Materials of Industry,* John Wiley and Sons, New York, 1979.

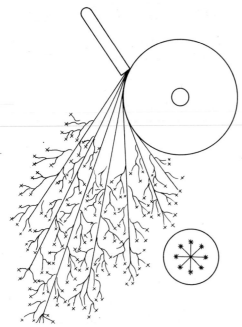

Figure 1. High carbon steel. Short, very white, or light yellow carrier lines with considerable forking, having many star-like bursts. Many of the sparks follow around the wheel.

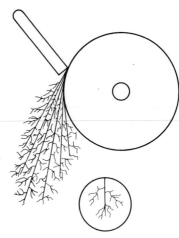

Figure 3. Cast iron. Short carrier lines with many bursts, which are red near the grinder and orange-yellow farther out. Considerable pressure is required on cast iron to produce sparks.

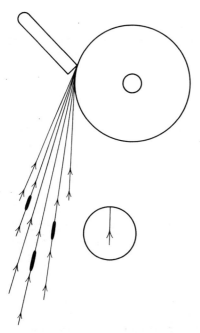

Figure 2. Low carbon steel. Straight carrier lines having a yellowish color with very small amount of branching and very few carbon bursts.

be test cut in a machine tool, using the same speed and feed for both. The ease of cutting should be compared, and chips observed for heating color and curl. See Section H, Unit 3, Table 2 for machinability ratings.

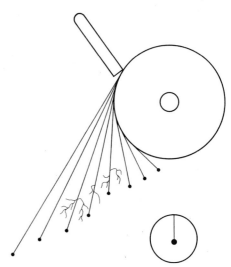

Figure 4. High speed steel. Carrier lines are orange, ending in pear-shaped globules with very little branching or carbon sparks. High speed steel requires moderate pressure to produce sparks.

Several properties should be considered when selecting a piece of steel for a job: strength, **machinability, hardenability, weldability, fatigue resistance,** and **corrosion** resistance.

Manufacturer's catalogs and handy reference books are available for selection of standard structural shapes, bars and other steel products (Figure 5). Others are available for the stainless steels, tool steels, finished carbon steel, and alloy shafting. Many of these steels are known by a trade name.

A machinist is often called upon to select a shaft material from which to machine finish a part. Shafting is

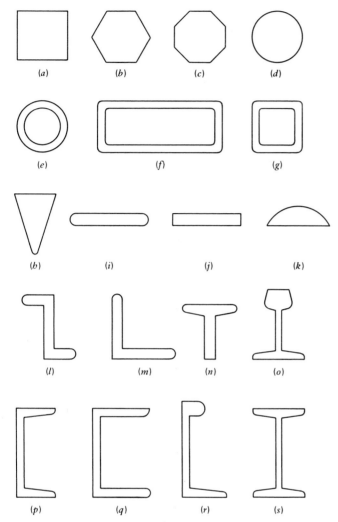

Figure 5. Steel shapes used in manufacturing (J. E. Neely. *Practical Metallurgy and Materials of Industry,* John Wiley and Sons, New York, 1979).

(a) Square HR or CR
(b) Hexagonal
(c) Octagon
(d) Round
(e) Tubing and pipe (round)
(f) HREW (hot rolled electric welded) rectangular steel tubing
(g) HREW square steel tubing
(h) Wedge
(i) HR flat bar (round edge spring steel flats)
(j) Flat bar (CR and HR)
(k) Half round
(l) Zee
(m) Angle
(n) Tee
(o) Rail
(p) Channel
(q) Car and ship channel
(r) Bulb angle
(s) Beams — I, H, and wide flange

manufactured with two kinds of surface finish: cold finished (CF) found on low carbon steel, and ground and polished (G and P) found mostly on alloy steel shafts. Tolerances are kept much closer on ground and polished

shafts. The following are some common alloy steels:

1. SAE 4140 is a chromium-molybdenum alloy with .40 percent carbon. It lends itself readily to heat treating, forging, and welding. It provides a high resistance to torsional and reversing stresses such as drive shafts.

2. SAE 1140 is a resulfurized, drawn, free machining bar stock. This material has good resistance to bending stresses because of its fibrous qualities and it has a high tensile strength. It is best used on shafts where the RPM (revolutions per minute) are high and the torque is low. SAE 1140 is also useful where stiffness is a requirement. It should not be heat treated or welded.

3. Leaded steels have all the free machining qualities and finishes of resulfurized steels. Leaded alloy steels such as SAE 41L40 have the superior strength of 4140, but are much easier to machine.

4. SAE 1040 is a medium carbon steel that has a normalized tensile strength of about 85,000 psi. It can be heat treated, but large sections will be hardened only on the surface and the core will still be in a soft condition. Its main advantage is that it is a less expensive way to obtain a higher strength part.

5. SAE 1020 is a low carbon steel that has good machining characteristics. It normally comes as CF shafting. It is very commonly used for shafting in industrial applications. It has a lower tensile strength than the alloy steels or higher carbon steels.

COSTS OF STEEL

Steel prices, as prices of most other products, change constantly, so costs can be shown only in example. Steel is usually priced by its weight. A cubic foot of mild steel weighs 489.60 pounds, so a square foot one inch thick weighs 40.80 pounds. From this, you can easily compute the weights for flat materials such as plate. For hexagonal and rounds, it would be much easier to consult a table in a catalog or handbook. Given a price per pound, you should then be able to figure the cost of a desired steel product.

EXAMPLE
A 1 by 6 in. mild steel bar is 48 in. long. If current steel prices are 30 cents per pound, how much does the bar cost?

$$\frac{6 \times 48}{144} = 2 \text{ sq. ft., 1 in. thick}$$

2 × 40.80 = 81.6 pounds

81.6 × .30 = 24.48 (cost of steel in dollars)

SELF-TEST

1. By what universal coding system is carbon and alloy steel designated?
2. What are three basic types of stainless steels and what is the number series assigned to them? What are their basic differences?
3. If your shop stocked the following steel shafting, how would you determine the content of an unmarked piece of each, using shop tests as given in this unit?
   (a) AISI C1020 CF
   (b) AISI B1140 (G and P)
   (c) AISI C4140 (G and P)
   (d) AISI 8620 HR
   (e) AISI B1140 (Ebony)
   (f) AISI C1040
4. A small part has obviously been made by a casting process. How can you determine whether it is a ferrous or a nonferrous metal, or if it is steel, or white or gray cast iron?
5. What is the meaning of the symbols O1 and W1 when applied to tool steels?
6. A $2\frac{7}{16}$ in. diameter steel shaft weighs 1.322 pounds per linear inch, as taken from a table of weights of steel bars. A 40 in. length is needed for a job. At 30 cents per pound, what would the shaft cost?
7. When checking the hardness of a piece of steel with the file test, the file slides over the surface without cutting.
   (a) Is the steel piece readily machinable?
   (b) What type of steel is it most likely to be?
8. Steel that is nonmagnetic is called.
9. What nonferrous metal is magnetic?
10. List at least four properties of steel that should be kept in mind when you select the material for a job.

UNIT 2 SELECTION AND IDENTIFICATION OF NONFERROUS METALS

Metals are designated as either ferrous or nonferrous. Iron and steel are ferrous metals, and any metal other than iron or steel is called nonferrous. Nonferrous metals such as gold, silver, copper, and tin were in use hundreds of years before the smelting of iron, and yet, some nonferrous metals have appeared relatively recently in common industrial use. For example, aluminum was first commercially extracted from ore in 1886 by the Hall-Heroult process, and titanium is a space age metal being produced in commercial quantities only after World War II.

In general, nonferrous metals are more costly than ferrous metals. It isn't always easy to distinguish a nonferrous metal from a ferrous metal, nor to separate one from another. This unit should help you to identify, select, and properly use many of these metals.

OBJECTIVES

After completing this unit, you should be able to:
1. Identify and classify nonferrous metals by a numerical system.
2. List the general appearance and use of various nonferrous metals.

Figure 1. Structural aluminum shapes used for building trim provides a pleasing appearance.

Table 1
Aluminum and Aluminum Alloys

Code Number	Major Alloying Element
1xxx	None
2xxx	Copper
3xxx	Manganese
4xxx	Silicon
5xxx	Magnesium
6xxx	Magnesium and silicon
7xxx	Zinc
8xxx	Other elements
9xxx	Unused (not yet assigned)

ALUMINUM

Aluminum is white or white-gray in color and can have any surface finish from dull to shiny and polished. An **anodized** surface is frequently found on aluminum products. Aluminum weighs 168.5 pounds per cubic foot as compared to 487 pounds per cubic foot for steel, and has a melting point of 1220°F (660°C) when pure. It is readily machinable and can be manufactured into almost any shape or form (Figure 1).

Magnesium is also a much lighter metal than steel, as it weighs 108.6 pounds per cubic foot, and looks much like aluminum. In order to distinguish between the two metals, it is sometimes necessary to make a chemical test. A zinc chloride solution in water, or a copper sulfate solution, will blacken magnesium immediately, but will not change aluminum.

There are several numerical systems used to identify aluminums, such as federal specifications, military specifications, the American Society for Testing Materials (ASTM), and SAE specifications. The system most used by manufacturers, however, is one adopted by the Aluminum Association in 1954.

From Table 1, you can see that the first digit of a number in the aluminum alloy series indicates the alloy type. The second digit, represented by an x in the table, indicates any modifications that were made to the original alloy. The last two digits indicate the numbers of similar aluminum alloys of an older marking system, except in the 1100 series, where the last two digits indicate the amount of pure aluminum above 99 percent contained in the metal.

EXAMPLES
An aluminum alloy numbered 5056 is an aluminum-magnesium alloy, where the first 5 represents the alloy magnesium, the 0 represents modifications to the alloy, and 56 are numbers of a similar aluminum of an older marking system. An aluminum numbered 1120 contains no major alloy, and has .20 percent pure aluminum above 99 percent.

Aluminum and its alloys are produced as castings or as wrought (cold worked) shapes such as sheets, bars, and tubing. Aluminum alloys are harder than pure aluminum and will scratch the softer (1100 series) aluminums. Pure aluminum and some of its alloys cannot be heat treated so their tempering is done by other methods. The temper designations are made by a letter that follows the four digit alloy series number:

- —F   as fabricated. No special control over strain hardening or temper designation is noted.
- —O   Annealed, recrystallized wrought products only. Softest temper.
- —H   Strain hardened, wrought products only. Strength is increased by work hardening.

This letter —H is always followed by two or more digits. The first digit, 1, 2, or 3, denotes the final degree of strain hardening:

- —H1   Strain hardened only
- —H2   Strain hardened and partially annealed
- —H3   Strain hardened and stabilized

and the second digit denotes higher strength tempers obtained by heat treatment:

$2 \frac{1}{4}$ hard
$4 \frac{1}{2}$ hard
$6 \frac{3}{4}$ hard
8 full hard

EXAMPLE
5056-H18 is an aluminum-magnesium alloy, strain hardened to a full hard temper.

Table 2
Cast Aluminum Alloy Designations

Code Number	Major Alloy Element
1xx.x	None, 99 percent aluminum
2xx.x	Copper
3xx.x	Silicon with Cu and/or Mg
4xx.x	Silicon
5xx.x	Magnesium
6xx.x	Zinc
7xx.x	Tin
8xx.x	Unused series
9xx.x	Other major alloys

Source. J. E. Neely. *Practical Metallurgy and Materials of Industry,* John Wiley and Sons, New York, 1979.

Some aluminum alloys can be hardened to a great extent by a process called **solution heat treatment** and **precipitation** or **aging.** This process involves heating the aluminum and its alloying elements until it is a **solid solution.** The aluminum is then quenched in water and allowed to age or is artificially aged by heating slightly. The aging produces an internal strain that hardens and strengthens the aluminum. Some other nonferrous metals are also hardened by this process. For these aluminum alloys the letter −T follows the four digit series number. Numbers 2 to 10 follow this letter to indicate the sequence of treatment.

- −T2   Annealed (cast products only)
- −T3   Solution heat treated and cold worked
- −T4   Solution heat treated, but naturally aged
- −T6   Solution heat treated and artificially aged
- −T8   Solution heat treated, cold worked, and artificially aged
- −T9   Solution heat treated, artificially aged, and cold worked
- −T10   Artificially aged and then cold worked

EXAMPLE
2024-T6 Aluminum-copper alloy, solution heat treated and artificially aged.

Cast aluminum alloys generally have lower tensile strength than wrought alloys. Sand castings, permanent mold, and die casting alloys are of this group. They owe their mechanical properties to solution heat treatment and precipitation or to the addition of alloys. A classification system similar to that of wrought aluminum alloys is used (Table 2).

The cast aluminum 108F, for example, has an ultimate tensile strength of 24,000 PSI in the as-fabricated condition and contains no alloy. The 220.T4 copper aluminum alloy has a tensile strength of 48,000 PSI.

OTHER NONFERROUS METALS

Cadmium

Cadmium has a blue-white color and is commonly used as a protective plating on parts such as screws, bolts, and washers. It is also used as an alloying element to make metal alloys that melt at low temperature, such as bearing metals, solder, type casting metals, and storage batteries. Cadmium compounds such as cadmium oxide are toxic and can cause illness when breathed. These toxic fumes can be produced by welding, cutting, or machining on cadmium plated parts. Breathing the fumes should be avoided by using adequate ventilation systems. The melting point of cadmium is 610°F (321°C). Its weight is 539.6 lb/ft³.

Copper and Copper Alloys

Copper is a soft, heavy metal that has a reddish color. It has high electrical and thermal conductivity when pure, but loses these properties to a certain extent when alloyed. It must be strain hardened when used for electric wire. Copper is very ductile and can be easily drawn into wire or tubular products. It is so soft that it is difficult to machine, and has a tendency to adhere to tools. Copper can be work hardened or hardened by solution heat treatment when alloyed with beryllium. The melting point of copper is 1981°F (1083°C). Its weight is 554.7 lb/ft³.

Beryllium Copper.   Beryllium copper is an alloy of copper and beryllium that can be hardened by heat treating for making nonsparking tools and other products. Machining of this metal should be done after solution heat treatment and aging, not when it is in the annealed state. Machining or welding beryllium copper can be very hazardous if safety precautions are not followed. Machining dust or welding fumes should be removed by a heavy coolant flow or by a vacuum exhaust system. A respirator type of face mask should be worn when around these two hazards. The melting point of beryllium is 2345°F (1285°C), and its weight is 115 lb/ft³.

Brass.   Brass is an alloy of zinc and copper. Brass colors usually range from white to yellow, and in some alloys, red to yellow. Brasses range from gilding metal used for jewelry (95 percent copper, 5 percent zinc) to Muntz metal (60 percent copper, 40 percent zinc) used for bronzing rod and sheet stock. Brasses are easily machined. Brass is usually tougher than bronze and produces a stringy chip when machined. The melting point of brasses ranges from 1616 to 1820°F (880 to 993°C), and their weights range from 512 to 536 lb/ft³.

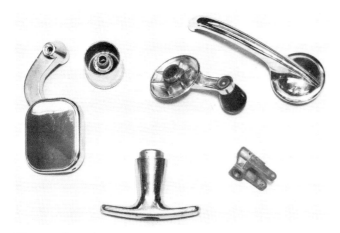

Figure 2. Die cast parts.

Figure 3. Babbitted pillow block bearings.

Bronze. Bronze is found in many combinations of copper and other metals; but copper and tin are its original elements. Bronze colors usually range from red to yellow. Phosphor bronze contains 92 percent copper, 0.05 percent phosphorus, and 8 percent zinc. Aluminum bronze is often used in the shop for making bushings or bearings that support heavy loads. (Brass is not normally used for making antifriction bushings.) The melting point of bronze is about 1841°F (1005°C) and its weight is about 548 lb/ft^3. Bronzes are usually harder than brasses, but are easily machined with sharp tools. The chip produced is often granular. Some bronze alloys are used as brazing rods.

Chromium

Chromium is a slightly gray metal that can take a high polish. It has a high resistance to corrosion by most reagents; exceptions are dilute hydrochloric and sulfuric acids. Chromium is widely used as a decorative plating on automobile parts and other products.

Chromium is not a very ductile or malleable metal and its brittleness limits its use as an unalloyed metal. It is commonly alloyed with steel to increase hardness and corrosion resistance. Chrome-nickel and chrome-molybdenum are two very common chromium alloys. Chromium is also used in electrical heating elements such as chromel or nichrome wire. The melting point of chromium is 2939°F (1615°C) and its weight is 432.4 lb/ft^3.

Die Cast Metals

Finished castings are produced with various metal alloys by the process of die casting. Die casting is a method of casting molten metal by forcing it into a mold. After the metal has solidified, the mold opens and the casting is ejected. Carburetors, door handles, and many small precision parts are manufactured using this process (Figure

2). Die cast alloys, often called ``pot metals,'' are classified in six groups:

1. Tin base alloys
2. Lead base alloys
3. Zinc base alloys
4. Aluminum base alloys
5. Copper, bronze, or brass alloys
6. Magnesium base alloys

The specific content of the alloying elements in each of the many die cast alloys may be found in handbooks or other references on die casting.

Lead and Lead Alloys

Lead is a heavy metal that is silvery when newly cut and gray when oxidized. It has a high density, low tensile strength, low ductility (cannot be easily drawn into wire), and high malleability (can be easily compressed into a thin sheet).

Lead has high corrosion resistance and is alloyed with antimony and tin for various uses. It is used as shielding material for nuclear and X-ray radiation, for cable sheathing, and battery plates. Lead is added to steels, brasses, and bronzes to improve machinability. Lead compounds are very toxic; they are also cumulative in the body. Small amounts ingested over a period of time can be fatal. The melting point of lead is 621°F (327°C); its weight is 707.7 lb/ft^3.

A **babbitt metal** is a soft, antifriction alloy metal often used for bearings and is usually tin or lead based (Figure 3). Tin babbitts usually contain from 65 to 90 percent tin with antimony, lead, and a small percentage of copper added. These are the higher grade and generally the more expensive of the two types. Lead babbitts contain up to 75 percent lead with antimony, tin, and some arsenic making up the difference.

Cadmium base babbitts resist higher temperatures than other tin and lead base types. These alloys contain from 1 to 15 percent nickel or a small percentage of copper and up to 2 percent silver. The melting point of babbitt is about 480°F (249°C).

Magnesium

When pure, magnesium is a soft, silver-white metal that closely resembles aluminum, but is less dense. In contrast to aluminum, magnesium will readily burn with a brilliant white light; thus, magnesium presents a fire hazard when machined. Magnesium, which is similar to aluminum in density and appearance, presents some quite different machining problems. Although magnesium chips can burn in air, applying water will only cause the chips to burn more fiercely. Sand or special compounds should be used to extinguish these fires. Thus, when working with magnesium, a water based coolant should never be used. Magnesium can be machined dry when light cuts are taken and the heat is dissipated. Compressed air is sometimes used as a coolant. Anhydrous (containing no water) oils having a high flash point and low viscosity are used in most production work. Magnesium is machined with very high surface speeds and with tool angles similar to those used for aluminum.

Cast and wrought magnesium alloys are designated by SAE and ASTM numbers, which may be found in metals reference handbooks such as the *Machinery's Handbook*. The melting point of magnesium is 1204°F (651°C), and its weight is 108.6 lb/ft^3.

Molybdenum

As a pure metal, molybdenum is used for high temperature applications and, when machined, it chips like gray cast iron. It is used as an alloying element in steel to promote deep hardening and to increase its tensile strength and toughness. Pure molybdenum is used for filament supports in lamps and in electron tubes. The melting point of molybdenum is 4748°F (2620°C). Its weight is 636.5 lb/ft^3.

Nickel

Nickel is noted for its resistance to corrosion and oxidation. It is a whitish metal used for electroplating and as an alloying element in steel and other metals to increase ductility and corrosion resistance. It resembles pure iron in some ways but has greater corrosion resistance. Electroplating is the coating or covering of another material with a thin layer of metal, using electricity to deposit the layer.

When spark tested, nickel throws short orange carrier lines with no sparks or sprigs (Figure 4). Nickel is attracted to a magnet, but becomes nonmagnetic near

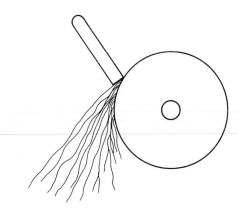

Figure 4. Spark test for nickel.

680°F (360°C). The melting point of nickel is 2646°F (1452°C), and its weight is 549.1 lb/ft^3.

Nickel Base Alloys

Monel is an alloy of 67 percent nickel and 28 percent copper, plus impurities such as iron, cobalt, and manganese. It is a tough, but machinable, ductile, and corrosion resistant alloy. Its tensile strength (resistance of a metal to a force tending to tear it apart) is 70,000 to 85,000 lb/in^2. Monel metal is used to make marine equipment such as pumps, steam valves, and turbine blades. On a spark test, monel shoots orange colored, straight sparks about 10 in. long, similar to those of nickel. K-monel contains 3 to 5 percent aluminum and can be hardened by heat treatment.

Chromel and nichrome are two nickel-chromium-iron alloys used as resistance wire for electric heaters and toasters. Nickel-silver contains nickel and copper in similar proportions to monel, but also contains 17 percent zinc. Other nickel alloys such as inconel are used for parts exposed to high temperatures for extended periods.

Inconel, a high temperature and corrosion resistant metal consisting of nickel, iron, and chromium, is often used for aircraft exhaust manifolds because of its resistance to high temperature oxidation (scaling). The nickel alloys melting point range is 2425 to 2950°F (1329 to 1621°C).

Precious Metals

Gold has a limited industrial value and is used in dentistry, electronic and chemical industries, and jewelry. In the past, gold has been used mostly for coinage. Gold coinage is usually hardened by alloying with about 10 percent copper. Silver is alloyed with 8 to 10 percent copper for coinage and jewelry. Sterling silver is 92.5 percent silver in English coinage and has been 90 percent silver for American coinage. Silver has many commercial

uses, such as an alloying element for mirrors, photographic compounds, and electrical equipment. It has a very high electrical conductivity. Silver is used in silver solders that are stronger and have a higher melting point than lead-tin solders.

Platinum, palladium, and iridium, as well as other rare metals, are even more rare than gold. These metals are used commercially because of their special properties such as extremely high resistance to corrosion, high melting points, and high hardness. The melting points of some precious metals are: gold 1945°F (1063°C), iridium 4430°F (2443°C), platinum 3224°F (1773°C), and silver 1761°F (961°C). Gold has a weight of 1204.3 lb/ft³. The weight of silver is about 654 lb/ft³. Platinum is one of the heaviest of metals with a weight of 1333.5 lb/ft³. Iridium is also a heavy metal, weighing 1397 lb/ft³.

Tantalum

Tantalum is a bluish-gray metal that is difficult to machine because it is quite soft and ductile and the chip clings to the tool. It is immune to attack from all corrosive acids except hydrofluoric and fuming sulfuric acids. It is used for high temperature operations above 2000°F (1093°C). It is also used for surgical implants and in electronics. Tantalum carbides are combined with tungsten carbides for cutting tools that have extreme wear resistance. The melting point of tantalum is 5162°F (2850°C). Its weight is 1035.8 lb/ft³.

Tin

Tin has a white color with a slightly bluish tinge. It is whiter than silver or zinc. Since tin has a good corrosion resistance, it is used to plate steel, especially for the food processing industry (Figure 5). Tin is used as an alloying element for solder, babbitt, and pewter. A popular solder is an alloy of 50 percent tin and 50 percent lead. Tin is alloyed with copper to make bronze. The melting point of tin is 449°F (232°C). Its weight is 454.9 lb/ft³.

Titanium

The strength and light weight of this silver-gray metal make it very useful in the aerospace industries for jet engine components, heat shrouds, and rocket parts; however, pure titanium can ignite and burn when heated to high temperatures. Pure titanium has a tensile strength of 60,000 to 110,000 PSI, similar to that of steel; by alloying titanium, its tensile strength can be increased considerably. Titanium weighs about half as much as steel and, like stainless steel, is a relatively difficult metal to machine. Machining can be accomplished with rigid setups, sharp tools, slower surface speed, and proper coolants. When spark tested, titanium throws a brilliant white spark with a single burst on the end of each car-

Figure 5. The most familiar tin plate product is the steel based tin can (Courtesy of American Iron & Steel Institute).

rier. The melting point of titanium is 3272°F (1800°C), and its weight is 280.1 lb/ft³.

Tungsten

Typically, tungsten has been used for incandescent light filaments. It has the highest known melting point (6098°F or 3370°C) of any metal, but is not resistant to oxidation at high temperatures. Tungsten is used for rocket engine nozzles and welding electrodes and as an alloying element with other metals. Machining pure tungsten is very difficult with single point tools, and grinding is preferred for finishing operations. Tungsten carbide compounds are used to make extremely hard and heat resistant lathe tools and milling cutters by compressing the tungsten carbide powder into a briquette and sintering it in a furnace. Tungsten weighs about 1180 lb/ft³.

Zinc

The familiar galvanized steel is actually steel plated with zinc and is used mainly for its high corrosion resistance. Zinc alloys are widely used as die casting metals. Zinc and zinc based die cast metals conduct heat much more slowly than aluminum. The rate of heat transfer on similar shapes of aluminum and zinc is a means of distinguishing between them. The melting point of zinc is 787°F (419°C), and it weighs about 440 lb/ft³.

Zirconium

Zirconium is similar to titanium in both appearance and physical properties. It was once used as an explosive

primer and as a flashlight powder for photography since, like magnesium, it readily combines with oxygen and rapidly burns when finely divided. Machining zirconium, like titanium, requires rigid setups and slow surface speeds. Zirconium has an extremely high resistance to corrosion from acids and sea water. Zirconium alloys are used in nuclear reactors, flash bulbs, and surgical implants such as screws, pegs, and skull plates. When spark tested, it produces a spark similar to that of titanium. The melting point of zirconium is 3182°F (1750°C). Its weight is 399 lb/ft³.

SELF-TEST

1. What advantages do aluminum and its alloys have over steel alloys? What disadvantages?
2. Describe the meaning of the letter "H" when it follows the four digit number that designates an aluminum alloy? The meaning of the letter "T"?
3. Name two ways in which magnesium differs from aluminum.
4. What is the major use of copper? How can copper be hardened?
5. What is the basic difference between brass and bronze?
6. Name two uses for nickel.
7. Lead, tin, and zinc all have one useful property in common. What is it?
8. Molybdenum and tungsten are both used in _____ steels.
9. Babbit metals, used for bearings, are made in what major basic types?
10. What type of metal can be injected under pressure into a permanent mold?

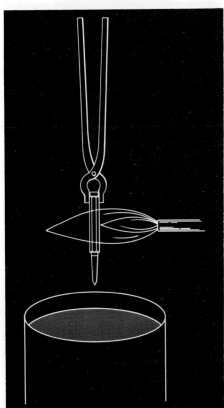

UNIT 3 HARDENING, CASE HARDENING, AND TEMPERING

Probably the most important property of carbon steels is their ability to be hardened through the process of heat treatments. Steels must be made hard if they are to be used as tools that have the ability to cut many materials including other soft steels. Various degrees of hardness are also desirable depending on the application of the tool steels. Heat treating carbon steels involves some very critical furnace operations. The proper steps must be carried out precisely, or a failure of the hardened steel will almost surely result. In some cases only surface hardening of a steel is required. This is accomplished through the process of surface and case hardening.

It is often desirable to slightly reduce the hardness of a steel tool in order to enhance other properties. For example, a chisel must have a hard cutting edge. It must also have a somewhat less hard but tough shank that will withstand hammering. The property of toughness is acquired through the process of tempering.

In this unit you will study the important processes and procedures for hardening, case hardening, and tempering of plain carbon steels.

OBJECTIVES

After completing this unit, you should be able to:
1. Correctly harden a piece of tool steel and evaluate your work.
2. Correctly temper the hardened piece of tool steel and evaluate your work.
3. Describe the proper heat treating procedures for more tool steels.

HARDENING METALS

Most metals (except copper used for electric wire) are not used commercially in their pure states because they are too soft and ductile and have low tensile strength. When they are alloyed with other elements, such as other metals, they become harder and stronger as well as more useful. A small amount (1 percent) of carbon greatly affects pure iron when alloyed with it. The alloy metal becomes a familiar tool steel used for cutting tools, files and punches. Iron with 2 to $4\frac{1}{2}$ percent carbon content yields **cast iron.**

Iron, steel, and other metals are composed of tiny grain structures that can be seen under a microscope when the specimen is polished and etched. This grain structure, which determines the strength and hardness of a steel, can be seen with the naked eye as small crystals in the rough broken section of a piece (Figure 1). These crystals or grain structures grow from a nucleus as the molten metal solidifies until the grain boundaries are formed. Grain structures differ according to the allotropic form of the iron or steel. An allotropic element is one able to exist in two or more forms with various properties without a change of chemical composition. Carbon exists in three **allotropic** forms: amorphous (charcoal, soot, coal), graphite, and diamond. Iron also exists in three allotropic forms (Figure 2): ferrite (at room temperature), austenite (above 1670°F, 911°C) and delta (between 2550°F and 2800°F or between 1498°C and 1371°C). The points where one phase changes to another are called critical points by heat treaters and transformation points by metallurgists. The critical points of water are the boiling point (212°F or 100°C) and the freezing point (32°F or 0°C). Figure 3 shows a critical temperature diagram for a carbon steel. The lower critical point is always about 1330°F (721°C) in equalibrium or very slow cooling, but the upper critical point changes as the carbon content changes (Figure 4).

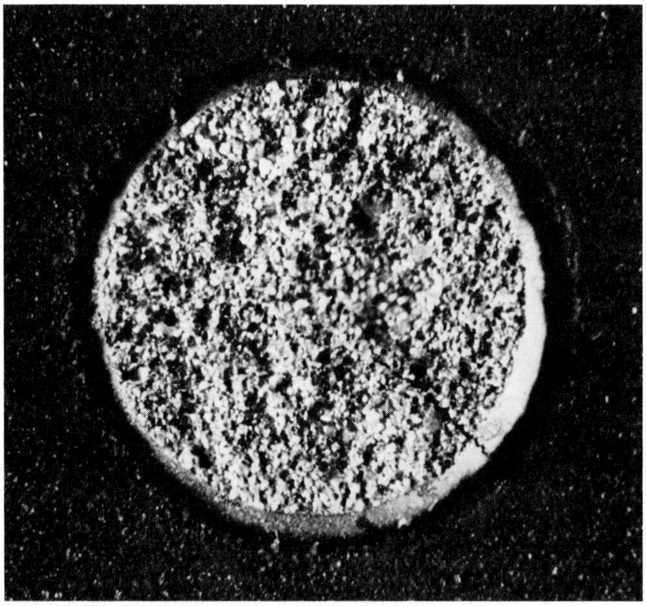

Figure 1. Single fracture of steel.

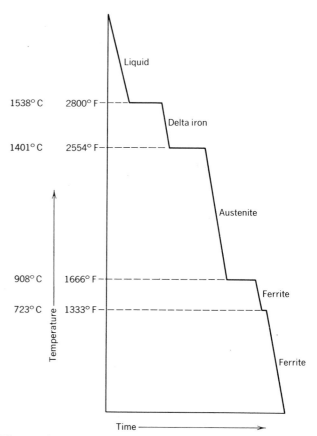

Figure 2. Cooling curve of iron.

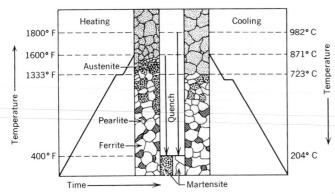

Figure 3. Critical temperature diagram of .83 percent steel showing grain structures in heating and cooling cycles. Center section shows quenching from different temperatures and the resultant grain structure.

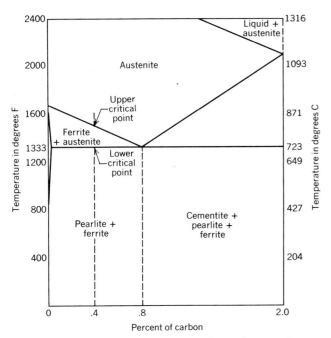

Figure 4. Simplified phase diagram for carbon steels.

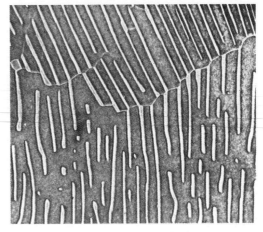

Figure 5. A replica electron micrograph. Structure consists of lamellar pearlite (11,000 ×). (By permission, from *Metals Handbook,* Volume 7, Copyright © American Society for Metals, 1972.)

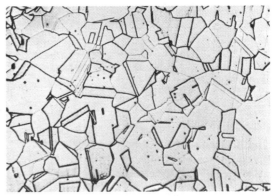

Figure 6. A microstructure of annealed 304 stainless steel that is austenitic at ordinary temperatures (250 ×). (By permission, from *Metals Handbook,* Volume 7, Copyright © American Society for Metals, 1972.)

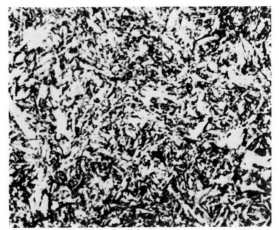

Figure 7. 1095 steel, water quenched from 1500°F (816°C) (1000 ×). The needlelike structure shows a pattern of fine untempered martensite. (By permission, from *Metals Handbook,* Volume 7, Copyright © American Society for Metals, 1972.)

HEAT TREATING STEEL

As steel is heated above the critical temperature of 1330°F, (721°C) the carbon that was in the form of layers of iron carbide or pearlite (Figure 5) begins to dissolve in the iron and forms a solid solution called **austenite** (Figure 6). When this solution of iron and carbon is suddenly cooled or quenched, a new microstructure is formed. This is called **martensite** (Figure 7). Martensite is very hard and **brittle,** having a much higher tensile strength than the steel with a **pearlite** microstructure. It is quite unstable, however, and must be tempered to relieve internal stresses in order to have the **toughness** needed

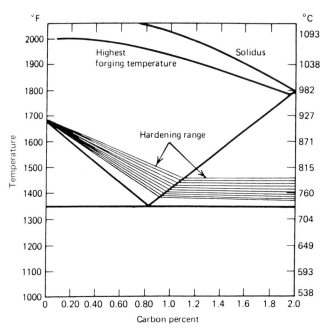

Figure 8. Temperature ranges used for hardening carbon steel (J. E. Neely. *Practical Metallurgy and Materials of Industry*, John Wiley and Sons, New York, 1979).

Figure 9. Fractured ends of $\frac{3}{8}$ in. diameter 1095 water quenched tool steel ranging from fine grain, quenched from 1475°F (802°C), to coarse grain, quenched from 1800°F (982°C).

to be useful. AISI-C1095, commonly known as water hardening (W1) steel, will begin to show hardness when quenched from a temperature just over 1330°F (721°C) but will not harden at all if quenched from a temperature lower than 1330°F (721°C). The steel will become as hard as it can get when heated to 1450°F (788°C) and quenched in water. This quenching temperature changes as the carbon content of the steel changes. It should be 50°F (10°C) above the upper critical limit into the hardening range (Figure 8).

Low carbon steels such as AISI 1020 will not, for all practical purposes, harden when they are heated and quenched. Oil and air hardening steels harden over a longer period of time and, consequently, are deeper hardening than water hardening types, which must be cooled to 200°F (93°C) within one or two seconds. As you can see, it is quite important to know the carbon content and alloying element so that the correct temperature and quenching medium can be used. Fine grained tool steels are much stronger than coarse grained tool steels (Figure 9). If a piece of tool steel is heated above the correct temperature for its specific carbon content, a phenomenon called grain growth will occur, and a coarse, weak grain structure develops. The grain growth will remain when the part is quenched and, if used for a tool such as a punch or chisel, the end may simply drop off when the first hammer blow is struck. Tempering will not remove the coarse grain structure. If the part has been overheated, simply cooling back to

the quenching temperature will not help, as the coarse grain persists well down into the hardening range as shown in Figure 3. The part should be cooled slowly and then reheated to the correct quenching temperature. Steels containing .83 percent carbon can get as hard as any carbon steel (Rc67) containing more carbon.

AISI-C1095, or water hardening tool steel (W1), can be quenched in oil, depending on the size of the part. For example, for a piece of AISI-C1095 drill rod, if the section is thin or the diameter is small, oil should be used as a quenching medium. Oil is not as severe as water because it conducts heat less rapidly than water, and thus avoids quench cracking. Larger sections or parts would not be fully transformed into martensite if they are oil quenched, but would instead contain some softer transformation structures. Water quench should be used, but remember that W1 is shallow hardening, and will only harden about $\frac{1}{8}$ in. deep.

When using a furnace to heat for quenching, the temperature control should be set for 1450°F (788°C). If the part is small, a preheat is not necessary; but if it is thick, it should be brought up to heat slowly. If the part is left in a furnace without a controlled atmosphere for any length of time, the metal will form an oxide scale and carbon will leave the surface. This decarburization of the surface will cause it to soften, while the metal directly under the surface will remain hard. This oxidation can be avoided by painting the part with a solution of boric acid and water before heating, or wrapping it in stainless steel foil. Place the part in the furnace with tongs, and wear gloves and face shields for protection. When the part has become the same color as the furnace bricks, remove it by grasping one end with the tongs and *immediately* plunge it into the quenching bath. If the part is long like a chisel or punch, it should be inserted into the quench vertically (straight up-and-down), not at a slant. Quenching at an angle can cause unequal cooling rates and bending of the part. Also, agitate the part in an up-and-down or a figure-8 motion to remove any gases or bubbles that might cause uneven quenching.

Oil is used to quench oil hardening steels (O1).

When hardening various tool steels, a manufacturer's catalog should be consulted for the correct temperature, time periods, and quenching media.

FURNACES

Electric, gas, or oil fueled furnaces are used for heat treating steels (Figure 10). They use various types of controls for temperature adjustment. These controls make use of the principle of the thermocouple (Figure 11). Temperatures generally range to 2500°F (1371°C). High temperature salt baths are also used for heating metals for hardening or annealing. One of the disadvantages of most electric furnaces is that they allow the atmosphere to enter the furnace, and the oxygen causes oxides to form on the heated metal. This causes scale and decar-

burization of the surface of the metal. A **decarburized** surface will not harden. One way to control this loss of surface carbon is to keep a slightly carbonizing atmosphere or an inert gas in the furnace.

One of the most important factors when heating steel is the rate at which heat is applied. When steel is first heated, it expands. If cold steel is placed in a hot furnace, the surface expands more rapidly than the still cool core. The surface will then have a tendency to pull away from the center, thus inducing internal stress. This can cause cracking and distortion in the part. Most furnaces can be adjusted for the proper rate of heat input (Figure 12) when bringing the part up to the soaking temperature (Figure 13). **Soaking** means holding the part for a given length of time at a specified temperature. Another factor is the time of soaking required for a certain size piece of steel. An old rule of thumb allows the steel to soak in the furnace for 1 hour for each inch of thickness, but there are considerable variations to this rule, since some steels require much more soaking time than others. The correct soaking period for any specific tool steel may be found in tool steel reference books.

Figure 10. Electric heat treating furnace. Part is being placed in furnace by heat treater wearing correct attire and using tongs (Lane Community College).

Figure 12. Input controls on furnace (Lane Community College).

Figure 11. Thermocouple (Lane Community College).

Figure 13. Temperature control (Lane Community College).

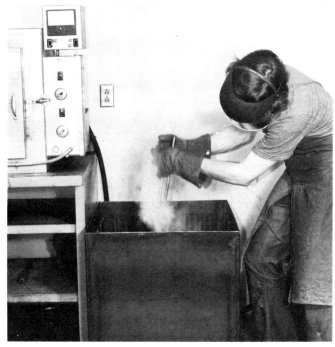

Figure 14. Heat treater is agitating part during quench (Lane Community College).

QUENCHING MEDIA

In general seven media are used to quench metals. They are listed here in their order of severity or speed of quenching.

1. Water and salt; that is, sodium chloride or sodium hydroxide. It is also called brine.
2. Tap water.
3. Fused or liquid salts.
4. Molten lead.
5. Soluble oil and water.
6. Oil.
7. Air.

Liquid quenching media goes through three stages. The **vapor-blanket** stage occurs first because the metal is so hot it vaporizes the media. This envelops the metal with vapor, which insulates it from the cold liquid bath. This causes the cooling rate to be relatively slow during this stage. The **vapor transport cooling** stage begins when the vapor blanket collapses, allowing the liquid medium to contact the surface of the metal. The cooling

rate is much higher during this stage. The **liquid cooling** stage begins when the metal surface reaches the boiling point of the quenching medium. There is no more boiling at this stage, so heat must be removed by conduction and convection. This is the slowest stage of cooling.

It is important in liquid quenching baths that either the quenching medium or the steel being quenched should be agitated (Figure 14). The vapor that forms around the part being quenched acts as an insulator and slows down the cooling rate. This can result in incomplete or spotty hardening of the part. Agitating the part breaks up the vapor barrier. An up and down motion works best for long, slender parts held vertically in the quench. A figure eight motion is sometimes used for heavier parts.

Gloves and face protection must be used in this operation for safety (Figure 15). Hot oil could splash up and burn the heat treater's face if a face shield is not worn.

Molten salt or lead is often used for **isothermal quenching.** This is the method of quenching used for **austempering.** Austempered parts (Figure 16) are superior in strength and quality to those produced by the two-stage process of quenching and tempering. The final austempered part is essentially a fine, lower **bainite** microstructure (Figure 17). As a rule, only parts that are thin in cross section are austempered.

Another form of isothermal quenching is called **mar-**

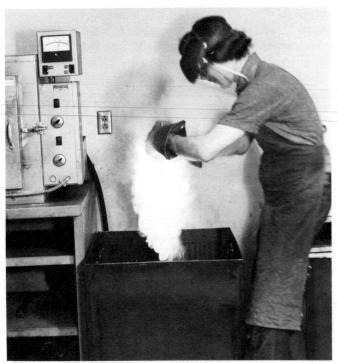

Figure 15. Beginning of quench. At this stage heat treater could be burned by hot oil if not adequately protected with gloves and face shield (Lane Community College).

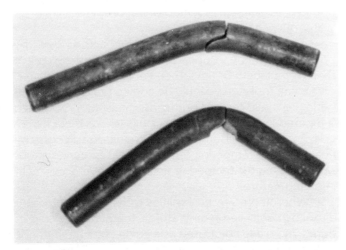

Figure 16. Austempered parts compared to the same kind of part hardened and tempered by the conventional method (Lane Community College).

tempering; the part is quenched in a lead or salt bath at about 400°F (204°C) until the outer and inner parts of the material are brought to the same uniform temperature. The part is next quenched below 200°F (93°C) to transform all of the austenite to martensite. Tempering is then carried out in the conventional manner.

Steels are often classified by the type of quenching

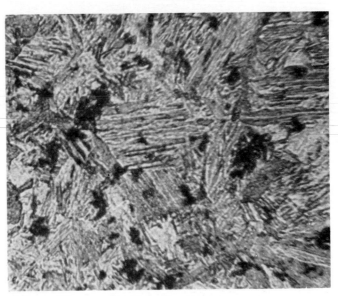

Figure 17. Lower bainite microstructure.

medium that is used to meet the requirements of the critical cooling rate. For example, water quenched steels, which are the plain carbon steels, must have a rapid quench. Oil quench steels are alloy steels, and they must be hardened in oil. The air cooled steels are alloy steels that will harden when allowed to cool from the austenitizing temperature in still air. Air is the slowest quenching medium; however, its cooling rate may be increased by movement (by use of fans, for example).

Step or multiple quenching is sometimes used when the part consists of both thick and thin sections. A severe quench will harden the thin section before the thick section has had a chance to cool. The resulting uneven contraction often results in cracking. With this method the part is quenched for a few seconds in a rapid quenching medium, such as water followed by a slower quench in oil. The surface is first hardened uniformly in the water quench, and time is provided by the slower quench to relieve stresses.

CASE HARDENING

Low carbon steels (.08 to .30 percent carbon) do not harden to any great extent even when combined with other alloying elements. Therefore, when a soft, tough core and an extremely hard outside surface is needed, one of several case hardening techniques is used. It should be noted that **surface** hardening is not necessarily **case hardening.** Flame hardening and induction hardening on the surfaces of gears, lathe ways, and many products depends on the carbon that is already contained in the ferrous metal. On the other hand, case hardening causes carbon from an outside source to penetrate the

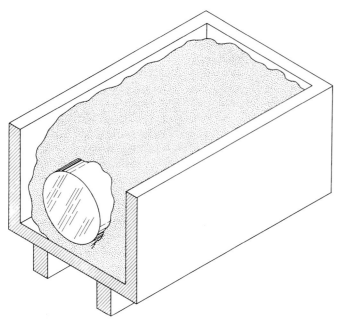

Figure 18. Pack carburizing. The workpiece to be pack carburized should be completely covered with carburizing sand. The metal box should have a close fitting lid.

surface of the steel, or carburizes it. Because it raises the carbon content, it also raises the hardenability of the steel.

Carburizing for case hardening can be done by either of two methods. If only a shallow hardened case is needed, roll carburizing may be used. This consists of heating the part to 1650°F (899°C) and rolling it in a carburizing compound, reheating, and quenching in water. In roll carburizing use only a nontoxic compound such as kasenite unless special ventilation systems are used. Roll carburizing produces a maximum case of about .003 in. but pack carburizing (Figure 18) can produce a case of $\frac{1}{16}$ in. in eight hours at 1700°F (925°C). The part is packed in carburizing compound in a metal box and placed in a furnace long enough to harden the case to the required depth. The part is then removed and quenched in water. After case hardening, tempering is not usually necessary since the core is still soft and tough. Therefore, unlike a hardened piece that is softened by tempering, the surface of a case hardened piece remains hard, usually Rc60 (as hard as a file) or above.

Some alloys and special heat treatments can be used to case harden steel parts. Liquid carburizing is an industrial method in which the parts are bathed in cyanide carbonate and chloride salts and held at a temperature between 1500 and 1700°F. Cyanide salts are extremely poisonous and adequate worker protection is essential.

Gas carburizing is a method in which the carbon is

supplied from a carburizing gas atmosphere in a special furnace where the part is heated. The same principle is used when a welder accidentally case hardens a piece of low carbon steel with an oxy-acetylene cutting torch that has a carbonizing flame adjustment. Of course, this torch hardening process makes the cut surface difficult to machine.

Nitriding is a method of case hardening in which the part is heated in a special container into which ammonia gas is released. Since the temperature used is only 950°F (510°C) to 1000°F (538°C) and the part is not quenched, warpage is kept to a minimum. The iron nitrides thus formed are even harder than the iron carbides formed by conventional carburizing methods.

TEMPERING

Tempering, or drawing, is the process of reheating a steel part that has been previously hardened to transform some of the hard martensite into softer structures. The higher the tempering temperature used, the more martensite is transformed, and the softer and tougher (less brittle) the piece becomes. Therefore, tempering temperatures are specified according to the strength and ductility desired. Mechanical properties charts, which may be found in steel manufacturer's handbooks and catalogs, gives this data for each type of alloy steel. Figure 19 is an example of a mechanical properties chart for water quenched 1095.

A part can be tempered in a furnace or oven by bringing it to the proper temperature and holding it there for a length of time, then cooling it in air or water.

Some tool steels should be cooled rapidly after tempering to avoid temper brittleness. Small parts are often tempered in liquid baths such as oil, salt, or metals. Specially prepared oils that do not ignite easily can be heated to the tempering temperature. Lead and various salts are used for tempering since they have a low melting temperature.

When there are no facilities to harden and temper a tool by controlled temperatures, tempering by color is done. The oxide color used as a guide in such tempering will form correctly on steel only if it is polished to the bare metal and is free from any oil or fingerprints. An oxy-acetylene torch, steel hot plate, or an electric hot plate can be used. If the part is quite small, a steel plate is heated from the underside, while the part is placed on top. Larger parts such as chisels and punches can be heated on an electric plate (Figure 20) until the needed color shows, then cooled in water. With this system the tempering process must cease when the part has come to the correct temperature, and the part must be dropped in water to stop further heating of the critical areas. There is no possible soaking time when this method is used.

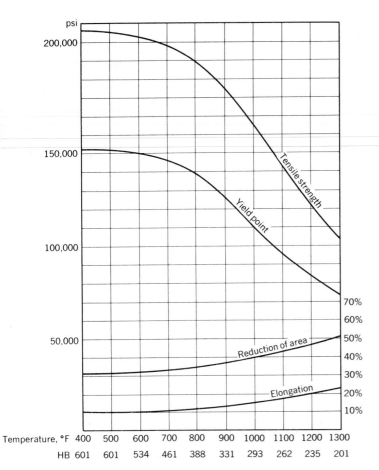

Figure 19. Mechanical properties chart, SAE 1095 steel, water quenched. The bottom two lines refer to tempering temperatures and the resultant hardness in Brinell reading. HB 601 is file hard (Courtesy of Bethlehem Steel Corporation, Bethlehem, Pa.).

Figure 20. Tempering a punch on a hot plate.

When grinding carbon steel tools, if the edge is heated enough to produce a color, you have in effect retempered the edge. If the temperature reached was above that of the original temper, the tool has become softer than it was before you began sharpening it. Table 1 gives the hardnesses of various tools as related to their oxide colors and the temperature at which they form.

Tempering should be done as soon as possible after

hardening. A part should not be allowed to cool completely, since untempered, it contains very high internal stresses and tends to split or crack. Tempering will relieve the internal stresses. A hardened part left overnight without tempering may develop cracks by itself. Furnace tempering is one of the best methods of controlling the final condition of the martensite to produce a tempered martensite of the correct hardness and toughness that the part requires. Tempering should be accomplished immediately after hardening. The part while still warm should be put into the furnace immediately. If it is left at room temperature for even a few minutes, it may develop a quench crack (Figure 21).

A soaking time should also be used when tempering as it is in hardening procedures, and the length of time is related to the type of tool steel used. A cold furnace should be brought up to the correct temperature for

Table 1
Temper Color Chart

| Degrees | | Oxide | |
C°	F°	Color	Suggested Uses for Carbon Tool Steels
220	425	Light straw	Steel cutting tools, files, and paper cutters
240	462	Dark straw	Punches and dies
258	490	Gold	Shear blades, hammer faces, center punches, and cold chisels
260	500	Purple	Axes, wood cutting tools, and striking faces of tools
282	540	Violet	Spring and screwdrivers
304	580	Pale blue	Springs
327	620	Steel gray	Cannot be used for cutting tools

Harder ——— Softer

Figure 21. These two breech plugs were made of Type L6 tool steel. Plug #1 cracked in the quench through a sharp corner and was therefore not tempered. Plug #2 was redesigned to incorporate a radius in the corners of the slot, and a soft steel plug was inserted in the slot to protect it from the quenching oil. Plug #2 was oil quenched and checked for hardness (Rockwell C 62) and, after tempering at 900°F (482°C), it was found to be cracked. The fact that the as-quenched hardness was measured proves that there was a delay between the quench and the temper that was responsible for the cracking. The proper practice would be to temper immediately at a low temper, check hardness, and retemper to desired hardness (Courtesy of Bethlehem Steel Corporation).

tempering. The residual heat in the bricks of a previously heated furnace may overheat the part, even though the furnace has been cooled down.

Double tempering is used for some alloy steels such as high speed steels that have incomplete transformation of the austenite when they are tempered for the first time. The second time they are tempered, the austenite transforms completely into the martensite structure.

PROBLEMS IN HEAT TREATING

Overheating of steels should always be avoided, and you have seen that if the furnace is set too high with a

Figure 22. This tool has been overheated and the typical ''chicken wire'' surface markings are evident. The tool must be discarded (Lane Community College).

Figure 23. Drawing die made of Type W1 tool steel shows characteristic cracking when water quenching is done without packing the bolt holes (Courtesy of Bethlehem Steel Corporation).

particular type of steel, a coarse grain can develop. The result is often a poor quality tool, quench cracking, or failure of the tool in use. Extreme overheating causes burning of the steel and damage to the grain boundaries, which cannot be repaired by heat treatment (Figure 22); the part must be scrapped. The shape of the part itself can be a contributing factor to quench failure and quench cracking. If there is a hole, sharp shoulder, or small extension from a larger cross section (unequal mass), a crack can develop in these areas (Figure 23). A part of the tool being held by tongs may be cooled to the extent that it may not harden. The tongs should therefore be heated prior to grasping the part for quenching (Figure 24). As mentioned before, decarburization is a problem in furnaces that do not have controlled atmosphere. This can be avoided in other ways, such as wrapping the part in stainless steel foil or covering it with cast iron chips.

Figure 24. Heating the tongs prior to quenching a part (Lane Community College).

A proper selection of tool steels is necessary to avoid failures in a particular application. If there is shock load on the tool being used, shock resisting tool steel must be selected. If there is to be heat applied in the use of the tool, a hot work type of tool steel is selected. If distortion must be kept to a minimum, an air hardening steel should be used.

Quench cracks have several characteristics that are easily recognized.

1. In general the fractures run from the surface toward the center in a relatively straight line. The crack tends to spread open.

2. Since quench cracking occurs at relatively low temperatures, the crack will not show any decarburization.

3. The fracture surfaces will exhibit a fine crystalline structure when tempered after quenching. The fractured surfaces may be blackened by tempering scale.

Some of the most common causes for quench cracks are:

1. Overheating during the austenitizing cycle causing the normally fine grained steel to become coarse.

2. Improper selection of the quenching medium; for example, the use of water or brine instead of oil for an oil hardening steel.

3. The improper selection of steel.

4. Time delays between quenching and tempering.

5. Improper design. Sharp changes of section such as holes and keyways (Figure 25).

6. Improper angle of the work into the quenching bath with respect to the shape of the part, causing non-uniform cooling.

Figure 25. (Top) Letter stamp made of Type S5 tool steel, which cracked in hardening through the stamped O. The other two form tools, made of Type T1 high speed steel, cracked in heat treatment through deeply stamped + marks. Stress raisers such as these deep stamp marks should be avoided. Although characters with straight lines are most likely to crack, even those with rounded lines are susceptible (Courtesy of Bethlehem Steel Corporation).

7. Failure to specify the correct size material to allow for cleaning up the outside decarburized surface of the bar before the final part is made.

It is sometimes desirable to normalize the part before hardening it. This is particularly appropriate for parts and tools that have been highly stressed by heavy machining or by prior heat treatment. If they are left unrelieved, the residual stresses from such operations may add to the thermal stress produced in the heating cycle and cause the part to crack even before it has reached the quenching temperature.

There is a definite relationship between grinding and heat treating. Development of surface temperatures ranging from 2000°F (1093°C) to 3000°F (1649°C) are generated during grinding. This can cause two undesirable effects on hardened tool steels: development of high internal stresses causing surface cracks to be formed, and changes in the hardness and metallurgical structure of the surface area.

One of the most common effects of grinding on hardened and tempered tool steels is that of reducing the hardness of the surface by gradual tempering where the hardness is lowest at the extreme surface but increases with distance below the surface. The depth of this tempering varies with the amount or depth of cut, the use of coolants, and the type of grinding wheel. If high temperatures are produced locally by the grinding wheel and the surface is immediately quenched by the coolant, a martensite having a Rockwell hardness of C65 to 70 can be formed. This gradient hardness, being much greater than that beneath the surface of the tempered part, sometimes causes very high stresses that contribute greatly to grinding cracks. Sometimes grinding cracks are visible in oblique or angling light, but they can be easily detected when present by the use of magnetic particles of fluorescent particle testing.

When a part is hardened but not tempered before it is ground, it is extremely liable to stress cracking (Figure 26). Faulty grinding procedures can also cause grinding cracks. Improper grinding operations can cause tools that have been properly hardened to fail. Sufficient stock should be allowed for a part to be heat treated so that grinding will remove any decarburized surface on all sides to a depth of .010 to .015 in.

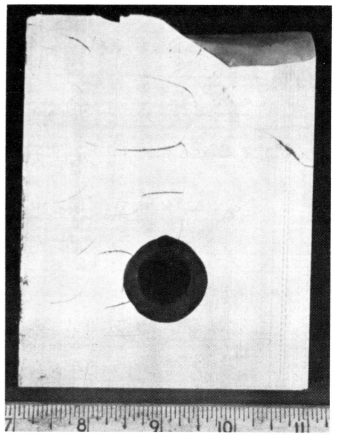

Figure 26. Severe grinding cracks in a shear blade made of Type A4 tool steel developed because the part was not tempered after quenching. Hardness was Rockwell C 64, and the cracks were exaggerated by magnetic particle test. Note the geometric scorch pattern on the surface and the fracture that developed from enlargement of the grinding cracks (Courtesy of Bethlehem Steel Corporation).

SELF-TEST

1. If you heated AISI C1080 steel to 1200°F (649°C) and quenched it in water, what would be the result?
2. If you heated AISI C1020 steel to 1500°F (815°C) and quenched it in water, what would happen?
3. List as many problems encountered with water hardening steels as you can think of.
4. Name some advantages in using air and oil hardening tool steels.
5. What is the correct temperature for quenching AISI C1095 tool steel? For any carbon steel?
6. Why is steel tempered after it is hardened?
7. What factors should you consider when you choose the tempering temperature for a tool?
8. The approximate temperature for tempering a center punch should be _____. The oxide color would be _____.
9. If a cold chisel became blue when the edge was ground on an abrasive wheel, to approximately what temperature was it raised? How would this affect the tool?
10. How soon after hardening should you temper a part?
11. What is the advantage of using low carbon steel for parts that are to be case hardened?
12. How can a deep case be made?
13. Are parts that are surface hardened always case hardened?
14. Name three methods by which carbon may be introduced into the surface of heated steel?
15. What method of case hardening uses ammonia gas?
16. Name three kinds of furnaces used for heat treating steels.
17. What can happen to a carbon steel when it is heated to high temperatures in the presence of air (oxygen)?
18. Why is it absolutely necessary to allow a soaking period for a length of time (that varies for different kinds of steels) before quenching the piece of steel?
19. Why should the part or the quenching medium be agitated when you are hardening steel?
20. Which method of tempering gives the heat treater the most control of the final product: by color or by furnace?

21. Describe two characteristics of quench cracking that would enable you to recognize them.
22. Name four or more causes of quench cracks.
23. In what ways can decarburization of a part be avoided when it is heated in a furnace?

24. Describe two types of surface failures of hardened steel when it is being ground.
25. When distortion must be kept to a minimum, which type of tool steel should be used?

UNIT 4 ANNEALING, NORMALIZING, AND STRESS RELIEVING

Since the machinability of steel is so greatly affected by heat treatments, the processes of annealing, normalizing, and stress relieving are important to a machinist. You will learn about these processes in this unit.

OBJECTIVES

After completing this unit, you should be able to:
Explain the principles of and differences between the various kinds of annealing processes.

ANNEALING

The heat treatment for iron and steel that is generally called annealing can be divided into several different processes: **full anneal, normalizing, spheroidize anneal, stress relief** (anneal), and **process anneal.**

Full Anneal

The full anneal is used to completely soften hardened steel, usually for easier machining of tool steels that have more than .8 percent carbon content. Lower carbon steels are full annealed for other purposes. For instance, when welding has been done on a medium to high carbon steel that must be machined, a full anneal is needed. Full annealing is done by heating the part in a furnace to 50°F (10°C) above the upper critical temperature (Figure 1), and then cooling very slowly in the furnace or in an insulating material. In the process, the microstructure becomes coarse pearlite and ferrite or pearlite and cementite, depending on the carbon content. It is necessary to heat above the critical temperature for grains containing iron carbides (pearlite) in order to recrystallize them and to reform new soft whole grains from the old hard distorted ones.

Normalizing

Normalizing is somewhat similar to annealing, but it is done for different purposes. Medium carbon steels are often normalized to give them better machining qualities. Medium (.3 to .6 percent) carbon steel may be "gummy" when machined after a full anneal, but can be made sufficiently soft for machining by normalizing. The finer, but harder, microstructure produced by normalizing gives the piece a better surface finish. The piece is heated to 100°F (38°C) above the upper critical line, and cooled in still air. When the carbon content is above or below .8 percent, higher temperatures are required (Figure 1).

Forgings and castings that have unusually large and mixed grain structures are corrected by using a normalizing heat treatment. Stresses are removed, but the

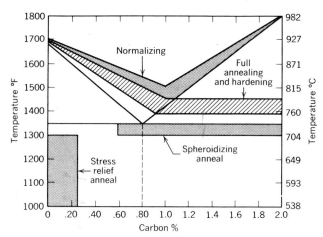

Figure 1.   Temperature ranges used for heat treating carbon steels.

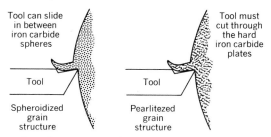

Figure 2.   Comparison of cutting action between spheroidized and normal carbon steels.

Figure 3.   Microstructure of flattened grains of .10 percent carbon steel, cold rolled (1000 ×). (By permission, from *Metals Handbook,* Volume 7, Copyright © American Society for Metals, 1972.)

Figure 4.   The same .10 percent carbon steel as in Figure 3, but annealed at 1025°F (552°C) (1000 ×). Ferrite grains are mostly reformed to their original state, but the pearlite grains are still distorted. (By permission, from *Metals Handbook* Volume 7, Copyright © American Society for Metals, 1972.)

metal is not as soft as with full annealing. The resultant microstructure is a uniform fine grained pearlite and ferrite, including other microstructures depending on the alloy and carbon content. Normalizing also is used to prepare steel for other forms of heat treatment such as hardening and tempering.

Spheroidizing

Spheroidizing is used to improve the machinability of high carbon steels (.8 to 1.7 percent). The cementite or iron carbide normally found in pearlite as flat plates alternating with plates of ferrite (iron) is changed into a spherical or globular form by spheroidization (Figure 2). Low carbon steels (.08 to .3 percent) can be spheroidized, but their machinability gets poorer since they become gummy and soft, causing tool edge build up and poor finish. The spheroidization temperature is close to 1300°F (704°C).

Stress Relief Anneal

Stress relief annealing is a process of reheating low carbon steels to 950°F (510°C). Stresses in the ferrite (mostly pure iron) grains caused by cold working steel such as rolling, pressing, forming, or drawing are relieved by this process. The distorted grains reform or recrystallize into new softer ones (Figures 3 and 4).

The pearlite grains and some other forms of iron carbide remain unaffected by this treatment, unless done at the spheroidizing temperature and held long enough to effect spheroidization. In the stress relieving of weldments, often one of the aims is to spheroidize the hard carbide and martensite grains to reduce brittleness in the junction of the weld.

Process Anneal

Process annealing is essentially the same as stress relief annealing. It is done at the same temperatures and with low and medium carbon steels. In the wire and sheet steel industry, the term is used for the annealing processes used in cold rolling or drawing processes and those used to remove the final residual stresses when necessary. Sometimes referred to as bright annealing, it is often carried out in a closed container with inert gas to prevent oxidation of the surface.

SELF-TEST

1. When might normalizing be necessary?
2. At what approximate temperature should you normalize .4 percent carbon steel?
3. What is the spheroidizing temperature of .8 percent carbon steel?
4. What is the essential difference between the full anneal and stress relieving?
5. When should you use stress relieving?
6. What kind of carbon steels would need to be spheroidized to give them free machining qualities?
7. Explain process annealing.
8. How should the piece be cooled for a normalizing heat treatment?
9. How should the piece be cooled for the full anneal?
10. What happens to machinability in low carbon steels that are spheroidized?

UNIT 5 ROCKWELL AND BRINELL HARDNESS TESTERS

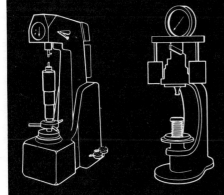

The Rockwell Hardness Tester and the Brinell Hardness Tester are the most commonly used types of hardness testers for industrial and metallurgical purposes. Heat treaters, inspectors, and many others in industry often use these machines. This unit will direct you into a proper understanding and use of both Rockwell and Brinell hardness testers.

OBJECTIVES

After completing this unit, you should be able to:
1. Make a Rockwell test using the correct penetrator, major load, and scale.
2. Make a Rockwell superficial test using the correct penetrator, major load, and scale.
3. Make a Brinell test, read the impression with a Brinell microscope, and determine the hardness number from a table.

The hardness of a metal is its ability to resist being permanently deformed. There are three ways that hardness is measured: resistance to penetration, elastic hardness, and resistance to abrasion. In this unit you will study the hardness of metals by their resistance to penetration.

Hardness varies considerably between different materials. This variation can be illustrated by making an indentation in a soft metal such as aluminum and in a

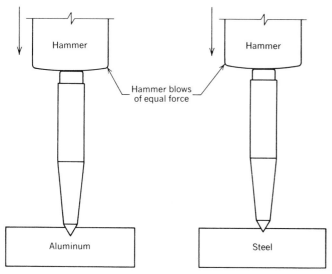

Figure 1. Indentations made by a punch in aluminum and alloy steel.

USING THE ROCKWELL HARDNESS TESTER

The Rockwell Hardness Test is made by applying two loads to a specimen and measuring the depth of penetration in the specimen between the first, or minor, load and the major load. The depth of penetration is indicated on the dial when the major load is removed (Figure 2). The amount of penetration decreases as the hardness of the specimen increases. Generally, the harder the material, the greater its tensile strength, or the ability to resist deformation and rupture when a load is applied. Table 1 compares hardness by Brinell and Rockwell testers to tensile strength.

There are two basic types of penetrators used on the Rockwell tester (Figure 3). One is a sphero-conical diamond called a *Brale* that is used only for hard materials; that is, for materials over B-100, such as hardened steel, nitrided steel, and hard cast irons. When the "C" Brale diamond penetrator is used, the recorded readings should be prefixed by the letter "C." The major load used is 150 kgf (kilograms of force). The C scale is *not* used to test extremely hard materials such as cemented carbides or shallow case hardened steels and thin steel. An A Brale penetrator is used in these cases and the A scale used with 60 kgf major load.

The second type penetrator is a $\frac{1}{16}$ in. diameter ball that is used for testing material in the range of B-100 to B-0, including such relatively soft materials as brass, bronze, and soft steel. If the ball penetrator is used on materials harder than B-100, there is a danger of flattening the ball. Ball penetrators for use on very soft bearing metals are available in sizes of $\frac{1}{2}$, $\frac{1}{4}$, and $\frac{1}{8}$ in. (Table 2).

hard metal such as alloy tool steel. The indentation could be made with an ordinary center punch and a hammer, giving a light blow of equal force on each of the two specimens (Figure 1). Just by visual observation you can tell which specimen is hardest in this case. Of course, this is not a reliable method of hardness testing, but it does show one of the principles of both the Rockwell and Brinell hardness testers: measuring penetration of the specimen by an indenter or penetrator, such as a steel ball or diamond cone.

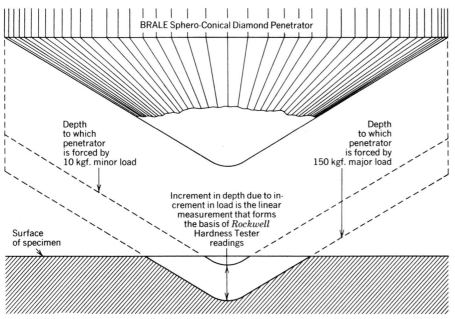

Figure 2. Schematic showing minor and major loads being applied (Courtesy of Wilson Instrument Division of Acco).

Table 1

Hardness and Tensile Strength Comparison Table

Hardness Conversion Table									
Brinell		Rockwell		Tensile Strength, (1000 psi, approximately)	Brinell		Rockwell		Tensile Strength, (1000 psi, approximately)
Indentation Diameter (mm)	No.[a]	B	C		Indentation Diameter (mm)	No.[a]	B	C	
2.25	745		65.3		3.75	262	(103.0)	26.6	127
2.30	712		—		3.80	255	(102.0)	25.4	123
2.35	682		61.7		3.85	248	(101.0)	24.2	120
2.40	653		60.0		3.90	241	100.0	22.8	116
2.45	627		58.7		3.95	235	99.0	21.7	114
2.50	601		57.3		4.00	229	98.2	20.5	111
2.55	578		56.0		4.05	223	97.3	(18.8)	—
2.60	555		54.7	298	4.10	217	96.4	(17.5)	105
2.65	534		53.5	288	4.15	212	95.5	(16.0)	102
2.70	514		52.1	274	4.20	207	94.6	(15.2)	100
2.75	495		51.6	269	4.25	201	93.8	(13.8)	98
2.80	477		50.3	258	4.30	197	92.8	(12.7)	95
2.85	461		48.8	244	4.35	192	91.9	(11.5)	93
2.90	444		47.2	231	4.40	187	90.7	(10.0)	90
2.95	429		45.7	219	4.45	183	90.0	(9.0)	89
3.00	415		44.5	212	4.50	179	89.0	(8.0)	87
3.05	401		43.1	202	4.55	174	87.8	(6.4)	85
3.10	388		41.8	193	4.60	170	86.8	(5.4)	83
3.15	375		40.4	184	4.65	167	86.0	(4.4)	81
3.20	363		39.1	177	4.70	163	85.0	(3.3)	79
3.25	352	(110.0)	37.9	171	4.80	156	82.9	(0.9)	76
3.30	341	(109.0)	36.6	164	4.90	149	80.8		73
3.35	331	(108.5)	35.5	159	5.00	143	78.7		71
3.40	321	(108.0)	34.3	154	5.10	137	76.4		67
3.45	311	(107.5)	33.1	149	5.20	131	74.0		65
3.50	302	(107.0)	32.1	146	5.30	126	72.0		63
3.55	293	(106.0)	30.9	141	5.40	121	69.8		60
3.60	285	(105.5)	29.9	138	5.50	116	67.6		58
3.65	277	(104.5)	28.8	134	5.60	111	65.7		56
3.70	269	(104.0)	27.6	130					

[a]Values above 500 are for tungsten carbide ball; below 500 for standard ball.

Note 1. This is a condensation of Table 2, Report J417b, SAE 1971 Handbook. Values in ( ) are beyond normal range, and are presented for information only.

Note 2. The following is a formula to approximate tensile strength when the Brinell hardness is known:

$$\text{Tensile strength} = BHN \times 500$$

Source. Bethlehem Steel Corporation, *Modern Steels and Their Properties,* Seventh Edition, Handbook 2757, 1972.

Figure 4 points out the parts used in the testing operation on the Rockwell Hardness Tester. You should learn the names of these parts before continuing with this unit.

When setting up the Rockwell Hardness Tester and making the test, follow these steps:

1. Using Table 2, select the proper weight (Figure 5) and penetrator. Make sure the crank handle is pulled completely forward.

2. Place the proper anvil (Figure 6) on the elevating screw, taking care not to bump the penetrator with the anvil. Make sure that the specimen to be tested is free from dirt, scale, or heavy oil on the underside.

3. Place the specimen to be tested on the anvil (Figure

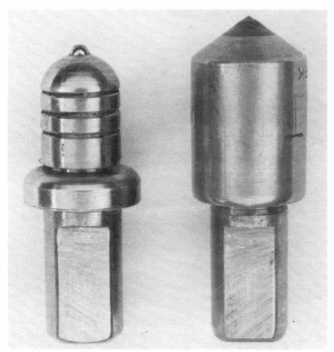

Figure 3. Brale and ball. These two penetrators are the basic types used on the Rockwell Hardness Tester. (*Note.* Brale is a registered trademark of American Chain & Cable Company, Inc., for sphero-conical diamond penetrators.)

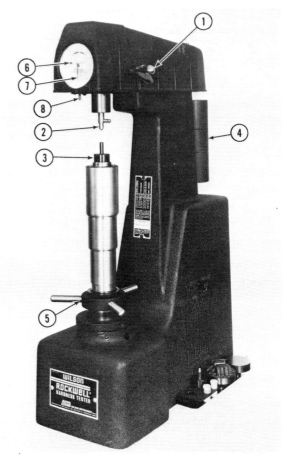

Figure 4. Rockwell Hardness Tester listing the names of parts used in the testing operations (Courtesy of Wilson Instrument Division of Acco).

1. Crank handle	5. Capstan handwheel
2. Penetrator	6. Small pointer
3. Anvil	7. Large pointer
4. Weights	8. Lever for setting the bezel

(*Note.* Rockwell is a registered trademark of American Chain & Cable Company, Inc., for hardness testers and test blocks.)

7). Then by turning the handwheel, gently raise the specimen until it comes in contact with the penetrator (Figure 8). Continue turning the handwheel slowly until the small pointer on the dial gage is nearly vertical (near the dot). Now watch the long pointer on the gage and continue raising the work until it is approximately vertical. It should not vary from the vertical position by more than five divisions on the dial. Set the dial to zero on the pointer by moving the bezel until the line marked **zero set** is in line with the pointer (Figure 9). You have now applied the **minor**

Figure 5. Selecting and installing the correct weight (Lane Community College).

Table 2
Penetrator and Load Selection

Scale Symbol	Penetrator	Major Load (kgf)	Dial Figures	Typical Applications of Scales
B	$\frac{1}{16}$ in. ball	100	Red	Copper alloys, soft steels, aluminum alloys, malleable iron, etc.
C	Brale	150	Black	Steel, hard cast irons, pearlitic malleable iron, titanium, deep case hardened steel, and other materials harder than B-100.
A	Brale	60	Black	Cemented carbides, thin steel, and shallow case hardened steel.
D	Brale	100	Black	Thin steel and medium case hardened steel and pearlitic malleable iron.
E	$\frac{1}{8}$ in. ball	100	Red	Cast iron and aluminum and magnesium alloys and bearing metals.
F	$\frac{1}{16}$ in. ball	60	Red	Annealed copper alloys and thin soft sheet metals.
G	$\frac{1}{16}$ in. ball	150	Red	Phosphor bronze, beryllium copper, and malleable irons. Upper limit G-92 to avoid possible flattening of ball.
H	$\frac{1}{8}$ in. ball	60	Red	Aluminum, zinc, and lead.
K	$\frac{1}{8}$ in. ball	150	Red	
L	$\frac{1}{4}$ in. ball	60	Red	Bearing metals and other very soft or thin
M	$\frac{1}{4}$ in. ball	100	Red	materials. Use the smallest ball and heaviest
P	$\frac{1}{4}$ in. ball	150	Red	load that does not give anvil effect.
R	$\frac{1}{2}$ in. ball	60	Red	
S	$\frac{1}{2}$ in. ball	100	Red	
V	$\frac{1}{2}$ in. ball	150	Red	

Source. *Wilson Instruction Manual,* ''Rockwell Hardness Tester Models OUR-a and OUS-a,'' American Chain & Cable Company, Inc., 1973.

load. This is the actual starting point for all conditions of testing.

4. Apply the major load by tripping the crank handle clockwise (Figure 10).
5. Wait two seconds after the pointer has stopped moving, then remove the major load by pulling the crank handle forward or counterclockwise.
6. Read the hardness number in Rockwell units on the dial (Figure 11). The black numbers are for the A and C scales and the red numbers are for the B scale. The specimen should be tested in several places and an average of the test results taken, since many materials vary in hardness even on the same surface.

Superficial Testing
After testing sheet metal, examine *the underside of the sheet.* If the impression of the penetrator can be seen, then the reading is in error and the superficial test should be used. If the impression can still be seen after the superficial test, then a lighter load should be used. A load

of 30 kgf is recommended for superficial testing. Superficial testing is also used for case hardened and nitrided steel having a very thin case.

A Brale marked N is needed for superficial testing, as A and C Brales are not suitable. Recorded readings should be prefixed by the major load and the letter **N,** when using the Brale for superficial testing; for example, 30N78. When using the $\frac{1}{16}$ in. ball penetrator, the same as that used for the B, F, and G hardness scales, the readings should always be prefixed by the major load and the letter **T;** for example, 30T85. The $\frac{1}{16}$ in. ball penetrator, however, should not be used on material harder than 30T82. Other superficial scales, such as W, X, and Y should also be prefixed with the major load when recording hardness. See Table 3 for superficial test penetrator selection.

A spot anvil, as shown in Figure 6, is used when the tester is being checked on a Rockwell test block. The spot anvil should not be used for checking cylindrical surfaces. The diamond spot anvil (Figure 12) is similar to

Figure 7. Placing the test block in the machine (Courtesy of Wilson Instrument Division of Acco).

Figure 6. Basic anvils used with Rockwell Hardness testers. (*a*) Plane, (*b*) Shallow V, (*c*) Spot, (*d*) Cylindron Jr. (Courtesy of Wilson Instrument Division of Acco).

Figure 8. Specimen being brought into contact with the penetrator. This establishes the minor load (Courtesy of Wilson Instrument Division of Acco).

Figure 9. Setting the bezel (Courtesy of Wilson Instrument Division of Acco).

Figure 10. Applying the major load by tripping the crank handle clockwise (Courtesy of Wilson Instrument Division of Acco).

the spot anvil, but it has a diamond set into the spot. The diamond is ground and polished to a flat surface. This anvil is used **only** with the superficial tester, and then **only** in conjunction with the steel ball penetrator for testing soft metal.

Surface Preparation and Proper Use
When testing hardness, surface condition is important for accuracy. A rough or ridged surface caused from

Figure 11. Dial face with reading in Rockwell units after completion of the test. The reading is RC 55 (Lane Community College).

Table 3
Superficial Tester Load and Penetrator Selection

Scale Symbol	Penetrator	Load (kgf)
15N	Brale	15
30N	Brale	30
45N	Brale	45
15T	$\frac{1}{16}$ in. ball	15
30T	$\frac{1}{16}$ in. ball	30
45T	$\frac{1}{16}$ in. ball	45
15W	$\frac{1}{8}$ in. ball	15
30W	$\frac{1}{8}$ in. ball	30
45W	$\frac{1}{8}$ in. ball	45
15X	$\frac{1}{4}$ in. ball	15
30X	$\frac{1}{4}$ in. ball	30
45X	$\frac{1}{4}$ in. ball	45
15Y	$\frac{1}{2}$ in. ball	15
30Y	$\frac{1}{2}$ in. ball	30
45Y	$\frac{1}{2}$ in. ball	45

Source. *Wilson Instruction Manual,* "Rockwell Hardness Tester Models OUR-a and OUS-a," American Chain & Cable Company, Inc., 1973.

Figure 12. Diamond spot anvil (Courtesy of Wilson Instrument Division of Acco).

coarse grinding will not produce as reliable results as a smoother surface. Any rough scale caused from hardening must be removed before testing. Likewise, if the workpiece has been decarburized by heat treatment, the test area should have this softer "skin" ground off.

Error can also result from testing curved surfaces. This effect may be eliminated by grinding a small flat spot on the specimen. Cylindrical workpieces must always be supported in a V-type centering anvil, and the surface to be tested should not deviate from the horizontal by more than five degrees. Tubing is often so thin that it will deform when tested. It should be supported on the inside by a mandrel or gooseneck anvil to avoid this problem.

Several devices are made available for the Rockwell Hardness Tester to support overhanging or large specimens. One type, called a jack rest (Figure 13), is used for supporting long, heavy parts such as shafts. It consists of a separate elevating screw and anvil support similar to that on the tester. Without adequate support overhanging work can damage the penetrator rod and cause inaccurate readings.

No test should be made near an edge of a specimen. Keep the penetrator at least $\frac{1}{8}$ in. away from the edge. The test block, as shown in Figure 7, should be used every day to check the calibration of the tester, if it is in constant use.

USING THE BRINELL HARDNESS TESTER

The Brinell hardness test is made by forcing a steel ball, usually 10 millimeters in diameter, into the test specimen by using a known load weight and measuring the diameter of the resulting impression. The Brinell hardness

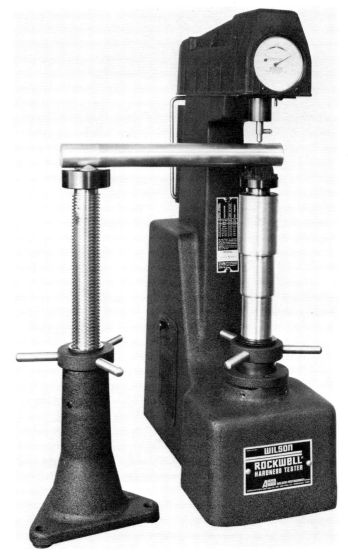

Figure 13. Correct method of testing long, heavy work requires the use of a jack rest (Courtesy of Wilson Instrument Division of Acco).

value is the load divided by the area of the impression, expressed as follows:

$$BHN = \frac{P}{\frac{\pi D}{2}(D - \sqrt{D^2 - d^2})}$$

BHN = Brinell Hardness Number in kilograms per square millimeter

D = Diameter of the steel ball in millimeters

P = Applied load in kilograms

d = Diameter of the impression in millimeters

A small microscope is used to measure the diameter of the impressions (Figure 14). Various loads are used for testing different materials: 500 kilograms for soft mate-

Figure 14. The Olsen Brinell microscope provides a fast, accurate means for measuring the diameter of the impression for determining the Brinell hardness number (Courtesy of the Tinius Olsen Testing Machine Co., Inc.).

rials such as copper and aluminum, and 3000 kilograms for steels and cast irons. For convenience, Table 1 gives the Brinell hardness number and corresponding diameters of impression for a 10 millimeter ball and a load of 3000 kilograms. The related Rockwell hardness numbers and tensile strengths are also shown. Just as for the Rockwell tests, the impression of the steel ball must not show on the underside of the specimen. Tests should not be made too near the edge of a specimen.

Figure 15 shows an air operated Brinell Hardness Tester. The testing sequence is as follows.

1. The desired load in kilograms is selected on the dial by adjusting the air regulator (Figure 16).
2. The specimen is placed on the anvil. Make sure the specimen is clean and free from burrs. It should be

Figure 15. Air-O-Brinell air-operated metal hardness tester (Courtesy of the Tinius Olsen Testing Machine Co., Inc.).

smooth enough so that an accurate measurement can be taken of the impression.

3. The specimen is raised to within $\frac{5}{8}$ in. of the Brinell ball by turning the handwheel.
4. The load is then applied by pulling out the plunger control (Figure 17). Maintain the load for 30 seconds for nonferrous metals and 15 seconds for steel. Release load (Figure 18).
5. Remove the specimen from the tester and measure the diameter of the impression.
6. Determine the Brinell Hardness Number (BHN) by calculation or by using the table. Soft copper should have a BHN of about 40, soft steel from 150 to 200, and hardened tools from 500 to 600. Fully hardened high carbon steel would have a BHN of 750. A Brinell test ball of tungsten carbide should be used for materials above 600 BHN.

Brinell Hardness testers work best for testing softer metals and medium hard tool steels.

Figure 16. Select load. Operator adjusts the air regulator as shown until the desired Brinell load in kilograms is indicated (Courtesy of the Tinius Olsen Testing Machine Co., Inc.).

Figure 17. Apply load. Operator pulls out plunger-type control to apply load to specimen smoothly (Courtesy of the Tinius Olsen Testing Machine Co., Inc.).

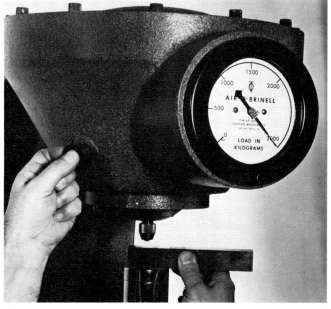

Figure 18. Release load. As soon as the plunger is depressed, the Brinell ball retracts in readiness for the next test (Courtesy of the Tinius Olsen Testing Machine Co., Inc.).

SELF-TEST

1. What one specific category of the property of hardness does the Rockwell and Brinell Hardness testers use and measure? How is it measured?
2. State the relationship that exists between hardness and tensile strength.
3. Explain which scale, major load, and penetrator should be used to test a block of tungsten carbide on the Rockwell tester.
4. What is the reason that the steel ball cannot be used on the Rockwell tester to test the harder steels?
5. When testing with the Rockwell superficial tester, is the Brale used the same one that is used on the A, C, and D scales? Explain.
6. The $\frac{1}{16}$ in. ball penetrator used for the Rockwell superficial tester is a different one than that used for the B, F, and G scales. True/False.
7. What is the diamond spot anvil used for?
8. How does roughness on the specimen to be tested affect the test results?
9. How does decarburization affect the test results?
10. What does a curved surface do to the test results?
11. On the Brinell tester what load should be used for testing steel?
12. What size ball penetrator is generally used on a Brinell tester?

SECTION E LAYOUT

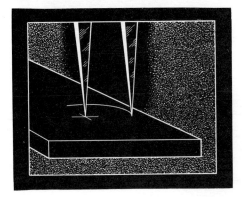

Layout is the process of placing reference marks on the workpiece. These marks may indicate the shape and size of a part or its features. Layout marks often indicate where machining will take place. A machinist may use layout marks as a guide for machining while checking his work by actual measurement. He may also cut to a layout mark. One of your first jobs after you have obtained material from stock will be to measure and lay out where the material will be cut. This kind of layout may be a simple pencil or chalk mark and is one of the basic tasks of semiprecision layout.

Precision layout can be a complex and involved operation making use of sophisticated tools. In the aircraft and shipbuilding industries, reference points, lines, and planes may be laid out using optical and laser instruments. In the machine shop, you will be primarily concerned with layout for stock cutoff, filing and offhand grinding, drilling, milling, and occasionally in connection with lathe work.

LAYOUT CLASSIFICATIONS

The process of layout can be generally classified as **semiprecision** and **precision**. Semiprecision layout is usually done by scale measurement to a tolerance of $\pm\frac{1}{64}$ in. Precision layout is done with tools that discriminate to .001 in. or finer, to a tolerance of $\pm$.001 in. if possible.

TOOLS OF LAYOUT

Surface Plates

The surface plate is an essential tool for many layout applications. A surface plate provides an accurate reference plane from which measurements for both layout and inspection may be made. In many machine shops, where a large amount of layout work is accomplished, a large area surface plate, perhaps 4 by 8 feet, may be used. These are often known as layout tables.

Any surface plate or layout table is a precision tool and should be treated as such. They should be covered when not in use and kept clean when being used. No surface plate should be hammered upon, since this will impair the accuracy of the reference surface. As you study machine tool practices, measurement, and layout, the surface plate will play an important part in many of your tasks.

Cast Iron and Semi-Steel Surface Plates. Cast iron and semisteel surface plates (Figure 1) are made from good quality castings that have been allowed to age, thus relieving internal stresses. Aging of the casting reduces distortion after its working surface has been finished to the desired degree of flatness. The cast iron or steel plate will also have several ribs on the underside to provide structural rigidity. Cast plates vary in size from small bench models, a few square inches in area, to larger sizes that may be four by eight feet or larger. The large cast plates are usually a foot or more in thickness with appropriate ribs on the underside to provide for sufficient rigidity. The large iron plate is generally mounted on a heavy stand or legs with provision for leveling. The plate is leveled periodically to insure that its working surface remains flat.

Figure 1. Cast iron surface plate (CSU, Fresno).

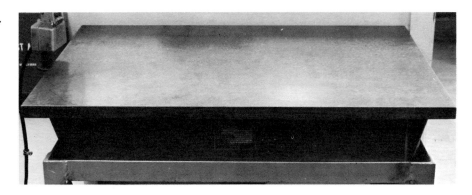

Figure 2. Granite surface plate (Courtesy of the DoAll Company).

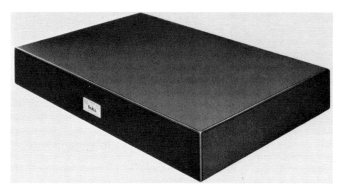

Granite Surface Plates. The cast iron and semisteel surface plate has all but given way to the granite plate (Figure 2). Granite is superior to metal because it is harder, denser, impervious to water and, if chipped, the surrounding flat surface is not affected. Furthermore, granite, because it is a natural material, has aged in the earth for a great deal of time. Therefore, it has little internal stress. Granite surface plates possess a greater temperature stability than their metal counterparts.

Granite plates range in size from about 12 by 18 inches to 4 by 12 feet. A large granite plate may be from 10 to 20 inches thick and weigh as much as 5 to 10 tons. Some granite plates are finished on two sides, thus permitting them to be turned over and their use extended.

Grades of Granite Surface Plates. The granite surface plate is available in three grades. Surface plate grade specifications are an indication of the plus and minus deviation of the working surface from an average plane.

Grade	Type	Tolerance
AA	Laboratory grade	± 25 millionths inch
A	Inspection grade	± 50 millionths inch
B	Shop grade	± 100 millionths inch

The tolerances are proportional to the size of the plate.
As the size increases, the tolerance widens.

Layout Dyes To make layout marks visible on the surface of the workpiece, a **layout dye** is used. Layout dyes are available in several colors. Among these are red, blue, and white. The blue dyes are very common. Depending on the surface

Figure 3. Applying layout dye to the workpiece (Courtesy of the L. S. Starrett Company).

Figure 4. Pocket scriber (Courtesy of Rank Scherr-Tumico, Inc.).

Figure 5. Engineer's scriber (Courtesy of Rank Scherr-Tumico, Inc.).

Figure 6. Machinist's scriber (Courtesy of Rank Scherr-Tumico, Inc.).

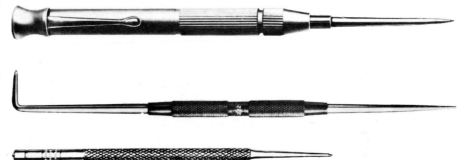

Scribers and Dividers

Figure 7. Rule scribe made from a high speed toolbit.

color of the workpiece material, different dye colors may make layout marks more visible. Layout dye should be applied sparingly in an even coat (Figure 3).

Several types of **scribers** are in common use. The pocket scriber (Figure 4) has a removable tip that can be stored in the handle. This permits the scriber to be carried safely in the pocket. The engineer's scriber (Figure 5) has one straight and one hooked end. The hook permits easier access to the line to be scribed. The machinist's scriber (Figure 6) has only one end with a fixed point. **Scribers must be kept sharp.** If they become dull, they must be reground or stoned to restore their points. Scriber materials include hardened steel and tungsten carbide.

When scribing against a rule, hold the rule firmly. Tilt the scriber so that the tip marks as close to the rule as possible. This will insure accuracy. An excellent scriber can be made by grinding a shallow angle on a piece of tool steel (Figure 7). This type of scriber is particularly well suited to scribing along a rule. The flat side permits the scriber to mark very close to the rule, thus obtaining maximum accuracy.

Several types of dividers are in common use. The **spring divider** is very

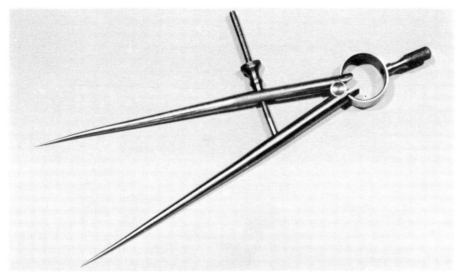

Figure 8. Spring dividers (DeAnza College).

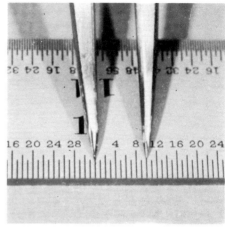

Figure 9. Setting divider points to an engraved rule (DeAnza College).

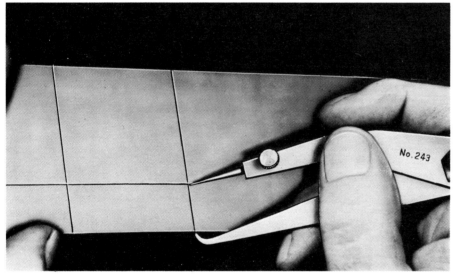

Figure 10. Scribing a line parallel to an edge using a hermaphrodite caliper (Courtesy of the L. S. Starrett Co.).

Figure 11. Scribing the centerline of round stock with the hermaphrodite caliper.

common (Figure 8). Spring dividers range in size from 2 to 12 in. The spacing of the divider legs is set by turning the adjusting screw. Dividers are usually set to rules. Engraved rules are best as the divider tips can be set in the engraved rule graduations (Figure 9). Like scribers, divider tips must be kept sharp and at nearly the same length.

Hermaphrodite Caliper   The **hermaphrodite caliper** has one leg similar to a regular divider. The tip is adjustable for length. The other leg has a hooked end that can be placed against the edge of the workpiece (Figure 10). Hermaphrodite calipers can be used to scribe a line parallel to an edge.

The hermaphrodite caliper can also be used to lay out the center of round stock (Figure 11). The hooked leg is placed against the round stock and an arc is marked on the end of the piece. By adjusting the leg spacing, tangent arcs can be laid out. By marking four arcs at 90 degrees, the center of the stock can be established.

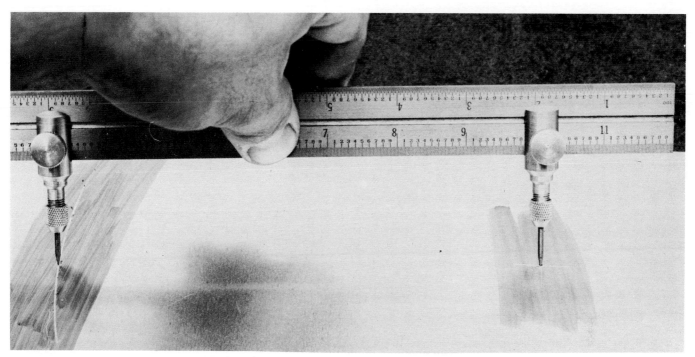

Figure 12. Trammel point attached to a rule.

Figure 13. Layout hammer and layout prick punch.

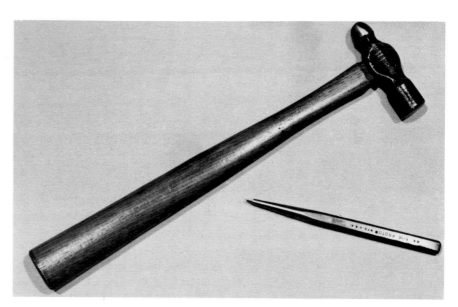

Trammel Points **Trammel points** are used for scribing circles and arcs when the distance involved exceeds the capacity of the divider. Trammel points are either attached to a bar and set to circle dimensions or they may be clamped directly to a rule where they can be set directly by rule graduations (Figure 12).

Layout Hammers and Punches **Layout hammers** are usually light weight machinist's ball peen hammers (Figure 13). A heavy hammer should not be used in layout as it tends to create punch marks that are unnecessarily large.

Figure 14. Toolmaker's hammer (CSU, Fresno).

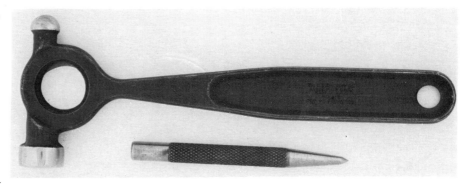

Figure 15. Using a toolmaker's hammer and layout punch (Courtesy of L. S. Starrett Co.).

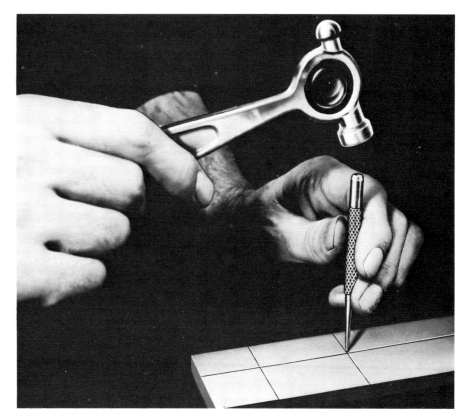

The **toolmaker's hammer** is also used (Figure 14). This hammer is equipped with magnifier that can be used to help locate a layout punch on a scribe mark (Figure 15).

There is an important difference between a layout punch and a center punch. The **layout** or **prick punch** (Figure 14) **has an included point angle of 30 degrees.** This is the only punch that should be used in layout. The slim point facilitates the locating of the punch on a scribe line. A prick punch mark is only used to preserve the location of a layout mark while doing minimum damage to the workpiece. On some workpieces, depending on the material used and the part application, layout punchmarks are not acceptable as they create a defect in the material. A punch mark may affect surface finish or metallurgical properties. Before using a layout punch, you must make sure that it is acceptable. In all cases, layout punch marks should be of minimum depth.

The **center punch** (Figure 16) **has an included point angle of 90 degrees**

Figure 16. Center punch (DeAnza College).

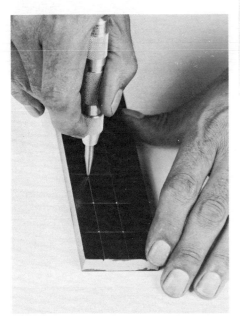

Figure 17. Using the automatic center punch in layout (Courtesy of the L. S. Starrett Co.).

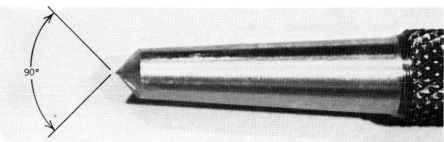

Figure 18. Automatic center punch (Courtesy of the L. S. Starrett Co.).

Figure 19. Optical center punch (CSU, Fresno).

and is used to mark the workpiece prior to such machining operations as drilling. A center punch should not be used in place of a layout punch. Likewise, a layout punch should not be used in place of a center punch. The center punch is used only to deepen the prick punch mark.

The **automatic center punch** (Figure 17) requires no hammer. Although called a center punch, its tip is suitably shaped for layout applications (Figure 18). Spring pressure behind the tip provides the required force. The automatic center punch may be adjusted for variable punching force by changing the spring tension. This is accomplished by an adjustment on the handle.

The **optical center punch** (Figure 19) consists of a locator, optical alignment magnifier, and punch. This type of layout punch is extremely useful in locating punch marks precisely on a scribed line or line intersection. The locator is placed over the approximate location and the optical alignment magnifier is inserted (Figure 20). The locator is magnetized so that it will

Figure 20. Locating the punch holder with the optical alignment magnifier (CSU, Fresno).

Figure 21. Inserting the punch into the punch holder (CSU, Fresno).

remain in position when used on ferrous metals. The optical alignment magnifier has crossed lines etched on its lower end. By looking through the magnifier, you can move the locator about until the cross lines are matched to the scribe lines on the workpiece. The magnifier is then removed and the punch is inserted into the locator (Figure 21). The punch is then tapped with a layout hammer (Figure 22).

Centerhead The **centerhead** is part of the **machinist's combination set.** Centerheads are used to lay out centerlines on round workpieces (Figure 23). When the centerhead is clamped to the combination set rule, the edge of the rule is in line with a circle center.

The other parts of the combination set are useful in layout. These include the **rule, square head,** and **bevel protractor.**

Figure 22. Tapping the punch with a layout hammer (CSU, Fresno).

Figure 23. Using the centerhead to lay out a centerline on round stock (Courtesy of the L. S. Starrett Co.).

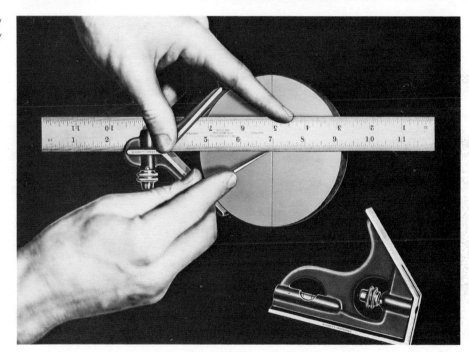

Surface Gage

The **surface gage** consists of a base, rocker, spindle adjusting screw, and scriber (Figure 24). The spindle of the surface gage pivots on the base and can be moved with the adjusting screw. The scriber can be moved along the spindle and locked at any desired position. The scriber can also swivel in its clamp. A surface gage may be used as a height transfer tool. The scribe is set to a rule dimension (Figure 25) and then transferred to the workpiece.

The hooked end of the surface gage scriber may be used to mark the centerline of a workpiece. The following procedure should be followed when doing this layout operation. The surface gage is first set as nearly as possible to a height equal to one half of the part height. The workpiece should be scribed for a short distance at this position. The part should be

Figure 24. Parts of the surface gage (Courtesy of Rank Scherr-Tumico, Inc.).

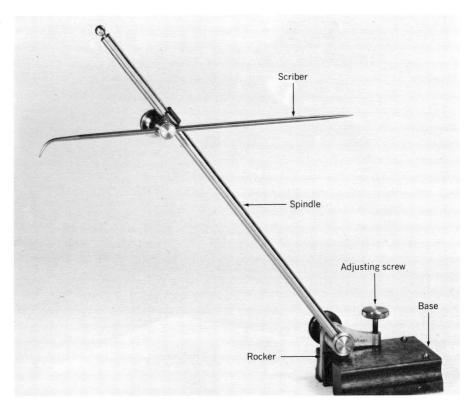

Figure 25. Setting a surface gage to a rule (DeAnza College).

turned over and scribed again (Figure 26). If a deviation exists, there will be two scribe lines on the workpiece. The surface gage scriber should then be adjusted so that it splits the difference between the two marks (Figure 27). This insures that the scribed line is in the center of the workpiece.

Height Gages   Height gages are some of the most important instruments for precision layout. The most common layout height gage is the vernier type. Use of this instrument will be discussed in the unit on precision layout. As a machinist, you may use several other types of height gages for layout applications.

Mechanical Dial and Electronic Digital Height Gages.
Mechanical dial (Figure 28) and electronic digital (Figure 29) height gages elim-

Figure 26. Finding the centerline of the workpiece using the surface gage (Courtesy of California Community Colleges IMC Project).

Figure 28. Mechanical dial height gage (Courtesy of Southwestern Industries, Inc. — Trav-A-Dial).

Figure 27. Adjusting the position of the scribe line to center by inverting the workpiece and checking the existing differences in scribe marks (Courtesy of the California Community Colleges IMC Project).

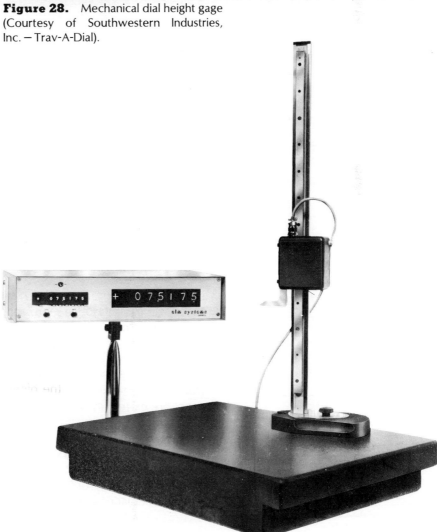

Figure 29. Electronic digital height gage (Courtesy of Elm Systems, Inc.).

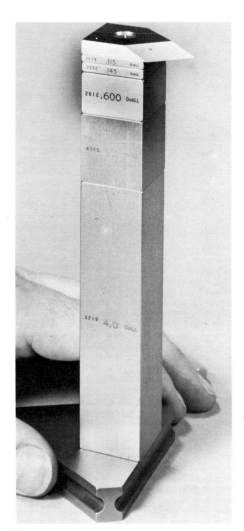

Figure 30. Height gage assembled from gage blocks (Courtesy of the DoAll Company).

Figure 31. Using the planer gage as a height gage in layout (DeAnza College).

inate the need to read a vernier scale. Often these height gages do not have beam graduations. Once set to zero on the reference surface, the total height reading is cumulative on the digital display. This makes beam graduations unnecessary. The electronic digital height gage will discriminate to .0001 in.

Gage Block Height Gages. Gage block height gages may be assembled from wrung stacks of gage blocks and accessories (Figure 30). These height gages are extremely precise as they make use of the inherent accuracy of the gage blocks from which they are assembled.

The Planer Gage as a Height Gage. The planer gage may be equipped with a scriber and used as a height gage (Figure 31). Dimensions are set by comparison to a precision height gage or height transfer micrometer. The planer gage can also be set with an outside micrometer.

Figure 32. Layout machine (Courtesy of Automation and Measurement Division — Bendix Corporation).

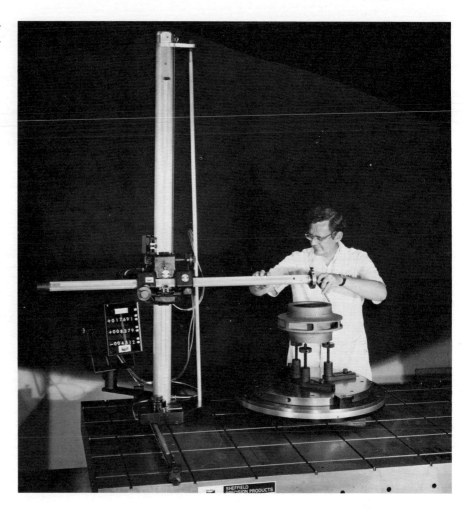

Layout Machines

The layout machine (Figure 32) consists of a vertical column with a horizontal crossarm that can move up and down, in and out. The vertical column also moves horizontally across the layout table. From a single setup, the layout machine can accomplish layout on all sides, bottom, top, and inside of the workpiece. The instrument is equipped with an electronic digital display discriminating to .0001 in.

LAYOUT ACCESSORIES

Layout accessories are tools that will aid you in accomplishing layout tasks. They are not specifically layout tools as they are used for many other purposes. The layout plate or surface plate used for layout is the most common accessory as it provides the reference surface from which to work. Other common accessories include vee-blocks and angle plates that hold the workpiece during layout operations (Figure 33).

Figure 33. Universal right angle plate and vee-block used as layout accessories (CSU, Fresno).

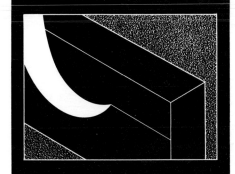

UNIT 1 BASIC SEMI-PRECISION LAYOUT PRACTICE

Before you can cut material for a certain job, you must perform a layout operation. Layout for stock cutoff may involve a simple chalk, pencil, or scribe mark on the material. No matter how simple the layout job may be, you should strive to do it neatly and accurately. In any layout, semiprecision or precision, accuracy is the watchword. Up to this point, you have been introduced to a large number of measuring and layout tools. It is now up to you to put these tools to work in the most productive manner possible. In this unit, you proceed through a typical semiprecision layout task that will familiarize you with basic layout practice.

OBJECTIVES

After completing this unit, you should be able to:
1. Prepare the workpiece for layout.
2. Measure for and scribe layout lines on the workpiece outlining the various features.
3. Locate and establish hole centers using a layout prick punch and center punch.
4. Layout a workpiece to a tolerance of $\pm \frac{1}{64}$ in.

PREPARING THE WORKPIECE FOR LAYOUT

After the material has been cut, all sharp edges should be removed by grinding or filing before placing the stock on the layout table. Place a paper towel under the workpiece to prevent layout dye from spilling on the layout table (Figure 1). Apply a **thin** even coat of layout dye to the workpiece. You will need a drawing of the part in order to do the required layout (Figure 2).

Study the drawing and determine the best way to proceed. The order of steps depends on the layout task. Before some features can be laid out, certain reference lines may have to be established. Measurements for other layout are made from these lines.

LAYOUT OF THE DRILL AND HOLE GAGE

If possible, obtain a piece of material the same size as indicated on the drawing. Depending on the part to be made, you may be able to use material that is the same size as the finished job. However, certain parts may require that the edges be machined to finished dimensions. This may necessitate using material that is larger

Figure 1. Applying layout dye with workpiece on a paper towel (Lane Community College).

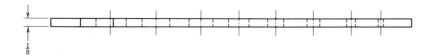

Figure 2. The drill and hole gage (Lane Community College).

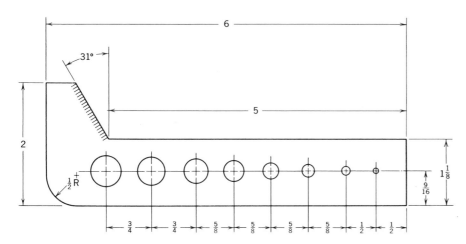

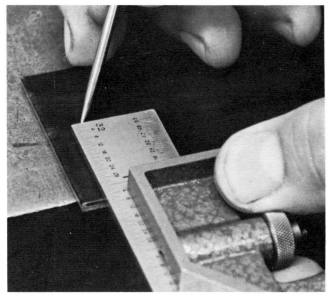

Figure 3. Measuring and marking the width of the gage using the combination square and rule (Lane Community College).

than the finished part in order to allow for machining of edges. Follow through each step as described in the reading. Refer to the layout drawings to determine where layout is to be done. The pictures will help you in selecting and using the required tools.

The first operation is to establish the width of the gage. Measure a distance of $1\frac{1}{8}$ in. from one edge of the material. Use the combination square and rule. Set the square at the required dimension and scribe a mark at each end of the stock (Figure 3 and Drawing A).

Remove the square and place the rule carefully on the scribe marks. Hold the rule **firmly** and scribe the line the full length of the material (Figure 4 and Drawing A). Be sure to use a sharp scribe and hold it so that the tip is against the rule. If the scribe is dull, regrind or stone it to restore its point. Scribe a clean visible line. Lay out the 5 in. length from the end of the piece to the angle vertex. Use the combination square and rule (Figure 5 and Drawing B).

Use a plate protractor to lay out the angle. The bevel protractor from the combination set is also a suit-

Drawing A. Width line.

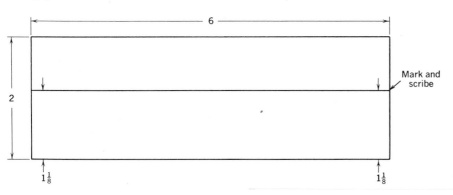

Figure 4. Scribing the width line (Lane Community College).

Figure 5. Measuring the 5 in. dimension from the end to the angle vertex (Lane Community College).

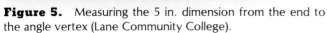

Drawing B. Angle line.

Figure 6. Scribing the angle line (Lane Community College).

able tool for this application. Be sure that the protractor is set to the correct angle. The edge of the protractor blade must be set exactly at the 5 in. mark (Figure 6 and Drawing B). The layout of the 31 degree angle establishes its complement of 59 degrees on the drill gage. The correct included angle for general purpose drill points will be 118 degrees, or twice 59 degrees.

The corner radius is $\frac{1}{2}$ in. Establish this dimension using the square and rule. Two measurements will be required. Measure from the side and from the end to establish the center of the circle (Figure 7 and Drawing C). Prick punch the intersection of the two lines with the 30 degree included point angle layout punch. Tilt the punch so that it can be positioned exactly on the scribe marks (Figure 8). A magnifier will be useful here. Move

the punch to its upright position and tap it lightly with the layout hammer (Figure 9 and Drawing C).

Set the dividers to a dimension of $\frac{1}{2}$ in. using the rule. For maximum reliability, use the one inch graduation for a starting point. Adjust the divider spacing until you feel the tips drop into the rule engravings (Figure 10). Place one divider tip into the layout punch mark and scribe the corner radius (Figure 11 and Drawing C).

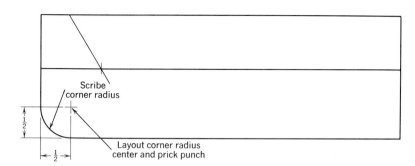

Drawing C. Corner radius.

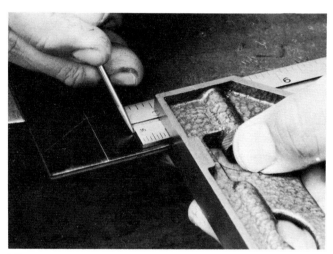

Figure 7. Establishing the center point of the corner radius (Lane Community College).

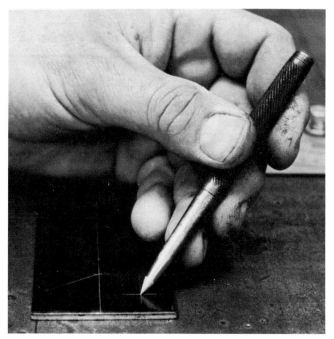

Figure 8. Setting the layout punch on the center point of the corner radius (Lane Community College).

Figure 9. Punching the center point of the corner radius (Lane Community College).

The centerline of the holes is $\frac{9}{16}$ in. from the edge. Use the square and rule to measure this distance. Mark at each end and scribe the line full length (Drawing D). Measure and lay out the center of each hole (Drawing D). Use the layout punch and mark each hole center. After prick punching each hole center, set the dividers to each indicated radius and scribe all hole diameters (Drawing D).

The last step is to center punch each hole center to deepen prick punch marks prior to drilling. Use a 90 degree included point angle center punch (Figure 12). Layout of the drill and hole gage is now complete (Figure 13).

Figure 10. Setting the dividers to the rule engravings (Lane Community College).

Figure 12. Center punching the hole centers (Lane Community College).

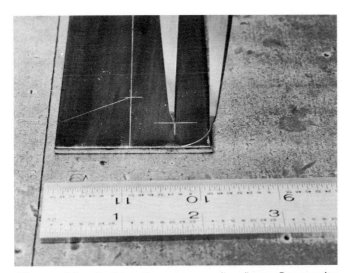

Figure 11. Scribing the corner radius (Lane Community College).

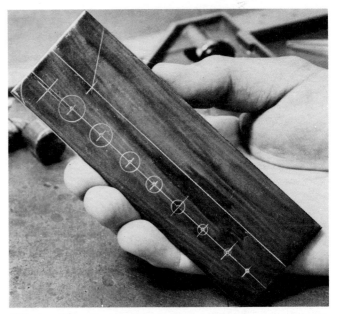

Figure 13. Completed layout for the drill and hole gage (Lane Community College).

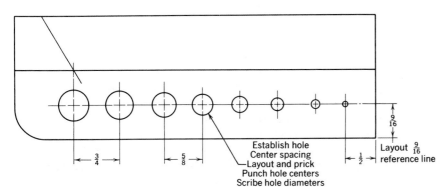

Establish hole
Center spacing
Layout and prick
Punch hole centers
Scribe hole diameters

$\frac{3}{4}$ $\frac{5}{8}$ $\frac{1}{2}$

$\frac{9}{16}$

Layout $\frac{9}{16}$ reference line

Drawing D. Hole locations.

SELF-TEST

1. How should the workpiece be prepared prior to layout?
2. What is the reason for placing the workpiece on a paper towel?
3. Describe the technique of using the layout punch.
4. Describe the use of the combination square and rule in layout.
5. Describe the technique of setting a divider to size using a rule.

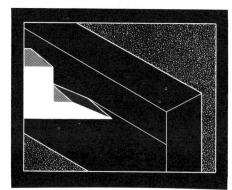

UNIT 2 BASIC PRECISION LAYOUT PRACTICE

Precision layout is generally more reliable and accurate than layout by semi-precision practice. On any job requiring maximum accuracy and reliability, precision layout practice should be used.

OBJECTIVES

After completing this unit, you should be able to:
1. Identify the major parts of the vernier height gage.
2. Describe applications of the vernier height gage in layout.
3. Read a vernier height gage in both metric and inch dimensions.
4. Accomplish layout using the vernier height gage.

THE VERNIER HEIGHT GAGE

The fundamental precision layout tool is the height gage. The vernier height gage is the most common type found in the machine shop. This instrument will discriminate to .001 in. With this ability, a much higher degree of accuracy and reliability is added to a layout task. Whenever possible, you should apply the height gage in all precision layout requirements. Major parts of the height gage include the **base, beam, vernier slide,** and **scriber** (Figure 1). The size of height gages is measured by the maximum height gaging ability of the instrument. Height gages range from 10 to 72 in.

Height gage scribers are made from tool steel or tungsten carbide. **Carbide scribers are subject to chipping and must be treated gently.** They do, however, retain their sharpness and scribe very clean narrow lines. Height gage scribers may be sharpened if they become dull. It is important that any **sharpening be done on the slanted surface so that the scriber dimensions will not be changed.**

The height gage scriber is attached to the vernier slide and can be moved up and down the beam. Scribers are either **straight** (Figure 2) or **offset** (Figure 3). The offset scriber permits direct readings with the height gage. The gage reads zero when the scriber rests down on the reference surface. With the straight scriber, the workpiece will have to be raised accordingly, if direct readings are to be obtained. This type of height gage scriber is less convenient.

READING THE VERNIER HEIGHT GAGE

On an inch height gage, the beam is graduated in inches with each inch divided into 10 parts. The tenth inch graduations are further divided into two or four parts depending on the divisions of the vernier. On the 25 division vernier, used on many older height gages, the $\frac{1}{10}$ in. divisions on the beam are graduated into four parts. The vernier permits discrimination to .001 in. Many newer height gages are making use of the 50 division

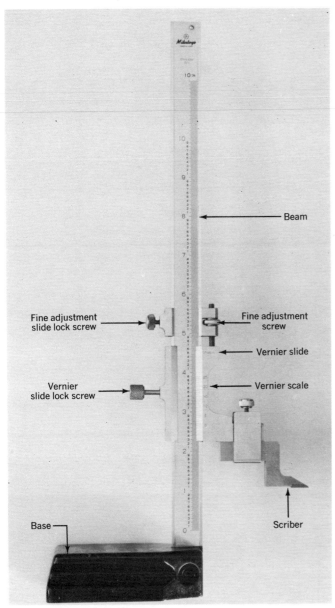

Figure 1. Parts of the vernier height gage.

inch vernier height gage with a 50 division vernier is read as follows (Figure 4, right-hand scale):

Beam reading	5.3
Vernier is coincident at 12 or .012 in.	.012
Total reading	5.312 in.

On the 50 division inch vernier height gage, the beam scale is graduated in $\frac{1}{10}$ in. graduations. Each $\frac{1}{10}$ in. increment is further divided into two parts. If the zero on the vernier is past the .050 in. mark on the beam, .050 in. must be added to the reading.

The metric vernier scale also has 50 divisions, each equal to $\frac{1}{50}$ or .02 millimeter (Figure 4, left-hand scale):

Beam scale reading	134 mm
Vernier coincident at line 49	
49 $\times$ .02 =	.98 mm
Total reading	134.98 mm

On the 25 division inch vernier height gage the $\frac{1}{10}$ in. beam graduations are divided into four parts, each equal to .025 in. Depending on the location of the vernier zero mark, .025, .050, or .075 in. may have to be added to the beam reading. The inch vernier height gage with a 25 division vernier is read as follows (Figure 5):

Beam	5.0
Vernier coincident at 17 or .017	.017
Total reading	5.017 in.

CHECKING THE ZERO REFERENCE ON THE VERNIER HEIGHT GAGE

The height gage scriber must be checked against the reference surface before attempting to make any height measurements of layouts. Clean the surface of the layout table and the base of the gage. Slide the scriber down until it just rests on the reference surface. Check the alignment of the zero mark on the vernier scale with the zero mark on the beam scale. The two marks should coincide exactly (Figure 6). Hold the height gage base firmly against the reference surface. Be sure that you do not tilt the base of the height gage by sliding the vernier slide past the zero point on the beam scale. If the zero marks on the vernier and beam do not coincide after the scriber has contacted the reference surface, an adjustment of the vernier scale is required.

Some height gages do not have an adjustable vernier scale. A misalignment in the vernier and the beam zero marks may indicate a loose vernier slide, an incorrect scriber dimension, or a beam that is out of perpendicular with the base. Loose vernier slides may be adjusted and scriber dimensions can be corrected. However, if the beam is out of perpendicular with the base, the instrument is unreliable because of cosine error. A

vernier, which permits easier reading. On a height gage with a 50 division vernier, the $\frac{1}{10}$ in. graduations on the beam will be divided into two parts. Discrimination of this height gage is also .001 in. The metric vernier height gage has the beam graduated in millimeters. The vernier contains 50 divisions permitting the instrument to discriminate to $\frac{1}{50}$ mm.

The vernier height gage is read like any other instrument employing the principle of the vernier. The line on the vernier scale that is coincident with a beam scale graduation must be determined. This value is added to the beam scale reading to make up the total reading. The

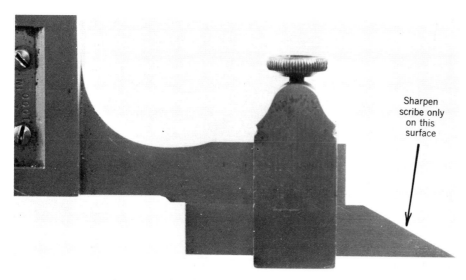

Figure 2.   Straight vernier height gage scriber (CSU, Fresno).

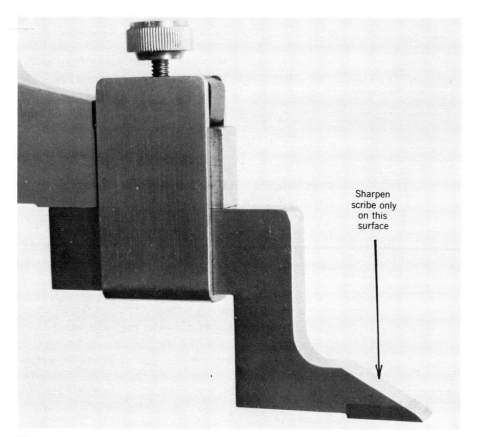

Figure 3.   Offset vernier height gage scriber.

determination of such a condition can be made by an appropriate calibration process. All height gages, particularly those with nonadjustable verniers, must be treated with the same respect as any precision instrument that you will use.

APPLICATIONS OF THE
VERNIER HEIGHT GAGE IN LAYOUT

The primary function of the vernier height gage in layout is to measure and scribe lines of known height on the workpiece (Figure 7). Perpendicular lines may be scribed

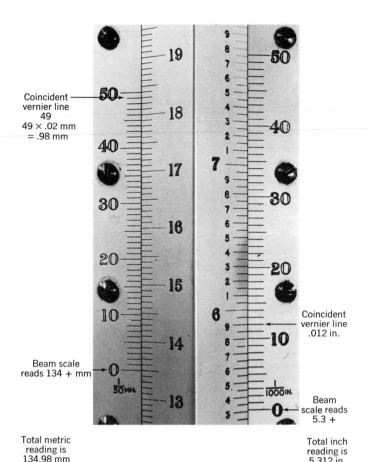

Coincident vernier line
49
49 × .02 mm
= .98 mm

Beam scale reads 134 + mm

Coincident vernier line .012 in.

Beam scale reads 5.3 +

Total metric reading is 134.98 mm

Total inch reading is 5.312 in.

Figure 4. Reading the 50 division inch/metric vernier height gage (DeAnza College).

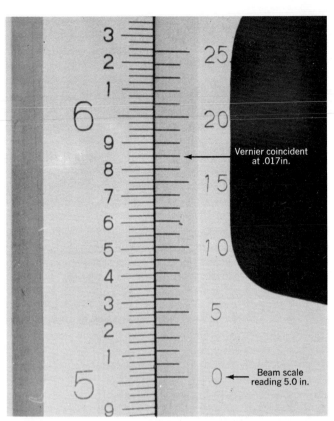

Vernier coincident at .017 in.

Beam scale reading 5.0 in.

Figure 5. Reading the 25 division inch vernier height gage.

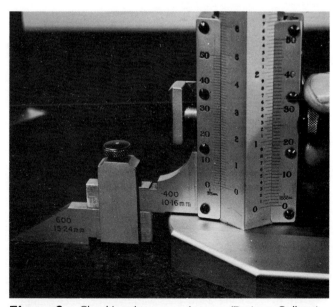

Figure 6. Checking the zero reference (DeAnza College).

on the workpiece by the following procedure. The work is first clamped to a right angle plate if necessary and the required lines are scribed in one direction. The height gage should be set at an angle to the work and the corner of the scriber pulled across while keeping the height gage base firmly on the reference surface (Figure 8). Only enough pressure should be applied with the scriber to remove the layout dye and not actually remove material from the workpiece.

After scribing the required lines in one direction, turn the workpiece by 90 degrees. Setup is quite critical if the scribe marks are to be truly perpendicular. A square (Figure 9) or a dial test indicator may be used (Figure 10) to establish the work at right angles. In both cases the edges of the workpiece must be machined smooth and square. After the clamp has been tightened, the perpendicular lines may be scribed at the required height (Figure 11).

The height gage may be used to lay out center lines on round stock (Figure 12). The stock is clamped in a vee-block and the correct dimension to center is deter-

mined. This can be done with the dial test indicator attached to the height gage. However, it must not be done with the height gage scriber.

Parallel bars (Figure 13) are a valuable and useful lay-

Figure 7. Scribing height lines with the vernier height gage (DeAnza College).

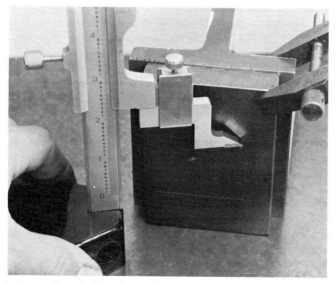

Figure 8. Scribing layout lines with the workpiece clamped to a right angle plate.

Figure 9. After turning the workpiece 90 degrees, it can be checked with a square.

Figure 10. Checking the work using a dial test indicator.

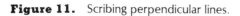

Figure 11. Scribing perpendicular lines.

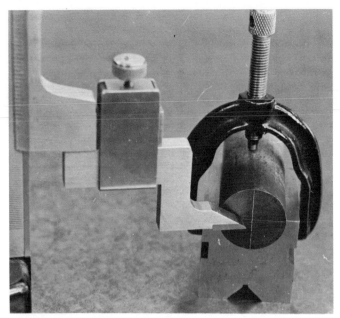

Figure 12. Scribing centerlines on round stock clamped in a vee-block.

Figure 14. Using parallel bars in layout.

Figure 13. Hardened steel parallel bars (CSU, Fresno).

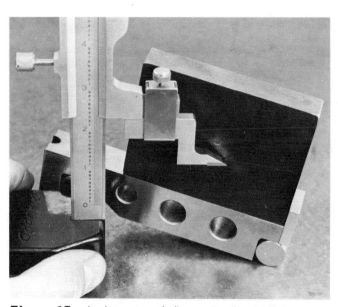

Figure 15. Laying out angle lines using the sine bar.

out accessory. These bars are made from hardened steel or granite, and they have extremely accurate dimensional accuracy. Parallel bars are available in many sizes and lengths. In layout with the height gage they can be used to support the workpiece (Figure 14).

Angles may be laid out by placing the workpiece on the sine bar (Figure 15).

BASIC PRECISION LAYOUT PRACTICE

The workpiece should be prepared as in semiprecision

layout. Sharp edges must be removed and a thin coat of layout dye applied. You will need a drawing of the part to be laid out (Figure 16). The order of steps will depend on the layout task.

Position One Layouts

In position one (Figure 17) the clamp frame is on edge. In any position, all layouts can be defined as heights above the reference surface. Refer to the drawing on position one layouts and determine all of the layout that can be accomplished there.

Start by scribing the $\frac{3}{4}$ in. height that defines the width of the clamp frame. Set the height gage to .750 in. (Figure 18). Attach the scriber (Figure 19). Be sure that the scriber is sharp and properly installed for the height

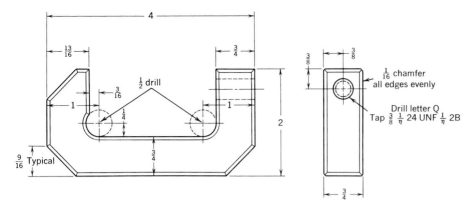

Figure 16. Clamp frame (Lane Community College).

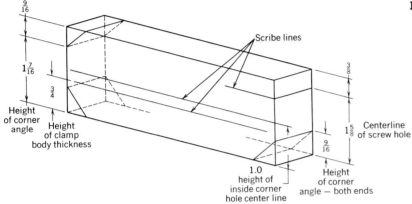

Figure 17. Clamp frame — position one layouts.

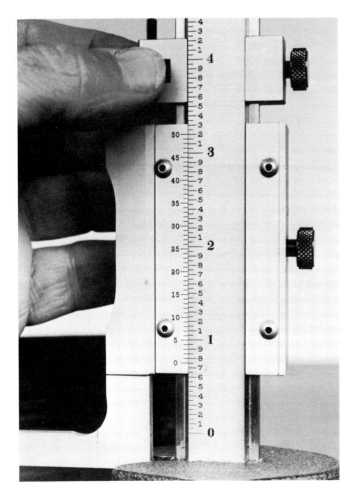

Figure 19. Attaching the scriber (Lane Community College).

Figure 18. Setting the height gage to a dimension of .750 in. (Lane Community College).

gage that you are using. Hold the workpiece and height gage firmly and pull the scriber across the work in a smooth motion (Figure 20). The height of the clamp screw hole can be laid out at this time. Refer to the part drawing and determine the height of the hole. Set the height gage at 1.625 in. and scribe the line on the end of the workpiece (Figure 21). The line may be projected around on the side of the part. This will facilitate setup in the drill press. Other layouts that can be accomplished at position one include the height equivalent of the inside corner hole centerlines.

The starting points of the corner angles on both ends may also be laid out. Refer to the drawing on position one layouts.

Position Two Layouts

In position two, the workpiece is on its side (Figure 22). Check the work with a micrometer to determine its exact thickness. Set the height gage to one-half this amount and scribe the centerline of the clamp screw hole. This layout will also establish the center point of the clamp screw hole. A height gage setting of .375 in. will probably be adequate providing that the stock is .750 in. thick. However, if the thickness varies above or below .750 in. the height gage can be set to one-half of whatever the thickness is. This will insure that the hole is in the center of the workpiece.

Position Three Layouts

In position three, the workpiece is on end clamped to an angle plate (Figure 23). The work must be established perpendicular using a square or dial test indicator. Set the height gage to .750 in. and scribe the height equiv-

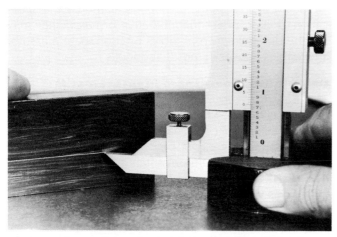

Figure 20. Scribing the height equivalent of the frame thickness (Lane Community College).

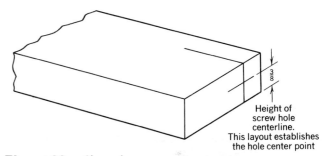

Figure 22. Clamp frame—position two layouts.

Figure 21. Scribing the height equivalent of the clamp screw hole (Lane Community College).

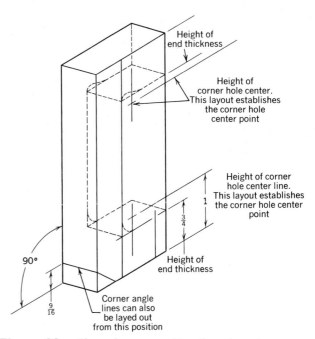

Figure 23. Clamp frame—position three layouts.

Figure 24. Scribing the height equivalent of the end thickness (Lane Community College).

Figure 25. Completed layout of the clamp frame (Lane Community College).

alent of the frame end thickness (Figure 24). Other layouts that can be done at position three include the height equivalent of the inside corner hole centerlines. This layout will also locate the center points of the inside corner holes (Figure 25). The height equivalent of the end thickness as well as the ending points of the corner angles can be scribed at position three.

HEIGHT GAGE LAYOUT BY COORDINATE MEASURE

Many layouts can be accomplished by calculating the coordinate position of the part features. Coordinate position simply means that each feature is located a certain distance from adjacent perpendicular reference lines. These are frequently known as the X and Y coordinates. You should begin to think of coordinates in terms of X and Y as this terminology will be important, especially in the area of numerical control machining. The X coordinate on a two dimensional drawing is horizontal. The Y coordinate is perpendicular to X and in the same plane. On a drawing, Y is the vertical coordinate. The X and Y coordinate lines can be and often are the edges of the workpiece, provided the edges have been machined true and square to each other.

Coordinate lengths can be calculated by the application of appropriate trigonometric formulas. They may also be determined from tables of coordinate measure. Such tables appear in most handbooks for machinists.

Calculating Coordinate Measurements

The drawing (Figure 26) shows a five hole equally spaced pattern centered on the workpiece. Since hole one is on the centerline, its coordinate position measured from the reference edges can be easily determined (Figure 27). The X coordinate (horizontal) is 2 in. The Y coordinate (vertical) is two inches plus the radius of the hole circle. This would be $3\frac{1}{4}$ in.

The coordinate position of hole two can be calculated by the following. Since there are five equally spaced holes the central angle is $\frac{360}{5}$ or 72 degrees. Right triangle ABC (Figure 28) is formed by constructing a perpendicular line from point B to point C. Angle A equals 18 degrees ($90 - 72 = 18$). To find the X coordinate, apply the following formula:

$$X_C = \text{circle radius} \times \cos 18°$$
$$= 1.250 \times .951$$
$$= 1.188 \text{ in.}$$

The X coordinate length from the reference edge is found by

$$2.0 - 1.188 = .812 \qquad \text{(Figure 26)}$$

The Y coordinate is found by the following formula:

$$Y_c = \text{circle radius} \times \sin 18°$$
$$= 1.250 \times .309$$
$$= .386$$

The Y coordinate length from the reference edge is found by

$$2.0 + .386 = 2.386 \text{ in.}$$

The coordinate position of hole three is calculated

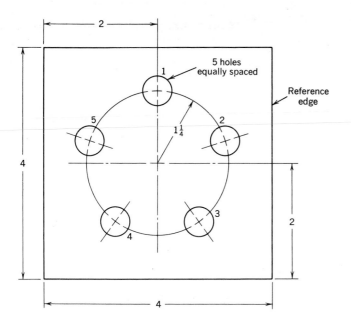

Figure 26.   Equally spaced five hole circle.

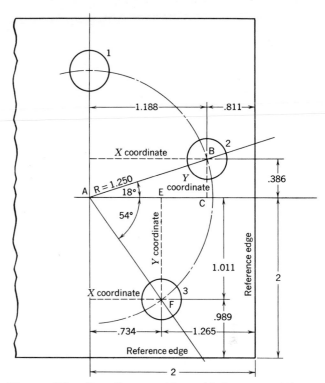

Figure 28.   Coordinate positions of holes two and three.

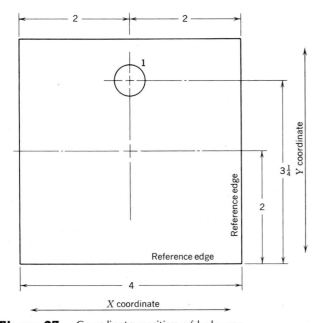

Figure 27.   Coordinate position of hole one.

in a similar manner. Right triangle *AEF* is formed by constructing a perpendicular line from point *F* to point *E* (Figure 28). Angle *FAE* equals 54 degrees (72 − 18 = 54). To find the *X* coordinate, apply the following formula:

$$X_c = \text{circle radius} \times \cos 54°$$
$$= 1.250 \times .587$$
$$= .734$$

The *X* coordinate length from the reference edge is found by

$$2.0 - .734 = 1.265 \qquad \text{(Figure 28)}$$

To find the *Y* coordinate, apply the following formula:

$$Y_c = \text{radius} \times \sin 54°$$
$$= 1.250 \times .809$$
$$= 1.011 \text{ in.}$$

The *Y* coordinate length from the reference edge is found by

$$2.0 - 1.011 = .989 \text{ in.} \qquad \text{(Figure 28)}$$

The coordinate positions of holes four and five are the same distance from the centerlines as holes two and three. Their positions from the reference edges can be calculated easily.

Since this layout involves scribing perpendicular lines, the workpiece must be turned 90 degrees. If the edges of the work are used as reference, they must be machined square. Either coordinate may be laid out first. The workpiece is then turned 90 degrees to the adjacent reference edge. This permits the layout of the perpendicular lines (Figure 29).

LAYING OUT ANGLES

Angles may be laid out using the height gage by calculating the appropriate dimensions using trigonometry. In

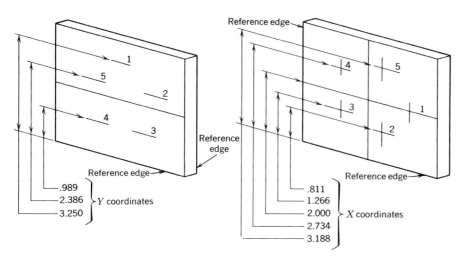

Figure 29. Height equivalents of coordinate positions for all holes.

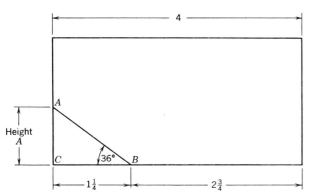

Figure 30. Laying out a 36 degree angle.

the example (Figure 30) the layout of height A will establish angle B at 36 degrees. Height A is calculated by the following formula:

$$\text{Height } A = 1.25 \times \tan B$$
$$= 1.25 \times .726$$
$$= .908 \text{ in.}$$

After scribing a height of .908 in., the workpiece is turned 90 degrees and the starting point of the angle established at point B. Scribing from point A to point B will establish the desired angle.

The sine bar can also be used in angular layout. In the example (Figure 31), the sine bar is elevated for the 25 degree angle. Sine bar elevation is calculated by the formula

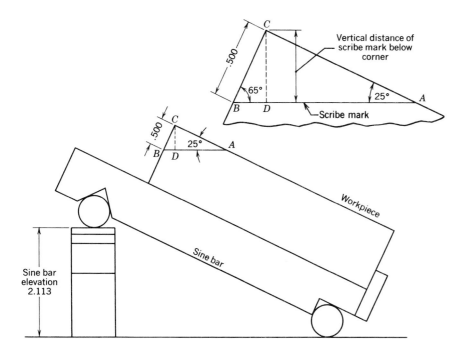

Figure 31. Laying out an angle using the sine bar.

Bar elevation = bar length × sine of required angle.

If we assume a 5 in. sine bar,

$$\text{Elevation} = 5 \times \sin 25°$$
$$= 5 \times .422$$
$$= 2.113 \text{ in.}$$

A gage block stack is assembled and placed under the sine bar. Now that the bar has been elevated, the vertical distance CD from the corner to the scribe line AB must be determined. To find distance DC, a perpendicular line must be constructed from point C to point D. Angle A is 65 degrees (90 − 25 = 65). Length CD is

found by the following formula:

$$CD = .500 \times \sin B$$
$$= .500 \times .906$$
$$= .453 \text{ in.}$$

The height of the corner must be determined and the length of CD subtracted from this dimension. This will result in the correct height gage setting for scribing line AB. The corner height should be determined using the height gage and dial test indicator. The corner height must not be determined using the height gage scriber.

SELF-TEST

Read and record the following 50 division inch/metric height gage readings.

1. (Figures 32–34)
Read and record the following 25 division inch height gage readings:
  (Figure 35)
  (Figure 36)

2. Describe the procedure for checking the zero reference.
3. How can the zero reference be adjusted?
4. How are perpendicular lines scribed with a height gage?
5. What is the measuring range of a typical height gage?
6. When laying out angles, what tool is used in conjunction with the height gage?

Figure 32.

Figure 33.

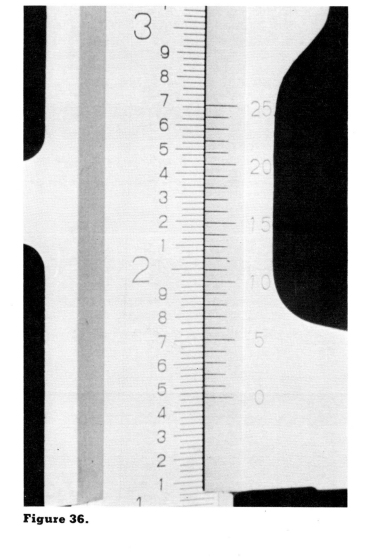

Figure 34.

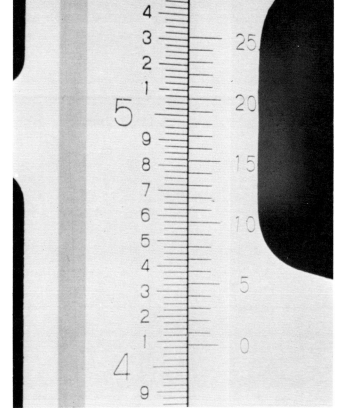

Figure 36.

Figure 35.

SECTION F SAWING MACHINES

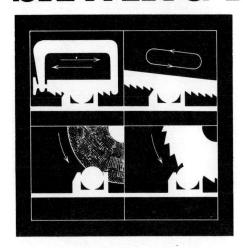

Sawing machines constitute some of the most important machine tools found in the machine shop. These machines can generally be divided into two classifications. The first class is **cutoff machines.** Common types of cutoff machines include reciprocating saws, horizontal endless band saws, universal tilt frame band saws, abrasive saws, and cold saws. Of the cutoff machines, the **horizontal band saw** is the most important type. The second class is the **vertical band machine** that can be used as a band saw or with other band tools. The vertical band machine is most commonly used as a **band saw.**

The first machine tool that you will probably encounter is a cutoff machine. In the machine shop, cutoff machines are generally found near the stock supply area. The primary function of the cutoff machine is to reduce mill lengths of bar stock material into lengths suitable for holding in other machine tools. In a large production machine shop where stock is being supplied to many machine tools, the cutoff machine will be constantly busy cutting many materials. The cutoff machine that you will most likely see in the machine shop will be some type of saw.

TYPES OF CUTOFF MACHINES

Reciprocating Saws

The **reciprocating** saw is often called a power hacksaw. Early saws were hand operated by a reciprocating or back-and-forth motion. It was logical that this principle be applied to power saws. The reciprocating saw is still used in the machine shop. However, they are giving way to the horizontal band machine. The reciprocating saw is built much like the metal cutting hand hacksaw. Basically, the machine consists of a frame that holds a blade. Reciprocating hacksaw blades are wider and thicker than those used in the hand hacksaw. The reciprocating motion is provided by hydraulics or a crankshaft mechanism.

Reciprocating saws are either the hinge type (Figure 1) or the column type (Figure 2). The saw frame on the hinge type pivots around a single point at the rear of the machine. On the column type, both ends of the frame rise vertically. Column-type reciprocating saws can accommodate larger sizes of material. The size of a reciprocating saw is determined by the largest piece of square material that can be cut. Sizes range from about 5 by 5 in. to 24 by 24 in. Large capacity reciprocating saws are often of the column design.

Horizontal Band Cutoff Machine

One disadvantage of the reciprocating saw is that it only cuts in one direction of the stroke. The band machine uses a steel band blade with the teeth on one edge. The band machine has a high cutting efficiency because the band is cutting at all times with no wasted motion. Band saws are the mainstay of production stock cutoff in the machine shop (Figure 3).

A modern band saw may be equipped with a variable speed drive. This permits the most efficient cutting speed to be selected for the material being cut. The feed rate through the material may also be varied. The size of the horizontal band machine is determined by the largest piece of square material that the machine can cut. Large capacity horizontal band saws (Figure 4) are

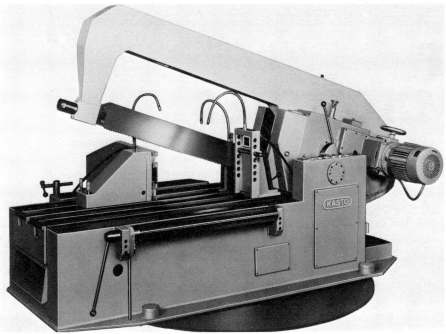

Figure 1. Hinge-type reciprocating cutoff saw (Courtesy of Kasto-Racine Inc.).

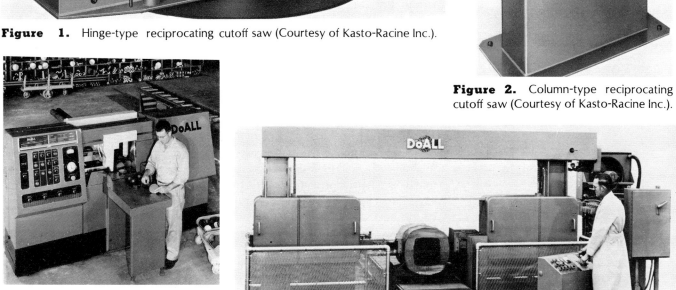

Figure 2. Column-type reciprocating cutoff saw (Courtesy of Kasto-Racine Inc.).

Figure 3. Horizontal endless band cutoff saw (Courtesy of the DoAll Company).

Figure 4. Large capacity horizontal band saw (Courtesy of the DoAll Company).

designed to handle large dimension workpieces that can weigh as much as 10 tons. With a wide variety of band types available, plus many special work-holding devices, the band saw is an extremely valuable and versatile machine tool.

Universal Tilt Frame Cutoff   The universal tilt frame band saw is much like its horizontal counterpart. This machine has the band blade vertical, and the frame can be tilted from side to

Figure 5. Tilt frame band saw (Courtesy of the DoAll Company).

Figure 6. Typical abrasive cutoff machine (CSU, Fresno).

Figure 7. Precision cold saw cutoff machine (Courtesy of Ameropean Industries, Inc.).

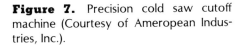

side (Figure 5). The tilt frame machine is particularly useful for making angle cuts on large structural shapes such as I-beams or pipe.

Abrasive Cutoff Machine

The abrasive cutoff machine (Figure 6) uses a thin circular abrasive wheel for cutting. Abrasive saws are very fast cutting. They can be used to cut a number of nonmetallic materials such as glass, brick, and stone. The major advantages of the abrasive cutoff machine are speed and the ability to cut nonmetals. Each particle of abrasive acts as a small tooth and actually cuts a small bit of material. Abrasive saws are operated at very high speeds. Blade speed can be as high as 10,000 to 15,000 surface feet per minute.

Cold Saw Cutoff Machines

The cold saw (Figure 7) uses a circular metal saw with teeth. These machine tools can produce extremely accurate cuts and are useful where length tol-

erance of the cut material must be held as close as possible. A cold saw blade that is .040 to .080 in. thick can saw material to a tolerance of plus or minus .002 in. Large cold saws are used to cut structural shapes such as angle and flat bar. These are also fast cutting machines.

CUTOFF MACHINE SAFETY

Reciprocating Saws

Be sure that all guards around moving parts are in place before starting the machine. The saw blade must be properly installed with the teeth pointed in the right direction. Check for correct blade tension. Be sure that the width of the workpiece is less than the distance of the saw stroke. The frame will be broken if it hits the workpiece during the stroke. This will damage the machine. Be sure that the speed of the stroke and the rate of feed is correct for the material being cut.

When operating a saw with coolant, see that the coolant does not run on the floor during the cutting operation. This can cause an extremely dangerous slippery area around the machine tool.

Horizontal Band Saws

Recent, new regulations require that the blade of the horizontal band machine be fully guarded except at the point of cut (Figure 8).

Make sure that blade tensions are correct on reciprocating and band saws. Check band tensions, especially after installing a new band. New bands may stretch and loosen during their run-in period. Band teeth are sharp. When installing a new band, it should be handled with gloves. This is one of the few places that gloves may be worn around the machine shop. They must not be worn when operating any machine tool.

Endless band blades are often stored in double coils. Be careful when unwinding them, as they are under tension. The coils may spring apart and could cause an injury.

Make sure that the band is tracking properly on the wheels and in the blade guides. If a band should break, it could be ejected from the machine and cause an injury.

Make sure that the material being cut is properly secured in the workholding device. If this is a vise, be sure that it is tight. If you are cutting off short pieces of material, the vise jaw must be supported at both ends (Figure 9). It is not good practice to attempt to cut pieces of material that are quite short. The stock cannot be secured properly and may be pulled from the vise by the pressure of the cut (Figure 10). This can cause damage to the machine as well as possible injury to the operator. Stock should extend at least halfway through the vise at all times.

Many cutoff machines have a rollcase that supports long bars of material while they are being cut. The stock should be brought to the saw on a rollcase (Figure 11) or a simple rollstand. The pieces being cut off can sometimes be several feet long and should be similarly supported. Sharp burrs left from the cutting should be removed immediately with a file. You can acquire a nasty cut by sliding your hand over one of these burrs.

Be careful around a rollcase, since bars of stock can roll, pinching fingers and hands. Also, be careful that heavy pieces of stock do not fall off the stock table or saw and injure feet or toes. Get help when lifting heavy bars of material. This will save your back and possibly your career.

Abrasive Saws

On an abrasive saw, inspect the cutting edge of the blade for cracks and chips (Figure 12). Replace the blade if it is damaged. Always operate an abrasive saw blade at the proper RPM (Figure 13). Overspeeding the blade can cause it to fly apart. If an abrasive saw blade should fail at high speed, pieces

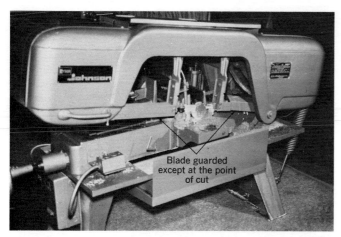

Figure 8. The horizontal band blade is guarded except in the immediate area of the cut.

Figure 9. Support both ends of the vise when cutting short material (CSU, Fresno).

Figure 10. Result of cutting stock that is too short.

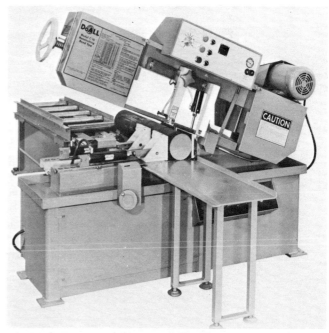

Figure 11. The material is brought into the saw on the roll-case (opposite side) and, when pieces are cut off, they are supported by the stand (this side of the saw). The stand prevents the part from falling to the floor (Courtesy of DoAll Company).

Figure 12. Inspecting the abrasive wheel for chips and cracks (CSU, Fresno).

Figure 13. Abrasive wheel must be operated at the correct RPM (CSU, Fresno).

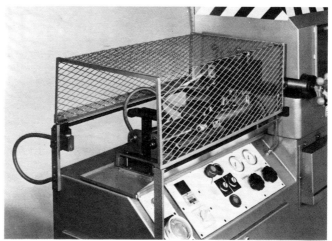

Figure 14. Wire mesh guard on the cold saw material feeding mechanism (Courtesy of Ameropean Industries, Inc.).

of the blade can be thrown out of the machine at extreme velocities. A very serious injury indeed can result if you happen to be in the path of these bulletlike projectiles.

Cold Saws   In terms of cold saws, safety is generally the same as with all cutoff machines. Guards must be in place around the saw and the feeding mechanism (Figure 14). Before starting the saw, check to see that speeds and feeds are correct and that the workpiece is properly secured.

Safety extends to the machine as well as the operator. Never abuse any machine tool. They cost a great deal of money and in many cases are purchased with your tax dollars.

VERTICAL BAND MACHINES

The vertical band machine (Figure 15) is often called the handiest machine tool in the machine shop. Perhaps the reason for this is the wide variety of work that can be accomplished on this versatile machine tool. The vertical band machine or vertical band saw is similar in general construction to its

horizontal counterpart. Basically, it consists of an endless band blade or other band tool that runs on a driven and idler wheel. The band tool runs vertically at the point of the cut where it passes through a worktable on which the workpiece rests. The workpiece is pushed into the blade and the direction of the cut is guided by hand or mechanical means.

ADVANTAGES OF BAND MACHINES

Shaping of material with the use of a saw blade or other band tool is often called **band machining.** The reason for this is that the band machine can perform other machining tasks aside from simple sawing. These include band friction sawing, band filing, and band polishing.

In any machining operation, a piece of stock material is cut by various processes to form the final shape and size of the part desired. In most machining operations, all of the unwanted material must be reduced to chips in order to uncover the final shape and size of the workpiece. With a band saw, only a small portion of the unwanted material must be reduced to chips in order to uncover the final workpiece shape and size (Figure 16). A piece of stock material can often be shaped to final size by one or two saw cuts. A further advantage is gained in that the band saw cuts a very narrow kerf. A minimum amount of material is wasted.

A second important advantage in band sawing machines is **contouring ability.** Contour band sawing is the ability of the saw to cut intricate curved shapes that would be nearly impossible to machine by other methods (Figure 17). The sawing of intricate shapes can be accomplished by a combination of hand and power feeds. On vertical band machines so equipped, the workpiece is steered by manual operation of the handwheel. The hydraulic table feed varies according to the saw pressure on the workpiece. This greatly facilitates contour sawing operations.

Band sawing and band machining have several other advantages. There is no limit to the length, angle, or direction of the cut (Figure 18). However, the throat capacity of the sawing machine will affect this depending on the dimension of the parts being sawed. Workpieces larger than the band machine can be cut (Figure 19). Since the band tool is fed continuously past the work, cutting efficiency is high. A band tool, whether it be a saw blade, band file, or grinding band, has a large number of cutting points passing the work. In most other machining operations, only one or a fairly low number of cutting points pass the work. With the band tool, wear is distributed over these many cutting points. Tool life is prolonged.

Figure 15. Leighton A. Wilkie bandsaw of 1933. (Courtesy of the DoAll Company).

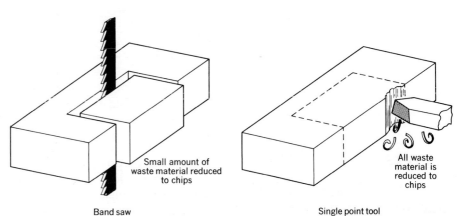

Small amount of waste material reduced to chips

All waste material is reduced to chips

Band saw

Single point tool

Figure 16. Sawing can uncover the workpiece shape in a minimum number of cuts.

Figure 17. Curved or contour band sawing can produce part shapes that would be difficult to machine by other methods (Courtesy of the DoAll Company).

Figure 18. Splitting a large diameter ring on the vertical band machine (Courtesy of the DoAll Company).

Figure 19. Workpieces larger than the machine tool can be cut (Courtesy of the DoAll Company).

TYPES OF BAND MACHINES

General Purpose Band Machine with Fixed Worktable

The general purpose band machine is found in most machine shops, (Figure 20). This machine tool has a nonpower-fed worktable that can be tilted in order to make angle cuts. The table may be tilted 10 degrees left (Figure 21). Tilt on this side is limited by the saw frame. The table may be tilted 45 degrees right (Figure 22). On large machines, table tilt left may be limited to 5 degrees.

Figure 20. General purpose vertical band machine (Courtesy of the DoAll Company).

Figure 21. Vertical band machine worktable can be tilted 10 degrees left (Courtesy California Community Colleges — IMC Project).

Figure 22. Vertical band machine worktable tilted 45 degrees right (Courtesy California Community Colleges — IMC Project).

The workpiece may be pushed into the blade by hand. Mechanical (Figure 23) or mechanical-hydraulic feeding mechanisms are also used. A band machine may be equipped with a hydraulic tracing attachment. This accessory uses a stylus contacting a template or pattern. The tracing accessory guides the workpiece during the cut (Figure 24).

Band Machines with Power-Fed Worktables

Heavier construction is used on these machine tools. The worktable is moved hydraulically. The operator is relieved of the need to push the workpiece into the cutting blade. The direction of the cut can be guided by a steering mechanism (Figure 25). A roller chain wraps around the workpiece and passes over a sprocket at the back of the worktable. The sprocket is connected to a steering wheel at the front of the worktable. The operator can then guide the workpiece and keep the saw cutting along the proper lines. The work-

Figure 23. Mechanical work feeding mechanism (Courtesy of the DoAll Company).

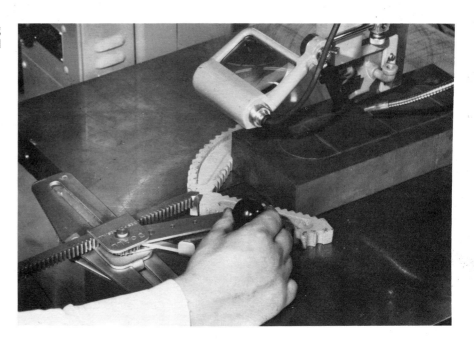

Figure 24. Hydraulic tracing accessory (Courtesy of the DoAll Company).

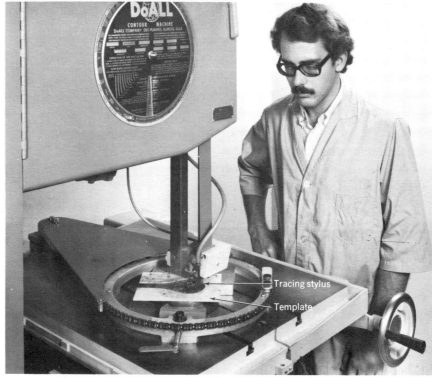

Figure 25. Heavy duty vertical band machine with power-fed worktable (Courtesy of the DoAll Company).

High Tool Velocity Band Machines

piece rests on roller bearing stands. These permit the workpiece to turn freely while it is being steered.

On the high tool velocity band machine (Figure 26), band speeds can range as high as 10 to 15,000 feet per minute (FPM). These machine tools are used in many band machining applications. They are frequently found cutting non-metal products. These include applications such as trimming plastic laminates (Figure 27) and cutting fiber materials (Figure 28).

Figure 26. High tool velocity vertical band machine (Courtesy of the DoAll Company).

Figure 27. Trimming plastic laminates on the high tool velocity band machine (Courtesy of the DoAll Company).

Figure 28. Cutting fiber material on the high tool velocity band machine (Courtesy of the DoAll Company).

Large Capacity Band Machines

This type of band machine is used on large workpieces. The entire saw is attached to a swinging column. The workpiece remains stationary and the saw is moved about to accomplish the desired cuts (Figure 29).

Figure 29. Large capacity vertical band machine (Courtesy of the DoAll Company).

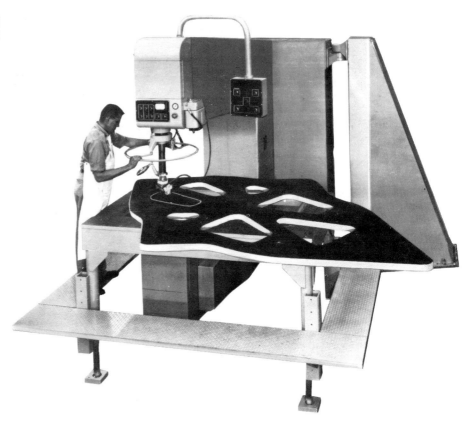

APPLICATIONS OF THE VERTICAL BAND MACHINE

Conventional and Contour Sawing

Vertical band machines are used in many conventional sawing applications. They are found in the foundry trimming sprues and risers from castings. The band machine can accommodate a large casting and make widely spaced cuts (Figure 30). Production trimming of castings is easily accomplished with the high tool velocity band machine (Figure 31). Band saws are also useful in ripping operations (Figure 32). In the machine shop, the vertical band machine is used in general purpose, straight line, and contour cutting mainly in sheet and plate stock.

Friction Sawing

Friction sawing can be used to cut materials that would be impossible or very difficult to cut by other means. In friction sawing, the workpiece is heated by friction created between it and the cutting blade. The blade melts its way through the work. Friction sawing can be used to cut hard materials such as files. Tough materials such as stainless steel wire brushes can be trimmed by friction sawing (Figure 33). Friction sawing can only be done on machines with sufficiently high band speeds.

Band Filing and Band Polishing

The band file consists of file segments attached to a spring steel band (D) (Figure 34). As the band file passes through the work an interlock closes and keeps the file segment tight (B). The interlock then releases, permitting the file segment to roll around the band wheel. A space is provided for chip clearance between the band and file segment (C). The band file has a locking slot so that the ends can be joined to form a continuous loop (A). Special guides are required for both file and polishing bands. Band files can be used in both internal (Figure 35) and external (Figure 36) filing applications. They are also

Figure 31. Production trimming of castings on the vertical band machine (Courtesy of the DoAll Company).

Figure 30. Trimming casting sprues and risers on the vertical band machine (Courtesy of the DoAll Company).

Figure 33. Trimming stainless steel wire brushes by friction sawing (Courtesy of the DoAll Company).

Figure 32. Ripping on the vertical band machine (Courtesy of the DoAll Company).

used in applications such as filing large gear teeth to shape and size (Figure 37).

In band polishing, a continuous abrasive strip is used (Figure 38). The grit of the abrasive can be varied depending on the surface finish desired.

Figure 34. Band file (Courtesy of the DoAll Company).

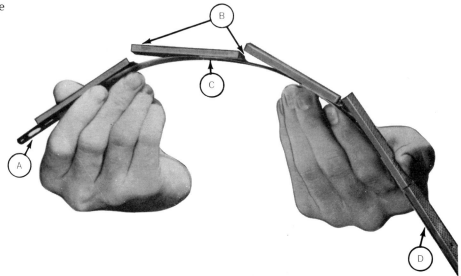

Figure 35. Internal band filing (Courtesy of the DoAll Company).

Figure 36. External band filing (Courtesy of the DoAll Company).

VERTICAL BAND MACHINE SAFETY

The **primary danger** in operating the vertical band machine is **accidental contact with the cutting blade.** Workpieces are often hand guided. One advantage in sawing machines is that the pressure of the cut tends to hold the workpiece against the saw table. However, hands are often in close proximity to the blade. If you should contact the blade accidentally, an injury is almost sure to occur. You will not have time even to think about withdrawing your fingers before they are cut. Keep this in mind at all times when operating a band saw.

Always use a **pusher** against the workpiece whenever possible. This will

keep your fingers away from the blade. Be careful as you are about to complete a cut. As the blade clears through the work, the pressure that you are applying is suddenly released and your hand or finger could be carried into the blade. As you approach the end of the cut, **reduce the feeding pressure** as the blade cuts through.

The vertical band machine is generally not used to cut round stock. This can be extremely hazardous and should be done on the horizontal band machine, where round stock can be secured in a vice. Hand-held round stock will turn if it is cut on the vertical band machine. This can cause an injury and may damage the blade as well. If round stock must be cut on the vertical band saw, it must be clamped securely in a vise, vee block, or other suitable workholding fixture.

Be sure to select the proper blade for the sawing requirements. Install it properly and apply the correct blade tension. Band tension should be rechecked after a few cuts. New blades will tend to stretch to some degree during their break-in period. Band tension may have to be readjusted.

The entire blade must be guarded except at the point of the cut. This is effectively accomplished by enclosing the wheels and blade behind guards that are easily opened for adjustments to the machine. Wheel and blade guard must be closed at all times during machine operation. The guidepost guard moves up and down with the guidepost (Figure 39). The operator is protected from an exposed blade at this point. For maximum safety, set the guidepost $\frac{1}{8}$ to $\frac{1}{4}$ in. above the workpiece.

Band machines may have one or two idler wheels. On machines with two idler wheels, a short blade running over only one wheel may be used. Under this condition an additional blade guard at the left side of the wheel is

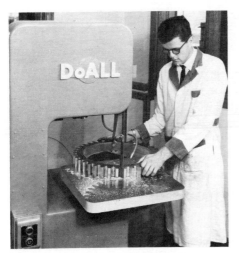

Figure 37. Band filing a large spur gear (Courtesy of the DoAll Company).

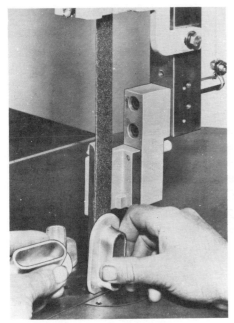

Figure 38. Band polishing (Courtesy of the DoAll Company).

Figure 39. Guidepost guard (CSU, Fresno).

Figure 40. Left side blade guard when using a short blade over one idler wheel (CSU, Fresno).

Figure 41. Roller blade guide shield (Courtesy of the California Community College — IMC Project).

required (Figure 40). This guard is removed when operating over two idler wheels as the blade is then behind the wheel guard.

Roller blade guides are used in friction and high speed sawing. A roller guide shield is used to provide protection for the operator (Figure 41). Depending on the material being cut, the entire cutting area may be enclosed. This would apply to the cutting of hard, brittle materials such as granite and glass. Diamond blades are frequently used in cutting these materials. The clear shield protects the operator while permitting him to view the operation. Cutting fluids are also prevented from spilling on the floor. In any sawing operation making use of cutting fluids, see that they do not spill on the floor around the machine. This creates an extremely dangerous situation, not only for you but for others in the shop as well.

Gloves should not be worn around any machine tool. An exception to this is for friction or high speed sawing or when handling band blades. Gloves will protect hands from the sharp saw teeth. If you wear gloves during friction or high speed sawing, be extra careful that they do not become entangled in the blade or other moving parts. Be prepared for teeth flying off the band. If this happens, gloves will not necessarily protect your hands.

UNIT 1 USING RECIPROCATING AND HORIZONTAL BAND CUTOFF MACHINES

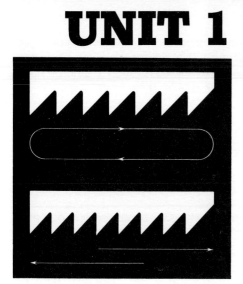

The reciprocating saw and the horizontal endless band saw are the most common cutoff machines you will encounter. Their primary function is to cut long lengths of material into lengths suitable for other machining operations on other machine tools. The cutoff machine is often the first step in machining a part to its final shape and size. In this unit, you are introduced to saw blades and the applications and operation of these important sawing machines.

OBJECTIVES

After completing this unit, you should be able to:
1. Use saw blade terminology.
2. Describe the conditions that define blade selection.
3. Identify the major parts of the reciprocating and horizontal band cutoff machine.
4. Properly install blades on reciprocating and horizontal band machines.
5. Properly use reciprocating and horizontal band machines in cutoff applications.

CUTTING SPEEDS

An understanding of cutting speeds is one of the most important aspects of machining you will encounter. Many years of machining experience have shown that certain tool materials are most effective if passed through workpiece materials at optimum speeds. If a tool material passes through the work too quickly, the heat generated by friction can rapidly dull the tool or cause it to fail completely. Too slow a passage of the tool through a material can result in premature dulling and low productivity.

A cutting speed refers to the amount of workpiece material that passes by a cutting tool in a given amount of time. Cutting speeds are measured in feet per minute. This is abbreviated FPM. In some machining operations, the tool can pass the work. Sawing is an example. The work may pass the tool as in the lathe. In both cases, FPM is the same. The shape of the workpiece does not affect the FPM. The circumference of a round part passing a cutting tool is still in FPM. In later units, FPM is discussed in terms of revolutions per minute of a round workpiece.

In sawing, FPM is simply the speed of each saw tooth as it passes through a given length of material in one minute. If one tooth of a band saw passes through one foot of material in one minute, the cutting speed is one foot per minute. This is true of reciprocating saws as well. However, remember that this saw only cuts in

one direction of the stroke. Cutting speeds are a critical factor in tool life. Productivity will be low if the sawing machine is stopped most of the time because a dull or damaged blade must be replaced frequently. The additional cost of replacement cutting tools must also be considered. In any machining operation, always keep cutting speeds in mind.

On a sawing machine, blade FPM is a function of RPM (revolutions per minute) of the saw drive. That is, the setting of a specific RPM on the saw drive will produce a specific FPM of the blade. Feet per minute is also related to the material being cut. Generally, hard, tough materials have low cutting speeds. Soft material has higher cutting speeds. In sawing, cutting speeds are affected by the material, size, and cross section of the workpiece.

SAW BLADES

The blade is the cutting tool of the sawing machine. In any sawing operation, at least three teeth on the saw blade must be in contact with the work at all times. This means that thin material requires a blade with more teeth per inch, while thick material can be cut with a blade having fewer teeth per inch. You should be familiar with the terminology of saw blades and saw cuts.

Blade Materials.   Saw blades for reciprocating and band saws are made from carbon steels and high speed alloy steels. Blades may also have tungsten carbide tipped teeth. Some blades are bimetallic.

Blade Kerf.   The kerf of a saw cut is the width of the cut as produced by the blade (Figure 1).

Blade Width.   The width of a saw blade is the distance from the tip of the tooth to the back of the blade (Figure 2).

Blade Gage.   Blade gage is the thickness behind the set of the blade (Figure 2). Reciprocating saw blades on large machines can be as thick as .250 in. Common band saw blades are .025 to .035 in. thick.

Blade Pitch.   The pitch of a saw blade is the number of teeth per inch (Figure 2). An eight pitch blade has eight teeth per inch (a tooth spacing of $\frac{1}{8}$ in.).

SAW TEETH

You should be familiar with saw tooth terminology (Figure 3).

Tooth Forms.   Tooth form is the shape of the saw tooth. Saw tooth forms are either standard, skip, or hook (Figure 4). Standard form gives accurate cuts with

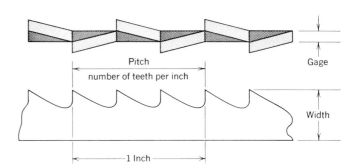

Figure 2.   Gage, pitch, and width.

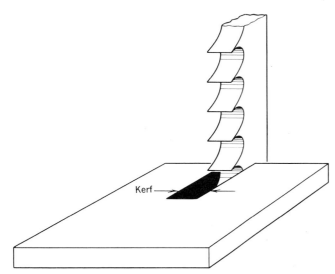

Figure 1.   Kerf.

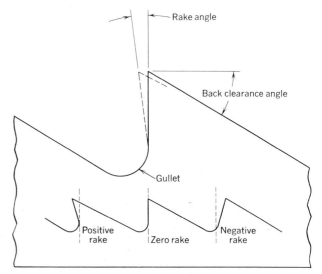

Figure 3.   Saw tooth terminology.

a smooth finish. Skip tooth gives additional chip clearance. Hook form provides faster cutting because of the positive rake angle especially in soft materials.

Set.   The teeth of a saw blade must be offset on each side to provide clearance for the back of the blade. This offset is called set (Figure 5). Set is equal on both sides of the blade. The set dimension is the total distance from the tip of a tooth on one side to the tip of a tooth on the other side.

Set Patterns.   Set forms include raker, straight, and wave (Figure 5). Raker and wave are the most common. Raker set is used in general sawing. Wave set is useful where the cross-sectional shape of the workpiece varies.

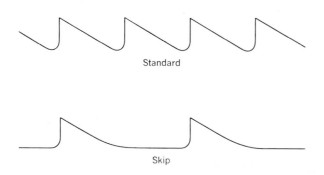

Standard

Skip

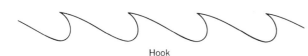

Hook

Figure 4.   Tooth forms.

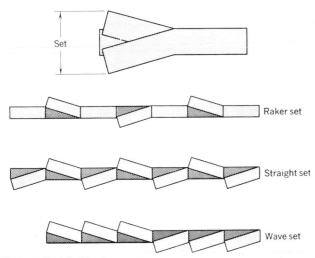

Set

Raker set

Straight set

Wave set

Figure 5.   Set and set patterns.

SELECTING A BLADE
FOR RECIPROCATING AND BAND SAWS

Blade selection will depend upon the material, thickness, and cross-sectional shape of the workpiece. Some band cutoff machines have a job selector (Figure 6). This will aid you greatly in selecting the proper blade for your sawing requirement. On a machine without a job selector, analyze the job and then select a suitable blade. For example, if you must cut thin tube, a fine pitch blade will be needed so that three teeth are in contact with the work. A particularly soft material may require a zero rake angle tooth form. Sawing through a workpiece with changing cross section may require a blade with wavy set to provide maximum accuracy.

USING CUTTING FLUIDS

Cutting fluids are an extremely important aid to sawing. The heat produced by the cutting action can become so great that the metallurgical structure of the blade teeth can be affected. Cutting fluids will dissipate much of this heat and greatly prolong the life of the blade. Besides their function as a coolant, they also lubricate the blade. Sawing with cutting fluids will produce a smoother finish on the workpiece. One of the most important functions of a cutting fluid is to transport chips out of the cut. This allows the blade to work more efficiently. Common cutting fluids are oils, oils dissolved in water or soluble oils, and synthetic chemical cutting fluids.

OPERATING THE RECIPROCATING
CUTOFF MACHINE

The reciprocating cutoff machine (Figure 7) is often

Figure 6.   Job selector on a horizontal band cutoff machine (Courtesy of the DoAll Company).

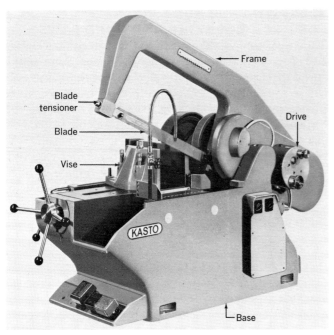

Figure 7. Reciprocating cutoff saw (Courtesy of Kasto-Racine, Inc.).

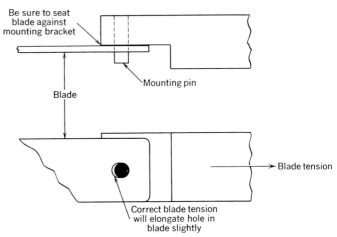

Figure 8. Blade mounting on the reciprocating cutoff saw.

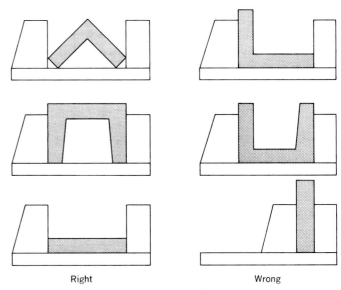

Figure 9. Cutting workpieces with sharp corners.

known as the power hacksaw. This machine is an outgrowth of the hand hacksaw. Basically, the machine consists of a frame supported blade that is operated in a back-and-forth motion. Power hacksaws may be hydraulically driven or driven by a crankshaft mechanism.

Installing the Blade on the Power Hacksaw

Obtain a blade of the correct length and make sure that the teeth are pointed in the direction of the cut. This will be on the back stroke. Make sure that the blade is seated against the mounting plates (Figure 8). Apply the correct tension. The blade may be tightened until a definite ring is heard when the blade is tapped. Do not overtighten the blade, as this may cause the pin holes to break out. If a new blade is installed, the tension should be rechecked after making a few cuts.

Making the Cut

Select the appropriate strokes per minute speed rate for the material being cut. Be sure to secure the workpiece properly. If you are cutting material with a sharp corner, begin the cut on a flat side if possible. Note that angle material presents a sharp corner to the blade. Start the saw gently until a small flat is established (Figure 9). Before making the cut, go over the safety checklist. Make sure that the length of the workpiece does not exceed the capacity of the stroke. This can break the frame if it should hit the workpiece. Bring the saw gently down until the blade has a chance to start cutting. Apply

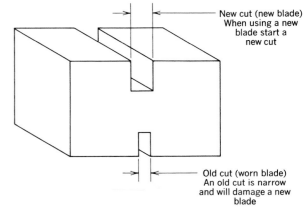

Figure 10. If the blade is changed, begin a new cut on the other side of the workpiece.

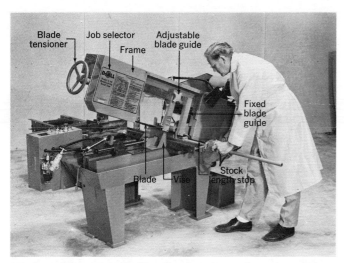

Figure 11. Horizontal endless band cutoff machine (Courtesy of the DoAll Company).

Figure 12. Comparison of kerf widths from band, reciprocating, and abrasive cutoff machines (Courtesy of the DoAll Company).

the proper feed. On reciprocating saws, feed is regulated with a sliding weight or feeding mechanism. If chips produced in the cut are blue, too much feed is being used. The blade will be damaged rapidly. Very fine powder like chips indicate too little pressure. This will dull the blade. If the blade is replaced after starting a cut, turn the workpiece over and begin a new cut (Figure 10). Do not attempt to saw through the old cut. This will damage the new blade. After a new blade has been used for a short time, recheck the tension and adjust if necessary.

OPERATING THE HORIZONTAL BAND CUTOFF MACHINE

The horizontal band cutoff machine (Figure 11) is the most common stock cutoff machine found in the machine shop. This machine tool uses an endless steel band blade with teeth on one edge. Since the blade passes through the work continuously, there is no wasted motion. Cutting efficiency is greatly increased over the reciprocating saw.

The kerf from the band blade is quite narrow as compared to the reciprocating hacksaw or abrasive saw (Figure 12). This is an added advantage in that minimum amounts of material are wasted in the sawing operation.

The size of the horizontal band saw is determined by the largest piece of square material that can be cut. Speeds on the horizontal band machine may be set by manual belt change (Figure 13), or a variable speed drive may be used. The variable speed drive permits an infinite selection of band speeds within the capacity of the machine. Cutting speeds can be set precisely. Many horizontal band machines are of the hinge design. The saw head, containing the drive and idler wheels, hinges around a point at the rear of the machine.

Figure 13. Changing speeds by shifting belts on a horizontal band saw (Courtesy of the DoAll Company).

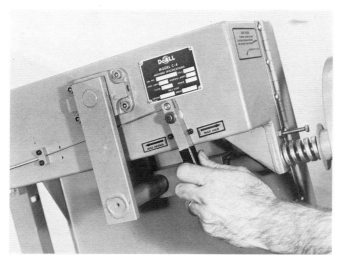

Figure 14. Horizontal band saw head release lever (Courtesy of the DoAll Company).

Figure 16. Coolant system on the horizontal band saw (Courtesy of the DoAll Company).

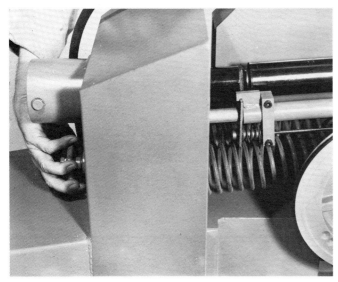

Figure 15. Adjusting the head tension on the horizontal band saw (Courtesy of the DoAll Company).

The saw head may be raised and locked in the up position while stock is being placed into or removed from the machine (Figure 14). Feeds are accomplished by gravity of the saw head. The feed rate can be regulated by adjusting the spring tension on the saw head (Figure 15). Some sawing machines use a hydraulic cylinder to regulate the feed rate. The head is held in the up position by the cylinder. A control valve permits oil to flow into the reservoir as the saw head descends. This permits the feed rate to be regulated.

Cutting fluid is pumped from a reservoir and flows on the blade at the forward guide. Additional fluid is permitted to flow on the blade at the point of the cut (Figure

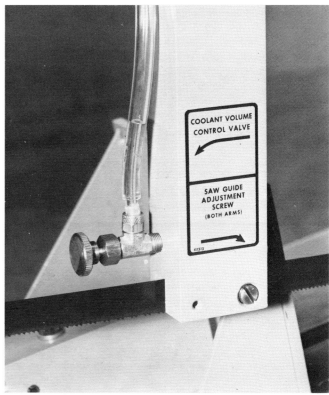

Figure 17. Coolant volume control valve on the horizontal band saw (Courtesy of the DoAll Company).

16). The saw shown does not have the now required full blade guards installed. Cutting fluid flow is controlled by a control valve (Figure 17). Chips can be cleared from the blade by a rotary brush that operates as the blade runs (Figure 18).

Figure 18. Rotary chip brushes on the band saw blade (Courtesy of the DoAll Company).

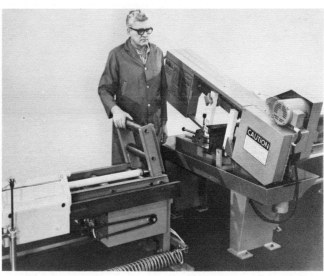

Figure 20. Roller stock table with access gate (Courtesy of the DoAll Company).

Figure 19. Setting the stock length gage (Courtesy of the DoAll Company).

Figure 21. Quick setting vise on the horizontal band saw (Courtesy of the DoAll Company).

Common accessories used on many horizontal band saws include workpiece length measuring equipment (Figure 19) and roller stock tables. The stock table shown has a hinged section that permits the operator to reach the rear of the machine (Figure 20).

Workholding on the Horizontal Band Saw

The vise is the most common workholding fixture. Rapid adjusting vises are very popular (Figure 21). These vises have large capacity and are quickly adjusted to the workpiece. After the vise jaws have contacted the workpiece, the vise is locked by operating the lock handle. The vise may be swiveled for miter or angle cuts (Figure 22). On some horizontal band cutoff machines, the entire saw frame swivels for making angle cuts (Figure 23).

The horizontal band saw is often used to cut several pieces of material at once. Stock may be held or nested in a special vise or nesting fixture (Figure 24).

Figure 22.   Band saw vise swiveled for angle cutting (Courtesy of the DoAll Company).

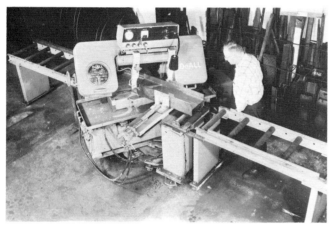

Figure 23.   Horizontal cutoff saw frame swiveled for angle cuts (Courtesy of the DoAll Company).

Figure 24.   Nesting fixture for sawing multiple workpieces (Courtesy of the DoAll Company).

Installing Blades on the Horizontal Band Machine

Blades for the horizontal band saw may be ordered prewelded in the proper length for the machine. Band blade may also be obtained in rolls. The required length is then cut and welded at the sawing machine location.

To install the band, shut off power to the machine and open the wheel guards. Release the tension by turning the tension wheel. Place the blade around the drive and idler wheels. Be sure that the teeth are pointed in the direction of the cut. This will be toward the rear of the machine. See that the blade is tracking properly on the idler and drive wheels (Figure 25). The blade will have to be twisted slightly to fit the guides. Guides should be adjusted so that they have .001 to .002 in. clearance with the blade. Adjust the blade tension using the tension gage (Figure 26) or the manual tension indicator built into the saw (Figure 27). The blade is tightened until the flange on the tension wheel contacts the tension indicator stop.

Making the Cut

Set the proper speed according to the blade type and material to be cut. If the workpiece has sharp corners, it should be positioned in the same manner as in the reciprocating saw (Figure 9). The blade guides must be adjusted so that they are as close to the work as possible (Figure 28). This will insure maximum blade support and maximum accuracy of the cut. Sufficient feed should be used to produce a good chip. Excessive feed can cause blade failure. Too little feed can dull the blade prematurely. Go over the safety checklist for horizontal band saws. Release the head and lower it by hand until the

Figure 25.   Make sure that the blade is tracking properly on the band wheel (CSU, Fresno).

Figure 26. Dial band tension indicator gage (Courtesy of the DoAll Company).

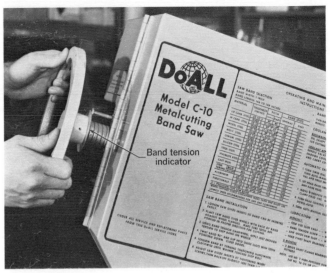

Figure 27. Band tension indicator attached to the machine (Courtesy of the DoAll Company).

blade starts to cut. Most saws are equipped with an automatic shutoff switch. When the cut is completed, the machine will shut off automatically.

SAWING PROBLEMS ON THE HORIZONTAL BAND MACHINE

You may use the stock stop to gage the length of duplicate pieces of material (Figure 29). It is important to swing the stop clear of the work after the vise has been tightened and before the cut is begun (Figure 30). A cutoff workpiece can bind between the stop and blade. This will destroy the blade set (Figure 31). A blade with a tooth set worn on one side will drift in the direction of the side that has a set still remaining (Figure 32). This is the principal cause of band breakage. As the saw progresses through the cut, the side draft of the blade will place the machine under great stress. The cut may drift so far as to permit the blade to cut into the vise (Figure 33).

Very thin and quite parallel workpieces can be cut by using a sharp blade in a rigid and accurate sawing machine (Figure 34). Chip removal is important to accurate cutting. If chips are not cleared from the blade prior to it entering the guides, the blade will be scored. This will make it brittle and subject to breakage.

Figure 28. Blade guide should be set as close to the workpiece as possible (CSU, Fresno).

Figure 29. Stock length stop in position (CSU, Fresno).

Figure 30. Stock length stop must be removed before beginning the cut (CSU, Fresno).

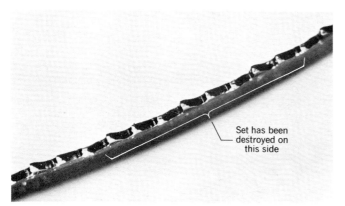

Figure 31. Band saw blade with the set worn on one side (Courtesy, California Community Colleges — IMC Project).

Figure 32. Using a band with the set worn on one side will cause the cut to drift toward the side of the blade with the set remaining (Courtesy, California Community Colleges — IMC Project).

Figure 33. The blade may drift far enough to damage the vise (Courtesy California Community Colleges — IMC Project).

Figure 34. Thin and parallel cuts may be made with a sharp blade and rigid sawing machine.

SELF-TEST

1. Name the most common saw blade set patterns.
2. Describe the conditions that define blade selection.
3. On a reciprocating saw, what is the direction of the cut?
4. What is set and why is it necessary?
5. What are common tooth forms?
6. What can happen if the stock stop is left in place during the cut?
7. What type of cutoff saw will most likely be found in the machine shop?
8. Of what value are cutting fluids?
9. What can result if chips are not properly removed from the cut?
10. If a blade is replaced after a cut has been started, what must be done with the workpiece?

UNIT 2 ABRASIVE AND COLD SAWS

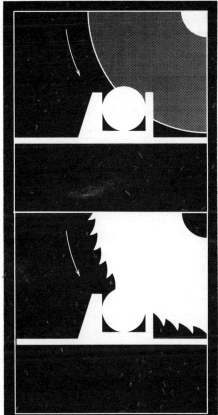

The abrasive saw is seldom used for stock cutoff in the machine shop. Small metal chips and abrasive wheel particles produced by the abrasive saw can damage other machine tools. However, the abrasive saw may be used in or around the machine shop or grinding room for the purpose of cutting hardened materials such as drills and endmills. Abrasive saws are very common in fabrication and welding shops. The abrasive saw has an advantage over other cutoff machines in that it can cut a number of nonmetallic materials such as slate, stone, brick, and glass.

The cold saw is seen in the machine shop. This type of cutoff machine uses a circular blade with teeth. Cold saws are useful in stock cutoff where length tolerances must be held as close as possible. You may see and possibly use a cold saw in stock cutoff applications.

OBJECTIVES

After completing this unit, you should be able to:
1. Identify abrasive and cold saws.
2. Identify abrasive wheel materials.
3. Identify abrasive wheel bonds.
4. Describe the operation of abrasive cold sawing machines.

ABRASIVE SAWING MACHINES

The **abrasive saw** (Figure 1) consists of a high speed motor driven abrasive wheel mounted on a swing arm. Abrasive saws are very fast cutting. The reason for this is that each particle of the abrasive wheel acts to cut a small bit of material. Since the abrasive wheel has a large number of abrasive particles, many "teeth" are involved in the cutting action. Abrasive wheels may operate at cutting speeds of 15 to 20 thousand feet per minute. A large number of abrasive particles delivered past the work at a high foot per minute rate makes for very fast cutting. One disadvantage of the abrasive saw is that common blades cut with a wide kerf. Considerable material may be wasted in the cut. However, some abrasive wheel materials permit a very thin wheel to be used. Abrasive sawing produces a large amount of heat in the workpiece. Cutting fluids act as coolants and are often used in abrasive sawing.

Abrasives

Abrasive saw wheels are made from aluminum oxide and silicon carbide. Aluminum oxide abrasives are used for most metals, including steel. Silicon carbide abrasive is used for nonmetallic materials such as stone. Diamond abrasives are used for extremely hard materials, such as glass.

Abrasive Saw Wheel Bonds

The **bond** of an abrasive saw wheel is the material that holds the abrasive particles together. The bond must be strong enough to withstand the large force placed on the wheel at high revolutions per minute as well as the heat generated in the cut. However, the bond must also be able to break down as the wheel cuts. This is necessary to expose new abrasive particles to the cut.

Shellac bond abrasive wheels are suited for cutting hard steels. **Resinoid bond** wheels are suitable for cut-

Figure 1. Typical abrasive cutoff machine (CSU, Fresno).

ting structural shapes and bar stock. **Rubber bond** wheels produce clean cuts when used with cutting fluids. Rubber bond wheels can be made as thin as .006 in.

Abrasive Saw Wheel Speeds

Abrasive saw wheel speeds vary as to the diameter of the wheel. A 12 in. diameter wheel can be operated at about 14,000 surface feet per minute. Twenty-inch wheels should be run at about 12,000 surface feet per minute. Surface feet is the speed of the wheel as measured at the circumference. Recommended wheel speeds will be marked on each wheel. **Abrasive saw wheels must not be operated at speeds faster than recommended.**

Selecting Abrasive Saws

The following factors affect the selection of an abrasive saw.

1. Material to be cut.
2. Size of material.
3. Cut to be made dry or with cutting fluid.
4. Degree of finish desired and acceptable burr (sharp edge left by the saw).

Quality of Abrasive Saw Cuts

Excessive heat generated in the cut may discolor the material or possibly affect metallurgical properties. This problem may be solved by selection of a different wheel. The use of a cutting fluid will produce a smooth cut with less of a burr. In some wet abrasive saw applications, the workpiece and part of the blade may be totally submerged in the cutting fluid. Fluids include a soda solution or plain water.

Abrasive Saw Feed Rates

An extremely light feed will heat the wheel excessively. Heavy feeding may result in excessive wheel wear or the wheel may break causing an extreme hazard. Feed rates depend on many factors, including the material to be cut, wheel type, speeds, and the condition of the abrasive sawing machine.

OPERATING THE ABRASIVE SAWING MACHINE

Inspect the abrasive wheel for chips and cracks. Be sure that it is rated at the proper RPM for the machine. Work-holding on the abrasive saw may be a simple vise or a quick setting production fixture such as an air operated chain vise. Here the chain passes over the workpiece and a link hooks into the chain catch (Figure 2). The chain

Figure 2. Quick setting chain vise (CSU, Fresno).

is tightened by a winder operated by an air cylinder (Figure 3).

Go over the safety checklist for abrasive saws. Start the machine and bring the abrasive wheel down until the cut begins. Use a feed rate that is suitable for the material being cut and the wheel being used (Figure 4). The abrasive saw may be swiveled to the side for miter cuts (Figure 5).

COLD SAWS

The **cold saw** (Figure 6) uses a circular metal blade with teeth. Cold saws are very useful in precision cutoff applications where length tolerance must be held as close as possible. A cold saw blade on a precision cutoff machine may be 7 to 8 in. in diameter with a thickness

of .040 to .080 in. The blade cuts a narrow kerf. A minimum amount of material is wasted in the cut. This is important when cutting expensive materials. Length tolerance and parallelism of the cut can be held to plus or minus .002 in. To obtain this degree of accuracy, hold

Figure 5.   The abrasive saw may be swiveled for angle cutting (CSU, Fresno).

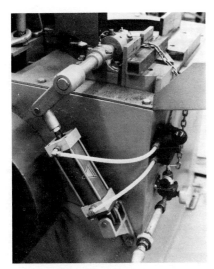

Figure 3.   Chain vise operating mechanism (CSU, Fresno).

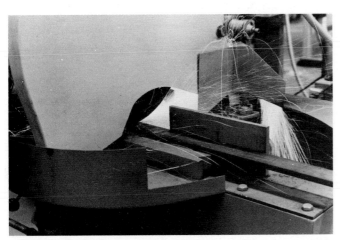

Figure 4.   Making a cut with the abrasive saw (CSU, Fresno).

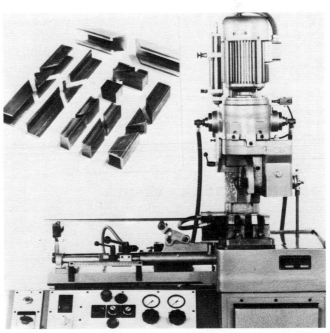

Figure 6.   The precision cold saw can make straight and angle cuts in materials with different cross sections (Courtesy of Ameropean Industries, Inc.).

the stock on both sides of the blade. A precision cold saw blade may be operated at speeds of 25 to 1200 RPM, depending on the size, shape, and material of the workpiece. Cold saws can be used to make straight and angle cuts in material with different cross sections (Figure 6). Cold saws with blade diameters of about 24 in. are also used for stock cutoff in machine and fabrication shops.

SELF-TEST

1. Are you likely to find an abrasive saw in a machine shop?
2. What are the advantages of the abrasive saw?
3. Name two types of abrasives.
4. Name two types of abrasive wheel bonds.
5. What is one advantage of a precision cold saw? This unit has no post-test.

UNIT 3 PREPARING TO USE THE VERTICAL BAND MACHINE

A machine tool can perform at maximum efficiency only if it has been properly maintained, adjusted, and set up. Before the vertical band machine can be used for a sawing or other band machining operation, several important preparations must be made. These include welding saw blades into bands and making several adjustments on the machine tool.

OBJECTIVES

After completing this unit, you should be able to:
1. Weld band saw blades.
2. Prepare the vertical band machine for operation.

WELDING BAND SAW BLADES

Band saw blade is frequently supplied in rolls. The required length is measured and cut and the ends are welded together to form an endless band. Most band machines are equipped with a band welding attachment. These are frequently attached to the machine tool. They may also be separate pieces of equipment (Figure 1).

The **band welder** is a resistance-type butt welder. They are often called **flash** welders because of the bright flash and shower of sparks created during the welding operation. The metal in the blade material has a certain resistance to the flow of an electric current. This resistance causes the blade metal to heat as the electric current flows during the welding operation. The blade metal is heated to a temperature that permits the ends to be forged together under pressure. When the forging temperature is reached, the ends of the blade are pushed together by mechanical pressure. They fuse, forming a resistance weld. The band weld is then annealed or softened and dressed to the correct thickness by grinding.

Welding band saw blades is a fairly simple operation and you should master it as soon as possible. Blade welding is frequently done in the machine shop. New blades

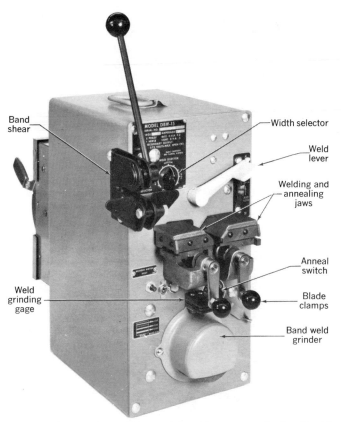

Figure 1. Band blade welder (Courtesy of the DoAll Company).

Figure 2. Blade shear (CSU, Fresno).

Figure 3. Placing the blade ends together with the teeth opposed (CSU, Fresno).

are always being prepared. Sawing operations, where totally enclosed workpiece features must be cut, require that the blade be inserted through a starting hole in the workpiece and then welded into a band. After the enclosed cut is made, the blade is broken apart and removed.

PREPARING THE BLADE FOR WELDING

The first step is to cut the required length of blade stock for the band machine that you are using. Blade stock can be cut with snips or with the band shear (Figure 2). Start the cut on the side of the band opposite the teeth. Many band machines have a blade shear near the welder. The required length of blade will usually be marked on the saw frame. Blade length, B_L, for two wheel sawing machines can be calculated by the formula

$$B_L = \pi D + 2L$$

where D is the diameter of the band wheel and L is the distance between band wheel centers. Set the tension adjustment on the idler wheel about midrange so that the blade will fit after welding. Most machine shops will have a permanent reference mark, probably on the

floor, that can be used for gaging blade length.

After cutting the required length of stock, the ends of the blade must be ground so that they are square when positioned in the welder. Place the ends of the blade together so that the teeth are opposed (Figure 3). Grind the blade ends in this position. The grinding wheel on the blade welder may be used for this operation. Blade ends may also be ground on the pedestal grinder

(Figure 4). Grinding the blade ends with the teeth opposed will insure that the ends of the blade are square when the blade is positioned in the welder. Any small error in grinding will be canceled when the teeth are placed in their normal position.

Proper grinding of the blade ends permits correct tooth spacing to be maintained. After the blade has been welded, the tooth spacing across the weld should be the **same** as any other place on the band. Tooth set should be aligned as well. A certain amount of blade material is consumed in the welding process. Therefore, the blade must be ground correctly if tooth spacing is to

be maintained. The amount consumed by the welding process may vary with different blade welders. You will have to determine this by experimentation. For example, if one-quarter in. of blade length is consumed in welding, this would amount to about one tooth on a four pitch blade. Therefore, one tooth should be ground from the blade. This represents the amount lost in welding (Figure 5). Be sure to grind only the tooth and not the end of the blade. The number of teeth to grind from a blade will vary according to the pitch and amount of material consumed by a specific welder. The weld should occur at the bottom of the tooth **gullet.** Exact tooth spacing

Figure 4. End grinding the blade on the pedestal grinder (CSU, Fresno).

Figure 6. Placing the blade in the welder (Courtesy, California Community Colleges — IMC Project).

Figure 5. The amount of blade lost in welding.

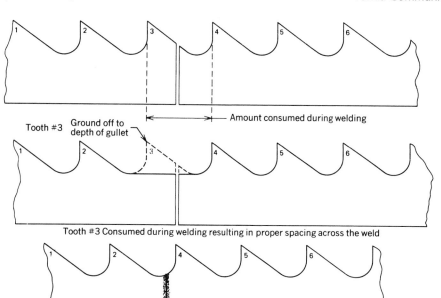

can be somewhat difficult to obtain. You may have to practice end grinding and welding several pieces of scrap blades until you are familiar with the proper welding and tooth grinding procedure.

The jaws of the blade welder should be clean before attempting any welding. Position the blade ends in the welder jaws (Figure 6). The saw teeth should point toward the back. This prevents scoring of the jaws when welding blades of different widths. A uniform amount of blade should extend from each jaw. The blade ends must contact squarely in the center of the gap between the welder jaws. Be sure that the blade ends are not off-set or overlapped. Tighten the blade clamps.

WELDING THE BLADE INTO AN ENDLESS BAND

Adjust the welder for the proper width of blade to be welded. **Wear eye protection** and stand to one side of the welder during the welding operation. Depress the weld lever. A flash with a shower of sparks will occur (Figure 7). In this brief operation, the movable jaw of the welder moved toward the stationary jaw. The blade ends were heated to forging temperature by a flow of electric current, and the molten ends of the blades were pushed together, forming a solid joint.

The blade clamps should be loosened before releasing the weld lever. This prevents scoring of the welder jaws by the now welded band. A correctly welded band will have the weld **flash** evenly distributed across the weld zone (Figure 8). Tooth spacing across the weld should be the same as the rest of the band.

ANNEALING THE WELD

The metal in the weld zone is hard and brittle immediately after welding. For the band to function, the weld must be **annealed** or **softened.** This improves strength qualities of the weld. Place the band in the annealing jaws with the teeth pointed out (Figure 9). This will concentrate annealing heat away from the saw teeth. A small amount of compression should be placed on the movable welder jaw prior to clamping the band. This permits the jaw to move as the annealing heat expands the band.

It is most important not to overheat the weld during the annealing process. Overheating can destroy an otherwise good weld, causing it to become brittle. The correct annealing temperature is determined by the color of the weld zone during annealing. This should be a dull red color. Depress the anneal switch and watch the band heat. When the dull red color appears, release the anneal switch immediately and let the band begin to cool. As the weld cools, depress the anneal switch

Figure 7. Welding the blade into a band (Courtesy of the DoAll Company).

Figure 8. Weld flash should be evenly distributed after welding (CSU, Fresno).

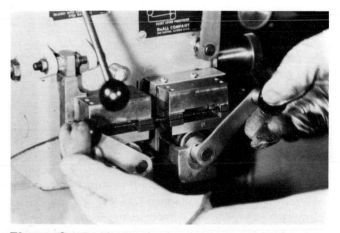

Figure 9. Positioning the band for annealing (Courtesy, California Community Colleges — IMC Project).

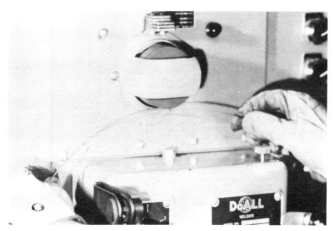

Figure 10. Grinding the band weld (Courtesy, California Community Colleges — IMC Project).

Figure 12. Band weld thickness gage (Courtesy, California Community Colleges — IMC Project).

Figure 11. The saw teeth must not be ground while grinding the band weld (CSU, Fresno).

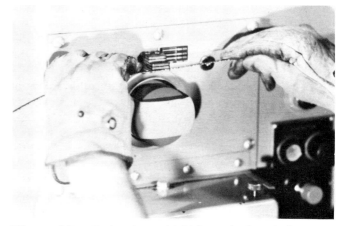

Figure 13. Gaging the weld thickness in the grinding gage (Courtesy, California Community Colleges — IMC Project).

briefly several times to slow the cooling rate. Too rapid cooling can result in a band weld that is not properly annealed.

GRINDING THE WELD

Some machinists prefer to grind the band weld prior to annealing. This permits the annealing color to be seen more easily. More often, the weld is ground after the annealing process. However, it is good practice to anneal the blade weld further after grinding. This will eliminate any hardness induced during the grinding operation. The grinding wheel on the band welder is designed for this operation. The top and bottom of the grinding wheel are exposed so that both sides of the

weld can be ground (Figure 10). **Be careful not to grind the teeth** when grinding a band weld. This will destroy the tooth set. Grind the band weld evenly on both sides (Figure 11). The weld should be ground to the same thickness as the rest of the band. If the weld area is ground thinner, the band will be weakened at that point. As you grind, check the band thickness in the gage (Figure 12) to determine proper thickness (Figure 13).

PROBLEMS IN BAND WELDING

Several problems may be encountered in band welding (Figure 14). These include misaligned pitch, blade misalignment, insufficient welding heat, or too much welding heat. You should learn to recognize and avoid these problems. The best way to do this is to obtain some scrap blades and practice the welding and grinding operations.

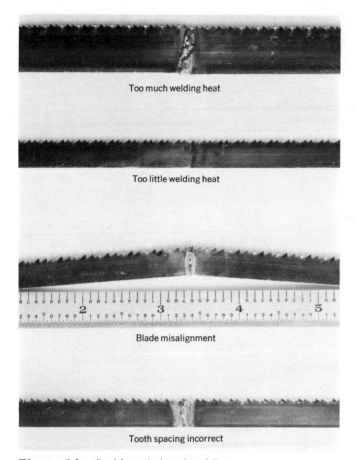

Figure 14. Problems in band welding.

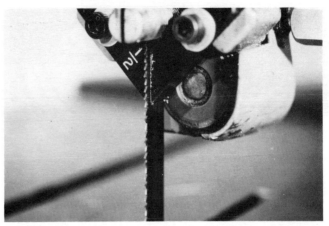

Figure 15. Band guides must fully support the band but must not extend over the saw teeth (Courtesy, California Community Colleges – IMC Project).

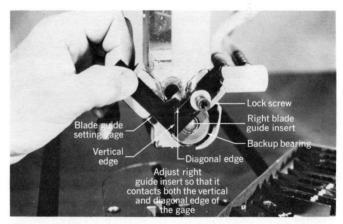

Figure 16. Using the saw guide setting gage (Courtesy, California Community Colleges – IMC Project).

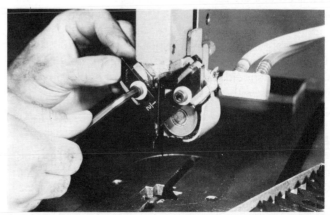

Figure 17. Adjusting the band guides for band thickness (Courtesy, California Community Colleges – IMC Project).

INSTALLING AND ADJUSTING BAND GUIDES ON THE VERTICAL BAND MACHINE

Band guides must be properly installed if the band machine is to cut accurately and if damage to the band is to be prevented. Be sure to use the **correct width guides** for the band (Figure 15). The band must be fully supported except for the teeth. Using wide band guides with a narrow band will destroy tooth set as soon as the machine is started.

Band guides are set with a **guide setting gage.** Install the right-hand band guide and tighten the lock screw just enough to hold the guide insert in place. Place the setting gage in the left guide slot and adjust the position of the right guide insert so that it is in contact with both the vertical and diagonal edges of the gage (Figure 16). Check the **backup bearing** at this time. Clear any chips that might prevent it from turning freely. If the backup bearing cannot turn freely, it will be scored by the band and damaged permanently.

Install the right-hand guide insert and make the adjustment for band thickness using the same setting gage (Figure 17). The thickness of the band will be

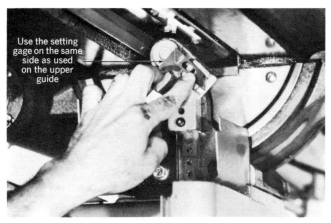

Figure 18. When adjusting the lower guide, use the setting gage on the same side as on the upper guide (Courtesy, California Community Colleges — IMC Project).

Figure 20. Coolant may be introduced directly ahead of the band (Courtesy of the DoAll Company).

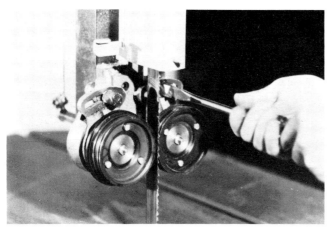

Figure 19. Adjusting roller band guides (Courtesy, California Community Colleges — IMC Project).

Figure 21. Mist and flood coolant nozzles (Courtesy, California Community Colleges — IMC Project).

marked on the tool. Be sure that this is the same as the band that will be used. The lower band guide is adjusted in a like manner. Use the setting gage on the same side as it was used when adjusting the top guides (Figure 18).

Roller band guides are used in high speed sawing applications where band velocities exceed 2000 FPM. They are also used in friction sawing operations. The roller guide should be adjusted so that it has .001 to .002 in. clearance with the band (Figure 19).

ADJUSTING THE COOLANT NOZZLE
A band machine may be equipped with flood or mist coolant. Mist coolant is liquid coolant mixed with air. Certain sawing operations may require only small amounts of coolant. With the mist system, liquid coolant is conserved and is less likely to spill on the floor. When cutting with flood coolant, be sure that the runoff

returns to the reservoir and does not spill on the floor. Flood coolant may be introduced directly ahead of the band (Figure 20).

Flood or mist coolant may be introduced through a nozzle in the upper guidepost assembly (Figure 21). Air and liquid are supplied to the inlet side of the nozzle by two hoses (Figure 22). The coolant nozzle must be installed (Figure 23) and preset (Figure 24) prior to installing the band. For mist coolant set the nozzle end $\frac{1}{2}$ in. from the face of the band guide. The setting for flood is $\frac{3}{8}$ in.

INSTALLING THE BAND ON
THE VERTICAL BAND MACHINE
Open the upper and lower wheel covers and remove the filler plate for the worktable. It is **safer to handle the band with gloves to protect your hands** from the sharp

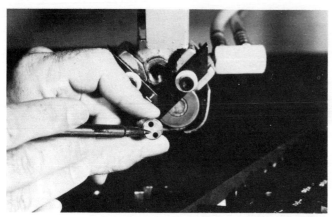

Figure 22. Inlet side of the coolant nozzle (Courtesy, California Community Colleges — IMC Project).

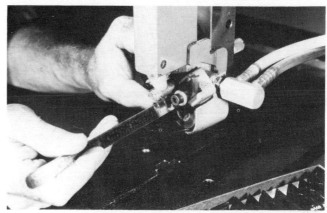

Figure 24. Presetting the coolant nozzle position before installing the band guides (Courtesy, California Community Colleges — IMC Project).

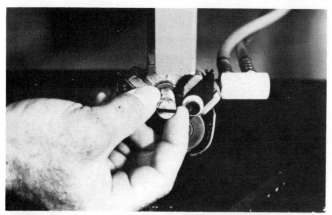

Figure 23. Installing the coolant nozzle (Courtesy, California Community Colleges — IMC Project).

saw teeth. The hand tension crank is attached to the upper idler wheel (Figure 25). Turn the crank to lower the wheel to a point where the band can be placed around the drive and idler wheels. Be sure to install the band so the teeth point in the direction of the cut. This is always in a **down direction toward the worktable.** If the saw teeth seem to be pointed in the wrong direction, the band may have to be turned inside out. This can be done easily. Place the band around the drive and idler wheels and turn the tension crank so that tension is placed on the band. Be sure that the band slips into the upper and lower guides properly. Replace the filler plate in the worktable.

Adjusting Band Tension
Proper **band tension** is important to accurate cutting. A high tensile strength band should be used whenever possible. Tensile strength refers to the strength of the band to withstand stretch. The correct band tension is

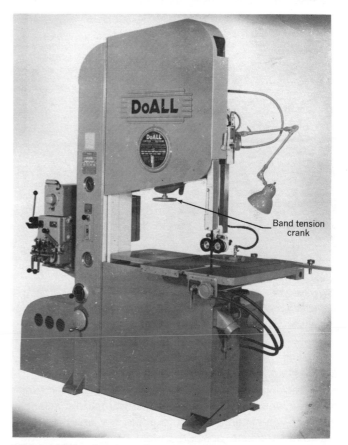

Band tension crank

Figure 25. Band tension crank (Courtesy of the DoAll Company).

indicated on the **band tension dial** (Figure 26). Adjust the tension for the width of band that you are using. After a new band has been run for a short time, recheck the tension. New bands tend to stretch during their initial running period.

Figure 26. Band tension dial (Courtesy of the DoAll Company).

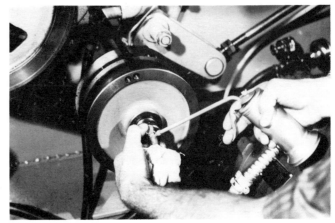

Figure 28. Lubricating the variable speed pulley hub (Courtesy, California Community Colleges — IMC Project).

Figure 27. Adjusting the band tracking position by tilting the idler wheel (Courtesy, California Community Colleges — IMC Project).

Adjusting Band Tracking

Band tracking refers to the position of the band as it runs on the idler wheel tires. On the vertical band machine, the idler wheel can be tilted to adjust tracking position. The band tracking position should be set so that the back of the band just touches the backup bearing in the guide assembly. Generally, you will not have to adjust band tracking very often. After you have installed a blade, check the tracking position. If it is incorrect, consult your instructor for help in adjusting the tracking position.

The tracking adjustment is made with the motor off and the speed range transmission in neutral. This permits

Figure 29. Band wheel chip brush (Courtesy, California Community Colleges — IMC Project).

the band to be rolled by hand. Two knobs are located on the idler wheel hub. The outer knob (Figure 27) tilts the wheel. The inner knob is the tilt lock. Loosen the lock knob and adjust the tilt of the idler wheel while rolling the band by hand. When the correct tracking position is reached, lock the inner knob. If the band machine has three idler wheels, adjust band tracking on the top wheel first. Then adjust tracking position on the back wheel.

OTHER ADJUSTMENTS ON THE VERTICAL BAND MACHINE

The hub of the variable speed pulley should be lubricated weekly (Figure 28). While the drive mechanism guard is open, check the oil level in the speed range transmission. The band machine may be equipped with a chip brush on the band wheel (Figure 29). This should be adjusted frequently. Chips that are transported through the band guides can score the band and make it brittle. The hydraulic oil level should be checked daily on band machines with hydraulic table feeds (Figure 30).

Figure 30. Checking the hydraulic oil level on the vertical band machine (Courtesy, California Community Colleges — IMC Project).

SELF-TEST

1. Describe the blade end grinding procedure.
2. Describe the band welding procedure.
3. Describe the weld grinding procedure.
4. What is the purpose of the band blade guide?
5. Why is it important to use a band guide of the correct width?
6. What tool can be used to adjust band guides?
7. What is the function of annealing the band weld?
8. Describe the annealing process.
9. What is band tracking?
10. How is band tracking adjusted?

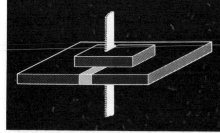

UNIT 4 USING THE VERTICAL BAND MACHINE

After a machine tool has been properly adjusted and set up, it can be used to accomplish a machining task. In the preceding unit, you had an opportunity to prepare the vertical band machine for use. In this unit, you will be able to operate this versatile machine tool.

OBJECTIVES

After completing this unit, you should be able to:
1. Use the vertical band machine job selector.
2. Operate the band machine controls.
3. Perform typical sawing operations on the vertical band machine.

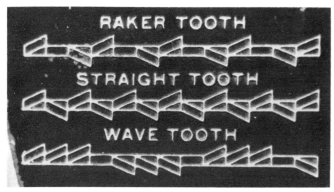

Figure 1. Blade set patterns (CSU, Fresno).

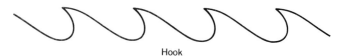

Figure 2. Saw tooth forms.

SELECTING A BLADE FOR
THE VERTICAL BAND MACHINE

Blade materials include standard carbon steel where the saw teeth are fully hardened but the back of the blade remains soft. The standard carbon steel blade is available in the greatest combination of width, set, pitch, and gage.

The carbon alloy steel blade has hardened teeth and also a hardened back. The harder back permits sufficient flexibility of the blade but, because of increased tensile strength, a higher band tension may be used. Because of this, cutting accuracy is greatly improved. The carbon alloy blade material is well suited to contour sawing.

High speed steel and bimetallic high speed steel blade materials are used in high production and severe sawing applications where blades must have long wearing characteristics. The high speed steel blade can withstand much more heat than the carbon or carbon alloy materials. On the bimetallic blade, the cutting edge is made from one type of high speed steel, while the back is made from another type of high speed steel that has been selected for high flexibility and high tensile strength. High speed and bimetallic high speed blades can cut longer, faster, and more accurately.

Band blade selection will depend on the sawing task. You should review saw blade terminology discussed in the cutoff machine unit. The first consideration is blade pitch. The pitch of the blade should be such that at least two teeth are in contact with the workpiece. This generally means that fine pitch blades with more teeth per inch will be used in thin materials. Thick material requires coarse pitch blades so that chips will be more effectively cleared from the kerf.

Remember that there are three tooth **sets** that can be used (Figure 1). **Raker** and **wave** set are the most common in the metalworking industries. **Straight** set may be used for cutting thin materials. Wave set is best for accurate cuts through materials with variable cross sec-

tions. Raker set may be used for general purpose sawing.

You also have a choice of **tooth forms** (Figure 2). **Precision** or **regular** tooth form is best for accurate cuts where a good finish may be required. **Hook** form is fast cutting but leaves a rougher finish. **Skip** tooth is useful on deep cuts where additional chip clearance is required.

Several special bands are also used. **Straight, scalloped,** and **wavy edges** are used for cutting nonmetallic substances where saw teeth would tear the material (Figure 3). **Continuous** (Figure 4) and **segmented** (Figure 5) **diamond edged band** are used for cutting very hard nonmetallic materials.

USING THE JOB SELECTOR
ON THE VERTICAL BAND MACHINE

Most vertical band machines are equipped with a **job selector.** This device will be of great aid to you in accomplishing a sawing task. Job selectors are usually attached to the machine tool. They are frequently arranged by material. The material to be cut is located on the rim of the selector. The selector disk is then turned until the sawing data for the material can be read (Figure 6).

The job selector yields much valuable information. Sawing velocity in feet per minute is the most important. The band must be operated at the correct cutting speed for the material. If it is not, the band may be damaged or productivity will be low. Saw velocity is read at the top

Figure 3. Straight, scalloped, and wavy edge bands (Courtesy of the DoAll Company).

Figure 4. Continuous edge diamond band (Courtesy of the DoAll Company).

Figure 5. Segmented diamond edge band (Courtesy of the DoAll Company).

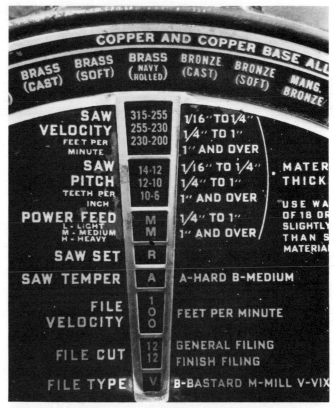

Figure 6. Job selector on the vertical band machine (CSU, Fresno).

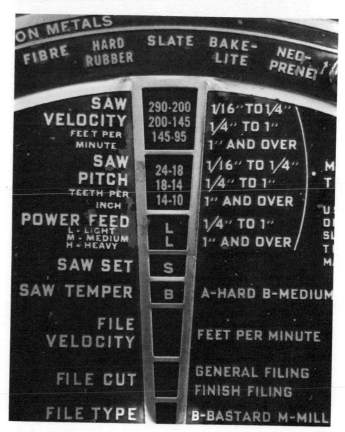

of the column and is dependent on material thickness. The job selector also indicates recommended pitch, set, feed, and temper. The job selector will provide information on sawing of nonmetallic materials (Figure 7). Information on band filing can also be determined from the job selector.

SETTING SAW VELOCITY ON THE VERTICAL BAND MACHINE

Most vertical band machines are equipped with a **variable speed drive** that permits a wide selection of band

Figure 7. The job selector set for a nonferrous material (CSU, Fresno).

Figure 8. Vertical band machine variable speed drive (Courtesy of the DoAll Company).

Figure 10. Speed range and band velocity controls (CSU, Fresno).

Figure 9. Band velocity indicator (CSU, Fresno).

velocities. This is one of the factors that make the band machine such a versatile machine tool. Saw velocities can be selected that permit successful cutting of many materials.

The typical variable speed drive uses a split flange pulley to vary the speed of the drive wheel (Figure 8). As the flanges of the pulley are spread apart by adjusting the speed control, the belt runs deeper in the pulley groove. This is the same as running the drive belt on a smaller diameter pulley. Slower speeds are obtained. As the flanges of the pulley are adjusted for less spread, the

belt runs toward the outside. This is equivalent to running the belt on a larger diameter pulley. Faster speeds are obtained.

Setting Band Velocity
Band velocity is indicated on the **band velocity indicator** (Figure 9). Remember that band velocity is measured in **feet per minute.** The inner scale indicates band velocity in the low speed range. The outer scale indicates velocity in the high speed range. Band velocity is regulated by adjusting the speed control (Figure 10). Adjust this control only while the motor is running, as this adjustment moves the flanges of the variable speed pulley.

Setting Speed Ranges
Most band machines with a variable speed drive have a **high** and **low speed range.** High or low speed range is selected by operating the **speed range shift lever** (Figure 10). This setting must be made while the band is stopped or is running at the lowest speed in the range. If the machine is set in high range and it is desired to go to low range, turn the band velocity control wheel until the band has slowed to the lowest speed possible. The

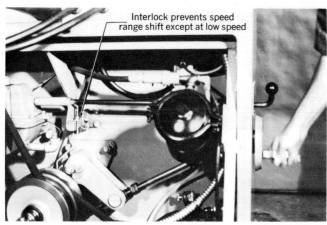

Figure 11. An interlock prevents shifting speed ranges except at low speed (Courtesy, California Community Colleges—IMC Project).

Figure 12. Adjusting the upper guide post (Courtesy of the DoAll Company).

Figure 13. Using too fine a pitch blade results in clogged teeth (Courtesy, California Community Colleges—IMC Project).

speed range shift may now be changed to low speed. If the machine is in low speed and it is desired to shift to high range, slow the band to the lowest speed before shifting speed ranges. A speed range shift made while the band is running at a fast speed may damage the speed range transmission gears. Some band machines are equipped with an interlock to prevent speed range shifts except at low band velocity (Figure 11).

STRAIGHT CUTTING ON THE VERTICAL BAND MACHINE

Adjust the upper guidepost so that it is as close to the workpiece as possible (Figure 12). This will maximize safety by properly supporting and guarding the band. Accuracy of the cut will also be aided. The guidepost is adjusted by loosening the clamping knob and moving the post up or down according to the workpiece thickness.

Be sure to use a band of the **proper pitch** for the thickness of the material to be cut. If the band pitch is too fine, the teeth will clog (Figure 13). This can result in stripping and breakage of the saw teeth due to overloading (Figure 14). Cutting productivity will also be reduced. Slow cutting will result from using a fine pitch

Figure 14. Stripped and broken teeth resulting from overloading the saw (Courtesy of the DoAll Company).

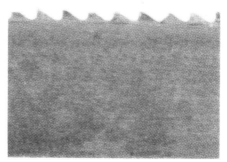

Figure 17. Chipped and fractured teeth resulting from shock and vibration (Courtesy of the DoAll Company).

Figure 15. Saw cut with a fine pitch blade in thick material (Courtesy, California Community Colleges — IMC Project).

Figure 16. Saw cut with correct pitch band for thick material (Courtesy, California Community Colleges — IMC Project).

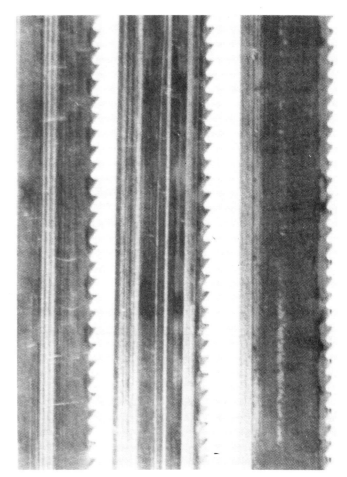

Figure 18. Scored bands can become brittle and lose flexibility (Courtesy of the DoAll Company).

band on thick material (Figure 15). The correct pitch for thick material (Figure 16) results in much more efficient cutting in the same amount of time and at the same feeding pressure.

As you begin a cut, feed the workpiece **gently** into the band. A sudden shock will cause the saw teeth to chip or fracture (Figure 17). This will quickly reduce band life. See that chips are cleared from the band guides. These can score the band (Figure 18), making it brittle and subject to breakage.

Figure 19. Adjusting the coolant and air mix on the vertical band machine (Courtesy, California Community Colleges — IMC Project).

Figure 20. Minimum radius per saw width chart on the job selector (CSU, Fresno).

Cutting Fluids

Cutting fluids are an important aid to sawing many materials. They **cool** and **lubricate** the band and **remove chips** from the kerf. Many band machines are equipped with a mist coolant system. Liquid cutting fluids are mixed with air to form a mist. With mist, the advantages of the coolant are realized without the need to collect and return large amounts of liquids to a reservoir. If your band machine uses mist coolant, set the liquid flow first and then add air to create a mist (Figure 19). Do not use more coolant than is necessary. Overuse of air may cause a mist fog around the machine. This is both unpleasant and hazardous, as coolant mist should not be inhaled.

CONTOUR CUTTING ON THE VERTICAL BAND MACHINE

Contour cutting is the ability of the band machine to cut around corners and produce intricate shapes. The ability of the saw to cut a specific radius depends on its **width**. The job selector will provide information on the minimum radius that can be cut with a blade of a given width (Figure 20). As you can see, a narrow band can cut a smaller radius than a wide band.

The set of the saw needs to be adequate for the corresponding band width. It is a good idea to make a test contour cut in a piece of scrap material. This will permit you to determine if the **saw set** is adequate to cut the desired radius. If the saw set is not adequate, you

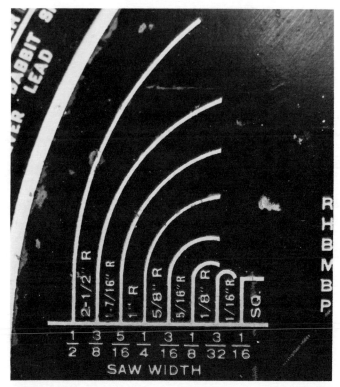

Figure 21. Band set must be adequate for the band width if the laid out radius is to be cut (Courtesy, California Community Colleges — IMC Project).

may not be able to keep the saw on the layout line as you complete the radius cut (Figure 21).

If you are cutting a totally enclosed feature, be sure to insert the saw blade through the starting hole in the workpiece before welding it into a band. Also, be sure that the teeth are pointed in the right direction.

SELF-TEST

1. Name three saw blade sets and describe the applications of each.
2. When might scalloped or wavy edged bands be used?
3. What information is found on the job selector?
4. In what units of measure are band velocities measured?
5. Explain the operating principle of the variable speed pulley.

6. Explain the selection of band speed ranges.
7. What machine safety precaution must be observed when selecting speed ranges?
8. Describe the upper guidepost adjustment.
9. What does band pitch have to do with sawing efficiency?
10. What does band set have to do with contouring?

SECTION G DRILLING MACHINES

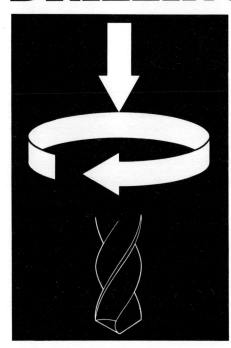

A modern machinist must be able to use several types of complex and powerful drilling machines. Safety is the first thing you should learn about drilling machines. Chips are produced in great quantities and must be safely handled. The operator must also be protected from these chips as they fly from the machine as well as from the rotating parts of the machine. It is most important for you to become familiar with the operation and major parts of drilling machines as soon as possible. Because of the great power exerted by these machines, workholding devices must be used to secure the work and to keep the operator safe.

There are three major types of drilling machines found in machine shops. The sensitive drill (Figure 1) is used for light drilling on small parts. The upright drill press (Figure 2) is used for heavy duty drilling. The radial drill press (Figure 3) is used for drilling large, heavy workpieces that are difficult to move.

There are a number of special purpose drilling machines, ranging from the microscopic drilling machine (Figure 4), which can drill a hole smaller than a human hair, to deep hole drilling machines and turret head drills, which are often tape controlled for automatic operation.

The gang drilling machine (Figure 5) is used when several successive operations must be performed on a workpiece. It has several drilling heads mounted over a single table, with each spindle tooled for drilling, reaming, or counterboring. Hand tooling, such as jigs and fixtures, is typically used on gang drilling machines. Tool guidance is provided by the jigs while the workpiece is clamped in the fixture. When one operation is completed, the workpiece is advanced to the next spindle. When a part requires the drilling of many holes, especially ones quite close together, a multispindle drilling machine (Figure 6) is used. This machine has a number of spindles connected to the main spindle through universal joints.

Turret drilling machines (Figure 7) have several drill tools on a turret, which allows a needed tool to be rotated into position for operating on a workpiece. Many of these machines are tape controlled so that the table position, spindle speed, and turret position are programmed to operate automatically. The operator simply clamps the workpiece in position and starts the machine.

Deep-hole drilling machines (Figure 8) are used to drill precision holes many times longer than the bore diameter. These machines are usually horizontal with lathe-type ways and drives. The workpiece is held in clamps and is fed into a rotating drill through which coolant is pumped at high pressure. Some machines use gun drills. The deep drilling machine has the advantage of a very high metal removal rate.

In the following units, you will learn about tooling, how to use basic drilling machines, and how to select drills and reamers. Drills typically cut rough holes, and reamers are used to finish the holes. Reaming in the drill press is one way of producing a precision hole with a good finish. Countersinking and counterboring are also important tooling operations that will be introduced to you.

Figure 1. The sensitive drill press (Courtesy of Wilton Corporation).

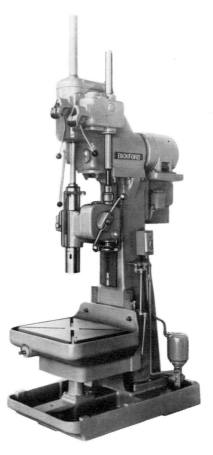

Figure 2. Upright drill press (Courtesy of Giddings & Lewis, Inc.).

Figure 3. Radial drill press (Courtesy of LeBlond Inc., Cincinnati, Ohio).

Figure 4. Microdrill press for drilling very small holes in miniature and microminiature parts (Courtesy of Louis Levin & Sons, Inc.).

Figure 5. Gang drilling machine (Courtesy of Giddings & Lewis, Inc.).

Figure 7. Turret drilling machine with multispindle heads (Courtesy of Jarvis Products Corporation).

Figure 8. Deep-hole drilling machine (Courtesy of Giddings & Lewis, Inc.).

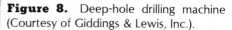

Figure 6. Multispindle drilling machine (Courtesy of Jarvis Products Corporation).

Since drills are used on a variety of materials and tend to take relatively heavy cuts, they often get dull or chipped. Sharpening can be done either by hand on a pedestal grinder or in a special machine. You will learn these sharpening methods in this section. Resharpening is kept to a minimum when the proper speeds, feeds, and coolants are used.

We have come a long way from the bow string and arrow drill. New ways of making holes in difficult materials are still being developed and used.

DRILLING MACHINE SAFETY

There is a tendency among students to dismiss the dangers involved in drilling since most drilling done in a school shop is performed in small sensitive drill presses with small diameter drills. This tendency, however, only increases the danger to the operator and has turned otherwise harmless situations into serious injuries. Clamps should be used to hold down workpieces, since hazards are always present even with small diameter drills.

One example of a safety hazard on even a small diameter drill is the "grabbing" of the drill when it breaks through the hole. If the operator is holding the workpiece with his hands and the piece suddenly begins to spin, his hand will likely be injured, especially if the workpiece is thin.

Figure 9. Drilling operation on upright drill press with tools properly located on adjacent work table (Lane Community College).

Figure 10. Properly clamped drill press vise holding work for hard steel drilling (DeAnza College).

Even if the operator were strong enough to hold the workpiece, the drill can break, continue turning, and with its jagged edge become an immediate hazard to the operator's hand. The sharp chips that turn with the drill can also cut the hand that holds the workpiece.

Poor work habits produce many injuries. Chips flying into unprotected eyes, heavy tooling, or parts dropping from the drill press onto toes, slipping on oily floors, and getting hair or clothing caught in a rotating drill are all hazards that can be avoided by safe work habits.

The following are safety rules to be observed around all types of drill presses:

1. Tools to be used while drilling should never be left lying on the drill press table, but should be placed on an adjacent worktable (Figure 9).

2. Get help when lifting heavy vises or workpieces.

3. Workpieces should always be secured with bolts and strap clamps, C-clamps, or fixtures. A drill press vise should be used when drilling small parts (Figure 10). If a clamp should come loose and a "merry-go-round" results, don't try to stop it from turning with your hands. Turn off the machine quickly; if the drill breaks or comes out, the workpiece may fly off the table.

4. Never clean the taper in the spindle when the drill is running, since this practice could result in broken fingers or worse injuries.

5. Always remove the chuck key immediately after using it. A key left in the chuck will be thrown out at high velocity when the machine is turned on. It is a good practice to **never let the chuck key leave your hand when you are using it.** It should not be left in the chuck even for a moment. Some keys are spring loaded so they will automatically be ejected from the chuck when released. Unfortunately, very few of these keys are in use in the industry.

6. Never stop the drill press spindle with your hand after you have turned off the machine. Sharp chips often collect around the chuck or spindle. Do not reach around, near, or behind a revolving drill.

7. When removing taper shank drills with a drift, use a piece of wood under the drills so they will not drop on your toes. This will also protect the drill points from being damaged by striking the machine base.

8. Interrupt the feed occasionally when drilling to break up the chip so it will not be a hazard and will be easier to handle.

9. Use a brush instead of your hands to clean chips off the machine. Never use an air jet for removing chips as this will cause the chips to fly at a high velocity and cuts or eye injuries may result. Do not clean up chips or wipe up oil while the machine is running.

10. Keep the floor clean. Immediately wipe up any oil that spills, or the floor will be slippery and unsafe.

11. Remove burrs from a drilled workpiece as soon as possible, since any sharp edges or burrs can cause severe cuts.

12. When you are finished with a drill or other cutting tool, wipe it clean with a shop towel and store it properly.

13. Oily shop towels should be placed in a closed metal container to prevent a cluttered work area and avoid a fire hazard.

14. When moving the head or table on sensitive drill presses, make sure a safety clamp is set just below the table or head on the column; this will prevent the table from suddenly dropping if the column clamp is prematurely released.

UNIT 1 THE DRILL PRESS

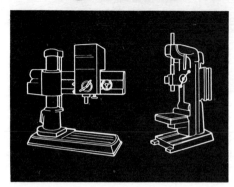

Before operating any machine, a machinist must know the names and the functions of all its parts. In this unit, therefore, you should familiarize yourself with the operating mechanisms of several types of drilling machines.

OBJECTIVES

After completing this unit, you should be able to:
1. Identify three basic drill press types and explain their differences and primary uses.
2. Identify the major parts of the sensitive drill press.
3. Identify the major parts of the radial arm drill press.

Drilling holes is one of the most basic of machining operations and one that is very frequently done by machinists. Metal cutting requires considerable pressure of feed on the cutting edge. A drill press provides the necessary feed pressure either by hand or power drive. The primary use of the drill press is to drill holes, but it can be used for other operations such as countersinking, counterboring, spot facing, reaming, and tapping, which are processes that modify the drilled hole.

There are three basic types of drill presses used for general drilling operations: the **sensitive drill press,** the **upright drilling machine,** and the **radial arm drill press.** The sensitive drill press (Figure 1), as the name implies, allows the operator to "feel" the cutting action of the drill as he hand feeds it into the work. These machines are either bench or floor mounted. Since these drill presses are used for light duty applications only, they usually have a maximum drill size of $\frac{1}{2}$ in. diameter. Machine capacity is measured by the diameter of work that can be drilled (Figure 2).

Figure 1. A sensitive drill press. These machines are used for light duty application (Courtesy of Wilton Corporation).

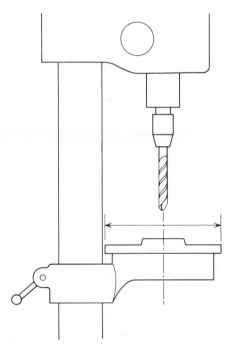

Figure 2. Drill presses are measured by the largest diameter of a circular piece that can be drilled in the center.

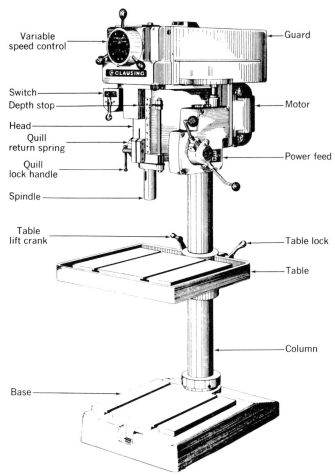

Variable speed control

Switch

Depth stop

Head

Quill return spring

Quill lock handle

Spindle

Table lift crank

Base

Guard

Motor

Power feed

Table lock

Table

Column

Figure 3. Drill press showing the names of major parts (Courtesy of Clausing Corporation).

Figure 5. View of a variable speed drive. Variable speed selector should only be moved when the motor is running. The exact speed choice is possible for the drill size and material with this drive (Courtesy of Clausing Corporation).

Figure 4. View of a vee-belt drive. Spindle speeds are highest when the belt is in the top steps and lowest at the bottom steps (Courtesy of Clausing Corporation).

Figure 6. Upright drill press (Courtesy of Wilton Corporation).

The sensitive drill press has four major parts, not including the motor: the head, column, table, and base. Figure 3 labels the parts of the drill press that you should remember. The spindle rotates within the quill, which does not rotate but carries the spindle up and down. The spindle shaft is driven by a **stepped-vee pulley and belt** (Figure 4) or by a **variable speed drive** (Figure 5). *The motor must be running and the spindle turning when changing speeds with a variable speed drive.*

The upright drill press is very similar to the sensitive drill press, but it is made for much heavier work (Figure 6). The drive is more powerful and many types are **gear** driven, so they are capable of drilling holes to two inches or more in diameter. *The motor must be stopped when changing speeds on a gear drive drill press.* If it doesn't shift into the selected gear, turn the spindle by hand until it meshes. Since power feeds are needed to drill these large size holes, these machines are equipped with power feed mechanisms that can be adjusted by the operator. The operator may either feed manually with a lever or hand wheel or he may engage the power feed. A mechanism is provided to raise and lower the table.

As Figures 7, 8, and 9 show, the radial arm drill press is the most versatile drilling machine. Its size is deter-

Figure 8. Heavy workpiece is mounted on a trunnion-type worktable that can be rotated for positioning (Courtesy of LeBlond Inc., Cincinnati, Ohio).

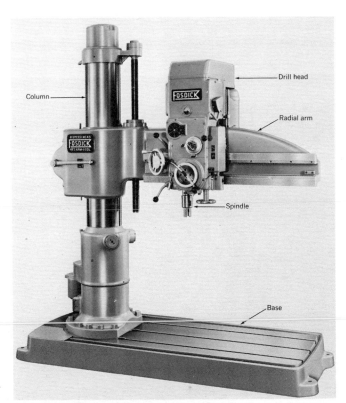

Figure 7. Radial arm drill press with names of major parts (Courtesy of LeBlond Inc., Cincinnati, Ohio).

Figure 9. Small holes are usually drilled by hand feeding on a sensitive radial drill. A workpiece is clamped on the tilting table so a hole may be drilled at an angle (Courtesy of LeBlond Inc., Cincinnati, Ohio).

mined by the diameter of the column and the length of the arm measured from the center of the spindle to the outer edge of the column. It is useful for operations on large castings that are too heavy to be repositioned by the operator for drilling each hole. The work is clamped to the table or base, and the drill can then be positioned where it is needed by swinging the arm and moving the head along the arm. The arm and head can be raised or lowered on the column and then locked in place. The radial arm drill press is used for drilling small to very large holes and for boring, reaming, counterboring, and countersinking. Like the upright machine, the radial arm drill press has a power feed mechanism and a hand feed lever.

SELF-TEST

1. List three basic types of drill presses and briefly explain their differences. Describe how the primary uses differ in each of these three drill press types.
2. Sensitive drill press. Match the correct letter with the name of that part shown on Figure 10.

   Spindle
   Quill lock handle
   Column
   Switch
   Depth stop
   Head
   Table
   Table lock
   Base
   Power feed
   Motor
   Variable speed control
   Table lift crank
   Quill return spring
   Guard

3. Radial drill press. Match the correct letter with the name of that part shown on Figure 11.

   Column
   Radial arm
   Spindle
   Base
   Drill head

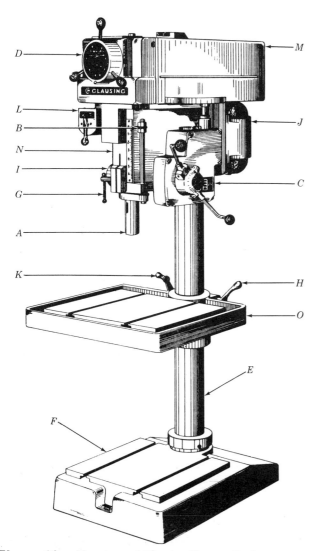

Figure 10.   (Courtesy of Clausing Corporation).

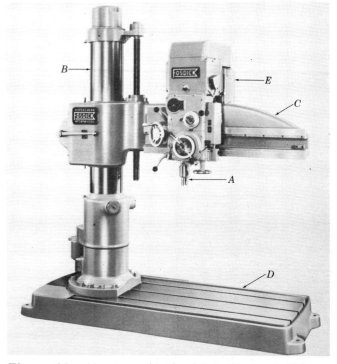

Figure 11.   (Courtesy of LeBlond, Inc., Cincinnati, Ohio).

UNIT 2 DRILLING TOOLS

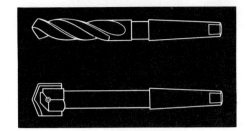

Before you learn to use drills and drilling machines, you will have to know of the great variety of drills and tooling available to the machinist. This unit will acquaint you with these interesting tools as well as show you how to select the one you should use for a given operation.

OBJECTIVES

After completing this unit, you should be able to:
1. Identify the various features of a twist drill.
2. Identify the series and size of 10 given decimal equivalent drill sizes.

The drill is an end cutting rotary-type tool having one or more cutting lips and one or more flutes for the removal of chips and the passage of coolant. Drilling is the most efficient method of making a hole in metals softer than Rockwell 30. Harder metals can be successfully drilled, however, by using special drills and techniques.

In the past, all drills were made of carbon steel and would lose their hardness if they became too hot from drilling. Today, however, most drills are made of high speed steel, although carbon steel drills are still made and can be identified by spark testing (see Section D, Unit 1 for identification of steel). High speed steel drills can operate at several hundred degrees Fahrenheit without breaking down, and, when cooled, will be as hard as before. Carbide tipped drills are used for special applications such as drilling abrasive materials and very hard steels. Other special drills are made from cast heat-resistant alloys.

Twist Drills

The twist drill is by far the most common type of drill used today. These are made with two or more flutes and cutting lips and in many varieties of design. Figure 1 illustrates several of the most commonly used types of twist drills. The names of parts and features of a twist drill are shown in Figure 2.

The twist drill has either a straight or tapered shank. The taper shank has a Morse taper, a standard taper of

about $\frac{5}{8}$ in. per foot, which has more driving power and greater rigidity than the straight shank types. Ordinary straight shank drills are typically held in drill chucks (Figure 3a). This is a friction drive, and slipping of the drill shank is a common problem. Straight shank drills with tang drives have a positive drive and are less expensive

Figure 1. Various types of twist drills used in drilling machines (Courtesy of the DoAll Company):
(a) High helix drill
(b) Low helix drill
(c) Left-hand drill
(d) Three flute drill
(e) Taper shank twist drill
(f) Standard helix jobber drill
(g) Center or spotting drill

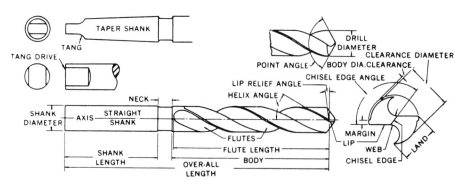

Figure 2. Features of a twist drill (Courtesy of Bendix Industrial Tools Division).

Figure 3a. Drill chucks such as this one are used to hold straight shank drills.

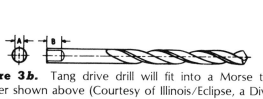

Figure 3b. Tang drive drill will fit into a Morse taper-adapter shown above (Courtesy of Illinois/Eclipse, a Division of Illinois Tool Works, Inc., Chicago, Illinois 60639).

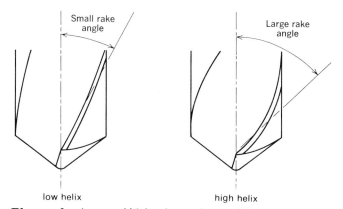

Figure 4. Low and high rake angles on drills.

than tapered shank drills. These are held in special drill chucks with a Morse taper (Figure 3b).

Jobbers drills have two flutes, a straight shank design, and a relatively short length-to-diameter ratio that helps to maintain rigidity. These drills are used for drilling in steel, cast iron, and nonferrous metals. Center drills and spotting drills are used for starting holes in workpieces. Oil hole drills are made so that coolant can be pumped through the drill to the cutting lips. This not only cools the cutting edges, but also forces out the chips along the flutes. Core drills have from three to six flutes making heavy stock removal possible. They are generally used for roughing holes to a larger diameter or for drilling out cores in castings. Left-handed drills are mostly used on multispindle drilling machines where some spindles are rotated in reverse of normal drill press rotation. The step drill generally has a flat or an angular

cutting edge, and can produce a hole with several diameters in one pass with either flat or countersunk shoulders.

Straight fluted drills are used for drilling brass and other soft materials because the zero rake angle eliminates the tendency for the drill to "grab" on breakthrough. For the same reason they are used on thin materials. Low helix drills, sometimes called slow spiral drills (Figure 4), are more rigid than standard helix drills and can stand more torque. Like straight fluted drills, they are less likely to "grab" when emerging from a hole, because of the small rake angle. For this reason the low helix and straight flute drills are used primarily for drilling in brass, bronze, and some other nonferrous metals. Because of the low helix angle, the flutes do not

Figure 5. Spotting drill (Courtesy of the DoAll Company).

remove chips very well from deep holes, but the large chip space allows maximum drilling efficiency in shallow holes. High helix drills, sometimes called fast spiral drills, are designed to remove chips from deep holes. The large rake angle makes these drills suitable for soft metals such as aluminum and mild steel. Spotting and centering drills (Figure 5) are used to accurately position holes for further drilling with regular drills. Centering drills are short and have little or no dead center. These characteristics prevent the drills from wobbling. Lathe center drills are often used as spotting drills.

Spade and Gun Drills

Special drills such as spade and gun drills are used in many manufacturing processes. A spade drill is simply a flat blade with sharpened cutting lips. The spade bit, which is clamped in a holder (Figure 6), is replaceable and can be sharpened many times. Some types provide for coolant flow to the cutting edge through a hole in the holder or shank for the purpose of deep drilling. These drills are made with very large diameters of 12 in. or more (Figure 7) but can also be found as microdrills, smaller than a hair. Twist drills by comparison are rarely found with diameters over $3\frac{1}{2}$ in. Spade drills are usually ground with a flat top rake and with chipbreaker grooves on the end. A chisel edge and thinned web are ground in the dead center (Figure 8).

Some spade drills are made of solid tungsten carbide, usually only in a small diameter. Twist drills with carbide inserts (Figure 9) require a rigid drilling setup. Gun drills (Figure 10) are also carbide tipped and have a single-vee-shaped flute in a steel tube through which coolant is pumped under pressure. These drills are used in horizontal machines that feed the drill with a positive guide. Extremely deep precision holes are produced with gun drills.

Another special drill, used for drilling very hard steel, is the Hard Steel Drill (Figure 11). A set of hard steel drills is shown in Figure 12. These drills are cast from a heat-resistant alloy, and the fluted end is ground to a triangular point. These drills work by heating the metal beneath the drill point by friction and then cutting out the softened metal as a chip. (Figures 13a–13d show this drill in use.)

Figure 6. Spade drill clamped in holder (Courtesy of the DoAll Company).

Drill Selection

The type of drill selected for a particular task depends upon several factors. The type of machine being used, rigidity of the workpiece, setup and size of the hole to be drilled are all important. The composition and hardness of the workpiece are especially critical. The job may require a starting drill or one for secondary operations such as counterboring or spot facing, and it might need to be a drill for a deep hole or a shallow one. If the drilling operation is too large for the size or rigidity of the machine, there wlll be chatter and the work surface will be rough or distorted.

A machinist also must make the selection on the size of the drill, the most important dimension of which is the diameter. Twist drills are measured across the margins near the drill point (Figure 14). Worn drills measure slightly smaller here. Drills are normally tapered back along the margin so that they will measure a few thousandths of an inch smaller at the shank.

Drilling is basically a roughing operation. This provides a hole that must be finished by other operations such as boring or reaming. Drills almost never make a hole smaller than their measured diameter, but often make a larger hole depending on how they have been sharpened. There are four drill size series: **fractional, number, letter,** and **metric** sizes. The fractional divisions are in $\frac{1}{64}$ in. increments, while the number, letter, and

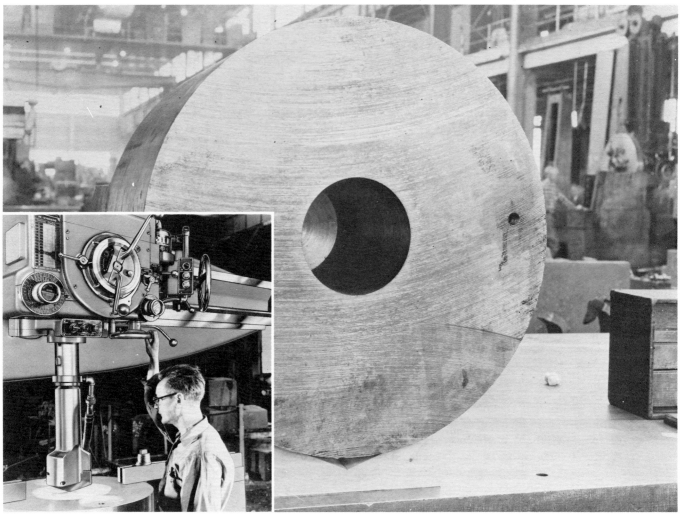

Figure 7. Large hole being drilled with spade drill. This 8 in. diameter hole $18\frac{7}{8}$ in. deep, was spade drilled in solid SAE #4145 steel rolling mill drive coupling housing with a Brinell hardness of 200-240. The machine that did the job is a 6 ft. 19 in. Chip master radial with a 25 hp motor (Courtesy of Giddings & Lewis, Inc.).

Figure 9. Carbide tipped twist drill (Courtesy of the DoAll Company).

Figure 8. Spade drill blades showing various grinds (Courtesy of the DoAll Company).

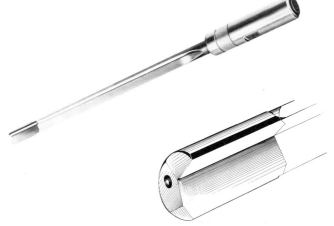

Figure 10. Single flute gun drill with insert of carbide cutting tip (Courtesy of the DoAll Company).

Figure 11. The hard steel drill (Courtesy of the DoAll Company).

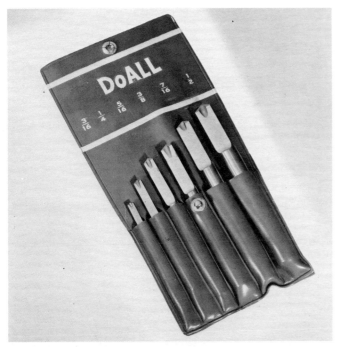

Figure 12. Set of hard steel drills (Courtesy of the DoAll Company).

Figure 13a. Hole started in file with a hard steel drill (DeAnza College).

Figure 13b. Drilling the hole (DeAnza College).

Figure 13c. Drill removed from file showing chip form (DeAnza College).

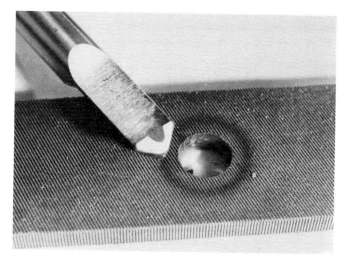

Figure 13d. Finished hole in file (DeAnza College).

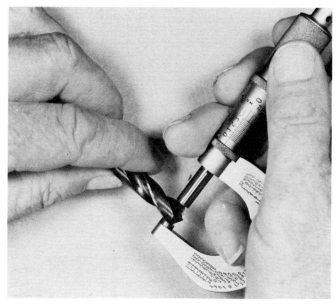

Figure 14. Drill being measured across the margins.

Figure 15. Morse taper drill sleeve (Courtesy of the DoAll Company).

Figure 16. Morse taper drill socket (Courtesy of the DoAll Company).

Figure 17. A drift is being used to remove a sleeve from a drill (Lane Community College).

metric series have drill diameters that fall between the fractional inch measures. Together, the four series make up a long-running series in decimal equivalents, as shown in Table 1.

Identification of a small drill is simple enough as long as the number or letter remains on the shank. Most shops, however, have several series of drills, and individual drills often become hard to identify since the markings become worn off by the drill chuck. The machinist must then use a decimal equivalent table such as Table 1. The drill in question is first measured by a micrometer,

the decimal reading is located in the table, and the equivalent fraction, number, letter, or metric size is found and noted.

Morse taper shanks on drills and Morse tapers in drill press spindles vary in size and are numbered from 1 to 6; for example, the smaller light duty drill press has a number 2 taper. Steel **sleeves** (Figure 15) have a Morse taper inside and outside with a slot provided at the end of the inside taper to facilitate removal of the drill shank. A sleeve is used for enlarging the taper end on a drill to fit a larger spindle taper. Steel **sockets** (Figure 16) function in the reverse manner of sleeves, as they adapt a smaller spindle taper to a larger drill. The tool used to remove a taper shank drill is called a drift (Figure 17), which is made in several sizes and is used to remove drills or sleeves. The drift is placed round side up, flat side against the drill (Figure 18), and is struck a light blow with a hammer. A block of wood should be placed under the drill to keep it from being damaged and from being a safety hazard.

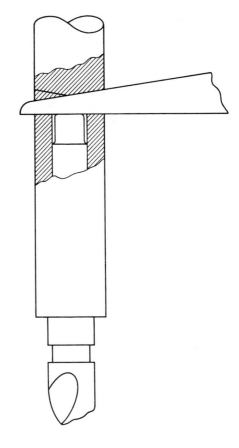

Figure 18. Cutaway of a drill and sleeve showing a drift in place.

Table 1
Decimal Equivalents for Drills

Decimals of an Inch	Inch	Wire Gage	Millimeter	Decimals of an Inch	Inch	Wire Gage	Millimeter	Decimals of an Inch	Inch	Wire Gage	Millimeter
.0135		80		.0320		67		.0520		55	
.0145		79		.0330		66		.0531			1.35
.0156	$\frac{1}{64}$			.0335			.85	.0550		54	
.0157			.4	.0350		65		.0551			1.4
.0160		78		.0354			.9	.0571			1.45
.0180		77		.0360		64		.0591			1.5
.0197			.5	.0370		63		.0595		53	
.0200		76		.0374			.95	.0610			1.55
.0210		75		.0380		62		.0625	$\frac{1}{16}$		
.0217			.55	.0390		61		.0630			1.6
.0225		74		.0394			1	.0635		52	
.0236			.6	.0400		60		.0650			1.65
.0240		73		.0410		59		.0669			1.7
.0250		72		.0413			1.05	.0670		51	
.0256			.65	.0420		58		.0689			1.75
.0260		71		.0430		57		.0700		50	
.0276			.7	.0433			1.1	.0709			1.8
.0280		70		.0453			1.15	.0728			1.85
.0293		69		.0465		56		.0730		49	
.0295			.75	.0469	$\frac{3}{64}$			.0748			1.9
.0310		68		.0472			1.2	.0760		48	
.0313	$\frac{1}{32}$			.0492			1.25	.0768			1.95
.0315			.8	.0512			1.3	.0781	$\frac{5}{64}$		

Table 1 Continued

Decimals of an Inch	Inch	Wire Gage	Milli-meter	Decimals of an Inch	Inch	Wire Gage	Milli-meter	Decimals of an Inch	Inch	Wire Gage	Milli-meter
.0785		47		.1220			3.1	.1772			4.5
.0787			2	.1250	$\frac{1}{8}$			.1800		15	
.0807			2.05	.1260			3.2	.1811			4.6
.0810		46		.1280			3.25	.1820		14	
.0820		45		.1285		30		.1850		13	
.0827			2.1	.1299			3.3	.1850			4.7
.0846			2.15	.1339			3.4	.1870			4.75
.0860		45		.1360		29		.1875	$\frac{3}{16}$		
.0866			2.2	.1378			3.5	.1890			4.8
.0886			2.25	.1405		28		.1890		12	
.0890		43		.1406	$\frac{9}{64}$			.1910		11	
.0906			2.3	.1417			3.6	.1929			4.9
.0925			2.35	.1440		27		.1935		10	
.0935		42		.1457			3.7	.1960		9	
.0938	$\frac{3}{32}$			.1470		26		.1969			5
.0945			2.4	.1476			3.75	.1990		8	
.0960		41		.1495		25		.2008			5.1
.0966			2.45	.1496			3.8	.2010		7	
.0980		40		.1520		24		.2031	$\frac{13}{64}$		
.0984			2.5	.1535			3.9	.2040		6	
.0995		39		.1540		23		.2047			5.2
.1015		38		.1563	$\frac{5}{32}$			.2055		5	
.1024			2.6	.1570		22		.2067			5.25
.1040		37		.1575			4	.2087			5.3
.1063			2.7	.1590		21		.2090		4	
.1065		36		.1610		20		.2126			5.4
.1083			2.75	.1614			4.1	.2130		3	
.1094	$\frac{7}{64}$			.1654			4.2	.2165			5.5
.1100		35		.1660		19		.2188	$\frac{7}{32}$		
.1102			2.8	.1673			4.25	.2205			5.6
.1110		34		.1693			4.3	.2210		2	
.1130		33		.1695		18		.2244			5.7
.1142			2.9	.1719	$\frac{11}{64}$			.2264			5.75
.1160		32		.1730		17		.2280		1	
.1181			3	.1732			4.4	.2283			5.8
.1200		31		.1770		16					

Table 1 Continued   329

Decimals of an Inch	Inch	Letter Sizes	Milli-meter
.2323			5.9
.2340		A	
.2344	$\frac{15}{64}$		
.2362			6
.2380		B	
.2402			6.1
.2420		C	
.2441			6.2
.2460		D	
.2461			6.25
.2480			6.3
.2500	$\frac{1}{4}$	E	
.2520			6.4
.2559			6.5
.2570		F	
.2598			6.6
.2610		G	
.2638			6.7
.2656	$\frac{17}{64}$		
.2657			6.75
.2660		H	
.2677			6.8
.2717			6.9
.2720		I	
.2756			7
.2770		J	
.2795			7.1
.2810		K	
.2812	$\frac{9}{32}$		
.2835			7.2
.2854			7.25
.2874			7.3
.2900		L	
.2913			7.4
.2950		M	
.2953			7.5
.2969	$\frac{19}{64}$		
.2992			7.6
.3020		N	
.3031			7.7
.3051			7.75
.3071			7.8
.3110			7.9
.3125	$\frac{5}{16}$		
.3150			8
.3160		O	
.3189			8.1
.3228			8.2
.3230		P	
.3248			8.25
.3268			8.3

Decimals of an Inch	Inch	Letter Sizes	Milli-meter
.3281	$\frac{21}{64}$		
.3307			8.4
.3320		Q	
.3346			8.5
.3386			8.6
.3390		R	
.3425			8.7
.3438	$\frac{11}{32}$		
.3345			8.75
.3465			8.8
.3480		S	
.3504			8.9
.3543			9
.3580		T	
.3583			9.1
.3594	$\frac{23}{64}$		
.3622			9.2
.3642			9.25
.3661			9.3
.3680		U	
.3701			9.4
.3740			9.5
.3750	$\frac{3}{8}$		
.3770		V	
.3780			9.6
.3819			9.7
.3839			9.75
.3858			9.8
.3860		W	
.3898			9.9
.3906	$\frac{25}{64}$		
.3937			10
.3970		X	
.4040		Y	
.4063	$\frac{13}{32}$		
.4130		Z	
.4134			10.5
.4219	$\frac{27}{64}$		
.4331			11
.4375	$\frac{7}{16}$		
.4528			11.5
.4531	$\frac{29}{64}$		
.4688	$\frac{15}{32}$		
.4724			12
.4844	$\frac{31}{64}$		
.4921			12.5
.5000	$\frac{1}{2}$		
.5118			13
.5156	$\frac{33}{64}$		
.5313	$\frac{17}{32}$		
.5315			13.5

Decimals of an Inch	Inch	Milli-meter
.5469	$\frac{35}{64}$	
.5512		14
.5625	$\frac{9}{16}$	
.5709		14.5
.5781	$\frac{37}{64}$	
.5906		15
.5938	$\frac{19}{32}$	
.6094	$\frac{39}{64}$	
.6102		15.5
.6250	$\frac{5}{8}$	
.6299		16
.6406	$\frac{41}{64}$	
.6496		16.5
.6563	$\frac{21}{32}$	
.6693		17
.6719	$\frac{43}{64}$	
.6875	$\frac{11}{16}$	
.6890		17.5
.7031	$\frac{45}{64}$	
.7087		18
.7188	$\frac{23}{32}$	
.7283		18.5
.7344	$\frac{47}{64}$	
.7480		19
.7500	$\frac{3}{4}$	
.7656	$\frac{49}{64}$	
.7677		19.5
.7812	$\frac{25}{32}$	
.7874		20
.7969	$\frac{51}{64}$	
.8071		20.5
.8125	$\frac{13}{16}$	
.8268		21
.8281	$\frac{53}{64}$	
.8438	$\frac{27}{32}$	
.8465		21.5
.8594	$\frac{55}{64}$	
.8661		22
.8750	$\frac{7}{8}$	
.8858		22.5
.8906	$\frac{57}{64}$	
.9055		23
.9063	$\frac{29}{32}$	
.9219	$\frac{59}{64}$	
.9252		23.5
.9375	$\frac{15}{16}$	
.9449		24
.9531	$\frac{61}{64}$	
.9646		245
.9688	$\frac{31}{32}$	
.9843		25
.9844	$\frac{63}{64}$	

Source: *Bendix Cutting Tool Handbook,* ''Decimal Equivalents — Twist Drill Sizes,'' The Bendix Corporation, Industrial Tools Division, 1972.

SELF-TEST

1. Match the correct letter from Figure 19 to the list of drill parts.

   Web
   Margin
   Drill point angle
   Cutting lip
   Flute
   Helix angle
   Axis of drill
   Shank length
   Body
   Lip relief angle
   Land
   Chisel edge angle
   Body clearance
   Tang
   Taper Shank
   Straight shank

2. Determine the letter, number, fractional, or metric equivalents of the 10 following decimal measurements of drills: .0781, .1495, .272, .159, .1969, .323, .3125, .4375, .201, and .1875.

Figure 19.   (Courtesy of Bendix Industrial Tools Division).

	Decimal Diameter	Fractional Size	Number Size	Letter Size	Metric Size
a.	.0781				
b.	.1495				
c.	.272				
d.	.159				
e.	.1969				
f.	.323				
g.	.3125				
h.	.4375				
i.	.201				
j.	.1875				

UNIT 3 HAND GRINDING OF DRILLS ON THE PEDESTAL GRINDER

Hand sharpening of twist drills has been until recent times the only method used for pointing a drill. Of course, various types of sharpening machines are now in use that can give a drill an accurate point. These precision machines are not found in every shop, however, so it is still necessary for a good machinist to learn the art of off-hand drill grinding.

OBJECTIVE

After completing this unit, you should be able to:
Properly hand sharpen a twist drill on a pedestal grinder so it will drill a hole not more than .010 in. times diameter oversize.

One of the advantages of hand grinding drills on the pedestal grinder is that special alterations of the drill point such as web thinning and rake modification can be made quickly. The greatest disadvantage to this method of drill sharpening is the possibility of producing inaccurate, oversize holes (Figure 1). If the drill has been sharpened with unequal angles, the lip with the large angle will do most of the cutting (Figure 1*a*), and will force the opposite margin to cut into the wall of the hole. If the drill has been sharpened with unequal lip lengths, both will cut with equal force, but the drill will wobble and one margin will cut into the hole wall (Figure 1*b*). When both conditions exist (Figure 1*c*), holes drilled may be out of round and oversize. When drilling with the inaccurate points, a great strain is placed on the drill and on the drill press spindle bearings. The frequent use of a drill point gage (Figure 2) during the sharpening process will help

to keep the point accurate and avoid such drilling problems.

The web of a twist drill (Figure 3) is thicker near the shank. As the drill is ground shorter a thicker web results near the point. Also the dead center or chisel point of the drill is wider and requires greater pressure to force it into the workpiece, thus generating heat. Web thinning (Figure 4) is one method of narrowing the dead center in order to restore the drill to its original efficiency.

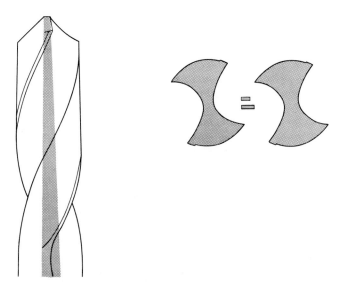

Figure 3. The tapered web of twist drills (Courtesy of Bendix Industrial Tools Division).

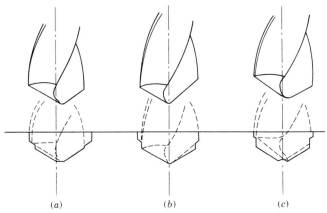

Figure 1. Causes of oversize drilling. (*a*) Drill lips ground to unequal lengths. (*b*) Drill lips ground to unequal angles. (*c*) Unequal angles and lengths.

Figure 2. Using a drill point gage (DeAnza College).

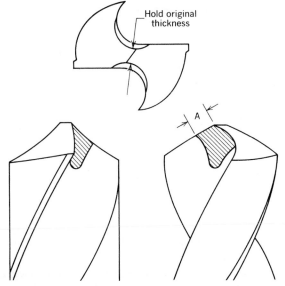

Figure 4. The usual method of thinning the point on a drill. The web should not be made thinner than it was originally when the drill was new and full length (Courtesy of Bendix Industrial Tools Division).

Figure 5. Split point design of a drill point (Courtesy of Bendix Industrial Tools Division).

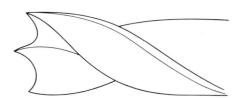

Figure 7. Sheet metal drill point.

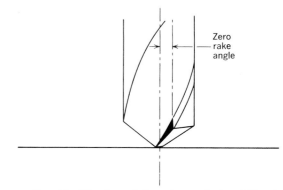

Figure 8. Modification of the rake angle for drilling brass.

Figure 6. Dupoint drill pointer (Courtesy of Mohawk Tools, Inc., Machine Tool Division).

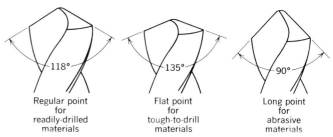

Figure 9. Drill point angles (Courtesy of Bendix Industrial Tools Division).

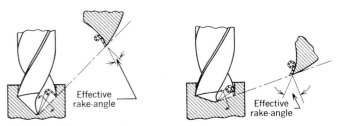

Figure 10. The effective rake angles (Courtesy of Bendix Industrial Tools Division).

Split-point design (Figure 5) is often used for drilling crankshafts and tough alloy steels. The shape of this point is quite critical and too difficult to grind by hand; it should be done on a machine (Figure 6). A sheet metal drill point (Figure 7) may be ground by an experienced hand. The rake angle on a drill can be modified for drilling brass as shown in Figure 8.

The standard drill point angle is an 118 degree included angle, while for drilling hard materials point angles should be from 135 to 150 degrees. A drill point angle from 60 to 90 degrees should be used when drilling soft materials, cast iron, abrasive materials, plastics,

and some nonferrous metals (Figure 9). Too great a decrease in the included point angle is not advisable, however, because it will result in an abnormal decrease in effective rake angle (Figure 10). This will increase the required feed pressure and change the chip formation and chip flow in most steels. Clearance angles (Figure 11) should be 8 to 12 degrees for most drilling.

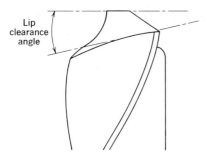

Figure 11.   Clearance angles on a drill point.

Figure 12.   Grinding wheel that is dressed and ready to use (DeAnza College).

Figure 13.   Trueing up a grinding wheel with a wheel dresser. The method shown here is often used in shops because it takes less time. The preferred method is to move the tool rest outward and to hook the lugs of the wheel dresser behind the tool rest, using it as a guide (DeAnza College).

Figure 14.   Starting position showing 59 degree angle with the wheel and the cutting lip horizontal (Lane Community College).

DRILL GRINDING PROCEDURE

Check to see if both the roughing and finishing wheels are true (Figure 12). If not, move a wheel dresser across them (Figure 13). If the end of the drill is badly damaged, use the coarse wheel to remove that part. If you over-heat the drill, let it cool in air; do not cool high speed steel drills in water.

The following method of grinding a drill is suggested:

1. Hold the drill shank with one hand and the drill near the point with the other hand. Rest your fingers that are near the point on the grinder tool rest. Hold the drill lightly at this point so you can manipulate it from the shank end with the other hand (Figure 14).

2. Hold the drill approximately horizontal with the cutting lip (Figure 15) that is being ground level. The axis of the drill should be at 59 degrees from the face of the wheel.

Figure 15.   Drill being held in the same starting position, approximately horizontal (Lane Community College).

Figure 16. Drill is now moved very slightly to the left with the shank being moved downward (Lane Community College).

Figure 18. Drill is now almost to final position of grinding. It has been rotated downward slightly from the starting position (Lane Community College).

Figure 17. Another view of the same position as shown in Figure 15 (Lane Community College).

Figure 19. After the sequence has been completed on both cutting lips, they are checked with a drill point gage for length and angle (DeAnza College).

3. Using the tool rest and fingers as a pivot, slowly move the shank downward and slightly to the left (Figure 16). The drill must be free to slip forward slightly to keep it against the wheel (Figure 17). Rotate the drill very slightly. It is the most common mistake of the beginner to rotate the drill until the opposite cutting edge has been ground off. Do not rotate small drills at all, only larger ones. As you continue the downward movement of the shank, crowd the drill into the wheel so that it will grind lightly all the way from the lip to the heel (Figure 18). This should all be one smooth movement. It is very important at this point to allow proper clearance (8 to 12 degrees) at the heel of the drill.

4. Without changing your body position, pull the drill back slightly and rotate 180 degrees so that the opposite lip is now in a level position. Repeat step 3.

5. Check *both cutting lips* with the drill point gage (Figure 19):
   a. For correct angle.
   b. For equal length.
   c. Check lip clearances visually. These should be between 8 and 12 degrees.
   If errors are found, adjust and regrind until they are correct.

6. When you are completely satisfied that the drill point angles and lip lengths are correct, drill a hole in a scrap metal that has been set aside for this purpose. Consult a drill speed table so you will be able to select the correct RPM. Use cutting oil or coolant.

7. Check the condition of the hole. Did the drill chatter and cause the start of the hole to be misshapen? This could be caused by too much lip clearance. Is the hole oversize more than .005 or .010 in.? Are the lips uneven or the lip angles off or both? Running the drill too slowly for its size will cause a rough hole; too fast will burn the drill. If the hole size is more than .010 in. × diameter over the drill size, resharpen and try again.

8. When you have a correctly sharpened drill, show this and the drilled hole to your instructor for his evaluation.

SELF-TEST
Sharpen drills on the pedestal grinder and submit them to your instructor for approval.

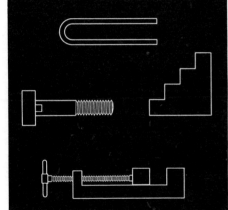

UNIT 4 WORK LOCATING AND HOLDING DEVICES ON DRILLING MACHINES

Workpieces of a great many sizes and shapes are drilled by machinists. In order to hold these parts safely and securely while they are drilled, several types of workholding devices are used. In this unit you will learn how to properly set up these devices for a machining operation.

OBJECTIVES

After completing this unit, you should be able to:
1. Identify and explain the correct uses for several workholding and locating devices.
2. Set up and drill holes in two parts of a continuing project; align and start a tap using the drill press.

Because of the great forces applied by the machines in drilling, some means must be provided to keep the workpiece from turning with the drill or from climbing up the flutes after the drill breaks through. This is necessary not only for safety's sake but also for workpiece rigidity and good workmanship.

One method of workholding is to use strap clamps (Figure 1) and T-bolts (Figure 2). The clamp must be kept parallel to the table by the use of step blocks (Figure 3) and the T-bolt should be kept as close to the workpiece as possible (Figure 4). Parallels (Figure 5) are placed under the work at the point where the clamp is holding. This provides a space for the drill to break through without making a hole in the table. A thin or narrow workpiece should not be supported too far from the drill, however, since it will spring down under the pressure of the drill-

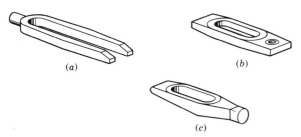

Figure 1. Strap clamps: (*a*) U-clamp, (*b*) Straight clamp, and (*c*) finger clamp.

Figure 2. T-bolts.

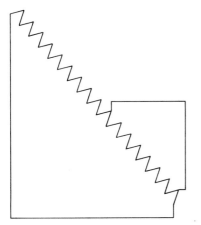

Figure 3. Adjustable step blocks.

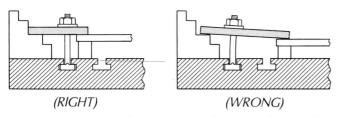

(RIGHT)   (WRONG)

Figure 4. Right and wrong setup for strap clamps. The clamp bolt should be as close to the workpiece as possible.

Figure 5. Parallels of various sizes (Lane Community College).

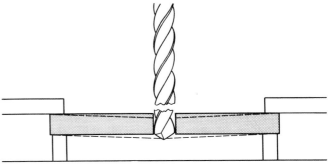

Figure 6. Thin, springy material is supported too far from the drill. Drilling pressure forces the workpiece downward until the drill breaks through, relieving the pressure. The work then springs back and the remaining "fin" of material is more than the drill can cut in one revolution. The result is drill breakage.

ing. This can cause the drill on breakthrough to suddenly "grab" more material than it can handle. The result is often a broken drill (Figure 6). Thin workpieces or sheet metal should be clamped over a wooden block to avoid this problem. C-clamps of various sizes are used to hold workpieces on drill press tables and on angle plates (Figure 7).

Angle plates facilitate the holding of odd shaped parts for drilling. The angle plate is either bolted or clamped to the table and the work is fastened to the angle plate. For example, a gear or wheel that requires a hole to be drilled into a projecting hub could be clamped to an angle plate.

Drill press vises (Figure 8) are very frequently used for holding small workpieces of regular shape and size with parallel sides. Vises provide the quickest and most efficient set up method for parallel work, but should not be used if the work does not have parallel sides. The

Figure 7. C-clamp being used on an angle plate to hold work that would be difficult to safely support in other ways (Lane Community College).

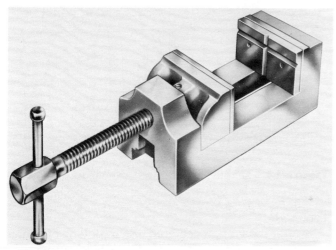

Figure 8. Drill press vise. Small parts are held for drilling and other operations with the drill press vise (Courtesy of Wilton Corporation).

Figure 9. Part set up in vise with parallels under it (Lane Community College).

workpiece must be supported so the drill will not go into the vise. If precision parallels are used for support, they and the drill can be easily damaged since they are both hardened (Figure 9). For rough drilling, however, cold finished (CF) keystock would be sufficient for supporting the workpiece. Angular vises can pivot a workpiece to a given angle so that angular holes can be drilled (Figure 10). Another method of drilling angular holes is by tilting the drill press table. If there is no angular scale on the vise or table, a protractor head with a level may be used to set up the correct angle for drilling. Angle plates are also sometimes used for drilling angular holes (Figure 11a). The drill press table must be level (Figure 11b).

Vee-blocks come in sets of two, often with clamps for holding small size rounds (Figure 12). Larger size round stock is set up with a strap clamp over the vee-blocks (Figure 13). The hole to be cross drilled is first laid out and center punched. The workpiece is lightly clamped in the vee-blocks and the punch mark is centered as shown in Figure 14. The clamps are tightened, and the drill is located precisely over the punch mark by means of a **wiggler**. A wiggler is a tool that can be put into a drill chuck to locate a punch mark to the exact center of the spindle.

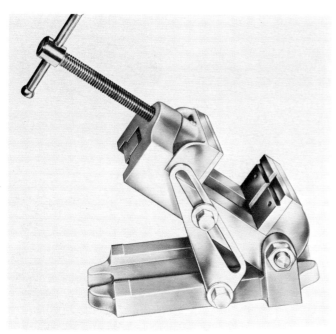

Figure 10. Angle vise. Parts that must be held at an angle to the drill press table while being drilled are held with this vise (Courtesy of Wilton Corporation).

Figure 11b. Checking the level of the table (Lane Community College).

Figure 11a. View of an adjustable angle plate on a drill press table using a protractor to set up (Lane Community College).

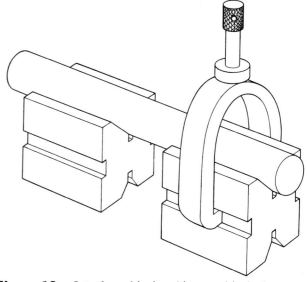

Figure 12. Set of vee-blocks with a vee-block clamp.

The wiggler is clamped into a drill chuck and the machine is turned on (Figure 15a). Push on the knob near the end of the pointer with a six inch rule or other piece of metal until it runs with no wobble (Figure 15b). With the machine still running, bring the pointer down into the punch mark. If the pointer begins to wobble again, the mark is not centered under the spindle and the workpiece will have to be shifted. When the wiggler enters the punch mark without wobbling, the workpiece is centered.

After the work is centered, use a spotting or center drill to start the hole. Then, for larger holes, use a pilot drill, which is always a little larger than the dead center of the next drill size used. Pilot drills are not usually used in industrial applications; only the spotting drill (if used) and the full size drill are used. Use the correct cutting speed and coolant. Chamfer both sides of the finished hole with a countersink or chamfering tool. Round stock

Figure 13. Setup of two vee-blocks and round stock with strap clamp (Lane Community College).

Figure 14. Round stock in vee-blocks. One method of centering layout line or punch mark using a combination square and rule (Lane Community College).

Figure 15a. Wiggler set in offset position (Lane Community College).

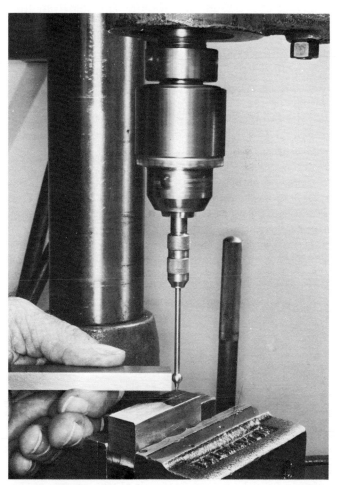

Figure 15b. Wiggler centered (Lane Community College).

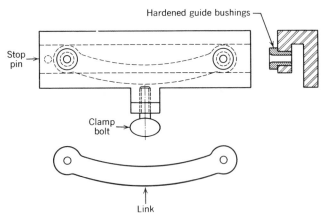

Figure 16. Simple box jig for drilling link. The link is shown below. Hardened guide bushings in the jig are used to limit wear.

can also be cross drilled when held in a vise, using the same technique as with vee-blocks.

A tap may be started straight in the drill press by hand. After tap drilling the workpiece and without removing any clamps, remove the tap drill from the chuck and replace it with a straight shank center. (An alternate method is to clamp the shank of the tap directly in the drill chuck and turn the spindle by hand two or three turns.) Insert a tap in the work and attach a tap handle. Then put the center into the tap, but *do not turn on the machine.* Apply sulfurized cutting oil and start the tap by turning the tap handle a few turns with one hand while feeding down with the other hand. Release the chuck while the tap is still in the work and finish the job of tapping the hole.

Jigs and fixtures are specially made tooling for production work. In general, fixtures reference a part to the cutting tool. Jigs guide the cutting tool (Figure 16). They both hold and support the part. The use of a jig assures exact positioning of the hole pattern in duplicate and eliminates layout work on every part.

DRILLING PROCEDURE C-CLAMP BODY

Given a combination square, wiggler, Q drill, countersink, $\frac{3}{8}-24$ tap, cutting oil, set of vee-blocks with clamps, drill press vise, the C-clamp body as it is finished up to this point, and a piece of $\frac{1}{2}$ in. diameter CF round stock $4\frac{1}{8}$ in. long:

1. Set up a workpiece square with the drill press table.
2. Locate punch mark and center drill in the mark.
3. Pilot drill and then tap drill.
4. Hand start the tap in the drill press.
5. Set up round stock in vee-blocks, locate center, then clamp in place and drill $\frac{3}{16}$ in. hole.

Figure 17. Setup of C-clamp project in vise by squaring it with combination square (Lane Community College).

Drilling the Clamp Body

1. Clamp the C-clamp body in the vise as shown in Figure 17 so the back side extends from the vise jaws about $\frac{1}{16}$ in. Square it with the table by using the combination square. Tighten the vise.

2. Put wiggler into the chuck and align the center as explained in this unit. Clamp the vise to the table, taking care not to move it.

3. Using the center drill or spotting drill, start the hole (Figure 18). Change to $\frac{1}{8}$ to $\frac{3}{16}$ in. pilot drill and make a hole clear through. Now change to the Q drill and enlarge the hole to this size (Figure 19). Chamfer the drilled hole with a countersink tool (Figure 20). The chamfer should measure about $\frac{3}{8}$ in. across. Use cutting oil or coolant for drilling.

4. Place a straight shank center in the chuck and tighten it. Insert a $\frac{3}{8}-24$ tap and tap handle in the tap-drilled hole and support the other end on the center. Apply sulfurized cutting oil. *Do not turn on the machine.* Feed lightly downward with one hand while hand turning the tap handle with the other hand (Figure 21). The tap will be started straight when part way into the work. Release the chuck and finish tapping with the tap handle.

Figure 18. Using a center drill to start the hole (Lane Community College).

Figure 20. Chamfering the drilled hole (Lane Community College).

Figure 19. Making the tap drill hole. Note the correct chip formation (Lane Community College.

Figure 21. Hand tapping in the drill press to assure good alignment (Lane Community College).

Cross Drilling the $\frac{1}{2}$ in. Round

1. Take the $\frac{1}{2}$ in. CF round; lay out the hole location and punch. Place it in one or two vee-blocks, depending on their size. Lightly clamp with about 1 in. extended from one end.
2. Set up the punch mark so it is centered and on top by using the combination square and a rule. Refer to Figure 13.

3. With a wiggler, locate the punch mark directly under the spindle.
4. Center drill; change to a $\frac{3}{16}$ in. drill and drill through. Chamfer both sides lightly. This part is now ready for lathe work.

Complete drawings for this project may be found in the instructor's manual. Ask your instructor.

SELF-TEST

1. What is the main purpose for using workholding devices on drilling machines?
2. List the names of all the workholding devices that you can remember.
3. Explain the uses of parallels for drilling setups.
4. Why should the support on a narrow or thin workpiece be as close to the drill as possible?
5. Angle drilling can be accomplished in several ways. Describe two methods. How would this be done if no angular measuring devices were mounted on the equipment?

6. What shape of material is the vee-block best suited to hold for drilling operations? What do you think its most frequent use would be?
7. What is the purpose of using a wiggler?
8. Why would you ever need an angle plate?
9. What is the purpose of starting a tap in the drill press?
10. Do you think jigs and fixtures are used to any great extent in small machine shops? Why?

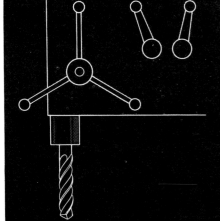

UNIT 5 OPERATING DRILLING MACHINES

You have already learned many things about drilling machines and tooling. You should now be ready to learn some very important facts about the use of these machines. How fast should the drill run? How much feed should be applied? Which kind of coolant should be used? These and other questions are answered in this unit.

OBJECTIVES

After completing this unit, you should be able to:
1. Determine the correct drilling speeds for five given drill diameters.
2. Determine the correct feed in steel by chip observation.
3. Set up the correct feed on a machine by using a feed table.

After the workpiece is properly clamped and operator safety is assured, the most important considerations for drilling are speeds, feeds, and coolants. Of these, the control and setting of speeds will have the greatest effect on the tool and the work.

CUTTING SPEEDS

Cutting speeds (CS) are normally given for high speed steel cutting tools and are based on surface feet per minute (FPM or SFM). Surface feet per minute means that either the tool moves past the work or the work moves past the tool at a rate based on the number of feet that passes a tool in one minute, whether it be on a flat surface or on the periphery of a cylindrical tool or workpiece. Since machine spindle speeds are given in revolutions per minute (RPM), this can be derived in the following manner:

$$\text{RPM} = \frac{\text{Cutting speed (in feet per minute)} \times 12}{\text{Diameter of cutter (in inches)} \times \pi}$$

If you use 3 to approximate π (3.1416), then the formula becomes

$$\frac{\text{CS} \times 12}{\text{D} \times 3} = \frac{\text{CS} \times 4}{\text{D}}$$

This simplified formula is certainly the most common one used in the machine shop practice and it applies to the full range of machine tool operations, which include the lathe and the milling machine, as well as the drill press. The simplified formula

$$\text{RPM} = \frac{\text{CS} \times 4}{\text{D}}$$

will be used throughout this text. The formula is used, for example, as follows, where D = the diameter of the drill and CS = an assigned cutting speed for a particular material: For a $\frac{1}{2}$ in. drill in low carbon steel the speed would be

$$\frac{90 \times 4}{1/2} = 720 \text{ RPM}$$

See Table 1 for cutting speeds for some metals.

Cutting speeds/RPM tables for various materials are available in handbooks and as wall charts. Excessive speeds can cause the outer corners and margins of the drill to break down. This will in turn cause the drill to bind in the hole, even if the speed is corrected and more cutting oil is applied. The only cure is to grind the drill back to its full diameter (Figure 1) using methods discussed in Unit 3 of this section.

A blue chip from steel indicates the speed is too high. The tendency with very small drills, however, is to set the RPM of the spindle too slow. This gives the drill

Table 1
Drilling Speed Table

Material	Cutting Speed (CS)
Low carbon steel	90
Aluminum	300
Cast iron	70
Alloy steel	50
Brass and bronze	120

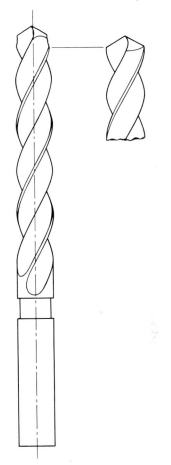

Figure 1. Broken down drill corrected by grinding back to full diameter margins and regrinding cutting lips.

a very low cutting speed and very little chip is formed unless the operator forces it with an excessive feed. The result is often a broken drill.

CONTROLLING FEEDS

The feed may be controlled by the "feel" of the cutting action and by observing the chip. A long, stringy chip indicates too much feed. The proper chip in soft steel should be a tightly rolled helix in both flutes (Figure 2).

Figure 2.   Properly formed chip (Lane Community College).

Table 2
Drilling Feed Table

Drill Size Diameter (in.)	Feeds per Revolution (in.)
Under $\frac{1}{8}$	.001 to .002
$\frac{1}{8}$ to $\frac{1}{4}$	.002 to .004
$\frac{1}{4}$ to $\frac{1}{2}$	.004 to .007
$\frac{1}{2}$ to 1	.007 to .015
over 1	.015 to .025

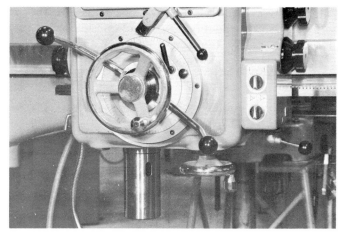

Figure 3.   Feed clutch handle. The power feed is engaged by pulling the handles outward. When the power feed is disengaged, the handles may be used to hand feed the drill (Lane Community College).

Figure 4a.   Speed and feed control dials (Lane Community College).

Figure 4b.   Large speed and feed plates on the front of the head of the upright drill press can be read at at a glance (Courtesy of Giddings & Lewis, Inc.).

Some materials such as cast iron will produce a granular chip. Drilling machines that have power feeds are arranged to advance the drill a given amount for each revolution of the spindle. Therefore, .006 in. feed means that the drill advances .006 in. every time the drill makes one full turn. The amount of feed varies according to the drill size and the work material. See Table 2.

It is a better practice to start with smaller feeds than those given in tables. Materials and setups vary, so it is safer to start low and work up to an optimum feed. You should stop the feed occasionally to break the chip and allow coolant to flow to the cutting edge of the drill.

There is generally no breakthrough problem when using power feed, but when hand feeding, the drill may catch and "grab" while coming through the last $\frac{1}{8}$ in. or so of the hole. Therefore, the operator should let up on the feed handle near this point and ease the drill through the hole. This "grabbing" tendency is especially true of brass and some plastics, but it is also a problem in steels

Figure 5. Tapping attachment (Lane Community College).

and other materials. Large upright drill presses and radial arm drills have power feed mechanisms with feed clutch handles (Figure 3) that also can be used for hand feeding when the power feed is disengaged. Both feed and speed controls are set by levers or dials (Figure 4a). Speed and feed tables on plates are often found on large drilling machines (Figure 4b).

Tapping with small taps is often done on a sensitive drill press with a tapping attachment (Figure 5) that has an adjustable friction clutch and reverse mechanism that screws the tap out when you raise the spindle. Large size taps are power driven on upright or radial drill presses. These machines provide for spindle reversal (sometimes automatic) to screw the tap back out.

COOLANTS AND CUTTING OILS

A large variety of coolants and cutting oils are used for drilling operations on the drill press. Emulsifying or soluble oils (either mineral or synthetic) mixed in water are used for drilling holes where the main requirement is an inexpensive cooling medium. Operations that tend to create more friction and, hence, need more lubrication to prevent galling (abrasion due to friction), require a cutting oil. Animal or mineral oils with sulfur or chlorine added are often used. Reaming, counterboring, countersinking, and tapping all create friction and require the use of cutting oils, of which the sulfurized type is most used. Cast iron and brass are usually drilled dry, but water soluble oil can be used for both. Aluminum can be drilled with water soluble oil or kerosene for a better finish. Both soluble and cutting oils are used for steel.

DRILLING PROCEDURES

Deep hole drilling requires sufficient drill length and quill stroke to complete the needed depth. A high helix drill

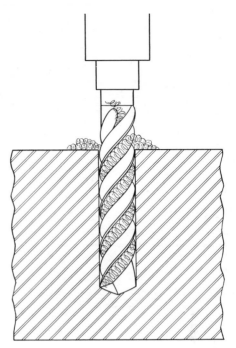

Figure 6. Drill jammed in hole because of packed chips.

helps to remove the chips, but sometimes the chips bind in the flutes of the drill and, if drilling continues, will cause the drill to jam in the hole (Figure 6). A method of avoiding this problem is called "pecking"; that is, when the hole is drilled a short distance, the drill is taken out from the hole allowing the accumulated chips to fly off. The drill is again inserted into the hole, a similar amount is drilled, and the drill is again removed. This pecking is repeated until the required depth is reached.

A depth stop is provided on drilling machines to limit the travel of the quill so that the drill can be made to stop at a predetermined depth (Figure 7). The use of a depth stop makes drilling several holes to the same depth quite easy. Spotfacing and counterboring should also be set up with the depth stop. Blind holes (holes that do not go through the piece) are measured from the edge of the drill margin to the required depth (Figure 8). Once measured, the depth can be set with the stop and drilling can proceed. One of the most important uses of a depth stop, from a maintenance standpoint, is that of setting the depth so that the machine table or drill press vise will not be drilled full of holes.

Holes that must be drilled partly into or across existing holes (Figure 9) may jam or bind a drill unless special precautions are taken. A special drill with a double margin and high helix could be used directly. However, an ordinary jobbers drill will do a satisfactory job if a tight plug made of the same material as the work is first tapped into the cross hole (Figure 10). The hole may then be drilled in a normal manner and the plug removed.

Figure 7. Using the depth stop (Lane Community College).

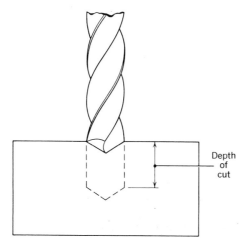

Figure 8. Measuring the depth of a drilled hole.

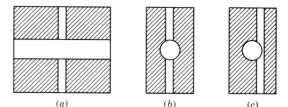

Figure 9. Hole drilled at 90 degree angle into existing hole. Cross drilling is done off center as well as on center. (*a*) Side view. (*b*) End view drilled on center. (*c*) End view drilled off center.

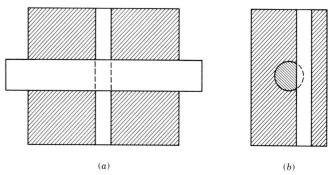

Figure 10. Existing hole is plugged to make the hole more easily drilled. (*a*) Hole is plugged with the same material that the workpiece consists of. (*b*) End view showing hole drilled through plug.

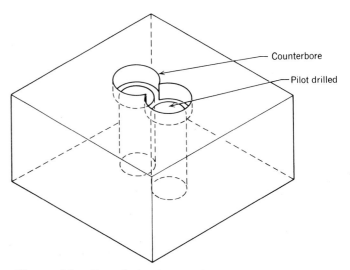

Figure 11. Deep holes that overlap are difficult to drill. The holes are drilled alternately with a smaller pilot drill and a counterbore for final size.

Holes that overlap may be made on the drill press if care is taken, and a set of counterbores with interchangeable pilots is available. First, pilot drill the holes with a size drill that does not overlap. Then counterbore to the proper size with the appropriate pilot on the counterbore (Figure 11).

Heavy duty drilling should be done on an upright or radial drill press (Figure 12). The workpiece should be made very secure since high drilling forces are used with the larger drill sizes. The work should be well clamped

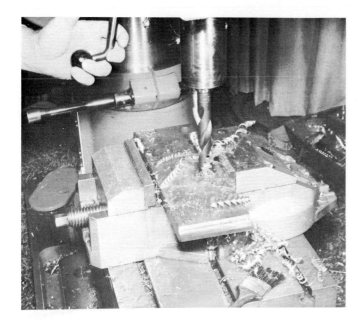

or bolted to the work table. The head and column clamp should always be locked when drilling is being done on a radial drill press. When several operations are performed in a continuing sequence, quick change drill and tool-holders are often used. Coolant is necessary for all heavy duty drilling.

Figure 12. Heavy duty drilling on a radial drill press.

SELF-TEST

1. Name three important things to keep in mind when using a drill press (not including operator safety and clamping work).
2. If RPM = $\dfrac{CS \times 4}{D}$ and the cutting speed for low carbon steel is 90, what would the RPMs be for the following drills: $\frac{1}{4}$, 2, $\frac{3}{4}$, $\frac{3}{8}$, $1\frac{1}{2}$ in. diameter.
3. What are some of the results of excessive drilling speed? What corrective measures can be taken?
4. Explain what can happen to small diameter drills when the cutting speed is too slow.
5. How can an operator tell by observing the chip if the feed is about right?
6. In what way are power feeds designated?
7. Name two differing cutting fluid types.
8. Such operations as counterboring, reaming, and tapping create friction that can cause heat. This can ruin a cutting edge. How can this situation be helped?
9. How can jamming of a drill be avoided when drilling deep holes?
10. Name three uses for the depth stop on a drill press.

UNIT 6 COUNTER-SINKING AND COUNTERBORING

In drill press work it is often necessary to make a recess that will leave a bolt head below the surface of the workpiece. These recesses are made with countersinks or counterbores. When holes are drilled into rough castings or angular surfaces, a flat surface square to these holes is needed, and spot facing is the operation used. This unit will familiarize you with these drill press operations.

OBJECTIVES

After completing this unit, you should be able to:
1. Identify tools for countersinking and counterboring.
2. Select speeds and feeds for countersinking and counterboring.

COUNTERSINKS

A countersink is a tool used to make a conical enlargement of the end of a hole. Figures 1 and 2 illustrate two types of common countersinks, both of which are designed to produce smooth surfaces, free from chatter marks. A countersink is used as a chamfering or deburring tool to prepare a hole for reaming or tapping. Unless a hole needs to have a sharp edge, it should be chamfered to protect the end of the hole from nicks and burrs. A chamfer from $\frac{1}{32}$ to $\frac{1}{16}$ in. wide is sufficient for most holes.

A hole made to receive a flathead screw or rivet should be countersunk deep enough for the head to be flush with the surface or up to .015 in. below the surface. A flathead fastener should never project above the surface. The included angles on commonly available countersinks are 60, 82, 90, and 100 degrees. Most flathead fasteners used in metalworking have an 82 degree head angle, except for the aircraft industry where the 100 degree angle is prevalent. The cutting speed used when countersinking should always be slow enough to avoid chattering.

A combination drill and countersink with a 60 degree angle (Figure 3) is used to make center holes in workpieces for machining on lathes and grinders. The illustration shown is a bell-type center drill that provides an additional angle for a chamfer of the center, protecting it from damage. The combination drill and countersink, known as a center drill, is also used for spotting holes when using a drill press or milling machine, since it is extremely rigid and will not bend under pressure.

COUNTERBORES

Counterbores are tools designed to enlarge previously drilled holes, much like countersinks, and are guided into the hole by a pilot to assure the concentricity of the two holes. A multiflute counterbore is shown in Figure 4, and a two flute counterbore is shown in Figure 5. The two flute counterbore has more chip clearance and a larger rake angle than the counterbore in Figure 4. Counterbored holes have flat bottoms, unlike the angled edges of countersunk holes, and are often used to recess a bolt head below the surface of a workpiece. Solid counterbores, such as shown in Figures 4 and 5, are used to cut recesses for socket head cap screws or filister head screws (Figure 6). The diameter of the counterbore is

Figure 1. Single flute countersink (Courtesy of the DoAll Company).
Figure 2. Chatterfree countersink (Courtesy of the DoAll Company).

Figure 3. Center drill or combination drill and countersink (Courtesy of the DoAll Company).

Figure 4. Multiflute counterbore.

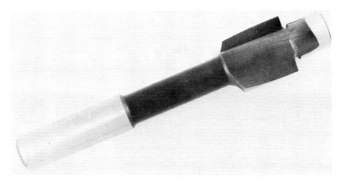

Figure 5. Two flute counterbore.

usually $\frac{1}{32}$ in. larger than the head of the bolt, so that the counterbore is freer cutting and better suited for soft and ductile materials.

When a variety of counterbore and pilot sizes is

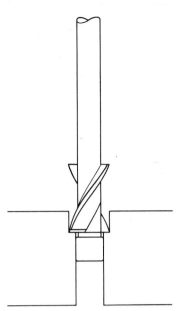

Figure 6. The counterbore is an enlargement of a hole already drilled.

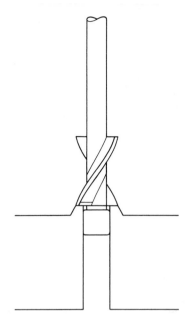

Figure 9. Spot facing on a raised boss.

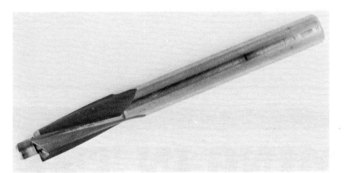

Figure 7. Interchangeable pilot counterbore.

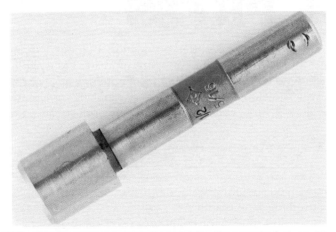

Figure 8. Pilot for interchangeable pilot counterbore.

necessary, a set of interchangeable pilot counterbores is available. Figure 7 shows a counterbore in which a number of standard or specially made pilots can be used. A pilot is illustrated in Figure 8.

Counterbores are made with straight or tapered shanks to be used in drill presses, milling machines, or even lathes. When counterboring a recess for a hex head bolt, remember to measure the diameter of the socket wrench so the hole will be large enough to accommodate it. For most counterboring operations the pilot should have from .002 to .005 in. clearance in the hole. If the pilot is too tight in the hole, it may seize and break. If there is too much clearance between the pilot and the hole, the counterbore will be out of round and will have an unsatisfactory surface finish.

It is very important that the pilot be lubricated while counterboring. Usually this lubrication is provided if a sulfurized cutting oil or soluble oil is used. When cutting dry, which is often the case with brass and cast iron, the hole and pilot should be lubricated with a few drops of lubricating oil.

Counterbores or spot facers are often used to provide a flat bearing surface for nut or bolt heads on rough castings or a raised boss (Figure 9). This operation is called spot facing. Because these rough surfaces may not be at right angles to the pilot hole, great strain is put on the pilot and counterbore, and can cause breakage of either one. To avoid breaking the tool, be very careful when starting the cut, especially when hand feeding. Prevent hogging into the work by tightening the spindle clamps slightly to remove possible backlash.

Recommended power feed rates for counterboring are shown in Table 1. The **feed** rate should be great enough to get under any surface scale quickly, thus preventing rapid dulling of the counterbore. The **speeds** used for counterboring are one third less than the

Table 1
Feeds for Counterboring

$\frac{3}{8}$ in. diameter up to .004 in. per revolution
$\frac{5}{8}$ in. diameter up to .005 in. per revolution
$\frac{7}{8}$ in. diameter up to .006 in. per revolution
$1\frac{1}{4}$ in. diameter up to .007 in. per revolution
$1\frac{1}{2}$ in. diameter up to .008 in. per revolution

speeds used for twist drills of corresponding diameters. The choice of speeds and feeds is very much affected by the condition of the equipment, the power available, and the material being counterbored.

SELF-TEST

1. When is a countersink used?
2. Why are countersinks made with varying angles?
3. What is a center drill?
4. When is a counterbore used?
5. What relationship exists between pilot size and hole size?
6. Why is lubrication of the pilot important?
7. As a rule, how does cutting speed compare between an

Before counterboring a workpiece, it should be securely fastened to the machine table or tightly held in a vise because of the great cutting pressures encountered. Workpieces also should be supported on parallels to allow for the protrusion of the pilot. To obtain several equally deep countersunk or counterbored holes on the drill press or milling machine, the spindle depth stop can be set.

Counterbores can be used on a lathe to rough out a hole before it is finished-bored. This is often more efficient than using a single cutting edge boring bar. It permits the use of a larger diameter boring bar for a more rigid setup.

equal size counterbore and twist drill?
8. What affects the selection of feed and speed when counterboring?
9. What is spot facing?
10. What important points should be considered when a counterboring setup is made?

UNIT 7 REAMING IN THE DRILL PRESS

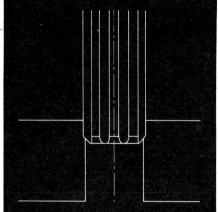

Many engineering requirements involve the production of holes having smooth surfaces, accurate location, and uniform size. In many cases, holes produced by drilling alone do not entirely satisfy these requirements. For this reason, the reamer was developed for enlarging or finishing previously formed holes. This unit will help you properly identify, select, and use machine reamers.

OBJECTIVES

After completing this unit, you should be able to:
1. Identify commonly used machine reamers.
2. Select the correct feeds and speeds for commonly used materials.
3. Determine appropriate amounts of stock allowance.
4. Identify probable solutions to reaming problems.

Reamers are tools used mostly to precision finish holes, but they are also used in the heavy construction industry to enlarge or align existing holes.

COMMON MACHINE REAMERS

Machine reamers have straight or taper shanks; the taper usually is a standard Morse taper. The parts of a

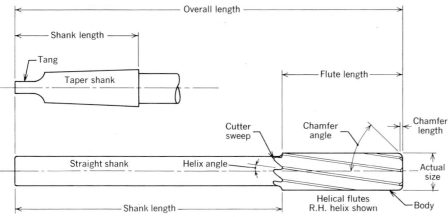

Figure 1. The parts of a machine reamer (Courtesy of Bendix Industrial Tools Division).

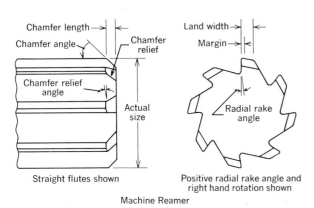

Figure 2. The cutting end of a machine reamer (Courtesy of Bendix Industrial Tools Division).

Figure 3. Straight shank straight flute chucking reamer (TRW Inc.).

Figure 4. Straight shank helical flute-chucking reamer (TRW Inc.).

Figure 5. Taper shank helical flute chucking reamer (TRW Inc.).

Figure 6. Taper shank straight flute jobbers reamer (TRW Inc.).

machine reamer are shown in Figure 1; the cutting end of a machine reamer is shown in Figure 2.

Chucking reamers (Figures 3, 4, and 5) are efficient in machine reaming a wide range of materials and are commonly used in drill presses, turret lathes, and screw machines. Helical flute reamers have an extremely smooth cutting action that finishes holes accurately and precisely. Chucking reamers cut on the chamfer at the end of the flutes. This chamfer is usually at a 45 degree angle.

Jobber's reamers (Figure 6) are used where a longer flute length than chucking reamers is needed. The additional flute length gives added guide to the reamer, especially when reaming deep holes.

The rose reamer (Figure 7) is primarily a roughing reamer used to enlarge holes to within .003 to .005 in. of finish size. The teeth are slightly backed off, which means that the reamer diameter is smaller toward shank end by approximately .001 in./in. of flute length. The lands on these reamers are ground cylindrically without radial relief, and all cutting is done on the end of the reamer. This reamer will remove a considerable amount of material in one cut.

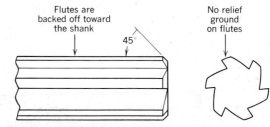

Figure 7. Rose reamer.

Shell reamers (Figure 8) are finishing reamers. They are more economically produced, especially in larger sizes, than solid reamers because a much smaller amount of tool material is used in making them. Two slots in the shank end of the reamer fit over matching driving lugs

Figure 8.   Shell reamer helical flute (TRW Inc.).

Figure 9.   Taper shank shell reamer arbor (TRW Inc.).

Figure 10.   Morse taper reamer (TRW Inc.).

Figure 11.   Helical taper pin reamer (TRW Inc.).

Figure 12.   Helical flute taper bridge reamer (TRW Inc.).

Figure 13.   Carbide tipped straight flute chucking reamer (TRW Inc.).

Figure 14.   Carbide tipped, helical flute chucking reamer, right-hand helix (TRW Inc.).

Figure 15.   Carbide tipped, helical flute chucking reamer, left-hand helix (TRW Inc.).

Figure 16.   Carbide tipped expansion reamer (TRW Inc.).

on the shell reamer or box (Figure 9). The hole in the shell reamer has a slight taper ($\frac{1}{8}$ in./ft) in it to assure exact alignment with the shell reamer arbor. Shell reamers are made with straight or helical flutes and are commonly produced in sizes from $\frac{3}{4}$ to $2\frac{1}{2}$ in. in diameter. Shell reamer arbors come with matching straight or tapered shanks and are made in designated sizes from numbers 4 to 9.

Morse taper reamers (Figure 10), with straight or helical flutes, are used to finish ream tapered holes in drill sockets, sleeves, and machine tool spindles. Helical taper pin reamers (Figure 11) are especially suitable for machine reaming of taper pin holes. There is no packing of chips in the flutes, which reduces the possibility of breakage. These reamers have a freecutting action that produces a good finish at high cutting speeds. Taper pin reamers have a taper of $\frac{1}{4}$ in. per foot of length and are manufactured in 18 different sizes ranging from smallest number 8/0 (eight naught) to the largest at number 10.

Taper bridge reamers (Figure 12) are used in structural iron or steel work, bridge work, and ship construc-

tion where extreme accuracy is not required. They have long tapered pilot points for easy entry in out-of-line holes often encountered in structural work. Taper bridge reamers are made with straight and helical flutes to ream holes with diameters from $\frac{1}{4}$ to $1\frac{5}{16}$ in.

Carbide tipped chucking reamers (Figure 13) are often used in production setups, particularly where abrasive materials or sand and scale as in castings are encountered. The right-hand helix chucking reamer (Figure 14) is recommended for ductile materials or highly abrasive materials or when machining blind holes. The carbide tipped left-hand helix chucking reamer (Figure 15) will produce good finishes on heat treated steels and other hard materials, but should be used on through holes only. All expansion reamers (Figure 16) after becoming worn can be expanded and resized by grinding. This feature offsets normal wear from abrasive materials and provides for a long tool life. These tools should not be adjusted for reaming size by loosening or tightening the expansion plug but only by grinding.

Reaming is intended to produce accurate and straight holes of uniform diameter. The required accuracy depends on a high degree of surface finish, tolerance on diameter, roundness, straightness, and absence of bellmouth at the ends of holes. To make an accurate hole it is necessary to use reamers with adequate support for the cutting edges; an adjustable reamer may not be adequate. Machine reamers are often made of either high speed steel or cemented carbide. Reamer cutting

Table 1
Reaming Speeds

Aluminum and its alloys	130–200[a]
Brass	130–200
Bronze, high tensile	50–70
Cast iron	
Soft	70–100
Hard	50–70
Steel	
Low carbon	50–70
Medium carbon	40–50
High carbon	35–40
Alloy	35–40
Stainless steel	
AISI 302	15–30
AISI 403	20–50
AISI 416	30–60
AISI 430	30–50
AISI 443	15–30

[a]Cutting speeds in surface feet per minute (FPM or SFM) for reaming with an HSS reamer.

action is controlled to a large extent by the cutting speed and feed used.

SPEED

The most efficient cutting speed for machine reaming depends on the type of material being reamed, the amount of stock to be removed, the tool material being used, the finish required, and the rigidity of the setup. A good starting point, when machine reaming, is to use $\frac{1}{2}$ to $\frac{1}{3}$ of the cutting speed used for drilling the same materials. Table 1 may be used as a guide.

Where conditions permit the use of carbide reamers, the speeds may often be increased over those recommended for HSS (high speed steel) reamers. The limiting factor is usually an absence of rigidity in the setup. Any chatter, which is often caused by too high a speed, is likely to chip the cutting edges of a carbide reamer. Always select a speed that is slow enough to eliminate chatter. Close tolerances and fine finishes often require the use of considerably lower speeds than those recommended in Table 1.

FEEDS

Feeds in reaming are usually 2 to 3 times greater than those used for drilling. The amount of feed may vary with different materials, but a good starting point would be between .0015 and .004 in. per revolution. Too low a feed may "glaze" the hole, which has the result of work hardening the material, causing occasional chatter and excessive wear on the reamer. Too high a feed

Table 2
Stock Allowance for Reaming

Reamer Size (in.)	Allowance (in.)
$\frac{1}{32}$ to $\frac{1}{8}$	.003 to .006
$\frac{1}{8}$ to $\frac{1}{4}$	.005 to .009
$\frac{1}{4}$ to $\frac{3}{8}$	.007 to .012
$\frac{3}{8}$ to $\frac{1}{2}$	.010 to .015
$\frac{1}{2}$ to $\frac{3}{4}$	$\frac{1}{64}$ or $\frac{1}{32}$
$\frac{3}{4}$ to 1	$\frac{1}{32}$

tends to reduce the accuracy of the hole and the quality of the surface finish. Generally, it is best to use as high a feed as possible to produce the required finish and accuracy.

When a drill press that has only a hand feed is used to ream a hole, the feed rate should be estimated just as it would be for drilling. About twice the feed rate should be used for reaming as would be used for drilling in the same setup when hand feeding.

STOCK ALLOWANCE

The stock removal allowance should be sufficient to assure a good cutting action of the reamer. Too small a stock allowance results in burnishing (a slipping or polishing action), or it wedges the reamer in the hole causing excessive wear or breakage of the reamer. The condition of the hole before reaming also has an influence on the reaming allowance since a rough hole will need a greater amount of stock removed than an equal size hole with a fairly smooth finish. See Table 2 for commonly used stock allowance for reaming. When materials that work harden readily are reamed, it is especially important to have adequate material for reaming.

CUTTING FLUIDS

To ream a hole to a high degree of surface finish, a cutting fluid is needed. A good cutting fluid will cool the workpiece and tool and will also act as a lubricant between the chip and the tool to reduce friction and heat buildup. Cutting fluids should be applied in sufficient volume to flush the chips away. Table 3 lists some coolants used for reaming different materials.

REAMING PROBLEMS

Chatter is often caused by the lack of rigidity in the machine, workpiece, or the reamer itself. Corrections may be made by reducing the speed, increasing the feed, putting a chamfer on the hole before reaming,

Table 3
Coolants Used for Reaming

Material	Dry	Soluble Oil	Kerosene	Sulfurized Oil	Mineral Oil
Aluminum		x	x		
Brass	x	x			
Bronze	x	x			x
Cast iron	x				
Steels					
Low carbon		x		x	
Alloy		x		x	
Stainless		x		x	

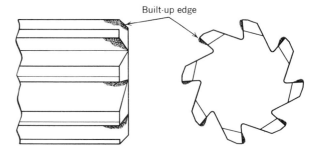

Figure 18. Reamer teeth having built-up edges.

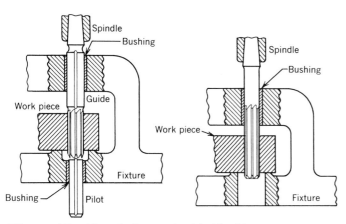

Figure 17. Use of pilots and guided bushings on reamers. Pilots are provided so that the reamer can be held in alignment and can be supported as close as possible while allowing for chip clearance (Courtesy of Bendix Industrial Tools Division).

using a reamer with a pilot (Figure 17), or reducing the clearance angle on the cutting edge of the reamer. Carbide tipped reamers especially cannot tolerate even a momentary chatter at the start of a hole, as such a vibration is likely to chip the cutting edges.

Oversize holes can be caused by inadequate workpiece support, worn guide bushings, worn or loose spindle bearings, or a bent reamer shank. When reamers gradually start cutting larger holes, it may be because of the work material galling or forming a built-up edge on reamer cutting surfaces (Figure 18). Mild steel and some aluminum alloys are particularly troublesome in this area. Changing to a different coolant may help. Reamers with highly polished flutes, margins, and relief angles or reamers that have special surface treatment may also improve the cutting action.

Bell-mouthed holes are caused by misalignment of the reamer with the hole. The use of accurate bushings or pilots may correct bell-mouth, but in many cases the only solution is the use of floating holders. A floating holder will allow movement in some directions while restricting it in others. A poor finish can be improved by decreasing the feed, but this will also increase the wear and shorten the life of the reamer. A worn reamer will never leave a good surface finish as it will score or groove the finish and often produce a tapered hole.

Too fast a feed will cause a reamer to break. Too large a stock allowance for finish reaming will produce a large volume of chips with heat build-up, and will result in a poor hole finish. Too small a stock allowance will cause the reamer teeth to rub as they cut, and not cut freely, which will produce a poor finish and cause rapid reamer wear. Coolant applied in insufficient quantity may also cause rough surface finishes when reaming.

SELF-TEST

1. How is a machine reamer identified?
2. What is the difference between a chucking and a rose reamer?
3. What is a jobbers reamer?
4. Why are shell reamers used?
5. How does the surface finish of a hole affect its accuracy?
6. How does the cutting speed compare between drilling and reaming for the same material?
7. How does the feed rate compare between drilling and reaming?
8. How much reaming allowance will you leave on a $\frac{1}{2}$ in. hole?
9. What is the purpose of using a coolant while reaming?
10. What can be done to overcome chatter?
11. What will cause oversize holes?
12. What causes a bell-mouthed hole?
13. How can poor surface finish be overcome?
14. When are carbide tipped reamers used?
15. Why is vibration harmful to carbide tipped reamers?

SECTION H
TURNING MACHINES

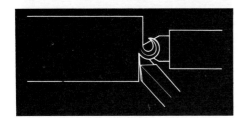

The power drive lathe or engine lathe is truly the father of all machine tools. With suitable attachments the engine lathe may be used for turning, threading, boring, drilling, reaming, facing, spinning, and grinding, although many of these operations are preferably done on specialized machinery. Sizes range from the smallest jeweler's or precision lathes (Figure 1) to the massive lathes used for machining huge forgings (Figure 2).

Engine lathes (Figures 3 and 4) are used by machinists to produce one-of-a-kind parts or a few pieces for a short run production. They are also used for toolmaking, machine repair, and maintenance.

Some lathes have a vertical spindle instead of a horizontal one with a large rotating table on which the work is clamped. These huge machines, called vertical boring mills (Figure 5), are the largest of our machine tools. A 25-foot diameter table is not unusual. Huge turbines, weighing many tons, can be placed on the table and clamped in position to be machined. The machining of such castings would be impractical on a horizontal spindle lathe.

A more versatile and higher production version of the boring mill is the vertical turret lathe (Figure 6). It does similar work to the vertical boring mill, but on a smaller scale. It is arranged with toolholders and turret with multiple tools much like that on a turret lathe, which give it flexibility and relatively high production.

Turret lathes are strictly production machines. They are designed to pro-

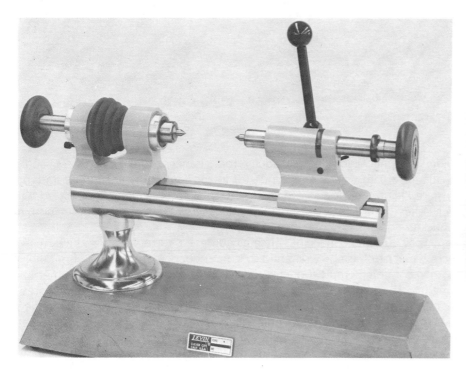

Figure 1. Jeweler's or instrument lathe (Courtesy of Louis Levin & Son, Inc.).

Figure 2. A massive forging being machined to exact specifications on a lathe (Courtesy of Bethlehem Steel Corporation, Bethlehem, Pa.).

Figure 3. Heavy duty engine lathe with $11\frac{1}{2}$ in. diameter hole through the spindle. The carriage has rapid power traverse feature (Courtesy of Lodge & Shipley Company).

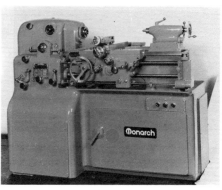

Figure 4. Ten in. toolmaker's lathe (Courtesy of The Monarch Machine Tool Company, Sidney, Ohio).

Figure 5. Vertical boring mill (Courtesy of El-Jay Inc., Eugene, Oregon).

Figure 6. Vertical turret lathe (Courtesy of Giddings & Lewis, Inc.).

vide short machining time and quick tool changes. Two types of semiautomatic turret lathes require an operator in constant attendance, the ram type (Figure 7) and the saddle type (Figure 8). Small, precision, hand operated turret lathes (Figure 9) are used to produce very small parts. Automatic bar chuckers require little operator action.

Fully automatic machines such as automatic turret lathes and automatic screw machines are programmed to do a sequence of machining operations to make a completed product. Automatic turret lathes are programmed by peg board or by numerical control (NC) on punched tape. Automatic screw machines, used for high production of small parts, are typically programmed with cams, although some are numerically controlled. There are several types of automatic machines: the single spindle machine, the sliding head (or Swiss type), the multiple spindle, and the revolving head wire feed type. Multiple

Figure 7. Ram-type turret lathe (Courtesy of The Warner & Swasey Company).

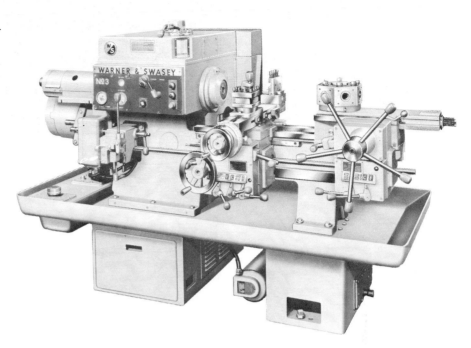

Figure 8. Saddle-type turret lathe (Courtesy of The Warner & Swasey Company).

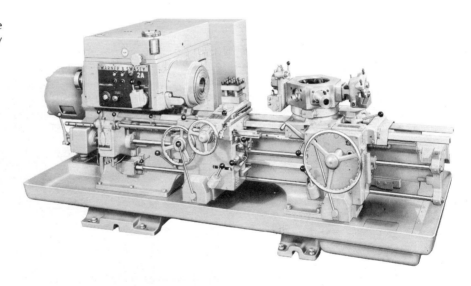

spindle bar and chucking machines are high production turning machines that can do a variety of operations at different stations.

Tracer lathes (Figure 10) follow a pattern or template to reproduce an exact shape on a workpiece. Tracing attachments (Figure 11) are often used on engine or turret lathes.

Lathes that are numerically controlled (NC) by programming and punching tape produce workpieces such as shafts with tapers and precision diameters. NC chuckers (Figure 12) are high production automatic lathes designed for chucking operations. Similar bar feeding NC types take a full length bar through the spindle and automatically feed it in as needed. Some automatic lathes operate as either chucking machines or bar feed machines.

Lathes are also used for metal spinning. Reflectors, covers, and pans, for example, are made by this method out of aluminum, copper, and other metals.

Figure 9. Small precision manually operated turret lathe (Courtesy of Louis Levin & Sons, Inc.).

Figure 10. Tracer lathe (Lane Community College).

Manufacturing methods for spinning heavy steel plate are entirely different. Hydraulic operated tools are used to form the steel (Figure 13). The dimensions of the part shaped by this Floturn process are shown in Figure 14.

Digital readout systems for machine tools such as the engine lathe in Figure 15 are becoming more common. This system features a completely self-guided rack and pinion that operates on the cross slide. The direct readout resolution is .001 in. on both the diameters and the cross slide movement. These systems can also be converted to metric measure.

In ordinary turning, metal is removed from a rotating workpiece with a

Figure 11. Tracer attachments on an engine lathe (Courtesy of Clausing Corporation).

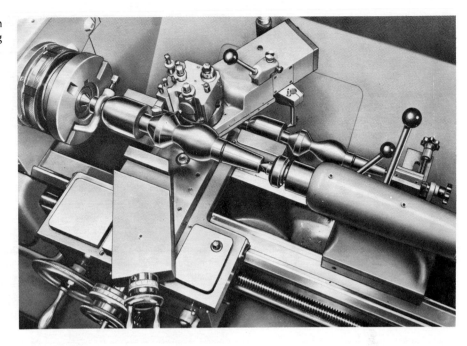

Figure 12. Numerically controlled chucking lathe with turret (Courtesy of The Monarch Machine Tool Company, Sidney, Ohio).

single point tool. The tool must be harder than the workpiece and held rigidly against it. Chips formed from the workpiece slide across the face of the tool. This essentially is the way chips are produced in all metal cutting operations. The pressures used in metal cutting can be as much as 20 tons per square inch. Tool geometry therefore is quite important to maintain the strength at the cutting edge of the tool bit.

In this section you will learn how to use common lathes, how to grind high speed tools, and how to select carbide tools for lathe work.

TURNING MACHINE SAFETY

The lathe can be a safe machine only if the machinist is aware of the hazards involved in its operation. In the machine shop as anywhere, you must always

Figure 13. Floturn lathe. The photograph (right) shows the completion of the first two operations. Starting with the flat blank, the workpiece is shear formed (Floturn) to the shape shown on the mandrel. In the process the 1 in. thickness of the blank is reduced to .420 in. The second operation, although performed on a Floturn machine, is more properly spinning than shear forming. In this operation, the workpiece is brought to the finished shape as seen in the background (Photo courtesy of Floturn, Inc., Division of the Lodge & Shipley Co.).

Figure 14. The principle of the Floturn process (Courtesy of Floturn, Inc., Division of the Lodge & Shipley Co.).

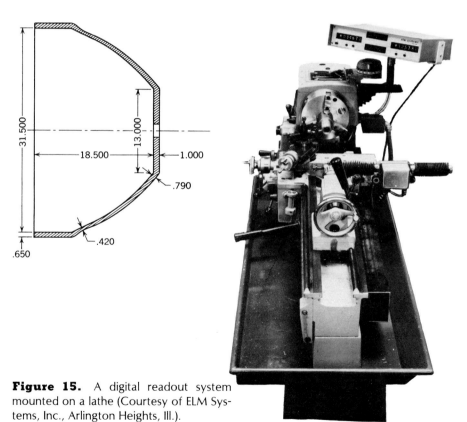

Figure 15. A digital readout system mounted on a lathe (Courtesy of ELM Systems, Inc., Arlington Heights, Ill.).

keep your mind on your work in order to avoid accidents. Develop safe work habits in the use of setups, chip breakers, guards, and other protective devices. Standards for safety have been established as guidelines to help you eliminate unsafe practices and procedures on lathes. Some of the hazards are as follows.

Figure 16a. A chuck wrench left in the chuck is a danger to everyone in the shop (Lane Community College).

Figure 16b. A safety-conscious lathe operator will remove the chuck wrench when he finishes using it (Lane Community College).

Pinch Points Due to Lathe Movement

A finger caught in gears or between the compound rest and a chuck jaw would be an example. The rule is to keep your hands away from such dangerous positions when the lathe is operating.

Hazards Associated with Broken or Falling Components

Heavy chucks or workpieces can be dangerous when accidentally dropped. Care must be used when handling them. If a threaded spindle is suddenly reversed, the chuck can come off and fly out of the lathe. A chuck wrench left in the chuck can become a missile when the machine is turned on. Always remove the chuck wrench immediately after using it (Figures 16a and 16b).

Hazards Resulting from Contact with High Temperature Components

Burns usually result from handling hot chips (up to 800°F or even more) or a hot workpiece. Gloves may be worn when handling hot chips or workpieces, but never worn when the machine is running.

Hazards Resulting from Contact with Sharp Edges, Corners, and Projections

These are perhaps the most common cause of hand injuries in lathe work. Dangerous sharp edges may be found many places: on a long stringy chip, on a tool bit, or on a burred edge of a turned or threaded part. Shields should be used for protection from flying chips and coolant. These shields are usually made of clear plastic and are hinged over the chuck or clamped to the carriage of engine lathes. Stringy chips must not be removed with bare hands; wear heavy gloves and use hook tools or pliers. Always turn off the machine before attempting to remove chips. Chips should be broken and 9-shaped rather than in a stringy mass or a long wire (Figure 17). Chip breakers on tools and correct feeds will help to produce safe, easily handled chips. Burred edges must be removed before the workpiece is removed from the lathe. Always remove the tool bit when setting up or removing workpieces from the lathe.

Hazards of Workholding Devices or Driving Devices

When workpieces are clamped, their components often extend beyond the outside diameter of the holding device. Guards, barriers, and warnings such as signs or verbal instructions are all used to make you aware of the hazards. On power chucking devices you should be aware of potential pinch points

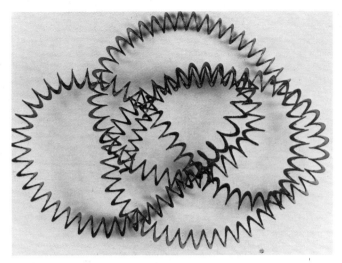

Figure 17. Unbroken lathe chips are sharp and hazardous to the operator (Lane Community College).

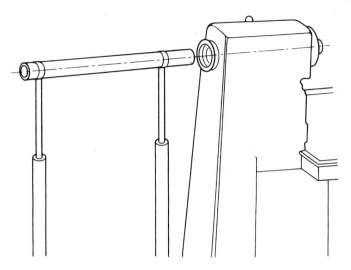

Figure 18. Stock tube is used to support long workpieces that extend out of the headstock of a lathe.

Figure 19. Polishing in the lathe with abrasive cloth (Lane Community College).

between workpiece and workholding device. Make certain sufficient gripping force is exerted by the jaws to safely hold the work. Never run a geared scroll chuck without having something being gripped in the jaws. Centrifugal force on the jaws can cause the scroll to unwind and the jaws to come out of the chuck. Keep tools, files, and micrometers off the machine. They may vibrate off into the revolving chuck or workpiece.

Spindle Braking The spindle or workpiece should never be slowed or stopped by hand gripping or by using a pry bar. Always use machine controls to stop or slow it.

Workpieces Extending Out of the Lathe Should Be Supported by a Stock Tube (Figure 18) If a slender workpiece is allowed to extend beyond the headstock spindle a foot or so without support, it can fly outward from centrifugal force. The piece will not only be bent, but it will present a very great danger to anyone standing near.

Figure 20. The skyhook in use bringing a large chuck into place for mounting (Syclone Products, Inc.).

Figure 21. Left-hand filing in the lathe (Lane Community College).

Other Safety Considerations Hold one end of abrasive cloth strips in each hand when polishing rotating work. Don't let either hand get closer than a few inches from the work (Figure 19). Keep rags, brushes, and fingers away from rotating work, especially when knurling. Roughing cuts tend to quickly drag in and wrap up rags, clothing, neckties, abrasive cloth, and hair. Move the carriage back out of the way and cover the tool with a cloth when checking boring work. When removing or installing chucks or heavy workpieces, use a board on the ways (a part of the lathe bed) so it can be slid into place. To lift a heavy chuck or workpiece (larger than an 8-in. diameter chuck) get help or use a crane (Figure 20). Remove the tool or turn it out of the way during this operation. Do not shift gears or try to take measurements while the machine is running and the workpiece is in motion. Never use a file without a handle as the file tang can quickly cut your hand or wrist if the file is struck by a spinning chuck jaw or lathe dog. Left-hand filing is considered safest in the lathe; that is, the left hand grips the handle while the right hand holds the tip end of the file (Figure 21).

UNIT 1 THE ENGINE LATHE

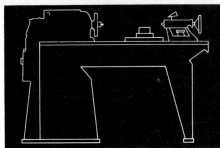

Modern lathes are highly accurate and complex machines capable of performing a great variety of operations. Before attempting to operate a lathe, you should familiarize yourself with its principal parts and their operation. Good maintenance is important to the life and accuracy of machine tools. A machinist depends on the lathe to make precision parts. A poorly maintained machine loses its usefulness to a machinist. This unit will show you how to make adjustments, lubricate, and properly maintain the machine that you use.

OBJECTIVES

After completing this unit, you should be able to:
1. Identify the most important parts of a lathe and their functions.
2. List all of the lubrication points for one lathe in your shop.
3. Determine the type of lubrication needed.
4. Adjust the cross slide, compound slide, and tailstock, and clamp the compound after rotating it.

One of the most important machine tools in the metal working industry is the lathe (Figure 1a). A lathe is a device in which the work is rotated against a cutting tool. As the cutting tool is moved lengthwise and crosswise to the axis of the workpiece, the shape of the workpiece is generated.

Figure 1b shows a lathe and its most important parts identified. A lathe consists of the following major component groups: headstock, bed, carriage, tailstock, quick-change gearbox, and a base or pedestal. The headstock is fastened on the left side of the bed. It contains the spindle that drives the various workholding devices. The spindle is supported by spindle bearings on each end. If they are sleeve-type bearings, a thrust bearing is also used to take up end play. Tapered roller spindle bearings are often used on modern lathes. Spindle speed changes are also made in the headstock, either with belts or with gears. Figure 2 shows a geared-type headstock. Speed changes are made in these lathes by shifting gears (Figure 3) in much the same way as in a standard automobile transmission.

Most belt-driven lathes have a slow speed range when back gears are engaged. Figure 4 shows a back geared headstock. Usually only older type lathes have belt drives and back gears. See Unit 5 for operating details on these various drives.

A feed reverse lever, also called a leadscrew direction control, is located on the headstock. Its function is simply to control the direction of rotation of the lead-

screw. This rotation determines the direction of feed and whether a thread cut on the lathe is left-hand or right-hand. The threading and feeding mechanisms of the lathe are also powered through the headstock.

The spindle is hollow to allow long slender workpieces to pass through. The spindle end facing the tailstock is called the spindle nose (Figure 5). Spindle noses usually are one of three designs: a long taper key drive (Figure 5), a cam lock type (Figure 6), or a threaded spindle nose (Figure 7). Lathe chucks and other workholding devices are fastened to and driven by the spindle nose. The hole in the spindle nose typically has a standard Morse taper. The size of this taper varies with the size of the lathe.

The bed (Figure 8) is the foundation and backbone of a lathe. Its rigidity and alignment affect the accuracy of the parts machined on it. Therefore, lathe beds are constructed to withstand the stresses created by heavy machining cuts. On top of the bed are the ways, which usually consist of two inverted vees and two flat bearing surfaces. The ways of the lathes are very accurately machined by grinding or by milling and hand scraping. Wear or damage to the ways will affect the accuracy of workpieces machined on them. A gear rack is fastened below the front way of the lathe. Gears that link the carriage handwheel to this rack make possible the lengthwise movement of the carriage by hand.

The carriage is made up of the saddle and apron (Figure 9). The apron is the part of the carriage facing the

Figure 1a. The engine lathe (Courtesy of Clausing Corporation).

Figure 2. Geared headstock for heavy duty lathe (Courtesy of the Lodge & Shipley Company).

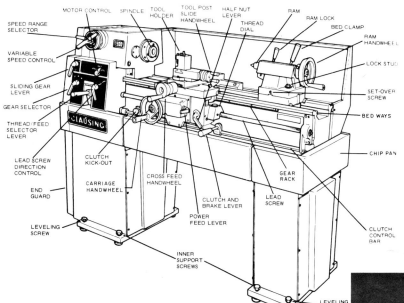

Figure 1b. Engine lathe with the parts identified (Courtesy of Clausing Corporation).

Figure 3. Spindle drive showing gears and shifting mechanism located in the headstock (Courtesy of the Lodge & Shipley Company).

operator; it contains the gears and feed clutches that transmit motion from the feed rod or leadscrew to the carriage and cross slide. The saddle slides on the ways and supports the cross slide and compound rest. The cross slide moves crosswise at 90 degrees to the axis of the lathe by manually turning the cross feed screw handle or by engaging the cross feed lever (also called power feed lever, and on some lathes the clutch knob), which is located on the apron for automatic feed. On some lathes a feed change lever (or plunger) on the

Figure 4. Speeds are changed on this lathe by moving the belt to various steps on the pulley (Lane Community College).

Figure 5. Long taper key drive spindle nose (Lane Community College).

Figure 6. Camlock spindle nose (DeAnza College).

Figure 7. Threaded spindle nose (Lane Community College).

Figure 8. Lathe bed (Courtesy of Clausing Corporation).

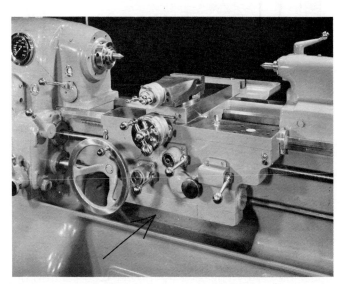

Figure 9. Lathe carriage. The arrow is pointing to the apron (Courtesy of The Monarch Machine Tool Company, Sidney, Ohio).

apron is used to direct power from the feed mechanism to either the longitudinal (lengthwise) travel of the carriage or to the cross slide. On other lathes, two separate levers or knobs are used to transmit motion to the carriage and cross slide.

A thread dial is fastened to the apron (usually on the right side), which indicates the exact moment to engage the half-nuts while cutting threads. The half-nut lever is used **only** for thread cutting and **never** for feeds for general turning. The entire carriage can be moved along the ways manually by turning the carriage handwheel or

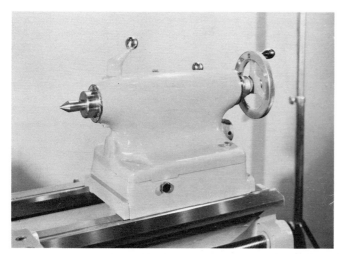

Figure 10. Tailstock (Courtesy of The Monarch Machine Tool Company, Sidney, Ohio).

Figure 11. Quick-change gearbox showing index plate (Lane Community College).

under power by engaging the power feed controls on the apron. Once in position, the carriage can be clamped to the bed by tightening the carriage lock screw.

The compound rest is mounted on the cross slide and can be swiveled to any angle horizontal with the lathe axis in order to produce bevels and tapers. The compound rest can only be moved manually by turning the compound rest feed screw handle. Cutting tools are fastened on a tool post that is located on the compound rest.

The tailstock (Figure 10) is used to support one end of a workpiece for machining or to hold various cutting tools such as drills, reamers, and taps. The tailstock slides on the ways and can be clamped in any position along

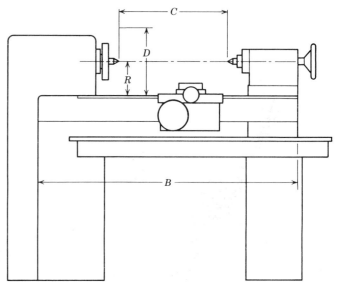

Figure 12. Measuring a lathe for size. C = maximum distance between centers; D = maximum diameter of workpiece over ways–swing of lathe; R = radius, one-half swing; B = length of bed.

the bed. The tailstock has a sliding spindle that is operated by a handwheel and locked in position with a spindle clamp lever. The spindle is bored to receive a standard Morse taper shank. The tailstock consists of an upper and lower unit and can be adjusted to make tapered workpieces by turning the adjusting screws in the base unit.

The quick-change gearbox (Figure 11) is the link that transmits power between the spindle and the carriage. By using the gear shift levers on the quick-change gearbox, you can select different feeds. Power is transmitted to the carriage through a feed rod, or as on smaller lathes, through the leadscrew with a keyway in it. The index plate on the quick-change gearbox indicates the feed in thousandths of an inch or as threads per inch for the lever positions.

The base of the machine is used to level the lathe and to secure it to the floor. The motor of the lathe is usually mounted in the base. Figure 12 shows how the lathe is measured.

ENGINE LATHE
MAINTENANCE AND ADJUSTMENTS

The engine lathe, a precision machine tool, is perhaps the most abused of all shop equipment. With proper care the lathe will maintain its accuracy for many years, but its service life will be shortened severely if it is misused. Even small nicks or burrs on the ways can prevent the carriage or tailstock from seating properly. Fine chips, filings, or grindings combine with the oil to form

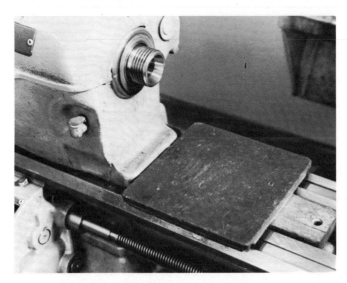

Figure 13. Wooden lathe board is used for handling chucks (Lane Community College).

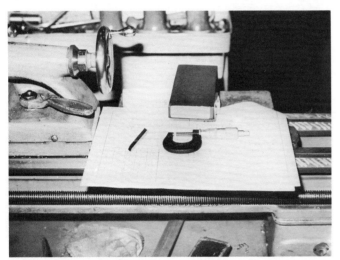

Figure 14. Precision tools are protected from damage by keeping them in a safe place such as a tool tray while working on a lathe (Lane Community College).

an abrasive mixture that can score and wear sliding surfaces and bearings. Frequent cleaning of way surfaces is helpful, but do not use an air jet, since this will blow the abrasive sludge into the bearing surfaces. Use a brush to remove chips and wipe off with a cloth, then apply a thin film of oil.

Nicks or burrs are often caused by dropping chucks and workpieces on the ways and by laying tools such as files across them. This should never be done. Wooden lathe boards are used for handling chucks and heavy work (Figure 13). Larger boards are often used for tool trays that are placed on an unused portion of the lathe way (Figure 14).

Occasionally it is advisable to clean the leadscrew.

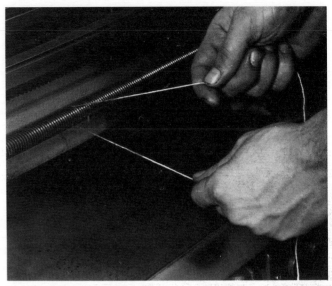

Figure 15. Cleaning the lead screw using a piece of string (Lane Community College).

To do this, loop a piece of string behind the leadscrew and hold each end of the string (Figure 15). With the machine on and the leadscrew turning, draw the string along the threads. Never hold the string by wrapping it around your fingers and, if the string grabs and begins winding on the leadscrew, let it go. Lathes should be completely lubricated daily or before using. Oil cups or holes should be given a few drops of oil (too much just runs out). Apron and headstock reservoirs should be checked for oil level. If they are low, use an oil recommended by the manufacturer or its equivalent.

Before operating any lathe, wipe the way surfaces, even if they look clean, as gritty dust can settle on them when the machine has been idle for a few hours. Wiped, the ways should then be given a thin film of way oil, which is specially compounded to remain on the way surfaces for a longer time than ordinary lubricating oil. After using the lathe, it should again be cleaned free of chips and grit, and the ways should be lightly oiled to prevent rusting. The chips and dirt on the surrounding floor space should be swept up and placed in a container.

Lathe maintenance and repair that requires extensive disassembly should only be done by qualified personnel. There are, however, many adjustments that a machinist should be able to perform. Adjustment of the gibs on the cross slide and compound slide may be needed if there is excess clearance between the gib and the dovetail slide. Adjust the gibs only when the slide is completely over its mating dovetail. Gibs adjusted without this backing may bend. Straight gibs are adjusted by tightening a number of screws (Figure 16) until the slide operates with just a slight drag. Too much tightening will

Figure 16. Gibs are adjusted by tightening screws while the compound is centered over its slide (Lane Community College).

Figure 17. Method of adjustment of tapered gibs. Thrust screw is being tightened. The lock screw is on the other end of the gib (Lane Community College).

cause binding. The gibs on the compound slide should be kept fairly tight when the compound is not being used. Lock nuts should be tightened after making the adjustment. Tapered gibs are adjusted by first loosening the lockscrew and then adjusting the thrust screw. When the proper fit has been obtained, tighten the lockscrew (Figure 17).

Lathes typically have some slack or backlash in the cross feed screw and compound screw. This slack must be removed before starting a cut by backing away from the work two turns and then bringing the tool to the work. Some lathes have backlash compensating cross feed nuts (Figure 18) that can be adjusted to remove most of the end play.

Sometimes a machinist must interchange gears in the gear train to the lead screw on the headstock end of the lathe. When the proper gears have been set in place, the mounting or clamping bolts should be tightened

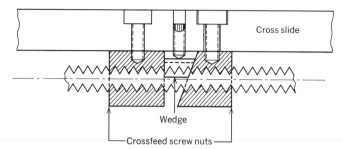

Figure 18. Backlash compensating crossfeed nuts. This is one kind of backlash compensator in which a wedge is forced between two nuts on the same screw.

Figure 19. Adjustment of feed change gears. Gear backlash should be approximately .005 in. (Lane Community College).

lightly and a strip of paper placed between the gears. The gears should then be pushed together against the paper shim. This spaces the gears approximately .005 in. The clamping bolts should then be tightened (Figure 19). If the gears are noisy, the adjustment must be made with more mating clearance between the gears.

The method by which the tailstock is clamped to the ways is simple and self-adjusting in many lathes, especially older ones. A large bolt and nut draws a cross bar up into the bed when the nut is tightened (Figure 20). A camlock type with a lever (Figure 21) is sometimes used alone or on larger lathes in conjunction with a standard

Figure 20. Tailstock is clamped to the ways by means of a bolt and crossbar (Lane Community College).

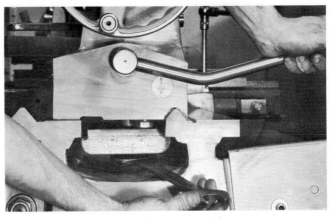

Figure 22. Adjustment of camlock clamp. When the bolt on the crossbar is tightened, the cam will lock with the lever in a lower position (Lane Community College).

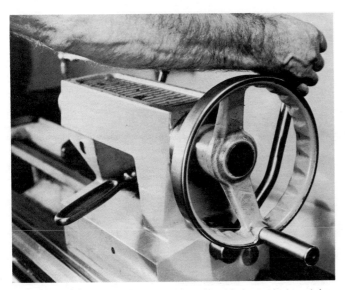

Figure 21. Camlock-type tailstock with lever being tightened (Lane Community College).

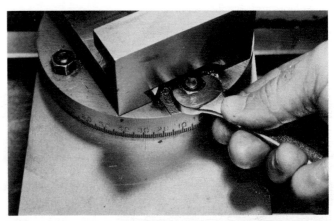

Figure 23. Compound being tightened with wrench on clamping nut (DeAnza College).

bolt and cross bar clamp. The clamping lever should never be forced. If it gets out of adjustment, it can be readjusted by means of a nut underneath the tailstock (Figure 22).

The compound is made to rotate on all lathes so that an angle may be machined. Degrees marked on its base are read against an index mark on the carriage. Various methods are used to clamp the compound, usually one or two bolts on each side (Figure 23). Some types have set screws.

SELF-TEST

At a lathe in the shop, identify the following parts and describe their functions. *Do not* turn on the lathe until you get permission from your instructor.

The Headstock:

1. Spindle
2. Spindle speed changing mechanism
3. Backgears

4. Bull gear lockpin
5. Spindle nose
6. What kind of spindle nose is on your lathe?
7. Feed reverse lever

The Bed

1. The ways
2. The gear rack

The Carriage

1. The cross slide
2. The compound rest
3. Saddle
4. Apron
5. Power feed lever
6. Feed change lever
7. Half-nut lever
8. Thread dial
9. Carriage handwheel
10. Carriage lock

The Tailstock

1. Spindle and spindle clamping lever
2. Tapered spindle hole and the size of its taper
3. The tailstock adjusting screws

The Quick-Chance Gearbox

1. The leadscrew
2. Shift the levers to obtain feeds of .005 and .013 in. per revolution. Rotating the leadscrew with your fingers aids in shifting these levers.
3. Set the levers to obtain 4 threads/in. and then 12 threads/in.
4. Measure the lathe and record its size.

---

1. Why should fine chips, filings, and grindings be cleaned from the ways and slides frequently?
2. How should cleaning of the ways and slides be done?
3. Nicks and scratches are very damaging to lathe ways. What means can be employed to avoid this?
4. How often should a lathe be lubricated?
5. Should you begin work immediately on a lathe that looks perfectly clean? Explain.
6. What should be done when you are finished using the lathe?
7. Name two types of gibs used on lathes.
8. How tight should the gibs be adjusted on the cross slide and on the compound?

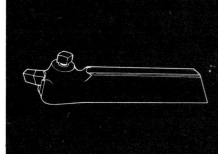

UNIT 2 TOOLHOLDERS AND TOOL HOLDING FOR THE LATHE

For lathe work, cutting tools must be supported and fastened securely in the proper position to machine the workpiece. There are many different types of toolholders available to satisfy this need. Anyone working with a lathe should be able to select the best tool holding device for the operation performed.

OBJECTIVES

After completing this unit, you should be able to:
1. Identify standard, quick-change, and turret-type toolholders mounted on a lathe carriage.
2. Identify tool holding for the lathe tailstock.

A cutting tool is supported and held in a lathe by a tool-holder that is secured in the tool post of the lathe with a clamp screw. A common tool post found on smaller or older lathes is shown in Figure 1. Tool height adjustments are made by swiveling the rocker in the tool post ring. Making adjustments in this manner changes the effective

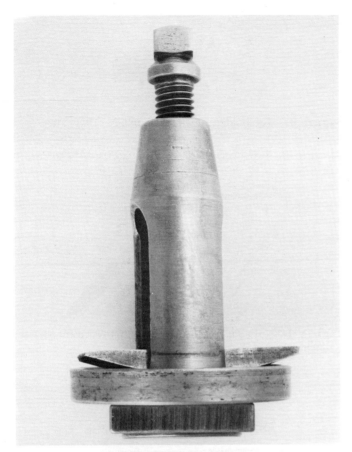

Figure 1.   Standard-type tool post with ring and rocker.

Figure 2.   Straight shank toolholder with built-in back rake holding a high speed right-hand tool (Lane Community College).

Figure 3.   Right-hand toolholder for carbide tool bits without back rake.

back rake angle and also the front relief angle of the tool.

Many types of toolholders are used with the standard tool post. A straight shank turning toolholder (Figure 2) is used with high speed tool bits. The tool bit is held in the toolholder at a $16\frac{1}{2}$ degree angle, which provides a positive back rake angle for cutting. Straight shank toolholders are used for general machining on

Figure 4.   Left-hand toolholder with right-hand tool (Lane Community College).

Figure 5.   Right-hand toolholder with left-hand tool (Lane Community College).

Figure 6.   Three kinds of cutoff toolholders with cutoff blades (TRW, Inc.).

lathes. The type shown in Figure 3 is used with carbide tools.

Offset toolholders (Figures 4 and 5) allow machining close to the chuck or tailstock of a lathe without tool post interference. The lefthand toolholder is intended for use with tools cutting from right to left or toward the headstock of the lathe.

A toolholder should be selected according to the machining to be done. The setup should be rigid and the toolholder overhang should be kept to a minimum to prevent chattering. A variety of cutoff toolholders (Figure 6) are used to cut off or make grooves in workpieces. Cutoff tools are available in a number of different thicknesses and heights. Knurling tools are made with one pair of rollers (Figure 7) or with three pairs of rollers (Figure 8) that make three different kinds of knurls.

Another tool used in a standard tool post is the boring bar toolholder (Figure 9). The boring bar tool post (Figure 10) can be used with a number of different boring bar sizes. Another advantage of boring bars is the interchangeability of tool holding end caps. End caps hold the boring tool square to the axis of the boring bar or at a 45 or 60 degree angle to it. The heavy duty boring bar

Figure 7. Knuckle-joint knurling tool (Lane Community College).

Figure 8. Triple head knurling tool (Lane Community College).

Figure 9. Toolholder for small boring bars (TRW, Inc.)

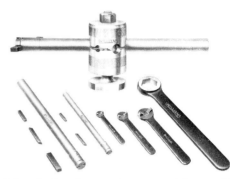

Figure 10. Boring bar tool post and bars with special wrench (TRW, Inc.).

Sleeve Bar

Figure 11. Heavy duty boring bar holder (TRW, Inc.).

holder in Figure 11 is not as rigid as the holder in Figure 10 because it is clamped in the tool post.

A quick-change tool post (Figure 12), so-called because of the speed with which tools can be interchanged, is more versatile than the standard post. The toolholders used on it are accurately held because of the dovetail construction of the post. This accuracy makes for more exact repetition of setups. Tool height adjustments are made with a micrometer adjustment collar, and the height alignment will remain constant through repeated tool changes.

A three-sided quick-change tool post (Figure 13) has the added ability to mount a tool on the tailstock side of the tool post. These tool posts are securely clamped to the compound rest. The tool post in Figure 13 uses double vees to locate the toolholders, which are clamped and released from the post by turning the top lever.

Toolholders for the quick-change tool posts include

Figure 12. Quick-change tool post, dovetail type (Copyright © 1975, Aloris Tool Company, Inc.).

Figure 13. Three-sided quick-change tool post (Lane Community College).

Figure 15 b. Threading is accomplished with the bottom edge of the blade with the lathe spindle in reverse. This assures cutting right-hand threads without hitting the shoulders (Copyright © 1975, Aloris Tool Company, Inc.).

Figure 14. Turning toolholder in use (Copyright © 1975, Aloris Tool Company, Inc.).

Figure 15 a. Threading toolholder, using the top of the blade (Copyright © 1975, Aloris Tool Company, Inc.).

Figure 16. Drill toolholder in the tool post. Mounting the drill in the tool post makes drilling with power feed possible (Copyright © 1975, Aloris Tool Company, Inc.).

those for turning (Figure 14), threading (Figures 15 a and 15 b), and holding drills (Figure 16). The drill holder makes it possible to use the carriage power feed when drilling holes instead of the tailstock hand feed. Figure 17 shows a boring bar toolholder in use; the boring bar is very rigidly supported.

An advantage of the quick-change tool post toolholders is that cutting tools of various shank thicknesses

Figure 17. Boring toolholder. This setup provides good boring bar rigidity (Copyright © 1975, Aloris Tool Company Inc.).

Figure 18. Toolholders are made with wide or narrow slots to fit tools with various shank thicknesses (Lane Community College).

Figure 19. Tailstock turret used in quick-change toolholder (Courtesy of Enco Manufacturing Company).

Figure 20. Quick-change cutoff toolholder (Courtesy of Enco Manufacturing Company).

Figure 21. Quick-change knurling and facing toolholder (Courtesy of Enco Manufacturing Company).

Figure 22. Facing cut with a turret-type toolholder (Courtesy of Enco Manufacturing Company).

can be mounted in the toolholders (Figure 18). Shims are sometimes used when the shank is too small for the setscrews to reach. Another example of quick-change tool post versatility is shown in Figure 19, where a tailstock turret is in use. Figure 20 shows a cutoff tool mounted in a toolholder. Figure 21 is a combination knurling tool and facing toolholder. A four-tool turret toolholder (Figure 22) can be set up with several different tools such as turning tools, facing tools, threading or boring tools.

Figure 23. Turning cut with a turret-type toolholder (Courtesy of Enco Manufacturing Company).

Figure 24. Chamfering cut with a turret-type toolholder (Courtesy of Enco Manufacturing Company).

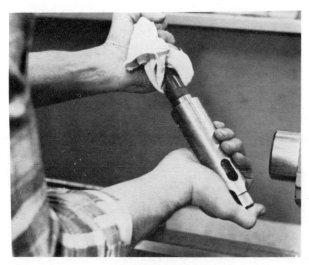

Figure 25. Taper shank drill with sleeve ready to insert in tailstock spindle (Lane Community College).

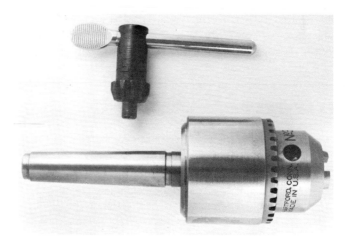

Figure 26. Drill chuck with Morse taper shank.

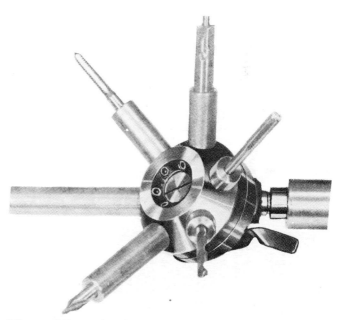

Figure 27. Tailstock turret (Courtesy of Enco Manufacturing Company).

Often one tool can perform two or more operations, especially if the turret can be indexed in 30 degree intervals. A facing operation (Figure 22), a turning operation (Figure 23), and chamfering of a bored hole (Figure 24) are all performed from this turret. Tool height adjustments are made by placing shims under the tool.

The toolholders studied so far are all intended for use on the carriage of a lathe. Toolholding is also done on the tailstock. Figure 25 shows how the tailstock spindle is used to hold Morse taper shank tools. One of the most common toolholding devices used on a tailstock is the drill chuck (Figure 26). A drill chuck is used for holding straight shank drilling tools. When a series of operations must be performed and repeated on several workpieces, a tailstock turret (Figure 27) can be used. The

illustrated tailstock turret has six tool positions, one of which is used as a workstop. The other positions are for center drilling, drilling, reaming, counterboring, and tapping. Tailstock tools are normally fed by turning the tailstock handwheel.

SELF-TEST

At a lathe in the shop, identify various toolholders and their functions.

1. What is the purpose of a toolholder?
2. How is a standard left-hand toolholder identified?
3. What is the difference between a standard-type toolholder for high speed steel tools and for carbide tools?
4. Which standard toolholder would be best used for turning close to the chuck?
5. How are tool height adjustments made on a standard toolholder?
6. How are tool height adjustments made on a quick-change toolholder?
7. How are tool height adjustments made on a turret-type toolholder?
8. How does the toolholder overhang affect the turning operation?
9. What is the difference between a standard toolholder and a quick-change toolholder?
10. What kind of tools are used in the lathe tailstock?
11. How are tools fastened in the tailstock?
12. When is a tailstock turret used?

UNIT 3 CUTTING TOOLS FOR THE LATHE

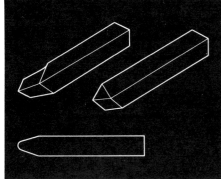

A machinist must fully understand the purpose of tool geometry, since it is the lathe tool that removes the metal from the workpiece. Whether this is done safely, economically, and with quality finishes depends to a large extent upon the shape of the point, the rake and relief angles, and the nose radius of the tool. In this unit, you will learn this tool geometry and also how to grind a lathe tool.

OBJECTIVES

After completing this unit, you should be able to:
1. Explain the purpose of rake and relief angles, chip breakers, and form tools.
2. Grind an acceptable right-hand roughing tool.

On a lathe, metal is removed from a workpiece by turning it against a single point cutting tool. This tool must be very hard and it should not lose its hardness from the heat generated by machining. High speed steel is used for many tools as it fulfills these requirements and is easily shaped by grinding. It should be noted, however, that their use is limited since most production machining today is done with carbide tools. High speed steel tools are required for older lathes that are equipped with only low speed ranges. They are also useful for finishing operations, especially on soft metals.

The most important aspect of a lathe tool is its geometric form: the side and back rake, front and side clearance or relief angles, and chip breakers. Figure 1 shows the parts and angles of the tool according to a commonly used industrial tool signature. The terms and definitions follow (the angles given are only examples and they could vary according to the application).

Back rake	BR	12°
Side rake	SR	12°
End relief	ER	10°
Side relief	SRF	10°
End cutting edge angle	ECEA	30°
Side cutting edge angle	SCEA	15°
Nose radius	NR	$\frac{1}{32}$ in.

1. The tool shank is that part held by the toolholder.
2. Back rake is very important to smooth chip flow, which is needed to have a uniform chip and a good finish.
3. The side rake directs the chip flow away from the point of cut and it provides for a keen cutting edge.
4. The end relief angle prevents the front edge of the tool from rubbing on the work.
5. The side relief angle provides for cutting action by allowing the tool to feed into the work material.
6. The cutting edge angle may vary considerably (from 5 to 32 degrees). For roughing, it should almost be square (5 degrees off 90 degrees), but tools used for squaring shoulders or for other light machining could have angles from 15 to 32 degrees.
7. The side cutting edge angle, which is usually 10 to 20 degrees, directs the cutting forces back into a stronger section of the tool point. It helps to direct the chip flow away from the workpiece. It also affects the thickness of the cut (Figure 2).
8. The nose radius will vary according to the finish required.

Grinding a tool provides both a sharp cutting edge and the shape needed for the cutting operation. When the purpose for the rake and relief angles on a tool are clearly understood, then a tool suitable to the job may be ground. Left-hand tools are shaped just the opposite to right-hand tools (Figure 3). The right-hand tool has the cutting edge on the left side and cuts to the left or toward the headstock. The hand of the lathe tool can be easily determined by looking at the end from the opposite side of the lathe; the cutting edge is to the right on a right-hand tool.

Tools are given a slight nose radius to strengthen the tip. A larger nose radius will give a better finish (Figure 4), but will also promote chattering (vibration) in a nonrigid setup. All lathe tools require some nose radius, however small. A sharp pointed tool is very weak at the point and will usually break off in use, causing a rough finish on the work. A facing tool (Figure 5) for shaft ends and mandrel work has very little nose radius and an included angle of 58 degrees. This facing tool is not used for chucking work, however, as it is a relatively weak

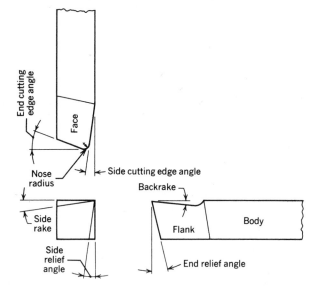

Figure 1. The parts and angles of a tool.

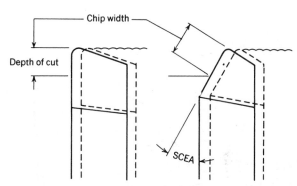

Figure 2. The change in chip width with an increase of the side cutting edge angle. A large SCEA can sometimes cause chatter (vibration of work or tool).

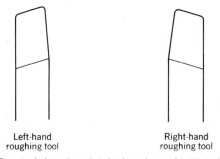

Figure 3. Left-hand and right-hand roughing tools.

tool. A right-hand (RH) or left-hand (LH) roughing or finishing tool is often used for facing in chuck mounted workpieces.

Some useful tool shapes are shown in Figure 6. These are used for general lathe work.

Tools that have special shaped cutting edges are

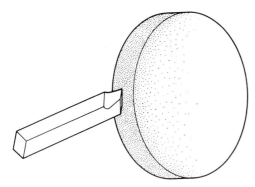

Figure 4. One method of grinding the nose radius on the point of the tool.

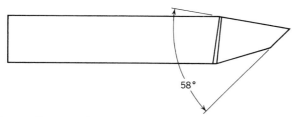

58°

Figure 5. A right-hand facing tool showing point angles. This tool is not suitable for roughing operations because of its acute point angle.

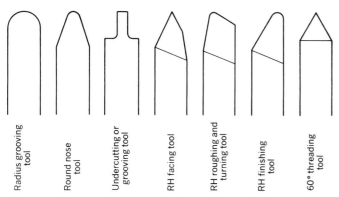

Radius grooving tool

Round nose tool

Undercutting or grooving tool

RH facing tool

RH roughing and turning tool

RH finishing tool

60° threading tool

Figure 6. Some useful tool shapes most often used. The first tool shapes needed are the three on the right, which are the roughing or general turning tool, finishing tool, and threading tool.

called form tools (Figure 7). These tools are plunged directly into the work, making the full cut in one operation.

Parting or cutoff tools are often used for necking or undercutting, but their main function is cutting off material to the correct length. The correct and incorrect ways to grind a cutoff tool are shown in Figure 8. Note that the width of the cutting edge becomes narrower than the blade as it is ground deeper, which causes the blade to bind in a groove that is deeper than the sharpened end.

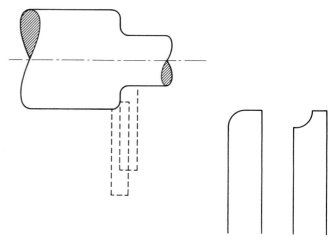

Figure 7. Form tools are used to produce the desired shape in the workpiece. External radius tools, for example, are used to make outside corners round, while fillet radius tools are used on shafts to round the inside corners on shoulders.

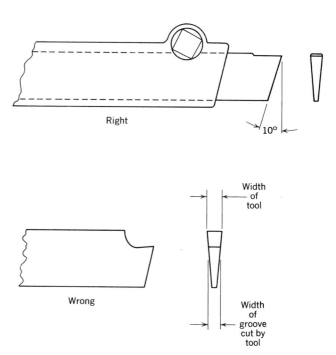

Right

10°

Width of tool

Wrong

Width of groove cut by tool

Figure 8. Correct and incorrect methods of grinding a cutoff tool for deep parting.

Tools are sometimes specially ground, however, for parting very soft metals or specially shaped grooves (Figure 9). The end is sometimes ground on a slight angle when a series of small hollow pieces is being cut off (Figure 10). This helps to eliminate the burr on small parts. This procedure is not recommended for deep parting.

Tools that have been ground back for resharpening too many times often form a "chip trap" causing the metal to be torn off or the tool to not cut at all (Figure

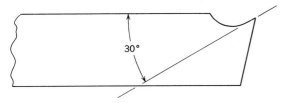

Figure 9. Cut-off tools are sometimes ground with large back rake angles for aluminum and other soft metals.

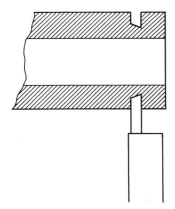

Figure 10. Parting tool ground on an angle to avoid burrs on the cut off pieces.

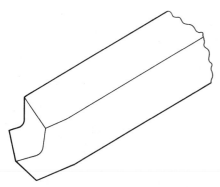

Figure 11. Deformed tool caused by many resharpenings. The chip trap should be ground off and a new point ground on the tool.

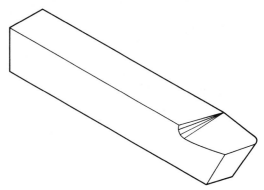

Figure 12. A properly ground right-hand roughing tool.

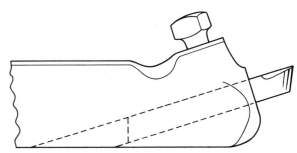

Figure 13. Toolholder with back rake.

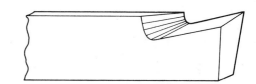

Figure 14. Right-hand roughing tool with back rake.

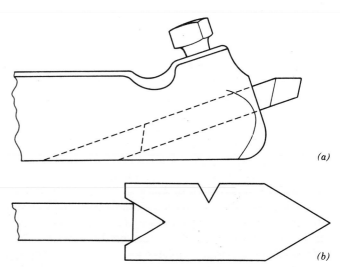

(a)

(b)

Figure 15. (*a*) Toolholder with back rake showing tool ground for zero rake. (*b*) Checking a threading tool with center gage.

11). A good machinist will never allow tools to get in this condition, but will grind off the useless end and regrind a proper tool shape (Figure 12).

Although many modern lathes have toolholders that hold the tool horizontally, some lathe toolholders have built-in back rake so it is not necessary to grind one into the tool as used in Figure 13. The tool in Figure 14, however, is ground with a back rake and can be used in a toolholder that does not have built-in back rake. Threading tools should have zero rake (Figure 15a). If a horizontal toolholder is used, the flat on top is unnecessary as the tool would have a zero rake. The tool should also be checked for the 60 degree angle with a center gage (Figure 15b) while grinding. Relief should be ground on

Table 1

Angle Degrees for High Speed Steel Tools

Material	End Relief	Side Relief	Side Rake	Back Rake
Aluminum	8 to 10	12 to 14	14 to 16	30 to 35
Brass, free cutting	8 to 10	8 to 10	1 to 3	0
Bronze, free cutting	8 to 10	8 to 10	2 to 4	0
Cast iron, gray	6 to 8	8 to 10	10 to 12	3 to 5
Copper	12 to 14	13 to 14	18 to 20	14 to 16
Nickel and monel	12 to 14	14 to 16	12 to 14	8 to 10
Steels, low carbon	8 to 10	8 to 10	10 to 12	10 to 12
Steels, alloy	7 to 9	7 to 9	8 to 10	6 to 8

Table 2

Machinability Ratings for Some Commonly Used Steels

AISI Number	Cutting Speed (Surface ft/min)	Machinability Index (% Relative Speed Based on AISI B1112 as 100%)
B1112	165	100
C1120	135	81
C1140	120	72
C1008	110	66
C1020	120	72
C1030	115	70
C1040	105	64
C1060 (annealed)	85	51
C1090 (annealed)	70	42
3140 (annealed)	110	66
4140 (annealed)	110	66
5140 (annealed)	115	70
6120	95	57
8620	110	66
301 (stainless)	60	36
302 (stainless)	60	36
304 (stainless)	60	36
420 (stainless)	60	36
440A (stainless)	40	24
440B (stainless)	40	24
440C (stainless)	40	24

Note. Speeds given are approximate and should be used only as a basis for determining correct cutting speeds for particular jobs and setups. Cutting speeds are for use with high speed tools.

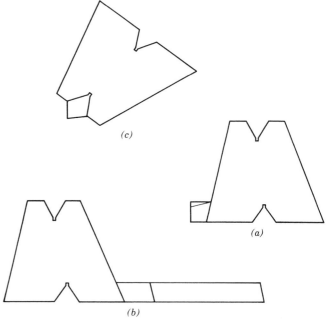

Figure 16. Using a tool gage for checking angles. (*a*) Checking the side relief angle; (*b*) checking end relief; and (*c*) checking the wedge angle for steel.

each side. A slight flat should be honed on the end with an oilstone. (See Unit 11, ''Cutting Unified External Thread,'' for this dimension.)

Tools for brass or plastics should have zero to negative rake to keep the tools from ''digging in.'' Side rake, back rake, and relief angles are given for tools in Table 1 for machining various metals.

The **machinability** of metals refers to the difficulty or ease of machining a metal. The factors considered are cutting tool life, horsepower required, and surface finish

obtained. Machinability is measured for roughing operations (heavy stock removal) by the length of cutting tool life in minutes or by the rate of stock removal in terms of cutting speed. Of course, that is determined by depth of cut. For finishing operations, machinability refers to the ease with which a good surface finish is produced and the length of cutting tool life. See Table 2 for the machinability ratings of some commonly used steels. Complete machinability tables and information may be found in machining data handbooks.

Figure 16 shows the use of a gage for checking angles when grinding a tool. It is designed to check tool angles on any flat surface. The angles are for tools to be used in toolholders having $16\frac{1}{2}$ degree back rake. Tools for straight or horizontal toolholders should have an end

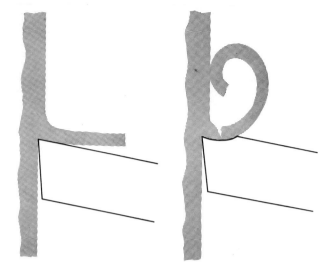

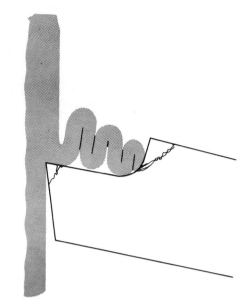

Figure 17. Chip flow with a plain tool and with a chip breaker.

Figure 19. Crowding of the chip is caused by a chip breaker that is ground too deeply.

Figure 18. A figure-9 chip is considered the safest kind of chip to produce (DeAnza College).

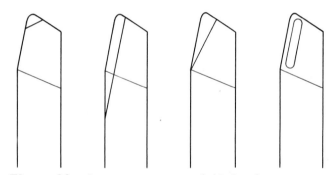

Figure 20. Four common types of chip breakers.

relief of 10 degrees; in these cases, change the end relief angle of the gage. A protractor or optical comparator can also be used to check tool angles.

For your safety, it is important to make tools that will produce chips that are not hazardous. Long, unbroken chips are extremely dangerous. Tool geometry, especially side and back rakes, has a considerable effect on chip formation. Side rakes with smaller angles tend to curl the chip more than those with large angles, and the curled chips are more likely to break up. Coarse feeds for roughing and maximum depth of cut also promote chip breaking. Feeds, speeds, and depth of cut will be further considered in Unit 7, "Turning Between Centers."

Chip breakers are extensively used on both carbide and high speed tools to curl the chip as it flows across the face of the tool. Since the chip is curled back into the work, it can go no further and breaks (Figure 17). A C-shaped chip is often the result, but a figure-9 shaped

chip is considered ideal (Figure 18). This chip should drop safely into the chip pan without flying out.

Grinding the chip breaker too deep will form a chip trap that may cause binding of the chip and tool breakage (Figure 19). The correct depth to grind a chip breaker is approximately $\frac{1}{32}$ inch. Chip breakers are typically of the parallel or angular types (Figure 20). More skill is needed to offhand grind a chip breaker on a high speed tool than is required to grind the basic tool angles. Therefore, the basic tool should be ground and an effort made to produce safe chips through the use of correct feeds and depth of cut before a chip breaker is ground.

Care must be exercised while grinding on high speed steel. A glazed wheel can generate heat up to 2000°F (1093°C) at the grinder-tool interface. Do not overheat the tool edge as this will cause small surface cracks that can result in the failure of the tool. Frequent cooling in water will keep the tool cool enough to handle. Do not quench in water, however, if you have

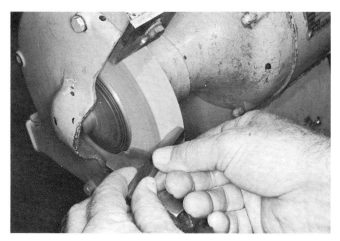

Figure 21. Roughing the side relief angle and the side cutting edge angle (Lane Community College).

Figure 22. Checking the side relief angle with a tool gage (Lane Community College).

overheated it. Let it cool in air.

Since the right-hand roughing tool is the one that is most commonly used by machinists and the first one that you will need, you should begin with it. A piece of keystock the same size as the tool bit should be used for practice until you are able to grind an acceptable tool.

GRINDING PROCEDURE, TOOL BIT

Given a tool blank, a piece of keystock about 3 in. long, a tool gage and a tool holder.

1. Grind one acceptable practice right-hand roughing tool. Have your instructor evaluate your progress.
2. Grind one acceptable right-hand roughing tool from a high speed tool blank.

Wear goggles and make certain the tool rest on the grinder is adjusted properly (about $\frac{1}{16}$ in. from the wheel). True up the wheels with a wheel dresser, if they are grooved, glazed, or out of round.

1. Using the roughing wheel, grind the side relief angle and the side cutting angle about 10 degrees by holding the blank and supporting your hand on the tool rest (Figure 21).
2. Check the angle with a tool gage (Figure 22). Correct if needed.
3. Rough out the end relief angle about 14 degrees and the end cutting edge angle (Figure 23).
4. Check the angle with the tool gage (Figure 24). Correct if needed.
5. Rough out the side rake. Stay clear of the side cutting edge by $\frac{1}{16}$ in. (Figure 25).
6. Check for wedge angle (Figure 26). Correct if needed.
7. Now change to the finer grit wheel and very gently

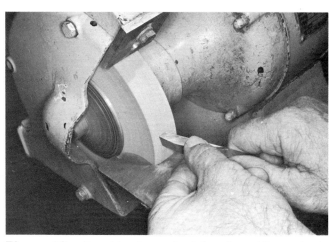

Figure 23. Roughing the end relief angle and the end cutting edge angle (Lane Community College).

Figure 24. Checking the end relief angle with a tool gage (Lane Community College).

finish grind the side and end relief angles. Try to avoid making several facets or grinds on one surface. A side to side oscillation will help to produce a good finish.

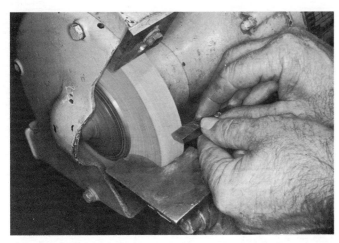

Figure 25. Roughing the side rake (Lane Community College)

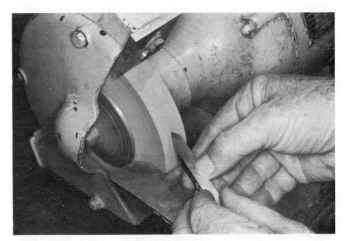

Figure 27. One method of grinding the nose radius is on the circumference of the wheel (Lane Community College).

Figure 26. Checking for wedge angle with a tool gage (Lane Community College).

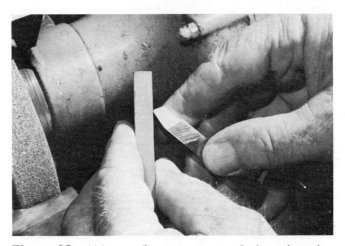

Figure 28. Using an oil stone to remove the burrs from the cutting edge (Lane Community College).

8. Grind the finish on the side rake as in Figure 25 and bring the ground surface just to the side cutting edge, but avoid going deeper.

9. A slight radius on the point of the tool should be ground on the circumference of the wheel (Figure 27) and all the way from the nose to the heel of the tool.

10. A medium to fine oilstone is used to remove the burrs from the cutting edge (Figure 28). The finished tool is shown in Figure 29.

Figure 29. The finished tool (Lane Community College).

SELF-TEST

1. Name the advantages to using high speed steel for tools.
2. Other than hardness and toughness, what is the most important aspect of a lathe tool?
3. How do form tools work?
4. A tool that has been reground too many times on the same place can form a chip trap. Describe the problems that result from this condition.
5. Why is it not always necessary to grind a back rake into the tool?
6. When should a zero or negative rake be used?

7. Explain the purpose of the side and end relief angles.
8. What is the function of the side and back rakes?
9. How can these angles be checked while grinding?
10. Why should chips be broken up?

11. In what ways can chips be broken?
12. Overheating a high speed tool bit can easily be done by using a glazed wheel that needs dressing or by exerting too much pressure. What does this cause in the tool?

UNIT 4 LATHE SPINDLE TOOLING

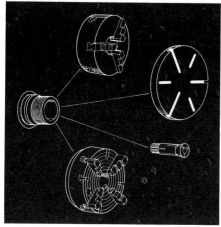

Workholding and driving devices that are fastened to the spindle nose are very important to machining on lathes. Various types of these workholding devices, their uses, and proper care are detailed in this unit.

OBJECTIVES

After completing this unit, you should be able to:
1. Explain the uses and care of independent and universal chucks.
2. Explain the limitations and advantages of collets and describe a collet setup.
3. Explain the use of a face driver or drive center.
4. Explain the uses and differences of drive plates and face plates.

The lathe spindle nose is the carrier of a variety of workholding devices that are fastened to it in several ways. The spindle is hollow and has an internal Morse taper at the nose end, which makes possible the use of taper shank drills or drill chucks (Figure 1). This internal taper is also used to hold live centers, drive centers, or collet assemblies. The outside of the spindle nose can have either a threaded nose (Figure 2), a long taper with key drive (Figure 3), or a camlock (Figure 4).

Threaded spindle noses are mostly used on older lathes. The chuck or face plate is screwed on a coarse, right-hand thread until it is forced against a shoulder on the spindle that aligns it. Two disadvantages of the threaded spindle nose are that the spindle cannot be rotated in reverse against a load and that it is sometimes very difficult to remove a chuck or face plate (Figure 5).

The **long taper key drive spindle nose** relies on the principle that a tapered fit will always repeat its original position. The key gives additional driving power. A large nut having a right-hand thread is turned with a spanner wrench. It draws the chuck into position and holds it there.

Camlock spindle noses use a short taper for alignment. A number of studs arranged in a circle fit into holes in the spindle nose. Each stud has a notch into which a cam is turned to lock it in place.

Figure 1.   Section view of the spindle.

Figure 2.   Threaded spindle nose (Lane Community College).

Figure 3. Long taper with key drive spindle nose (Lane Community College).

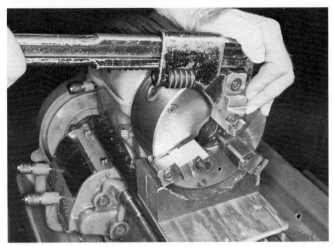

Figure 5. The chuck can be removed by using a large monkey wrench on one of the chuck jaws while the spindle is locked in a low gear. A long steel bar may also be used between the jaws. The knockout bar should never be used to remove a chuck as it is too light and will bend (Lane Community College).

Figure 4. Camlock spindle nose (DeAnza College).

Figure 6. A spring cleaner is used for cleaning internal threads on chucks.

All spindle noses and their mating parts must be carefully cleaned before assembly. Small chips or grit will cause a workholding device to run out of true and be damaged. A spring cleaner (Figure 6) is used on mating threads for threaded spindles. Brushes and cloths are used for cleaning. A thin film of light oil should be applied to threads and mating surfaces.

Independent four-jaw and **universal** three-jaw chucks and, occasionally, drive or face plates are mounted on the spindle nose of engine lathes. Each of the four jaws of the independent chuck moves independently of the others, which makes it possible to set up oddly shaped pieces (Figure 7). The concentric rings on the chuck face help to set the work true before starting the machine. Very precise setups also can be made with the four-jaw chuck by using a dial indicator, especially on round material. Each jaw of the chuck can be removed and reversed to accommodate irregular shapes. Some types are fitted with top jaws that can be reversed after removal of bolts on the jaw. Jaws in the reverse position can grip larger diameter workpieces (Figure 8). The independent chuck will hold work more securely for heavy cutting than will the three-jaw universal chuck.

Universal chucks usually have three jaws, but some are made with two jaws (Figure 9) or six jaws (Figure 10).

Figure 7. Four-jaw independent chuck holding an offset rectangular part (DeAnza College).

Figure 8. Four-jaw chuck in reverse position holding a large diameter workpiece (Lane Community College).

All the jaws are moved in or out equally in their slides by means of a scroll plate located back of the jaws. The scroll plate has a bevel gear on its reverse side that is driven by a pinion gear. This gear extends to the outside of the chuck body and is turned with the chuck wrench (Figure 11). Universal chucks provide quick and simple chucking and centering of round stock. Uneven or irregularly shaped material will damage these chucks.

The jaws of universal chucks will not reverse as with independent chucks, so a separate set of reverse jaws

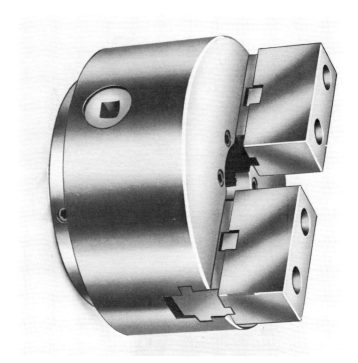

Figure 9. Two-jaw universal chuck (Courtesy of Hardinge Brothers, Inc., Elmira, N.Y.).

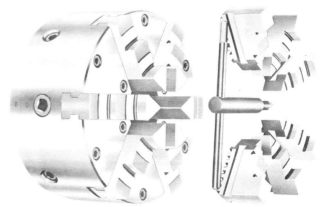

Figure 10. Six-jaw universal chuck (Courtesy of Buck Tool Company).

is used (Figure 12) to hold pieces with larger diameters. The chuck and each of its jaws are stamped with identification numbers. Do not interchange any of these parts with another chuck or both will be inaccurate. Also each jaw is stamped 1, 2, or 3 to correspond to the same number stamped by the slot on the chuck. The jaws are removed from the chuck in the order 3, 2, 1 and should be returned in the reverse order, 1, 2, 3.

A universal chuck with **top jaws** (Figure 13) is reversed by removing the bolts in the top jaws and by reversing them. They must be carefully cleaned when this is done. Soft top jaws are frequently used when special gripping problems arise. Since the jaws are machined to fit the shape of the part (Figure 14), they can grip it securely for heavy cuts (Figure 15).

Figure 11. Exploded view of a universal three-jaw chuck (Adjust-tru) showing the scroll plate and gear drive mechanism (Courtesy of Buck Tool Company).

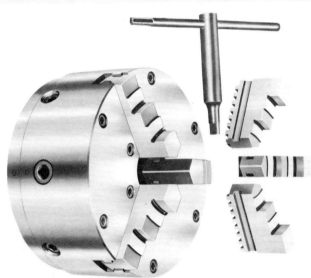

Figure 12. Universal three-jaw chuck (Adjust-tru) with a set of outside jaws (Courtesy of Buck Tool Company).

Figure 14. Machining soft jaws to fit an odd-shaped workpiece on a jaw turning fixture (Courtesy of The Warner & Swasey Company).

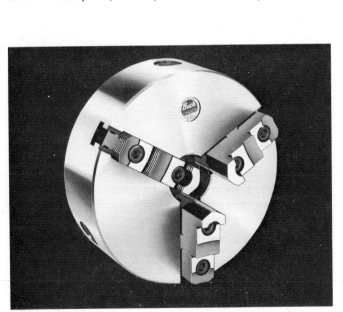

Figure 13. Universal chuck with top jaws (Courtesy of Buck Tool Company).

Figure 15. Soft jaws have been machined to fit the shape of this cast steel workpiece in order to hold it securely for heavy cuts (Courtesy of The Warner & Swasey Company).

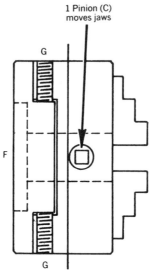

1 Pinion (C)
moves jaws

Figure 16. Universal chuck (Adjust-tru) with special adjustment feature (G) makes it possible to compensate for wear (Courtesy of Buck Tool Company).

Figure 17. Magnetic chuck (Courtesy of Enco Manufacturing Company).

One disadvantage of most universal chucks is that they lose their accuracy when the scroll and jaws wear, and normally there is no compensation for wear other than regrinding the jaws. The three-jaw adjustable chuck in Figure 16 has a compensating adjustment for wear or misalignment.

Combination universal and independent chucks also provide for quick opening and closing and have the added advantage of independent adjustment on each jaw. These chucks are like the universal type since three or four jaws move in or out equally, but each jaw can be adjusted independently as well.

Magnetic chucks (Figure 17) are sometimes used for making light cuts on ferromagnetic material. They are useful for facing thin material that would be difficult to hold in conventional workholding devices. Magnetic chucks do not hold work very securely and so are not used much in lathe work.

All chucks need frequent cleaning of scrolls and jaws. These should be lightly oiled after cleaning and chucks with grease fittings should be pressure lubricated. Chucks come in all diameters and are made for light, medium, and heavy duty uses.

Drive plates are used together with lathe dogs to drive work mounted between centers (Figure 18). The live center fits directly into the spindle taper and turns with the spindle. A sleeve is sometimes used if the spindle taper is too large in diameter to fit the center. The live center is usually made of soft steel so the point can be machined as needed to keep it running true. Live centers are removed by means of a knockout bar (Figure 19).

Figure 18. Drive plate for turning between centers (Lane Community College).

Often when a machinist wants to machine the entire length of work mounted between centers without the interference of a lathe dog, specially ground and hardened drive centers are used (Figure 20). These are serrated so they will turn the work, but only light cuts can be made. Modern drive centers or face drivers (Figure 21) can also be used to machine a part without interference from a lathe dog. Quite heavy cuts are possible with these drivers, which are used especially for manufacturing purposes.

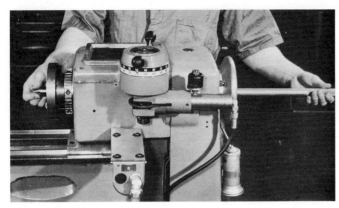

Figure 19. Knockout bar is used to remove centers (Courtesy of California Community Colleges, IMC Project).

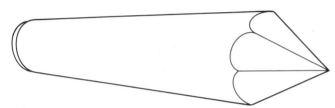

Figure 20. Hardened and serrated drive center is used for very light turning between centers.

Figure 21. Face driver is mounted in headstock spindle and work is driven by the drive pins that surround the center (Courtesy of Madison-Kosta®, Madison Industries, a Division of Amtel, Inc.) (Madison-Kosta® is a registered trademark of Madison Industries, A Division of Amtel, Inc.).

Figure 22. T-slot face plate. Workpieces are clamped on the plate with T-bolts and strap clamps (Courtesy of The Monarch Machine Tool Company, Sidney, Ohio).

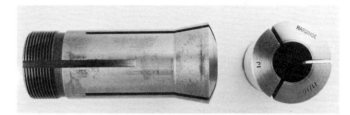

Figure 23. Side and end views of a spring collet for round work.

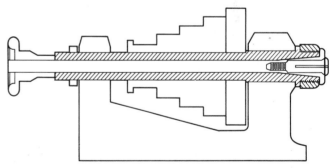

Figure 24. Cross section of spindle showing construction of draw-in collet chuck attachment.

Face plates are used for mounting workpieces or fixtures. Unlike drive plates that have only slots, face plates have T slots and are more heavily built (Figure 22). Face plates are made of cast iron and so must be operated at relatively slow speeds. If the speed is too high, the face plate could fly apart.

Collet chucks (Figure 23) are very accurate workholding devices and are used in producing small high precision parts. Steel spring collets are available for holding and turning hexagonal, square, and round workpieces. They are made in specific sizes (which are stamped on them) with a range of only a few thou-

sandths of an inch. Rough and inaccurate workpieces should not be held in the collet chuck since the gripping surfaces of the chuck would form an angle with the workpiece. The contact area would then be at one point on the jaws instead of along the entire length, and the piece would not be held firmly. If it is not held firmly, workpiece accuracy is impaired and the collet may be damaged. An adapter called a collet sleeve is fitted into the spindle taper and a draw bar is inserted into the spindle at the opposite end (Figure 24). The collet is placed

Figure 25.   Rubber flex collet.

Figure 26.   Collet handwheel attachment for rubber flex collets (Courtesy of The Monarch Machine Tool Company, Sidney, Ohio).

in the adapter, and the draw bar is rotated, which threads the collet into the taper and closes it. *Never tighten a collet without a workpiece in its jaws* as this will damage it. Before collets and adapters are installed, they should be cleaned to insure accuracy.

The rubber flex collet (Figure 25) has a set of tapered steel bars mounted in rubber. It has a much wider range than the spring collet, each collet with a range of about $\frac{1}{8}$ in. A large handwheel is used to open and close the collets instead of a draw bar (Figure 26).

The concentricity that you could expect from each type of workholding device is as follows:

Device	Centering Accuracy in Inches (Indicator Reading Difference)
Centers	Within .001
Four-jaw chuck	Within .001 (depending on the ability of machinist)
Collets	.0005 to .001
Three-jaw chuck	.001 to .003 (good condition) .005 or more (poor condition)

SELF-TEST

1. Briefly describe the lathe spindle. How does the spindle support chucks and collets?
2. Name the spindle nose types.
3. What is an independent chuck and what is it used for?
4. What is a universal chuck and what is it used for?
5. What chuck types make possible the frequent adjusting of chucks so they will hold stock with minimum runout?
6. Workpieces mounted between centers are driven with lathe dogs. Which type of plate is used on the spindle nose to turn the lathe dog?
7. What is a live center made of? How does it fit in the spindle nose?
8. Describe a drive center and a face driver.
9. On which type of plate are workpieces and fixtures mounted? How is it identified?
10. Name one advantage of using steel spring collets. Name one disadvantage.

UNIT 5 OPERATING THE MACHINE CONTROLS

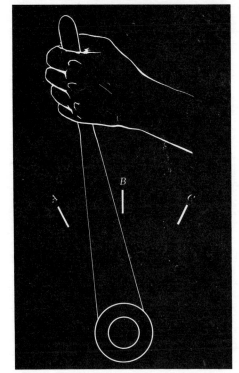

Before using any machine, you must be able to properly use the controls, know what they are for, and how they work. You must also be aware of the potential hazards that exist for you and the machine if it is mishandled. This unit prepares you to operate lathes.

OBJECTIVES

After completing this unit, you should be able to:
1. Explain drives and shifting procedures for changing speeds on lathes.
2. Describe the use of various feed control levers.
3. Explain the relationship between longitudinal feeds and cross feeds.
4. State the differences in types of cross feed screw micrometer collars.

Most lathes have similar control mechanisms and operating handles for feeds and threading. Some machines, however, have entirely different driving mechanisms as well as different speed controls.

DRIVES

Spindle speed is controlled on some lathes by a belt on a step cone pulley in the headstock (Figure 1). The speed is changed by turning the belt tension lever to loosen the belt, moving the belt to the proper step for the desired speed, and then moving the lever to its former position. Several more lower speeds are available by shifting to back gear. To do this, pull out or release the bull gear lockpin to disengage the spindle from the step cone pulley and engage the back gear lever as shown in Figure 1. It may be necessary to rotate the spindle by hand slightly to bring the gear into mesh. The back gears must **never** be engaged when the spindle is turning with power. Do not forget to close the gear and pulley guards before starting the lathe.

Another drive system uses a variable speed drive (Figure 2) with a high and low range using a back gear. On this drive system, the motor must be running to change the speed on the vari-drive, but the motor must be turned off to shift the back gear lever. Geared head lathes are shifted with levers on the outside of the headstock (Figure 3). Several of these levers are used to set up the various speeds within the range of the machine. The gears will not mesh unless they are perfectly aligned, so it is sometimes necessary to rotate the spindle by hand. **Never try to shift gears with the motor running and the clutch lever engaged.**

FEED CONTROL LEVERS

The carriage is moved along the ways by means of the lead screw when threading, or by a separate feed rod when using feeds. On most small lathes, however, a lead screw-feed rod combination is used. In order to make left-hand threads and reverse the feed, the feed reverse lever is used. This lever reverses the leadscrew. It should never be moved when the machine is running.

The quick-change gearbox (Figures 4a and 4b) typically has two or more sliding gear shifter levers. These are used to select feeds or threads per inch. On those lathes also equipped with metric selections, the threads are expressed in pitches (measured in millimeters).

Figure 1a. View of headstock showing back gear disengaged and lock pin engaged for direct belt drive (Lane Community College).

Figure 1b. View of headstock showing flat belt drive, the back gear engaged, and the lock pin disengaged (Lane Community College).

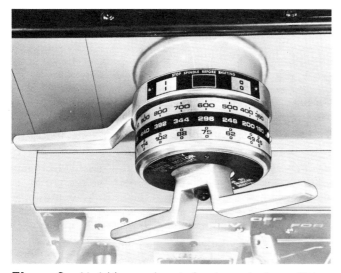

Figure 2. Variable speed control and speed selector (Courtesy of Clausing Corporation).

Figure 3. Speed change levers and feed selection levers on a geared head lathe (Lane Community College).

The carriage apron (Figure 5) contains the handwheel for hand feeding and a power feed lever that engages a clutch to a gear drive train in the apron.

Hand feeding should not be used for long cuts as there would be lack of uniformity and a poor finish would result. When using power feed and approaching a shoulder or the chuck jaws, disengage the power feed and hand feed the carriage for the last $\frac{1}{8}$ in. or so. The handwheel is used to quickly bring the tool close to the work before engaging the feed and for rapidly returning to the start of a cut after disengaging the feed. A feed change lever diverts the feed to either the carriage for longitudinal movement or to the cross feed screw to move the cross slide. There is generally some slack or backlash in the cross feed and compound screws. As long as the tool is being fed in one direction against the work load, there is no problem, but if the screw is *slightly* backed off, the readings will be in error. To correct this problem, back off two turns and come back to the desired position.

Figure 4a. Quick-change gearbox with index plate (Lane Community College).

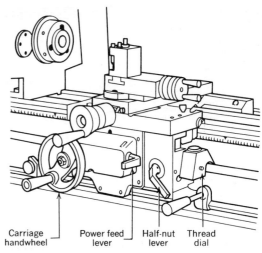

Figure 5. View of carriage apron with names of parts (Courtesy of Clausing Corporation).

Figure 4b. Exposed quick-change gear mechanism for a large, heavy duty lathe (Courtesy of Lodge & Shipley Company).

Figure 6. Facing on a lathe (Lane Community College).

Cross feeds are geared differently than longitudinal feeds. On most lathes the cross feed is approximately one-third to one-half that of the longitudinal feed, so a facing job (Figure 6) with the quick-change gearbox set at about .012 in. feed would actually only be .004 in. for facing. The cross feed ratio for each lathe is usually found on the quick-change gearbox index plate.

The **half-nut** or split-nut lever on the carriage engages the thread on the lead screw directly and is used **only** for threading. It cannot be engaged unless the feed change lever is in the neutral position.

Both the cross feed screw handle and the compound rest feed screw handle are fitted with **micrometer collars** (Figure 7). These collars traditionally have been graduated in English units, but metric conversion collars (Figure 8) will help in the transition to the metric system.

Some micrometer collars are graduated to read single depth; that is, the tool moves as much as the reading shows. When turning a cylindrical object such as a shaft, dials that read single depth will remove twice as much from the diameter (Figure 9). For example, if the cross feed screw is turned in .020 in. and a cut is taken, the diameter will have been reduced by .040 in. Sometimes only the compound is calibrated in this way. Many lathes, however, are graduated on the micrometer dial to compensate for double depth on cylindrical turning. On this type of lathe if the cross feed screw is turned in until .020 in. shows on the dial and a cut is taken, the diameter will have been reduced .020 in. The tool would have actually moved into the work only .010 in. This is sometimes called radius and diameter reduction.

To determine which type of graduation you are using, set a fractional amount on the dial (such as .250 in. = $\frac{1}{4}$ in.) and measure on the cross slide with a rule. The actual slide movement you measure with the rule will be either the same as the amount set on the dial, for

Figure 7. Micrometer collar on the crossfeed screw that is graduated in English units. Each division represents .001 in. (Lane Community College).

Figure 8. Crossfeed and compound screw handles with metric-English conversion collars (Courtesy of The Monarch Machine Tool Company, Sidney, Ohio).

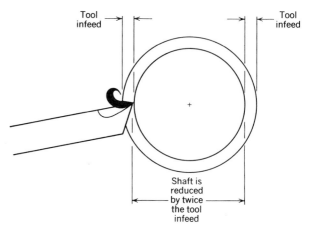

Figure 9. The diameter of the workpiece is reduced twice the amount in which the tool is moved.

Figure 10. Clutch rod is actuated by moving the clutch level. This disengages the motor from the spindle (Lane Community College).

the single depth collar, or one half that amount, for the double depth collar.

Some lathes have a brake and clutch rod that is the same length as the lead screw. A clutch lever connected to the carriage apron rides along the clutch rod (Figure 10). The spindle can be started and stopped without

turning off the motor by using the clutch lever. Some types also have a spindle brake that quickly stops the spindle when the clutch lever is moved to the stop position. An adjustable automatic clutch kickout is also a feature of the clutch rod.

When starting a lathe for the first time use the following checkout list:

1. Move carriage and tailstock to the right to clear workholding device.
2. Locate feed clutches and half-nut lever and disengage before starting spindle.
3. Set up to operate at low speeds.
4. Read any machine information panels that may be located on the machine and observe precautions.
5. Note the feed direction; there are no built-in travel limits or warning devices to prevent feeding into the chuck or against the end of the slides.
6. When you are finished with a lathe, disengage all clutches, clean up chips, and remove any attachments or special setups.

SELF-TEST

1. How can the shift to the low speed range be made on the belt drive lathes that have the step cone pulley?
2. Explain speed shifting procedure on the variable speed drive.
3. In what way can speed changes be made on gearhead lathes?
4. What lever is shifted in order to reverse the lead screw?
5. The sliding gear shifter levers on the quick-change gearbox are used for just two purposes. What are they?
6. When is the proper time to use the carriage handwheel?
7. Why will you not get the same surface finish (tool marks per inch) on the face of a workpiece as you would get on the outside diameter when on the same power feed?
8. The half-nut lever is not used to move the carriage for turning. Name its only use.
9. Micrometer collars are attached on the cross feed handle and compound handle. In what ways are they graduated?
10. How can you know if the lathe you are using is calibrated for single or double depth?

UNIT 6 FACING AND CENTER DRILLING

Facing and center drilling the workpiece are often the first steps taken in a turning project to produce a stepped shaft or a sleeve from solid material. Much lathe work is done in a chuck and requires considerable facing and some center drilling. These important lathe practices will be covered in detail in this unit.

OBJECTIVES

After completing this unit, you should be able to:
1. Correctly set up a workpiece and face the ends.
2. Correctly center drill the ends of a workpiece.
3. Determine the proper feeds and speeds for a workpiece.
4. Explain how to set up to make facing cuts to a given depth and how to measure them.

SETTING UP FOR FACING

Facing is done to obtain a flat surface on the end of cylindrical workpieces or on the face of parts clamped in a chuck or face plate (Figures 1a and 1b). The work most often is held in a three- or four-jaw chuck. If the chuck is to be removed from the lathe spindle, a lathe board must first be placed on the ways. Figure 2 shows a camlock mounted chuck being removed. The correct procedure for installing a chuck on a camlock spindle nose is shown in Figures 3a to 3f. The cams should be tightly snugged (Figure 3f) for one or two revolutions around the spindle.

Setting up work in an independent chuck is simple, but mastering the setup procedures takes some practice. Round stock can be set up by using a dial indicator (Figure 4). Square or rectangular stock can either be set up with a dial indicator or by using a toolholder turned backwards (Figure 5).

Begin the set up by aligning two opposite jaws with the same concentric ring marked in the face of the chuck while the jaws are near the workpiece. This will roughly

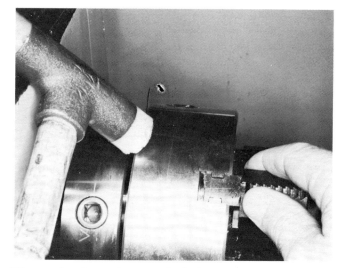

Figure 2. Removing a camlock chuck that is mounted on a lathe spindle (DeAnza College).

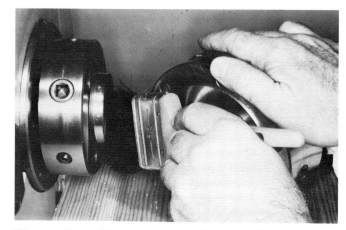

Figure 3a. Chips are cleaned from spindle nose with a brush (DeAnza College).

Figure 1a. Facing a workpiece in a chuck (Lane Community College).

Figure 1b. Facing the end of a shaft (Lane Community College).

Figure 3b. Cleaning the chips from the chuck with a brush (DeAnza College).

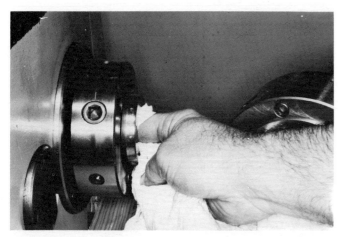

Figure 3c. Spindle nose is thoroughly cleaned with a soft cloth (DeAnza College).

Figure 3d. Chuck is thoroughly cleaned with a soft cloth (DeAnza College).

Figure 3e. Chuck is mounted on spindle nose (DeAnza College).

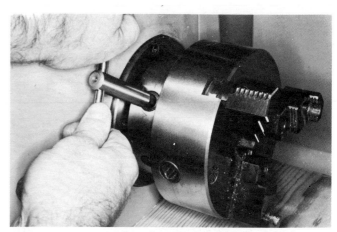

Figure 3f. All cams are turned clockwise until locked securely (DeAnza College).

Figure 4. Setting up round stock in an independent chuck with a dial indicator (Lane Community College).

center the work. Set up the other two jaws with a concentric ring also when they are near the work. Next, bring all of the jaws firmly against the work. When using the dial indicator, zero the bezel at the lowest reading. Now rotate the chuck to the opposite jaw with the high reading and tighten it half the amount of the runout. It might be necessary to loosen the jaw on the low side

Figure 5a. Rectangular stock being set up by using a tool-holder turned backwards. The micrometer dial is used to center the workpiece (Lane Community College).

Figure 5b. Adjusting the rectangular stock at 90 degrees from Figure 5a (Lane Community College).

slightly. Always tighten the jaws at the position where the dial indicator contacts the work since any other location will give erroneous readings. When using the back of the toolholder, the micrometer dial on the cross slide will show the difference in runout. Chalk is sometimes used for setting up rough castings and other work too irregular to be measured with a dial indicator. Workpieces can either be chucked normally, internally, or externally (Figures 6a to 6c).

FACING

The material to be machined usually has been cut off in

Figure 6a. Normal chucking position (Lane Community College).

Figure 6b. Internal chucking position (Lane Community College).

Figure 6c. External chucking position (Lane Community College).

Figure 8. Facing from the outside toward the center of the workpiece (Courtesy of Clausing Corporation).

Figure 9. Setting the tool to the center of the work using the tailstock center (Lane Community College).

Figure 7. Facing from the center to the outside of a workpiece (Lane Community College).

a power saw and so the piece is not square on the end or cut to the specified length. Facing from the center out (Figure 7) produces a better finish, but it is difficult to cut on a solid face in the center. Facing from the outside (Figure 8) is more convenient since heavier cuts may be taken and it is easier to work to the scribed lines on the circumference of the work. When facing from the center out, a right-hand turning tool in a left-hand toolholder is the best arrangement, but when facing from the outside to the center, a left-hand tool in a right-hand or straight toolholder can be used. Facing or other tool machining should not be done on workpieces extending more than five diameters from the chuck jaws.

The point of the tool should be set to the center of the work (Figure 9). This is done by setting the tool to the tailstock center point or by making a trial cut to the center of the work. If the tool is below center, a small uncut stub will be left. The tool can then be reset to the center of the stub.

The carriage must be locked when taking facing cuts as the cutting pressure can cause the tool and carriage to move away (Figure 10), which would make the faced surface curved rather than flat. Finer feeds should be used for finishing than for roughing. Remember, the cross feed is one-half to one-third that of the longitudinal feed. The ratio is usually listed on the index plate of the

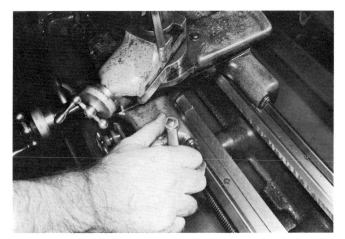

Figure 10. Carriage must be locked before taking a facing cut (Lane Community College).

Figure 12. The compound set at 90 degrees for facing operations (Lane Community College).

Figure 11. Facing to length using a hook rule for measuring (Lane Community College).

Figure 13. Setting the compound at 30 degrees (Lane Community College).

quick-change gear box. A roughing feed could be from .005 to .015 in. and a finishing feed from .003 to .005 in. Use of cutting oils will help produce better finishes on finish facing cuts.

Facing to length may be accomplished by trying a cut and measuring with a hook rule (Figure 11) or by facing to a previously made layout line. A more precise method is to use the graduations on the micrometer collar of the compound. The compound is set so its slide is parallel to the ways (Figure 12). The carriage is locked in place and a trial cut is taken with the micrometer collar set on zero index. The workpiece is measured with a micrometer and the desired length is subtracted from the measurement; the remainder is the amount you should remove by facing. If more than .015 to .030 in. (depth left for finish cut) has to be removed, it should be taken off in two or more cuts by moving the compound micrometer dial the desired amount. A short trial cut (about $\frac{1}{8}$ in.) should again be taken on the finish cut and

adjustment made if necessary. Roughing cuts should be approximately .060 in. in depth.

Quite often the compound is kept at 30 degrees for threading purposes (Figure 13). It is convenient to know that at this angle the tool feeds into the face of the work .001 in. for every .002 in. that the slide is moved. For example, if you wanted to remove .015 in. from the workpiece, you would turn in .030 in. on the micrometer dial (assuming it reads single depth).

A specially ground tool is used to face the end of a workpiece that is mounted between centers. The right-hand facing tool is shaped to fit in the angle between the

Figure 14.   Half centers make facing shaft ends easier.

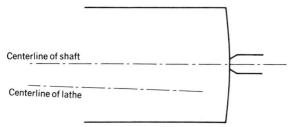

Figure 15a   Convex shaft ends caused by the tailstock being moved off center away from the operator.

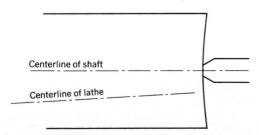

Figure 15b.   Concave shaft ends caused by the tailstock being moved toward the operator.

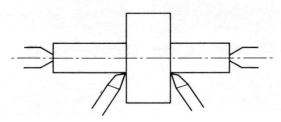

Figure 16.   Work that is held between centers on a mandrel can be faced on both sides with right-hand and left-hand facing tools.

center and the face of the workpiece. Half centers (Figure 14) are made to make the job easier, but they should be used only for facing and not for general turning. If the tailstock is moved off center away from the operator, the shaft end will be convex and, if it is moved toward the operator, it will be concave (Figure 15). Both right-hand and left-hand facing tools are used for facing work held on mandrels (Figure 16).

SPEEDS
Speeds (RPM) for lathe turning a workpiece are determined in essentially the same way as speeds for drilling tools. The only difference is that the diameter of the

work is used instead of the diameter of the drill. For facing work, the outside diameter is always used to determine RPM. Thus:

$$RPM = \frac{CS \times 4}{D}, \text{ where}$$

D = diameter of workpiece (where machining is done)
RPM = revolutions per minute
CS = cutting speed (surface feet per minute)

EXAMPLE 1
The cutting speed for low carbon steel is 90 SFM (surface feet per minute) and the workpiece diameter to be faced is 6 in. Find the correct RPM.

$$RPM = \frac{90 \times 4}{6} = 60$$

EXAMPLE 2
A center drill has a $\frac{1}{8}$ in. drill point. Find the correct RPM to use on low carbon steel (CS 90).

$$RPM = \frac{90 \times 4}{\frac{1}{8}} = \frac{360}{1} \times \frac{8}{1} = 2880$$

These are only approximate speeds and will vary according to the conditions. If chatter marks (vibration marks) appear on the workpiece, the RPM should be reduced. If this does not help, ask your instructor for assistance. For more information on speeds and feeds, see the next unit, "Turning Between Centers."

CENTER DRILLS AND DRILLING
When work is held and turned between centers, a center hole is required on each end of the workpiece. The center hole must have a 60 degree angle to conform to the center and have a smaller drilled hole to clear the center's point. This center hole is made with a combination drill and countersink, sometimes referred to as a center drill. These drills are available in a range of sizes from $\frac{1}{8}$ to $\frac{3}{4}$ in. body diameter and are classified by numbers from 00 to 8, which are normally stamped on the drill body. For example, a number 3 center drill has a $\frac{1}{4}$ in. body diameter and a $\frac{7}{64}$ in. drill diameter. Full listings can be found in the *Machinery's Handbook*.

Center drills are usually held in a drill chuck in the tailstock, while the workpieces are most often supported and turned in a lathe chuck for center drilling (Figure 17). A workpiece could also be laid out and supported in a vertical position for center drilling in a drill press. This method, however, is not used very often.

Round stock could be clamped in a vee block and drill press vise (Figure 18) or on an angle plate. Crossed layout lines are scribed on round stock by means of a

Figure 17. Center drilling a workpiece held in a chuck (Lane Community College).

Figure 18. Center being drilled in round stock that is held in drill press vise (Lane Community College).

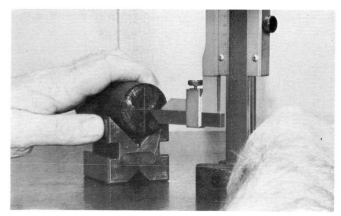

Figure 19. Layout lines for center drilling are scribed on round stock by using a height gage and a vee block on a surface plate (Lane Community College).

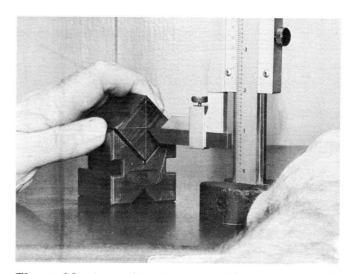

Figure 20. Layout lines for center drilling on square stock are made from corner to corner (Lane Community College).

height gage (Figure 19), and a punch mark is made where they intersect. Layout for square or rectangular stock to be placed between centers is done simply by scribing two diagonal lines from corner to corner (Figure 20). Center layout may also be done with a center head.

As a rule, center holes are drilled by rotating the work in a lathe chuck and feeding the center drill into the work by means of the tailstock spindle. Long workpieces, however, are generally faced by chucking one end and supporting the other in a steady rest (Figure 21). Since the end of stock is never sawed square, it should be center drilled only after spotting a small hole with the lathe tool. A slow feed is needed to protect the small, delicate drill end. Cutting oil should be used and the drill should be backed out frequently to remove chips. The greater the work diameter and the heavier the cut, the larger the center hole should be.

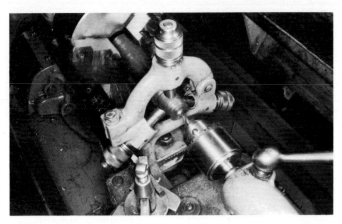

Figure 21. Center drilling long material that is supported in a steady rest (Lane Community College).

Figure 23. Center drill is brought up to work and lightly fed into material (DeAnza College).

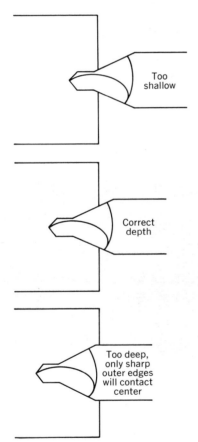

Figure 22. Correct and incorrect depth for center drilling.

Too shallow

Correct depth

Too deep, only sharp outer edges will contact center

Figure 24. Center drill is fed into work with a slow even feed (DeAnza College).

The size of the center hole can be selected by the center drill size and then regulated to some extent by the depth of drilling. You must be careful not to drill too deeply (Figure 22) as this causes the center to contact only the sharp outer edge of the hole, which is a poor bearing surface. It soon becomes loose and out of round and causes such machining problems as chatter and roughness. Center drills are broken often from feeding the drill too fast with the lathe speed too slow or with the tailstock off center.

Center drills are often used as starting or spotting drills when a drilling sequence is to be performed (Figures 23 and 24). This keeps the drill from "wandering" off the center and making the hole run eccentric. Spot drilling is done when work is chucked or is supported in a steady rest. Care must be taken that the workpiece is centered properly in the steady rest or the center drill will be broken.

SELF-TEST

1. You have a rectangular workpiece that needs a facing operation plus center drilling, and a universal chuck is mounted on the lathe spindle. What is your procedure to prepare for machining?
2. Should the point of the tool be set above, below, or at the center of the spindle axis when taking a facing cut?
3. If you set the quick-change gearbox to .012 in., would that be considered a roughing feed for facing?
4. An alignment step must be machined on a cover plate .125 in., plus or minus .003 in., in depth (Figure 25). What procedure should be taken to face to this depth? How can you check your final finish cut?
5. What tool is used for facing shaft ends when they are mounted between centers? In what way is this tool different from a turning tool?
6. If the cutting speed of aluminum is 300 SFM and the workpiece diameter is 4 in., what is the RPM? The formula is

$$RPM = \frac{CS \times 4}{D}$$

7. Name two reasons for center drilling a workpiece in a lathe.

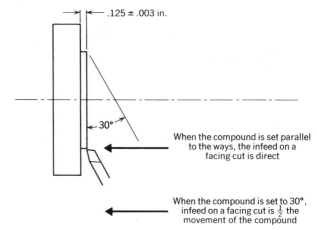

Figure 25.

.125 ± .003 in.

30°

When the compound is set parallel to the ways, the infeed on a facing cut is direct

When the compound is set to 30°, infeed on a facing cut is $\frac{1}{2}$ the movement of the compound

8. How is laying out and drilling center holes in a drill press accomplished?
9. Name two causes for center drill breakage.
10. What happens when you drill too deeply with a center drill?

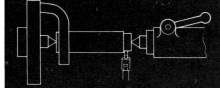

UNIT 7 TURNING BETWEEN CENTERS

Since for a large percentage of lathe work the workpiece is held between centers or between a chuck and a center, turning between centers is a good way for you to learn the basic principles of lathe operation. The economics of machining time and quality will be detailed in this unit, as heavy roughing cuts are compared to light cuts, and speeds and feeds for turning operations are presented.

OBJECTIVES

After completing this unit, you should be able to:
1. Describe the correct setup procedure for turning between centers.
2. Select correct feeds and speeds for a turning operation.
3. Detail the steps necessary for turning to size predictably.
4. Turn a $1\frac{1}{4}$ in.-diameter shaft with six shoulders to a tolerance of plus 0.0, minus .002 in.

SETUP FOR TURNING BETWEEN CENTERS

To turn a workpiece between centers, it is supported between the dead center (tailstock center) and the live center in the spindle nose. A lathe dog (Figure 1) clamped to the workpiece is driven by a drive or dog plate (Figure 2) mounted on the spindle nose. Machining with a single point tool can be done anywhere on the workpiece except near or at the location of the lathe dog.

Turning between centers has some disadvantages. A workpiece cannot be cut off with a parting tool while being supported between centers as this will bind and break the parting tool and ruin the workpiece. For drilling, boring, or machining the end of a long shaft, a steady rest is normally used to support the work. But these operations cannot very well be done when the shaft is supported only by centers.

The advantages of turning between centers are many. A shaft between centers can be turned end for end to continue machining without eccentricity if the centers are in line (Figure 3). This is why shafts that are to be subsequently finish-ground between centers must be machined between centers on a lathe. If a partially threaded part is removed from between centers for checking, and everything is left the same on the lathe, the part can be returned to the lathe, and the threading resumed where it was left off.

A considerable amount of straight turning on shafts is done with the work held between a chuck and the tailstock center (Figure 4). The advantages of this method are quick setup and a positive drive. One disadvantage is that eccentricities in the shaft are caused by inaccuracies in the chuck jaws. Another is the tendency for the workpiece to slip endwise into the chuck jaws under a heavy cut, thus allowing the workpiece to loosen or to come out of the tailstock center.

As in other lathe operations, chip formation and handling are important to safety. Coarser feeds, deeper cuts, and smaller rake angles all tend to increase chip curl, which breaks up the chip into small, safe pieces. Fine feeds and shallow cuts, on the other hand, produce a tangle of wiry, sharp hazardous chips (Figures 5a and 5b) even with a chip breaker on the tool. Long strings may come off the tool, suddenly wrap in the work and

Figure 1. Lathe dog.

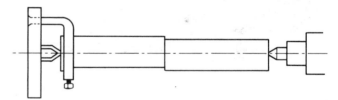

Figure 3. Eccentricity in the center of the part because of the live center being off center.

Figure 2. Dog plate or drive plate on spindle nose of the lathe (Courtesy of the Monarch Machine Tool Company, Sidney, Ohio).

Figure 4. Work being machined between chuck and tailstock center. Note chip formation. Chip guard has been removed for clarity (Lane Community College).

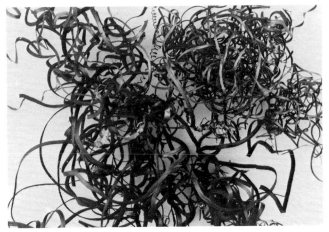

Figure 5a. A tangle of wiry chips. These chips can be hazardous to the operator (Lane Community College).

Figure 5b. A better formation of chips. This type of chip will fall into the chip pan and is more easily handled (Lane Community College).

be drawn back rapidly to the machine. The edges are like saws and can cause very severe cuts.

The center for the headstock spindle is called a live center and it is usually not hardened since its point frequently needs machining to keep it true. Thoroughly clean the inside of the spindle with a soft cloth and wipe off the live center. If the live center is too small for the lathe spindle taper, use a tapered bushing that fits the lathe (Figure 6). Seat the bushing firmly in the taper (Figure 7) and install the center (Figure 8). Set up a dial indicator on the end of the center (Figure 9) to check for runout. If there is runout, remove the center by using a knockout bar through the spindle. Be sure to catch the center with one hand. Check the outside of the center for nicks or burrs. These can be removed with a file. Check the inside of the spindle taper with your finger for nicks or grit. If nicks are found, *do not* use a file but check with your instructor. After removing nicks, if the

Figure 6. Inserting the tapered spindle nose sleeve (DeAnza College).

Figure 7. Make sure the bushing is firmly seated in the taper (Lane Community College).

Figure 8. Installing the center (DeAnza College).

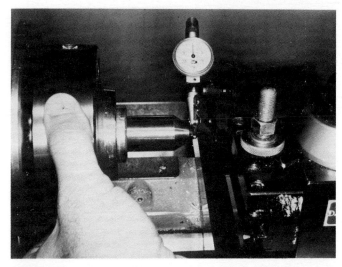

Figure 9. Checking the live center for runout with a dial indicator (DeAnza College).

Figure 10. Live center being machined in a four-jaw chuck. The lathe dog on the workpiece is driven by one of the chuck jaws (Lane Community College).

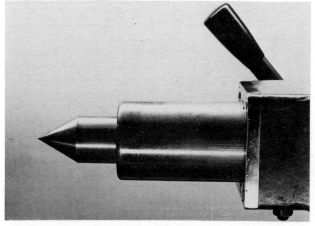

Figure 11. The dead center is hardened to resist wear. It is made of high speed steel or steel with a carbide insert (Courtesy of California Community Colleges, IMC Project).

center still runs out more than the acceptable tolerances (usually .0001 to .0005 in.) a light cut by tool or grinding can be taken with the compound set at 30 degrees.

A live center is often machined from a short piece of soft steel mounted in a chuck (Figure 10). It is then left in place and the workpiece is mounted between it and the tailstock center. A lathe dog with the bent tail against a chuck jaw is used to drive the workpiece. This procedure sometimes saves time on large lathes where changing from the chuck to a drive plate is cumbersome and the amount of work to be done between centers is small.

The tailstock center (Figure 11) is hardened to withstand machining pressures and friction. Clean inside the taper and on the center before installing. Ball bearing, antifriction centers are often used in the tailstock as they will withstand high speed turning without the overheating problems of dead centers. Pipe centers are used for turning tubular material (Figures 12a to 12c).

Figure 12a. Pipe center used for turning (Courtesy of The Monarch Machine Tool Company, Sidney, Ohio).

Figure 12b. Antifriction ball bearing center (Courtesy of the Monarch Machine Tool Company, Sidney, Ohio).

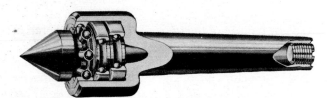

Figure 12c. Cutaway view of a ball bearing tailstock center (Courtesy of the DoAll Company).

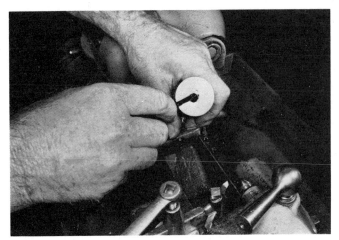

Figure 13. Antifriction compound put in the center hole before setting the workpiece between centers. This step is not necessary when using an antifriction ball bearing center (Lane Community College).

Figure 14. Lathe dog in position (Lane Community College).

To set up a workpiece that has been previously center drilled, slip a lathe dog on one end with the bent tail toward the drive plate. Do not tighten the dog yet. Put antifriction compound into the center hole toward the tailstock and then place the workpiece between centers (Figure 13). The tailstock spindle should not extend out too far as some rigidity in the machine would be lost and chatter or vibration may result. Set the dog in place and avoid any binding of the bent tail (Figure 14). Tighten the dog and then adjust the tailstock so there is no end play, but so the bent tail of the dog freely clicks in its slot. Tighten the tailstock binding lever. The heat of machining will expand the workpiece and cause the dead center to heat from friction. If overheated, the center may be ruined and may even be welded into your workpiece. Periodically, or at the end of each heavy cut, you

Figure 15a. Incorrect position of toolholder for roughing. If the toolholder should turn when using heavy feeds, the tool will gouge more deeply into the work (Lane Community College).

Figure 15b. Correct position of toolholder for roughing. The toolholder will swing away from the cut with excessive feeds (Lane Community College).

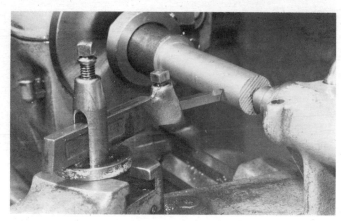

Figure 16. Tools with excessive overhang. Both tool and toolholder extend too far from the tool post for roughing operations (Lane Community College).

Figure 17. Tool and toolholder in the correct position (Lane Community College).

Figure 18. Centering a tool by means of a steel rule (Lane Community College).

for turning between centers by using the same formula as given for facing operations in the last unit:

$$RPM = \frac{CS \times 4}{D}$$

where,

RPM = revolutions per minute
D = diameter of workpiece
CS = cutting speed in surface feet per minute (SFM)

Cutting speeds for various materials are given in Table 1.

EXAMPLE
If the cutting speed is 40 for a certain alloy steel and the workpiece is 2 in. in diameter, find the RPM.

$$RPM = \frac{40 \times 4}{2} = 80$$

After calculating the RPM, use the nearest or next lower speed on the lathe and set the speed.

Feeds are expressed in inches per revolution (IPR) of the spindle. A .010 in. feed will move the carriage and tool .010 in. for one full turn of the headstock spindle. If the spindle speed is changed, the feed ratio still remains the same. Feeds are selected by means of an index chart (Figure 19) either found on the quick-change gearbox or on the side of the headstock housing (Figure 20). The sliding gear levers are shifted to different positions to obtain the feeds indicated on the index plate. The lower decimal numbers on the plate are feeds and the upper numbers are threads per inch.

Feeds and depth of cut should be as much as the tool, workpiece, or machine can stand without undue

should check the adjustment of the centers and reset if necessary.

When a tool post and toolholder are used, the tool-holder must be positioned so it will not turn into the work when heavy cuts are taken (Figures 15a and 15b). The tool and toolholder should not overhang too far (Figure 16) for rough turning, but should be kept toward the tool post as far as practical (Figure 17). Tools should be set on or slightly above the center of the workpiece for roughing and on center for finishing. The tool may be set to the dead center or to a steel rule on the workpiece (Figure 18).

SPEEDS AND FEEDS FOR TURNING

Since machining time is an important factor in lathe operations, it is necessary for you to fully understand the principles of speeds and feeds in order to make the most economical use of your machine. Speeds are determined

Table 1
Cutting Speeds and Feeds for High Speed Steel Tools

	Low Carbon Steel	High Carbon Steel Annealed	Alloy Steel Normalized	Aluminum Alloys	Cast Iron	Bronze
Roughing speed SFM	90	50	45	200	70	100
Finishing speed SFM	120	65	60	300	80	130
Feed IPR roughing	.010–.020	.010–.020	.010–.020	.015–.030	.010–.020	.010–.020
Feed IPR finishing	.003–.005	.003–.005	.003–.005	.005–.010	.003–.010	.003–.010

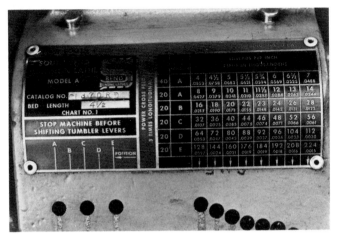

Figure 19. Index chart on the quick-change gearbox (Lane Community College).

Figure 20. Index chart for feed mechanism on a modern geared head lathe with both metric and inch thread and feed selections (Lane Community College).

stress. The *feed rate for roughing should be from one-fifth to one-tenth as much as the depth of cut.* A small 10 or 12 in. swing lathe should handle $\frac{1}{8}$ in. depth of cut in soft steel, but in some cases this may have to be reduced to $\frac{1}{16}$ in. If .100 in. were selected as a trial depth of cut, then the feed could be anywhere from .010 to .020 in. If the machine seems to be overloaded, reduce the feed. Finishing feeds can be from .003 to .005 in. for steel. Use a tool with a larger nose radius for finishing.

TURNING TO SIZE

The cut-and-try method of turning to size a workpiece, or making a cut and measuring how close you came to the desired result, was used in the past when calipers and rule were used for measuring work diameters. A more modern method of turning to size predictably uses the compound and cross feed micrometer collars and micrometer calipers for measurement. If the micrometer collar on the cross feed screw reads in single depth, it will remove twice the amount from the diameter of the

work as the reading shows. A micrometer collar that reads directly or double depth will remove the same amount from the diameter that the reading shows, though the tool will actually move in only half that amount.

After taking one or several roughing cuts (depending on the diameter of the workpiece), .015 to .030 in. should be left for finishing. This can be taken in one cut if the tolerance is large, such as plus or minus .003 in. If the tolerance is small (plus or minus .0005 in.), two finish cuts should be taken, but enough stock must be left for the second cut to make a chip. If insufficient material is left for machining, .001 in. for example, the tool will rub and will not cut. Between .005 and .010 in. should be left for the last finish cut.

The position of the tool is set in relation to the micrometer dial reading, and the first of the two finish cuts is made (Figure 21). *The tool is then returned to the start of the cut without moving the cross feed screw.* The diameter of the workpiece is checked with a micrometer (Figure 22) and the remaining amount to be

Figure 21. A trial cut is made to establish a setting of a micrometer dial in relation to the diameter of the workpiece (Lane Community College).

Figure 22. Measuring the workpiece with a micrometer (Lane Community College).

cut is dialed on the cross feed micrometer dial. A short trial cut is taken (about $\frac{1}{8}$ in. long) and the lathe stopped. A final check with a micrometer is made to validate the tool setting, and then the cut is completed. If the lathe makes a slight taper, see the next unit on ''Alignment of the Lathe Centers'' to correct this problem.

Finishing of machined parts with a file and abrasive cloth should not be necessary if the tools are sharp and honed and if the feeds, speeds, and depth of cut are correct. A machine-finished part looks better than a part finished with a file and abrasive cloth. In the past, filing and polishing the precision surfaces of lathe workpieces were necessary because of lack of rigidity and repeatability of machines. In the same way, worn lathes are not dependable for close tolerances and so an extra allowance must be made for filing. The amount of surface material left for filing ranges from .0005 to .005 in., depending on the final finish, and diameter. If more than the tips of the tool marks are removed with a file and abrasive cloth, a wavy surface will result. For most purposes .002 in. is sufficient material to leave for finishing.

When filing on a lathe, use a low speed, long

Figure 23. Filing in the lathe, left-handed (Lane Community College).

strokes and file left handed (Figure 23). For polishing with abrasive cloth, set the lathe for a high speed and move the cloth back and forth across the work. Hold an end of the cloth strip in each hand (Figures 24a and 24b). Abrasive cloth leaves grit on the ways of the lathe, so a

Figure 24a.   Using abrasive cloth for polishing (Lane Community College).

Figure 24b.   Using a file for backing abrasive cloth for more uniform polishing (Lane Community College).

Figure 25.   Measuring the workpiece length to a shoulder with a machinist's rule (Lane Community College).

Figure 26.   Carriage micrometer stop set to limit tool travel in order to establish a shoulder (Lane Community College).

thorough cleaning of the ways should be done after polishing.

Machining shoulders to specific lengths can be done in several ways. Using a machinist's rule (Figure 25) to measure workpiece length to a shoulder is a very common but semiprecision method. Preset carriage micrometer stops (Figure 26) can be used to limit carriage movement and establish a shoulder. This method can be very accurate if it is set up correctly. Another very accurate means of machining shoulders is by using special dial indicators with long travel plunger rods. These indicators show the longitudinal position of the carriage. Whichever method is used, *the power feed should be turned off one-eighth in. short of the workpiece shoulder* and the tool handfed to the desired length. If the tool should be accidentally fed into an existing shoulder, the feed mechanism may jam and be very difficult to release. A broken tool, toolholder, or lathe part may be the result.

Mandrels, sometimes called lathe arbors, are used to hold work that is turned between centers (Figures 27a and 27b). Tapered mandrels are made in standard sizes

Figure 27 a. Tapered mandrel or arbor.

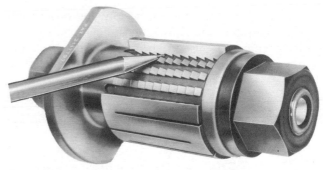

Figure 28. Operating principle of a special type of an expanding mandrel. The "Saber-tooth" design provides a uniform gripping action in the bore (Courtesy of Buck Tool Company).

Figure 27 b. Tapered mandrel and workpiece set up between centers (Courtesy of Clausing Corporation).

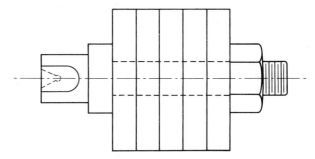

Figure 29. Expanding mandrel and workpiece set up between centers (Lane Community College).

Figure 30. Many similar parts are machined at the same time with a gang mandrel.

and have a taper of only .006 in./ft. A flat is milled on one end of the mandrel for the lathe dog set screw. High pressure lubricant is applied to the bore of the workpiece and the mandrel is pressed into the workpiece with an arbor press. The assembly is mounted between centers and the workpiece is turned or faced on either side.

Expanding mandrels (Figure 28) have the advantage of providing a uniform gripping surface for the length of the bore (Figure 29). A tapered mandrel grips tighter on one end than the other. Gang mandrels (Figure 30) grip several pieces of similar size, such as discs, to turn their circumference. These are made with collars, thread, and nut for clamping.

Stub mandrels (Figures 31a to 31c) are used in chucking operations. These are often quickly machined for a single job and then discarded. Expanding stub mandrels (Figures 32a and 32b) are used when production of many similar parts is carried out. Threaded stub mandrels are used for machining the outside surfaces of parts that are threaded in the bore.

Coolants are used for heavy duty and production turning. Oil-water emulsions and synthetic coolants are the most commonly used, while sulfurized oils usually are not used for turning operations except for threading.

Most job work or single piece work is done dry. Many shop lathes do not have a coolant pump and tank, so, if any coolant or cutting oil is used, it is applied with a pump oil can. Coolants and cutting oils for various materials are given in Table 2.

Figure 31a. Stub mandrel being machined to size with a slight taper, about .006 in./ft (Lane Community College).

Figure 31c. Part being machined after assembly on mandrel (Lane Community College).

Figure 31b. Part to be machined being affixed to the mandrel. The mandrel is oiled so that the part can be easily removed (Lane Community College).

Figure 32a. Special stub mandrel with adjust-tru feature (Courtesy of Buck Tool Company).

Table 2
Coolants and Cutting Oils Used for Turning

Material	Dry	Water Soluble Oil	Synthetic Coolants	Kerosene	Sulfurized Oil	Mineral Oil
Aluminum		x	x	x		
Brass	x	x	x			
Bronze	x	x	x			x
Cast iron	x					
Steel						
Low carbon		x	x		x	
Alloy		x	x		x	
Stainless		x	x		x	

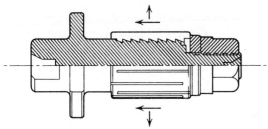

MC standard between centers nut actuated

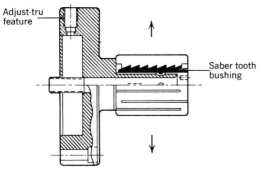

Adjust-tru feature

Saber tooth bushing

MLDR — flange mount — draw bolt actuated
stationary sleeve

Figure 32.b. Precision adjustment can be maintained on
the expanding stub mandrels with the adjust-tru feature on the
flange mount (Courtesy of Buck Tool Company).

SELF-TEST

1. Name two advantages and two disadvantages of turning between centers.
2. What other method besides turning between centers is extensively used for turning shafts and long workpieces that are supported by the tailstock center?
3. What factors tend to promote or increase chip curl so that safer chips are formed?
4. Name three kinds of centers used in the tailstock and explain their uses.
5. How is the dead center correctly adjusted?
6. Why should the dead center be frequently adjusted when turning between centers?
7. Why should you avoid excess overhang with the tool and toolholder when roughing?
8. Calculate the RPM for roughing a $1\frac{1}{2}$-in. diameter shaft of machine steel.
9. What would the spacing or distance between tool marks on the workpiece be with a .010 in. feed?
10. How much should the feed rate be for roughing?
11. How much should be left for finishing?
12. Describe the procedure in turning to size predictably.

UNIT 8 ALIGNMENT OF THE LATHE CENTERS

As a machinist, you must be able to check a workpiece for taper and properly set the tailstock of a lathe. Without these skills, you will lose much time in futile attempts to restore precision turning between centers when the workpiece has an unintentional taper. This unit will show you several ways to align the centers of a lathe.

OBJECTIVES

After completing this unit, you should be able to:

1. Check for taper with a test bar and restore alignment by adjusting the tailstock.
2. Check for taper by taking a cut with a tool and measuring the workpiece and restore alignment by adjusting the tailstock.

The tailstock will normally stay in good alignment on a lathe that is not badly worn. If a lathe has been used for taper turning with the tailstock offset, however, the tailstock may not have been realigned properly (Figure 1). The tailstock also could be slightly out of alignment if an improper method of adjustment was used. It is therefore a good practice to occasionally check the center alignment of the lathe you usually use and to always check the alignment before using a different lathe.

It is often too late to save the workpiece by realigning centers if a taper is discovered while making a finish cut. A check for taper should be made on the workpiece while it is still in the roughing stage. You can do this by taking a light cut for some distance along the workpiece or on each end *without resetting* the cross feed dial. Then check the diameter on each end with a micrometer; the difference between the two readings is the amount of taper in that distance.

Four methods are used for aligning centers on a lathe. In one method, the center points are brought together and visually checked for alignment (Figure 2). This is, of course, not a precision method for checking alignment.

Another method of aligning centers is by using the

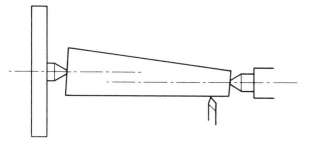

Figure 1. Tailstock out of line causing a tapered workpiece.

Figure 2. Checking alignment by matching center points (DeAnza College).

tailstock witness marks. Adjusting the tailstock to the witness marks (Figure 3), however, is only an approximate means of eliminating taper. The tailstock is moved by means of a screw or screws. A typical arrangement is shown in Figure 4, where one set screw is released and the opposite one is tightened to move the tailstock on its slide (Figure 5). The tailstock clamp bolt must be released before the tailstock is offset.

Two more accurate means of aligning centers are by using a test bar and by machining and measuring. A test bar is simply a shaft that has true centers (is not off center) and has no taper. Some test bars are made with two diameters for convenience. When checking align-

Figure 3. Adjusting the tailstock to the witness marks for alignment (DeAnza College).

Figure 4. Hexagonal socket set screw which, when turned, moves the tailstock provided that the opposite one is loosened (DeAnza College).

ment with a test bar, no dog is necessary as the bar is not rotated. A dial indicator is mounted, preferably in the tool post, so it will travel with the carriage (Figure 6). Its contact point should be on the center of the test bar.

Begin with the indicator at the headstock end, and set the indicator bezel to zero (Figure 7). Now move the setup to the tailstock end of the test bar (Figure 8), and check the dial indicator reading. If no movement of the needle has occurred, the centers are in line. If the needle has moved clockwise, the tailstock is misaligned toward the operator. This will cause the workpiece to taper with the smaller end near the tailstock. If the needle has moved counterclockwise, the tailstock is away from the operator too far and the workpiece will taper with the smaller end at the headstock.

In either case, move the tailstock until both diameters have the same reading.

Since usually only a minor adjustment is needed while a job is in progress, the most common method of aligning lathe centers is by cutting and measuring. It is also the most accurate. This method, unlike the bar test method, usually uses the workpiece while it is in the roughing stage (Figure 9). A light cut is taken along the length of the test piece and both ends are measured with a micrometer. If the diameter at the tailstock end is smaller, the tailstock is toward the operator, and if the diameter at the headstock end is smaller, the tailstock is away from the operator. Set up a dial indicator (Figure 10) and move the tailstock half the difference of the two micrometer readings. Make another light cut and check for taper.

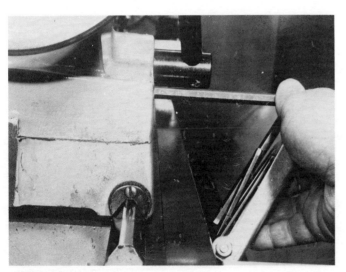

Figure 5. The opposite set screw being adjusted (DeAnza College).

Figure 6. Test bar setup between centers with a dial indicator mounted in the tool post (DeAnza College).

Figure 7. Indicator is moved to measuring surface at headstock end and the bezel is set on zero (DeAnza College).

Figure 8. The carriage with the dial indicator is moved to the measuring surface near the tailstock. In this case the dial indicator did not move, so the tailstock is on center (DeAnza College).

Figure 9. Checking for taper by taking a cut on a workpiece. After the cut is made for the length of the workpiece, a micrometer reading is taken at each end to determine any difference in diameter (Lane Community College).

Figure 10. Using a dial indicator to check the amount of movement of the tailstock when it is being realigned (Lane Community College).

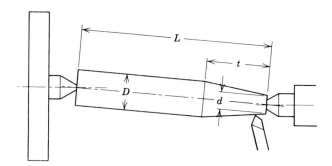

Figure 11. A short taper is made on a longer shaft.

When only a short distance of the total length of a shaft (Figure 11) can be turned to check for taper, the amount of tailstock setover may be calculated by the following formula:

$$\text{Offset} = \frac{L \times (D - d)}{2t}$$

where,

L = total length of shaft
t = length of taper
D = diameter at large end
d = diameter at small end

EXAMPLE

L = 14 in.
t = 4 in.
D = 1.495 in.
d = 1.490 in.

$$\text{Offset} = \frac{14 \times (1.495 - 1.490)}{2 \times 4} = .010 \text{ in.}$$

In this case, the tailstock should be moved away from the operator .010 in.

SELF-TEST

1. What is the result on the workpiece when the centers are out of line?
2. What happens to the workpiece when the tailstock is offset toward the operator?
3. Name three methods of aligning the centers.
4. Which measuring instrument is used when using a test bar?
5. By what means is the measuring done when checking taper by taking a cut?

This unit has no post test.

UNIT 9 DRILLING, BORING, REAMING, KNURLING, RECESSING, PARTING, AND TAPPING IN THE LATHE

Much of the versatility of the lathe as a machine tool is due to the variety of tools and workholding devices used. This equipment makes possible the many special operations that you will begin to do in this unit.

OBJECTIVES

After completing this unit, you should be able to:
1. Explain the procedures for drilling, boring, reaming, knurling, recessing, parting, and tapping in the lathe.
2. Set up to drill, ream bore, and tap on the lathe and complete each of these operations.
3. Set up for knurling, recessing, die threading, and parting on the lathe and complete each of these operations.

DRILLING

The lathe operations of boring, tapping, and reaming usually begin with spotting and drilling a hole. The workpiece, often a solid material that requires a bore, is mounted in a chuck , collet, or faceplate, while the drill is typically mounted in the tailstock spindle that has a Morse taper. If there is a slot in the tailstock spindle, the drill tang must be aligned with it when inserting the drill.

Drill chucks with Morse taper shanks are used to hold straight shank drills and center drills (Figure 1a). Center drills are used for spotting or making a start for drilling (Figure 1b). When drilling with large size drills, a pilot drill should be used first. If a drill wobbles when started, place the heel of a toolholder against it near the point to steady the drill while it is starting in the hole. Taper shank drills (Figure 2) are inserted directly into the tailstock spindle. The friction of the taper is usually all that is needed to keep the drill from turning while a hole is being drilled (Figures 3 and 4), but when using larger drills, the friction is not enough. A lathe dog is sometimes clamped to the drill just above the flutes (Figure 5) with the bent tail resting on the compound. Hole depth can be measured with a rule or by means of the graduations on top of the tailstock spindle. The alignment of the tailstock with the lathe center line should be checked before drilling or reaming.

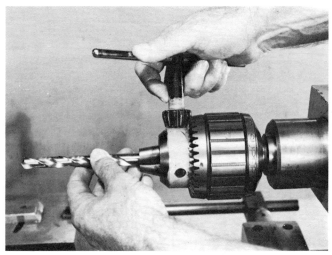

Figure 1a. Mounting a straight shank drill in a drill chuck in the tailstock spindle (Lane Community College).

Figure 1b. Center drilling is the first step prior to drilling, reaming, or boring (DeAnza College).

Drilled holes are not accurate enough for many applications, such as for gear or pulley bores, which should not be made over the nominal size more than .001 to .002 in. Drilling typically produces holes that are oversize and run eccentric to the center axis of the lathe (Figure 6). This is not true in the case of some manufacturing types such as gun drilling. However, truer axial alignment of holes is possible when the work is turned and the drill remains stationary, as in a lathe operation, in comparison to operations where the drill is turned and the work is stationary, as on a drill press. Drilling also produces holes with rough finishes, which along with size errors can be corrected by boring or reaming. The hole must first be drilled slightly smaller than the finish diameter in order to leave material for finishing by either of these methods.

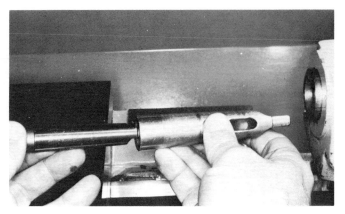

Figure 2. A drill sleeve is placed on the drill so that it will fit the taper in the tailstock spindle (DeAnza College).

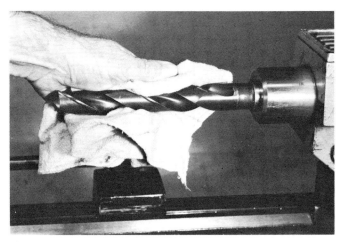

Figure 3. The drill is then firmly seated in the tailstock spindle (Lane Community College).

Figure 4. The feed pressure when drilling is usually sufficient to keep the drill seated in the tailstock spindle, thus keeping the drill from turning (DeAnza College).

Figure 5. A lathe dog is used when the drill has a tendency to turn in the tailstock spindle (Lane Community College).

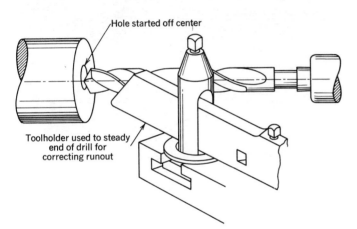

Figure 6. An exaggerated view of the runout and eccentricity that is typical of drilled holes.

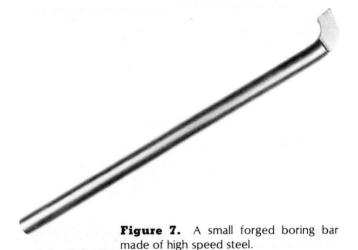

Figure 7. A small forged boring bar made of high speed steel.

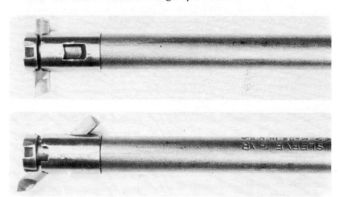

Figure 8. Two boring bars with inserted tools set at different angles.

BORING

Boring is the process of enlarging and truing an existing or drilled hole. A drilled hole for boring can be from $\frac{1}{32}$ to $\frac{1}{16}$ in. undersize, depending on the situation. Speeds and feeds for boring are determined in the same way as they are for external turning. Boring to size predictably is also done in the same way as in external turning except that the cross feed screw is turned counterclockwise to move the tool into the work.

An inside spring caliper and a rule are sometimes useful for rough measurement. Vernier calipers are also used by machinists for internal measuring, though the telescoping gage and outside micrometer are most commonly used for the precision measurement of small bores. Inside micrometers are used for larger bores. Other means of measurement are an inside spring caliper used with an outside micrometer, and on large bores an inside micrometer used with an outside caliper. Pre-cision bore gages are used where many bores are checked for similar size, such as for acceptable tolerance.

A boring bar is clamped in a holder mounted on the carriage compound. Several types of boring bars and holders are used. Boring bars designed for small holes ($\frac{1}{2}$ in. and smaller) are usually the forged type (Figure 7). The forged end is sharpened by grinding. When the bar gets ground too far back, it must be reshaped or discarded. Boring bars for holes with diameters over $\frac{1}{2}$ in. (Figure 8) use high speed tool inserts, which are typically hand ground in the form of a left-hand turning tool. These tools can be removed from the bar for resharpening when needed. The cutting tool can be held at various angles to obtain different results, which makes the boring bar useful for many applications. Standard bars generally come with a tool angle of 30, 45, or 90 degrees. Some boring bars are made for carbide inserts (Figure 9).

Chatter is the rattle or vibration between a workpiece and a tool because of the lack of rigid support for the tool. Chatter is a great problem in boring operations since the bar must extend away from the support of the

Figure 9. A boring bar with carbide insert. When one edge is dull, a new one is selected (Courtesy of Kennametal Inc., Latrobe, Pa.).

Figure 12. Boring tools must have sufficient side relief and side rake to be efficient cutting tools. Back rake is not normally used (Lane Community College).

Figure 10. A boring bar setup with a large overhang for making a deep bore. It is difficult to avoid chatter with this arrangement (DeAnza College).

Figure 11. Tuned boring bars contain dampening slugs of heavy material that can be adjusted by applying pressure with a screw (Courtesy of Kennametal Inc., Latrobe, Pa.).

Figure 13. A tool with insufficient end relief will rub on the heel of the tool (arrow) and will not cut (Lane Community College).

compound (Figure 10). For this reason boring bars should be kept back into their holders as far as practicable. Tuned boring bars can be adjusted so that their vibration is dampened (Figure 11). If chatter occurs when boring, one or more of the following may help to eliminate the vibration of the boring tool.

1. Shorten the boring bar overhang, if possible.
2. Make sure the tool is on center.
3. Reduce the spindle speed.
4. Use a boring bar as large in diameter as possible without it binding in the hole.
5. Reduce the nose radius on the tool.
6. Apply cutting oil to the bore.

Boring bars sometimes spring away from the cut and cause bell-mouth, a slight taper at the front edge of a bore. One or two extra cuts (called free cuts) taken

without moving the cross feed will usually eliminate this problem.

A large variety of boring bar holders are used. Some types are designed for small, forged bars while others of more rigid construction are used for larger, heavier work.

Boring tools are made with side relief and end relief, but usually with zero back rake (Figure 12). Insufficient end relief will allow the heel of the tool to rub on the workpiece (Figure 13). The end relief should be between 10 and 20 degrees. The machinist must use judgment when grinding the end relief because the larger the bore, the less end relief is required (Figure 14). If the end of the tool is relieved too much, the cutting edge will be weak and break down.

The point of the cutting tool should be positioned exactly on the center line of the workpiece (Figures 15a to 15c). There must be a space to allow the chips to pass

Figure 14. End relief angle varies depending on the diameter of the workpiece bore. These views are looking outward from inside the chuck (Lane Community College).

Figure 15b. If the boring tool is too low, the heel of the tool will rub and the tool will not cut, even if the tool has the correct relief angle (Lane Community College).

Figure 15a. The point of the boring tool must be positioned on the centerline of the workpiece (Lane Community College).

Figure 15c. If the tool is too high, the back rake becomes excessively negative and the tool point is likely to be broken off. A poor quality finish is the result of this position (Lane Community College).

between the bar and the surface being machined, or the chips will wedge and bind on the back side of the bar, forcing the cutting tool deeper into the work (Figure 16).

"Through boring" is the boring of a workpiece from one end to the other or all the way through it. For through boring, the tool is held in a bar that is perpendicular to the axis of the workpiece. A slight side cutting edge angle is often used for through boring (Figure 17).

Figure 16. Allowance must be made so the chips can clear the space between the bar and the surface being machined This setup has insufficient chip clearance (where the arrow is pointing) (Lane Community College).

Figure 17. Bar and tool arrangement for through boring (Lane Community College).

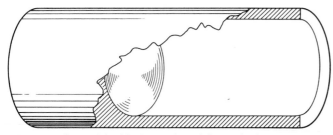

Figure 18. A blind hole machined flat in the bottom.

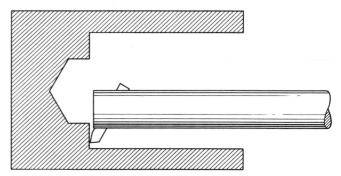

Figure 19. A bar with an angled tool used to square the bottom of a hole with a drilled center.

Figure 20. Workpiece clamped on face plate has been located, drilled, and bored (California Community Colleges IMC Project).

Back facing is sometimes done to true up a surface on the back side of a through bore. This is done with a straight ground right-hand tool also held in a bar perpendicular to the workpiece. This amount of facing that can be done in this way is limited to the movement of the bar in the bore.

A blind hole is one that does not go all the way through the part to be machined (Figure 18). Machining the bottom or end of a blind hole to a flat is easier when the drilled center does not need to be cleaned up. A bar with the tool set at an angle, usually 30 or 45 degrees, is used to square the bottom of a hole with a drilled center (Figure 19).

Most boring is performed on workpieces mounted in a chuck. But it is also done in the end of workpieces supported by a steady rest. Boring and other operations are infrequently done on workpieces set up on a face plate (Figure 20).

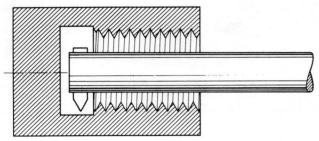

Figure 21. Ample thread relief is necessary when making internal threads.

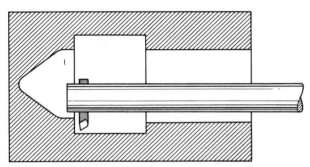

Figure 22. The hole is drilled deeper than necessary to allow room for the boring bar.

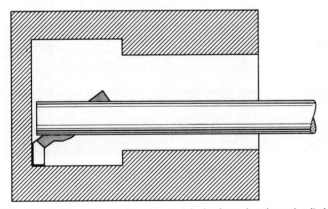

Figure 23. A special tool is needed when the thread relief must be next to a flat bottom.

A thread relief is an enlargment of a bore at the bottom of a blind hole. The purpose of a thread relief is to allow a threading tool to disengage the work at the end of a pass (Figure 21). When the work will allow it, a hole can be drilled deeper than necessary. This will give the end of the boring bar enough space so that the tool can reach into the area to be relieved and still be held at a 90 degree angle (Figure 22). When the work will not allow for the deeper drilling, a special tool must be ground (Figure 23).

Grooves in bores are made by feeding a form tool (Figure 24) straight into the work. Snap ring, O-ring, and

Figure 24. A tool that is ground to the exact width of the desired groove can be moved directly into the work to the correct depth (Lane Community College).

Figure 25. A square shoulder is made with a counterboring tool (Lane Community College).

oil grooves are made in this way. Cutting oil should always be used in these operations.

Counterboring in a lathe is the process of enlarging a bore for definite length (Figure 25). The shoulder that is produced in the end of the counterbore is usually made square (90 degrees) to the lathe axis. Boring and counterboring are also done on long workpieces that are supported in a steady rest. All boring work should have the edges and corners broken or chamfered.

REAMING

Reaming is done in the lathe to quickly and accurately finish drilled or bored holes to size. Machine reamers, like drills, are held in the tailstock spindle of the lathe. Floating reamer holders are sometimes used to assure alignment of the reamer, since the reamer follows the eccentricity of drilled holes. This helps eliminate bell-mouth bores that result from reamer wobble, but does not eliminate the hole eccentricity. Only boring will remove the bore runout.

Roughing reamers (rose reamers) are often used in drilled or cored holes followed by machine or finish reamers. When drilled or cored holes have excessive

Figure 26. Hand reaming in the lathe (Lane Community College).

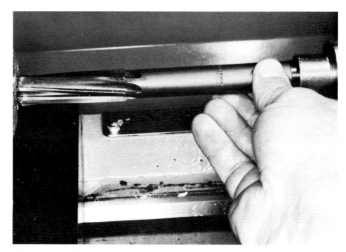

Figure 27. The reamer must be seated in the taper (DeAnza College).

eccentricity, they are bored .010 to .015 in. undersize and machine reamed. If a greater degree of accuracy or a better finish is required, the hole is bored to within .003 to .005 in. of finish size and hand reamed (Figure 26). For hand reaming, the machine is shut off and the hand reamer is turned with a tap wrench. Types of machine reamers are shown in Section G, Unit 7, "Reaming in the Drill Press." Hand reamers are shown in Section B, Unit 6, "Hand Reamers."

Cutting oils used in reaming are similar to those used for drilling holes (see Table 2, "Coolants Used for Reaming," in Section G, Unit 7, "Reaming in the Drill Press"). Cutting speeds are dependent on machine and workpiece material finish requirements. A rule of thumb for reaming speeds is to use one-half the speed used for drilling (see Table 1, Cutting Speeds in SFPM for Reaming with an HSS Reamer," in Section G, Unit 7, "Reaming in the Drill Press").

Feeds for reaming are about twice that used for drilling. The cutting edge should not rub without cutting as it causes glazing, work hardening, and dulling of the reamer.

A simple machine reaming sequence would be as follows:

1. Assuming that the hole has been drilled $\frac{1}{64}$ in. undersize, a taper shank machine reamer is seated in the taper by hand pressure (Figure 27).

2. Cutting oil is applied to the hole and the reamer is started into the hole by turning the tailstock handwheel (Figure 28). The hole is completed and the reamer is removed from the hole. Never reverse the machine when reaming.

3. The reamer is removed from the tailstock spindle and cleaned with a cloth (Figure 29).The reamer is then returned to the storage rack.

4. The lathe is cleaned with a brush (Figure 30).

Figure 28. Starting the reamer in the hole. Kerosene is being used as a cutting fluid (DeAnza College).

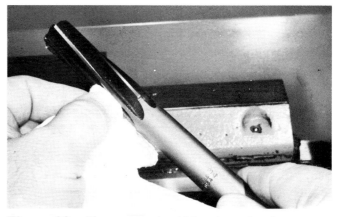

Figure 29. The reamer should be cleaned and put away after using it (DeAnza College).

Figure 30. The chips are brushed into the chip pan (DeAnza College).

TAPPING

The tapping of work mounted in a chuck is a quick and accurate means of producing internal threads. Tapping in the lathe is similar to tapping in the drill press but it is generally reserved for small size holes, as tapping is the only way they can be internally threaded. Large internal threads are made in the lathe with a single point threading tool held in a boring bar. A large tap requires considerable force or torque to turn, more than can be provided by hand turning. A tap that is aligned by the dead center will make a straight tapped hole that is in line with the lathe axis.

A plug tap (Figure 31) or spiral point tap (Figure 32) may be used for tapping through holes. When tapping blind holes, a plug tap could be followed by a bottoming tap (Figure 33), if threads are needed to the bottom of the hole. A good practice is to drill a blind hole deeper than the required depth of threads.

Two approaches may be taken for hand tapping. Power is not used in either case. One method is to turn the tap by means of a tap wrench or adjustable wrench with the spindle engaged in a low gear so it will not turn (Figure 34). The other method is to disengage the spindle and turn the chuck by hand while the tap wrench handle rests on the compound (Figure 35). In both cases the tailstock is clamped to the ways, and the dead center is kept in the center of the tap by slowly turning the tailstock handwheel. The tailstock on small lathes need not be clamped to the ways for small taps, but held firmly with one hand. Cutting oil should be used and the tap

Figure 35. Tapping by turning the chuck (Lane Community College).

Figure 31. Plug tap (TRW, Inc.).

Figure 32. Spiral point tap or gun tap (TRW, Inc.).

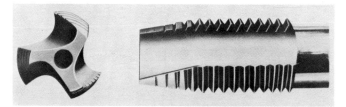

Figure 33. Bottoming tap (TRW, Inc.).

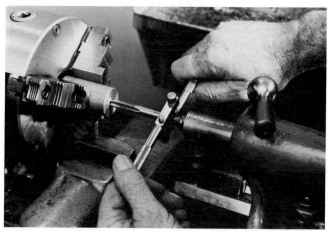

Figure 34. Hand tapping in the lathe by turning the tap wrench (Lane Community College).

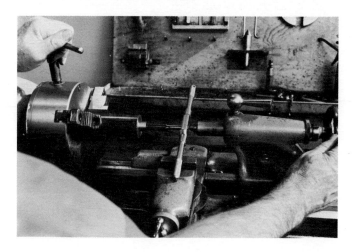

Figure 36. Starting die on rod to be threaded in the lathe. The tailstock spindle (without a center) is used to start the die squarely onto the work (Lane Community College).

Figure 37. Button die holder being used to cut a small diameter thread on a parallel clamp screw (Lane Community College).

backed off every one or two turns to break chips unless it is a spiral point tap, sometimes called a gun tap.

The correct tap drill size should be obtained from a tap drill chart. Drills tend to drill slightly oversize, and tapping the oversize hole can produce poor internal thread with only a small percentage of thread cut. Make sure the drill produces a correctly sized hole by drilling first with a slightly smaller drill, then use the tap drill as a reamer.

Tapping can be done on the lathe with power, but it is recommended that it be done only if the spindle rotation can be reversed, if a spiral point tap is used, and if the hole is clear through the work. The tailstock is left free to move on the ways. Insert the tap in a drill chuck in the tailstock and set the lathe on a low speed. Use cutting oil and slide the tailstock so the tap engages the work. Reverse the rotation and remove the tap from the work every $\frac{3}{8}$ to $\frac{1}{2}$ in. When reversing, apply light hand pressure on the tailstock to move it to the right until the tap is all of the way out.

External threads cut with a die should only be used for nonprecision purposes, since the die may wobble and the pitch (the distance from a point on one thread to the same point on the next) may not be uniform. The rod to be threaded extends a short distance from the chuck and a die and diestock are started on the end (Figure 36). Cutting oil is used. The handle is rested against the compound. The chuck may be turned by hand, but if power is used, the machine is set for low speed and reversed every $\frac{3}{8}$ to $\frac{1}{2}$ in. to clear the chips. Finish the last $\frac{1}{4}$ in. by hand if approaching a shoulder. Reverse the lathe to remove the die.

Die holders are sometimes used on the lathe to hold and guide the die from the tailstock spindle. The thread is much better aligned with less pitch error than it is with a die stock (though not as accurate as in single point threading). The button die holder shown in Figure 37 is hollow and is guided by a bar that is seated in the tailstock spindle. The lathe is running at low speed and the thread is cut when the knurled body is gripped, preventing its turning. As in other die cutting, the cutting action is stopped every 2 to 5 turns to break the chips. Fairly long threads on small diameter stock (not over $\frac{1}{2}$ in.) can be produced by this method.

RECESSING, GROOVING, AND PARTING

Recessing and grooving on external diameters (Figures 38a to 38c) is done to provide grooves for thread relief, snap rings, and O-rings. Special tools (Figure 39) are ground for both external and internal grooves and recesses. Parting tools are sometimes used for external grooving and thread relief.

Parting or cutoff tools (Figure 40) are designed to withstand high cutting forces, but if chips are not sufficiently cleared or cutting oil is not used, these tools can quickly jam and break. Parting tools must be set on center and square with the work (Figure 41). Lathe tools are often specially ground as parting tools for small or delicate parting jobs (Figure 42). Diagonally ground parting tools leave no burr.

Parting alloy steels and other metals is sometimes difficult, and step parting (Figure 43) may help in these cases. When deep parting difficult material, extend the cutting tool from the holder a short distance and part to that depth. Then back off the cross feed and extend the

Figure 38a. The undercutting tool is brought to the workpiece and the micrometer dial is zeroed. Cutting oil is applied to the work (Lane Community College).

Figure 38c. The finished groove (Lane Community College).

Figure 38b. The tool is fed to the single depth of the thread or the required depth of the groove. If a wider groove is necessary, the tool is moved over and a second cut is taken as shown (Lane Community College).

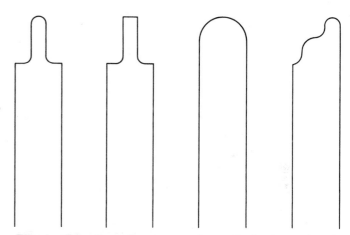

Figure 39. Recessing or grooving tools for internal and external use.

tool a bit farther; part to that depth. Repeat the process until the center is reached. Sulfurized cutting oil works best for parting unless the lathe is equipped with a coolant pump and a steady flow of soluble oil is available. Parting tools are made in either straight or offset types. A right-hand offset cutoff tool is necessary when parting very near the chuck.

All parting and grooving tools have a tendency to chatter; therefore any setup must be as rigid as possible.

Figure 40. Parting tool making a cut (Lane Community College).

Figure 41. Parting tools must be set to the center of the work (Lane Community College).

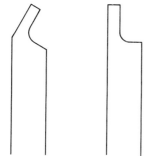

Figure 42. Special parting tools that have been ground from lathe tools for small or delicate parting jobs.

Figure 43. Step parting (Lane Community College).

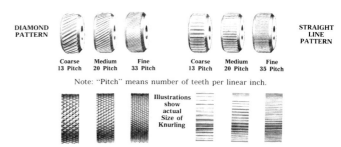

Figure 44. Set of straight knurls and diagonal knurls (TRW, Inc.).

Figure 45a. Knuckle-joint knurling toolholder.

A low speed should be used for parting; if the tool chatters, reduce the speed. Work should not extend very far from the chuck when parting or grooving, and no parting should be done in the middle of a workpiece or at the end near the dead center. A feed that is too light can cause a chatter, but a feed that is too heavy can jam the tool. The tool should always be making a chip. Hand feeding the tool is best at first.

KNURLING

A knurl is a raised impression on the surface of a workpiece produced by two hardened rolls, and is usually of two patterns: diamond or straight (Figure 44). The diamond pattern is formed by a right-hand and a left-hand helix mounted in a self-centering head. The straight pattern is formed by two straight rolls. These common knurl patterns can be either fine, medium, or coarse.

Diamond knurling is used to improve the appearance of a part and to provide a good gripping surface for levers and tool handles. Straight knurling is used to increase the size of a part for press fits in light duty applications. A disadvantage to this use of knurls is that the fit has less contact area than a standard fit.

Three basic types of knurling toolholders are used: the knuckle-joint holder (Figure 45a), the revolving head holder (Figure 45b), and the straddle holder (Figure 45c). The straddle holder allows small diameters to be knurled with less distortion. This principle is used for knurling on production machines.

Knurling works best on workpieces mounted between centers. When held in a chuck and supported by a center, the workpiece tends to crawl back into the chuck and out of the supporting center with the high

Figure 45 b. Revolving head knurling toolholder.

Figure 46. Knurls are centered on the workpiece (Lane Community College).

Figure 45 c. Straddle knurling toolholder (Courtesy of Ral-mike's Tool-A-Rama).

Figure 47. Angling the toolholder 5 degrees often helps establish the diamond pattern (Lane Community College).

pressure of the knurl. This is especially true when the knurl is started at the tailstock end and the feed is toward the chuck. Long slender pieces push away from the knurl and will stay bent if the knurl is left in the work after the lathe is stopped.

Knurls do not cut, but displace the metal with high pressures. Lubrication is more important than cooling, so a lard oil or lubricating oil is satisfactory. Low speeds (about the same as for threading) and a feed of about .015 to .030 in. are used for knurling.

The knurls should be centered on the workpiece vertically (Figure 46) and the knurl toolholder should be square with the work, unless the knurl pattern is difficult to establish, as it often is in tough materials. In that case, the toolholder should be angled about 5 degrees to the work so the knurl can penetrate deeper (Figure 47).

A knurl should be started in soft metal about half depth and the pattern checked. An even diamond pattern should develop (Figure 48). But, if one roll is dull or placed too high or too low, a double impression will develop (Figure 49) because the rolls are not tracking evenly. If this happens, move the knurls to a new position along the workpiece, readjust up or down, and try

again. The knurls should be cleaned with a wire brush between passes.

Material that hardens as it is worked, such as high carbon or spring steel, should be knurled in one pass if at all possible, but in not more than two passes. Even in ordinary steel, the surface will work harden after a diamond pattern has developed to points. It is best to stop knurling just before the points are sharp (Figure 50).

Figure 48. The knurl is started approximately half depth. Notice the diamond pattern is not fully developed (Lane Community College).

Figure 50. More than one pass is usually required to bring the knurl to full depth (Lane Community College).

Figure 49. Double impression on the left is the result of the rolls not tracking evenly (Lane Community College).

Figure 51. A knurling tool that cuts a knurl rather than forming it by pressure.

Figure 52. A knurl being cut showing formation of chip (Lane Community College).

Metal flaking off the knurled surface is evidence that work hardening has occurred. Avoid knurling too deeply as it produces an inferior knurled finish.

Knurls are also produced with a type of cutting tool (Figure 51) similar in appearance to a knurling tool. The serrated rolls form a chip on this edge (Figure 52). Material difficult to knurl by pressure rolling, such as tubing and work hardening metals, can be knurled by this cutting tool. Sulfurized cutting oil should be used when knurling steel with this kind of knurling tool.

SELF-TEST

1. Why are drilled holes not used for bores in machine parts such as pulleys, gears, and bearing fits?
2. Describe the procedure used to produce drilled holes on workpieces in the lathe with minimum oversize and runout.
3. What is the chief advantage of boring over reaming in the lathe?
4. List five ways to eliminate chatter in a boring bar.
5. Explain the differences between through boring, counterboring, and boring blind holes.
6. By what means are grooves and thread relief made in a bore?
7. Reamers will follow an eccentric drilled hole, thus producing a bell-mouth bore with runout. What device can be used to help eliminate bell-mouth? Does it help remove the runout?
8. Machine reamers produce a better finish than is obtained by boring. How can you get an even better finish with a reamer?
9. Cutting speeds for reaming are (twice, half) that used for drilling; feeds used for reaming are (twice, half) that used for drilling.
10. Are large internal threads produced with a tap or a boring tool? Explain the reason for your answer.
11. How can you avoid drilling oversize with a tap drill?
12. Standard plug or bottoming taps can be used when hand tapping in the lathe. If power is used, what kind of tap works best?
13. Why would threads cut with a hand die in a lathe not be acceptable for using on a feed screw with a micrometer collar?
14. By what means are thread relief on external grooves produced?
15. If cutting oil is not used on parting tools or chips do not clear out of the groove because of a heavy feed, what is generally the immediate result?
16. How can you avoid chatter when cutting off stock with a parting tool?
17. State three reasons for knurling.
18. Ordinary knurls do not cut. In what way do they make the diamond or straight pattern on the workpiece?
19. If a knurl is producing a double impression, what can you do to make it develop a diamond pattern?
20. How can you avoid producing a knurled surface on which the metal is flaking off?

UNIT 10 SIXTY DEGREE THREAD INFORMATION AND CALCULATIONS

$P = \dfrac{1}{}$ $d = \dfrac{.613}{}$

To cut threads, a good machinist must know more than how to set up the lathe. He or she must know the thread form, class of fit, and thread calculation. This unit prepares you for the actual cutting of threads, which you will do in the next unit.

OBJECTIVES

After completing this unit, you should be able to:
1. Describe the several 60 degree thread forms, noting their similarities and differences.
2. Calculate thread depth, infeeds, and minor diameters of threads.

THE SHARP VEE THREAD FORM

Various screw thread forms are used for fastening and for moving or transmitting parts against loads. The most widely used of these forms are the 60 degree thread types. These are mostly used for fasteners. An early form of the 60 degree thread is the sharp V (Figure 1). The sides of the thread form a 60 degree angle with each other. Theoretically, the sides and the base between two thread roots would form an equilateral triangle, but in practice this is not the case; it is necessary to make a slight flat on top of the thread in order to deburr it. Also, the tool will always round off and leave a slight flat at the thread root. The greatest drawback to this thread form is that it is so easily damaged while handling. The sharp V thread will fit closer and seal better than most threads, but is seldom used today. The depth (*d*) for the sharp V thread is calculated as follows:

$$d = \text{pitch} \times \cos 30 = .866 \text{ pitch}$$
$$= \frac{.866}{\text{number of threads per inch}}$$

The relationship between pitch and threads per inch should be noted (Figure 2). Pitch is the distance between a point on one screw thread and the corresponding point on the next thread, measured parallel to the thread axis. Threads per inch means the number of threads in one inch. The pitch (P) may be derived by dividing the number of threads per inch (TPI) into one:

$$P = \frac{1}{\text{TPI}}$$

EXAMPLE
Find the pitch of a $\frac{1}{2}$ in. diameter-20 TPI machine screw thread.

$$P = \frac{1}{20} = .050 \text{ in.}$$

Pitch is checked on a screw thread with a screw pitch gage (Figures 3*a* and 3*b*). General dimensions and symbols for screw threads are shown in Figure 4.

UNIFIED AND AMERICAN NATIONAL FORMS

The American National form (Figure 5), formerly United States Standard, was used for many years for screws,

bolts, and other products. These National form threads are in either the national fine (NF) or the national coarse (NC) series. Other screw threads are listed in machinist's handbooks.

Taps and dies are marked with letter symbols to designate the series of the threads they form. For example, the symbol for American Standard Taper pipe thread is NPT, for Unified coarse thread it is UNC, and for Unified fine thread the symbol is UNF.

Thread Depth

The American Standard for Unified threads (Figure 6) is very similar to the American National Standard with certain modifications. The thread forms are practically the same and the basic 60 degree angle is the same. The

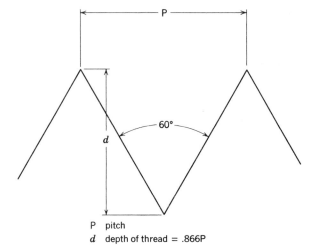

P pitch
d depth of thread = .866P

Figure 1. The 60 degree sharp V thread.

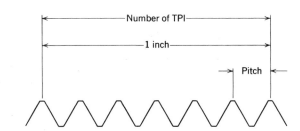

Figure 2. The difference between threads per inch and pitch.

Figure 3a. Screw pitch gage for inch threads.

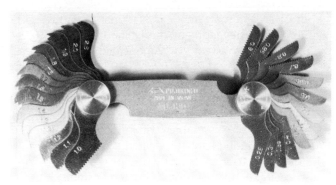

Figure 3b. Screw pitch gage for metric threads.

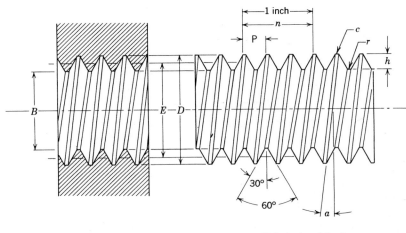

D Major Diameter
E Pitch Diameter
B Minor Diameter
n Number of threads per inch (TPI)
P Pitch

a Helix (or Lead) Angle
c Crest of Thread
r Root of Thread
h Basic Thread Height (or depth)

Figure 4. General dimensions of screw threads.

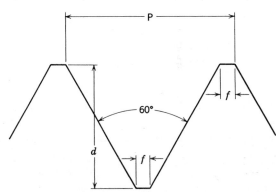

P pitch
d depth of thread = .6495P
f flat at crest and root of thread = $\frac{P}{8}$

Figure 5. The American National form of thread.

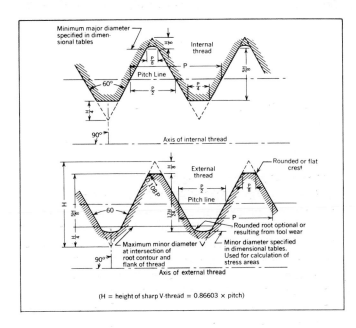

(H = height of sharp V-thread = 0.86603 × pitch)

Unified Thread Form Data

$$\text{Pitch} = \frac{1}{\text{Number of threads per inch}}$$

Depth (external thread)	= 0.613 × pitch
Depth (internal thread)	= 0.541 × pitch
Flat at crest (external thread)	= 0.125 × pitch
Flat at crest (internal thread)	= 0.25 × pitch
Flat at root [internal thread (tool flat)]	= 0.125 × pitch
Flat at root [external thread (tool flat)]	= 0.125 × pitch

Figure 6. Unified screw threads (Illustration: Reprinted from ASA B1.1 − 1960, Unified Screw Threads, with permission of the publisher, The American Society of Mechanical Engineers. Data from: John E. Neely, *Practical Machine Shop,* John Wiley & Sons, Inc., New York).

depth of an external American National thread is .6495 × pitch, and the depth of the Unified thread is .6134 × pitch. The constant for American National thread depth may be rounded off from .6495 to .65, and the constant for Unified thread depth may be rounded to .613. The thread depth and the root truncation (tool flat) of the American National thread is fixed or definite, but these factors are variable within limits for Unified threads. A rounded root for Unified threads is desirable whether from tool wear or by design. A rounded crest is also desirable but not required. The constants .613 for thread depth and .125 for the flat on the end of the tool were selected for calculations on Unified threads in this unit.

Thread Fit Classes and Thread Designations

Unified and American National Standard form threads are interchangeable. An NC bolt will fit an UNC nut. The principal difference between the two systems is that of tolerances. The Unified system, a modified version of the old system, allows for more tolerances of fit. Thread fit classes 1, 2, 3, 4, and 5 were used with the American National Standard; one being a very loose fit, two a free fit, three a close fit, four a snug fit, and five a jam or interference fit. The Unified system expanded this number system to include a letter, so the threads could be identified as class 1A, 1B, 2A, 2B, and so on. ''A'' indicates an external thread and ''B'' an internal thread. Because of this expansion in the Unified system, tolerances are now possible on external threads and are 30 percent greater on internal threads. These changes make easier the manufacturer's job of controlling tolerances to insure the interchangeability of threaded parts. See the *Machinery's Handbook* for tables of Unified thread limits. Limits are the maximum and minimum allowable dimensions of a part, in this case, internal and external threads.

Threads are designated by the nominal bolt size or major diameter, the threads per inch, the letter series, the thread tolerance, and the thread direction. Thus, $1\frac{1}{4}$ in.–12 UNF-2BLH would indicate a $1\frac{1}{4}$ in. Unified nut with 12 threads per inch, a class 2 thread fit, and a left-hand helix.

Unified screw thread systems are the American Standard for fastening types of screw threads. Manufacturing processes where V threads are produced are based on the Unified system. Many job and maintenance machine shops, on the other hand, still use the American National thread system when chasing a thread with a single point tool on an engine lathe.

Tool Flats and Infeeds for Thread Cutting

The flat on the crest of the thread on both the Unified and American National systems is P/8 or P × .125. The root flat (flat on the end of the external threading tool) is calculated P/8 or P × .125 for the American National system, but it varies in the Unified system. However, for purposes of convenience in cutting threads on a lathe, the same tool flat (P/8) may also be used for the Unified form thread.

To cut 60 degree form threads, the tool is fed into the work with the compound (Figure 7), which is set at 30 degrees. However, in practice, the compound is actually set to 29 degrees to provide a light finishing cut on the trailing side of the threading tool. The one degree difference will make no significant difference in calculations. The infeed depth along the flank of the thread at 30 degrees is greater than the depth at 90 degrees from the work axis. This depth may be calculated for American National threads by dividing the number of threads per inch (n) into .75,

$$\text{Infeed} = \frac{.75}{n} \quad \text{or} \quad P \times .75$$

Thus, for a thread with 10 threads per inch (.100 inch pitch):

$$\text{Infeed} = \frac{.75}{10} = .075 \text{ in.}$$

or

$$\text{Infeed} = .75 \times .100 = .075 \text{ in.}$$

For external Unified threads the infeed at 29 degrees may be calculated by the formula:

$$\text{Infeed} = \frac{.708}{n} \quad \text{or} \quad .708P$$

Thus, for a thread with 10 threads per inch (.100 in. pitch):

$$\text{Infeed} = \frac{.708}{10} = .0708 \text{ in.}$$

or

$$\text{Infeed} = .708 \times .100 = .0708 \text{ in.}$$

PITCH DIAMETER, HELIX ANGLE, AND PERCENT OF THREADS

The making of external and internal threads that are interchangeable depends upon the selection of thread fit classes. The clearances and tolerances for thread fits are derived from the pitch diameter. The pitch diameter on a straight thread is the diameter of an imaginary cylinder that passes through the thread profiles at a point where the width of the groove and thread are equal. The mating surfaces are the flanks of the thread.

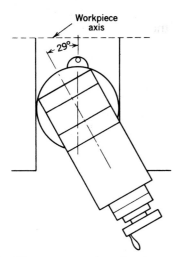

Figure 7. The compound at 29 degrees for cutting 60 degree threads.

Figure 9. Checking the relief and helix angle on the threading tool with a protractor (Lane Community College).

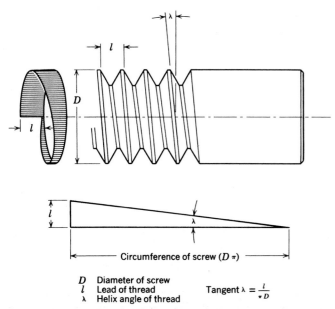

Figure 8. Screw thread helix angle. D = diameter of screw; l = lead of thread, and λ = helix angle of thread. Tangent $\lambda = \dfrac{l}{\pi D}$

D Diameter of screw
l Lead of thread
λ Helix angle of thread

Tangent $\lambda = \dfrac{l}{\pi D}$

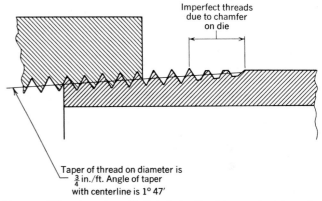

Figure 10. American National standard taper pipe thread.

The percent of thread has little to do with fit, but refers to the actual minor diameter of the internal thread. The typical nut for machine screws has 75 percent threads, which are easier to tap than 100 percent threads and retain sufficient strength for most thread applications.

The helix angle of a screw thread (Figure 8) is larger for greater lead threads than for smaller leads; and the larger the diameter of the workpiece, the smaller the helix angle for the same lead. Helix angles should be taken into account when grinding tools for threading.

The relief and helix angles must be ground on the leading or cutting edge of the tool (Figure 9). A protractor may be used to check this angle.

Helix angles may be determined by the following formula:

$$\text{Tangent of helix angle} = \frac{\text{lead of thread}}{\text{circumference of screw}}$$

$$= \frac{\text{lead of thread}}{\pi D}$$

where π = 3.1416, D = the major diameter of the screw. (Also note that pitch and lead are the same for single lead screws.) Helix angles are given for Unified and other thread series in handbooks such as the *Machinery's Handbook*.

A taper thread is made on the internal or external surface of a cone. An example of a 60 degree taper thread is the American National Standard pipe thread (Figure 10). A line bisecting the 60 degree thread is per-

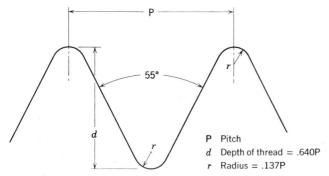

Figure 11. Whitworth thread. P = pitch; d = depth of thread, .640P; r = radius, .137P.

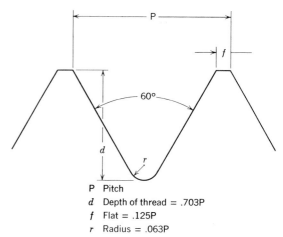

Figure 12. The SI metric thread form. P = pitch; d = depth of thread, .703P; f = flat; .125P; r = radius, .063P.

pendicular to the axis of the workpiece. On a taper thread the pitch diameter at a given position on the thread axis is the diameter of the pitch cone at that position.

The British Standard Whitworth thread (Figure 11) has rounded crests and roots and has an included angle of 55 degrees. This thread form has been largely replaced by the Unified and metric thread forms.

METRIC THREAD FORMS

Several metric thread systems such as the SAE standard spark plug threads and the British Standard for spark plugs are in use today. The Système Internationale (SI) thread form (Figure 12), adopted in 1898, is similar to the American National Standard. Metric bolt sizes differ slightly from one European country to the next. The British Standard for ISO (International Organization for Standardization) metric screw threads was set up to standardize metric thread forms. The basic form of the ISO metric thread (Figure 13) is similar to the Unified thread form. These and other metric thread systems are listed in the *Machinery's Handbook*. See Table 1 for ISO metric tap drill sizes.

A new metric standard was endorsed by the Industrial Fasteners Institute (IFI) January 31, 1974. It is called the IFI-500 Trial Standard. For further information on the new thread system, refer to *Machinery's Handbook*.

BASIC DESIGNATIONS

ISO Metric Threads are designated by the letter "M" followed by the *nominal size* in millimeters, and the *pitch* in millimeters, separated by the sign "X."

Example: M16 X 1.5

Above designation format is followed for all thread series except *coarse* pitch series as explained below.

Coarse Pitch ISO Metric Threads are designated by only the letter "M" and the *nominal size* in millimeters.

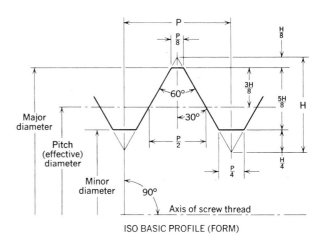

ISO BASIC PROFILE (FORM)

Figure 13. ISO metric thread form (TRW, Inc.).

Example: M16

This is a 16 millimeter diameter, 2 millimeter pitch ISO metric thread. Although the ISO standards use the above designations for coarse pitch, USA practice has been to include the pitch symbol even for the coarse pitch series. The inclusion of the pitch symbol should not create any problems, and will serve to avoid confusion.

TOLERANCE SYMBOLS

3   4   5 $\boxed{6}$
         7   8   9

Numbers are used to define the amount of product tolerance permitted on either internal or external threads. Smaller grade numbers carry smaller tolerances, that is, grade 4 tolerances are smaller than grade 6 tolerances, and grade 8 tolerances are larger than grade 6 tolerances.

Table 1
Metric Tap Drill Sizes

	Recommended Metric Drill				Closest Recommended Inch Drill			
Metric Tap Size	Drill Size (mm)	Inch Equivalent	Probable Hole Size (in.)	Probable Percent of Thread	Drill Size	Inch Equivalent	Probable Hole Size (in.)	Probable Percent of Thread
M1.6 × .35	1.25	.0492	.0507	69	—	—	—	—
M1.8 × .35	1.45	.0571	.0586	69	—	—	—	—
M2 × .4	1.60	.0630	.0647	69	#52	.0635	.0652	66
M2.2 × .45	1.75	.0689	.0706	70	—	—	—	—
M2.5 × .45	2.05	.0807	.0826	69	#46	.0810	.0829	67
M3 × .5	2.50	.0984	.1007	68	#40	.0980	.1003	70
M3.5 × .6	2.90	.1142	.1168	68	#33	.1130	.1156	72
M4 × .7	3.30	.1299	.1328	69	#30	.1285	.1314	73
M4.5 × .75	3.70	.1457	.1489	74	#26	.1470	.1502	70
M5 × .8	4.20	.1654	.1686	69	#19	.1660	.1692	68
M6 × 1	5.00	.1968	.2006	70	#9	.1960	.1998	71
M7 × 1	6.00	.2362	.2400	70	15/64	.2344	.2382	73
M8 × 1.25	6.70	.2638	.2679	74	17/64	.2656	.2697	71
M8 × 1	7.00	.2756	.2797	69	J	.2770	.2811	66
M10 × 1.5	8.50	.3346	.3390	71	Q	.3320	.3364	75
M10 × 1.25	8.70	.3425	.3471	73	11/32	.3438	.3483	71
M12 × 1.75	10.20	.4016	.4063	74	Y	.4040	.4087	71
M12 × 1.25	10.80	.4252	.4299	67	27/64	.4219	.4266	72
M14 × 2	12.00	.4724	.4772	72	15/32	.4688	.4736	76
M14 × 1.5	12.50	.4921	.4969	71	—	—	—	—
M16 × 2	14.00	.5512	.5561	72	35/64	.5469	.5518	76
M16 × 1.5	14.50	.5709	.5758	71	—	—	—	—
M18 × 2.5	15.50	.6102	.6152	73	39/64	.6094	.6144	74
M18 × 1.5	16.50	.6496	.6546	70	—	—	—	—
M20 × 2.5	17.50	.6890	.6942	73	11/16	.6875	.6925	74

Table 1 (Continued)
Metric Tap Drill Sizes

Metric Tap Size	Recommended Metric Drill				Closest Recommended Inch Drill			
	Drill Size (mm)	Inch Equivalent	Probable Hole Size (in.)	Probable Percent of Thread	Drill Size	Inch Equivalent	Probable Hole Size (in.)	Probable Percent of Thread
M20 × 1.5	18.50	.7283	.7335	70	—	—	—	—
M22 × 2.5	19.50	.7677	.7729	73	49/64	.7656	.7708	75
M22 × 1.5	20.50	.8071	.8123	70	—	—	—	—
M24 × 3	21.00	.8268	.8327	73	53/64	.8281	.8340	72
M24 × 2	22.00	.8661	.8720	71	—	—	—	—
M27 × 3	24.00	.9449	.9511	73	15/16	.9375	.9435	78
M27 × 2	25.00	.9843	.9913	70	63/64	.9844	.9914	70
M30 × 3.5	26.50	1.0433						
M30 × 2	28.00	1.1024						
M33 × 3.5	29.50	1.1614			Reaming Recommended to the Drill Size Shown			
M33 × 2	31.00	1.2205						
M36 × 4	32.00	1.2598						
M36 × 3	33.00	1.2992						
M39 × 4	35.00	1.3780						
M39 × 3	36.00	1.4173						

Formula for Metric Tap Drill Size:

$$\text{Basic major diameter} - \frac{\% \text{ Thread} \times \text{Pitch (mm)}}{76.980} = \text{Drilled Hole Size (mm)}$$

Formula for Percent of Thread:

$$\frac{76.980}{\text{Pitch (mm)}} \times \left[\begin{array}{c} \text{Basic Major Diameter -Drilled Hole Size} \\ \text{(mm)} \qquad \text{(mm)} \end{array} \right] = \text{Percent of Thread}$$

Source. Material courtesy of TRW, Inc., *New Greenfield Geometric ISO Metric Screw Thread Manual*, 1973.

e   H   G   g

Letters are used to designate the "position" of the product thread tolerances relative to basic diameters. Lower case letters are used for external threads, and capital letters for internal threads.

In some cases the "position" of the tolerance establishes an allowance (a definite clearance) between external and internal threads.

By combining the tolerance amount number and the tolerance position letter, the *tolerance symbol* is established that identifies the actual maximum and minimum product limits for external or internal threads. Generally the first number and letter refer to the pitch diameter symbol. The second number and letter refer to the crest diameter symbol (minor diameter of internal threads or major diameter of external threads.)

Example:

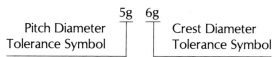

Pitch Diameter
Tolerance Symbol

5g   6g

Crest Diameter
Tolerance Symbol

Where the pitch diameter and crest diameter tolerance symbols are the same, the symbol need only be given once.

Example:

6g

Pitch Diameter and Crest
Diameter Tolerance Symbol

It is recommended that the *coarse* series be selected whenever possible, and that *general purpose grade* 6 be used for both internal and external threads. *Tolerance positions* ''g'' for external threads and ''H'' for internal threads are preferred.

Other product information may also be conveyed by the ISO metric thread designations. Complete specifications and product limits may be found in the ISO Recommendations or in the B1 report ''ISO Metric Screw Threads.''

Some examples of ISO Metric Thread designations are as follows (material courtesy of TRW Inc. New Greenfield Geometric Screw ISO Metrec Thread Manual, 1973):

M10
M18 × 1.5
M6 − 6H
M4 − 6g
M12 × 1.25 − 6H
M20 × 2 − 6H/6g
M6 × 0.75 − 7g 6g

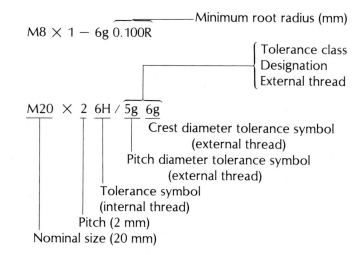

M8 × 1 − 6g 0.100R

Minimum root radius (mm)

Tolerance class
Designation
External thread

M20 × 2 6H / 5g 6g

Crest diameter tolerance symbol
(external thread)

Pitch diameter tolerance symbol
(external thread)

Tolerance symbol
(internal thread)

Pitch (2 mm)

Nominal size (20 mm)

SELF-TEST

1. Name one disadvantage of the sharp V thread.
2. Explain the difference between the threads per inch and the pitch of the thread.
3. Name two similarities and two differences between American National and Unified threads.
4. What is a major reason for thread allowances and classes of fits?
5. What does $\frac{1}{2}$-20 UNC − 2A describe?
6. The root truncation for unified threads and for American National threads is found by .125P. What should the flat on the end of the threading tools be for both systems on a $\frac{1}{2}$-20 thread?
7. How far should the compound set at 30 degrees move to cut a $\frac{1}{2}$-20 Unified thread? The formula is .708/n. How far should the compound move to cut a $\frac{1}{2}$-20 American National thread? The formula is .75/n.
8. Explain the difference between the fit of threads and the percent of thread.
9. Name two metric thread standard systems.
10. In metric tolerance symbols, which is a closer or smaller tolerance, a grade 3 or a grade 6?

UNIT 11 CUTTING UNIFIED EXTERNAL THREADS

A machinist is frequently called upon to cut threads of various forms on the engine lathe. The threads most commonly made are the V form, American National, or Unified. This unit will show you how to make these threads on a lathe. You will need much practice to gain confidence in your ability to make external Unified threads on any workpiece.

OBJECTIVES

After completing this unit, you should be able to:
1. Detail the steps and procedures necessary to cut a Unified thread to the correct depth.
2. Set up a lathe for threading and cut several different thread pitches and diameters.
3. Identify tools and procedures for thread measurement.

HOW THREADING IS DONE ON A LATHE

Thread cutting on a lathe with a single point tool is done by taking a series of cuts in the same helix of the thread. This is sometimes called chasing a thread. A direct ratio exists between the headstock spindle rotation, the leadscrew rotation, and the number of threads on the leadscrew. This ratio can be altered by the quick-change gearbox to make a variety of threads. When the halfnuts are clamped on the thread of the leadscrew, the carriage will move a given distance for each revolution of the spindle. This distance is the lead of the thread.

If the infeed of a thread is made with the cross slide (Figure 1), equal size chips will be formed on both cutting edges of the tool. This causes higher tool pressures that can result in tool breakdown, and sometimes causes tearing of the threads because of insufficient chip clearance. A more accepted practice is to feed in with the compound, which is set at 29 degrees (Figure 2) toward the right of the operator, for cutting right-hand threads. This assures a cleaner cutting action than with 30 degrees with most of the chip taken from the leading edge and a scraping cut from the following edge of the tool.

SETTING UP FOR THREADING

Begin setup by obtaining or grinding a tool for cutting Unified threads of the required thread pitch. The only difference in tools for various pitches is the flat on the end of the tool. For Unified threads this is .125P, as discussed in the last unit. If the toolholder you are using has no back rake, no grinding on the top of the tool is necessary. If the toolholder does have back rake, the tool must be ground to provide zero rake (Figure 3).

A center gage (Figure 4) or an optical comparator may be used to check the tool angle. An adequate allowance for the helix angle on the leading edge will assure sufficient side relief.

The part to be threaded is set up between centers, in a chuck, or in a collet (Figures 5a to 5c). An undercut of .005 in. less than the minor diameter should be made at the end of the thread. Its width should be sufficient to clear the tool.

The tool is clamped in the holder and set on the centerline of the workpiece (Figures 6a to 6c). A center gage is used to align the tool to the workpiece (Figure 7). The toolholder is clamped tightly after the tool is properly aligned.

Figure 1. An equal chip is formed on each side of the threading tool when the infeed is made with the cross slide (Lane Community College).

Figure 2. A chip is formed on the leading edge of the tool when the infeed is made with the compound set at 29 degrees to the right of the operator to make right-hand threads (Lane Community College).

Setting Dials on the Compound and Cross Feed

The point of the tool is brought into contact with the work by moving the cross feed handle, and the micrometer collar is set on the zero mark (Figure 8). The compound micrometer collar should also be set on zero (Figure 9), but first be sure all slack or backlash is removed by turning the compound feed handle clockwise.

Setting Apron Controls

On some lathes a feed change lever, which selects either

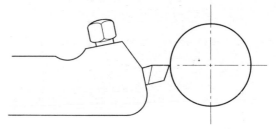

Figure 3. The tool must have zero rake and be set on the center of the work in order to produce the correct form.

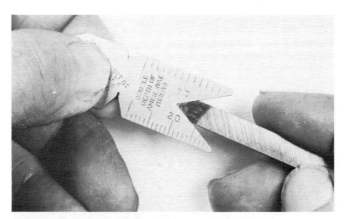

Figure 4. Checking the tool angle with a center gage.

cross or longitudinal feeds, must be moved to a neutral position for threading. This action locks out the feed mechanism so that no mechanical interference is possible. All lathes have some interlock mechanism to prevent interference when the half-nut lever is used. The half-nut lever causes two halves of a nut to clamp over the leadscrew. The carriage will move the distance of the lead of the thread on the leadscrew for each revolution of the leadscrew.

Threading dials operate off the leadscrew and continue to turn when the leadscrew is rotating and the carriage is not moving. When the half-nut lever is engaged, the threading dial stops turning and the carriage moves. The marks on the dial indicate when it is safe to engage the half-nut lever. If the half-nuts are engaged at the wrong place, the threading tool will not track in the same groove as before but may cut into the center of the thread and ruin it. With any even number of threads such as 4, 6, 12, and 20, the half-nut may be engaged at *any line*. Odd numbered threads such as 5, 7, 13 may be engaged at any *numbered line*. With fractional threads it is safest to engage the half-nut at the same line every time.

The Quick-Change Gearbox

The settings for the gear shift levers on the quick-change

Figure 5a. Lathe is set up for a threading project by inserting collet in collet sleeve (DeAnza College).

Figure 5b. A stub mandrel is inserted in the collet and the collet is tightened (DeAnza College).

Figure 5c. The sleeve to be threaded externally is mounted on the stub mandrel (DeAnza College).

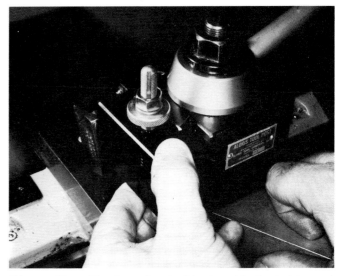

Figure 6a. The threading tool is placed in the holder and lightly clamped (DeAnza College).

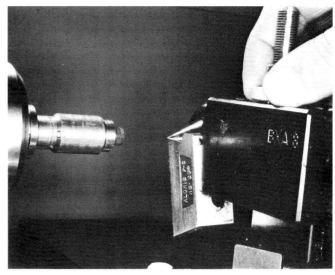

Figure 6b. The tool is adjusted to the dead center for height. A tool that is set too high or too low will not produce a true 60 degree angle in the cut thread (DeAnza College).

gearbox are selected according to the threads per inch desired (Figure 10). If the lathe has an interchangeable stud gear, be sure the correct one is in place.

Spindle Speeds

Spindle speeds for thread cutting are approximately one-fourth turning speeds. The speed should be slow enough so you will have complete control of the thread cutting operation.

Figure 6c. An alternate method of adjusting the tool for height is to use the steel rule. It will be in a vertical position when the tool is on center (DeAnza College).

Figure 8. After the tool is brought into contact with the work, the cross feed micrometer collar is set to the zero index (DeAnza College).

Figure 7. The tool is properly aligned by using a center gage. The toolholder is adjusted until the tool is aligned. The toolholder is then tightened (DeAnza College).

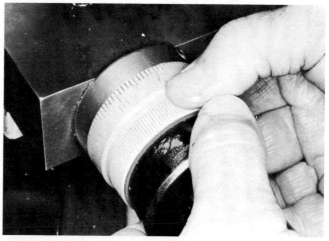

Figure 9. The operator will then set the compound micrometer collar to the zero index (DeAnza College).

Figure 10. The threads per inch selection is made on the quick-change gearbox (DeAnza College).

CUTTING THE THREAD

The following is the procedure for cutting right-hand threads:

1. Move the tool off the work and turn the cross feed micrometer dial back to zero.
2. Feed it in .002 in. on the compound dial.
3. Turn on the lathe and engage the half-nut lever (Figure 11).
4. Take a scratch cut without using cutting oil (Figure 12). Stop the lathe at the end of the cut and back out the tool using the cross feed. Disengage the half-nut. Return the carriage to the starting position.
5. Check the thread pitch with a screw pitch gage or a rule (Figure 13). If the pitch is wrong, it can still be corrected.
6. Apply sulfurized cutting fluid to the work (Figure 14).
7. Feed the compound in .005 in. and reset the cross feed dial to zero. Make the second cut (Figure 15).
8. Continue this process until the tool is within .010 in. of the finish depth (Figure 16).
9. Brush the threads to remove the chips. Check the

Figure 13. The pitch of the thread is being checked with a screw pitch gage (DeAnza College).

Figure 11. The half-nut lever is engaged at the correct line or numbered line depending upon whether the thread is odd, even, or a fractional numbered thread (DeAnza College).

Figure 12. A light scratch cut is taken for the purpose of checking the pitch (DeAnza College).

Figure 14.   Cutting fluid is applied before taking the first cut (DeAnza College).

Figure 15.   The second cut is taken after feeding in the compound .005 in. (DeAnza College).

Figure 16.   The finish cut is taken with infeed of .001 to .002 in. (DeAnza College).

Left-Hand Threads

The procedure for cutting left-hand threads (Figure 18a) is the same as that used for cutting right-hand threads with two exceptions. The compound is set at 29 degrees to the left of the operator (Figure 18b) and the lead-screw rotation is reversed so the cut is made from the left to the right. The feed reverse lever is moved to reverse the leadscrew. Sufficient undercut must be made for a starting place for the tool. Also, sufficient relief must be provided on the *right* side of the tool.

Methods of Terminating Threads

Undercuts are often used for terminating threads. They should be made the single depth of the thread plus .005 in. The undercut should have a radius to lessen the possibility of fatigue failure resulting from stress concentration in the sharp corners.

Machinists sometimes simply remove the tool quickly at the end of the thread while disengaging the half-nuts. If a machinist misjudges and waits too long, the point of the threading tool will be broken off. A dial indicator is sometimes used to locate the exact position for removing the tool. When this tool withdrawal method is used, an undercut is not necessary.

thread fit with a ring gage (Figure 17a), standard nut or mating part (Figure 17b), or comparison thread micrometer (Figure 17c). The work may be removed from between centers and returned without disturbing the threading setup, provided that the tail of the dog is returned to the same slot.

10. Continue to take cuts of .001 or .002 in. (as shown in Figure 16) and check the fit between each cut. Thread the nut with your fingers; it should go on easily but without end play. A class 2 fit is desirable for most purposes.

11. Chamfer the end of the thread to protect it from damage.

Figure 17a. The thread is checked with a ring gage (DeAnza College).

Figure 17b. A standard nut is often used to check a thread (DeAnza College).

Figure 17c. A thread comparison micrometer may be used to check the threads against a known standard such as a precision thread plug gage (DeAnza College).

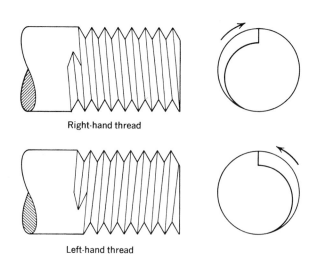

Right-hand thread

Left-hand thread

Figure 18a. The difference between right-hand and left-hand threads as seen from the side and end.

Angle of compound

29°

Infeed

Figure 18b. Compound set for cutting a left-hand thread (Lane Community College).

Figure 19. A threading tool that is used for threading to a shoulder (Lane Community College).

Figure 21a. Carbide threading insert for external threading. Inserts are made for many different thread forms and for boring bars (Courtesy of Kennametal Inc., Latrobe, Pa.).

Figure 21b. Threads being turned at high speed with carbide insert threading tool (Courtesy of Kennametal Inc., Latrobe, Pa.).

Figure 20. By placing the blade of the threading tool in the upper position, this tool can be made to thread on the bottom side. The lathe is reversed and the thread is cut from left to right making the job easier when threading next to a shoulder (Copyright 1975, Aloris Tool Company, Inc.).

Terminating threads close to a shoulder requires specially ground tools (Figure 19). Sometimes it is convenient to turn the tool upside down and reverse the lathe when cutting right-hand threads to a shoulder. Some commercial threading tools are made for this purpose (Figure 20).

Other Tool Types

Since the crest of the Unified thread form should be rounded, some commercial threading tools provide this and other advantages (Figures 21a and 21b). Another form of threading tool used in the lathe is shown in Figures 22a to 22c. This is a multiple point tool that will produce a full form of thread. The advantages are rapid threading, good finishes, and the ability to thread close to shoulders.

Picking Up a Thread

It sometimes becomes necessary to reset the tool when its position against the work has been changed during a threading operation. This position change may be caused by removing the threading tool for grinding, by the work slipping in the chuck or lathe dog, or by the tool moving from the pressure of the cut.

To reposition the tool the following steps may be taken:

1. Check the tool position with reference to the work by using a center gage. If necessary, realign the tool.
2. With the tool backed away from the threads, engage the half-nuts with the machine running. Turn off the machine with the half-nut still engaged and the tool located over the partially cut threads.
3. Position the tool in its original location in the threads by moving both the cross feed and compound handles (Figure 23).
4. Set the micrometer dial to zero on the cross feed collar and set the dial on the compound to the last setting used.
5. Back off the cross feed and disengage the half-nuts. Resume threading where you left off.

BASIC THREAD MEASUREMENT

The simplest method for checking a thread is to try the mating part for fit. The fit is determined solely by feel with no measurement involved. While a loose, medium, or close fit may be determined by this method, the

Figure 22a. Uni-chaser. A single tangent threading tool chaser that is a multiple point tool and will produce a bottom and top radius on the thread (Courtesy of Geometric Tool Division of TRW, Inc.).

Figure 22c. Thread being cut with the bottom side of the Uni-chaser (Courtesy of Geometric Tool Division of TRW, Inc.).

Figure 23. Repositioning the tool (DeAnza College).

Figure 22b. A right-hand thread being cut with a Uni-chaser (TRW, Inc.).

Figure 24. Thread plug gage (Courtesy of PMC Industries).

Figure 26. Thread roll snap gage (Courtesy of PMC Industries).

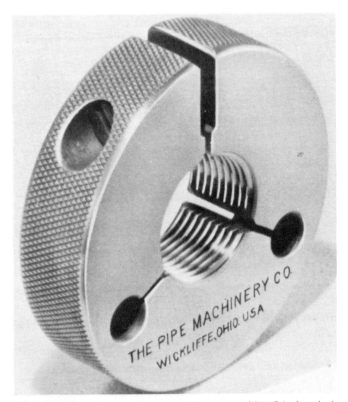

Figure 25. Thread ring gage (Courtesy of PMC Industries).

threads cannot be depended upon for interchangeability with others of the same size and pitch.

More precise methods of checking threads depend on the Go/No Go principle. The thread plug gage (Figure 24) is used for checking internal threads. These gages are available in various sizes, which are stamped on the handle. A *male* screw thread is on each end of the handle. The longer threaded end is called the ''Go'' gage, while the shorter end is called the ''No Go'' gage. The No Go end is made to a slightly larger dimension than the pitch diameter for the class of fit that the gage tests. To test an internal thread, both the Go and No Go gages should

be tried in the hole. If the part is within the range or tolerance of the gage, the Go end should turn in flush to the bottom of the internal thread, but the No Go end should just start into the hole and become snug with no more than three turns. The gage should never be forced into the hole.

Thread ring gages are used to check the accuracy of external threads (Figure 25). The outside of the ring gage is knurled and the No Go gage can be easily identified by a groove on the knurled surface. When these gages are used, the Go ring gage should enter the thread fully. The No Go gage should not exceed more than $1\frac{1}{2}$ turns on the thread being checked.

Thread roll snap gages are used to check the accuracy of external screw threads (Figure 26). These common measuring tools are easier and faster to use than thread micrometers or ring gages. The part size is compared to a preset dimension on the roll gage. The first set of rolls are the Go and the second the No Go rolls.

Thread roll snap gages, ring gages, and plug gages are used in production manufacturing where quick gaging methods are needed. These gaging methods depend on the operator's ''feel'' and the level of precision is only as good as the accuracy of the gage. The thread sizes are not measurable in any definite way.

The thread comparator micrometer (Figure 27) has two conical points. This micrometer does not measure the pitch diameter of a thread, but is used only to make a comparison with a known standard. The micrometer is first set to the threaded part and then it is compared to the reading obtained from a plug gage.

Figure 27. Thread comparator micrometer (DeAnza College).

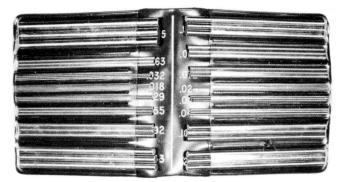

Figure 28. Set of "best" three-wires for various thread sizes.

ADVANCED METHODS OF THREAD MEASUREMENT

The most accurate place to measure a screw thread is on the flank or angular surface of the thread at the pitch diameter. The outside diameter measured at the crest or the minor diameter measured at the root could vary considerably. Threads may be measured with standard micrometers and specially designated wires (Figure 28) or with a screw thread micrometer. The pitch diameter is measured directly by these methods.

The Three-Wire Method

The three-wire method of measuring threads is considered one of the best and most accurate. Figure 29 shows three wires placed in the threads with the micrometer measuring over them. Different sizes and pitches of threads require different size wires. For greatest accuracy a wire size that will contact the thread at the pitch diameter should be used. This is called the "best" wire size.

The pitch diameter of a thread can be calculated by subtracting the wire constant (which is the single depth of a sharp V thread, or .866 × P) from the measurement over the three wires when the best wire size is used. The wires used for three-wire measurement of threads are hardened and lapped steel, and are available in sets that cover a large range of thread pitches.

A formula by which the best size wire may be found is as follows:

$$\text{Wire size} = \frac{.57735}{n}$$

where n = the number of threads per inch.

Figure 29. Measuring threads with the three-wire and micrometer method (Lane Community College).

EXAMPLE
To find the best size wire for measuring a $1\frac{1}{4}$ in. – 12 UNC screw thread:

$$\text{Wire size} = \frac{.57735}{12} = .048$$

The best wire size to use for measuring a 12 pitch thread would be .048 in.

If the best wire sizes are not available, smaller or larger wires may be used within limits. They should not be so small that they are below the major diameter of the thread, or so large that they do not contact the flank of the thread. Subtract the constant (.866 × P) for best wire size from the pitch diameter and add three times the diameter of the available wire when the best wire size is not available.

EXAMPLE
The best wire size for $1\frac{1}{4}$ – 12 is .048 in., but only $\frac{3}{64}$-in. diameter drill rod is available, which has a diameter of .0469 in.

1.1959   Pitch diameter of $1\frac{1}{4}$–12
−.0722   constant for best wire size
_____
1.1237
+.1407   3 × .0469 available wire size
_____   measurement over wires
= 1.2644

The measurement over the wires will be slightly different than that of the best wire size because of the difference in wire size.

After the best size wire is found, the wires are positioned in the thread grooves as shown in Figure 29. The anvil and spindle of a standard outside micrometer are then placed against the three wires and the measurement is taken.

To calculate what the reading of the micrometer should be if a thread is the correct finished size, use the following formula when measuring Unified coarse threads or American National threads.

$$M = D + 3W - \frac{1.5155}{n}$$

where

M = micrometer measurement over wires
D = diameter of the thread
n = number of threads per inch
W = diameter of wire used

EXAMPLE
To find M for a $1\frac{1}{4}$–12 UNC thread proceed as follows:

where

$$W = .048$$
$$D = 1.250$$
$$n = 12$$

then

$$M = 1.250 + (3 \times .048) - \frac{1.5155}{12}$$
$$= 1.250 + 1.44 - .126$$
$$M = 1.268 \text{ (micrometer measurement)}$$

When measuring a Unified fine thread, the same method and formula are used, except that the constant should be 1.732 instead of 1.5155.

The wire method of thread measurement is also used for other thread forms such as Acme and Buttress. Information and tables may be found in the *Machinery's Handbook*.

The screw thread micrometer (Figure 30) may be used to measure sharp V, Unified, and American National threads. The spindle is pointed to a 60 degree included angle. The anvil, which swivels, has a double-V shape to contact the pitch diameter. The thread microm-

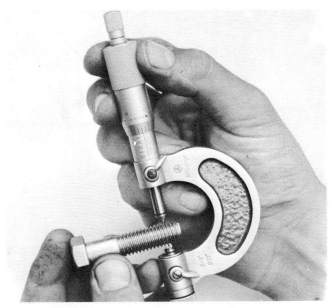

Figure 30. Screw thread micrometer (Yuba College).

eter measures the pitch diameter directly from the screw thread. This reading may be compared with pitch diameters given in handbook tables. Thread micrometers have interchangeable anvils that will fit a wide range of thread pitches. Some are made in sets of four micrometers that have a capacity up to one inch, and each covers a range of threads. The range of these micrometers depends on the manufacturer. Typical ranges are as follows:

No. 1   8 to 14 threads per inch
No. 2   14 to 20 threads per inch
No. 3   22 to 30 threads per inch
No. 4   32 to 40 threads per inch

The optical comparator is sometimes used to check thread form, helix angle, and depth of thread on external threads (Figure 31). The part is mounted in a screw thread accessory that is adjusted to the helix angle of the thread so that the light beam will show a true profile of the thread.

Since internal threads are most often made by tapping, the pitch diameter and fit are determined by the tap used. Internal threads cut with a single point tool, however, need to be checked. A precision Go/No Go plug gage is generally sufficient in this case. If no gage is available, a shop gage can be made by cutting the required external thread to very precise dimensions. If only one threaded part of a kind is to be made and no interchangeability is required, the mating part may be used as a gage.

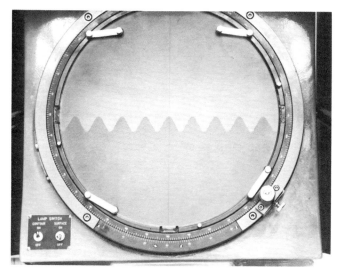

Figure 31. Profile of thread as shown on the screen of the optical comparator (Lane Community College).

SELF-TEST

1. By what method are threads cut or chased with a single point tool in a lathe? How can a given helix or lead be produced?
2. The better practice is to feed the tool in with the compound set at 29 degrees rather than with the cross slide when cutting threads. Why is this so?
3. By what means should a threading tool be checked for the 60 degree angle?
4. How can the number of threads per inch be checked?
5. How is the tool aligned with the work?
6. Is the carriage moved along the ways by means of gears when the half-nut lever is engaged? Explain.
7. Explain which positions on the threading dial are used for engaging the half-nuts for even, odd, and fractional numbered threads.
8. How fast should the spindle be turning for threading?
9. What is the procedure for cutting left-hand threads?
10. If for some reason it becomes necessary for you to temporarily remove the tool or the entire threading setup before a thread is completed, what procedure is needed when you are ready to finish the thread?

UNIT 12 CUTTING UNIFIED INTERNAL THREADS

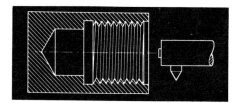

While small internal threads are tapped, larger sizes from one inch and up are often cut in a lathe. The problems and calculations involved with cutting internal threads differ in some ways from those of cutting external threads. This unit will help you understand these differences.

OBJECTIVE

After completing this unit, you should be able to:
Calculate the dimensions for a given internal Unified thread.

Many of the same rules used for external threading apply to internal threading: the tool must be shaped to the exact form of the thread, and the tool must be set on the center of the workpiece. When cutting an internal thread with a single point tool, the inside diameter of the workpiece should be the **minor diameter** of the internal thread (Figure 1). On the other hand, if the thread is made by tapping in the lathe, the inside diameter of the workpiece can be varied to obtain the desired percent of thread.

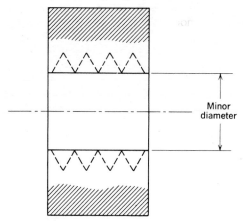

Figure 1. Diagram of internal thread showing minor diameter.

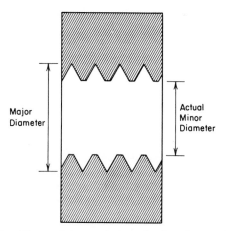

Figure 2. View of internal threads showing major and actual minor diameters.

TAPPING INTERNAL THREADS

Full depth or 100 percent threads are very difficult to tap in soft metals and impossible in tough materials. Tests have proven that above 60 percent of thread very little additional strength is gained. Lower percentages provide less flank surface for wear, however. Most commercial internal threads in steel are about 75 percent. Tap drill charts are generally based on 75 percent thread calculations for American National threads. The larger the tap drill, the lower the percent of thread. These figures are correct, however, only if the drilled hole is not oversize.

The probable percent of thread may be 5 to 10 percent lower than the calculated percent since drills usually make an oversize hole. In practice, a drill slightly under the tap drill size should first be used so the tap drill will make a more accurate hole. Reaming can be done for more precise tapping.

The major and minor diameters of the internal thread are shown in Figure 2. For tapped internal threads, the minor diameter is varied according to the percent of thread desired. The percent of thread for American National threads is calculated: the basic major diameter minus the **actual minor diameter**, divided by two times the basic thread height, expressed as a percentage. Thus,

Percent of thread

$$= \frac{\text{major } D - \text{actual minor } D}{2 \times \text{basic thread height}} \times 100$$

If you should need to select a tap drill size, or determine the bore size for tapping an internal thread, use this formula in a different form. Solving for the actual minor diameter, which should be the inside diameter of the hole, the formula becomes:

Actual minor D = major D − 2 × basic thread height × Percent of thread

EXAMPLE
Determine the bore size for tapping an 80 percent 1 in.-8 NC internal thread.

$$\text{Actual minor } D = 1 - \left(\frac{.65}{8} \times 2 \times .8 \right) = .870$$

or top drill size

A bolt or external thread is made with 100 percent threads, and the outside diameter is always close to its nominal size within tolerances. There is a clearance of a few thousandths of an inch between the flank of the internal thread or nut and the flank of the bolt, which is provided by making the major diameter of the internal thread .002 to .005 in. oversize.

SINGLE POINT TOOL THREADING

The advantages of making internal threads with a single point tool are that large threads of various forms can be made and that the threads are concentric to the axis of the work. The threads may not be concentric when they are tapped. There are some difficulties encountered when making internal threads. The tool is often hidden from view and tool spring must be taken into account.

The hole to be threaded is first drilled to $\frac{1}{16}$ in. diameter less than the minor diameter. Then a boring bar is set up, and the hole is bored to the minor diameter of the thread. If the thread is to go completely through the work, no recess is necessary, but if threading is done in a blind hole, a recess must be made. The compound rest should be swiveled 29 degrees to the left of the operator for cutting right-hand threads (Figures 3a and 3b). A threading tool is clamped in the bar and aligned by means of a center gage (Figure 4).

Figure 3a. For right-hand internal threads, the compound is swiveled to the left (Lane Community College).

Figure 3b. The compound rest is swiveled to the right for left-hand internal threads (Lane Community College).

The compound micrometer collar is moved to the zero index after the slack has been removed by turning the screw outwards or counterclockwise. The tool is brought to the work with the cross slide handle and its collar is set on zero. Threading may now proceed in the same manner as it is done with external threads. The compound is advanced outwards a few thousandths of an inch, a scratch cut is made, and the thread pitch is checked with a screw pitch gage.

The cross slide is backed out of the cut and reset to zero before the next pass. Cutting oil is used. The compound is advanced a few thousandths (.001 to .010 in.).

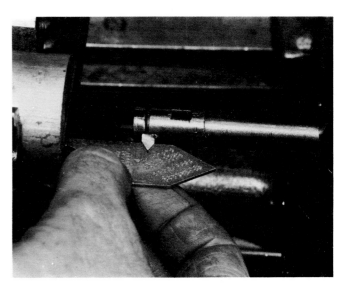

Figure 4. Aligning the threading tool with a center gage (Lane Community College).

The exact amount of infeed depends on how rigid the boring bar and holder are and how deep the cut has progressed. Too much infeed will cause the bar to spring away and produce a bell-mouth internal thread.

If a slender boring bar is necessary or there is more than usual overhang, lighter cuts must be used to avoid chatter. The bar may spring away from the cut causing the major diameter to be less than the calculated amount, or that amount fed in on the compound. If several passes are taken through the thread with the same setting on the compound, this problem can often be corrected.

The single depth of the Unified internal thread (Figure 5) equals P $\times$ .541. The minor diameter is found by subtracting the double depth of the thread from the major diameter.

Thus, if

$$D = \text{Major diameter}$$
$$d = \text{Minor diameter}$$
$$P = \text{Thread pitch}$$
$$P \times .541 = \text{Single depth}$$

the formula is

$$d = D - (P \times .541 \times 2)$$

EXAMPLE
A $1\frac{1}{2}$–6 UNC nut must be bored and threaded to fit a stud. Find the dimension of the bore.

$$P = \tfrac{1}{6} = .1666$$
$$d = 1.500 - (.1666 \times .541 \times 2)$$
$$d = 1.500 - .180$$
$$d = 1.320$$

Thus, the bore should be made 1.320 in.

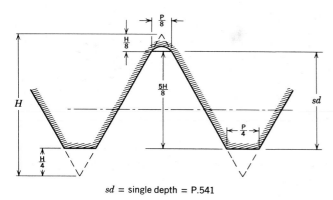

sd = single depth = P.541

Figure 5.   Single depth of the Unified internal thread.

The infeed on the compound is calculated in the same way as with external threads; for Unified internal threads, use the formula:

$$\text{Infeed} = P \times .625$$

for the depth of cut with the compound set at 29 degrees. Using the pitch from the previous example

$$\text{Infeed} = .1666 \times .625 = .104 \text{ in.}$$

The single depth of the American National thread equals $P \times .6495$ and the infeed on the compound set at 29 degrees is $P \times .75$. These figures may be substituted in the previous calculations to determine the single depth and infeed for a $1\frac{1}{2}$–6 NC internal thread.

Often it is necessary to realign an internal threading tool with the thread when the tool has been moved for sharpening or when the setup has moved during the cut. The tool is realigned in the same way as it is done for external threads: by engaging the half-nut and positioning the tool in a convenient place over the threads, then moving both the compound and cross slides to adjust the tool position.

SELF-TEST

1. When internal threads are made with a tool, what should the bore size be?
2. In what way is percent of thread obtained? Why is this done?
3. What percent of thread are tap drill charts usually based on?
4. Drills often make an oversize hole that lowers the percent of thread that a tap will cut. How can a more precise hole be drilled?
5. Your specifications call for a 60 percent thread in a tough stainless steel casting for a $\frac{1}{2}$–13 tapped thread. The tap drill size = Major $D - 2 \times$ basic thread height $\times$ percent of thread. What would your tap drill size be?
6. Name two advantages of making internal threads with a single point tool on the lathe.
7. When making internal right-hand threads, which direction should the compound be swiveled?
8. After a scratch cut is made, what would the most convenient method be to measure the pitch of the internal thread?
9. What does deflection or spring of the boring bar cause when cutting internal threads?
10. Using $P \times .541$ as a constant for Unified single depth internal threads, what would the minor diameter be for a 1–8 thread?

UNIT 13 TAPER TURNING, TAPER BORING, AND FORMING

Tapers are very useful machine elements that are used for many purposes. The machinist should be able to quickly calculate a specific taper and to set up a machine to produce it. The machinist should also be able to accurately measure tapers and determine proper fits. This unit will help you understand the various methods and principles involved in making a taper.

OBJECTIVE

After completing this unit, you should be able to:
Describe different types of tapers and the methods used to produce and measure them.

USES OF TAPERS

Tapers are used on machines because of their capacity to align and hold machine parts and to realign when they are repeatedly assembled and disassembled. This repeatability assures that tools such as centers in lathes, taper shank drills in drill presses, and arbors in milling machines will run in perfect alignment when placed in the machine. When a taper is slight, such as a Morse taper that is about $\frac{5}{8}$ in. taper/ft, it is called a self-holding taper since it is held in and driven by friction (Figure 1). A steep taper, such as a quick-release taper of $3\frac{1}{2}$ in./ft and used on most milling machines, must be held in place with a draw bolt (Figure 2).

A taper may be defined as a uniform increase in diameter on a workpiece for a given length measured parallel to the axis. Internal or external tapers are expressed in taper per foot (TPF), taper per inch (TPI), or in degrees. The TPF or TPI refers to the difference in diameters in the length of one foot or one inch, respectively (Figure 3). This difference is measured in inches. Angles of taper, on the other hand, may refer to the included angles or the angles with the centerline (Figure 4).

Some machine parts that are measured in taper per foot are mandrels (.006 in./ft), taper pins and reamers ($\frac{1}{4}$ in./ft), the Jarno taper series (.600 in./ft), the Brown and Sharpe taper series (approximately $\frac{1}{2}$ in./ft), and the Morse taper series (about $\frac{5}{8}$ in./ft). Morse tapers include eight sizes that range from size 0 to size 7. Tapers and dimensions vary slightly from size to size in both the Brown and Sharpe and the Morse series. For instance, a No. 2 Morse taper has .5944 in./ft taper and a No. 4 has .6233 in./ft taper. See Table 1 for more information on Morse tapers.

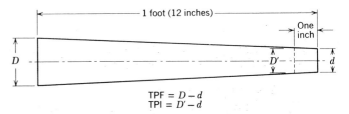

Figure 2. The milling machine taper is driven by lugs and held in by a draw bolt (Lane Community College).

$$TPF = D - d$$
$$TPI = D' - d$$

Figure 3. The difference between taper per foot (TPF) and taper per inch (TPI).

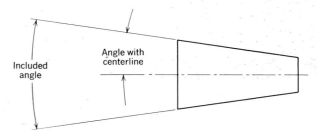

Figure 1. The Morse taper shank on this drill keeps the drill from turning when the hole is being drilled (Lane Community College).

Figure 4. Included angles and angles with centerline.

Table 1
Morse Tapers Information

Number of Taper	Taper per Foot	Taper per Inch	P Standard Plug Depth	D Diameter of Plug at Small End	A Diameter at End of Socket	H Depth of Hole
0	.6246	.0520	2	.252	.356	$2\frac{1}{32}$
1	.5986	.0499	$2\frac{1}{8}$	.396	.475	$2\frac{3}{16}$
2	.5994	.0500	$2\frac{9}{16}$	.572	.700	$2\frac{5}{8}$
3	.6023	.0502	$3\frac{3}{16}$	.778	.938	$3\frac{1}{4}$
4	.6232	.0519	$4\frac{1}{16}$	1.020	1.231	$4\frac{1}{8}$
5	.6315	.0526	$5\frac{3}{16}$	1.475	1.748	$5\frac{1}{4}$
6	.6256	.0521	$7\frac{1}{4}$	2.116	2.494	$7\frac{3}{8}$
7	.6240	.0520	10	2.750	3.270	$10\frac{1}{8}$

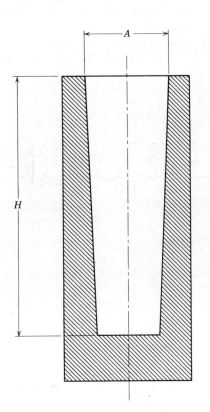

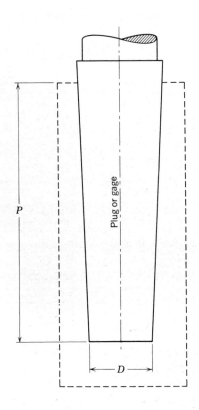

METHODS OF MAKING A TAPER

There are four methods of turning a taper on a lathe. They are the compound slide method, the offset tailstock method, the taper attachment method, and the use of a form tool. Each method has its advantages and disadvantages, so the kind of taper needed on a workpiece should be the deciding factor in the selection of the method that will be used.

The Compound Slide Method

Both internal and external short steep tapers can be turned on a lathe by hand feeding the compound slide (Figure 5). The swivel base of the compound is divided in degrees. When the compound slide is in line with the ways of the lathe, the 0 degree line will align with the index line on the cross slide (Figure 6). When the compound is swiveled off the index, which is parallel to the

Figure 5. Making a taper using the compound slide (Lane Community College).

Figure 6. Alignment of the compound parallel with the ways (Lane Community College).

Figure 7. An angle may be set off the axis of the lathe from this index (Lane Community College).

Figure 8. The compound set 14½ degrees off the axis of the cross slide (Lane Community College).

centerline of the lathe, a direct reading may be taken for the half angle or angle to centerline of the machined part (Figure 7). When a taper is machined on the lathe centerline, its included angle will be twice the angle that is set on the compound. Not all lathes are indexed in this manner.

When the compound slide is aligned with the axis of the cross slide and swiveled off the index in either direction, an angle is directly read off the cross slide centerline (Figure 8). Since the lathe centerline is 90 degrees from the cross slide centerline, the reading on the lathe centerline index is the complementary angle. So, if the compound is set off the axis of the cross slide 14½ degrees, the lathe centerline index reading is 90 − 14½ = 75½ degrees, as seen in Figure 8.

Tapers of any angle may be cut by this method, but the length is limited to the stroke of the compound slide.

Since tapers are often given in TPF, it is sometimes convenient to consult a TPF to angle conversion table, as in Table 2. A more complete table may be found in the *Machinery's Handbook*.

If a more precise conversion is desired, the following formula may be used to find the included angle: Divide the taper in inches per foot by 24; find the angle that corresponds to the quotient in a table of tangents and double this angle. If the angle with centerline is desired, do not double the angle.

EXAMPLE
What angle is equivalent to a taper of 3½ in./ft?

Table 2

Tapers and Corresponding Angles

Taper per Foot	Included Angle		Angle with Centerline		Taper per Inch
	Degrees	Minutes	Degrees	Minutes	
$-\frac{1}{8}$	0	36	0	18	.0104
$-\frac{3}{16}$	0	54	0	27	.0156
$-\frac{1}{4}$	1	12	0	36	.0208
$-\frac{5}{16}$	1	30	0	45	.0260
$-\frac{3}{8}$	1	47	0	53	.0313
$-\frac{7}{16}$	2	5	1	2	.0365
$-\frac{1}{2}$	2	23	1	11	.0417
$-\frac{9}{16}$	2	42	1	21	.0469
$-\frac{5}{8}$	3	00	1	30	.0521
$-\frac{11}{16}$	3	18	1	39	.0573
$-\frac{3}{4}$	3	35	1	48	.0625
$-\frac{13}{16}$	3	52	1	56	.0677
$-\frac{7}{8}$	4	12	2	6	.0729
$-\frac{15}{16}$	4	28	2	14	.0781
1	4	45	2	23	.0833
$-1\frac{1}{4}$	5	58	2	59	.1042
$-1\frac{1}{2}$	7	8	3	34	.1250
$-1\frac{3}{4}$	8	20	4	10	.1458
2	9	32	4	46	.1667
$-2\frac{1}{2}$	11	54	5	57	.2083
3	14	16	7	8	.2500
$-3\frac{1}{2}$	16	36	8	18	.2917
4	18	56	9	28	.3333
$-4\frac{1}{2}$	21	14	10	37	.3750
5	23	32	11	46	.4167
6	28	4	14	2	.5000

$$\frac{3.5}{24} = .14583$$

The angle of this tangent is 8 degrees 18 minutes, and the included angle is twice this, or 16 degrees 36 minutes.

THE OFFSET TAILSTOCK METHOD

Long, slight tapers may be produced on shafts and external parts *only* between centers. Internal tapers cannot be made by this method. Power feed is used so good finishes are obtainable. The taper per foot or taper per inch must be known so the amount of offset for the tailstock can be calculated. Since tapers are of different lengths, they would not be the same TPI or TPF for the same offset (Figure 9). When the taper per inch is known, the offset calculation is as follows: Where

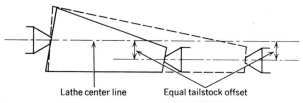

Figure 9. When tapers are of different lengths, the TPF is not the same with the same offset.

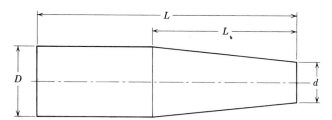

Figure 10. Long workpiece with a short taper.

$$TPI = \text{taper per inch}$$
$$L = \text{length of workpiece}$$
$$\text{Offset} = \frac{TPI \times L}{2}$$

When the taper per foot is known, use the following formula:

$$\text{Offset} = \frac{TPF \times L}{24}$$

If the workpiece has a short taper in any part of its length (Figure 10) and the TPI or TPF is not given use the following formula:

$$\text{Offset} = \frac{L \times (D - d)}{2 \times L_1}$$

where,

$$D = \text{diameter at large end of taper}$$
$$d = \text{diameter at small end of taper}$$
$$L = \text{total length of workpiece}$$
$$L_1 = \text{length of taper}$$

When you set up for turning a taper between centers, remember that the contact area between the center and the center hole is limited (Figure 11). Frequent lubrication of the centers may be necessary.

You should also note the path of the lathe dog bent tail in the drive slot (Figure 12). Check to see that there is adequate clearance.

To measure the offset on the tailstock, use either the centers and a rule (Figure 13) or the witness mark and a rule (Figure 14); both methods are adequate for some purposes. A more precise measurement is possible

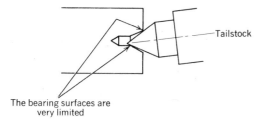

Figure 11. The contact area between the center hole and the center is small.

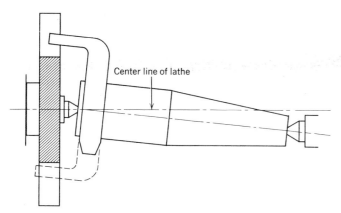

Figure 12. The bent tail of the lathe dog should have adequate clearance.

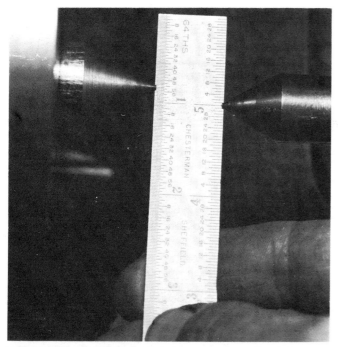

Figure 13. Measuring the offset on the tailstock by use of the centers and the rule (Lane Community College).

Figure 14. Measuring the offset with the witness mark and a rule (Lane Community College).

Figure 15. Using the dial indicator to measure the offset (Lane Community College).

with a dial indicator as shown in Figure 15. The indicator is set on the tailstock spindle while the centers are still aligned. A slight loading of the indicator is advised since the first 0.010 or 0.020 in. movement of the indicator may be inaccurate or the mechanism loose due to wear, causing fluctuating readings. The bezel is set at zero and the tailstock is moved toward the operator the calculated amount. Clamp the tailstock to the way. If the indicator reading changes, loosen the clamp and readjust.

Another accurate method for offsetting the tailstock is to use the cross slide (Figures 16a to 16c). With the centers aligned, bring the reverse end of the toolholder in contact with the tailstock spindle. A paper strip may

Figure 16a. The toolholder is brought to the tailstock spindle using a paper strip as a feeler gage. The micrometer dial is set to zero (Lane Community College).

Figure 16b. The cross slide is backed off the desired amount plus one full turn (Lane Community College).

be used as a feeler gage. Set the micrometer dial to zero. Back off the cross slide the calculated amount plus a full turn to remove backlash; then turn back in to the calculated amount. Move the tailstock until it contacts the paper strip held at the end of the toolholder.

When cutting tapered threads such as pipe threads, the tool should be square with the centerline of the workpiece, not the taper (Figure 17). When you have finished making tapers by the offset tailstock method, realign the centers to .001 in. or less in 12 in. When more than one part must be turned by this method, all parts must have identical lengths and center hole depths if the tapers are to be the same.

The Taper Attachment Method

The taper attachment features a slide independent to the ways that can be angled and will move the cross slide according to the angle set. Slight to fairly steep tapers ($3\frac{1}{2}$ in./ft) may be made, but length is limited to

Figure 16c. The toolholder is brought forward to the desired setting and the tailstock is moved over until it contacts the paper strip (Lane Community College).

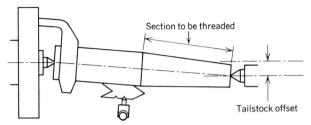

Figure 17. Adjusting the threading tool for cutting tapered threads. The tool is set square to the centerline of the work rather than the taper.

Figure 18. The plain taper attachment (Lane Community College).

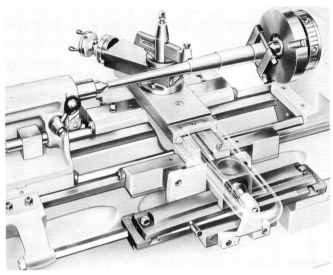

Figure 19. The telescopic taper attachment (Courtesy of Clausing Corporation).

Figure 20. Adjusting the taper attachment to a given taper with a dial indicator (Lane Community College).

the stroke of the taper attachment. Centers may remain in line without distortion of the center holes. Work may be held in a chuck and both external and internal tapers may be made, often with the same setting for mating parts. Power feed is used. Taper attachments are graduated in taper per foot (TPF) or in degrees.

There are two types of taper attachments: the plain taper attachment (Figure 18) and the telescoping taper attachment (Figure 19). The cross feed binding screw must be removed to free the nut when the plain type is set up. The depth of cut must then be made by using the compound feed screw handle. The cross feed may be used for depth of cut when using the telescoping taper attachment since the cross feed binding screw is not disengaged with this type.

When a workpiece is to be duplicated or an internal

taper is to be made for an existing external taper, it is often convenient to set up the taper attachment by using a dial indicator (Figure 20). The contact point of the dial indicator must be on the center of the workpiece. The workpiece is first set up in a chuck or between centers so there is no runout when it is rotated. With the lathe spindle stopped, the indicator is moved from one end of the taper to the other. The taper attachment is adjusted until the indicator does not change reading when moved.

The angle, the taper per foot, or the taper per inch must be known to set up the taper attachment to cut specific tapers. If none of these are known, proceed as follows.

If the end diameters (D and d) and the length of taper (L) are given in inches, the following applies.

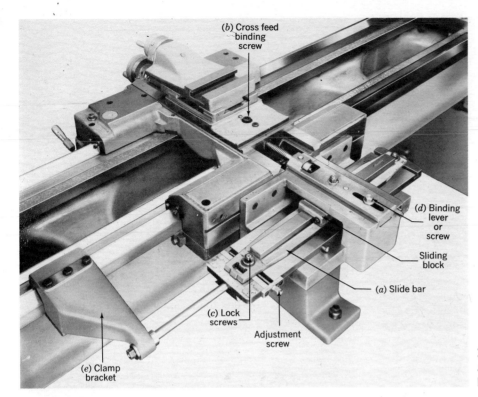

Figure 21. The parts of the taper attachment (Courtesy of the Lodge & Shipley Company).

$$\text{Taper per foot} = \frac{D - d}{L} \times 12$$

If the taper per foot is given, but you want to know the amount of taper in inches for a given length, use the following formula.

$$\text{Amount of taper} = \frac{\text{TPF}}{12} \times \text{given length of tapered part}$$

When the TPF is known, to find TPI divide the TPF by 12. When the TPI is known, to find TPF multiply the TPI by 12.

To set up the taper attachment (Figure 21), proceed as follows:

1. Clean and oil the slide bar (*a*).
2. Set up the workpiece and the cutting tool on center. Bring the tool near the workpiece and to the center of the taper.
3. Remove the cross feed binding screw (*b*) that binds the cross feed screw nut to the cross slide. *Do not remove* this screw if you are using a telescoping taper attachment. The screw is removed *only* on the plain type. Put a temporary plug in the hole to keep chips out.
4. Loosen the lock screws (*c*) on both ends of the slide bar and adjust to the required degree of taper.
5. Tighten the lock screws.

6. Tighten the binding lever (*d*) on the slotted cross slide extension at the sliding block, *plain type only.*
7. Lock the clamp bracket (*e*) to the lathe bed.
8. Move the carriage to the right so that the tool is from $\frac{1}{2}$ to $\frac{3}{4}$ in. past the start position. This should be done on every pass to remove any backlash in the taper attachment.
9. Feed the tool in for the depth of the first cut with the cross slide unless you are using a plain-type attachment. Use the compound slide for the plain type.
10. Take a trial cut and check for diameter. Continue the roughing cut.
11. Check the taper for fit and readjust the taper attachment, if necessary.
12. Take a light cut, about .010 in. and check the taper again. If it is correct, complete the roughing and final finish cuts.

Internal tapers (Figure 22) are best made with the taper attachment. They are set up in the same manner as prescribed for external tapers.

Other Methods of Making Tapers

A tool may be set with a protractor to a given angle (Figures 23*a* and 23*b*) and a single plunge cut may be made to produce a taper. This method is often used for cham-

Figure 22. Internal taper being made with a plain taper attachment. Note that the cross feed nut locking screw has been removed and the hole has not been plugged. This hole *must* be plugged and the screw stored in a safe place. (Lane Community College).

Figure 23a. Tool is set up with protractor to make an accurate chamfer or taper (Lane Community College).

fering a workpiece to an angle such as the chamfer used for hexagonal bolt heads and nuts. Tapered form tools sometimes are used to make V-shaped grooves. Only very short tapers can be made with form tools.

Tapered reamers are sometimes used to produce a specific taper such as a Morse taper. A roughing reamer is first used, followed by a finishing reamer. Finishing Morse taper reamers are often used to true up a badly nicked and scarred internal Morse taper.

Figure 23b. Making the chamfer with a tool (Lane Community College).

Figure 24. Taper plug gage (Lane Community College).

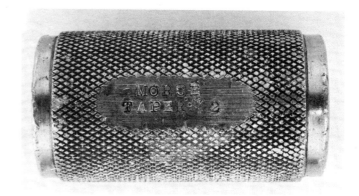

Figure 25. Taper ring gage (Lane Community College).

METHODS OF MEASURING TAPERS

The most convenient and simple way of checking tapers is to use the taper plug gage (Figure 24) for internal tapers and the taper ring gage (Figure 25) for external tapers. Some taper gages have Go and No Go limit marks on them (Figure 26).

To check an internal taper, a chalk or prussian blue mark is first made along the length of the taper plug gage (Figures 27a and 27b). The gage is then inserted into the internal taper and turned slightly. When the gage is taken out, the chalk mark will be partly rubbed off where contact was made. Adjustment of the taper

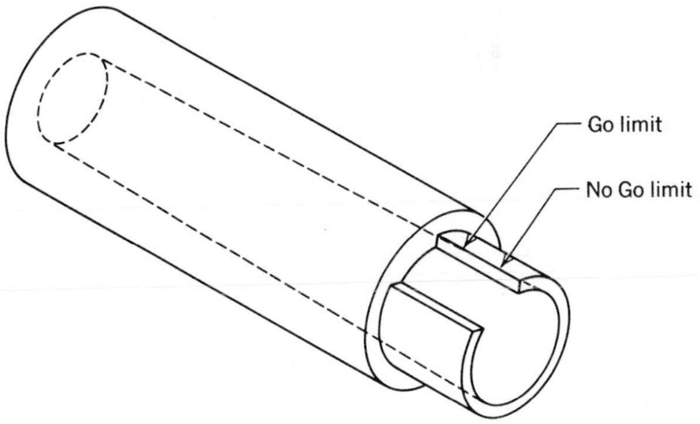

Figure 26. Go/No Go taper ring gage.

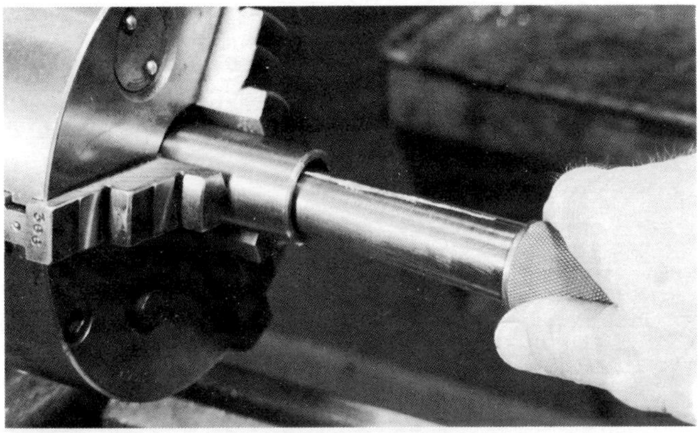

Figure 27*a*. Chalk mark is made along a taper plug gage prior to checking an internal taper (Lane Community College).

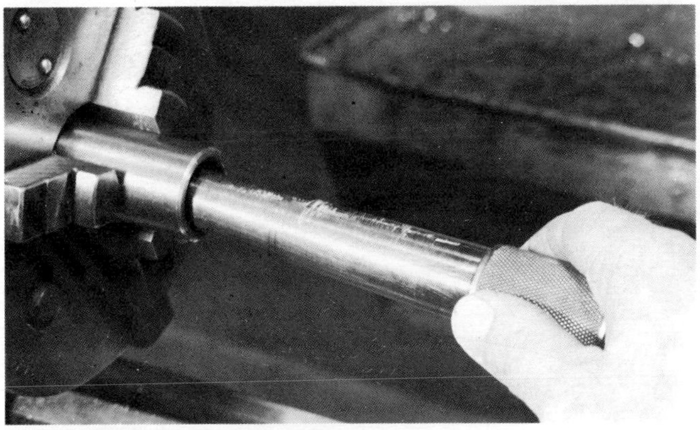

Figure 27*b*. The taper has been tested and the chalk mark has been rubbed off evenly, indicating a good fit (Lane Community College).

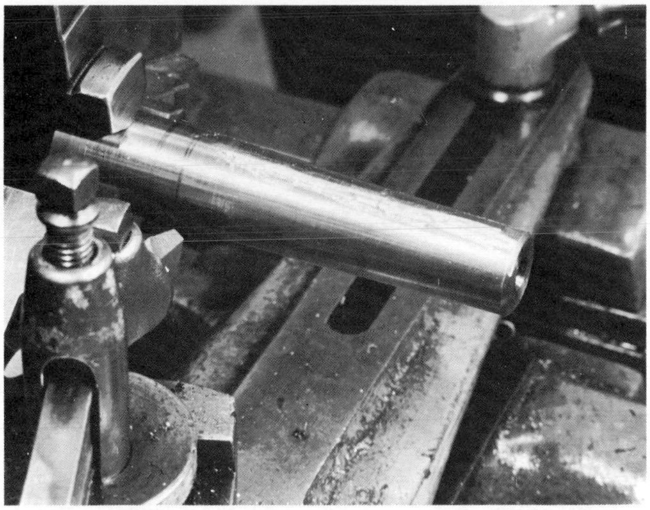

Figure 28*a*. The external taper is marked with chalk or prussian blue before being checked with a taper ring gage (Lane Community College).

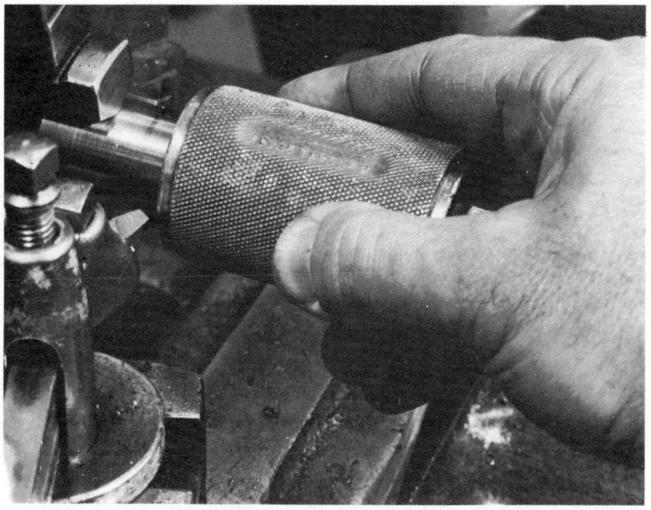

Figure 28*b*. The ring gage is placed on the taper snugly and is rotated slightly (Lane Community College).

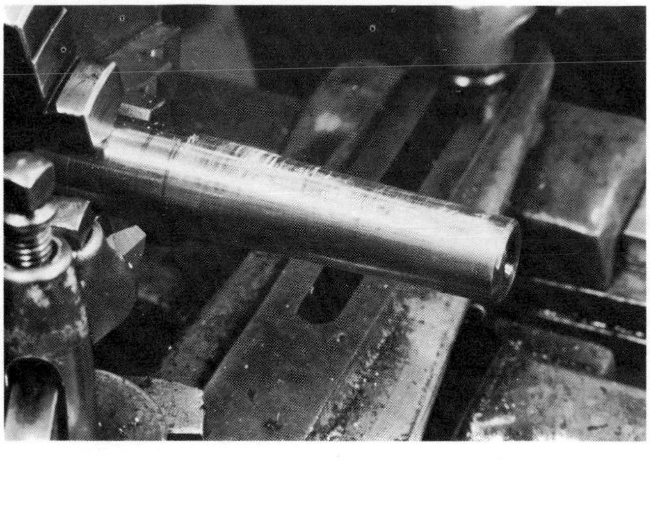

Figure 28*c*. The ring gage is removed and the chalk mark is rubbed off evenly for the entire length of the ring gage, which indicates a good fit (Lane Community College).

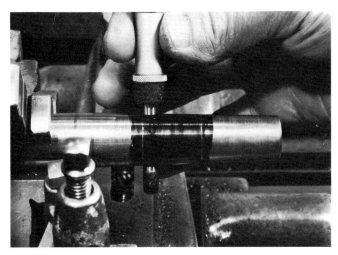

Figure 29a. Measuring the taper per inch (TPI) with a micrometer. The larger diameter is measured on the line with the edge of the spindle and the anvil of the micrometer contacting the line (Lane Community College).

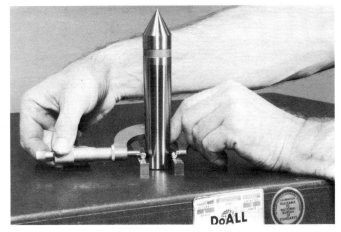

Figure 30a. Checking the taper on a surface plate with precision parallels, drill rod, and micrometer. The first set of parallels is used so that the point of measurement is accessible to the micrometer (Lane Community College).

Figure 29b. The second measurement is taken on the smaller diameter at the edge of the line in the same manner (Lane Community College).

Figure 30b. When one inch wide parallels are in place, a second measurement is taken. The difference is the taper per inch (Lane Community College).

should be made until the chalk mark is rubbed off along its full length of contact, indicating a good fit. An external taper is marked with chalk to be checked in the same way with a taper ring gage (Figures 28a to 28c).

The taper per inch may be checked with a micrometer by scribing two marks one inch apart on the taper and measuring the diameters (Figures 29a and 29b) at these marks. The difference is the taper per inch. A more precise way of making this measurement is shown in Figures 30a and 30b. A surface plate is used with precision parallels and drill rods. The tapered workpiece would have to be removed from the lathe if this method is used, however.

Figure 31. Using a sine bar and gage blocks with a dial indicator to measure a taper (Lane Community College).

Perhaps an even more precise method of measuring a taper is with the sine bar and gage blocks on the surface plate (Figure 31). When this is done, it is important to keep the centerline of the taper parallel to the sine bar and to read the indicator at the highest point.

Tapers may be measured with a taper micrometer. Refer to Section C, Unit 4 for a description of this instrument.

SELF-TEST

1. State the difference in use between steep tapers and slight tapers.
2. In what three ways are tapers expressed (measured)?
3. Briefly describe the four methods of turning a taper in the lathe.
4. When a taper is produced by the compound slide method, is the reading in degrees on the compound swivel base the same as the angle of the finished workpiece? Explain.
5. If the swivel base is set to a 35 degree angle at the cross slide centerline index, what would the reading be at the lathe centerline index?
6. Calculate the offset for the taper shown in Figure 32. The formula is

$$\text{Offset} = \frac{L \times (D - d)}{2 \times L_1}$$

7. Name four methods of measuring the offset on the tailstock for making a taper.

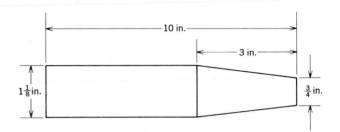

Figure 32.

8. What are the two types of taper attachments and what are their advantages over other means of making a taper?
9. What is the most practical and convenient way to check internal and external tapers when they are in the lathe? Name four methods of measuring tapers.
10. Describe the kinds of tapers that may be made by using a form tool or the side of a tool.

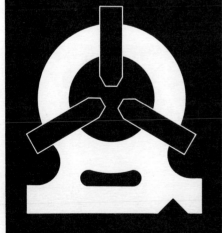

UNIT 14 USING STEADY AND FOLLOWER RESTS IN THE LATHE

Many lathe operations would not be possible without the use of the steady and follower rests. These valuable attachments make internal and external machining operations on long workpieces possible on a lathe.

OBJECTIVES

After completing this unit, you should be able to:
1. Identify the parts and explain the uses of the steady rest.
2. Explain the correct uses of the follower rest.
3. Correctly set up a steady rest on a straight shaft.
4. Correctly set up a follower rest on a prepared shaft.

THE STEADY REST

On a lathe, long shafts tend to vibrate when cuts are made, leaving chatter marks. Even light finish cuts will often produce chatter when the shaft is long and slender. To help eliminate these problems, use a steady rest to support workpieces that extend from a chuck more than four or five diameters of the workpiece for turning, facing, drilling, and boring operations.

The steady rest (Figure 1) is made of a cast iron or steel frame that is hinged so it will open to accommodate workpieces. It has three or more adjustable jaws that are tipped with bronze, plastic, or ball bearing rollers. The base of the frame is machined to fit the ways of the lathe and it is clamped to the bed by means of a bolt and crossbar.

A steady rest is also used to support long workpieces for various other machining operations such as threading, grooving, and knurling (Figure 2). Heavy cuts can be made by using one or more steady rests along a shaft.

Adjusting the Steady Rest

Workpieces should be mounted and centered in a chuck whether a tailstock center is used or not. If the shaft has centers and finished surfaces that turn concentric (have no runout) with the lathe centerline, setup of the steady rest is simple. The steady rest is slid to a convenient location on the shaft, which is supported in the dead center and chuck, and the base is clamped to the bed. The two lower jaws are brought up to the shaft finger tight only (Figure 3). A good high pressure lubricant is applied to the shaft and the top half of the steady rest is closed and clamped. The upper jaw is brought to the shaft finger tight, and then all three lockscrews are tightened. Some clearance is necessary on the upper jaw to avoid scoring of the shaft. As the shaft warms or heats up from friction during machining, readjustment of the upper jaw is necessary.

A finished workpiece can be scored if any hardness or grit is present on the jaws. To protect finishes, brass or copper strips or abrasive cloth is often placed between the jaws and the workpiece; with the abrasive cloth, the abrasive side is placed outward against the jaws.

Figure 1. The parts of the steady rest (Lane Community College).

Figure 2. A long, slender workpiece is supported by a steady rest near the center to limit vibration or chatter (Lane Community College).

Figure 3. Adjusting the steady rest jaws to a centered shaft (Lane Community College).

When there is no center in a finished shaft of the same diameter, setup procedure is as follows.

1. Position the steady rest near the end of the shaft with the other end lightly chucked in a three- or four-jaw chuck.
2. Scribe two cross center lines with a center head on the end of the shaft and prick punch (Figures 4a and 4b).
3. Bring up the dead center near to the punch mark.
4. Adjust the lower jaws of the steady rest to the shaft and lock.

5. Tighten the chuck. If it is a four-jaw chuck, check for runout with a dial indicator.
6. The steady rest may now be moved to any location along the shaft.

Stepped shafts may be set up by using a similar procedure, but the steady rest must remain on the diameter on which it is set up.

Using the Steady Rest

A frequent misconception among students is that the steady rest may be set up properly by using a dial indicator near the steady rest on a rotating shaft. This procedure would never work since the indicator would show no offset or runout, no matter where the jaws were moved.

Steady rest jaws should never be used on rough surfaces. When a forging, casting, or hot rolled bar must be placed in a steady rest, a concentric bearing with a good finish must be turned (Figure 5). Thick walled tubing or other materials that tend to be out of round also should have bearing surfaces machined on them. The usual practice is to remove no more in diameter than necessary to clean up the bearing spot.

When the piece to be set up is very irregular, such as a square or hexagonal part, a cat head is used (Figure 6). The piece is placed in the cat head and the cat head is mounted in the steady rest while the other end of the workpiece is centered in the chuck. The workpiece is made to run true near the steady rest by adjusting screws on the cat head. In most cases the workpiece is given a center to provide more support for turning operations. A centered cat head (Figures 7a and 7b) is sometimes used when a permanent center is not required in the workpiece. Internal cat heads (Figure 8)

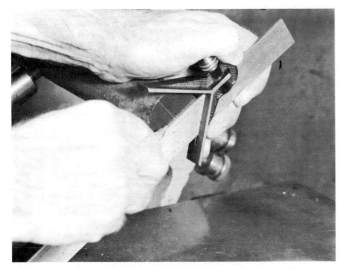

Figure 4a. Laying out the center of a shaft (Lane Community College).

Figure 4b. Aligning the shaft center with the dead center (Lane Community College).

Figure 5. Turning a concentric bearing surface on rough stock for the steady rest jaws (Lane Community College).

Figure 6. Using a cat head for supporting a square piece. Drilling and boring in the end of a heavy square bar requires the use of an external cat head (Lane Community College).

Figure 7a. Using a centered cat head to provide a center when the end of the shaft or tube cannot be centered conveniently (Lane Community College).

Figure 7b. The cat head is adjusted over the irregular end of the shaft (Lane Community College).

Figure 8. Tubing being set up with a cat head using a dial indicator to true the inside diameter (Lane Community College).

are used for truing to the inside diameter of tubing that has an irregular wall thickness, so that a steady rest bearing spot can be machined on the outside diameter. These also have adjustment screws.

THE FOLLOWER REST

Long, slender shafts tend to spring away from the tool, vary in diameter, chatter, and often climb the tool. To avoid these problems when machining a slender shaft along its entire length, a follower rest (Figure 9) is often used. Follower rests are bolted to the carriage and follow along with the tool. Most follower rests have two jaws placed to back up the work opposite to the tool thrust. Some types are made with different size bushings to fit the work.

Using the Follower Rest

The workpiece should be one to two inches longer than the job requires to allow room for the follower rest jaws. The end is turned to smaller than the finish size. The tool is adjusted ahead of the jaws about one and one-half inches and a trial cut of two or three inches is made with the jaws backed off. Then the lower jaw is adjusted finger tight (Figure 10) followed by the upper jaw. Both locking screws are tightened. A cutting oil should be used to lubricate the jaws.

The follower rest is often used when cutting threads

Figure 9. A follower rest is used to turn this long shaft (Lane Community College).

Figure 11. Long, slender Acme threaded screw being machined with the aid of a follower rest (Lane Community College).

Figure 10. Adjusting the follower rest (Lane Community College).

Figure 12. Both steady and follower rests being used (Lane Community College).

on long, slender shafts, especially when cutting square or Acme threads (Figure 11). Burrs should be removed between passes to prevent them cutting into the jaws.

Jaws with rolls are sometimes used for this purpose. On quite long shafts, sometimes both a steady rest and follower rest are used (Figure 12).

SELF-TEST

1. When should a steady rest be used?
2. In what ways can a steady rest be useful?
3. How is the steady rest set up on a straight finished shaft when it has centers in the ends?
4. What precaution can be taken to prevent scoring of a finished shaft?
5. How can a steady rest be set up when there is no center hole in the shaft?
6. Is it possible to correctly set up a steady rest by using a dial indicator on the rotating shaft in order to watch for runout?
7. Should a steady rest be used on a rough surface? Explain.

8. How can a steady rest be used on an irregular surface such as square or hex stock?

9. When a long, slender shaft needs to be turned or threaded for its entire length, which lathe attachment could be used?

10. The jaws of the follower rest are usually one or two inches to the right of the tool on a setup. If the workpiece happens to be smaller than the dead center or tailstock spindle, how would it be possible to bring the tool to the end of the work to start a cut without interference by the follower rest jaws?

UNIT 15 ADDITIONAL THREAD FORMS

Many thread forms other than the 60 degree types are to be found on machines. Each of the forms is unique and has a special use. To be able to recognize and measure these various thread forms will be very helpful to you as an apprentice machinist.

As a machinist, you may occasionally be called upon to make a multiple lead thread. When this happens, you should be prepared to select a method that is best for the job and proceed as efficiently as you would in cutting a single lead thread. This unit will acquaint you with the various methods and precedures for cutting multiple lead threads.

OBJECTIVES

After completing this unit, you should be able to:

1. Identify five different thread forms and explain their uses.
2. Calculate the dimensions needed to machine the five thread forms.
3. Described the methods and procedures for machining multiple lead threads.

Transmitting (translating) screw threads are primarily used to transmit or impart power or motion to a mechanical part. Often these transmitting screws are of multiple lead to effect rapid motion. Bench vises and house jacks are familiar applications of single lead transmitting screws. The lead screw on a lathe and the table feed screws on milling machines are examples of these screw threads being used to impart power along the axis of the screw to move a part.

The earliest type of transmitting screws were of the square thread form (Figure 1). Thrust on the flanks of the thread is fully axial, thus reducing friction to a minimum. The square thread is more difficult to produce than other types and is not now widely used. The thread has a depth and thickness that is one-half the pitch. Clearance must be provided on the flanks and major diameter of the thread.

The modified square thread form (Figure 2) was designed to replace the square thread. It is easier to produce than the square thread, yet it has all of the advantages and some of the drawbacks of the square thread. It, like the square thread, is not widely used.

The Acme thread (Figure 3) is generally accepted throughout the mechanical industries as an improved thread form over that of the square and modified square. The Acme thread is easier to machine and

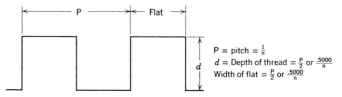

P = pitch = $\frac{1}{n}$
d = Depth of thread = $\frac{P}{2}$ or $\frac{.5000}{n}$
Width of flat = $\frac{P}{2}$ or $\frac{.5000}{n}$

Figure 1. The square thread. P = pitch = $\frac{1}{n}$; D = depth of thread = $\frac{P}{2}$ or $\frac{.5000}{n}$. Width of flat = $\frac{P}{2}$ or $\frac{.5000}{n}$.

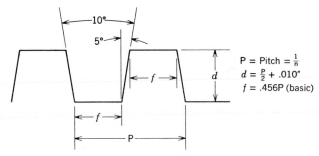

Figure 2. Modified square thread. P = pitch = $\frac{1}{n}$; d = $\frac{P}{2} + \frac{.010}{in.}$; f = .456P (basic).

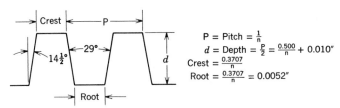

Figure 3. Acme thread. P = pitch = $\frac{1}{n}$; d = depth = $\frac{P}{2}$ = $\frac{.500}{n}$ + .010 in.; crest = $\frac{.3707}{n}$; root = $\frac{.3707}{n}$ = .0052 in.

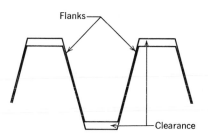

Figure 4. General purpose Acme threads bear on the flanks.

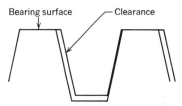

Figure 5. Centralizing Acme threads bear at the major diameter.

Figure 6a. American Standard Stub Acme thread. P = pitch = $1/n$; d = depth = .3P; F_c = basic flat at crest = .4224P; F_r = basic flat at root = .4224P − .0052.

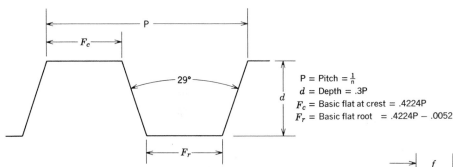

P = Pitch = $\frac{1}{n}$
d = Depth = .3P
F_c = Basic flat at crest = .4224P
F_r = Basic flat root = .4224P − .0052

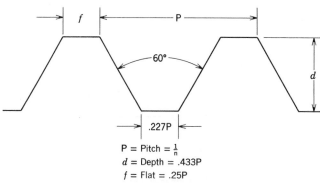

P = Pitch = $\frac{1}{n}$
d = Depth = .433P
f = Flat = .25P

Figure 6b. Stub Acme thread. P = pitch = $1/n$; d = depth = .433P; f = flat = .25P.

stronger than the square form thread since the Acme root cross section is thicker than its root clearance. Acme thread screws are used on milling machines and lathes. Like the square thread, the Acme has a basic depth equal to one-half the pitch; however, clearance is added both at the crest and the root of the thread for the general purpose fit. The Acme general purpose threads bear on the flanks (Figure 4). Centralizing fits bear at the major diameter (Figure 5). For more detailed information on Acme thread fits, see the *Machinery's Handbook*.

Three classes of general purpose Acme threads 2G, 3G, and 4G are used. Class 2G is preferred for general purpose assemblies. If less backlash or end play is desired, classes 3G and 4G are given. Internal threads of any class may be combined with any external class to provide other degrees of fit. The included angle of Gen-eral Purpose Acme threads is 29 degrees. Depth of thread is one-half the pitch plus .010 in. for 10 TPI and coarser. For finer pitches the depth of thread is one-half the pitch plus .005 in.

Stub Acme threads (Figures 6a and 6b) are used

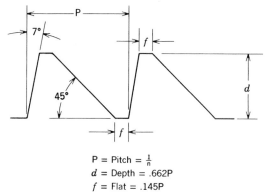

$$P = \text{Pitch} = \frac{1}{n}$$
$$d = \text{Depth} = .662P$$
$$f = \text{Flat} = .145P$$

Figure 7. Buttress thread. P = pitch = 1/n; d = depth = .662P; = f = flat = .145P.

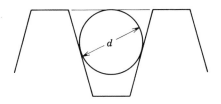

$d = \text{Diameter of wire} = .48725P$

Figure 8. The one-wire method for measuring Acme threads. d = diameter of wire = .48725P.

where a coarse pitch thread with a shallow depth is required. The depth for the Stub Acme is only .3P and .433P for the American Standard Stub, as compared to .5P for the standard Acme threads.

The Buttress thread (Figure 7) is not usually used for translating motion. It is often used where great pressures are applied in one direction only, such as on vise screws and the breech of large guns. Acme threads are gradually replacing square and Buttress thread forms.

Acme threads may be measured by using the one-wire method (Figure 8). If a wire with a diameter equal to .48725 × P is placed in the groove of an Acme thread, the wire will be flush with the top of the thread. For further information on one-wire and three-wire methods for checking Acme threads, see the *Machinery's Handbook*.

MULTIPLE LEAD THREADS

Multiple threads, though not often used, are usually found on industrial machines, valves, fire hydrants, and aircraft landing gear. They are also used on jars or other containers.

Most screws and bolts have single lead threads, which are formed by cutting one groove with a single point tool. A double lead thread has two grooves, a triple lead thread has three grooves, and a quadruple lead

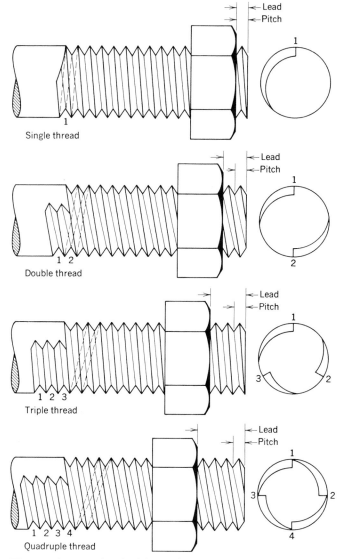

Figure 9. Single, double, triple, and quadruple threads.

thread has four grooves. Double, triple, and quadruple threads are also known as multiple threads, meaning more than one thread. You may determine whether a bolt or screw is single or multiple threaded by looking at its end (Figure 9) and counting the grooves that have been started. Multiple threads have less holding power, and less force is produced when these screws are tightened. A single lead thread should be used for fasteners where locking power is required.

Multiple lead threads offer several advantages:

1. They furnish more bearing surface area than single threads.

2. They have larger minor diameters and, therefore, a bolt is stronger than one with a single thread.

Figure 10. Using the face plate and lathe dog method of indexing multiple lead threads (Lane Community College).

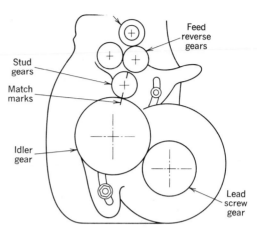

Figure 11. Using the stud gear in the drive train for indexing.

3. They provide rapid movement.
4. They are more efficient as they lose less power to friction than do single lead threads.

The lead is the distance that a nut travels in one revolution. In one turn on a single lead screw, a nut moves forward the distance of one thread; in one turn on a double lead thread it moves twice as far; on a triple lead thread it moves three times as far; and on a quadruple thread, it moves four times as far. On a single lead screw the lead and pitch are the same; but on a two lead screw, the lead is twice the pitch. Pitch is measured in the same way for single and multiple lead thread. It is the distance from a point on one thread to the corresponding point on the next thead.

The form and depth of thread for multiple lead threads can be based on any recognized thread form: Buttress, square, sharp V, Acme, American National, metric or Unified, both left- and right-hand, as discussed in Units 13 and 19 of this section. The thread depth is based on the pitch of the thread and not the lead.

CUTTING MULTIPLE LEAD THREADS
Several methods are used for indexing or dividing multiple lead threads. One method is to use an accurately slotted face plate (Figure 10). The lathe dog is moved 180 degrees for two leads, 120 degrees for three leads, and 90 degrees for four leads. This method will only work on external threading. Another method is to mark the stud gear at 180 degrees for two leads, disengage the gear, rotate it 180 degrees, and reset it (Figure 11). This procedure will work only if the spindle and stud gear have a 1:1 (1 to 1) ratio.

Figure 12. A thread chasing dial. May be used to cut double lead threads (Lane Community College).

A thread chasing dial (Figure 12) may be used to cut double threads if they are fractional or odd numbered. The first lead is cut on the numbered lines; the second lead is cut on the unnumbered lines. Some experimentation on various lathes will be useful to determine where the divisions may be found. If you cut the thread with the compound set at 29 degrees, be sure to back the compound out to its original position when you move to the next lead.

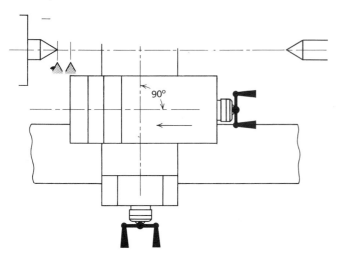

Figure 13. Setting the compound parallel to the ways for cutting multiple lead threads. To index, move the compound a distance equal to the pitch, always in the same direction.

Many machinists prefer to index the thread with the compound set at 90 degrees, or parallel to the ways (Figure 13). With this method, the tool must be fed straight into the work, so lighter cuts should be taken to keep from tearing the thread. Begin by taking up the slack in the compound feed screw and setting the tool to cut the first lead. Set the compound and cross feed micrometer dials to zero. Cut the first thread to the correct depth and move the compound forward one pitch of the thread using the micrometer dial or a dial indicator. Be sure the slack is out of the screw at all times. It is a good idea to tighten the compound gibs for this operation.

Make the cut for the second lead and check the fit.

If it is a two start thread, for example, use a gage or two start nut to check it. If the thread is too tight, move the cross slide in a few thousandths of an inch, take a cut, then advance the compound *forward* to the other position and take the same depth cut. This method may be used for a thread with any number of starts. On coarse threads (under 12 threads per inch), rough out both threads before taking the finishing cuts. Setups or tools may slip out of place slightly on heavy cuts, thus allowing for no adjustment if one thread were already finished.

An example of using this method to cut multiple lead threads is as follows.

If a two start, double lead unified screw thread with .100 inch pitch is required, the following steps can be used to make this thread.

1. The lead is .200 in. or 5 threads per inch (TPI). The quick-change gearbox is set at 5 TPI.
2. The compound is set at 90 degrees, or parallel to the axis of the lathe, and the tool is set up.
3. The micrometer dials are zeroed and a scratch cut is taken. The compound is advanced .100 in. and the second scratch cut is taken. The pitch should now be .100 in. or 10 TPI when checked with a screw pitch gage.
4. The depth of the external unified thread is P × .613.
5. Feed in no more than .005 in. per pass but leave .010 in. for finishing. Now repeat this process in the second lead.
6. Both leads may now be cut to finish diameter.

If you use a dial indicator instead of the micrometer dial to measure the movement of the compound, the two lead threads can be within .001 in. of true position.

SELF-TEST

1. For what two major purposes are translating-type screw threads used?
2. Name five thread forms used as translating screws.
3. What would the depth of thread be for a square thread that is 4 TPI?
4. What would the depth of thread be for a general purpose Acme thread that is 4 TPI?
5. What is the main difference between general purpose Acme threads and centralizing Acme threads?
6. What is the included angle of Acme threads?
7. Explain the general use of stub Acme threads.
8. Which thread form has a 10 degree included angle?
9. Of the translating thread forms, which type is most used and is easiest to machine?
10. What are Buttress threads mostly used for?

11. A $\frac{1}{8}$ in. pitch single lead thread will move .125 in. in one revolution of the nut. How far will a $\frac{1}{8}$ in. pitch, three-start thread move in one revolution?
12. Define the *pitch*.
13. Define the *lead*.
14. Which thread has more force or holding power for fasteners, a single or a multiple lead?
15. Name four methods of indexing the lathe for multiple threads.
16. Name three advantages offered by multiple lead threads.
17. What kinds of threads can be made multiple lead?
18. How can you determine the number of leads?
19. Why should both leads be roughed out before taking the finish cut on coarse threads?
20. Why are lighter cuts taken when using the compound slide method of indexing?

UNIT 16 CUTTING ACME THREADS ON THE LATHE

Machinists are sometimes required to cut internal and external Acme threads. These threads are, in most cases, larger and coarser than 60 degree form threads, and require greater skill to produce them well. In this unit, you will learn the procedure for cutting these threads.

OBJECTIVE

After completing this unit, you should be able to:
Describe set up and procedure for making external and internal Acme threads.

Cutting Acme threads is similar to cutting 60 degree threads in many ways. The threads per inch and infeeds are calculated in the same way. Some calculations, tool form and relief angles, and finishes for Acme threads, however, involve different problems and procedures.

GRINDING THE TOOL FOR ACME THREADS

The cutting tool form must be checked with the Acme tool gage (Figures 1a and 1b) when the 29 degree included angle is ground. Side relief must be ground at the same time. The end of the tool is ground flat and perpendicular to the bisector of the angle. The flat is checked (Figure 2) with the tool gage at the number corresponding to the threads per inch you will cut. It is very important to have the flat the exact width needed for the particular thread being cut.

The relief angles on the tool (Figure 3a and 3b) are of greater importance when coarse threads are cut, since if the heel of the tool rubs on either side, a rough, inaccurate thread will result. When the helix angle has been determined, it should be added to the relief angle (8 to 12 degrees) of the tool on the leading edge and similar relief provided on the trailing edge of the tool (Figure 4). As in other threading operations, the tool must be ground for 0 degree rake and set on the center of the work to maintain the correct thread form.

SETTING UP TO CUT EXTERNAL ACME THREADS ON THE LATHE

The threads per inch are set up normally and the lead screw rotation is set for right- or left-hand threads. The

gears, leadscrew, and carriage should be lubricated before cutting coarse threads. The compound is most often set at $14\frac{1}{2}$ degrees to the right for right-hand external threads. The workpiece must be set up and held very securely in the workholding device; a four-jaw chuck

Figure 1a.   Acme tool gage.

Figure 1b.   Checking the tool angle with the Acme tool gage (Lane Community College).

Figure 2. Checking the flat on the end of the tool with the Acme tool gage (Lane Community College).

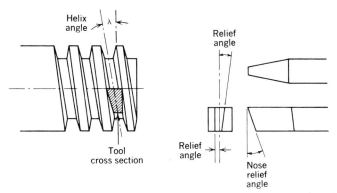

Figure 3a. Acme threads showing the importance of the relief angles on both sides of the tool.

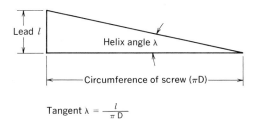

Tangent $\lambda = \dfrac{l}{\pi D}$

Figure 3b. The screw thread helix angle may be determined by dividing the lead by the circumference of the screw. The number thus obtained is the tangent of the helix angle, which can then be found in a table of tangents. D = diameter of screw, l = lead of thread, and λ = helix angle of thread.

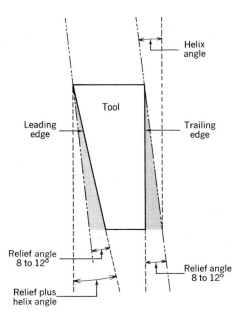

Figure 4. The relationship of the helix angle of the thread to the relief angle of the tool.

Figure 5. Aligning the tool with the work using the Acme gage (Lane Community College).

and dead center would be most secure. The tool is aligned with the work by using the Acme gage (Figure 5). With this setup, the tool is fed into the work by advancing the compound in small steps as with 60 degree threads. An undercut must be made at the end of the threads to clear the tool.

When Acme threads coarser than 5 TPI are cut, a square or round nose roughing tool that is smaller than the Acme tool should be used to make a first cut. The roughing tool does not cut to full depth or width and the Acme form tool is used to finish the thread. This procedure is also used when making threads in tough alloy materials.

Some machinists prefer to set the compound parallel to the ways so they can "shave" both flanks of the thread for a good finish. When this is done, the tool must

Figure 6. Taking the scratch cut (Lane Community College).

be made a few thousandths of an inch narrower to allow for the "shaving" operation.

Making the Cut

A scratch cut is taken (Figure 6) and measured. The cross slide is moved out and the carriage returned. The cross slide is again set on zero and the compound is advanced .005 to .010 in., depending on what the lathe and setup will handle without chatter. Use sulfurized cutting oil. The total depth of the cut is .5P + .010 in. Feed in on the cross slide for the last few thousandths of an inch so that the trailing flank will also receive a finish cut. For other Acme thread fits, see the *Machinery's Handbook*.

INTERNAL THREADS

The bore size for making an Acme General Purpose internal thread is the major diameter of the screw minus the pitch. As with Unified threads, the actual minor diameter of an Acme thread is the inside diameter of the bore; thus the minor diameter of an Acme 1–5 thread would be 1 − .200 = .800 in. The internal major diameter should be the major diameter of the screw plus .010 in. for 10 or more TPI and .020 in. for pitches less than 10 TPI.

The compound is set $14\frac{1}{2}$ degrees to the left for cutting right-hand internal threads (Figure 7). An internal Acme threading tool is ground, checked (Figure 8) and set up, then fed into the work with the compound .002 to .005 in. for each pass. An Acme screw plug gage or the mating external thread should be used to check the fit as the internal thread nears completion (Figure 9).

When internal Acme threads are too small in diameter to be cut with a boring bar and tool, an Acme tap (Figure 10) is used to make the thread. Acme taps are made in sets of two or three taps; each tap cuts more of the thread, the last tap for the finishing cut. Two taps are sometimes made on the same shank as in Figure 10. The part is drilled or bored to the minor diameter of the thread and the Acme tap is turned in by hand. Use cut-

Figure 7. Compound is set $14\frac{1}{2}$ degrees to the left of the operator for right-hand internal threads (Lane Community College).

Figure 8. Aligning the Acme tool with a gage for cutting internal threads (Lane Community College).

ting oil when tapping steel, but cut threads in bronze dry.

A problem often encountered when threading coarse threads on small lathes is that of producing a thicker than normal last thread; the plug gage will go in the nut all the way except for the final thread. This hap-

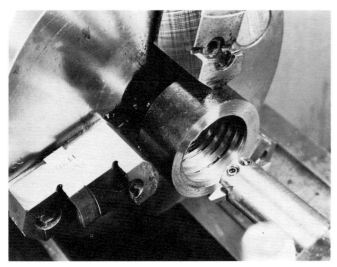

Figure 9. Completed internal Acme threads (Lane Community College).

Figure 10. An Acme tap (Lane Community College).

pens because the carriage is not heavy enough to provide sufficient drag to keep the tool cutting on its following side when the leading side of the tool is emerging from the cut. The result is a pitch error on the last thread. The slack in the half-nuts allows this to happen. Providing a slight drag on the carriage handwheel will eliminate this problem.

External Acme threads must often have a good finish. A final honing of the tool before the last few shaving passes will help. The setup must be very rigid and the gibs tight. Low speeds are essential. The grade of cutting oil is extremely important in this finishing operation.

The thread may be finished after it is cut by using a thin, safe edge file at low RPM and by using abrasive cloth at a higher RPM. A thin piece of wood is sometimes used to back up the abrasive cloth while each flank is being polished.

SELF-TEST

1. What is the major difference between V-form threads and Acme threads?
2. When grinding an Acme threading tool, what three important parts should be carefully measured?
3. Why should the gears, ways, leadscrew, and carriage be lubricated before cutting coarse threads?
4. Where is the compound most frequently set when cutting Acme threads? What setup is preferred by some machinists?
5. What is the depth of thread for a $\frac{3}{4}$–6 external general purpose Acme thread?
6. How is the tool aligned with the workpiece?
7. Determine the bore size to make a $\frac{3}{4}$–6 general purpose internal Acme thread.
8. Which is the best way to make small internal Acme threads?
9. What can you use to check internal threads for fit?
10. Explain how a good tool finish may be obtained on an Acme thread.

UNIT 17 USING CARBIDES AND OTHER TOOL MATERIALS ON THE LATHE

The cutting tool materials such as carbon steels and high speed steel that served the needs of machining in the past years are not suitable in many applications today. Tougher and harder tools are required to machine the tough, hard, space age metals and new alloys. The constant demand for higher productivity led to the need for faster stock removal and quick-change tooling. You, as a machinist, must learn to achieve maximum productivity at minimum cost. Your knowledge of carbide cutting tools and ability to select them for specific machining tasks will effect your productivity directly.

OBJECTIVES

After completing this unit, you should be able to:
1. List six different cutting tool materials and compare some of their machining properties.
2. Select a carbide tool for a job by reference to operating conditions, carbide grades, nose radii, tool style, rake angles, shank size, and insert size, shape, and thickness.
3. Identify carbide inserts and toolholders by number systems developed by the American Standards Association.

The various tool materials are high carbon steel, high speed steel, nonferrous cast alloys, cemented carbides, ceramics, and diamond.

HIGH CARBON STEELS

High carbon tool steels are used for hand tools such as files, chisels, and only to a limited extent for drilling and turning tools. They are oil or water hardening plain carbon steels with .9 to 1.4 percent carbon content. These tools maintain a keen edge and can be used for metals that produce low tool-chip interface temperatures; for example, aluminum, magnesium, copper, and brass. These tools, however, tend to soften at machining speeds above 50 feet per minute (FPM) in mild steels.

HIGH SPEED STEELS

High speed steels (HSS) may be used at higher speeds (100 FPM in mild steels) without losing their hardness.

The relationship of cutting speeds to the approximate temperature of tool-chip interface is as follows:

100 FPM — 1000°F (538°C)
200 FPM — 1200°F (649°C)
300 FPM — 1300°F (704°C)
400 FPM — 1400°F (760°C)

High speed steel is sometimes used when special tool shapes are needed, especially for boring tools.

CAST ALLOYS

Cast alloys are referred to as such because they are nonferrous (not containing iron) alloys. These materials are somewhat softer than HSS at room temperature, but retain their hardness to higher temperatures. This property in tools is known as red hardness. The cast alloys can be used at speeds of nearly 200 FPM or up to 1200°F (649°C) in steels. The approximate composition of cast

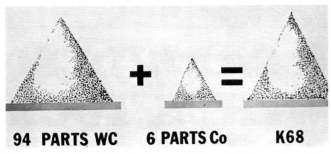

94 PARTS WC   6 PARTS Co   K68

Figure 1. The three basic materials needed to produce the straight grades of tungsten carbide (Courtesy of Kennametal, Inc., Latrobe, Pa.).

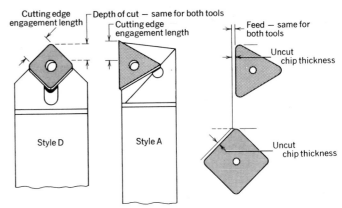

Figure 2. The difference in Style A and Style D holders for depth of cut and cutting edge engagement length (Copyright General Electric Company).

alloy materials is 12 to 17 percent tungsten or tantalum, 30 to 35 percent chromium, 45 to 55 percent cobalt, and 2 to 3 percent carbon.

CEMENTED CARBIDES

A carbide, generally, is a chemical compound of carbon and a metal. The term carbide is commonly used to refer to cemented carbides, the cutting tools composed of tungsten carbide, titanium carbide, or tantalum carbide, and cobalt in various combinations. A typical composition of cemented carbide is 85 to 95 percent carbides of tungsten and the remainder a cobalt binder for the tungsten carbide powder.

Cemented carbides are made by compressing various metal powders (Figure 1) and sintering (heating to weld particles together without melting them) the briquettes. Cobalt powder is used as a binder for the carbide powder used, either tungsten, titanium, or tantalum carbide powder or a combination of these. Increasing the percentage of cobalt binder increases the toughness of the tool material and at the same time reduces its hardness or wear resistance. Carbides have greater hardness at both high and low temperatures than high speed steel or cast alloys. At temperatures of 1400°F (760°C) and higher, carbides maintain the hardness required for efficient machining. This makes possible machining speeds of approximately 400 FPM in steels. The addition of tantalum increases the red hardness of a tool material. Cemented carbides are extremely hard tool materials (above RA90), have a high compressive strength, and resist wear and rupture.

SELECTING CARBIDE TOOLS

The following steps may be used in selecting the correct carbide tool for a job.

1. Establish the operating conditions.
2. Select the cemented carbide grade.
3. Select nose radius.
4. Select insert shape.
5. Select insert size.
6. Select insert thickness.
7. Select tool style.
8. Select rake angle.
9. Select shank size.

Step 1. Establishing the Operating Conditions

The tool engineer or machinist must use three variables to establish metal removal rate: speed, feed, and depth of cut. Cutting speed has the greatest effect on tool life. A 50 percent increase in cutting speed will decrease tool life by 80 percent. A 50 percent increase in feed will decrease tool life by 60 percent. The cutting edge engagement or depth of cut (Figure 2) is limited by the size and thickness of the carbide insert and the hardness of the workpiece material. Hard workpiece materials require decreased feed, speed, and depth of cut.

Figure 2 shows how the lead angle affects both cutting edge engagement length and chip thickness by comparing a Style D square insert tool, using a 45 degree lead angle, to a Style A triangular insert tool, using a 0 degree lead angle. The two tools are shown making an identical depth of cut at an identical feed rate. The feed rate is the same as the chip thickness with the Style A tool or any tool with a 90 degree lead angle. The chip would be wider but thinner using the Style D with the same feed rate. When large lead angles are used, the Style D tool has a much greater strength than the Style A tool since the cutting forces are directed into the solid part of the holder. Large lead angles can cause chatter to develop, however, if the setup is not rigid.

The depth of cut is limited by the strength and thickness of the carbide insert, the rigidity of the machine and setup, the horsepower of the machine and, of course, the amount of material to be removed. An example of

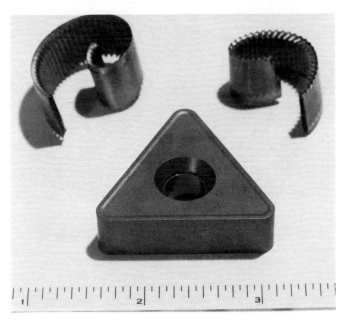

Figure 3. Large, well-formed chips were produced by this tool with built-in chip breaker (Courtesy of Kennametal, Inc., Latrobe, Pa.).

Figure 5. Tool point breakdown caused by built-up edge.

Figure 4. Normal edge wear.

Figure 6. Chipped or broken inserts. The triangular insert shows the typical breakage on straight tungsten carbide inserts. The square titanium-coated insert shows a stratified failure because of an edge impact.

a relatively large depth of cut with an insert that produced large 9-shaped chips is shown in Figure 3.

Edge wear and cratering are the most frequent tool breakdowns that occur. Edge wear (Figure 4) is simply the breaking down of the tool relief surface caused by friction and abrasion and is considered normal wear. Edge breakdown is also caused by the tearing away of minute carbide particles by the built-up edge (Figure 5). The cutting edge is usually chipped or broken in this case. Lack of rigidity, too much feed, or too slow a speed results in chipped or broken inserts (Figure 6).

Thermal shock, caused by sudden heating and cooling, is the cracking and checking of a tool that leads to breakage (Figure 7). This condition is most likely to occur when an inadequate amount of coolant is used. It is better to machine dry if the work and tool cannot be kept flooded with coolant.

If edge wear occurs:

1. Decrease machining speed.
2. Increase feed.
3. Change to a harder, more wear-resistant carbide grade.

If the cutting edge is chipped or broken:

Breakage

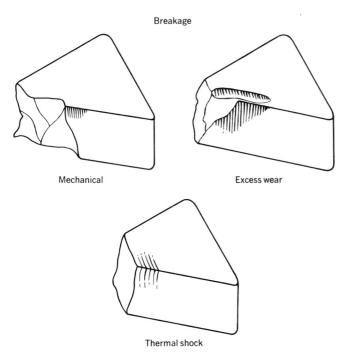

Mechanical   Excess wear

Thermal shock

Figure 7. Three causes of tool breakage (Courtesy of Kennametal, Inc., Latrobe, Pa.).

1. Increase speed.
2. Decrease feed and/or depth of cut.
3. Change to a tougher grade carbide insert.
4. Use negative rake.
5. Hone the cutting edge before use.
6. Check the rigidity and tool overhang.

When there is a buildup on the cutting edge:

1. Increase speed.
2. Change to a positive rake tool.
3. Change to a grade containing titanium.

For cutting edge notching:

1. Increase side cutting edge angle.
2. Decrease feed.

Cratering (Figure 8) is the result of high temperatures and pressures that cause the steel chip to weld itself to the tungsten carbide and tear out small particles of the tool material. The addition of titanium carbide to the mixture of tungsten carbide and cobalt provides an antiweld quality, but there is some loss in abrasive wear and strength in these tools.

Step 2. Selecting Cemented Carbide Grades

There are two main groups of cemented carbides from which to select most grades: First, the straight carbide

Figure 8. Cratering on a carbide tool.

grades composed of tungsten carbide and cobalt binder, which are used for cast iron, nonferrous metals and non-metalics where resistance to edge wear is the primary factor; second, grades composed of tungsten carbide, titanium carbide, and tantalum carbide plus cobalt binder, which are usually used for machining steels. Resistance to cratering and deformation is the major requirement for these steel grades.

Cemented carbides have been organized into grades. Properties that determine grade include hardness, toughness, and resistance to chip welding or cratering. The properties of carbide tools may be varied by the percentages of cobalt and titanium or tantalum carbides. Increasing the cobalt content increases toughness but decreases hardness. Properties may also be varied during the processing by the grain size of carbides, density, and other modifications. Some tungsten carbide inserts are given a titanium carbide coating (about .0003 in. thick) to resist cratering and edge breakdown. Tantalum carbide is added to sintered carbide principally to improve hot hardness characteristics. This increases the composition's resistance to deformation at cutting temperatures.

The grades of carbides have been organized according to their suitable uses by the Cemented Carbide Producers Association (CCPA). It is recommended that carbides be selected by using such a table rather than by their composition. Cemented carbide grades with specific chip removal applications are:

C-1 Roughing cuts (cast iron and nonferrous materials)
C-2 General purpose (cast iron and nonferrous materials)

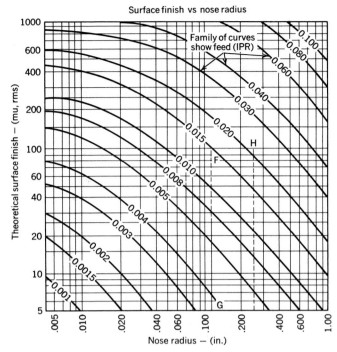

Figure 9. Surface finish vs. nose radius (Copyright General Electric Company).

C-3 Light finishing (cast iron and nonferrous materials)

C-4 Precision boring (cast iron and nonferrous materials)

C-5 Roughing cuts (steel)

C-6 General purpose (steel)

C-7 Finishing cuts (steel)

C-8 Precision boring (steel)

The hardest of the nonferrous-cast iron grades would be C-4 and the hardest of the steel grades would be C-8.

This system does not specify the particular materials or alloy, and the particular machining operations are not specified. One must use the judgment of an experienced machinist in order to select a grade of carbide, for example, for turning a chromium-molybdenum steel. Factors to be considered would include the difficulty of machining such an alloy because of its toughness. Given this example, a grade of C-5 or C-6 carbide would probably be best suited to this operation. The proof of the selection would come only with the actual machining. Cemented carbide tool manufacturers often supply tables designating uses and machining characteristics of their various grades. See Table 1.

Grade classification-comparison tables that convert each manufacturer's carbide designations to CCPA "C" numbers are available. See Table 2. There is, however, one major caution. The tables are intended to correlate grades on the basis of composition and not according to

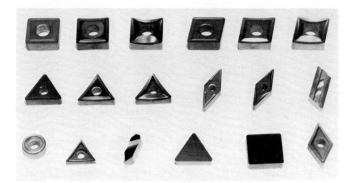

Figure 10. Insert shapes for various applications (Courtesy of Kennametal, Inc., Latrobe, Pa.).

tested performance. Grades from different manufacturers having the same "C" number may vary in performance. Some general guidelines to grade selection are as follows:

1. Select the grade with the highest hardness with sufficient strength to prevent breakage.
2. Select straight grades of tungsten carbide for the highest resistance to abrasion.

Step 3. Select Nose Radius

Selecting the nose radius can be important because of tool strength, surface finish, or perhaps the forming of a fillet or radius on the work. To determine the nose radius according to strength requirements, use the nomograph in Figure 9. Consider that the feed rate, depth of cut, and workpiece condition determine strength requirements, since a larger nose radius makes a stronger tool.

Large radii are strongest and can produce the best finishes, but they also can cause chatter between tool and workpiece. For example, the dashed line on the chart indicates that a $\frac{1}{8}$ in. radius would be required for turning with a feed rate of .015 in., and to obtain a 100 microinch finish, a $\frac{1}{4}$ in. radius would be required with a .020 in. feed rate.

Step 4. Select Insert Shapes

Indexable inserts (Figure 10), also called throwaway inserts, are clamped in toolholders of various design. These inserts provide a cutting tool with several cutting edges. After every or all edges have been used, the insert is discarded.

The round inserts have the greatest strength and, as with large radius inserts, make possible higher feed rates with equal finishes. Round inserts also have the greatest number of cutting edges possible, but are limited to workpiece configurations and operations that are not affected by a large radius. Round inserts would be ideally suited, for example, to straight turning operations.

Table 1

Grade and Machining Applications

<table>
<tr><th colspan="2"></th><th>Grade</th><th>Hardness
R_A</th><th>Typical Machining Applications</th></tr>
<tr><td rowspan="12" style="writing-mode:vertical">Combined Crater and Edge-Wear Resistance</td><td rowspan="4" style="writing-mode:vertical">Maximum Crater Resistance</td><td>CO6</td><td>Ceramic^a</td><td>The hardest of this group. For finishing most ferrous and nonferrous alloys and nonmetals as in high speed, light chip load precision machining, or for use at moderate speeds and chip loads where long tool life is desired.</td></tr>
<tr><td>K165</td><td>93.5</td><td>Titanium carbide for finishing steels and cast irons at high to moderate speeds and light chip loads.</td></tr>
<tr><td>K7H</td><td>93.5</td><td>For finishing steels at higher speeds and moderate chip loads.</td></tr>
<tr><td>K5H</td><td>93.0</td><td>For finishing and light roughing steels at moderate speeds and chip loads through light interruptions.</td></tr>
<tr><td rowspan="5" style="writing-mode:vertical">KC75</td><td>K45</td><td>92.5</td><td>The hardest of this group. General purpose grade for light roughing to semifinishing of steels at moderate speeds and chip loads, and for many low speed, light chip load applications.</td></tr>
<tr><td>K4H</td><td>92.0</td><td>For light roughing to semifinishing of steels at moderate speeds and chip loads, and for form tools and tools that must dwell.</td></tr>
<tr><td>K2S</td><td>91.5</td><td>For light to moderate roughing of steels at moderate speeds and feeds through medium interruptions.</td></tr>
<tr><td colspan="3" align="center">**For general purpose use in machining of steels over a wide range of speeds in moderate roughing to semifinishing applications.**</td></tr>
<tr><td>K21</td><td>91.0</td><td>For moderate to heavy roughing of steels at moderate speeds and heavy chip loads through medium interruptions where mechanical and thermal shock are encountered.</td></tr>
<tr><td>K42</td><td>91.3</td><td>For heavy roughing of steels at low to moderate speeds and heavy chip loads through interruptions where mechanical and severe thermal shocks are encountered.</td></tr>
<tr><td rowspan="4" style="writing-mode:vertical">Maximum Edge-Wear Resistance</td><td>K11</td><td>93.0</td><td>The hardest of this group. For precision finishing of cast irons, nonferrous alloys, nonmetals at high speeds and light chip loads, and for finishing many hard steels at low speeds and light chip loads.</td></tr>
<tr><td>K68</td><td>92.6</td><td>General purpose grade for light roughing to finishing of most high temperature alloys, refractory metals, cast irons, nonferrous alloys, and nonmetals at moderate speeds and chip loads through light interruptions.</td></tr>
<tr><td>K6</td><td>92.0</td><td>For moderate roughing of most high temperature alloys, cast irons, nonferrous alloys, and nonmetals at moderate to low speeds and moderate to heavy chip loads through light interruptions.</td></tr>
<tr><td>K1</td><td>90.0</td><td>The most shock resistant of this group. For heavy roughing of most high temperature alloys, cast irons, and nonferrous alloys at low speeds and heavy chip loads through heavy interruptions.</td></tr>
</table>

^a The hardness of CO6 is 91 Rockwell 45N (or about 94R_A).

Source: *Kentrol Inserts* (*Supplement 5 to Catalog 73*, ''Kennametal Grade Systems and Machining Applications,'' 1975 (data courtesy of Kennametal, Inc., Latrobe, Pa.).

Square inserts have lower strength and fewer possible cutting edges than round tools, but are much stronger than triangular inserts. The included angle between cutting edges (90 degrees) is greater than for triangular inserts (60 degrees), and there are eight cutting edges possible as compared to six for the triangular inserts.

Triangular inserts have the greatest versatility. They can be used, for example, for combination turning and facing operations, while round or square inserts are often not adaptable to such combinations. Because the included angle between cutting edges is less than 90 degrees, the triangular inserts are also capable of tracing operations. The disadvantages include their reduced strength and fewer cutting edges per insert.

For tracing operations where triangular inserts cannot be applied, diamond-shaped inserts with smaller included angles between edges are available. The included angles on these diamond-shaped inserts range from 35 to 80 degrees. The smaller angle inserts in par-

Table 2

Carbide Grade Classification–Comparison Table with CCPA "C" Numbers and Manufacturers Designations

APPLICATION				Newcomer	Adamas	Atrax	Carboloy	Carmet	Ex-cell-o	Firth Sterling	Greenleaf	Kennametal	Metal Carbides	Sandvik	Valenite	V-R Wesson	Walmet	Wendt-Sonis
CHIP REMOVAL	Cast Irons	Roughing cuts	C-1	N10	B	FA5	44A	CA3	E8	H HB	G10	K1	C89	H20	VC-1	VR54 2A68	WA-1 WA-159	CQ12 CQ22
	Nonferrous, Nonmetallic, Hi-Temperature alloys	General purpose	C-2	N20 N22	A AM	FA6 FA-62	883 860	CA4 CA443	E6 XL620	HA HTA	G20 G25	K6 K68	C91	H20	VC-2 VC-28	2A5 VR82	WA-69 WA-2	CQ2 CQ23
		Light finishing	C-3	N30	PWX	FA7	905	CA7	E5	HE HTA	G30	K8 K68	C93	R1P	VC-3	2A7 VR82	WA-35 WA3	CQ3 CQ23
	200 & 300 series stainless	Precision boring	C-4	N40	AAA	FA8	999 895	CA8	E3	HF	G40	K11	C95	H1P HO5	VC-4	2A7	WA4	CQ4
	Carbon steels	Roughing cuts	C-5	N50 N52	499 434	FT-3 FT-35	370 78B	CA721 CA740	10A 945	NTA TXH	G50 G55	K42 K21	S-880	S-6	VC-55 VC-125	VR77 WM	WA5 WA55	CY12 CY17
		General purpose	C-6	N60	6X T-60	FT-4 FT-6	78B	CA720	BA 606	T22 T25	G60	K2S K21	S-900 S-901	S-4	VC-6	26 VR75	WA6	CY5 CY16
	Alloy steels	Finishing cuts	C-7	N70 N72	495 548	FT-6 FT-62	78 350	CA711	6A XL70 6AX	T25 T31	G70 G74	K45 K5H	S-92 S-900	SM	VC7 VC-76	WH VR73	WA7 WA168	CY2 CY14
	400 Series stainless	Precision boring	C-8	N80 N93	490 T-80	FT-7 FT-71	330 210	CA704	6AX XL88	T31	G80	K7H K165	S-94	FO2	VC-8 VC-83	VR71 VR65	WA8 WA800	CY31 Ti8
		Hi-velocity	C-80	N95			0-30					CO6				VR97		

Source. Newcomer Products, Inc. *Reference card.*

ticular may be plunged into the workpiece as required for tracing. A typical setup for tracing is shown in Figure 11. Note that small clearance angles are used for each cutting edge to permit plunging.

Step 5.   Select Insert Size
The insert selected should be the smallest insert capable of sustaining the required depth of cut and feed rate. The depth of cut should always be as great as possible. A rule of thumb is to select an insert with cutting edges $1\frac{1}{2}$ times the length of cutting edge engagement. The feed for roughing mild steel should be approximately $\frac{1}{10}$ the depth of cut.

Step 6.   Select Insert Thickness
Insert thickness is also important to tool strength. The required depth of cut and feed rate are criteria that determine insert thickness. The nomograph in Figure 12 simplifies the relationship of depth of cut and feed rate to insert thickness. Lead angle is also important in converting the depth of cut to a length of cutting edge engagement.

The dashed line on the nomograph in Figure 12 represents an operation with a $\frac{3}{4}$ in. length of engagement (not depth of cut) and a feed rate of .020 IPR. Depending on the grade of carbide used (tough or hard), an insert of $\frac{1}{4}$ or $\frac{3}{8}$ inch thickness should be used.

Step 7.   Select Tool Style
Tool style pertains to the configuration of toolholder for a carbide insert. To determine style, some familiarity with the particular machine tool and the operations to be performed is required. Figure 13 shows some of the styles available for toolholders.

Step 8.   Select Rake Angle
When selecting the rake angles, you need to consider the machining conditions. Negative rake should be used where there is maximum rigidity of the tool and work and where high machining speeds can be maintained. More horsepower is needed when using negative rake tools. Under these conditions, negative rake tools are stronger and produce satisfactory results (Figure 14).

Negative rake inserts may also be used on both

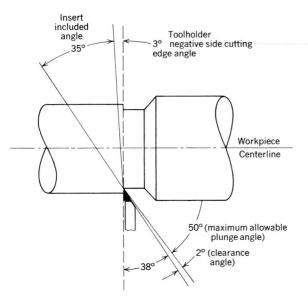

Insert included angle 35°

Toolholder 3° negative side cutting edge angle

Workpiece Centerline

50° (maximum allowable plunge angle)

2° (clearance angle)

38°

Figure 11. A 38 degree triangular insert used for a tracing operation (Copyright General Electric Company).

DETERMINING INSERT THICKNESS TO MEET STRENGTH REQUIREMENTS

Use ¼ in. thick insert in regular cut with impact resistant cemented carbide, 3/8 in. with wear resistant carbide grade.

STANDARD INSERT THICKNESS FOR INTERRUPTED CUTS, ECCENTRIC FORGINGS, ETC.

STANDARD INSERT THICKNESS FOR REGULAR CUTS

FEED (IN./REV)

CUTTING EDGE ENGAGEMENT (IN.)

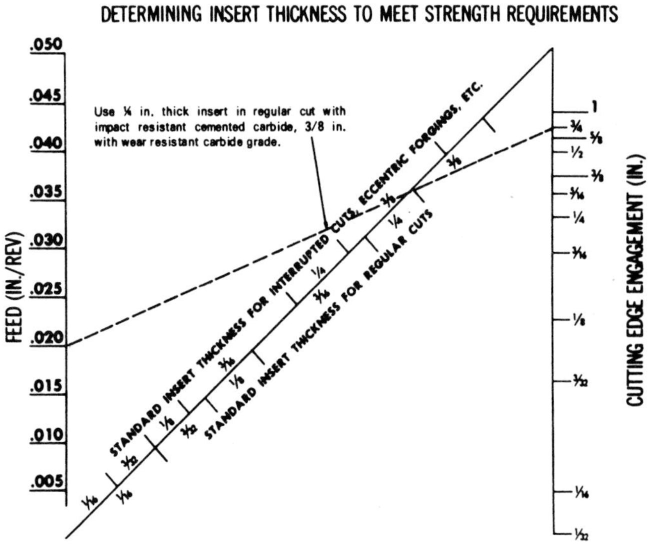

Figure 12. Insert thickness as determined by length of cutting edge engagement and feed rate (Copyright General Electric Company).

sides, doubling the number of cutting edges per insert. This is possible because end and side relief are provided by the angle of the toolholder rather than by the shape of the insert.

Positive rake inserts should be used where rigidity of the tool and work is reduced and where high cutting speeds are not possible; for example, on a flexible shaft of small diameter. Positive rake tools cut with less force so deflection of the work and toolholder would be

Figure 13. Several of the many tool styles available (Courtesy of Kennametal, Inc., Latrobe, Pa.).

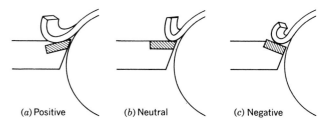

(a) Positive   (b) Neutral   (c) Negative

Figure 14. Side view of back rake angles.

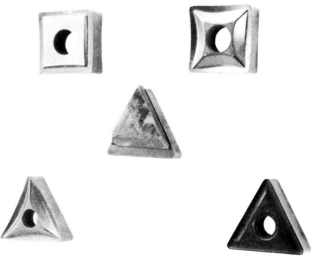

Figure 15. Chip breakers used are the adjustable chip deflector (center) with a straight insert and the type with the built-in chip control groove.

reduced. High cutting speeds (SFPM) are often not possible on small diameters because of limitations in spindle speeds. Some insert types are plain and others have built-in chip-breakers (Figure 15).

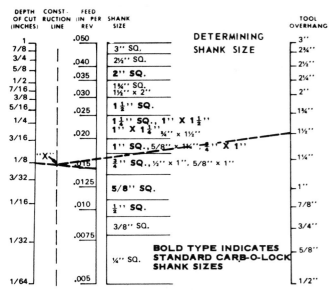

Figure 16. Determining shank size according to depth of cut, feed rate, and tool overhang (Copyright General Electric Company).

Figure 17. A boring bar with various interchangeable adjustable heads (Courtesy of Kennametal, Inc., Latrobe, Pa.).

Step 9. Select Shank Size

As with insert thickness and rake angles, the rate of feed and depth of cut are important in determining shank size. Overhang of the tool shank is extremely important for the same reason. Heavy cuts at high feed rates create high downward forces on the tool. These downward forces acting on a tool with excessive overhang would cause tool deflection that would make it difficult or impossible to maintain accuracy or surface finish quality.

Having established the feed rate, depth of cut, and tool overhang, use the nomograph in Figure 16 to determine the shank size. Begin by drawing a line from the depth of cut scale to the feed rate scale. From the point where this line intersects the vertical construction line, draw a line to the correct point on the tool overhang

scale. Determine the shank size from where this last line crosses through the shank size scale.

In the example shown on the graph, a line has been drawn from the $\frac{1}{8}$ in. depth of cut point to the .015 IPR feed rate point. Another line has been drawn from the point of intersection on the vertical construction line to the amount of tool overhang. The second line drawn passes through the shank size scale at the $\frac{3}{4}$ square in. (cross sectional area) point. Toolholders $\frac{1}{2} \times 1$ in. or $\frac{5}{8} \times 1$ in. would meet the requirements. Throwaway carbide inserts are also used for boring bars (Figure 17) of various shapes and sizes. Brazed carbide tips are sometimes put on the end of a boring bar for special applications.

TOOLHOLDER IDENTIFICATION

The carbide manufacturers and the American Standards Association (ASA) have adopted a system of identifying toolholders for inserted carbides. This system is used to call out the toolholder geometry and for ordering tools from manufacturers or distributors. The system is shown in Table 3.

As an example, use this system to determine the geometry of a toolholder called out as TANR-8:

    T — Triangular insert shape

    A — 0 degree side cutting edge angle

    N — Negative rake

    R — Right hand turning (from left to right)

    8 — Square shank, $\frac{8}{16}$ in. per side

CARBIDE INSERT IDENTIFICATION

As with toolholder identification, a system has been adopted by the carbide manufacturers and the American Standard Association for identifying inserts. See Table 4.

For example, use this system to determine the specifications for an insert called out as T N M G-323 E:

    T — Triangular shape

    N — 0 degree relief (relief provided by holder)

    M — Plus or minus .005 in. tolerance on thickness

    G — With hole and chipbreaker

    3 — $\frac{3}{8}$ in. inscribed circle (inside square and triangular insert)

    2 — $\frac{2}{16}$ in. thickness

    3 $\frac{3}{64}$ in. radius

    E — Unground, honed

Brazed carbide tools have been used for many years and are still used on many machining jobs. These

Table 3
ASA Tool Holder Identification System

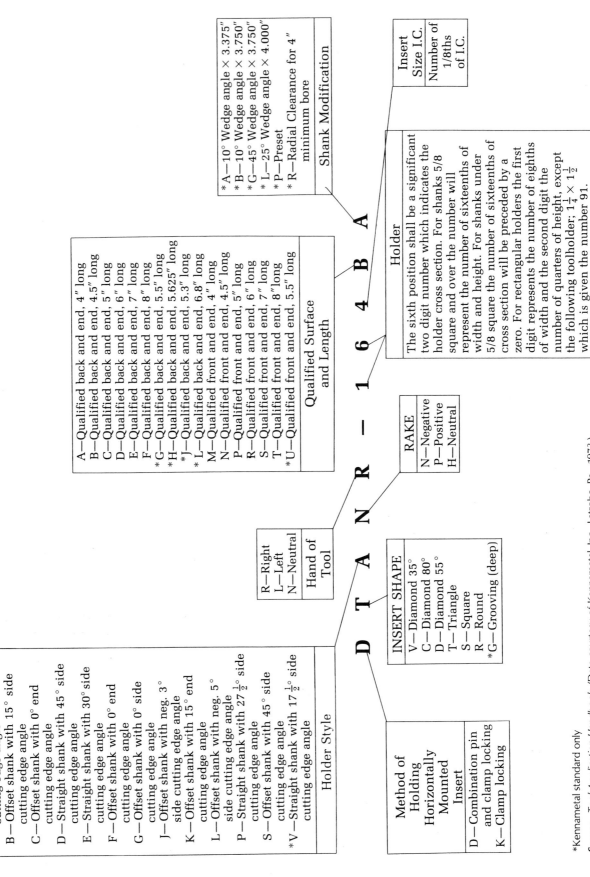

D T A N R – 1 6 4 B A

Holder Style

A—Straight shank with 0° side cutting edge angle
B—Offset shank with 15° side cutting edge angle
C—Offset shank with 0° end cutting edge angle
D—Straight shank with 45° side cutting edge angle
E—Straight shank with 30° side cutting edge angle
F—Offset shank with 0° end cutting edge angle
G—Offset shank with 0° side cutting edge angle
J—Offset shank with neg. 3° side cutting edge angle
K—Offset shank with 15° end cutting edge angle
L—Offset shank with neg. 5° side cutting edge angle
P—Straight shank with 27 $\frac{1}{2}$° side cutting edge angle
S—Offset shank with 45° side cutting edge angle
*V—Straight shank with 17 $\frac{1}{2}$° side cutting edge angle

Method of Holding Horizontally Mounted Insert

D—Combination pin and clamp locking
K—Clamp locking

INSERT SHAPE

V—Diamond 35°
C—Diamond 80°
D—Diamond 55°
T—Triangle
S—Square
R—Round
*G—Grooving (deep)

RAKE

N—Negative
P—Positive
H—Neutral

Hand of Tool

R—Right
L—Left
N—Neutral

Qualified Surface and Length

A—Qualified back and end, 4" long
B—Qualified back and end, 4.5" long
C—Qualified back and end, 5" long
D—Qualified back and end, 6" long
E—Qualified back and end, 7" long
F—Qualified back and end, 8" long
*G—Qualified back and end, 5.5" long
*H—Qualified back and end, 5.625" long
*J—Qualified back and end, 5.3" long
*L—Qualified back and end, 6.8" long
M—Qualified front and end, 4" long
N—Qualified front and end, 4.5" long
P—Qualified front and end, 5" long
R—Qualified front and end, 6" long
S—Qualified front and end, 7" long
T—Qualified front and end, 8" long
*U—Qualified front and end, 5.5" long

Shank Modification

*A—10° Wedge angle × 3.375"
*B—10° Wedge angle × 3.750"
*G—45° Wedge angle × 3.750"
*L—25° Wedge angle × 4.000"
*P—Preset
*R—Radial Clearance for 4" minimum bore

Insert Size I.C.
Number of 1/8ths of I.C.

Holder

The sixth position shall be a significant two digit number which indicates the holder cross section. For shanks 5/8 square and over the number will represent the number of sixteenths of width and height. For shanks under 5/8 square the number of sixteenths of cross section will be preceded by a zero. For rectangular holders the first digit represents the number of eighths of width and the second digit the number of quarters of height, except the following toolholder; $1\frac{1}{4} \times 1\frac{1}{2}$ which is given the number 91.

*Kennametal standard only

Source. *Tool Application Handbook.* (Data courtesy of Kennametal, Inc., Latrobe, Pa., 1973.)

Table 4
ASA Carbide Insert Identification

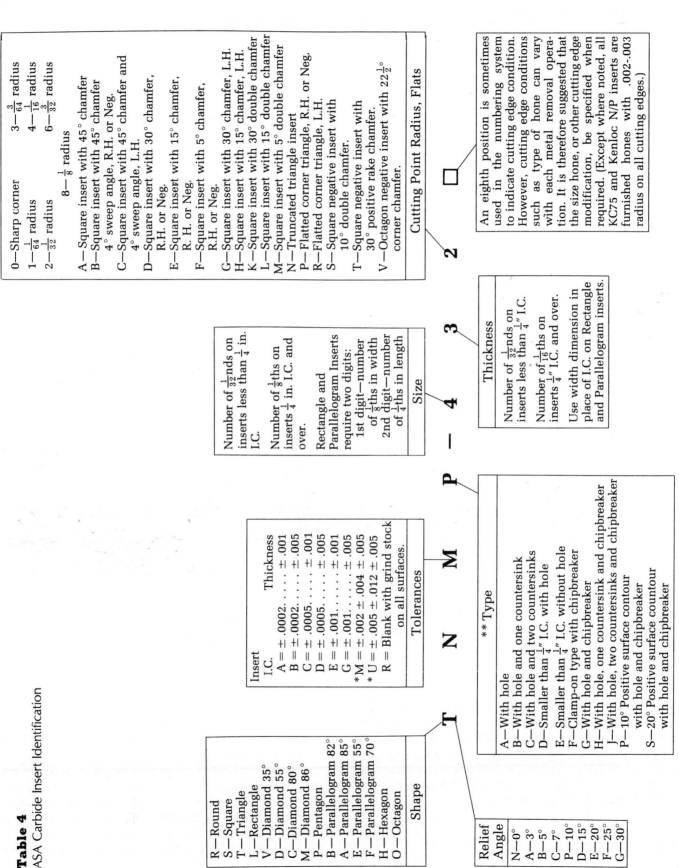

Insert code example: T — N — M — P — 4 — 4 — 3 — 2

Shape (T)

R—Round
S—Square
T—Triangle
L—Rectangle
V—Diamond 35°
D—Diamond 55°
C—Diamond 80°
M—Diamond 86°
P—Pentagon
B—Parallelogram 82°
A—Parallelogram 85°
E—Parallelogram 55°
F—Parallelogram 70°
H—Hexagon
O—Octagon

Relief Angle (N)

N—0°
A—3°
B—5°
C—7°
P—10°
D—15°
E—20°
F—25°
G—30°

Tolerances (M)

Insert I.C.	Thickness
A = ±.0002	±.001
B = ±.0002	±.005
C = ±.0005	±.001
D = ±.0005	±.005
E = ±.001	±.001
G = ±.001	±.005
*M = ±.002 ±.004	±.005
*U = ±.005 ±.012	±.005
R = Blank with grind stock on all surfaces.	

**Type (P)

A—With hole
B—With hole and one countersink
C—With hole and two countersinks
D—Smaller than $\frac{1}{4}$" I.C. with hole
E—Smaller than $\frac{1}{4}$" I.C. without hole
F—Clamp-on type with chipbreaker
G—With hole and chipbreaker
H—With hole, one countersink and chipbreaker
J—With hole, two countersinks and chipbreaker
P—10° Positive surface contour with hole and chipbreaker
S—20° Positive surface countour with hole and chipbreaker

Size (4)

Number of $\frac{1}{32}$nds on inserts less than $\frac{1}{4}$ in. I.C.

Number of $\frac{1}{8}$ths on inserts $\frac{1}{4}$ in. I.C. and over.

Rectangle and Parallelogram Inserts require two digits:
1st digit—number of $\frac{1}{8}$ths in width
2nd digit—number of $\frac{1}{4}$ths in length

Thickness (3)

Number of $\frac{1}{32}$nds on inserts less than $\frac{1}{4}$" I.C.

Number of $\frac{1}{16}$ths on inserts $\frac{1}{4}$" I.C. and over.

Use width dimension in place of I.C. on Rectangle and Parallelogram inserts.

Cutting Point Radius, Flats (2)

0—Sharp corner
1—$\frac{1}{64}$ radius   3—$\frac{3}{64}$ radius
2—$\frac{1}{32}$ radius   4—$\frac{1}{16}$ radius
                             6—$\frac{3}{32}$ radius
8—$\frac{1}{8}$ radius

A—Square insert with 45° chamfer
B—Square insert with 45° chamfer 4° sweep angle, R.H. or Neg.
C—Square insert with 45° chamfer and 4° sweep angle, L.H.
D—Square insert with 30° chamfer, R.H. or Neg.
E—Square insert with 15° chamfer, R. H. or Neg.
F—Square insert with 5° chamfer, R.H. or Neg.
G—Square insert with 30° chamfer, L.H.
H—Square insert with 15° chamfer, L.H.
K—Square insert with 30° double chamfer
L—Square insert with 15° double chamfer
M—Square insert with 5° double chamfer
N—Truncated triangle insert
P—Flatted corner triangle, R.H. or Neg.
R—Flatted corner triangle, L.H.
S—Square negative insert with 10° double chamfer.
T—Square negative insert with 30° positive rake chamfer.
V—Octagon negative insert with $22\frac{1}{2}$° corner chamfer.

An eighth position is sometimes used in the numbering system to indicate cutting edge condition. However, cutting edge conditions such as type of hone can vary with each metal removal operation. It is therefore suggested that the size hone, or other cutting edge modification, be specified when required. (Except where noted, all KC75 and Kenloc N/P inserts are furnished hones with .002-.003 radius on all cutting edges.)

Source. *Tool Application Handbook.* (Data courtesy of Kennametal, Inc., Latrobe, Pa., 1973.)

*Exact tolerance is determined by size of insert **Shall be used only when required

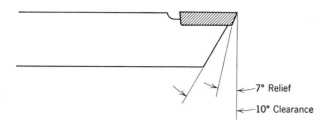

Figure 18. Relief and clearance compared.

Figure 19. Ceramic tool with carbide seat and chip deflector shown assembled in toolholder behind the parts (Courtesy of Kennametal, Inc., Latrobe, Pa.).

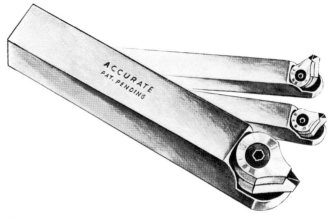

Figure 20a. Diamond tools are mounted in round or square shank holders as replaceable inserts (Courtesy of Accurate Diamond Tool Corp.). (Universal Turning and Boring Tool is a patented item. Patent is owned by: Accurate Diamond Tool Corp.).

tools can be sharpened by grinding many times, while the insert tool is thrown away after its cutting edges are dull. Grinding the tool often causes thermal shock by the sudden heating of the carbide surface. This is evident when "crazing" or several tiny checks appear on the edge or when a large crack can be seen in the tool. To prevent crazing when grinding these tools:

1. Avoid the use of aluminum oxide wheels (except to rough grind the steel shank for clearance). Use only silicon carbide wheels with a soft bond.
2. Avoid excessive grinding pressure in a small area.
3. Avoid poor cutting action of a low concentration diamond wheel.
4. Avoid dry grinding.

Chipbreakers may be ground on the edge of brazed carbide tools with diamond wheels on a surface grinder.

The side and end clearance angles are not to be confused with relief angles on carbide tools (Figure 18). Clearance refers to the increased angle ground on the shank of a carbide tipped tool. Clearance provides for a narrow flank on the carbide and for regrinding of the carbide without contacting steel.

CERAMIC TOOLS

Ceramic or "cemented oxide" tools (Figure 19) are made

Figure 20b. Turning at 725 SFM .010 inch stock is removed on each of two passes at a rate of $5\frac{1}{2}$ in. per minute (.0023 IPR) along the 29 in. length of the casting. A coolant is not required for this turning (Courtesy of Accurate Diamond Tool Company).

primarily from aluminum oxide with a binder. Some manufacturers add titanium, magnesium, or chromium oxides in quantities of 10 percent or less. The tool materials are molded at pressures over 4000 PSI (pounds per square inch) and sintered at temperatures of approximately 3000°F (1649°C). This process partly accounts for the high density and hardness of cemented oxide tools.

Cemented oxides are brittle and require that machines and setups be rigid and free of vibration. Some machines cannot obtain the spindle speeds required to use cemented oxides at their peak capacity in terms of FPM. When practicable, however, cemented oxides can

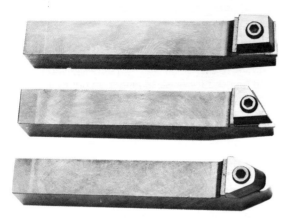

Figure 21. Sintered diamond inserts are clamped in tool-holders (Courtesy of Megadiamond Industries).

Figure 22. To make abrasive fused silica tubes absolutely round where they fit into tundish valves, FloCon turns the tubes with a sintered diamond tool insert. After limited experience, the Megadiamond sintered diamond inserts appear to give about 200 times as much wear as carbides in the same application (Courtesy of Megadiamond Industries).

be used to machine relatively hard materials at high speeds.

Ceramic tools should be used as a replacement for carbide tools that are wearing rapidly, but not to replace carbide tools that are breaking.

DIAMOND TOOLS

Industrial diamonds are sometimes used to machine extremely hard workpieces. Only relatively small removal rates are possible with diamond tools (Figure 20a), but very high speeds are used and good finishes are obtained (Figure 20b). Nonferrous metals are turned at 2000 to 2500 FPM, for example. Sintered diamond tools (Figure 21), available in shapes similar to those of ceramic tools, are used for materials (Figure 22) that are abrasive and difficult to machine.

Each of the cutting tool materials varies in hardness. The differences in hardness tend to become more pronounced at high temperatures, as can be seen in Table 5. Hardness is related to the wear resistance of a tool and its ability to machine materials that are softer than it is. Temperature change is important since the increase of temperature during machining results in the softening of the tool material.

Diamond or ceramic tools should never be used for interrupted cuts such as on splines or keyseats because they could chip or break. They must never be used at low speeds or on machines that are not capable of attaining the higher speeds at which these tools should operate.

Since heavy forces and high speeds are involved when using carbides, safety considerations are essential. Chip forms such as the ideal 9 or C-shape are convenient to handle, but shields, chip deflectors, or guards are required to direct chips away from workers in the shop.

Make sure the setup is secure, that centers are large enough to support the work, and that work cannot slip in the chuck. If a long, slender work is machined at high speeds and there is a possibility of it being thrown out, guards should be provided.

Table 5
Hardness of Cutting Materials at High and Low Temperatures

Tool Material	Hardness at Room Temperature	Hardness at 1400°F (760°C)
High speed steel	RA 85	RA 60
Cast alloy	RA 81	RA 70
Carbide	RA 92	RA 82
Cemented oxide (ceramic)	RA 93-94	RA 84
Diamond		Hardest known substance

SELF-TEST

1. List the major materials used in "straight" cemented carbides.
2. What effect does increasing the cobalt content have on cemented carbides?
3. How can you identify normal wear on a carbide tool?
4. Is chip thickness the same as feed on a Style A tool?
5. Is the cutting edge engagement length the same as depth of cut on Style B tools?
6. What effect does the addition of titanium carbides have on tool performance?
7. What effect does the addition of tantalum carbides have on tool performance?
8. What change in tool geometry can make possible an increased rate of feed with equal surface finish quality in turning operations?
9. How does increasing the nose radius affect tool strength?
10. What is the hazard in using too large a nose radius?
11. In respect to carbide turning tools, how is clearance different from relief?
12. What are ceramic tools made of?
13. When should ceramic tools be used?
14. According to the CCPA chart, what designation of carbide would be used for finish-turning aluminum?
15. According to the CCPA chart, what designation of carbide is used for roughing cuts on steel?
16. According to the Grade Classification chart, what Carboloy designation of carbide would be used for rough cuts in cast iron?
17. According to the Grade Classification chart, what number on the CCPA table would a Kennametal K5H have?
18. Extremely hard or abrasive materials are machined with diamond tools. Is the material removal rate very high? What kind of finishes are produced?
19. Polycrystalline diamond tools are similar in some ways to ceramic inserts. What is their major advantage?
20. When brazed carbide tools are sharpened, should you use an aluminum oxide wheel or a silicon carbide wheel?

SECTION I VERTICAL MILLING MACHINES

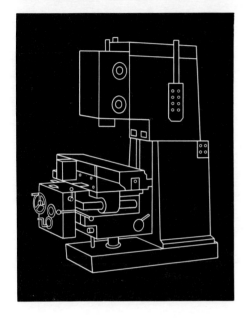

The standard vertical milling machine (Figure 1) is one of the most versatile machine tools found in the machine shop. This machine can accomplish a wide variety of machining tasks including **milling, drilling, slotting,** and **boring.** The spindle assembly of the vertical mill is designed to take the heavy side loads encountered in milling. The overall versatility of the vertical mill is further improved by taking advantage of new developments in drives and control systems. Two of these developments are hydraulic tracing controls (Figure 2) and line tracing by optical sensor (Figure 3). Electronic and computer control systems (N/C, C N/C) have also been applied to the vertical milling machine contributing to the development of the vertical spindle machining center (Figure 4).

VERTICAL MILLING MACHINE SAFETY

Be careful when handling tools and sharp edged workpieces to avoid getting cut. Use a rag to protect your hand. Workpieces should be rigidly supported and tightly clamped to withstand the usually high cutting forces encountered in machining. When a workpiece comes loose while machining, it is usually ruined and, often, so is the cutter. The operator can also be hurt by flying particles from the cutter or workpiece.

The cutting tools should be securely fastened in the machine spindle to prevent any movement during the cutting operation. Cutting tools need to be operated at the correct revolutions per minute (RPM) and feedrate for any given material. Excessive speeds and feeds can break the cutting tools. On vertical milling machines, care has to be exercised when swiveling the workhead to make angular cuts. After loosening the clamping bolts that hold the workhead to the overarm, retighten them lightly to create a slight drag. There should be enough friction between the workhead and the overarm that the head only swivels when pressure is applied to it. If the clamping bolts are completely loosened, the weight of the heavy spindle motor will flip the workhead upside down or until it hits the table, possibly smashing the operator's hand or a workpiece.

Measurements are frequently made during machining operations. Do not make any measurements until the spindle has come to a complete stop or standstill.

Figure 1. A popular type of manually operated vertical milling machine with accessory slotting attachment. This is called a ram-type turret mill (Courtesy Bridgeport Milling Machines, Division of Textron, Inc.).

Figure 3. Line tracing vertical milling machine (Courtesy Bridgeport Milling Machines, Division of Textron, Inc.).

Figure 2. Hydraulic tracing controls on a vertical milling machine especially developed for die sinking (Courtesy of Cincinnati Milacron).

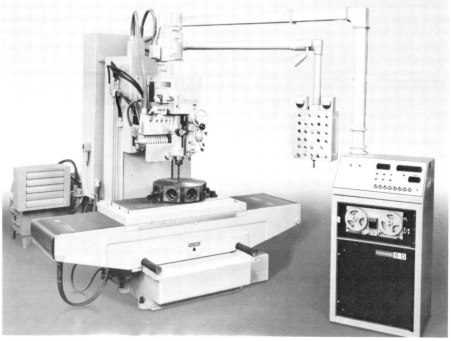

Figure 4. Numerically controlled vertical milling machine (Courtesy of Cincinnati Milacron).

UNIT 1 THE VERTICAL SPINDLE MILLING MACHINE

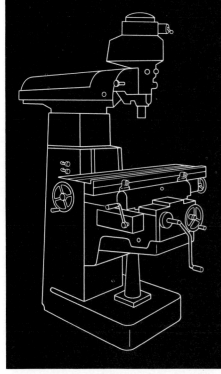

The first step in efficient and safe operation of any machine tool is to know the names of the machine parts and its various controls. The next step is to know the function of each part and control so that you can operate the machine without damage to it, the workpiece, or possible injury to yourself. The purpose of this unit is to acquaint you with the nomenclature of the vertical milling machine and to identify the machine controls and their functions. Before starting any milling job, take a short time to operate all the machine controls and observe their functions.

OBJECTIVES

After completing this unit, you should be able to:
1. Identify the important components and controls on the vertical milling machine.
2. Describe the functions of machine parts and controls.
3. Perform routine maintenance on the machine.

IDENTIFYING MACHINE PARTS, CONTROLS, AND THEIR FUNCTIONS

The major assemblies of the vertical milling machine are: base and column, knee and saddle, table, ram, and tool head (Figure 1).

Base and Column

The **base** and **column** are one piece and are the major structural component of this machine tool. A **dovetail slide** is machined on the face of the column to provide a vertical guide for the knee. A similar slide is machined on the top of the column to provide a guide for the ram. The top column slide and ram can be swiveled right and left of center to permit wide area positioning of the tool head over the table.

Knee

The **knee** engages the slide on the face of the column and is moved up and down by turning the **vertical traverse crank.** The knee supports the saddle and table. Knee locks are provided that will securely lock the knee at a given position.

Saddle

The **saddle** engages the slide on the top of the knee and can be moved in and out by turning the **cross traverse crank.** The saddle supports the table. Saddle locks are provided for the purpose of locking the saddle at a given position.

Table

The **table** engages the slide on the top of the saddle and is moved right and left by turning the **table traverse crank.** The workpiece or workholding device is secured to the table. Table locks are provided so that the table may be locked at a given position. Some milling machines have a power feed mechanism on the table. This permits a variable table feed rate in either direction during a milling operation.

Ram

The **ram** engages the swiveling slide on the top of the column. The ram is moved in and out by turning the **ram positioning pinion** gear. Ram locks are provided to secure the ram position.

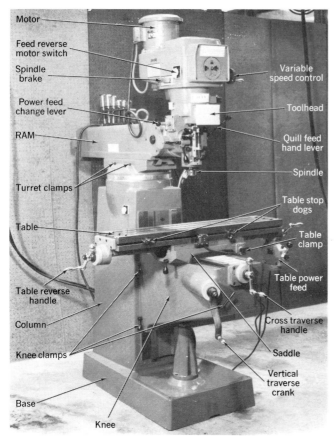

Figure 1. The important parts of a vertical milling machine (Lane Community College).

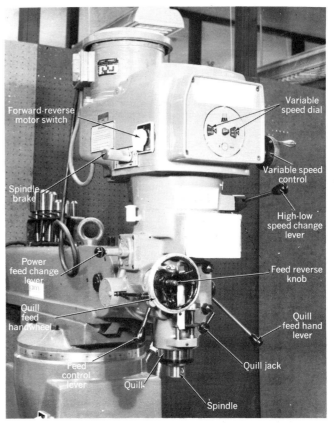

Figure 2. The toolhead (Lane Community College).

Tool Head

The **tool head** (Figure 2) is attached to the end of the ram, and is a complex assembly consisting of the following components.

1. **Drive motor** with **on/off switch**
2. **Drive belt** or **gear train for speed changing**
3. **Quill, spindle,** and **drawbolt**
4. **Quill feed** and **stop mechanism**

On many vertical milling machines, the entire tool head assembly can be swiveled with reference to the table and saddle axes.

Drive Motor, Switch, and Speed Changing.

The motor provides the driving force for the machine spindle and may contain the on/off switch. This is usually a three position switch that will reverse the rotation of the motor and spindle. **Be sure spindle is turning in the proper direction when you turn on the machine.** This will depend on the type of machining operation you may be doing and the type of milling cutter or drill you may be using.

Motor connection to the spindle is usually made through a **V-belt drive** or by a **direct coupled gear train.** On V-drives, spindle speed changes are made by loosening the motor swivel locks and moving the motor forward so as to loosen the belt tension. **All belt changing must be made with the machine off and the motor stopped. Do not attempt to make any adjustments to the belt drive mechanism while the machine is running.** To change speeds, the drive belt is shifted to the desired pulley stops and then the motor is swiveled back to position to provide proper belt tension.

Many milling machines have a high and low speed range. Speed ranges on belt driven mills are selected much in the same way that a lathe is placed in back gear. Follow the instructions on the tool head instruction plate for selection of speed ranges and **make sure that the motor is off** before making any adjustments.

On variable speed gear driven tool heads, spindle speeds are changed by moving the variable speed controls. Unlike the belt drive, this must be done while the machine is running. However, since the gear drive assemblies are totally enclosed, there is no danger to hands while making this adjustment.

The gear driven tool head has an advantage over its belt driven counterpart. Spindle speeds are continuously

Figure 3. Quill stop (Lane Community College).

Figure 4. Clamping devices (Lane Community College).

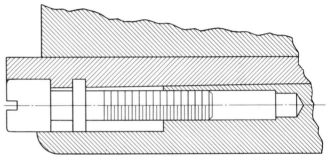

Figure 5. Gib adjusting screw (Courtesy Cincinnati Milacron).

variable within the range of the drive thus permitting an exact setting of spindle RPM based on cutting speed calculations. Speed changing with gear drives is also faster and more convenient than belt drives.

Quill, Spindle, Drawbolt, and Brake. The **quill** is nonrotating and contains the rotating spindle and bearings. The tool head contains the mechanism and controls that feed the quill up and down by power during such machining operations as drilling and boring. Quill feed rates are variable, usually .003, .006, and .015 per spindle revolution. Quill feed rate is selected by the control handle on the side of the tool head. The quill feed can be disengaged from the feed worm permitting it to be fed by hand using the hand wheel. The quill is also equipped with an automatic feature that will disengage the feed at a preset depth setting established by the quill stop (Figure 3). Some milling machines may have a turret quill stop (Section O, Unit 3, Figure 2). This permits a selection of depth settings to be preset and is useful for multiple or several different machining operations. The quill feed hand lever will rapidly position the quill or can be used for drill press operations. A quill lock is provided that will lock the quill at a preset position. Be sure to release this lock before engaging the quill power

feed. Engaging any power feeds with any locks in place can damage the feed mechanism.

The rotating part contained in the quill is the spindle. The lower end of the spindle accepts the collet (cutter holder) which is secured by the **spindle drawbolt.** The drawbolt extends through the hole in the center of the spindle and threads into the upper end of the collet. When the drawbolt is tightened, the collet is drawn into the taper in the spindle thus aligning and also holding the milling cutter.

To tighten the drawbolt, the **spindle brake** is applied so that the spindle will not turn. After the drawbolt is tight, the brake must be released before turning on the motor.

LOCKS, ADJUSTMENTS, AND MAINTENANCE

The knee, saddle, table, quill, and ram are all equipped with locks that will prevent movement of these parts (Figure 4). During machining, all axes except the moving one should be locked. This will increase the rigidity of the setup. Do not use these clamping devices to compensate for wear on the machine slides. If the machine slides become loose, make adjustments with the **gib adjustment screws** (Figure 5). Turning this screw in will

tighten a tapered gib. Make a partial turn on the screw, then try moving the unit with the hand sheel. Repeat this operation until a free but not loose movement is obtained. Too tight an adjustment squeezes the lubricant from the slides, resulting in rapid wear.

All machine tools require periodic adjustment and lubrication. Many mills are equipped with "one shot" lubricators often located on the side of the knee. Oil from the lubricator is pressure fed to the knee, saddle, and table slides. Any other oil cups on the machine should be kept filled with light oil as specified by the manufacturer.

SELF-TEST

1. Name the six major components of a vertical milling machine.
2. Which parts are used to move the table longitudinally?
3. Which parts are used to move the saddle?
4. What moves the quill manually?
5. What is the purpose of the table clamp?
6. What is the purpose of the spindle brake?
7. What is important when changing the spindle speed range from high to low?
8. Why is the toolhead fastened to a ram?
9. How is a loose table movement adjusted?
10. What is the purpose of the quill clamp?

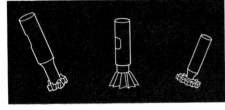

UNIT 2 CUTTING TOOLS AND CUTTER HOLDERS FOR THE VERTICAL MILLING MACHINE

The metal cutting versatility of the vertical milling machine can be fully realized and utilized by understanding, identifying, and selecting from the many types of milling cutters available for use on this machine tool. The purpose of this unit is to describe many of these common types of cutters and aid you in selecting the one that best fits your needs for a specific machining task.

OBJECTIVES

After completing this unit, you should be able to:
1. Identify common cutters for the vertical mill.
2. Select a proper cutter for a given machining task.

END MILLS

The most popular and frequently used cutting tool for the vertical milling machine is the **end mill**. End mills are so named because their primary cutting is done on their ends. End mills may have two, three, four, or more **flutes** and may be **right-hand** or **left-hand** cutting. To determine the cutting direction of an end mill, observe the cutter from its cutting end (Figure 1). A right-handed cutter will cut while turning in a counterclockwise direction.

A left-handed cutter will cut turning in a clockwise direction. The direction of flute twist or helix may also be right or left handed. For example, a right-handed helix twists to the right.

Two flute end mills can be used much like a drill for **plunge cutting**. These are called **center cutting** because they can make their own starting hole (Figure 2). Four flute end mills may also be center cutting. However, if these are center drilled or gashed on the end, they cannot start their own holes. This type of end mill will only cut on its periphery, but may be used in end milling provided the cut is begun off the workpiece or in a premachined hole or other cavity.

High Speed Steel Helical and Straight Flute End Mills

The **high speed steel end mill** is a very common cutter for the vertical mill. These cutters may be single ended (Figure 3) or double ended (Figure 4). They may also have straight flutes (Figure 5). **Slow, regular,** and **fast helix angles** are also available. An example of slow helix is where the helix angle of the cutter is about 12 degrees. A regular helix angle may be 30 degrees and a fast helix 40 degrees or more. Selection of helix angle will depend on the machining task. For example, aluminum can be efficient-machined with a high helix angle cutter (45 degrees) and with a highly polished cutting face to minimize chip adherence (Figure 6). Chips sticking to the cutting face can mar the surface finish of the part being machined. High speed steel end mills are readily available at reasonable cost in a wide variety of styles, shapes, and sizes.

Carbide End Mills

Carbide (tungsten carbide) end mills may be carbide tipped or made from solid carbide. These end mills are more expensive than high speed types. However, they are extremely efficient in difficult-to-machine materials and for production machining applications. Two common carbide end mills are: a two flute cutter with a negative axial rake and slow helix (Figure 7) designed to cut

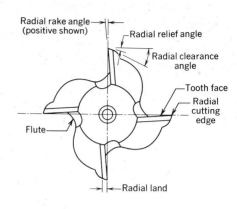

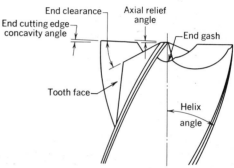

Figure 1. End mill nomenclature (Copyright © National Twist Drill & Tool Div., Lear Siegler, Inc.).

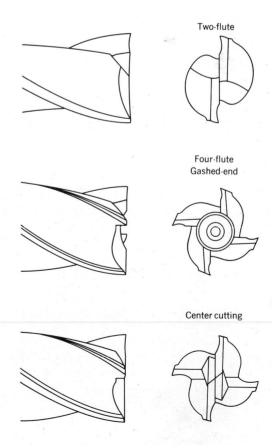

Figure 2. Types of end teeth on end mills (Copyright © National Twist Drill & Tool Div., Lear Siegler, Inc.).

Figure 3. Single end helical teeth end mill (Courtesy of Weldon Tool Company, Cleveland, Ohio).

Figure 4. Two flute, double end, helical teeth end mill (Courtesy of Weldon Tool Company, Cleveland, Ohio).

Figure 5. Straight tooth, single end end mill (Courtesy of Weldon Tool Company, Cleveland, Ohio).

Figure 6. Forty-five degree helix angle aluminum end mill (Courtesy of Weldon Tool Company, Cleveland, Ohio).

Figure 7. Two flute, carbide tipped end mill (Courtesy of Brown & Sharpe Mfg. Co.).

Figure 8. Four flute, carbide tipped end mill (Courtesy of Brown & Sharpe Mfg. Co.).

steel, and a four flute cutter with a positive rake for nonferrous materials such as brass and aluminum (Figure 8).

The **disposable insert** carbide end mill (Figure 9) has carbide inserts providing the cutting edges. When the edges of the insert become dull, they are turned to expose a new cutting edge to the work. When all edges are dull the insert is discarded and a new one installed. No sharpening of the cutter is required. Various grades

Figure 9. Disposable insert.

Figure 10. Roughing mill (Copyright © Illinois Tool Works, Inc., 1976).

Figure 11. Three flute, tapered end mill (Courtesy of Weldon Tool Company, Cleveland, Ohio).

of carbide are also used depending on the material to be machined.

Roughing and Tapered End Mills

The **roughing end mill** (Figure 10) is used when large amounts of material must be quickly removed (roughed) from the workpiece. These end mills are also called **hogging** end mills and have a wavy tooth form cut on their periphery. These waved teeth form many individual cutting edges. The tip of each wave contacts the work and produces one short compact chip. Each succeeding wave tip is offset from the next one, which results in a relatively smooth surface finish. During the cutting operation, a number of teeth are in contact with the work. This reduces the possibility of vibration or chatter.

Tapered end mills (Figure 11) are used in mold making, die work, and pattern making, where precise tapered surfaces need to be made. Tapered end mills have included tapers ranging from 1 degree to over 10 degrees. Tapered end mills are also called diesinking mills.

Geometry Forming, Dovetail, T-Slot, Woodruff Key, and Shell End Mills

Several types of end mills are used to form a particular geometry on the workpiece.

Figure 12. Two flute, single end, ball end mill (Courtesy of Weldon Tool Company, Cleveland, Ohio).

Figure 13. Corner rounding milling cutter (Copyright © Illinois Tool Works, Inc., 1976).

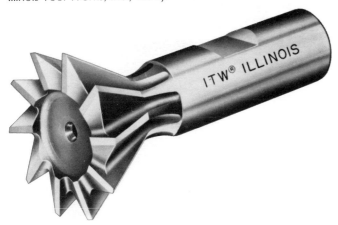

Figure 14. Single angle milling cutter (Copyright © Illinois Tool Works, Inc., 1976).

Ball-end end mills (Figure 12) have two or more flutes and form an inside radius or fillet between surfaces. Ball-end end mills are used in tracer milling and in die sinking operations. Round bottom grooves can also be machined with them. Precise convex radii can be machined on a milling machine with **corner rounding end mills** (Figure 13). Dovetails are machined with single angle milling cutters (Figure 14). The two commonly

Figure 15. T-slot milling cutter (Courtesy of Weldon Tool Company, Cleveland, Ohio).

Figure 16. Woodruff keyslot milling cutter (Copyright © Illinois Tool Works, Inc., 1976).

available angles are 45 degrees and 60 degrees. T-slots in machine tables and workholding devices are machined with **T-slot cutters** (Figure 15). T-slot cutters are made in sizes to fit standard T-nuts.

Woodruff key ways are cut into shafts to retain a woodruff key as a driving and connecting member between shafts and pulleys or gears. **Woodruff key way** cutters (Figure 16) come in many different standardized sizes. When larger flat surfaces need to be machined, a **shell end mill** (Figure 17) can be used. Shell end mills are more economical to produce because less of the costly tool material is needed to make one than for a solid shank end mill of the same size. To obtain rapid metal removal, shell end mills are made as a roughing type mill (Figure 18) with a wavy thread forming many cutting edges. Shell mills are also made with carbide inserts (Figure 19). The ease with which new sharp cutting edges can be installed makes this a very practical, efficient cutting tool. The great number of different carbide grades available makes it possible to select a grade suitable for all work materials.

Flycutters
A **flycutter** is a single point tool often consisting of a high speed or carbide tool secured in an appropriate holder (Figure 20). Although a flycutter is not truly an end mill, it is used for end milling applications. Flycutters are often used to take light face cuts from large surface areas. The tool bit in the flycutter must be properly ground to obtain the correct rake and clearance angles for the

Figure 17.   Shell end mill (Copyright © Illinois Tool Works, Inc., 1976).

Figure 19.   Shell mill with carbide inserts (Lane Community College).

Figure 20.   Fly cutter (Lane Community College).

Figure 18.   Shell-type roughing mill (Copyright © Illinois Tool Works, Inc., 1976).

material being machined. Flycutters may also be used for boring operations.

CUTTER HOLDING ON THE VERTICAL MILL

No matter which of the previously discussed milling cutters that you might be using, they all must be securely

mounted in the machine spindle before beginning a machining operation. **Collet holders** are widely used for this purpose.

The most rigid type of these is the **solid collet** (Figure 21), sometimes called an **end mill holder.** The solid collet has a precision ground shank that fits the spindle on the milling machine. Most common vertical spindle milling machines have an R 8 spindle, meaning that they will accept all standard R 8 tooling. The solid collet has a hole that just fits the shank of the end mill. The end mill

Figure 21. Solid collet (Lane Community College).

Figure 22. Split collet (Lane Community College).

Figure 23. Quick-change adapter and tool holders (Lane Community College).

is secured with set screws that bear against a flat on the cutter shank. Solid collets will accommodate many different sizes of end mill shanks.

The **split collet** (Figure 22) is widely used to hold cutters on the vertical mill. When the tapered part of the collet is pulled into the spindle taper by the drawbolt, the split in the collet permits it to squeeze tightly against the shank of the end mill. Although split collets are very effective cutter holding devices, it is possible for a cutter to be pulled from the collet because of heavy feedrates or the tool being dull. Helical flute end mills may tend to be pulled from the collet as well. In this respect the solid collet has an advantage over the split type since here the set screws prevent slippage of the cutter.

Quick Change Systems

To facilitate and speed tool changing, a **quick change** tooling system may be used. Different tools can be mounted in their individual tool holders and preset to different lengths if desired. The tool holders are then mounted and removed from the master holder in the machine spindle by means of a clamping ring (Figure 23).

Figure 24. Shell mill arbor (Courtesy of Weldon Tool Company, Cleveland, Ohio).

Arbors

Shell end mills or saws can be mounted on **arbors** where the cutter is secured by a nut. The shank of the arbor is the same as the shank of either the solid or split collet (Figure 24).

SELF-TEST

1. How is a right-hand cut end mill identified?
2. What is characteristic of end mills that can be used for plunge cutting?
3. What is the main difference between a general purpose end mill and one designed to cut aluminum?
4. When are carbide tipped end mills chosen over high speed steel end mills?
5. To remove a considerable amount of material, what kind of end mill is used?
6. Where are tapered end mills used?
7. Why are tools with carbide inserts used?
8. How are straight shank tools held in the machine spindle?
9. How are shell end mills driven?
10. Why are quick-change tool holders used?

UNIT 3 SETUPS ON THE VERTICAL MILLING MACHINE

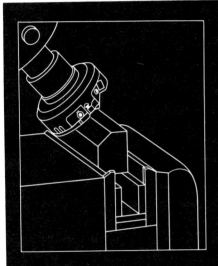

Before any machining can be done on the vertical mill, the toolhead must be squared to the table and saddle axes. Also, the workpiece or workholding device must be secured to and aligned with the table and saddle axes. These common machine setups must be made or rechecked each time the machine is used. The purpose of this unit is to describe the procedure for squaring the tool head and discuss common workpiece setups.

OBJECTIVES

After completing this unit, you should be able to:
1. Square the toolhead.
2. Setup and align a workpiece on the table.
3. Setup and align a mill vise.
4. Locate the edges of a workpiece relative to the spindle and position the spindle over a hole center.

SQUARING THE TOOL HEAD

On many vertical mills, although not all, the toolhead can be swiveled relative to the table and saddle axes (Figure 1). This feature adds to the versatility of the machine tool since it permits drilling and milling on angled surfaces. However, by far the largest number of milling and drilling operations are done with the tool head set square to the table and saddle axes. This alignment is quite critical as it is directly responsible for square mill cuts and straight drilled holes. The following procedure is used to square the toolhead:

1. Fasten a dial indicator in the machine spindle (Figure 2). The indicator should sweep a circle slightly smaller than the width of the table.
2. Lower the quill until the indicator contact point is depressed .015 to .020 in. Lock the quill in this position. The spindle indicator will be turned by hand and used to determine the position of the toolhead relative to the table and saddle. There is a tendency for the indicator tip to catch in the table T-slot as it is turned. To prevent this, an accurately machine ring can be used as an indicating surface. A large

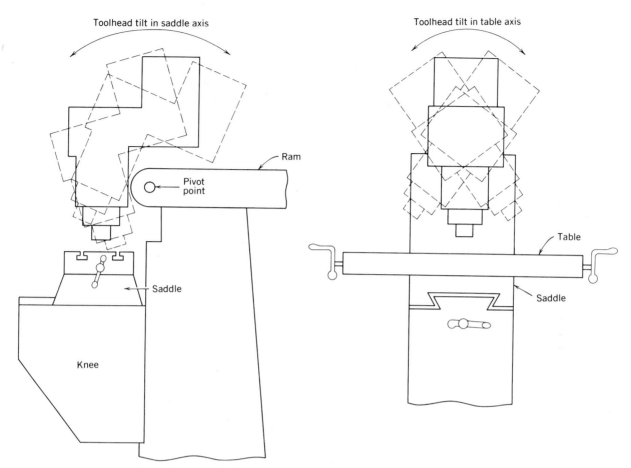

Figure 1. Vertical mill toolhead tilting capability.

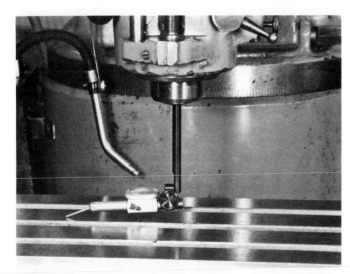

Figure 2. Aligning the toolhead square to the table with a dial indicator (Lane Community College).

bearing race or the swivel base from a precision mill vise can be used for this purpose. If you use a ring for an indicating surface, be sure that the table is clean and that there are no burrs on the ring. **The ring must also be accurately machined.**

3. **Tighten the knee clamp locks.** If this is neglected, the knee will sag in the front and introduce an error in the indicator reading.

4. Loosen the head toolhead clamping bolts one at a time and retighten them to provide a slight drag on the toolhead. Fine adjustments will be easier if the toolhead is just loose enough to be moved by slight pressure.

5. Rotate the spindle by hand until the indicator is to the left or right of the spindle and in line with the table axis.

6. Set the indicator bezel to zero. The example shown will aid you in the alignment procedure (Figure 3).

7. Rotate the spindle 180 degrees so that the indicator is positioned on the opposite side and in line with the table axis. Note the reading at this position.

8. Tilt the toolhead using the tilt screw until the indicator moves back toward zero, one-half the amount showing.

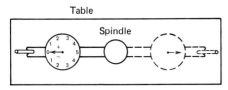

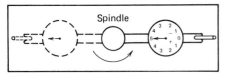

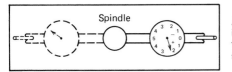

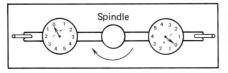

	Set indicator to zero and rotate 180°
	Observe reading (in this example +.005)
	Adjust toolhead until indicator moves back toward zero ½ amount shown (.0025)
	Reset indicator to zero and move back 180°. Readings should be the same on both sides

Figure 3. Indicator readings while squaring the toolhead.

Figure 4. Work aligned by locating against stops in T-slots (Lane Community College).

9. Turn the indicator 180 degrees and see if the reading varies. If both readings are the same, tighten the toolhead clamping bolts and recheck the readings. Tightening the toolhead clamps will sometimes displace the head slightly requiring a small additional adjustment.

10. Repeat this procedure for the toolhead alignment relative to the saddle axis.

11. After the toolhead has been squared in both axes, recheck its position and be sure that all clamping bolts are tight.

WORKHOLDING ON THE VERTICAL MILL
The two most common workholding methods on the vertical mill are securing parts *directly to the table* by means of clamps, or holding in a **mill vise.**

Mounting Directly to the Table
Mounting a workpiece directly to the machine table is an excellent workholding method. The same clamping techniques that you learned in drilling are applied in milling. Be careful not to distort the workpiece when applying clamping pressure.

In many cases, the workpiece must be aligned with the table or saddle axis to insure parallel or perpendicular cuts. A workpiece can be quite accurately aligned by placing it against **stops** that just fit the table T-slots

Figure 5. Measuring the distance from the edge of the table to the workpiece (Lane Community College).

(Figure 4). Another method is to **measure** from the edge of the table to the workpiece (Figure 5).

Probably the most accurate method of workpiece alignment is to use a **dial indicator** fastened in the machine spindle or to the toolhead (Figure 6). The workpiece is brought into contact with the indicator and the table or saddle is run back and forth while the workpiece position is adjusted so that the indicator reads zero.

Using a Mill Vise
A precision **mill vise** may also be used to hold the part

Figure 6. Aligning a workpiece with the aid of a dial indicator (Lane Community College).

Figure 7. Offset edgefinder (Lane Community College).

Figure 8. Work approaches the tip of the offset edgefinder (Lane Community College).

being machined. The vise must also be aligned with the table or saddle axis. Once again, use a dial indicator for this purpose and always indicate a vise on its solid jaw. Mill vises are precision tools. Always treat them gently when setting them down on the machine table. Be sure that the table is clean and that there are no burrs on the bottom of the vise.

Soft Vise Jaws. Sometimes a mill vise may be equipped with soft steel or aluminum jaws instead of the regular hardened steel types. After the vise has been bolted to the mill table and roughly aligned, a light cut can be taken on the soft jaws. The result of this procedure is a vise jaw that has been machined true to the axis of the saddle or table. Soft jaws are often used in production machining operations or where it might be desirable to shape the vise jaw in a certain way in order to hold a particular part to be machined.

WORK EDGE AND HOLE CENTERLINE LOCATING

After a workpiece has been set up on the mill, it may be necessary to position the machine spindle relative to the edge of the part, or to center the spindle over an existing hole. **Edge finding** and **centerline finding** are very common operations that you will encounter almost daily in general milling machine operations.

Using an Edgefinder

A very useful tool for edge finding is the **offset edgefind-** er (Figure 7). The edgefinder consists of a shank with a floating tip that is retained by an internal spring. The diameter of the edgefinder tip is accurately machined to a known diameter usually .200 or .500 in. Follow this procedure for using the edgefinder.

1. Secure the edgefinder in a collet or chuck in the machine spindle.

2. Set the spindle speed to about 600 to 800 RPM, and slide the edgefinder tip over so that it is off center.

3. Start the spindle and lower the quill or raise the knee so that the edgefinder tip can contact the edge of the part to be located.

4. Turn the table or saddle cranks and move the workpiece until it contacts the rotating edgefinder tip. *Continue to slowly advance the workpiece against the edgefinder tip until the tip suddenly springs sideways. Stop movement at this moment* (Figure 8). The machine spindle is now positioned a distance equal to *one-half of the edgefinder tip diameter from the edge of the workpiece.* If you are using a .200 diameter tip, the centerline of the spindle is .100 from the edge of the workpiece. **If you are unsure of the situation, back off and repeat the procedure.** Watch the movement of the edgefinder tip.

5. When you are sure that the positioning is correct, lower the workpiece or raise the spindle and set the

Figure 9.   Dial indicator locating the center of a hole (Lane Community College).

table or saddle micrometer collars to zero. Then move the table or saddle the additional .100 *in the same direction* that it was moving as it approached the workpiece. This will prevent a backlash error from being introduced due to slack in the table or saddle nuts.

Hole Center Locating
Many vertical milling machine operations require that the machine spindle be positioned over the center of an existing hole in the workpiece. Use a dial test indicator and follow the procedure listed.

1. Secure a dial test indicator in the machine spindle.
2. Lower the quill or raise the knee until the indicator tip is below the top surface that the hole is through.
3. Turn the spindle by hand and roughly position the table and saddle until the indicator can be turned completely around in the hole.
4. Move the indicator tip out until it contacts the side of the hole and suitable amount of indication appears on the indicator dial.
5. Position the indicator in line with either the table or saddle axis and set the bezel to zero. Turn the indicator 180 degrees and observe the reading.
6. Adjust the table or saddle position so that the indicator reading is reduced by one-half (moving back toward zero). Turn the spindle 180 degrees and

observe the reading once again. If an offset remains, reduce the amount showing on the indicator by one-half and recheck the reading on the opposite side.

7. When a zero reading is obtained on opposite points in the hole, check the part in the perpendicular axis and position by the above procedure. A mirror can be used to see the indicator face when it is turned to the back (Figure 9).

Provided the hole to be located is round, the indicator will read zero both on the table and saddle axes. However, if the hole is out of round (eccentric), zero indicator readings can be obtained only on one axis unless the bezel is reset for the perpendicular axis. Nonetheless, the centerline of the hole can be found by positioning the part such that **independent but equal** readings are obtained on the table and saddle axes. For example, after establishing a zero reading on the table axis, the saddle axis reads plus or minus, but equally plus or minus on each side of the hole because the hole is eccentric. The machine spindle will still be accurately positioned over the center of the feature.

PROCEDURE

Machining Holes in Vise Body (Figure 10)

1. Align the workhead square to the machine table.
2. Align and fasten a machine vise on the table so its jaw is parallel to the long axis of the table.
3. Mount the vise body in the machine vise with the bottom surface against the solid jaw of the machine vise.
4. Mount an edgefinder in a spindle collet and align the spindle axis with the base surface of the vise body.
5. Move the table the required .452 in. distance and lock the table cross slide.
6. Now pick up the outside of the solid jaw of the vise body.
7. Move to the first hole location 1.015 in. from the outside edge.
8. Center drill this hole.
9. Use a $\frac{1}{4}$ in. diameter twist drill and drill this hole $1\frac{1}{2}$ in. deep.
10. Repeat steps 8 and 9 for the remaining eight holes. Accurate positioning is done with the micrometer dials.
11. Remove the workpiece from the machine vise. Turn it over so that the just drilled holes are down and the bottom surface of the vise body is again against the solid jaw.
12. Use the edgefinder to pick up the two sides, as for the first drilling operation.

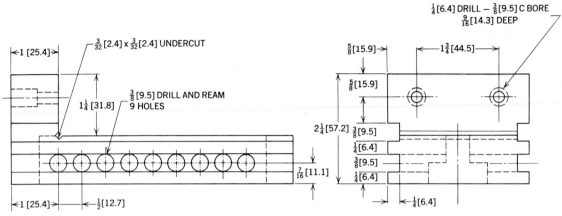

Figure 10.   Machining the holes in the vise body.

Figure 11.   Drilling $\frac{11}{32}$ in. diameter holes in the vise body (Lane Community College).

13. Position the spindle over the first hole location, again with the first hole on the solid jaw side.

14. Center drill this hole.

15. Drill this hole with a $\frac{1}{4}$ in. diameter drill deep enough to meet the hole from below.

16. Switch to an $\frac{11}{32}$ in. diameter drill and drill completely through the vise body (Figure 11). The $\frac{1}{4}$ in. hole acts as a pilot hole to let the $\frac{11}{32}$ in. drill come out in the correct place on the bottom side.

17. Change from the $\frac{11}{32}$ in. drill to a $\frac{3}{8}$ in. diameter machine reamer and ream this hole completely through also (Figure 12).

Figure 12.   Reaming $\frac{3}{8}$ in. diameter holes in the vise body (Lane Community College).

18. Repeat steps 14 to 17 for the remaining eight holes.
19. Reposition the workpiece so it is upright in the machine vise with the solid jaw of the vise body up.
20. With an edgefinder, pick up the edges of the workpiece.
21. Position for the two hole locations and drill the $\frac{17}{64}$ in. diameter holes with their $\frac{13}{32}$ in. diameter counterbores (Figure 13).
22. Remove all burrs.

Figure 13. Drill and counterbore holes in the solid jaw of the vise body (Lane Community College).

SELF-TEST

1. How can workpieces be aligned when they are clamped to the table?
2. How is a vise aligned on a machine table?
3. When is the toolhead alignment checked?
4. Why is it important that the knee clamping bolts are tight before aligning a toolhead?
5. Why does the toolhead alignment need to be checked again after all the clamping bolts are tightened?
6. How can the machine spindle be located exactly over the edge of a workpiece?
7. With a .200 in. edgefinder tip, when do you know that the spindle axis is .100 in. away from the edge of the workpiece?
8. What is the recommended RPM to use with an offset edgefinder?
9. When locating a number of positions on a workpiece, how can you eliminate the backlash in the machine screws?
10. How is the center of an existing hole located?

UNIT 4 FEEDS AND SPEEDS FOR END MILLING

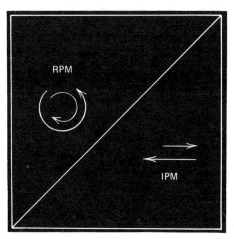

In the preceding units you learned the nomenclature of the vertical milling machine, how to square the toolhead, select a proper cutter, setup, and locate the workpiece. Equally important is the selection of cutting speeds and feeds for the milling work you will be doing. The purpose of this unit is to describe and discuss cutting speeds and feeds and to familiarize you with the calculations in determining these factors:

OBJECTIVES

After completing this unit, you should be able to:
Calculate cutting speeds and feeds for end milling operations.

CUTTING SPEEDS

Cutting speed in milling is the rate at which a point on the cutter passes by a point on the workpiece in a given period of time. Cutting speed is often abbreviated **CS** and is an extremely important factor in all machining operations. For rotating milling cutters, CS is expressed as a function of cutter RPM by the formula

$$RPM = \frac{CS \times 4}{D}$$

where **RPM is revolutions per minute of the cutter, CS is the cutting speed of the material being machined in feet per minute of tool passing by the workpiece, and D is the diameter of the cutter in inches.**

Cutting speed constants (Table 1) are influenced by the cutting tool material, workpiece material, rigidity of the machine setup and the use of coolants. As a rule, lower cutting speeds are used to machine hard or tough materials or where heavy cuts are taken and it is desirable to minimize tool wear and thus maximize tool life. Higher cutting speeds are used in machining softer materials in order to achieve better surface finishes. Higher speeds also apply when using small diameter cutters for light cuts on frail workpieces and in delicate setups. Table 2 gives starting values for common materials. These may have to be varied up or down depending on the specific machining task. Always observe the cutting action carefully and make appropriate speed corrections as needed. Until you gain some experience in milling, **use the lower values** in the table when selecting cutting speeds.

Table 1

Cutting Speeds and Starting Values for Some Commonly Used Materials

Work Material	Tool Material	
	High Speed Steel	Cemented Carbide
Aluminum	300–800	1000–2000
Brass	200–400	500–800
Bronze	65–130	200–400
Cast iron	50–80	250–350
Low carbon steel	60–100	300–600
Medium carbon steel	50–80	225–400
High carbon steel	40–70	150–250
Medium alloy steel	40–70	150–350
Stainless steel	30–80	100–300

Table 2

Feeds for End Mills (Feed per Tooth in Inches)

Cutter Diameter	Aluminum	Brass	Bronze	Cast Iron	Low Carbon Steel	High Carbon Steel	Medium Alloy Steel	Stainless Steel
$\frac{1}{8}$	.002	.001	.0005	.0005	.0005	.0005	.0005	.0005
$\frac{1}{4}$	.002	.002	.001	.001	.001	.001	.0005	.001
$\frac{3}{8}$	.003	.003	.002	.002	.002	.002	.001	.002
$\frac{1}{2}$	.005	.003	.003	.0025	.003	.002	.001	.002
$\frac{3}{4}$	.006	.004	.003	.003	.004	.003	.002	.003
1	.007	.005	.004	.0035	.005	.003	.003	.004
$1\frac{1}{2}$	.008	.005	.005	.004	.006	.004	.003	.004
2	.009	.006	.005	.005	.007	.004	.003	.005

FEEDRATES

Another equally important factor in safe and efficient machining is **feedrate.** Feedrate is the rate at which the material is advanced into the cutter or where the cutter is advanced into the work material. Since each tooth of a multitooth milling cutter is cutting, a chip of a given thickness will be removed depending on the rate of feed. Chip thickness affects the life of the milling cutter. Very thick chips will dull the cutting edges rapidly. Excessive feedrates can cause a chipped cutting edge or a broken cutter. The highest possible feedrate per tooth will give the longest tool life between resharpenings. Feedrate in milling is measured in inches per minute, or IPM, and is calculated by the formula

$$IPM = F \times N \times RPM$$

where IPM = feedrate in inches per minute, N = number of teeth in the cutter being used, and RPM = revolutions per minute of the cutter.

CUTTING SPEED AND FEEDRATE CALCULATIONS

The first step is to calculate the **correct RPM** for the cutter. Refer to Table 1 for the cutting speed starting value.

EXAMPLE
Calculate RPM for a $\frac{1}{2}$ in. diameter HSS end mill machining aluminum.

$$RPM = \frac{CS \times 4}{D} = \frac{300 \times 4}{1/2} = \frac{1200}{.5} = 2400$$

The next step is to calculate the **feedrate.** Refer to Table 2 for the starting values.

$$
\begin{aligned}
IPM &= F \times N \times RPM \\
&= .005 \text{ (feed per tooth, Table 2)} \\
&\quad \times N \text{ (number of teeth)} \times RPM \\
&= .005 \times 2 \times 2400 = 24 \text{ in. per minute}
\end{aligned}
$$

Therefore, the cutter should revolve at 2400 RPM and the feedrate should be 24 inches per minute. Feed rates can also be expressed in terms of inches per revolution of the cutter (IPR).

DEPTH OF CUT

The third factor to be considered in using end mills is the depth of cut. The depth of cut is limited by the amount of material that needs to be removed from the workpiece, by the power available at the machine spindle, and by the rigidity of the workpiece, tool, and setup. As a rule, the depth of cut for an end mill should not exceed one-half of the diameter of the tool. But if deeper cuts need to be made, the feedrate needs to be reduced to

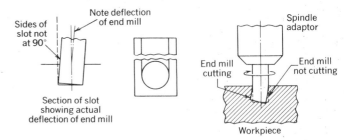

Figure 1.   The causes of a leaning slot in end milling.

prevent tool breakage. The end mill must be sharp and should run concentric in the end mill holder. The end mill should be mounted with no more tool overhang than necessary to do the job.

A problem that occasionally arises when using end mills to machine grooves or slots is a slot with nonperpendicular sides. Grooves with leaning sides are caused by worn spindles, excessive tool projection from the spindle, dull end mills, or excessive feedrates. The leaning slot is produced by an end mill that is deflected by high cutting forces (Figure 1). To reduce the tendency of the tool to cut a leaning slot, reduce the feedrate, use end mills with only a short projection from the spindle, and use end mills with straight or low helix angle flutes.

COOLANTS

Milling as well as other machining operations is often done using a coolant or cutting fluid. Coolants serve to **dissipate heat** generated by the friction of the cutter against the workpiece. They also help to **lubricate** the interface between the cutting edge and work and to **wash chips** from the cut. Many machining operations are greatly facilitated with coolants. **Productivity is increased, tool life extended, and surface finish on the workpiece improved.**

Typical coolants are water based soluble oils, petroleum oils, and synthetic oils. Water based coolants have excellent heat transfer qualities; other oils result in good surface finishes. Coolants may be applied to the cut in a flood stream or by an air/coolant mist mix. When using coolants with carbide cutters, sufficient flow must be maintained at the cutting edge so that the carbide does not experience intermittent heating and cooling. This can result in thermal cracking of the carbide and premature tool failure. If you are milling without the use of pumped coolant, the application of a standard cutting oil with a pump oil can will greatly facilitate your work.

Some materials such as cast iron, brass, and plastics are often machined dry. A stream of compressed air can be used to cool tools and keep the cutting area clear of chips. **Take precautions to prevent flying chips from causing an injury.**

SELF-TEST

1. When are the lower cutting speeds recommended?
2. When are the higher cutting speeds used?
3. Should you always use calculated RPM?
4. When are cutting fluids used?
5. When should machining be performed dry?
6. How is the tool life of an end mill affected by the chip thickness of a cut?
7. What is normally considered the maximum depth of cut for an end mill?
8. What are the limitations on the depth of cut?
9. Calculate the RPM for a $\frac{3}{4}$ in. diameter HSS end mill to machine brass.
10. Calculate the feedrate for a two flute $\frac{1}{4}$ in. diameter carbide end mill to machine medium alloy steel.

UNIT 5 VERTICAL MILLING MACHINE OPERATIONS

The vertical milling machine is one of the most versatile machine tools found in the machine shop. The purpose of this unit is to explore some of this versatility and give you an idea of the wide scope of machining capability on this machine.

OBJECTIVE

After completing this unit, you should be able to: Identify and select vertical milling machine setups and operations for a variety of machining tasks.

CLIMB AND CONVENTIONAL MILLING

In milling, the direction that the workpiece is being fed can either be the same as the direction of cutter rotation or can be opposed to the direction of cutter rotation. When the direction of feed is opposed to the direction of rotation, this is said to be conventional or up milling (Figure 1). When the direction of feed is the same as the direction of cutter rotation, this is said to be climb or down milling, because the cutter is attempting to climb onto the workpiece as it is fed into the cutter. If there is any large amount of backlash in the table or saddle nuts, the workpiece can be pulled into the cutter during climb milling. This can result in a broken cutter, damaged workpiece, and possible injury from flying metal. Climb milling should be avoided in most every case. However, in certain situations it may be desirable to climb mill. For

example, if the milling machine has ball nuts and screws where backlash is virtually eliminated, climb milling is an acceptable technique. Even on conventional machines, climb milling with a **very light cut** can result in a better surface finish since chips are not swept back through the cut.

During any milling operation, all table movements should be locked except the one that is moving. This will insure the most rigid setup possible. Spiral fluted end mills may work their way out of a split collet when deep heavy cuts are made or when the end mill gets dull. As a precaution, to warn you that this is happening, you can make a mark with a felt tip pen on the revolving end mill shank where it meets the collet face. Observing this mark during the cut will give you an early indication if the end mill is changing its position in the collet.

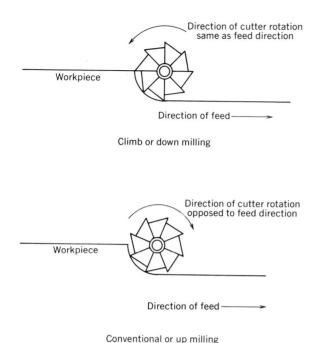

Climb or down milling

Conventional or up milling

Figure 1. Climb and conventional milling.

COMMON MILLING OPERATIONS

Machining Steps and Squaring

Common milling operations on the vertical mill include machining steps (Figure 2) and squaring or machining two surfaces perpendicular to each other (Figure 3). The ends of the workpiece can be machined square and to a given length by using the peripheral teeth of an end mill.

Milling a Cavity

Center cutting end mills make their own starting hole when used to mill a pocket or cavity (Figure 4). Prior to making any mill cuts, the outline of the cavity should be laid out on the workpiece. Only when finish cuts are made should these layout lines disappear. Good milling practice is to rough out the cavity to within .030 in. of finished size before making any finish cuts.

When you are milling a cavity, the direction of the feed should be against the rotation of the cutter (Figure 5). This assures positive control over the distance the cutter travels and prevents the workpiece from being pulled into the cutter because of backlash. When you reverse the direction of table travel, you will have to compensate for the backlash in the table feed mechanism.

End Milling a Shaft Keyway

A common end milling operation on the vertical mill is keyway milling. A shaft keyway must be both centered

Figure 2. Using an end mill to mill steps (Lane Community College).

Figure 3. Using an end mill to square stock (Lane Community College).

on the shaft and cut to the correct depth. The following procedure may be used.

1. Secure the workpiece to the machine table or in an indicator aligned mill vise.

Figure 4. Using an end mill to machine a pocket (Lane Community College).

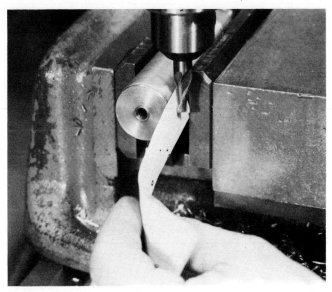

Figure 6. Setting an end mill to the side of a shaft with the aid of a paper feeler (Lane Community College).

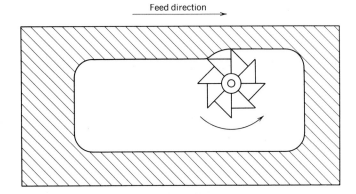

Feed direction

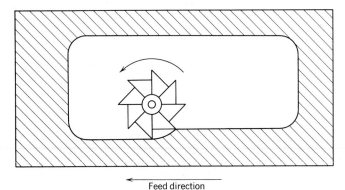

Feed direction

Figure 5. Feed direction is against cutter rotation.

2. Select the correct size of cutter either in a two flute or center cutting multiflute type and preferably one that has not been reduced in diameter by resharpenings. Install the cutter in the machine spindle.

3. Move the workpiece aside and lower the cutter beside the part. With the spindle motor off, insert a slip of paper between cutter and workpiece.

4. Use the saddle crank and move the workpiece toward the cutter until the paper feeler is pulled between cutter and work as you rotate the spindle by hand. At this point, the cutter is about .002 in. from the cutter (Figure 6).

5. Set the saddle micrometer collar to zero compensating for the .002 in. of paper thickness.

6. Add the diameter of the shaft and cutter and divide by two. This is the total distance to move the workpiece for centering.

7. Raise the cutter clear of the work and move the workpiece over the correct amount **in the same direction that it was moving as it approached the cutter.**

8. Raise the quill to its top position and lock saddle in place.

9. Move the table crank to position the cutter at the point where the keyway is to begin.

10. Start the spindle and raise the knee until the cutter makes a circular mark equal to the cutter diameter (Figure 7). Set the knee micrometer collar to zero. Raise the knee a distance equal to $\frac{1}{2}$ the cutter diameter plus .005 in. and lock knee in this position. Using correct speeds and feeds mill the keyway to required length (Figure 8).

Machining T-Slots, Dovetails, Angle Milling, and Drilling

To machine a T-slot or a dovetail into a workpiece, two operations are performed. First, a slot is cut with a regular end mill and then a T-slot cutter or a single angle milling cutter is used to finish the contour (Figures 9 and

Figure 7. Cutter centered over the shaft and lowered to make a circular mark (Lane Community College).

Figure 9. Milling a slot and then the dovetail (Lane Community College).

Figure 8. After centering and setting depth, keyway is milled to required length (Lane Community College).

Figure 10. First a slot is milled and then the T-slot cutter makes the T-slot (Lane Community College).

10). Angular cuts on workpieces can be made by tilting the workpiece in a vise with the aid of a protractor (Figure 11) and its built-in spirit level.

Machining the angle can be performed with an end mill (Figure 12) or with a shell mill (Figure 13). Another possibility for machining angles is the tilting of the workhead (Figures 14 and 15).

Accurate holes can be drilled at any angle that the head can be swiveled to. These holes can be drilled by using the sensitive quill feed lever or the power feed mechanism (Figure 16) or, in the case of vertical holes, the knee can be raised.

Figure 11. Setting up a workpiece for an angular cut with a protractor (Lane Community College).

Figure 12. Machining an angle with an end mill (Lane Community College).

Figure 13. Using a shell mill to machine an angle (Lane Community College).

Figure 14. Cutting an angle by tilting the workhead and using the end teeth of an end mill (Lane Community College).

Figure 15. Cutting an angle by tilting the workhead and using the peripheral teeth of an end mill (Lane Community College).

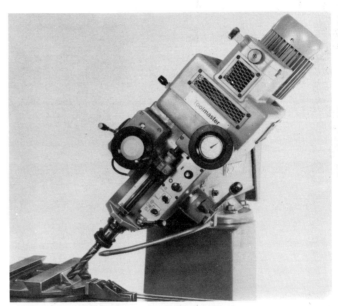

Figure 16. Drilling of accurately located holes (Courtesy of Cincinnati Milacron).

Other Vertical Mill Operations and Accessories

Holes can be machine tapped by using the sensitive quill feed lever and the instant spindle reversal knob (Figure 17). When an offset boring head is mounted in the spindle, precisely located and accurately dimensioned holes can be bored (Figure 18). Circular slots can be milled

Figure 17. Tapping in a vertical milling machine (Courtesy of Cincinnati Milacron).

Figure 18. Boring with an offset boring head (Courtesy of Cincinnati Milacron).

Figure 19. Using a rotary table to mill a circular slot (Courtesy of Cincinnati Milacron).

Figure 20. A dividing head in use (Courtesy of Cincinnati Milacron).

when a rotary table is used (Figure 19). Precise indexing can be performed when a dividing head is mounted on the milling machine. Figure 20 shows the milling of a square on the end of a shaft. On many vertical milling machines a shaping attachment is mounted on the rear of the ram. This shaping attachment can be brought over the machine table by swiveling the ram 180 degrees.

Figure 21. A shaping head used to cut a square corner hole (Lane Community College).

Figure 22. Using a right angle milling attachment (Courtesy of Cincinnati Milacron).

Shaping attachments are used to machine irregular shapes on or in workpieces such as the square corner hole shown in Figure 21. When a right angle milling attachment (Figure 22) is mounted on the spindle, it is possible to machine hard to get at cavities at often difficult angles on workpieces.

SELF-TEST

1. How is an end mill centered over a shaft prior to cutting a keyway?
2. Why should the feed direction be against the cutter rotation when milling a cavity?
3. What can cause an end mill to work itself out of a collet while cutting?
4. Describe two methods of cutting angular surfaces in a vertical milling machine.
5. How are circular slots milled?
6. What milling machine attachment is used to mill a precise square or hexagon on a shaft?
7. How can a square hole in a workpiece be machined on the vertical milling machine?
8. When is a right angle milling attachment used?
9. Why should workpieces be laid out before machining starts?
10. Why are two operations necessary to mill a T-slot?

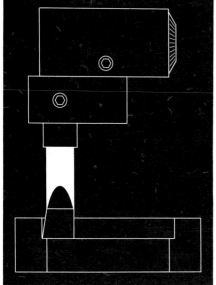

UNIT 6 USING THE OFFSET BORING HEAD

The offset boring head is used on the vertical mill to machine accurately located holes of precisely controlled diameters. Boring heads can also be used to machine external surfaces and to cut grooves and recesses. The purpose of this unit is to describe the setup and operation of this very useful accessory tool for the vertical mill.

OBJECTIVE

After completing this unit, you should be able to:
Set up and use the offset boring head in common boring operations.

THE OFFSET BORING HEAD

Most holes in workpieces are machined by drilling. When a better surface finish and better diameter accuracy is required, reaming may follow drilling. However, drilling and reaming are limited to standard sizes in which these tools are available. In addition, drilled holes may drift off position during a machining operation.

To machine holes of any size and at exact locations, the **offset boring** head may be used. A boring head can only be used to enlarge existing holes already in the workpiece. The workpiece must be predrilled on the mill or drill press. If you are boring holes that are considerably larger than the largest diameter drill available, time may be saved by using a high speed hole saw to cut out most of the unwanted material. This will save many additional boring steps required to enlarge a hole to its finished size.

Parts of the Offset Boring Head

The offset boring head consists of the **body** with **shank** and the **tool slide** (Figure 1). The shank permits the body to be secured in the machine spindle. The tool slide contains several holes that will accommodate the several sizes of **boring bars.** Boring bar materials include HSS, brazed carbide, and disposable insert carbide. A typical boring bar set (Figure 2) consists of several HSS or brazed carbide bars in assorted diameters and lengths.

All bars have standard shanks that fit the holes in the tool slide.

WORKPIECE PREPARATION AND SETUP

The workpiece should be pre-drilled or otherwise machined to within about one-sixteenth in. of finished size. If the hole in the part is rough, leave additional material so that clean up machining will be insured.

A workpiece to be bored may be clamped directly to the machine table by standard methods or held in a vise or other workholding fixture. If the part is to be

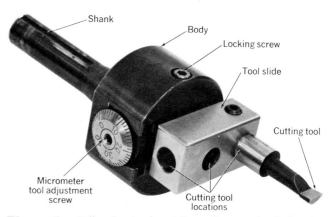

Figure 1.   Offset boring head (Lane Community College).

Figure 2. Set of boring tools for the offset boring head (Lane Community College).

Figure 3. Workpiece supported on parallels. Note the clearance for the penetrating boring tool (Lane Community College).

bored through, **it must be supported on parallels so that the boring bar will not hit the machine table (Figure 3). The parallels must also be set far enough apart so that the bar will clear as it turns.**

Positioning the Boring Head

Before boring can begin, the boring head must be positioned over the hole to be bored. If the predrilled hole is accurately positioned, the boring head may be centered over the hole by using a dial indicator clamped to the boring head or held in the machine spindle. Use the same procedure that you learned in Unit 3 to position the boring head over the hole.

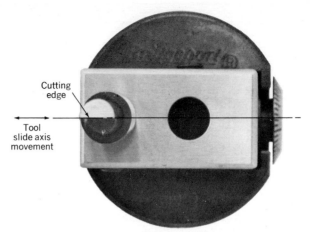

Figure 4. Boring tool cutting edge is on the centerline of the boring head (Lane Community College).

If the pre-drilled hole is off location, the position of the final bored hole can still be correct if the machine spindle is first positioned in the saddle and table axes relative to the edge of the workpiece or other reference point or feature. Use the positioning techniques that you have already learned.

USING THE OFFSET BORING HEAD

Bar Setup

When a boring tool is mounted in a boring head, it is very important that the cutting edge is on the centerline of the boring head and in line with the axis of the tool slide movement (Figure 4). Only in this position are the rake angles and clearance angles correct as ground on the tool. This is also the only position when the tool's cutting edge moves the same distance as the tool slide when adjustments are made. When selecting a boring bar, always pick the largest diameter bar that will fit the hole to be bored. This insures maximum rigidity of the setup.

When using any boring head, it is important to determine the amount of tool slide advance when the micrometer adjusting screw is rotated one graduation. On some boring heads **the tool slide advances twice the amount on the micrometer dial.** This will increase the diameter of the bore by twice the movement on the dial. Other boring heads are **direct reading** where the tool slide advance will increase the bore diameter by the same amount indicated on the dial. Movement of the tool slide is in thousandths of an inch and the ratio of tool slide advance to micrometer graduations will usually be indicated on the boring head.

Feeds and Speeds in Boring

The kind of tool material and the workpiece material

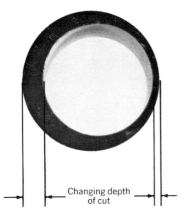

Figure 5. When the hole is eccentric to the spindle center-line, it will cause a variable depth of cut for the boring tool (Lane Community College).

Figure 6. A radius is machined on a workpiece with the offset boring head (Lane Community College).

determine the cutting speed that should be used. But the rigidity of the machine spindle and the setup often require a lower than calculated RPM because the imbalance of the offset boring head creates heavy machine vibrations.

The quill feed on many vertical milling machines is limited to .0015, .003, and .006 in. of feed per spindle revolution. Roughing cuts should be made at the higher figure and finishing cuts should be made with the two lower values. Roughing cuts are usually made with the tool feeding down into the hole. Finishing cuts are made with the tool feeding down and often the tool is fed back up thru the hole by changing the feed direction at the bottom of the hole. Because of the tool deflection, a light cut will be made without resetting the tool on that second cut. When cuts are made with the tool only feeding down but not out, the spindle rotation is stopped before the tool is withdrawn from the hole. If the spindle rotates while the quill is raised, a helical groove will be cut into the wall of the just completed hole, possibly spoiling it.

Controlling the Bore Diameter

To obtain a predictable change in hole size for a given tool slide adjustment, certain conditions have to be met. The depth of cut of the boring tool needs to be the same around the circumference of the hole and not like the varying depth of cut illustrated in Figure 5. Roughing cuts should be taken until the hole is round and concentric with the spindle centerline. The depth of cut needs to be equal for successive cuts. As an example, assume that a hole has been rough bored to be concentric with the spindle axis. The tool is now resharpened and fastened in the tool slide. The tool slide is advanced until the tool just touches the wall of the hole. After raising the tool above the work, the tool is moved 20 graduations, or a

Figure 7. A boring and facing head (Lane Community College).

distance that should increase the hole diameter by .020 in. The spindle is turned on, and with a feed of .003 in. per revolution, the cut is made thru the hole. The spindle is stopped and the tool is withdrawn from the hole. Measuring the hole shows the diameter to have

increased by only .015 in. What has happened is that the tool was deflected by the cutting pressure to produce a hole .005 in. smaller than expected. The tool is now advanced to again give an increase of .020 in. in the hole diameter. With the same feed as for the last cut, the hole is bored.

Measuring the hole again shows the hole to be .020 in. larger. Additional cuts made with the same depth of cut and the same feed will give additional .020 in. diameter increases. If the depth of cut is increased, more tool deflection will take place, resulting in a smaller than expected diameter increase. If the depth of cut is decreased, the tool will be deflected less, resulting in a larger than expected diameter.

When the same depth of cut is maintained but the feed per revolution is increased, higher cutting pressures will produce more tool deflection and a smaller than expected hole diameter. With an equal depth of cut and a smaller feed per revolution, less cutting pressure will produce a larger than expected hole diameter. Another factor that affects the hole diameter with a given depth of cut is tool wear. As a tool cuts, it becomes dull. A dull tool will produce higher cutting pressures with a resultant larger tool deflection.

Machining Radii and Facing with the Boring Head

An offset boring head can also be used to machine a precise radius on a workpiece (Figure 6). The workpiece is positioned the specified distance from the spindle axis. A scrap piece of metal is clamped to the table opposite the workpiece. As cuts are being made with the offset boring head, the tool cuts on both the workpiece and the scrap piece. The diameter of the cuts is measured between the pieces being machined.

With a boring and facing head (Figure 7), it is possible to machine flat surfaces with the same tool that was used to bore a hole to size. The tool can be moved sideways while the spindle is rotating.

SELF-TEST

1. When is an offset boring head used?
2. Why is the workpiece normally placed on parallels?
3. Why is the locking screw tightened after tool slide adjustments have been made?
4. Why does the tool slide have a number of holes to hold boring tools?
5. Why is it important to determine the amount of tool movement for each graduation on the adjustment screw?
6. What would be the best boring tool to use on a job?
7. How important is the alignment of the tool's cutting edge with the axis of the tool slide?
8. What factors affect the size of the hold obtained for a given amount of tool adjustment?
9. Name three causes for changes in boring tool deflection.
10. What determines the cutting speed in boring?

SECTION J HORIZONTAL MILLING MACHINES

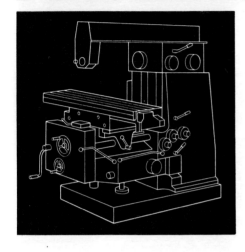

In the preceding section you studied the vertical milling machine where the machine spindle is primarily in the vertical axis. This section deals with the horizontal milling machine where the spindle is primarily in the horizontal axis.

The horizontal milling machine, like its vertical counterpart, is an extremely versatile machine tool and capable of accomplishing a variety of machining tasks.

TYPES OF HORIZONTAL MILLING MACHINES

Bed-Type

A **bed-type** milling machine is one in which the position of the milling spindle, but not the height of the table, can be changed. There are many configurations of bed-type milling machines. One type has the general appearance of a knee and column. One type of very large milling machine is known as a planer mill (Figure 1) or adjustable rail milling machine. The example shown is equipped with two separate tables so that one table can be set up while machining is taking place on the other table. These machines often have 250 hp to their spindles. Other bed-type milling machines that employ two or more cutting heads are called **duplex** or **triplex milling machines** (Figure 2). These are commonly used in high production setups.

A particularly common form of bed milling machine is called the **manufacturing milling machine** (Figure 3). On this machine the spindle assembly is positioned and secured at the correct height and parts are passed under the cutter. These machines are usually equipped with means for automatic cycling of the table; and they often have twin fixtures so that one part can be added while the other part is being machined. This is called **reciprocal milling.** This design of machine can also be found with hydraulic tracer controls that move the spindle carrier and cutter vertically in response to a stylus following a cam. These are termed **tracer-type manufacturing milling machines** (Figure 4).

Another bed-type milling machine also has a table traverse motion with a spindle assembly that can be moved vertically (Figure 5). This type of machine is found with either horizontal or vertical head configuration and, by general appearance, is often mistaken for a knee- and column-type milling machine.

Figure 1. A large planer-type milling machine with two tables. A setup can be made on one table while machining is taking place on the other (Courtesy Ingersoll Milling Machine Company).

KNEE AND COLUMN MILLING MACHINES

Knee and column milling machines are derived from the heritage of Joseph Brown's universal milling machines in the 1860s. Universal means that the machine table can swivel on its horizontal axis (Figure 6) so that the work can be presented to the cutter at an angle in conjunction with a suitable indexing head permitting **helical milling.** The plain knee and column milling machine (Figure 7) omits the table swiveling feature in the interest of greater machine rigidity.

There is one type of knee and column milling machine used in manufacturing that is capable of vertical table positioning and longitudinal table travel, but it does not have transverse or cross feeding capability. On this type of machine (Figure 8), the spindle bearings are carried in a quill so that the cutter can be positioned traversely over the part and locked into position. Eliminating the cross feeding saddle adds to the machine rigidity.

Figure 2. Triplex bed-type milling machine (Courtesy of Cincinnati Milacron).

Figure 3. Plain manufacturing-type milling machine (Courtesy of Cincinnati Milacron).

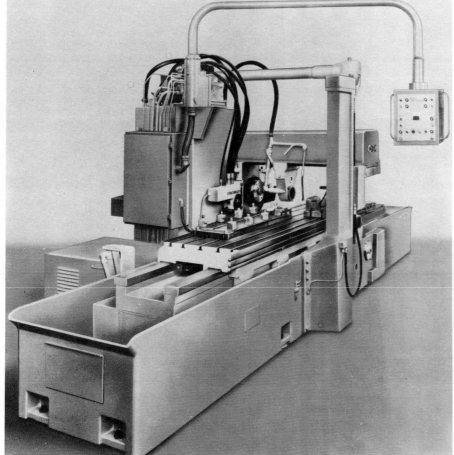

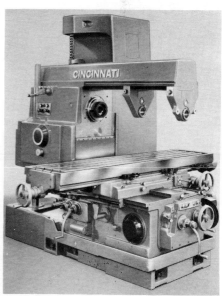

Figure 4. Plain tracer controlled milling machine (Courtesy of Cincinnati Milacron).

Figure 5. Bed-type horizontal milling machine with transverse table motion. This type mill is also found in a vertical spindle design (Courtesy of Cincinnati Milacron).

Figure 6. The main features of the knee, saddle, and table assembly on the universal knee and column milling machine (Courtesy of Cincinnati Milacron).

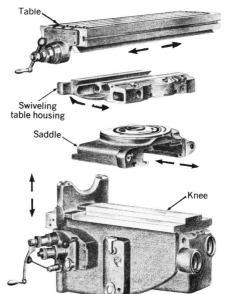

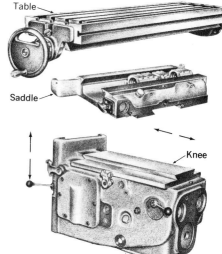

Figure 7. The feature of the knee, saddle, and column milling machine. The swiveling table housing is omitted in this design (Courtesy of Cincinnati Milacron).

Figure 8. Small, plain, automatic knee, and column milling machine (Courtesy of Cincinnati Milacron).

Figure 9. Backlash eliminator to permit climb milling (Courtesy of Cincinnati Milacron).

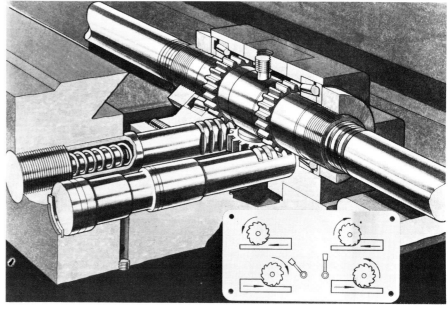

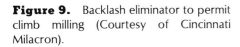

On the bed-type manufacturing milling machines, the table is moved by a hydraulic-mechanical means that includes **backlash control.** This control permits the cut to be made easily in either direction without the danger of having the milling cutter suddenly grab the work and take up the backlash, as can happen with most ordinary nut and screw table feeds. This sudden taking up of backlash results in many broken cutter teeth if it is not controlled by the method of milling or by special devices. One of these devices is called a **backlash eliminator** (Figure 9), which automatically takes up the backlash by applying a preload between two nuts following the leadscrew. Another method, employed mainly with numerically controlled machine tools, is a ring ball nut, commonly called ball screw, which is essentially free of backlash.

Figure 10. The overarm can reduce cutting vibration (Courtesy of Cincinnati Milacron).

Since much of the concern in the development of the milling machine and its cutters has been toward the highest possible machine rigidity by various means such as minimum number of moving components, overarm supports, and devices like backlash eliminators, another technique should be mentioned. Machine castings often vary in their ability to absorb vibration, even with the most careful design of internal webbing. Another means to attack the problem has been the **tuning out** of vibration by special vibration dampening devices. Figure 10 shows the milling machine overarm equipped with a device to reduce the resonance of vibration passing through the casting. This capability permits increased cutting loads before chatter sets in.

ATTACHMENTS AND ACCESSORIES FOR THE HORIZONTAL MILL

A number of attachments are available to increase the capabilities of milling machines, particularly for toolroom applications where a few parts are made or for limited production where the expense of a special machine would not be warranted. The **vertical milling attachment** (Figure 11) is used on horizontal milling machines to obtain the capability of both vertical and angular machining. The **universal milling attachments** (Figure 12) permit an additional motion so that spiral milling may be done on a plain table milling machine in addition to vertical and angular cuts.

Another attachment is the **independent overhead spindle** with an **angular swivel head** (Figure 13), which is powered separately from the horizontal machine spindle. This device replaces the standard overarm and can be used in conjunction with the horizontal spindle as needed to machine angular surfaces without moving the workpiece. When not needed, it can be swiveled out of the way, and the regular overarm brackets can be attached.

A **slotting attachment** (Figure 14) is also available for horizontal milling machines to utilize a single point tool for operations like internal keyway cutting, where a vertical slotter is not available. It may be set at an angle as well as being set vertically.

Devices for tool holding, such as arbors and adapters for horizontal milling, will be studied in this section. Table-mounted attachments such as rotary tables, indexing/dividing heads, and workholding devices such as clamps and vises will also be studied.

Milling machines can be equipped with accessory measuring equipment, called direct readouts (DRO), to reduce the chance of operator error when machining expensive complex parts (Figure 15). These measuring systems can be switched to present information in either inch or metric form, which is a great time-saver and eliminates the possibility of making errors in conversion between the two systems.

Figure 11. A vertical milling attachment with quill feeding capability (Courtesy of Cincinnati Milacron).

Figure 12. Universal milling attachment (Courtesy of Cincinnati Milacron).

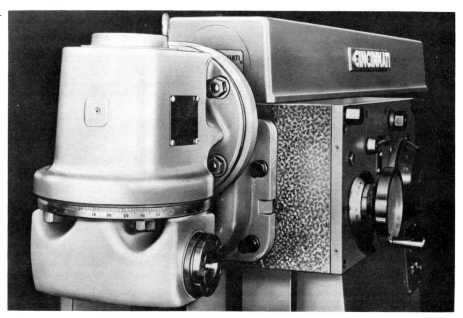

Figure 13. Independent overhead spindle with angular head (Courtesy of Cincinnati Milacron).

Figure 14. A slotting attachment for the horizontal milling machine (Courtesy of Cincinnati Milacron).

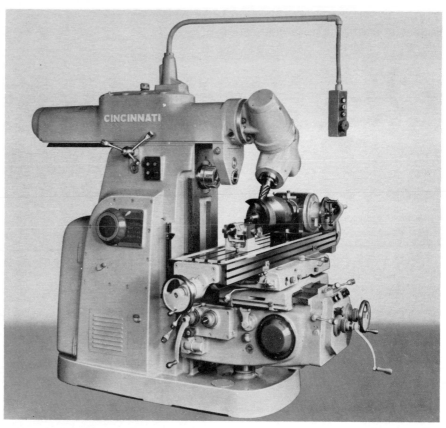

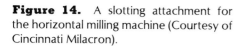

The horizontal milling machine, in combination with its wide array of accessories, is an extremely versatile machine tool. It should be pointed out that since the advent of numerical control, many of the functions of the horizontal and vertical milling machines are being displaced, especially on the production of highly complex parts with large numbers of interrelated or repeated dimensions. When you are milling a part with more than 100 related hole positions and depths, it is very difficult to avoid making at least one mistake. Consequently, much of the work that was formerly done by milling machines and by the accessories shown is now numerically programmed, even to make a single complex part.

It is important for you to learn to use vertical and horizontal milling machines competently because the cutting and locating principles apply to the most complex numerically controlled machine tool. Few companies are willing to risk damage to an expensive and complex numerically controlled machine by an operator without a background in conventional milling practice. An operator must be able to determine readily when there is something going wrong with the cutting operation and make appropriate corrections by replacing tools or manually overriding the machine control. Numerically controlled milling centers are sometimes equipped with five programmable machine axes or motions that can permit the spindle to be presented to the work at any angle between the horizontal and vertical besides moving up and down (Figure 16) under the guidance of a programmed tape or by direct computer control.

In this section you will observe specific safety precautions that relate to horizontal milling, identify components and functions of horizontal mills, and perform routine maintenance. Various mounting systems used to drive milling

Figure 15. Direct readout (DRO) fitted to a horizontal milling machine (Courtesy of Cincinnati Milacron).

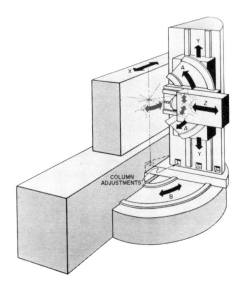

COLUMN ADJUSTMENTS

Figure 16. Diagram of five axes of machine motion for complex milling under numerical control (Courtesy of Cincinnati Milacron).

cutters will be studied, and you will be able to match cutters to their respective applications. You will calculate RPM and feedrates for milling cutters and set the values into the machine controls. You will learn about a variety of workholding methods and alignment procedures and how to mill a square workpiece. In addition, you will use side milling cutters in various combinations and you will use face milling cutters to machine flat surfaces.

Horizontal and vertical milling machines are as basic as the lathe, particularly where one-of-a-kind or small quantities of workpieces are involved. Both of these machine types will be in use for a long time to come. It is important for you to learn to set up and use these machines quickly, accurately, and safely.

HORIZONTAL MILLING MACHINE SAFETY

Safe operation of a machine tool requires that you think before you do something. Before starting up a machine, **know the location and operation of its controls.** Operate all controls on the machine yourself. Do not have another person start or stop the machine for you. Chances are good that he will turn a control at the wrong time. While operating a milling machine, **observe the cutting action at all times** so that you can **stop the machine immediately** when you see or hear something unfamiliar. Always stay within reach of the

controls while the machine is running. An unexpected emergency may require quick action on your part. **Never leave a running machine unattended.**

Before operating the rapid traverse control on a milling machine **loosen the locking devices** on the machine axis to be moved. Check that the hand wheels or hand cranks are disengaged, or they will spin and injure anyone near them when the rapid traverse is engaged. The rapid traverse control will move any machine axis that has its feed lever engaged singularly or simultaneously. **Do not try to position a workpiece too close to the cutter with this control,** but approach the final 2 in. by using the hand wheels or hand cranks.

A person concentrating on a machining operation should not be approached quietly from behind, since it may annoy and alarm him and he may ruin a workpiece or injure himself. Do not lean on a running machine; moving parts can hurt you. Signs posted on a machine indicating a dangerous condition or a repair in progress should only be removed by the person making the repair or by a supervisor.

Measurements should only be taken on a milling machine after the cutter has stopped rotating and after the chips have been cleared away. Milling machine chips are dangerously sharp and often hot and contaminated with cutting fluids. They should not be handled with bare hands. **Chips should be removed with a brush. Compressed air should not be used to clean off chips from a machine** because it will make small missiles out of chips that can injure a person, even one who's quite a distance away. A blast of air will also force small chips into the ways and sliding surfaces of the milling machine where they will cause scoring and rapid premature wear. Cleaning chips and cutting fluids from the machine or workpiece should only be done after the cutter has stopped turning. Before and during the operation of a milling machine, **keep the area around the machine clean of chips, oil spills, cutting fluids, and other obstructions to prevent the operator from slipping or stumbling.**

Many milling machine attachments and workpieces are heavy; **use a hoist to lift them on or off the table. Do not walk under a hoisted load.** The hoist may release and drop the load on you. If a hoist is not available, ask for assistance.

Injuries can be caused by improper setups or the use of wrong tools. **Use the correct size wrench when loosening or tightening nuts or bolts, preferably a box wrench** or a socket wrench. An oversized wrench will round off the corners on bolts and nuts and prevent sufficient tightening or loosening; a slipping wrench can cause smashed fingers or other injuries to the hands or arms. **Milling machine cutters have very sharp cutting edges.** Handling cutters carefully and with a cloth will avoid cuts on the hands.

All machine guards should be checked to see that they are in good condition and in place to increase milling machine safety. Workpieces should be centered in a vise with only enough extending out to permit machining. Clean the working area after a job is completed. A clean machine is safer than one buried under chips.

UNIT 1 PLAIN AND UNIVERSAL HORIZONTAL MILLING MACHINES

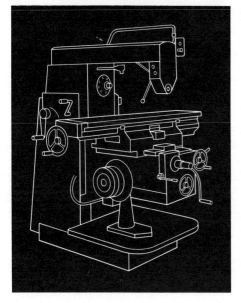

Before operating a horizontal mill, you must know the names of the machine parts, controls, and their functions. You must also know how to perform routine maintenance on the machine required to preserve its accuracy and provide ease of operation. The purpose of this unit is to identify the parts, controls, and control functions of the horizontal mill and to describe routine maintenance procedures.

OBJECTIVES

After completing this unit, you should be able to:
1. Identify the important components and controls on the vertical milling machine.
2. Describe the functions of machine parts and controls.
3. Perform routine maintenance on the machine.

PLAIN HORIZONTAL MILLING MACHINE
Determining the Size of the Machine
The size of a horizontal milling machine is usually given as the range of movement possible and the power rating of the main drive motor of the machine. An example would be a milling machine with a 28 in. longitudinal travel, 10 in. cross travel, and 16 in. vertical travel with a 5 hp main drive motor. As the physical capacity of a machine increases, more power is also available at the spindle through a larger motor.

Identifying Major Parts, Controls and Their Functions
The major assemblies of the horizontal mill are: **base and column, knee, saddle, table, spindle, and overarm** (Figure 1).

Base and Column.   The **base** along with the **column** form the one-piece major structural component of the machine tool. A dovetail slide is machined on the vertical face of the column providing an accurate guide for the

vertical travel of the knee. A dovetail slide is also machined on the top of the column providing a guide for the overarm. The column also contains the machine spindle, main drive motor, spindle speed selector mechanism, and spindle rotation direction selector.

Knee.   The **knee** engages the slide on the face of the column and is moved vertically by turning the vertical feed crank. A slide on the top of the knee provides a guide for the saddle.

Saddle.   The **saddle** engages the slide on the top of the knee and is moved horizontally toward or away from the face of the column by turning the cross feed handwheel crank. The saddle supports the table.

Table.   The **table** engages the slide on the top of the saddle and can be moved horizontally right and left by turning the table hand wheel. The table is equipped with T-slots for direct mounting of the workpiece, vise, or other fixture.

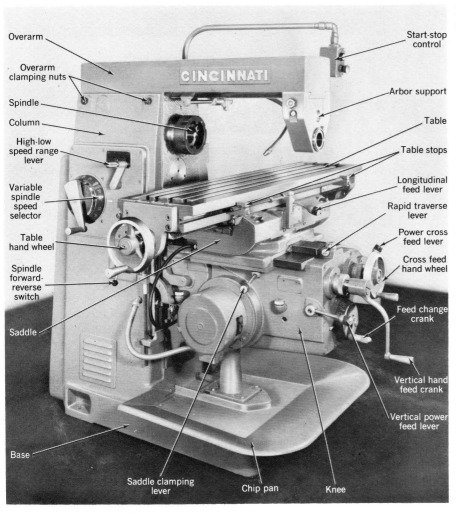

Figure 1. Horizontal milling machine (Courtesy of Cincinnati Milacron).

Spindle. The machine **spindle** is located in the upper part of the column and is used to hold, align, and drive the various cutters, chucks, and arbors. The front end or **nose** of the spindle has a tapered socket in a **standard milling machine taper.** This taper aligns the milling machine adaptor or cutter arbor. Driving force is provided by two keys located on the nose of the spindle. These engage slots on the adaptor or arbor.

Arbors and adaptors are held in place by means of a drawbolt extending through the hollow center of the spindle to the rear of the machine. Like the vertical mill, the drawbolt is threaded on one end and is designed to screw into the thread in the end of the arbor or adaptor shank. Tightening the drawbolt lock nut draws the taper shank of the arbor into the spindle taper.

Overarm and Arbor Support. The **overarm** engages the slide on the top of the column and may be moved in and out by loosening the overarm clamps and sliding this part to the desired position. The **arbor support** engages the dovetail on the overarm. The arbor support contains a bearing that is exactly in line with the

spindle of the mill. The arbor support provides a rigid bearing support for the outer end of the mill arbor.

Machine Controls

Most horizontal milling machines are equipped with **power feeds** for the **table, saddle,** and **knee.** This machine tool is also equipped with a **rapid traverse** feature that permits rapid positioning of a workpiece without the need to turn table, saddle, and knee cranks by hand. This capability necessitates a few more controls be added to the machine than were needed on the vertical mill.

Controls for Manual Movements. Cranks and crank handwheels are provided to elevate the knee and move table and saddle. All of these controls are equipped with a micrometer collar graduated in .001 in. increments.

Feedrate Selector and Feed Engage Controls. The **feedrate selector** is located on the knee (Figure 2) and is used to select the power feedrate for

Figure 2. Feed change crank (Courtesy of Cincinnati Milacron).

Figure 3. Rapid traverse lever (Courtesy of Cincinnati Milacron).

table, saddle, and knee in **inches per minute (IPM)**. Power feeds are engaged by individual controls on the table, saddle, and knee. However, engaging all of these at the same time will cause all these components to move under power at the same time. On most mills, power feeds will not function unless the spindle is turning. Safety stops on each axis prevent damage to the feed mechanism by automatically disengaging the power feed when a component arrives at the end of its travel. Adjustable power feed trip dogs are also provided so that you may preset the point at which the feed is to be disengaged.

Using the Rapid Traverse. To expedite the positioning of the knee, saddle, and table in order to rapidly move the workpiece up to the cutter or clear of the overarm, a rapid traverse feature is provided. When the rapid traverse control is engaged (Figure 3) it overrides the feedrate selector rate and rapidly moves the table, saddle, or knee depending on which feed control is engaged. The direction of rapid traverse is in the same direction as that of the feed. Furthermore, the rapid traverse will rapidly move the knee, saddle, and table all at the same time if all these parts should happen to have their feed controls engaged. **Be careful when using the rapid traverse function not to run the work or table into the cutter or overarm.** This will damage the work, cutter, and machine and could cause an injury.

Spindle Controls. Spindle controls include the **main motor switch, clutch, spindle speed,** and **speed range controls.** The motor switch will usually reverse the motor and spindle direction electrically. On some mills, spindle rotation is changed mechanically. A clutch is sometimes used to connect spindle and motor.

Spindle speeds are selected from the control on the

Figure 4. Speed change levers (Courtesy of Cincinnati Milacron).

side of the column (Figure 4). Several spindle speeds are available in both a **low and high speed range.** Variable speed controls are also used. The speed range selector is adjacent to the speed selector. This control has a **neutral** position between high and low speed settings. In the neutral position, the spindle may be turned by hand during machine setups. **Spindle speed and direction must be selected and set while the motor and spindle are stopped.** Shifting gears while the spindle is turning can

damage the drive mechanism. However, on variable speed drives, speeds must be set while the spindle is in motion.

Locks

Locks are provided on the table, saddle, and knee. These permit the components to be locked in place during a machining operation in order to increase rigidity of the setup. **All locks must be released before moving any part either by hand or under power.** During machining, locks should be set except the one on the moving axis. Locks should not be used to compensate for wear in the machine slides.

UNIVERSAL HORIZONTAL MILLING MACHINE

The **universal milling machine** (Figure 5) closely resembles a plain horizontal milling machine. The main difference between these machines is that the universal machine has an additional housing that swivels on the saddle and supports the table. This allows the table to be swiveled 45 degrees in either direction in a horizontal plane. The universal milling machine is especially designed to machine helical slots or grooves as in twist drills and milling cutters. Other than these special applications, a universal mill and a plain milling machine can perform the same operations.

Figure 5.   Universal milling machine (Courtesy of Cincinnati Milacron).

ROUTINE MAINTENANCE ON MILLS

Before any machine tool is operated, it should be lubricated. A good starting point is to wipe clean all sliding surfaces and to apply a coat of a good way lubricant to them. Way lubricant is a specially formulated oil for sliding surfaces. Dirt, chips, and dust will act like an abrasive compound between sliding members and cause excessive machine wear. Most machine tools have a lubrication chart that outlines the correct lubricants and lubrication procedures. When no lubrication chart is available, check all oil sight gages for the correct oil level and refill, if necessary. Too much oil causes leakage. Lubrication should be performed progressively, starting at the top of the machine and working down. Machine points that are hand oiled should only receive a small amount of oil at any one time, but this should be repeated at regular intervals, at least daily. Motor or pulley bearings should not get too much grease, since this may destroy the seals.

SELF-TEST

1. Go to a plain or universal horizontal milling machine and locate the following parts:

overarm	crossfeed and	switch for coolant pump	knee clamping lever
column	vertical feed	table	spindle forward-
saddle clamping lever	rapid traverse lever	knee	reverse switch
speed change lever	switch for spindle	feed change lever	trip dogs for all
powerfeed levers for	ON-OFF	spindle nose	three axes
longitudinal feed,	arbor support	saddle	

2. Lubricate a plain horizontal milling machine.

UNIT 2 TYPES OF SPINDLES, ARBORS, AND ADAPTORS

Several different devices are used to hold and drive cutters on the horizontal mill. As a machinist, part of your job is to know what these are and to select the one that best fits your needs. The purpose of this unit is to identify and describe types of spindles, arbors, and adaptors used on the horizontal mill.

OBJECTIVE

After completing this unit, you should be able to:
Identify machine spindles and set up different cutting tool mounting systems used to drive milling cutters.

MILL SPINDLE TAPERS

The milling machine spindle provides the driving force for the milling cutter. A milling cutter may be attached directly to the spindle nose (Figure 1) or held in a **taper shank adaptor** or on a **taper shank arbor.** The arbor and adaptor is then secured in the tapered socket located in the end of the spindle.

Mill spindle tapers may be self-holding or self-releasing. **Self-holding tapers** have a small included taper angle of usually 5 degrees or less. When a taper shank tool is firmly seated in a self-holding taper, the high wedging force will hold it in place. In order to separate self-holding tapered parts, it is usually necessary to drive them apart.

Self-releasing tapers have a large included taper angle of about 15 degrees. With this much steeper taper angle, the wedging of two tapered parts is precluded and the parts will separate with no difficulty. Most modern milling machines have self-releasing tapers in their spindle sockets. These permit quick and easy installing and removal of tooling.

The **standard national milling machine taper** is 3 and one-half inches per foot (IPF), making an included angle of about 16 and one-half degrees. Since the spindle taper in most milling machines is self-releasing, tooling must be held in place by a **draw-in bolt** or **drawbolt** extending through the center of the spindle. National milling machine tapers are available in four different sizes and are identified by the numbers **30, 40, 50,** and **60. Number 50 is the most common.** Positive drive of tapered shank tooling is provided through two keys on the spindle nose that engage keyways in the flange on the arbor or adaptor.

TYPES OF MILLING MACHINE ARBORS

Two common arbor styles are shown in Figure 2. **Style A arbor** has a cylindrical pilot on the end opposite the shank. The pilot is used to support the free end of the arbor. Style A arbors are used mostly on small milling machines. But they are also used on larger machines when a style B arbor support cannot be used because of a small diameter cutter or interference between the arbor support and the workpiece.

Style B arbors are supported by one or more bearing collars and arbor supports. Style B arbors are used to obtain rigid setups in heavy duty milling operations.

Style C arbors are also known as shell end mill arbors or as stub arbors (Figure 3). Shell end milling cutters are face milling cutters up to 6 in. in diameter. Because of their relatively small diameter, these cutters cannot be counterbored so that they can be mounted directly on the spindle nose, as are face mills, but they are mounted on shell end mill arbors.

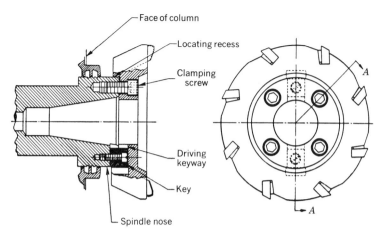

Face of column
Locating recess
Clamping screw
Driving keyway
Key
Spindle nose

Figure 1. Mounting a face mill on the spindle nose of a milling machine (Courtesy of Cincinnati Milacron).

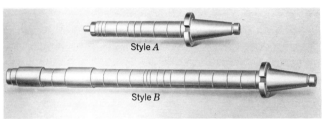

Style A

Style B

Figure 2. Arbors, styles A and B (Courtesy of Cincinnati Milacron).

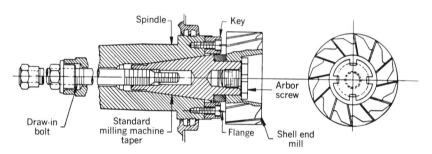

Spindle
Key
Arbor screw
Draw-in bolt
Standard milling machine taper
Flange
Shell end mill

Figure 3. Style C arbor; shell end mill arbor (Courtesy of Cincinnati Milacron).

Spacing and Bearing Collars

Precision spacing collars are used to take up the space between the cutter and the ends of the arbor. Shims may also be used to obtain exact cutter spacings in straddle milling operations. **Bearing collars** are larger in diameter than spacing collars. These collars ride in the arbor support bearing. On style A arbors, the end of the arbor rides in the arbor support bearing.

All collars are manufactured to very close tolerances with their ends or faces being parallel and also square to the hole. It is very important that the collars and other parts fitting on the arbor are handled carefully to avoid damaging the collar faces. **Any nicks, chips, or dirt between the collar faces will misalign the cutter or deflect the arbor and cause cutter run-out.**

Arbor Support Bearings

The **arbor support bearing** has a very important function in supporting the outer end of the arbor (Figure 4). The arbor bearing collar or arbor pilot fits this bearing that is located in the arbor support. The arbor support bearing may be a sleeve bushing, or on some mills, a sealed ball bearing may be used. On mills where a sleeve bushing is used for the arbor support bearing, the **fit of the arbor bearing collar or pilot can be quite critical.**

A provision for adjusting the fit of the arbor support bushing to the arbor collar or pilot is provided. Too loose a fit will cause inaccuracies in the mill cuts or permit chatter to occur. Too tight a fit will cause frictional heating and can damage the arbor collar, pilot, or the arbor support bushing. An arbor turning at high RPM will require more clearance than at slow RPM.

Arbor support bushings must be lubricated properly. Some mills have an oil reservoir in the arbor support for supplying oil to the arbor bushing. Check the oil level and method of lubrication before operating the machine, and consult with your instructor regarding the adjustment of the bushing to fit the arbor you are using.

Figure 4. Section through arbor showing locations of arbor collars, keys, bearing collars, and various arbor supports (Courtesy of Cincinnati Milacron).

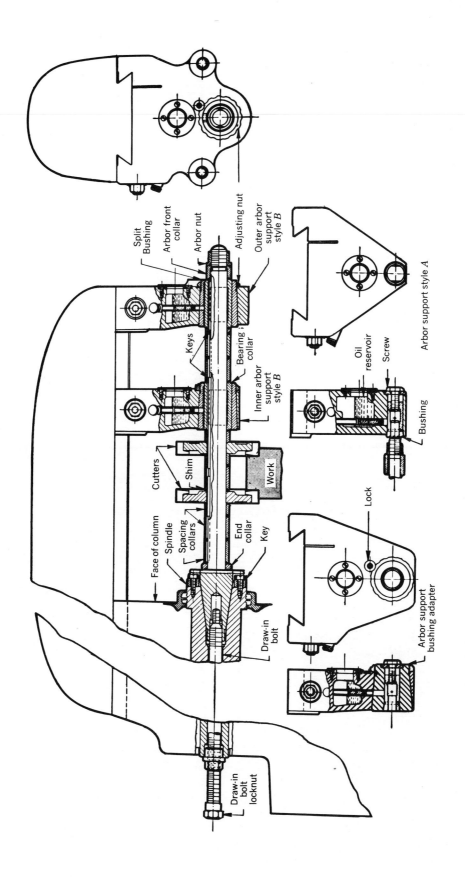

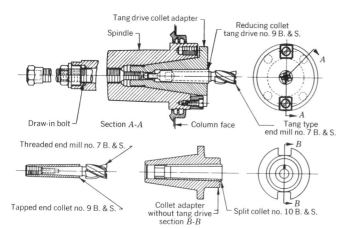

Figure 5. Adaptors and collets for self-releasing and self-holding tapers (Courtesy of Cincinnati Milacron).

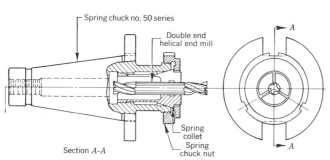

Figure 6. Spring chuck adaptor (Courtesy of Cincinnati Milacron).

Figure 7. Quick-change adaptor mounted on spindle nose (Courtesy of Cincinnati Milacron).

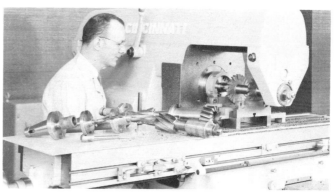

Figure 8. A number of tools mounted on quick-change tool holders ready to use (Courtesy of Cincinnati Milacron).

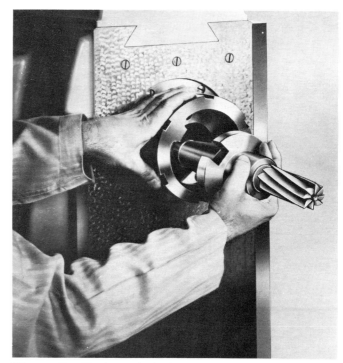

Figure 9. Tools are locked into the spindle with a partial turn of the clamp ring (Courtesy of Cincinnati Milacron).

ADAPTORS, COLLETS, AND QUICK-CHANGE TOOLING SYSTEMS

Adaptors are used on milling machines to mount cutters that cannot be mounted on arbors. Adaptors can be used to hold and drive taper shank tools (Figure 5).

Collets used with these adaptors increase the range of tools that can be used in a milling machine having a given size spindle socket. The **spring chuck adaptor** (Figure 6), with different size removable spring collets, is used with straight shank tools such as drills and end mills. With a **quick-change adaptor** (Figure 7) mounted on the spindle nose, a number of milling machine operations such as drilling, end milling, and boring can be per-

formed without changing the setup of the part being machined. The different tools are mounted on quick-change adaptors that are ready for use (Figure 8). The adaptor is held in the spindle taper by a clamping ring (Figure 9). Tool changing with this system is greatly facilitated.

SELF-TEST

1. What kind of cutters are mounted directly on the spindle nose?
2. Milling machine spindle sockets have two classes of taper. What are they?
3. What is the amount of taper on a national milling machine taper?
4. When is a style *A* arbor used?
5. What is a style *C* arbor?
6. Why are milling machine adaptors used?
7. Describe the function and care of spacing and bearing collars.
8. What is the result of dirty or nicked collars?
9. Describe clearances and lubrication requirements for the arbor support bearing and collar.
10. What is the advantage of quick-change tooling?

UNIT 3 ARBOR-DRIVEN MILLING CUTTERS

The metal cutting versatility of the horizontal mill can be fully realized and utilized by understanding, identifying, and selecting from the many types of milling cutters available for use on this machine tool. The purpose of this unit is to describe many of these common milling cutters and aid you in selecting the one that best fits your needs for a specific machining task.

OBJECTIVE

After completing this unit, you should be able to:
Identify common milling cutters, list their names, and select a suitable cutter for a given machining task.

CLASSIFYING MILLING CUTTERS

Most milling cutters are designed to perform specific machining operations. You should learn to identify common types by sight and know their capabilities and limitations. Milling cutters can be generally classified as to:

1. Material of manufacture
2. Profile sharpened or form relieved
3. Arbor-driven or shank types
4. Rotation and helix hand

Material of Manufacture

Many milling cutters are made from high speed steel (HSS). They also have cemented carbide cutting edges. Large cutters have inserted blades or teeth.

Profile Sharpened or Form Relieved

Profile sharpened cutters are resharpened by grinding a narrow land (Figure 1) back of the cutting edge. Form relieved cutters are resharpened by grinding the face of the teeth parallel to the axis of the cutter.

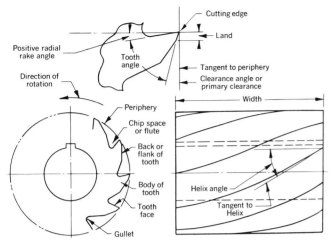

Figure 1. Nomenclature of plain milling cutter (Courtesy of Cincinnati Milacron).

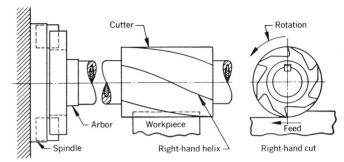

Figure 2. Plain milling cutter with right-hand helix and right-hand cut (Courtesy of Cincinnati Milacron).

Arbor-Driven or Shank Types

Milling cutters for the horizontal mill are designed to be driven by the mill arbor, or they may have their own tapered shanks for direct mounting in the machine spindle socket. Although there are many instances where you will use a tapered shank mounted cutter in the horizontal mill, probably the most common cutters you will be using are arbor mounted types.

Rotation and Helix Hand

Milling cutters are either for right-hand rotation cutting or left-hand rotation cutting. The way in which a cutter is mounted on an arbor determines the hand or cut. Counterclockwise rotation determines right-hand cutting direction. Clockwise rotation determines a left-hand cutting direction (Figure 2).

Helix hand is determined by looking at the direction of cutting rotation and determining which direction the flutes twist. Flutes twisting to the right are right-hand helix and to the left are left-hand helix.

PLAIN ARBOR-DRIVEN CUTTERS

Plain milling cutters are designed for milling plain surfaces where the width of the work is narrower than the cutter (Figure 3). Plain milling cutters less than $\frac{3}{4}$ in. wide have straight teeth. On straight tooth cutters, the cutting edge will cut along its entire length at the same time. Cutting pressure increases until the chip is completed. At this time the sudden change in tooth load causes a shock that is transmitted through the drive and often leaves chatter marks or an unsatisfactory surface finish. Light duty milling cutters have a large number of teeth, which limits their use to light or finishing cut because of insufficient chip space for heavy cutting. **Heavy duty plain**

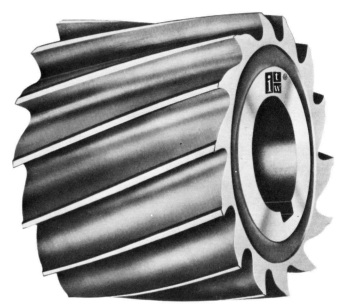

Figure 3. Light duty plain milling cutters (Illinois Tool Works Inc.).

mills (Figure 4) have fewer coarse teeth, which makes for strong teeth with ample chip clearance. The helix angle of heavy duty mills is about 45 degrees. The helical form enables each tooth to take a cut gradually, which reduces shock and lowers the tendency to chatter. Plain milling cutters are also called **slab mills**. Plain milling cutters with a helix angle over 45 degrees are known as **helical mills** (Figure 5). These milling cutters produce a smooth finish when used for light cuts or on intermittent surfaces. **Plain milling cutters do not have side cutting teeth and should not be used to mill shoulders or steps on workpieces.**

SIDE MILLING CUTTERS

Side milling cutters are used to machine steps or grooves. These cutters are made from $\frac{3}{16}$ to 1 in. in width. Figure 6 shows a straight tooth side milling cutter. To cut

Figure 4. Heavy duty plain milling cutter (Illinois Tool Works Inc.).

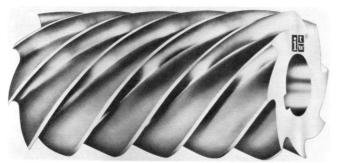

Figure 5. Helical plain milling cutter (Illinois Tool Works Inc.).

Figure 7. Stagger tooth milling cutter (Illinois Tool Works Inc.).

Figure 6. Side milling cutter (Lane Community College).

deep slots or grooves, a **staggered tooth side milling cutter** (Figure 7) is preferred because the alternate right-hand and left-hand helical teeth reduce chatter and give more chip space for higher speeds and feeds than are possible with straight tooth side milling cutters. To cut slots over 1 in. wide, two or more side milling cutters may be mounted on the arbor simultaneously. Shims between the hubs of the side mills can be used to get any precise width cutter combination or to bring the cutter again to the original width after sharpening.

Half side milling cutters are designed for heavy duty milling where only one side of the cutter is used (Figure 8). For straddle milling, a right-hand and a left-hand cutter combination is used.

Plain metal slitting saws are designed for slotting and cutoff operations (Figure 9). Their sides are slightly relieved or **dished** to prevent binding in a slot. Their use is limited to a relatively shallow depth of cut. These saws are made in widths from $\frac{1}{32}$ to $\frac{5}{16}$ in.

To cut deep slots or when many teeth are in contact with the work, a **side tooth metal slitting saw** will perform better than a plain metal slitting saw (Figure 10). These saws are made from $\frac{1}{16}$ to $\frac{3}{16}$ in. wide.

Figure 8.   Half side milling cutter (Illinois Tool Works Inc.).

Figure 10.   Side tooth metal slitting saw (Illinois Tool Works Inc.).

Extra deep cuts can be made with a **staggered tooth metal slitting saw** (Figure 11). Staggered tooth saws have greater chip carrying capacity than other saw types. All metal slitting saws have a slight clearance ground on the sides toward the hole to prevent binding in the slot and the scoring of the walls of the slot. Stagger tooth saws are made from $\frac{3}{16}$ to $\frac{5}{16}$ in. wide.

Angular milling cutters are used for angular milling such as cutting of dovetails, V-notches, and serrations. **Single angle cutters** (Figure 12) form an included angle of 45 or 60 degrees, with one side of the angle at 90 degrees to the axis of the cutter.

Figure 9.   Plain metal slitting saw (Illinois Tool Works Inc).

552

Figure 12. Single angle milling cutter (Illinois Tool Works Inc.).

Figure 13. Double angle milling cutter (Illinois Tool Works Inc).

Figure 11. Staggered tooth metal slitting saw (Illinois Tool Works Inc.).

Double angle milling cutters (Figure 13) usually have an included angle of 45, 60, or 90 degrees. Angles other than those mentioned are special milling cutters.

Convex milling cutters (Figure 14) produce concave bottom grooves or they can be used to make a radius in an inside corner. Concave milling cutters (Figure 15) make convex surfaces. **Corner rounding milling cutters** (Figure 16) make rounded corners. The cutters illustrated in Figures 14 to 17 are form relieved cutters.

Involute gear cutters (Figure 17) are commonly available in a set of eight cutters for a given pitch, depending on the number of teeth for which the cutter is to be used. The ranges for the individual cutters are as follows.

Number of Cutter	Range of Teeth
1	135 to rack
2	55 to 134
3	35 to 54
4	26 to 53
5	21 to 25
6	17 to 20
7	14 to 16
8	12 and 13

These eight cutters are designed so that their forms are correct for the lowest number of teeth in each range. If an accurate tooth form near the upper end of a range is required, a special cutter is needed.

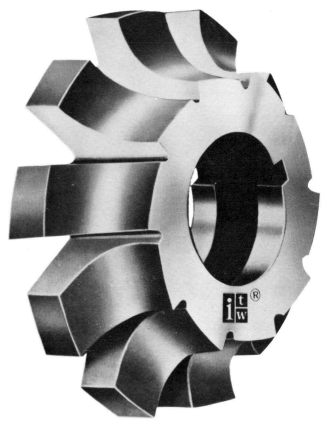

Figure 14.   Convex milling cutter (Illinois Tool Works Inc.).

Figure 16.   Corner rounding milling cutter (Illinois Tool Works Inc.).

Figure 17.   Involute gear cutter (Lane Community College).

Figure 15.   Concave milling cutter (Illinois Tool Works Inc.).

SELF-TEST

1. What are the two basic kinds of milling cutters with reference to their tooth shape?
2. What is the difference between a light duty and a heavy duty plain milling cutter?
3. Why are plain milling cutters not used to mill steps or grooves?
4. What kind of cutter is used to mill grooves?
5. How does the cutting action of a straight tooth side milling cutter differ from a stagger tooth side milling cutter?
6. Give an example of an application of half side milling cutters.
7. When are metal slitting saws used?
8. Give two examples of form relieved milling cutters.
9. When are angular milling cutters used?
10. When facing the spindle, in which direction should the right-hand cutter be rotated in order to cut?

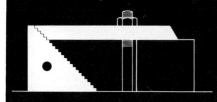

UNIT 4 WORKHOLDING METHODS AND STANDARD SETUPS

Before any machining can be done on the horizontal mill, the workpiece or workholding fixture must be secured and aligned on the machine table. A specific setup will depend on the particular workpiece and the machining task to be done. Considerable ingenuity on your part is required to make a safe and secure setup that will not distort or damage the workpiece. Milling machine setups are almost infinite in number and it would not be possible to discuss them all. The purpose of this unit is to introduce you to the equipment and techniques for common setups on this machine.

OBJECTIVES

After completing this unit, you should be able to:
1. Select a workholding method and device for common milling tasks.
2. Safely set up a workpiece on the machine using common standard techniques.

DIRECT MOUNTING TO THE TABLE

A large variety of milling **clamps** are available for **direct to table mounting of the workpiece.** Always follow the rules of good clamping. Clamping studs or bolts should be fully screwed into their T-nuts. Clamp nuts should have full thread engagement on studs. **Studs or clamp bolts should be located as close to the workpiece as possible and clamp support blocks arranged so that clamping pressure is applied to the workpiece** (Figure 1). Clamps should be located on both sides of the work-

piece if possible. This will ensure maximum safety (Figure 2). Clamp supports **must be the same height as the workpiece. Never use clamp supports that are lower than the workpiece.** Adjustable step blocks are extremely useful for this as the height of the clamp bar may be adjusted to insure maximum clamping pressure.

To protect a soft or finished surface from damage by clamping pressure, place a shim between the clamp and work (Figure 3). If you are machining a rough casting or weldment (Figure 4), **protect the machine table from**

Figure 1. Work clamped to the table with T-slot bolts and clamps (Courtesy of Cincinnati Milacron).

Figure 4. Protect the machine table surface from rough workpieces (Lane Community College).

Figure 2. Clamping bolt close to the work gives effective clamping.

Figure 5. Workpiece supported under the clamp.

Figure 3. Highly finished surfaces should be protected from clamping damage (Lane Community College).

damage by using a shim under the workpiece. Paper, plywood, and sheet metal are shim materials. Their selection depends on the accuracy of the machine cuts.

Workpieces can be easily distorted, broken, or otherwise damaged by excessive or improper clamping. One solution to this problem is to use a **screw jack** to support the workpiece (Figure 5). The jack should be placed **directly under the clamp.** Screw jacks are available in a variety of sizes and styles (Figure 6). In lieu of a screw jack, solid blocks of the correct size may be used both as workpiece supports and clamp supports (Figure 7).

In machining operations where heavy cuts are involved, **top clamps alone may not be sufficient to restrain the workpiece.** A **workpiece stop** may be used to prevent slippage of the part being machined (Figure 8).

Figure 6. Examples of screw jacks (Courtesy of Cincinnati Milacron).

Figure 8. Stop block prevents work slippage.

Figure 7. Work set up and clamped on table (Courtesy of Cincinnati Milacron).

Figure 9. Quick action jaws holding workpiece (Courtesy of Cincinnati Milacron).

Quick action jaws (Figure 9) may be used in direct table clamping. These can be positioned at any location on the table. Clamping action is independent of the clamp mounting, permitting the workpiece to be clamped or released without actually moving the clamp itself.

MILL VISES

Probably the most common method of workholding on a milling machine is a **vise.** Vises are simple to operate and can quickly be adjusted to the size of the work-

piece. A vise should be used to hold work with parallel sides if it is within the size limits of the vise, because it is the fastest and most economical workholding method. The **plain vise** (Figure 10) is bolted to the machine table. Alignment with the table is provided by two slots at right angles to each other on the underside of the vise. These slots are fitted with removable keys that align the vise with the table T-slots either lengthwise or crosswise. A plain vise can be converted to a **swivel vise** (Figure 11) by mounting it on a **swivel base.** The swivel plate is graduated in degrees. This allows the upper section to be swiveled to any angle in the horizontal plane. When

Figure 10. Plain vise (Courtesy of Cincinnati Milacron).

Figure 11. Swivel vise (Courtesy of Cincinnati Milacron).

Figure 12. Universal vise (Courtesy of Cincinnati Milacron).

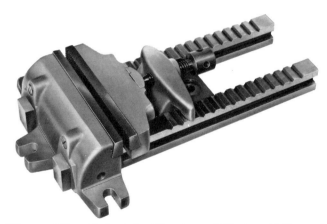

Figure 13. All-steel vise (Courtesy of Cincinnati Milacron).

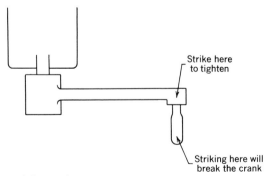

Figure 14. Tightening a vise.

swivel bases are added to a plain vise, the versatility increases, but the rigidity is lessened.

For work involving compound angles, a **universal vise** (Figure 12) is used. This vise can be swiveled 90 degrees in the vertical plane and 360 degrees in the horizontal plane.

The strongest setup is the one where the workpiece is clamped close to the table surface. Castings, forgings, or other rough workpieces can be securely fastened in an **all-steel vise** (Figure 13). The movable jaw can be set in any notch on the two bars to accommodate different workpieces. The short clamping screw makes for a very strong and rigid setup. The hardened and serrated jaws grip the workpiece securely.

Air or **hydraulically operated vises** are often used in production work, but in general toolroom work, vises are opened and closed by cranks or levers. To hold

workpieces securely without slipping under high cutting forces, a vise must be tightened by striking the crank with a lead hammer (Figure 14) or other soft face hammer.

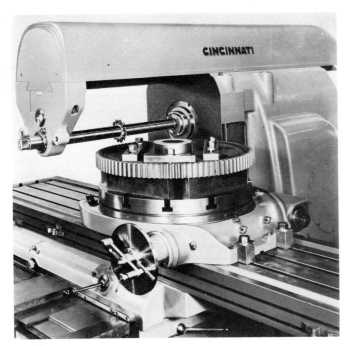

Figure 15. Rotary table (Courtesy of Cincinnati Milacron).

Figure 17. Dividing head used to drill equally spaced holes (Courtesy of Cincinnati Milacron).

Figure 18. Round shaft being held in vee-blocks.

Figure 16. Dividing head and foot stock (Courtesy of Cincinnati Milacron).

OTHER WORKHOLDING ACCESSORIES FOR THE HORIZONTAL MILL

A **rotary table or circular milling attachment** (Figure 15) is used to provide rotary movement to a workpiece. The rotary table can be used for angular indexing, milling circular grooves, or to cut radii. The rotary table is shown in Figure 15 in a gear cutting operation.

The **dividing head** (Figure 16) is used to divide the circumference of a workpiece into any number of equally spaced divisions. Work is held **between centers, in collets,** or in a **chuck.** The supporting member opposite the dividing head is the **foot stock.** The dividing head can be swiveled from below a horizontal line to beyond the vertical. The dividing head can also be used to drill equally spaced holes in workpieces held in a chuck (Figure 17). **Round workpieces can be securely fastened in a set of vee blocks** (Figure 18). To prevent the shaft from bending under cutting pressure, a screw jack such as those shown in Figure 7 can be used to support the shaft halfway between the vee blocks. If a number of identical workpieces are to be machined, a **milling fixture** (Figure 19) may be the most efficient way of holding them. A fixture is used when the savings resulting from its use are greater than the cost of making the fixture.

Figure 19. Milling fixture used for many identical parts (Courtesy of Cincinnati Milacron).

SELF-TEST

1. In relationship to the workpiece, where should the clamping bolt be located?
2. What precautions should be taken when clamping finished surfaces?
3. When are screw jacks used?
4. What is the reason for clamping a stop block to the table?
5. What are quick action jaws?
6. What is the difference between a swivel vise and a universal vise?
7. When is an all-steel vise used?
8. When is a rotary table used?
9. When is a dividing head used?
10. When is a fixture used?

UNIT 5 FEEDS AND SPEEDS FOR HORIZONTAL MILLING

In the preceding units, you have learned the nomenclature of the horizontal mill, different types of spindles, cutter holders, and cutters, and been introduced to common machine setups. Equally important is the selection of cutting speeds and feeds for milling work. The purpose of this unit is to describe and discuss cutting speeds and feeds for horizontal milling and to familiarize you with the calculations in determining these factors.

OBJECTIVES

After completing this unit, you should be able to:

1. Select cutting speeds for different materials and calculate the RPM for different milling cutters.
2. Select and calculate feedrates for different materials and milling cutters.
3. Set speeds and feeds on a horizontal milling machine.

CUTTING SPEEDS

As in vertical milling, **cutting speed** (CS) is expressed as a function of cutter RPM by the general formula:

$$RPM = \frac{CS \times 4}{D}$$

where **RPM is the cutter speed in revolutions per minute, CS is the cutting speed of the material being machined expressed in surface feet per minute (SFPM), and D is the diameter of the milling cutter.**

Table 1
Cutting Speeds for Milling

	Cutting Speed SFM	
Material	High Speed Steel Cutter	Carbide Cutter
Free machining steel	100–150	400–600
Low carbon steel	60–90	300–550
Medium carbon steel	50–80	225–400
High carbon steel	40–70	150–250
Medium alloy steel	40–70	150–350
Stainless steel	30–80	100–300
Gray cast iron	50–80	250–350
Bronze	65–130	200–400
Aluminum	300–800	1000–2000

Cutting speeds (Table 1) are influenced by the same factors as in vertical milling. Some additional factors relative to horizontal milling further influence their selection. Among these are: cutting edges not remaining in the work continuously, a chip of variable thickness being formed, the type of milling being done (slab, face, or end), and the way in which heat is transferred from the cutting edge. Table values are approximate and may have to be varied up or down to fit specific machining tasks. Until you gain experience in horizontal milling, **use the lower values** when selecting cutting speeds. Computations are done in the same way as for vertical milling.

FEEDRATES

Horizontal mill feedrates are expressed in **inches per minute (IPM)** and are calculated by the formula:

$$IPM = F \times N \times RPM$$

where **IPM is the inch/minute feed rate, F is the feed per tooth (Table 2), N is the number of teeth on the milling cutter, and RPM is the revolutions per minute of the cutter.**

To calculate a feed rate, first find RPM by the preceding formula, then refer to Table 2 and calculate the feedrate by IPM = F × N × RPM.

Table 2
Feed in Inches per Tooth (Instructional Setting)

	Aluminum		Bronze		Cast Iron		Free Machining Steel		Alloy Steel	
Type of Cutter	HSS	Carbide	HSS	Carbide	HSS	Carbide	HSS	Carbide	HSS	Carbide
Face mills	.007 to .022	.007 to .020	.005 to .014	.004 to .012	.004 to .016	.006 to .020	.003 to .012	.004 to .016	.002 to .008	.003 to .014
Helical mills	.006 to .018	.006 to .016	.003 to .011	.003 to .010	.004 to .013	.004 to .016	.002 to .010	.003 to .013	.002 to .007	.003 to .001
Side cutting mills	.004 to .013	.004 to .012	.003 to .008	.003 to .007	.002 to .009	.003 to .012	.002 to .007	.003 to .009	.001 to .005	.002 to .008
End mills	.003 to .011	.003 to .010	.003 to .007	.002 to .006	.002 to .008	.003 to .010	.001 to .006	.002 to .008	.001 to .004	.002 to .007
Form relieved cutters	.002 to .007	.002 to .006	.001 to .004	.001 to .004	.001 to .005	.002 to .006	.001 to .004	.002 to .005	.001 to .003	.001 to .004
Circular saws	.002 to .005	.002 to .005	.001 to .003	.001 to .003	.001 to .004	.002 to .006	.001 to .003	.001 to .004	.005 to .002	.001 to .004

EXAMPLE

Find RPM and feedrate for a 3 in. diameter high speed helical mill cutting free machining steel.

$$RPM = \frac{CS \times 4}{D}$$
$$= \frac{4 \times 100 \text{ feet per minute (Table 1)}}{3 \text{ in. dia. cutter}}$$
$$= 134$$
$$IPM = F \times N \times RPM$$
$$= .002 \text{ in. feed/tooth (Table 2)} \times 6 \text{ teeth}$$
$$\times 134 \text{ RPM}$$
$$= 1.608 \text{ inches per minute feed}$$

To calculate the starting feedrate, use the low figure from the feed per tooth chart and, if conditions permit, increase the feedrate from there. **The most economical cutting takes place when the most cubic inches of metal per minute are removed and a long tool life is obtained. The tool life is longest when a low speed and high feed rate is used.** Try to avoid feedrates of less than .001 in. per tooth because this will cause rapid dulling of the cutter. Exceptions to this limit are small diameter end mills when used on harder materials. The depth and width of cut also affect the feedrate. **Wide and deep cuts require a smaller feedrate than do shallow, narrow cuts.** Rough-ing cuts are made to remove material rapidly. The depth of cut may be $\frac{1}{8}$ in. or more, depending on the rigidity of the machine, the setup, and the horsepower available. **Finishing cuts are made to produce precise dimensions and acceptable surface finishes. The depth of cut on a finishing cut should be between .015 and .030 in.** A depth of cut of .005 in. or less will cause the cutter to rub instead of cut and also results in excessive cutting edge wear.

COOLANTS AND CUTTING FLUIDS

Cutting fluids should be used when machining most metals with high speed steel cutters. A cutting fluid cools the tool and the workpiece. It lubricates, which reduces friction between the tool face and chip. Cutting fluids prevent rust and corrosion and, if applied in sufficient quantity, will flush away chips. Cutting fluids will, through these characteristics, increase production through higher speeds and produce better surface finishes. Most milling with carbide cutters is done dry unless a large constant flow of cutting fluid can be directed at the cutting edge. An interrupted coolant flow on a carbide tool causes thermal cracking and results in subsequent chipping of the tool.

SELF-TEST

1. What is cutting speed?
2. Why should cuts be started at the low end of the cutting speed range?
3. If the cutting speed is 100 FPM with an HSS tool, what would it be with a carbide tool for the same material?
4. What is the effect of too low a cutting speed?
5. How is the feedrate expressed on a milling machine?
6. How is the feedrate calculated?
7. Why is a feed per tooth given instead of a feed per revolution?
8. What is the effect of too low a feedrate?
9. What RPM is used with a 3 in. diameter HSS cutter on low carbon steel?
10. What is the feedrate for a 4 in. diameter, five tooth carbide face mill machining alloy steel?

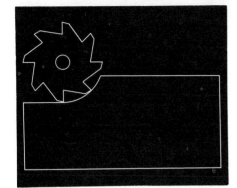

UNIT 6 MACHINE SETUP AND TECHNIQUES FOR PLAIN MILLING

Plain milling is the machining operation of milling a flat surface parallel to the cutter axis and machine table. Plain milling is accomplished most frequently on the plain horizontal milling machine and involves setting up the machine, selecting an appropriate arbor and cutter, and calculating correct speeds, feeds, and depth of cuts. Plain milling on the universal mill involves the additional operation of aligning the machine table. The purpose of this unit is to describe the procedure for preparing the machine tool and to acquaint you with the actual processes of plain milling.

OBJECTIVES

After completing this unit, you should be able to:
1. Set up the mill for plain milling.
2. Select and set up a workholding system.
3. Select and set up an appropriate cutter and arbor.
4. Mill surfaces flat and square to each other.

SETTING UP THE MILL

The machine table and all sliding surfaces should be cleaned prior to setup or operation. Any nicks or burrs found on the table or workholding devices should be removed with a stone.

Table Alignment on the Universal Mill

The table on the universal mill should be checked and adjusted if necessary for alignment prior to any machining. The following procedure may be used.

1. Clean the face of the column and the machine table.
2. Fasten a dial indicator to the table using a magnetic base or other mounting system (Figure 1). **Never** try to align the table with the indicator mounted on the column since this would always show the table to be in alignment.
3. Preload the indicator about one-half revolution. If the table is set at an extreme angle, loosen the locking bolts and swing back to a position of approximate alignment.

4. Turn the crank handwheel and move the indicator until it is positioned near one edge of the column. Set the bezel to zero.
5. Move the table so that the indicator moves across the

Figure 1. Aligning the universal milling machine table (Lane Community College).

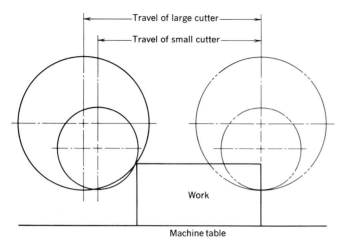

Figure 2. Different travel distances between different diameters of cutters.

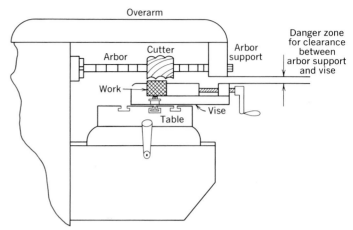

Figure 3. Always check clearance between arbor support and vise when setting up the machine.

face of the column and observe the reading at the opposite edge.

6. Adjust the position of the table so that one-half of the total indicated runout is cancelled (back toward zero on the indicator).

7. Reset the bezel to zero and move the indicator back across the face of the column.

8. If an error is observed, cancel by one-half and recheck on the opposite edge of the column.

9. Tighten all locking bolts securely and **recheck the alignment.** A zero indicator reading should be observed at both edges of the column.

Selecting the Cutter

For a flat surface, use a plain milling cutter that is wider than the surface to be machined. The diameter of the milling cutter selected should be as small as practical. A larger diameter cutter must travel farther than one with a smaller diameter (Figure 2). Therefore, a smaller diameter cutter is more efficient since time will be saved. Use a sharp cutter to minimize cutting pressure and to obtain a good surface finish.

Whatever diameter cutter is used, it is important to have sufficient clearance between the arbor supports and the vise or other workholding fixture (Figure 3). As material is machined from the workpiece, this clearance is reduced and it may become necessary to reset the workpiece if the vise and arbor supports will not clear each other before the final cut is taken.

Climb and Conventional Milling

In milling, the direction that the workpiece is being fed can either be in the same direction as cutter rotation or can be opposed to the direction of cutter rotation (Figure 4). When the direction of **feed is opposed** to the

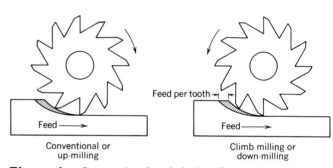

Figure 4. Conventional and climb milling.

rotation direction of the cutter, this is said to be **up or conventional milling.** When the direction of **feed is the same** as the rotation direction, this is said to be **down or climb milling** because the cutter is attempting to climb onto the workpiece. If any appreciable amount of backlash exists in the table or saddle, the workpiece may be pulled into the cutter during climb milling. This can result in a bent arbor, broken cutter, damaged workpiece, and possible injury to the operator. Climb milling should be avoided unless the mill is equipped with adequate backlash control. Remember that any cutter can be operated in an up milling or down milling mode depending only on which side of the workpiece the cut is started.

Selecting and Setting Up Mill Arbors

When selecting a mill arbor, use one that has minimum overhang beyond the outer arbor support. Excessive overhang can cause vibration and chatter. After selecting the proper arbor, insert the tapered shank into the spindle socket. Be sure that the socket is **clean** and **free** from **burrs or nicks.** Large mill arbors are heavy and you may need some help holding them in place until the drawbolt is engaged. **Don't let the arbor fall out onto**

the machine table. Thread the drawbolt into the arbor shank all the way, then draw the arbor into the spindle taper by turning the **drawbolt locknut.** Tighten the locknut with a wrench.

Remove the arbor nut and spacing collars. Place these on a clean surface so that their precision surfaces are not damaged. Position the cutter on the arbor as close to the spindle as the machining task will permit. Place a sufficient number of spacing collars on either side of the cutter so as to position it correctly. The cutter, spacing collars, and bearing collar should be a smooth sliding fit on the arbor.

A **key** is generally used to insure a positive drive between cutter and arbor. However, a milling cutter can be driven without a key. **Consult with your instructor and follow instructions regarding the use of keys.**

Place the bearing collar on the arbor and locate as close to the cutter as the machining task will permit. Place the arbor support on the overarm and slide it in until the arbor bearing collar slips through the arbor support bearing. Tighten overarm and support clamps. Tighten the arbor nut only after the support is in place. Tightening the arbor nut before the support is in place may bend the arbor. Do not overtighten the arbor nut and always use a wrench of the correct type and size.

Removing and Storing Mill Arbors

Care should be exercised in removing the arbor from the spindle. Loosen the drawbolt locknut about one turn. You may have to tap the drawbolt lightly to release the arbor taper shank from the spindle socket. Hold the arbor in place or get help while you unscrew the drawbolt from the arbor shank. Remove the arbor from the machine and store in an upright position. Long arbors stored in a flat position may bend.

Workholding

Selection of a workholding device and method will depend on the machining task to be done. Review Unit 4 and if you are clamping directly to the mill table, **be sure to follow the rules of good clamping.** Use a work stop if necessary to prevent workpiece slippage from cutting pressure.

Mill Vises. A **mill vise** is an accurate and dependable workholding tool. When milling only on the top of the workpiece, it is not necessary to set up the vise square to the column or parallel to the table. However, if the workpiece has already machined outside surfaces, steps, or grooves, the vise must be precisely aligned to the machine table.

Many mill vises are equipped with **keys** that fit snugly into the table T-slots (Figure 5). Once the keys are engaged, the vise is accurately aligned. Before mounting

Figure 5. Fixture alignment keys (Lane Community College).

a vise or any other mill fixture, inspect the bottom for small chips, nicks, and burrs. Use a stone to remove these and make sure that the tooling and table are clean. Set the vise gently on the table and position it according to the job to be done. Install the holddown bolts and tighten just enough to permit the vise to be moved by gentle tapping with a lead or other soft hammer. If the mill vise does not have alignment keys, the following procedures may be used to align it parallel or perpendicular to the machine table.

Parallel to Table Alignment

1. Fasten a dial indicator on a magnetic base and attach to the arbor or overarm (Figure 6). Be sure that overarm clamps are tight. Position the indicator to contact the **solid jaw** of the vise. Preload the indicator about one-half revolution.

2. Move the table by hand so that the indicator is positioned at one end of the solid jaw. Set the bezel to zero. Crank the table so that the vise jaw moves past the indicator tip and note the reading at the opposite end of the jaw.

3. Tap the vise gently with a soft hammer so that one-half of the total indicated runout is cancelled (back toward zero on the indicator). When tapping the vise, **move it in such a direction that the solid jaw moves away from the indicator tip.** Moving the jaw against the indicator tip can damage the delicate indicator because of the shock delivered to the indicator movement. Reset the bezel to zero.

4. Crank the table back and observe the indicator reading. If a zero reading is obtained, tighten the holddown bolts securely and **recheck** the alignment.

Figure 6. Aligning vise parallel to table (Lane Community College).

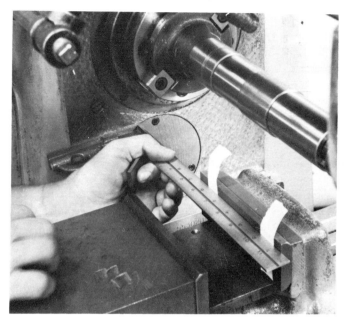

Figure 8. Using a square to align vise on table (Lane Community College).

Figure 7. Aligning vise square to table travel (Lane Community College).

Perpendicular to Table Alignment. A vise may be aligned at right angles to the table (Figure 7) by the same technique previously discussed. Once again, **always indicate on the solid jaw** and move the saddle in order to carry the vise jaw past the indicator. **Always recheck after tightening holddown bolts.**

Squaring a Vise to the Column. A vise may be aligned by squaring the solid jaw to the column. Two paper strips may be used as feeler gages between the beam of

the square and the vise jaw (Figure 8). This technique will quite accurately align a vise, but it is not as reliable as the dial indicator methods previously discussed.

Angular Alignment. A protractor may be used to set a vise at an angle other than 90 degrees to the table (Figure 9). The accuracy of the angle is dependent on the type of tool used and the technique. Errors can be introduced from the angle setting on the protractor and the relative alignment of the vise jaw along the protractor blade. Considerable care must be exercised in making a setup by this technique.

Securing the Workpiece. The vise will effectively secure a workpiece in most cases. Whenever possible, set up the vise so that **cutting pressure is applied to the solid jaw** (Figure 10). Avoid applying cutting pressure against the movable jaw. If the workpiece is sufficiently high, it may be seated on the bottom of the vise. If not, **parallels** may be used to elevate the work to a point where it can be machined. In many cases it will be necessary to apply the cutting pressure parallel to the vise jaws (Figure 11). Remember that friction between the vise jaws and workpiece holds it in place. The more contact area that there is will result in improved holding power. When cutting pressure is applied parallel to the vise jaws, there is always a possibility that the part will be pushed from the vise. Therefore, if you must use parallels to elevate the workpiece, only raise it high enough to accomplish the required machining since this reduces contact area and the vise may not be able to hold the workpiece safely and securely.

Figure 9. Using a protractor to align a vise on table (Lane Community College).

Figure 10. Cutting pressure against solid jaw (Lane Community College).

Figure 11. Workpiece held in vise (Lane Community College).

Figure 12. Using a paper strip to set the depth of cut (Lane Community College).

PLAIN MILLING

Good milling practice is to take a **roughing cut** and then a **finish cut.** Better surface finish and higher dimensional accuracy are achieved when roughing and finishing cuts are made. The depth of the roughing cut often is limited by the horsepower of the machine or the rigidity of the setup. A good **starting depth for roughing is .100 to .200 in.**

The **finishing cut** should be **.015 to .030 in. deep.** Depth of cut less than .015 in. should be avoided because a milling cutter, especially in conventional or up milling, has a strong rubbing action before the cutter actually starts cutting. This rubbing action causes a cutter to dull rapidly.

Roughing Cuts

Assuming that a roughing cut .100 in. deep is to be taken, the following procedure may be used.

1. Loosen the knee locking clamp and the cross slide lock.
2. Turn on the spindle and check its rotation.
3. Position the table so that the workpiece is under the cutter.
4. A paper strip may be used to determine when the cutter is about .002 in. away from the workpiece (Figure 12). Although this should be done with the spindle off and turned by hand, the experienced machinist may do it with the spindle running. **There**

is considerable danger present and it is much safer to stop the spindle when hands are near the cutter.

5. Set the micrometer dial on the knee crank on zero.

6. Lower the knee approximately one-half revolution of the hand feed crank. If the knee is not lowered, the cutter will leave tool marks on the workpiece in the following operation.

7. Move the table right or left until the cutter is clear of the workpiece. Start the cut on whichever side of the part that results in up or conventional milling.

8. Raise the knee past the zero mark to the 100 mark on the micrometer dial.

9. Tighten the knee lock and the cross slide lock. **Always** prior to starting a machining operation, tighten all locking clamps except the one that would restrict table movement while cutting. This aids in making a rigid chatterfree setup.

10. The machine is now ready for the cut. Turn on the coolant (Figure 13). Move the table slowly into the revolving cutter until the full depth of cut is obtained before engaging the power feed.

11. When the cut is completed, disengage the power feed, stop the spindle rotation, and turn off the coolant before returning the table to its starting position. If the revolving cutter is returned over the newly machined surface, it will leave cutter marks and mar the finish.

12. After brushing off the chips and wiping the workpiece clean, the part should be measured while it is still fastened in the machine. If the workpiece is parallel at this time, additional cuts can be made if more material needs to be removed.

Squaring a Workpiece

Often a piece of stock shaped like a parallelogram (Figure 14) must be machined square. This can be accomplished by machining all four sides in the correct sequence. The workpiece should be set up in a mill vise; it may be placed on parallels if necessary. This will facilitate measurements and will also raise a short part above the vise jaws. The following procedure may be used.

1. Set the workpiece in the vise and mill a reference surface on top.

2. Deburr and place this surface (side 1, Figure 15) against the solid jaw of the vise.

3. Place a short length of soft round rod between the work and the movable jaw of the vise. Tighten vise and seat workpiece down on the parallels with a lead hammer. The rod will insure that the reference surface is pressed flat against the solid vise jaw.

4. Mill side 2 (Figure 15).

5. Deburr and place side 2 down keeping side 1 against

Figure 13. Coolant cools the cutter and washes away chips (Lane Community College).

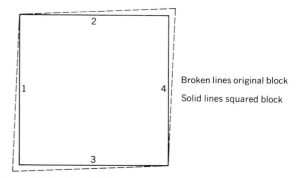

Figure 14. Machining a square from a parallelogram.

Broken lines original block

Solid lines squared block

Figure 15. Setup to machine side 2 (Lane Community College).

the solid jaw. Be sure that side 2 is carefully seated against the parallels. Test by trying to move the parallels. If they can be moved, use the lead hammer and tap the workpiece down so that it will be firmly seated.

Figure 16. Setup to machine side 3 (Lane Community College).

Figure 18. Setup to machine side 4 (Lane Community College).

Figure 17. Location of shim to square up work (Lane Community College).

Figure 19. Setup of a workpiece to machine an end square (Lane Community College).

6. Mill side 3 (Figure 16).

7. Use a micrometer and measure across sides 2 and 3. These should measure parallel and furthermore should be square to the reference side 1 since it is against the solid jaw. If they are not, paper shims (Figure 17) may be used to square the workpiece. An additional test cut may be made and measurements rechecked.

8. Deburr and place side 1 down and sides 2 or 3 against the solid jaw of the vise. Be sure that side 1 is well seated on the parallels. Since sides 2 and 3 are parallel, the rod between the work and movable jaw will not be necessary.

9. Mill side 4 (Figure 18).

Milling Ends of the Workpiece

After the sides of the workpiece have been machined

square, the end may also be finished by placing the work in a vise end up (Figure 19). A square is used to position the workpiece. Tighten the vise lightly and tap the work with a soft hammer to bring it into a square position. A dial indicator can also be used to position the workpiece in a perpendicular position. Attach the indicator to the overarm or arbor with the tip in contact with the workpiece. Run the knee up and down and adjust the workpiece until a zero indicator reading is obtained.

Figure 20.   Work clamped off center needs a spacer (Lane Community College).

Figure 21.   Use of angle plate to mill ends of workpieces (Lane Community College).

If the workpiece is quite long, it may still be end machined in a vise by setting it off center. In this setup, always support the opposite end of the vise jaw with a piece of material that is the same thickness as the work-piece (Figure 20). The end of a long workpiece may also be machined by clamping to an angle plate (Figure 21) and adjusting the position of the workpiece with a square or dial indicator.

SELF-TEST

1. Why is the solid jaw used to align a vise on a milling machine table?
2. Which is more accurate, using a precision square or a dial indicator to square a vise on a machine table?
3. What is the purpose of the keys used on the base of machine vises?
4. Should you mount the indicator on the column to align the table on a universal milling machine?
5. Should the solid vise jaw be in a specific position in relation to the direction of the cut?
6. Is a large or small diameter cutter more efficient?
7. What is the difference between conventional milling and climb milling?
8. How deep should a finish cut be?
9. Why are all table movements locked except the one being used during machining?
10. Why is the cutter rotation stopped while the table is returned over the newly cut surface to its starting position?

UNIT 7 USING SIDE MILLING CUTTERS

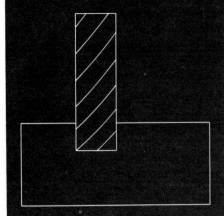

Machining a flat surface is only one of the many machining operations that can be accomplished on the horizontal mill. Steps and grooves, straddle and gang milling involve the use of side milling cutters. The purpose of this unit is to introduce you to these useful milling cutters and their applications.

OBJECTIVES

After completing this unit, you should be able to:
1. Set up side milling cutters and cut steps and grooves.
2. Use side milling cutters for straddle milling.
3. Use side milling cutters in gang milling.

SIDE MILLING CUTTERS AND SIDE MILLING

Milling cutters with side teeth are called **side milling cutters.** These are used to machine steps and grooves or, when only the sides of the workpiece are to be machined, in **straddle** setups. An example of this would be cutting hexes on bolt heads. Grooves are best machined in the workpiece with **full side mills** that have cutting teeth on both sides (Figure 1). Steps may be cut with **half side mills** having cutting teeth only on one side (Figure 2).

The size, type, and diameter of side milling cutter to use will depend on the machining task. As a rule, the smallest diameter cutter that will do the job should be used as long as sufficient clearance is maintained between the arbor support and work or vise (Figure 3).

Frequently side milling cutters will cut a slot or groove that is slightly wider than the nominal width of the cutter. Reasons for this include: cutter wobble due to chips or dirt between the cutter and arbor spacing collars, making multiple cuts through the workpiece, and a dull or worn cutter. Other factors contributing to wider than desired slots are the rate of feed and the type of material being machined. A slow feed will give the side mill more time to cut a slightly wider slot. A fast feed will crowd the cutter resulting in a narrower slot. Wider slots may occur in softer materials more than they do in harder materials.

If the specifications call for a slot width of .375 in., using a .375 (three-eighth) in. wide side mill may result in

a slot width that ranges from .3755 to .376 in. In order to hold the required dimension, it may be necessary to use a narrower side mill, say .3125 (five-sixteenth) in., and make additional passes through the workpiece until the required width dimension is obtained.

Preparing and Setting Up the Workpiece

A good machinist will mark the workpiece with layout lines before securing it in the machine. The layout should be an exact outline of the final part shape and size. The reason for making the layout prior to beginning work is that reference surfaces are often removed during machining. After the layout has been made, diagonal lines should be chalked on the workpiece indicating the portions that are to be cut away. This helps to identify on which side of the layout lines the cut is to be made (Figure 4).

The workpiece may be mounted by any of the traditional methods previously discussed. If you are using a vise, be sure it is aligned along with the table. If you are clamping directly to the table, **follow the rules of good clamping.**

Positioning a Side Milling Cutter

In order to machine a slot or groove at a particular location on the workpiece, the side mill must be positioned both horizontally (for location) and vertically (for feature depth). To position the cutter for location, lower below the top surface of the workpiece. With the spindle off and free to turn by hand, insert a paper strip between

Figure 1. Full side milling cutter machining a groove (Lane Community College).

Figure 2. Half side milling cutter machining a step (Lane Community College).

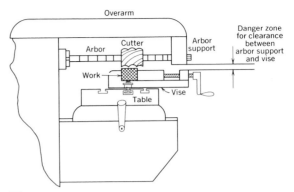

Figure 3. Always check clearance between arbor support and vise when setting up the machine.

Figure 4. Work laid out for milling (Lane Community College).

to zero compensating for the .002 of paper thickness.

Position for depth by lowering the knee and moving the workpiece under the cutter. Then, raise the knee and use the paper strip gage to determine when the cutter is about .002 in. above the workpiece. Set the knee micrometer collar to zero. Move the table until the cutter is clear of the workpiece and then raise the knee the amount required for the depth of the feature.

A less accurate, but quicker method of cutter alignment is by direct measurement (Figure 6). A rule may be used to measure the position of the cutter relative to the edge of the workpiece after which the saddle micrometer collar should be set to zero.

Making the Cut. After the cutter has been positioned for location, raise the knee the amount required for the depth of the feature. Machining to full depth may

cutter and work (Figure 5) and move the workpiece toward the cutter until the paper is pulled between the work and cutter. At this point, the cutter is about .002 in. from the workpiece. Set the saddle micrometer collar

Figure 5. Setting up a cutter by using a paper strip (Lane Community College).

Figure 7. Taking a trial cut (Lane Community College).

Figure 6. Positioning a cutter using a steel rule (Lane Community College).

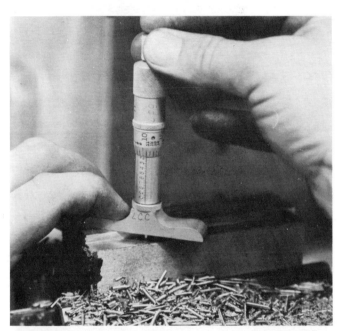

Figure 8. Measuring depth of a step (Lane Community College).

be accomplished in one pass dependent on the width of the cut and the material being machined. A deep slot may have to be machined in more than one pass, each pass somewhat deeper than the one before. Until you gain some experience in milling, hold depth setting to about .100 in.

Set proper feeds and speeds and turn on the spindle. Approach the workpiece in an up milling mode. Hand feed the cutter into the work until a small nick is machined on the corner (Figure 7, point X). Stop spindle, back away, and check the dimension relative to the edge of the workpiece. If you are machining a slot, check the width. If dimensions are correct, complete the required cuts. Final depth can be measured with a depth micrometer (Figure 8). Slot width can be measured with a dial/vernier caliper or adjustable parallel.

Side Milling Shaft Keyways
Side milling is an excellent way to machine a shaft keyway especially if the keyway is quite long. The proce-

Figure 9. Setting the side mill alongside the shaft (Lane Community College).

Figure 11. Side milling a shaft keyway (Lane Community College).

Figure 10. After centering, cutter is brought into contact with shaft (Lane Community College).

dure for keyway milling is much the same as in vertical milling. The cutter must be centered over the shaft and set for depth.

After selecting and mounting a cutter of the proper width, raise the workpiece beside the cutter (Figure 9) and use the paper feeler technique to position the cutter alongside the shaft. Lower the knee and move the work-

piece over a distance equal to one-half the total of cutter width and shaft diameter. Raise the knee until the cutter contacts the shaft and cuts a full width cut (Figure 10). Set the knee micrometer collar to zero. Lower the knee and move the cutter clear of the workpiece in the table axis only. Raise the knee to obtain the correct keyway depth. Using proper feeds and speeds, approach the workpiece in an up milling mode, and mill the keyway to the proper length (Figure 11).

Straddle and Gang Milling

Side milling cutters are combined to perform **straddle milling.** In straddle milling, two side milling cutters are mounted on an arbor and set at an exact spacing (Figure 12). Two sides of the workpiece are machined simultaneously and final width dimensions are exactly controlled. Straddle milling has many useful applications· in production machining. Parallel slots of equal depth can be milled by using straddle mills or equal diameters.

In **gang milling,** several cutters are mounted on the arbor and used to machine special shapes and contours on the workpiece (Figure 13). The difference in cutter diameter determines the depths of steps and grooves. Cutter RPM is calculated for the largest diameter cutter in the gang.

Interlocking Tooth and
Right- and Left-Hand Helical Side Mills

Wide slots and grooves can be machined with right- and

Figure 12. Straddle milling (Lane Community College).

Figure 13. Gang milling (Courtesy of Cincinnati Milacron).

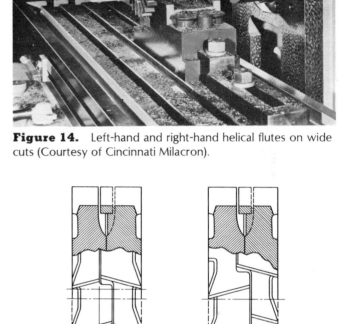

Figure 14. Left-hand and right-hand helical flutes on wide cuts (Courtesy of Cincinnati Milacron).

Overlapping teeth

Figure 15. Interlocking side milling cutters.

left-hand **helical side mills.** The heavy side thrust created by the cutter helix is cancelled by placing right- and left-hand helices opposite each other (Figure 14).

Interlocking side mills are used when grooves of a precise width are machined in one operation (Figure 15).

Shims inserted between individual cutters make precise adjustment possible. The overlapping teeth leave a smooth finish in the bottom of the groove. Cutters that have become thinner from resharpenings can also be adjusted to their full width by adding shims.

SELF-TEST

1. When are full side milling cutters used?
2. When are half side milling cutters used?
3. What diameter side milling cutter is most efficient?
4. Is a groove the same width as the cutter that produces it?
5. Why should a layout be made on workpieces?
6. How can a side milling cutter be positioned for a cut without marring the workpiece surface?
7. Why should measurements be made before removing a workpiece from the workholding device?
8. How is the width of a workpiece controlled in a straddle milling operation?
9. What determines the depth of the steps in gang milling?
10. When are interlocking side mills used?

SECTION K ROTARY TABLES AND INDEXING DEVICES

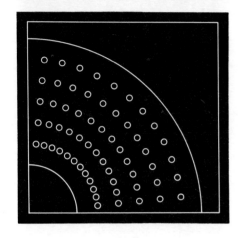

Since the circle forms the basic geometric shape for so many mechanical devices, the ability to divide a circle circumference into almost any number of divisions is extremely useful. Furthermore, the ability to machine a circular feature on a workpiece has contributed greatly to the development of many useful devices.

The group of tools known as **rotary tables** or circular milling attachments divides the circle in angular terms—that is, by degrees and fractions of degrees. The group of tools known as **indexing** or **dividing heads** divides the circle in terms of the number of circumference divisions desired. Naturally, angles and numbers of circumference divisions can be equated to each other and the tools may often be applied interchangeably depending on the specific machining task to be done. However, a tool from one group or the other may be better suited to a specific application. Part of your job is to be able to select the one that best fits the need. The purpose of this section is to identify these useful accessories, describe their applications, aid you in selecting the one that best fits the job, and familiarize you with calculations relative to indexing requirements.

ROTARY TABLES

The **rotary table** is an extremely useful accessory for the milling machine. A rotary table consists of a precision worm and wheel unit that can be attached to the milling machine table (Figure 1). One common application of the rotary table is machining a circular feature on the workpiece (Figure 2). Rotary tables may be power driven by mechanical connection to the mill table feed mechanism (Figure 3). When using a rotary table for the more precise requirements of an indexing operation, it may be equipped with an indexing attachment (Figure 4). The typical rotary table is graduated in degrees and fractions. Discriminations range from one minute of arc down to fractions of seconds (Figure 5). An optical microscope may be used to further increase discrimination (Figure 6). Rotary tables may be designed so they can be mounted on a machine tool in either a vertical or horizontal position (Figure 7). Inspection (Figure 8) and calibration make use of high resolution rotary tables discriminating to $\frac{1}{10}$ second of arc (Figure 9).

INDEXING DEVICES

Indexing devices divide the circle in terms of the number of circumference spacings required. Indexing devices may also be called indexing heads or dividing heads. One of the simplest types is the **collet index fixture** (Figure 10). This tool can be mounted horizontally or vertically and is suitable for indexing low numbers or divisions (2, 4, 6, 8, 10, 12, etc.). The workpiece is held in a split collet.

Many types of horizontal and universal indexing heads have been devel-

Figure 1. Circular milling table (Courtesy of Cincinnati Milacron).

Figure 2. Circular milling attachment being used to mill a circular T-slot (Courtesy of Cincinnati Milacron).

Figure 3. A circular milling table with power feed is termed a circular milling attachment (Courtesy of Cincinnati Milacron).

Figure 4. Circular milling attachment equipped with an indexing attachment (Courtesy of Cincinnati Milacron).

oped. The indexing capability is accomplished by making use of an **index plate.** An index plate consists of several circles of equally spaced holes into which the index crank pin can be engaged. Although the hole circles in the index plate are equally spaced, the number of holes varies in different circles permitting many different numbers of circumference divisions to be

Figure 5. Ultraprecise rotary table (Courtesy of Moore Special Tool Co., Inc., Bridgeport, Conn.).

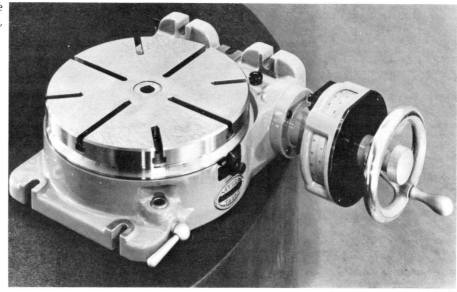

Figure 6. Optical dividing table (Courtesy of American SIP Corporation).

Figure 7. Using the rotary table on a jig boring machine (Courtesy of Moore Special Tool Co., Inc., Bridgeport, Conn.).

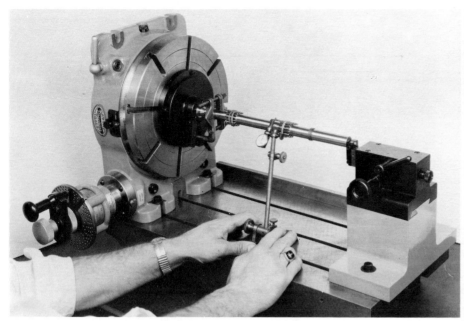

Figure 8. Rotary table with tailstock and adjustable center being used for inspection (Courtesy of Moore Special Tool Co., Inc., Bridgeport, Conn.).

Figure 9. Precision index — a master tool for master tools (Courtesy of Moore Special Tool Co.).

Figure 10. Collet index fixture (Courtesy of Hardinge Brothers, Inc.).

Figure 11. Direct indexing head (Courtesy of Cincinnati Milacron).

obtained. Sets of index plates containing a variety of hole circles are also available, further increasing the range of circumference divisions possible.

The direct index head (Figure 11) has the spindle connected directly to the index crank. The index plate is located on the back of the head. Indexing is accomplished by first setting the crank pin to the desired circle of holes, then moving the crank from hole to hole to achieve indexing of the work-

Figure 12. Gear cutting attachment (Courtesy of Cincinnati Milacron).

Figure 13. Milling a bevel gear with a universal index head (Courtesy of Cincinnati Milacron).

Figure 14. Dividing heads are also useful for making graduations on conical surface (Courtesy of Cincinnati Milacron).

Figure 15. Dividing head with wide range divider (Courtesy of Cincinnati Milacron).

piece. Direct index heads are limited to the maximum number of holes in the index plate, usually 50.

By adding a 40:1 worm and wheel to the index head, the ratio of crank turns to spindle turns can be greatly increased, thus permitting the circle circumference to be divided into many more parts. This type of plain index head is regularly used in spur gear cutting (Figure 12).

The **universal indexing head** is much like the plain index head with the added feature that the spindle may be swiveled out of the horizontal. The workpiece may still be indexed, but milling can now be done on an angled surface (Figure 13). Circular graduating on an angled surface is another operation that can be done with a universal index head (Figure 14).

The **wide range indexing head** (Figure 15) uses the standard 40:1 ratio plus an additional 100:1 ratio. The ratios are multiplied resulting in a total of 4000:1. Divisions of 2 to 400,000 can be obtained with this tool.

Figure 16. Inspecting a cam using a dividing head (Courtesy of Cincinnati Milacron).

Figure 17. Helical milling head (Courtesy of Cincinnati Milacron.)

Indexing heads may be applied in special inspection requirements (Figure 16). For example, a cam lobe may be inspected by rotating the workpiece indexed accord1ing to the lobe positions.

Index Heads and Helical Milling Processes

Helical milling is a process where the workpiece is rotated at the same time that it is being fed into the cutter. The result is a helical cut such as the flute of a drill, helix of a milling cutter, or the helical teeth of a gear. By varying the rate of rotation relative to the distance the workpiece travels longitudinally, the amount of helical twist or lead can be changed depending on the machining requirements. For example, a drill would have a relatively long or slow helix whereas a high helix milling cutter would have a short or fast helix. You will probably not encounter a great deal of helical milling in routine machine shop work unless you happen to become involved with the more specialized manufacturing making use of this process. However, the process is quite interesting and machine setup is probably one of the more involved processes done by the general machinist.

To accomplish helical milling, the spindle of the index head (Figure 17) is

Figure 18. Standard universal dividing head driving mechanism (Courtesy of Cincinnati Milacron).

Figure 19. Short and long lead driving mechanism (Courtesy of Cincinnati Milacron).

coupled to the mill table screw. This will cause the index head spindle to rotate as the machine table is moved back and forth. The indexing capability of the index head permits the manufacture of a helical gear on the universal milling machine. However, it should be noted that milling of helical gears on a universal mill is not that common a process since the end result may not meet the exact specifications required on precision gears. Helical gear cutting for manufacturing purposes is done on sophisticated gear generators discussed in later sections.

Helical leads are obtained through the gear train connecting the table screw and index head spindle (Figure 18). The short and long lead attachment (Figure 19) permits the selection of over 13,000 leads ranging from .010 to 3000 in. Various accessories can be combined to accomplish complex helical milling operations (Figure 20).

Gear hobbing is another job that can be done by synchronizing an indexing device with the machine spindle (Figure 21).

Figure 20. A combination of attachments for the milling of a leadscrew (Courtesy of Cincinnati Milacron).

Figure 21. A special hobbing attachment for the horizontal milling machine (Courtesy of Cincinnati Milacron).

UNIT 1 SETUP AND OPERATION OF INDEXING HEADS AND ROTARY TABLES

The **indexing head** and **rotary table** are versatile and useful milling machine accessories. They serve to rotate the workpiece a full or partial turn for the purpose of indexing a specific number of divisions, an angle, or to machine a circular feature. The purpose of this unit is to discuss the operation and setup of common indexing heads and rotary tables.

OBJECTIVES

After completing this unit, you should be able to:
1. Identify the major parts of indexing heads and rotary tables.
2. Set up these tools on the milling machine.

INDEXING HEADS

Probably the most common **index head** used in the machine shop is either the **plain** or **universal** type. These tools consist of a precision worm and wheel unit housed in appropriate bearings (Figure 1). The index head worm engages the spindle worm wheel and is turned by operating the index crank. The crank is geared to the worm usually in the ratio of 40:1. **This means that 40 turns of the index crank are required to rotate the spindle one revolution.**

On most indexing heads, the spindle can be disengaged from the crank worm permitting the spindle to be turned by hand. This facilitates setup of the tool and also permits **direct indexing.** Direct indexing may be accomplished by engaging the direct index plunger and pin in holes on the spindle nose (Figure 2). Smaller numbers of division can be indexed in this manner.

The index head spindle has a tapered bore that will accept tapered shank tooling. Some index head spindles are threaded to accept screw on chucks. A lock is provided so that the spindle may be secured at a particular setting in order to increase rigidity of a setup.

The index crank contains a pin on a spring-loaded plunger that engages the holes in the index plate. Hole circles in the index plate provide the indexing function. The pattern on the plate consists of a number of equally spaced hole circles, and the crank pin is adjusted in and out so that the desired circle may be used. Some plates have additional circles of holes on the reverse side.

Two **sector arms** rotate about the crank hub and can be adjusted to indicate the correct number of holes for a partial turn of the crank. For example, if you are indexing one turn plus five holes for each division, the sector arms can be set so that you will not have to count the five extra holes each time around.

Setting Up the Index Head

The index head is secured to the mill table in the same manner as any other machine accessory. Many heads have alignment keys that fit the table T-slots. If the head has no keys, it must be aligned with the table using the dial indicator alignment techniques discussed in previous units. Furthermore, the universal indexing head must be aligned in the horizontal if it is used for parallel to table machining setups.

The ends of long workpieces or gear arbors are

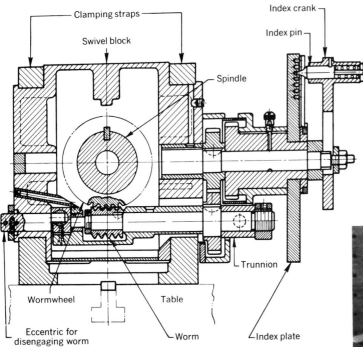

Figure 1. Section through dividing head showing worm and worm shaft (Courtesy of Cincinnati Milacron).

Figure 3. Footstock (Lane Community College).

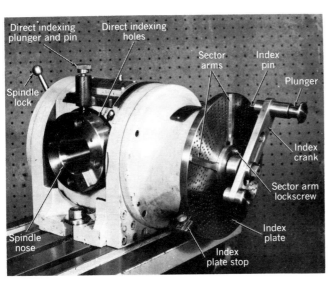

Figure 2. Indexing components of a dividing head (Lane Community College).

supported by a **footstock** (Figure 3). Similar in function to the lathe tailstock, the footstock center can be adjusted in and out as well as up and down. Long or slender workpieces may be further supported by an **adjustable center rest** (Figure 4).

Figure 4. Adjustable center rest (Lane Community College).

ROTARY TABLES

The common **rotary table** is also a precision worm and wheel unit. Many rotary table setups use the tool in its horizontal position (Figure 5). However, some rotary

Figure 5.   Rotary table (Lane Community College).

tables are designed to be used in both vertical and horizontal positions.

Rotary tables position the workpiece by **degrees of arc,** but may be used much like the index head with the addition of an indexing attachment. The rotary table is equipped with T-slots so that the workpiece may be secured.

Discriminations on rotary tables vary from one minute to fractions of seconds. Full degrees are graduated on the circumference of the table. Fractions of degrees are read on the worm crank scale usually with the aid of a vernier. Ratios of common rotary tables are 40:1, 80:1, and 120:1. A lock is provided to increase the rigidity of the setup during machining.

Setting Up and Using Rotary Tables

If the rotary table is used to machine features equidistant from center, the tool must be accurately positioned under the machine spindle. This is done by the same techniques discussed in previous units. Use a dial test indicator and pick up center from the hole in the center of the rotary table. Once the table has been centered under the spindle in both table and saddle axes, it may be moved off center in either axis an amount equal to the pitch circle radius of the features to be machined. It may also be **necessary to center the workpiece** on the table so that concentric features may be obtained during a machining operation.

SELF-TEST

1. When are indexing devices used?
2. What makes indexing devices so accurate?
3. When is the worm disengaged from the worm wheel?
4. When is the hole circle on the spindle nose used?
5. What is a commonly used index ratio on dividing heads?
6. Why does the index plate have a number of different hole circles?
7. What is the purpose of the sector arms?
8. What does the spindle lock do?
9. How can divisions be made that are not possible with a standard index plate?
10. Why should the index crank be rotated in one direction only while indexing?

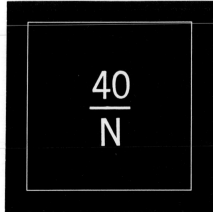

UNIT 2 DIRECT AND SIMPLE INDEXING

$$\frac{40}{N}$$

Most indexing for routine machining operations can be done by the **direct** and **simple** methods. Accuracy and the number of divisions required determine the method to use. Common machining operations that involve indexing include spline and gear cutting, keyways, hexagons, octagons, squares, and other geometric shapes. The purpose of this unit is to familiarize you with the calculations required for indexing tasks.

OBJECTIVE

After completing this unit, you should be able to calculate full and fractional turns of the index head spindle to index the workpiece a required number of equal divisions.

DIRECT INDEXING

Direct indexing is the simplest method dividing a circle into a required number of equally spaced divisions. The number of divisions that can be obtained by the direct method is limited by the number of holes in the index plate or in the spindle nose. Direct index head plates contain 24, 30, and 36 hole circles. The following formula may be used to make the index calculation:

$$\frac{\text{Number of holes in the indexing circle}}{\text{Required number of divisions}} = \frac{\text{holes}}{\text{division required for indexing}}$$

The result of this calculation must be a **whole number,** as it is obvious that only full holes are available into which the index may be engaged.

EXAMPLES
The available hole circles for direct indexing may be evenly divided in the following manner.

24 divided by:	30 divided by:	36 divided by:
2 = 12 holes/division	2 = 15 holes/division	2 = 18 holes/division
3 = 8	3 = 10	3 = 12
4 = 6	5 = 6	4 = 9
6 = 4		
8 = 3	6 = 5	6 = 6
12 = 2	10 = 3	9 = 4
24 = 1	15 = 2	12 = 3
	30 = 1	18 = 2
		36 = 1

Calculate direct indexing for 6 divisions:

$$24/6 = 4 \text{ holes per division}$$

If you were using a 24 hole circle, the spindle would have to be rotated the partial turn corresponding to 4 holes. The 30 and 36 hole circles could also be used for 6 divisions. However, only the 30 hole circle could have been used for 5 divisions and only the 36 hole circle for 9 divisions.

When direct indexing, count the required number of new holes to the next division. *Do not count the hole in which the index pin is engaged.* After engaging the pin, always lock the spindle to increase rigidity of the

setup. To avoid an indexing error, you may mark the hole circle with a felt pen or chalk.

Direct indexing may be done on a plain index head by disengaging the worm from the spindle so that the spindle may be turned by hand. The hole circles in the spindle nose are used for the indexing circles.

SIMPLE INDEXING

Simple indexing, also known as plain indexing, makes use of the gear ratio between crank and spindle. On most common index heads this ratio is **40:1. Forty turns of the index crank are required to rotate the spindle one revolution.**

Required numbers of circle divisions involving less than one full turn of the spindle now become fractions of 40 and the indexing calculation is made by applying the formula:

$$\textbf{Index crank turns} = \textbf{40/}N$$

where N is the required number of divisions. Index plates with the following hole circles are available: 24, 25, 28, 30, 34, 37, 38, 39, 41, 42, 43, 46, 47, 49, 51, 53, 54, 57, 58, 59, 62, 66.

EXAMPLE
Calculate indexing for 20 divisions.

$$40/N = 40/20 = 2 \text{ full turns of the index crank}$$

In this case any index plate may be used since no partial turn is required. However, to calculate indexing for 52 divisions:

$$40/N = 40/52$$

This means that less than one full turn is required for each division, $\frac{40}{52}$ of a turn to be exact. A 52 hole circle is not available so a **proportional fraction** must be generated. This can be done by the following procedure. Reduce the index fraction to its lowest terms:

$$40/52 = 10/13$$

Take the **denominator** of lowest terms, 13, and determine into which of the available hole circles it can be **evenly divided.** In this case, 13 may be divided into the available 39 hole circle exactly 3 times. Use this result 3 as a **multiplier** to generate the proportional fraction required.

$$\frac{10 \times 3}{13 \times 3} = \frac{30}{39}$$

Therefore, **30 holes on a 39 hole circle** is the correct indexing for 52 divisions.

EXAMPLE
Calculate indexing for 27 divisions.

$$\frac{40}{N} = \frac{40}{27} = 1\frac{13}{27}$$

or 1 full turn plus $\frac{13}{27}$ fractional turn. If a 27 hole circle were available, then 13 holes of the 27 would give the fractional turn required. However, a 27 hole circle is not available so a proportional fraction must be generated containing a denominator corresponding to an available hole circle.

The fraction $\frac{13}{27}$ is already at lowest terms, so take the denominator and determine which of the available hole circles it will divide into evenly. When divided into the 54 hole circle, 27 goes exactly 2 times. This result becomes the multiplier used to generate the proportional fraction,

$$\frac{13 \times 2}{27 \times 2} = \frac{26}{54}$$

Therefore, **26 holes on the 54 hole circle** will give the correct partial turn fraction. Indexing will then be one full turn plus 26 of the 54 holes for each of the required divisions.

EXAMPLE
Calculate indexing for 35 divisions.

$$\frac{40}{N} = \frac{40}{35} = 1\frac{5}{35}$$

Figure 1. Dividing head sector arms set for indexing 11 spaces (Lane Community College).

or 1 full turn plus $\frac{5}{35}$ fractional turn. Reducing $\frac{5}{35}$ to lowest terms equals $\frac{1}{7}$. The lowest term denominator 7 divides evenly into:

28 hole circle (4 times)
42 hole circle (6 times) } multipliers
49 hole circle (7 times)

Therefore, any of these indexing circles may be used by generating the proportional fractions in the following manner:

$$\frac{1 \times 4}{7 \times 4} = \frac{4}{28} \quad \text{(4 holes on 28 hole circle)}$$
$$\frac{1 \times 6}{7 \times 6} = \frac{6}{42} \quad \text{(6 holes on 42 hole circle)}$$
$$\frac{1 \times 7}{7 \times 7} = \frac{7}{49} \quad \text{(7 holes on 49 hole circle)}$$

EXAMPLE
Calculate indexing for 51 divisions

$$\frac{40}{N} = \frac{40}{51}$$

Since a 51 hole circle is available, 40 holes on a 51 hole circle will provide the correct indexing.

Using the Index Head

It would be very unhandy to have to count numbers of holes for fractional turns each time around. To facilitate and to reduce possible errors in indexing, the **sector arms** are used. The sector arms rotate about the index crank hub and are locked in place by a lock screw. The facing edges of the arms are beveled (Figure 1) and the number of holes required for fractional turns is established between the beveled edges. Remember that the number of holes required for a fractional turn will be **new holes**. The hole where the crank pin is engaged is not counted.

To operate the index head, unlock the spindle and pull back the crank pin plunger. Rotate the crank the required number of turns plus fractions. Set the sector arms to keep track of additional holes beyond one full turn of the crank. *Bring the crank pin around until it just drops into the required hole.* If you overshoot the position, back off well past the required hole and come up to it once again. This will eliminate any backlash in the worm and wheel. **Always index only in one direction and always lock the spindle before beginning the machining operation.**

After each indexing move, the sector arms must be shifted so that they will be properly positioned for the next move. For example, if you are indexing one full turn plus 11 holes, set the sector arms to include **11 new holes** between the beveled faces. Turn the index crank

one full turn plus the 11 additional holes. Then, shift the sector arms around so that 11 new holes will be available for the next move.

COMPOUND AND DIFFERENTIAL INDEXING

To obtain indexing of divisions that cannot be done on standard index plates, high number plates or the wide range indexing head may be used. Nonstandard numbers of divisions can also be obtained by the processes of **differential** or **compound indexing.** This is accomplished by rotating the index plate backward or forward in order to increase the combinations of hole circles and obtain the required number of indexing divisions. Consult a machinist's handbook for more information regarding compound or differential indexing.

SELF-TEST

1. When are indexing devices used?
2. What makes indexing devices so accurate?
3. When is the worm disengaged from the worm wheel?
4. When is the hole circle on the spindle nose used?
5. What is a commonly used index ratio on dividing heads?
6. Why does the index plate have a number of different hole circles?
7. What is the purpose of the sector arms?
8. What does the spindle lock do?
9. How can divisions be made that are not possible with a standard index plate?
10. Why should the index crank be rotated in one direction only while indexing?

UNIT 3 ANGULAR INDEXING

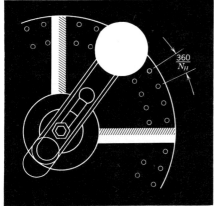

Circumference divisions on a circle can be defined in terms of specific numbers of equal spaces, or they may be defined in **angular terms—that is, degrees or minutes of arc.** Hole spacings in index plates can then become equivalent to angular measurement. The purpose of this unit is to define indexing plate hole circles in angular measure and familiarize you with the calculations for angular indexing.

OBJECTIVE

After completing this unit you should be able to perform calculations required for angular indexing.

DIRECT ANGULAR INDEXING

Since there are 360 degrees in a circle, each hole in any index plate circle can be equated to degrees and fractions by the formula

Degrees per hole = $360/N_H$

where **N_H = number of holes in the index circle.** Transposing this formula to determine the number of holes corresponding to an angle gives

$N_H = 360/$degrees in angle desired

EXAMPLE
Calculate direct indexing for 15 degrees.

$$N_H = 360/15 = 24$$

Therefore, a 24 hole circle would equate to 15 degrees per hole.

To determine the number of index plate holes that

define a specific angle, **divide the degrees per hole of a specific index circle into the angle.**

EXAMPLE
Calculate indexing for 75 degrees using a 24 hole index circle.

$$\frac{75 \text{ deg}}{15 \text{ deg/hole}} = 5 \text{ holes for 75 deg}$$

SIMPLE ANGULAR INDEXING

On the simple index head making use of a 40:1 ratio, 40 turns of the index crank are required to turn the spindle 360 degrees or one full revolution. Therefore, one turn of the index crank is equal to

$$\frac{360 \text{ deg}}{40 \text{ turns}} = 9 \text{ deg per turn}$$

Any index plate circle that is divisible by nine can be used for angular indexing.

EXAMPLE

$$\frac{27 \text{ hole circle}}{9} = 3 \text{ holes per deg}$$
$$(1 \text{ hole} = \tfrac{1}{3} \text{ deg or 20 min})$$
$$\frac{36 \text{ hole circle}}{9} = 4 \text{ holes per deg}$$
$$(1 \text{ hole} = \tfrac{1}{4} \text{ deg or 15 min})$$
$$\frac{45 \text{ hole circle}}{9} = 5 \text{ holes per deg}$$
$$(1 \text{ hole} = \tfrac{1}{5} \text{ deg or 12 min})$$
$$\frac{54 \text{ hole circle}}{9} = 6 \text{ holes per deg}$$
$$(1 \text{ hole} = \tfrac{1}{6} \text{ deg or 10 min})$$

The index crank turns required for an angle can be calculated by the formula:

$$\text{Turns} = \frac{\text{Degrees required}}{9 \text{ deg/turn}}$$

EXAMPLE
Calculate indexing for 37 degrees.

$$\frac{37}{9} = 4\frac{1}{9}$$

or 4 full turns plus $\tfrac{1}{9}$ additional turn. The $\tfrac{1}{9}$ partial turn is found by the same method described in the previous unit. Determine which of the available index circles the lowest term denominator 9 will divide into evenly.

$$\frac{54 \text{ hole circle}}{9} = 6 \text{ holes}$$

Therefore, indexing is **4 full turns plus 6 holes** on a 54 hole circle.

Angular Indexing in Minutes

Since one full turn of the index crank in a 40:1 ratio head is equal to 9 degrees, **it is also equal to 9 × 60 or 540 minutes.** Therefore, to index by minutes, apply the formula:

$$\text{Crank turns} = \frac{\text{Minutes required}}{540 \text{ min/turn}}$$

EXAMPLES
Calculate indexing for 8 deg, 50 min. Convert angle to minutes:

$$8 \text{ deg 50 min} = 530 \text{ min}$$

Apply the formula:

$$\text{Crank turns} = \frac{\text{Minutes required}}{540 \text{ min/turn}} = \frac{530}{540}$$

Reduce the fraction to lowest terms:

$$\frac{530}{540} = \frac{53}{54}$$

Take the lowest term denominator 54, and determine the available hole circle that it will divide into evenly. Since a 54 hole circle is available, 53 holes on a 54 hole circle will index 8 degrees and 53 minutes.

Uneven Minute Calculations. In some cases, it may not be possible to determine an exact partial turn on the index crank.

EXAMPLE
Calculate indexing for 1 deg and 35 min. Convert to minutes:

$$1 \text{ deg 35 min} = 95 \text{ min}$$

Apply the formula:

$$\frac{\text{Minutes required}}{540 \text{ min/turn}} = \frac{95}{540}$$

Reduce fraction to lowest terms:

$$\frac{95}{540} = \frac{19}{108}$$

If a 108 hole circle were available, then 19 holes would index the required 95 minutes. However, 108 is not available so a proportional fraction must be generated containing a denominator equal to an available hole circle.

The method of creating a proportional fraction is not apparently obvious. The task is to determine which

of the available hole circles will be closest to the requirements. A proportion may be established and evaluated for various hole circles:

$$\frac{19}{108} = \frac{X \text{ holes}}{\text{available circles}}$$

Evaluating this expression for a 51 hole circle, the result is

$$\frac{19}{108} = \frac{X}{51} \qquad X = \frac{19 \times 51}{108} = 8.972$$

This means that 8.972 holes on the available 51 hole circle will result in proper indexing. Obviously it is not possible to have .972 holes, the number may be rounded to the nearest full hole. In this case, 9 would be the closest. Since 9 holes, on the 51 hole circle would be $\frac{9}{51}$ of 540 min, the actual indexed angle would be 95.294 min or 95'17". The error is quite small. For more accuracy in angular indexing, it would be better to use the wide range indexing head.

SELF-TEST

1. If there are 24 holes in the direct indexing plate, how many degrees are between holes?
2. How many holes movement is necessary to index 45 degrees using the direct indexing method?
3. How many degrees in the movement produced by one complete turn of the index crank?
4. Which hole circles on the index plate can be used to index by whole degrees?
5. How many turns of the index crank are necessary to index 17 degrees?
6. What fraction of one degree is represented by 1 space on the 18 hole circle?
7. What fraction of one degree is represented by 1 space on the 36 hole circle?
8. What fraction of one degree is represented by 1 space on the 54 hole circle?
9. How many minutes movement is produced by one turn of the index crank?
10. How many turns of the index crank are necessary to index 54 deg 30 min using the 54 hole circle?

SECTION L
GEARS AND GEAR CUTTING

It would be difficult to envision a world without gears. Historically, the evolution of gears from pin cogs to the modern involute type is one of the more interesting developments in mechanical technology.

PURPOSE OF GEARS

Gears provide positive (nonslip) power transmission. They are also used to increase torque (turning effort) in many kinds of mechanical devices. Gears are used to increase and decrease speed in geared speeders and speed reducers. Mechanical timing requirements make extensive use of gears; they are widely used to establish set speed ratios between shafts.

Two or more gears running in mesh form a gear train. If the gears in a train are of different sizes, the smaller gear is called the **pinion.** Any two gears in mesh will always turn in opposite directions. To achieve same direction rotation, a third gear must be placed in mesh between two gears, or internal gears may be used.

Gears are often used to connect shafts at relatively short center distances. However, large marine reduction gear units may connect shafts that are several feet apart and are capable of transmitting many thousands of horsepower.

GEAR MANUFACTURING PROCESSES

Originally gears were milled with form cutters. This led to the involute geometry of modern gears and the method of gear cutting known as **hobbing** (Figures 1 and 2). **Gear hobbers** are a type of milling machine designed with both horizontal (Figure 3) and vertical spindles (Figure 4).

Another important type of gear cutting machine is the **gear shaper** (Figure 5). The shaper can make external, internal, spur, and helical gears. It can also form a gear next to a shoulder or next to another gear of the type found in many transmission gear clusters. Automotive differential gears that must be accurate, quiet, and long running are made on a **hypoid gear generator** (Figure 6). The gear shaper will also form gears of very unusual geometry (Figure 7).

As the need for high production of accurate gears increased, methods such as **gear broaching** were developed. Broaching is well suited to producing individual and nonclustered gears with straight teeth, or helical gears with low helix angles (Figure 8).

Figure 1. Schematic view of the generating action of a hob (Barber-Colman Company).

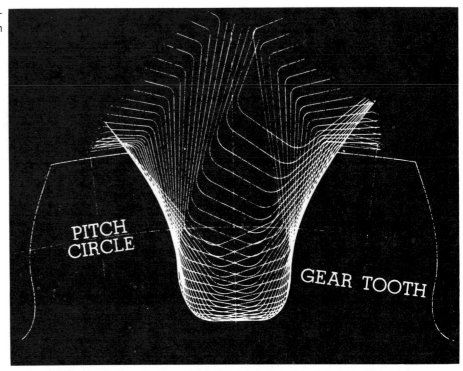

Figure 2. Schematic view of the performance of an individual hob tooth (Barber-Colman Company).

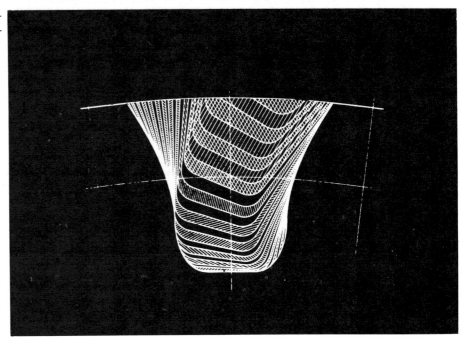

GEAR FINISHING PROCESSES

For commercial use, gear teeth are usually finished after they are cut and after the gear has been heat treated. The finishing process depends on the required accuracy of the gear, hardness, noise limitations, and where the gear will be used.

To finish gear teeth that are not harder than Rockwell C30, the **shaving process** may be used. Shaving can result in surface finishes from 32 to 16 microinches. One shaving method uses a shaving cutter that is meshed with

Figure 3. Small horizontal spindle hobbing machine (DeAnza College).

Figure 4. A huge vertical spindle gear hobbing machine. Notice the operator with the pendant control at the upper left (Courtesy of Ex-Cell-O Corporation).

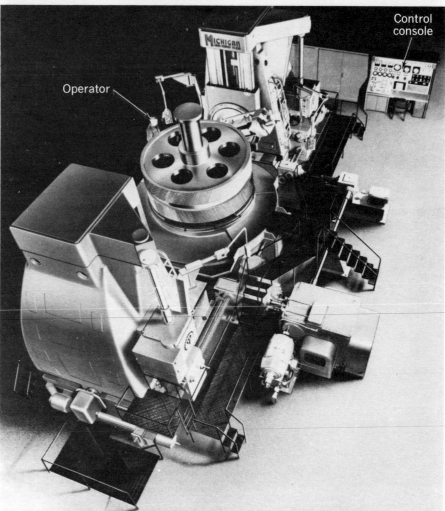

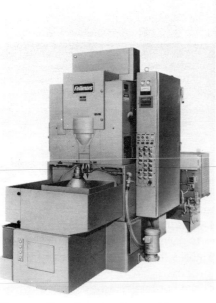

Figure 5. A gear shaper. The cutter moves up and down with the same twist as the helix angle of the gear (Courtesy of Fellows Corporation).

Figure 6. Hypoid gear generator (Courtesy of Gleason Works).

Figure 7. The gear shaper can produce unusual gear shapes (Courtesy of Fellows Corporation).

Figure 8. Pot broaching tool that produces a helical gear (Courtesy of National Broach and Machine Division, Lear Siegler, Inc.).

the gear to be finished. The shaving roll and gear are set at an angle (Figure 9). This process is called **diagonal shaving.**

Roll finishing is used on unhardened gears (Figure 10). This is a cold forming process that produces surface finishes to 10 microinches. Hardened gears may also be finished by **form grinding** (Figures 11 and 12). Finishes of 30 to 10 microinches can be obtained by this process.

Gear honing on hardened gears can obtain finishes of 10 to 5 microinches (Figure 13). The gear hone is an abrasive impregnated mating gear that rolls in mesh with the gear to be finished. Gear honing is also applied to internal gears.

Figure 9. Gear shaving (Courtesy of National Broach and Machine Division, Lear Siegler, Inc.).

Figure 10. Roll finishing of unhardened gears (Courtesy of National Broach and Machine Division, Lear Siegler, Inc.).

Figure 11. Finishing a gear by form grinding (Courtesy of National Broach and Machine Division, Lear Siegler, Inc.).

Figure 12. Finishing a gear by generating the ground surface (Courtesy of Fellows Corporation).

Figure 13. Finishing a hardened gear by honing. The honing tool has the helical teeth (Courtesy of National Broach and Machine Division, Lear Siegler, Inc.).

Figure 14. Inspecting gear profiles (Courtesy of Fellows Corporation).

GEAR INSPECTIONS

Due to the high degree of precision required in the manufacture and applications of gears, measurement and inspection is a highly refined technology (Figure 14). Special testing and gear measuring tools are used to check the involute profile of a gear tooth, the tooth spacing, or the accuracy of the helix on a helical gear. Mesh is checked with a master gear engaged to the manufactured gear. In this section, you will have the opportunity to learn about common gear measuring techniques used in the machine shop.

COMMON GEAR CUTTING IN THE MACHINE SHOP

Gear cutting in the job or school machine shop is done in order to make a part for a slow speed drive or emergency situation, where an unhardened gear will meet needs. Although it would be possible to properly heat treat a gear, a required finishing process might not be available. In the school shop, gear cutting is often limited to spur types, although the milling of helical gears is sometimes done for instructional purposes.

Nonetheless, the processes of gear cutting make use of many of the setups and machining procedures that you have studied up to now. The work of gear cutting is very much in line with the overall work of the machine shop. Exposure to this technology will enhance both your experience and knowledge in machining. In this section, you will study types and applications of gears, machine setup and calculations for gear cutting, fundamental spur gear cutting techniques, and common methods for gear inspection and measurement.

UNIT 1 INTRODUCTION TO GEARS

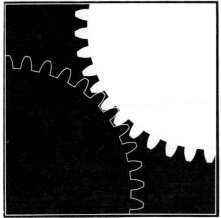

Gears play an extremely important part in mechanical devices of all kinds. To meet a variety of gearing requirements, many types of gears have been developed. The purpose of this unit is to identify and familiarize you with several common types of gears and the materials from which they are made.

OBJECTIVE

After completing this unit, you should be able to identify common gear types and describe common gear materials.

TYPES OF GEARS

Spur Gears
Spur gears have straight teeth and are used to connect parallel shafts (Figure 1). Spur gears are found in a wide variety of mechanisms ranging from watches and clocks to mechanical drives for large machinery.

Internal Gears
Internal gears may be **spur** or **helical** (Figure 2) types. Two internal gears in mesh rotate in the same direction. Internal gears permit closer shaft center distances and these gears have stronger teeth than equivalent external gears.

Helical and Herringbone Gears
When gear teeth are cut at an angle to the gear axis, a **helical gear** is formed (Figure 3). Helical gears are smoother and quieter running than spur gears because several teeth are in mesh at any given time. However, due to the helix of the teeth, an end thrust is created. Two helical gears in mesh will tend to push each other sideways. To overcome this tendency, **herringbone** or **double helical gears** are used. The right- and left-hand helixes cancel each other's end thrust (Figure 4).

Crossed helical gears will connect shafts at a 90 degree angle, but not in the same plane (Figure 5).

Bevel Gears
Bevel gears connect shafts at an angle (Figure 6) in the same plane since the conical axis of the gears must intersect. Two meshed bevel gears of the same size connecting shafts at a 90 degree angle are called **miter gears**

(Figure 7). Shafts are connected at other angles by **angular bevel gears.**

Worm Gears
Worm gears connect shafts at 90 degree angles, but not in the same plane. Worm gears are extensively used in speed reducers because of the large ratio differences that can be obtained using only two components, the **worm** and **worm gear** or **wheel.** In worm gear systems, the worm is the driving component while the gear or wheel is the driven component.

Two basic designs of worm gears are used. These

Figure 1. Spur Gears in lathe headstock (Courtesy of B&K Mfg.).

Figure 2. Helical internal gears (Lane Community College).

Figure 4. Herringbone gear (Lane Community College).

Figure 3. Helical gears (Lane Community College).

Figure 5. Crossed helical gear (Lane Community College).

are the **single enveloping worm** (Figure 8) and the **double enveloping worm** (Figure 9). In the double enveloping design, the worm is hourglass shaped and envelops the worm wheel on both sides of center. Greater loads can be transmitted through this type of worm gear. Worms may be single or multiple **leads** depending on the speed ratio desired and they will only mesh with corresponding wheels.

Hypoid Gears

A type of gear related to both the worm and crossed helical gear is the **hypoid** (Figure 10). Hypoids connect shafts at right angles, but displaced in two planes. Hypoids are widely used in automotive differentials.

Rack and Pinion

Gear teeth cut side by side on a flat bar form a **rack.** A

Figure 6. Bevel gears (Lane Community College).

Figure 7. Miter gears (Lane Community College).

Figure 8. Worm and worm gear (Lane Community College).

Figure 9. Double enveloping worm and gear (Lane Community College).

Figure 10. Hypoid gears (Lane Community College).

pinion gear meshes with the rack forming a **rack and pinion** (Figure 11). The rack and pinion is used to convert rotary motion to linear motion or the other way around depending on which one is the driven component. A rack and pinion may be either spur or helical in tooth form; this device is found in numerous applications on machine tools and in many other mechanical devices.

Figure 11. Spur gear and gear rack (Lane Community College).

GEAR MATERIALS

Gears are made from **ferrous** and **non-ferrous metals** as well as **non-metallic materials.**

Ferrous Materials

Steel and **cast iron** are typical **ferrous gear materials.** High carbon steel gears can be hardened and tempered to exact specifications. The metallurgy of steels can be varied to suit gear specifications ranging from long wear to machinability.

Cast iron gears are easily machined, but this material is not as well suited for load carrying as steel. Cast iron gears have low impact strength and are poorly suited for shock loads. **Ductile** and **malleable iron** as well as **sintered metals** are also used as gear materials.

Non-Ferrous Materials

Gears for light applications such as clocks are often made from **brass** and **aluminum** alloys. **Bronze** is a superior gear material because of its tough and wear-resistant qualities.

Low cost gears of non-ferrous material may be made by die casting finished pieces. No machining is needed. Die cast gear materials include zinc, aluminum, magnesium, and copper based alloys.

Non-Metallic Materials

A large number of gears for numerous applications are made from many types of **plastic** materials including phenolic resins, nylon, and micarta. Non-metallic gears have excellent wear resistance and often need no lubrication. Non-metallic gears run very well meshed with steel or iron gears in many applications.

GEAR TRAIN MECHANICS

In many instances, gear trains are made up with different gear materials. Many worm drives use a bronze worm gear with a hardened steel worm. Cast iron gears work well with steel gears. To equalize the wear in gear trains, the pinion is made harder than the gear. Even wear in gear trains can be obtained when a gear ratio is used that allows for a **hunting tooth.** For example, a gear train ratio of approximately 4:1 is needed. This is possible by using an 80 tooth gear in mesh with a 20 tooth gear. In this gear arrangement, the same tooth of the pinion will mesh with the same tooth of the gear in every revolution. If an 81 tooth gear were used, the teeth of the pinion will not equally divide into it, but each tooth of one gear will mesh with **all of the mating teeth** one after the other, distributing wear evenly over all teeth.

SELF-TEST

1. Name two types of gears used to connect parallel shafts.
2. What are some advantages and some disadvantages of helical gears?
3. What is the direction of rotation of a pinion in relation to an internal gear when they are meshed together?
4. Two helical gears of the same hand and a 45 degree helix angle are in mesh. What relationship exists between the axis of the two shafts?
5. What is the gear reduction in a worm gear set when the worm has a double lead thread and the worm gear has 100 teeth?
6. Can a worm gear set ratio be changed by substituting a single start worm with a triple start worm?
7. What kind of gear material gives the greatest load carrying capacity for a given size?
8. What kind of material can be used for gears to run quietly at high speed?
9. How can the wear on the gear teeth be equalized when a large and a small gear are running together?
10. What kind of gear materials give corrosion resistance to gear sets?

UNIT 2 SPUR GEAR TERMS AND CALCULATIONS

Although most gear cutting is done on specialized machine tools, a spur gear may be cut on the milling machine by straightforward machining techniques. Gears and gear cutting in general involve a number of terms, numerous dimensions, and calculations. The purpose of this unit is to familiarize you with gear terminology and calculations involved in gear cutting.

OBJECTIVE

After completing this unit, you should be able to identify gear tooth parts and to calculate their dimensions.

SPUR GEAR TERMINOLOGY

Spur gear terms are illustrated in Figure 1. The definitions of these terms are as follows:

Addendum. The radial distance from the pitch circle to the outside diameter.

Dedendum. The radial distance between the pitch circle and the root diameter.

Circular thickness. The distance of the arc along the pitch circle from one side of a gear tooth to the other.

Circular pitch. The length of the arc of the pitch circle from one point on a tooth to the same point on the adjacent tooth.

Pitch diameter. The diameter of the pitch circle.

Outside diameter. The major diameter of the gear.

Root diameter. The diameter of the root circle measured from the bottom of the tooth spaces.

Chordal addendum. The distance from the top of the tooth to the chord connecting the circular thickness arc.

Chordal thickness. The thickness of a tooth on a straight line or chord on the pitch circle.

Whole depth. The total depth of a tooth space equal to the sum of the addendum and dedendum.

Working depth. The depth of engagement of two mating gears.

Clearance. The amount by which the tooth space is cut deeper than the working depth.

Backlash. The amount by which the width of a tooth space exceeds the thickness of the engaging tooth on the pitch circles.

Diametral pitch. The number of gear teeth to each inch of pitch diameter.

Pressure angle. The angle between a tooth profile and a radial line at the pitch circle (Figure 2).

Center distance. The distances between the centers of the pitch circles.

PRESSURE ANGLES

Three spur gear tooth forms are generally used with pressure angles of $14\frac{1}{2}$, 20, and 25 degrees. The $14\frac{1}{2}$ degree tooth form is being replaced and made obsolete by the 20 and 25 degree forms. Figure 3 illustrates these three pressure angles as applied to a gear rack with all

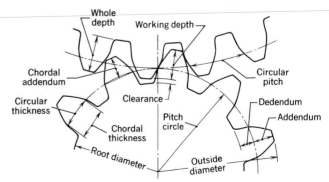

Figure 1. Spur gear terms.

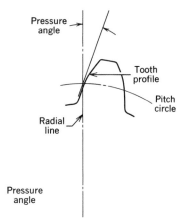

Figure 2. Pressure angle.

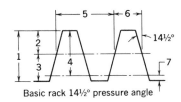

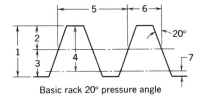

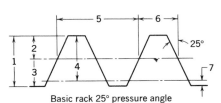

Legend for all three
tooth forms

1 – Whole depth
2 – Addendum
3 – Dedendum
4 – Working depth
5 – Circular pitch
6 – Tooth thickness
7 – Clearance

Figure 3. Comparison of tooth shape on gear rack with different pressure angles.

teeth being the same depth. **The larger pressure angle makes teeth with a much larger base, which also makes these teeth much stronger.** The larger pressure angles also allow the production of gears with fewer teeth. Any two gears in mesh with each other must be of the same pressure angle and the same diametral pitch.

Information in this unit will include constants for $14\frac{1}{2}$ degree pressure angle gear calculations because many existing gears and gear cutters are of this tooth form. When gear tooth measurements are to be made with gear tooth calipers, the chordal tooth thickness and also the chordal addendum must be calculated. Most of the gear tooth dimensions that you will calculate in this unit can be found in tables in the *Machinery's Handbook*.

SPUR GEAR CALCULATIONS

The following symbols are used to represent gear tooth terms in spur gear calculations.

P = **diametral pitch**
D = **pitch diameter**
D_o = **outside diameter**
N = **number of teeth in gear**
t = **tooth thickness—circular**
a = **addendum**
b = **dedendum**
c = **clearance**
C = **center distance**
h_k = **working depth**
h_t = **whole depth**
t_c = **tooth thickness—chordal**
a_c = **addendum—choral**

Table 1 gives the formulas to calculate the gear dimensions in the following examples.

EXAMPLE 1
Determine the dimensions for a 30 tooth gear, $14\frac{1}{2}$ degree pressure angle, and a 2.500 in. pitch diameter.

1. Number of teeth $N = 30$.
2. Pitch diameter $D = 2.500$ in.
3. Diametral pitch $P = \dfrac{N}{D} = \dfrac{30}{2.500} = 12$
4. Addendum $a = \dfrac{1}{P} = \dfrac{1}{12} = .083$ in.
5. Dedendum $b = \dfrac{1.157}{P} = \dfrac{1.157}{12} = .096$ in.
6. Tooth thickness
   $t = \dfrac{1.5708}{P} = \dfrac{1.5708}{12} = .131$ in.
7. Clearance $c = \dfrac{.157}{P} = \dfrac{.157}{12} = .013$ in.
8. Whole depth $h_t = \dfrac{2.157}{P} = \dfrac{2.157}{12} = .179$ in.
9. Working depth $h_k = \dfrac{2}{P} = \dfrac{2}{12} = .166$ in.
10. Chordal tooth thickness
    $t_c = D \sin\left(\dfrac{90 \text{ deg.}}{N}\right)$
    $= 2.500 \times \sin\left(\dfrac{90 \text{ deg.}}{30}\right)$
    $= 2.500 \times \sin 3 \text{ deg.}$
    $= 2.5 \times .0523 = .1307$ in.
11. Chordal addendum

Table 1
Spur Gear Formulas

To Find	Spur Gear Formulas	
	$14\frac{1}{2}$ degree Pressure Angle	20 and 25 degree Pressure Angles
Addendum, a	$a = \dfrac{1.0}{P}$	$a = \dfrac{1.0}{P}$
Dedendum, b	$b = \dfrac{1.157}{P}$	$b = \dfrac{1.250}{P}$
Pitch diameter, D	$D = \dfrac{N}{P}$	$D = \dfrac{N}{P}$
Outside diameter, D_o	$D_o = \dfrac{N+2}{P}$	$D_o = \dfrac{N+2}{P}$
Number of teeth, N	$N = D \times P$	$N = D \times P$
Tooth thickness, t	$t = \dfrac{1.5708}{P}$	$t = \dfrac{1.5708}{P}$
Whole depth, h_t	$h_t = \dfrac{2.157}{P}$	$h_t = \dfrac{2.250}{P}$
Clearance, c	$c = \dfrac{.157}{P}$	$c = \dfrac{.250K}{P}$
Center distance, C	$C = \dfrac{N_1 + N_2}{2 \times P}$	$C = \dfrac{N_1 + N_2}{2 \times P}$
Working depth, h_k	$h_k = \dfrac{2}{P}$	$h_k = \dfrac{2}{P}$
Chordal tooth thickness, t_c	$t_c = D \sin\left(\dfrac{90 \text{ degs}}{N}\right)$	$t_c = D \sin\left(\dfrac{90 \text{ degs}}{N}\right)$
Chordal addendum, a_c	$a_c = a + \dfrac{t^2}{4D}$	$a_c = a + \dfrac{t^2}{4D}$
Diametral pitch, P	$P = \dfrac{N}{D}$	$P = \dfrac{N}{D}$
Center distance, C	$C = \dfrac{D_1 + D_2}{2}$	$C = \dfrac{D_1 + D_2}{2}$

$$a_c = a + \frac{t^2}{4D}$$
$$= .083 + \frac{.131^2}{4 \times 2.5}$$
$$= .083 + \frac{.017}{10}$$
$$= .083 + .0017 = .0847 \text{ in.}$$

12. Outside diameter

$$D_o = \frac{N+2}{P}$$
$$= \frac{30+2}{12}$$
$$= \frac{32}{12} = 2.6666 \text{ in.}$$

EXAMPLE 2
Determine the gear dimensions for a 45 tooth gear, 8 diametral pitch, 20 degree pressure angle.

1. Number of teeth $N = 45$
2. Diametral pitch $P = 8$
3. Pitch diameter $D = \dfrac{N}{P} = \dfrac{45}{8} = 5.625 \text{ in.}$
4. Addendum $a = \dfrac{1}{P} = \dfrac{1}{8} = .125 \text{ in.}$
5. Dedendum $b = \dfrac{1.250}{P} = \dfrac{1.250}{8} = .1562 \text{ in.}$
6. Tooth thickness
$$t = \frac{1.5708}{P}$$
$$= \frac{1.5708}{8}$$
$$= .1963 \text{ in.}$$
7. Clearance $c = \dfrac{.250}{P} = \dfrac{.250}{8} = .031 \text{ in.}$

8. Whole depth $h_t = \dfrac{2.250}{P} = \dfrac{2.250}{8} = .281$ in.

9. Working depth $h_k = \dfrac{2}{P} = \dfrac{2}{8} = .250$ in.

10. Outside diameter

$$
\begin{aligned}
D_o &= \frac{N + 2}{P} \\
&= \frac{45 + 2}{8} \\
&= \frac{47}{8} = 5.875 \text{ in.}
\end{aligned}
$$

11. Chordal tooth thickness

$$
\begin{aligned}
t_c &= D \sin \frac{90 \text{ deg.}}{N} \\
&= 5.625 \times \sin \frac{90 \text{ deg.}}{45} \\
&= 5.625 \times \sin 2 \text{ deg.} \\
&= 5.625 \times .0349 = .1963 \text{ in.}
\end{aligned}
$$

12. Chordal addendum

$$
\begin{aligned}
a_c &= a + \frac{t^2}{4D} \\
&= .125 \text{ in.} + \frac{.1963^2}{4 \times 5.625} \\
&= .125 \text{ in.} + .0017 \text{ in.} = .1267 \text{ in.}
\end{aligned}
$$

The center distance between gears can be calcu-lated when the number of teeth in the gears and the dia-metral pitch is known. Two gears in mesh make contact at their pitch diameters.

EXAMPLE 3
Determine the center distance between gears with 25 and 40 teeth and a diametral pitch of 14.

$$
\begin{aligned}
\text{Center distance } C &= \frac{N_1 + N_2}{2 \times P} \\
&= \frac{25 + 40}{2 \times 14} \\
&= \frac{65}{28} = 2.3214 \text{ in.}
\end{aligned}
$$

Another method of finding the center distance if the pitch diameters are known is to add both pitch diame-ters and divide that sum by 2.

EXAMPLE 4
What is the center distance of two gears when their pitch diameters are 2.500 and 3.000 in., respectively?

$$
\begin{aligned}
\text{Center distance } C &= \frac{D_1 + D_2}{2} \\
&= \frac{2.500 + 3.000}{2} \\
&= \frac{5.500}{2} = 2.750 \text{ in.}
\end{aligned}
$$

SELF-TEST

1. What are commonly found pressure angles for gear teeth?
2. Why are larger pressure angles used on gear teeth?
3. What is the center distance between two gears with 20 and 30 teeth and a diametral pitch of 10?
4. What is the center distance between two gears with pitch diameters of 3.500 and 2.500 in.?
5. What is the difference between the whole depth of a tooth and the working depth of a tooth?
6. What relationship does the addendum and the dedendum have with the pitch diameter on a tooth?
7. What is the outside diameter and the tooth thickness on a 50 tooth gear with a diametral pitch of 5?
8. What is the diametral pitch of a gear with 36 teeth and a pitch diameter of 3.000 in.?
9. What is the outside diameter, whole depth, pitch diame-ter, and dedendum for a 40 tooth, 8 diametral pitch, 20 degree pressure angle gear?
10. What is the outside diameter, clearance, whole depth, tooth thickness, and pitch diameter for a 48 tooth, 6 dia-metral pitch, $14\frac{1}{2}$ degree pressure angle gear?

UNIT 3 CUTTING A SPUR GEAR

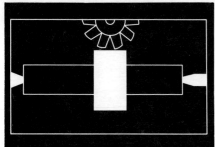

Spur gear cutting, like any machining job, includes setting up the machine, workpiece, selecting the correct cutter, and performing all calculations necessary to the task. The purpose of this unit is to describe and familiarize you with these procedures.

OBJECTIVE

After completing this unit, you should be able to set up the mill and cut a spur gear.

INVOLUTE GEAR CUTTERS

Spur gears are cut with **involute gear cutters.** The gear cutter set consists of eight cutters numbered 1 to 8, for typical pressure angles of $14\frac{1}{2}$ or 20 degrees. The eight gear cutters have eight **different** tooth forms for each diametral pitch, depending on the number of teeth on the gear to be cut. Each gear cutter can be used to cut a range of teeth (Table 1). However, the cutter will only produce the **exact tooth form** for the **lowest number of teeth in the range** For example, a #5 cutter will cut 21 to 25 teeth, but will produce the exact form only for 21 teeth. Other numbers of teeth will be less accurate in form.

Half-step cutters are also available. These serve to cut more accurate tooth forms within a cutter's range. An example would be a #$5\frac{1}{2}$ for 19 and 20 teeth. Special cutters designed for specific numbers of teeth or for low numbers of teeth (6–11) are also used.

Gear cutters are identified and marked with the following information.

Cutter number	Pressure angle
Diametral pitch	**Whole depth of tooth**
Number of teeth	

Table 1

Number of Cutter	Number of Teeth Cut	Number of Cutter	Number of Teeth Cut
1	135 to rack	5	21 to 25
2	55 to 134	6	17 to 20
3	35 to 54	7	14 to 16
4	26 to 34	8	12 and 13

MACHINING AND MOUNTING THE GEAR BLANK

The first step in gear cutting is to machine the gear blank. The outside diameter is the most critical dimension and should be held as close as possible to the calculated size. For example, a gear is to be cut to the following specifications:

Number of teeth — 48
Diametral pitch — 12
Pressure angle — $14\frac{1}{2}$ degrees

The gear blank is turned on the lathe to its correct outside diameter. This is calculated by the formula:

$$\text{Outside diameter } D_0 = \frac{N + 2}{P}$$

where N = number of teeth, P = diametral pitch.

$$\frac{N + 2}{P} = \frac{48 + 2}{12} = 4.167 \text{ in.}$$

If the gear has a hub, the outside diameter may be machined by chucking the gear on the hub. Better accuracy can be obtained by turning the outside diameter while the gear blank is mounted on the same arbor that will be used while milling the teeth.

If more than one gear of the same size is to be made, a solid blank may be machined that is sufficiently long to accommodate the required number of gears. After teeth have been milled, individual gears may be cut off on the band saw or parted off in the lathe.

If you are using an arbor to hold the gear blank during turning or milling, **be sure to lubricate the bore** of the blank before pressing it onto the arbor.

Figure 1. Checking the axis of the mandrel to be parallel with the table surface (Lane Community College).

Figure 2. Aligning the cutter centrally over the gear blank (Lane Community College).

MACHINE AND WORKPIECE SETUP

Mount the index head on the mill table. The index head spindle must be aligned with the table in both the **horizontal and vertical axes.** Secure the footstock to the mill table and use it to support the small end of the arbor.

From Table 1, select the correct gear cutter for 48 teeth and a pressure angle of $14\frac{1}{2}$ degrees. This will be a number 3 cutter (35–54 teeth). Keep the saddle as close to the column as possible and position the gear cutter on the mill arbor as close to the spindle as possible, allowing clear access to the gear blank. **Cutting pressure should always be applied toward the index head spindle holding the big end of the arbor.** Install mill arbor spacing and bearing collars and the arbor support.

Attach a driving dog to the large end of the gear arbor. Place the arbor between the index head and footstock centers. Tighten the footstock center to hold the arbor in place. Use a dial test indicator to check the height of the gear arbor at both ends (Figure 1). Allow for the taper of the gear arbor and adjust the footstock center height if necessary. The gear blank **must be parallel** to the machine table.

Centering the Workpiece

The gear blank must be exactly centered under the gear cutter. Several methods may be used for this. A direct measurement (Figure 2) can be made by placing a square against the gear blank and measuring the distance to the cutter to determine the amount of saddle setover required. A more accurate method is to use the saddle micrometer collar to determine the setover dimension. Place a square against the gear blank and move the saddle until the cutter just touches the square (Figure 3). Set the saddle micrometer to zero. Measure the width of the square with a micrometer and add this amount to the sum of half the cutter thickness plus half the diameter of the gear blank. Move the saddle over this amount to center the gear blank under the cutter.

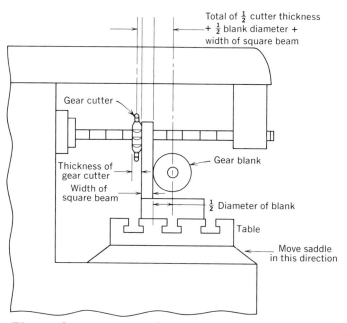

Figure 3. Determining the saddle setover dimension for centering the gear cutter.

Calculating Indexing

Calculate indexing for 48 teeth by the following formula:

$$\frac{40}{N} = \frac{40}{48} = \frac{5}{6}$$

Create the proportional fraction required by dividing the lowest term denominator 6 into the available index plate hole circles to determine the multiplier. Any hole circle divisible by 6 can be used.

$$\frac{5 \times 5}{6 \times 5} = \frac{25 \text{ holes}}{30 \text{ hole circle}}$$
$$\frac{5 \times 7}{6 \times 7} = \frac{35 \text{ holes}}{42 \text{ hole circle}}$$
$$\frac{5 \times 9}{6 \times 9} = \frac{45 \text{ holes}}{54 \text{ hole circle}}$$

Figure 4. Marking all the tooth spaces around the circumference of the gear blank (Lane Community College).

Figure 5. Finish cut the gear teeth (Lane Community College).

Adjust the index crank pin to the correct hole circle and set the sector arms to include the correct number of new holes for the partial turn required. If you start the first cut with the index pin in the **numbered hole** of the index plate circle, you can double check the indexing by coming back to the starting location.

CUTTING THE GEAR

Calculate the depth of cut by the formula:

$$\text{Whole depth} = \frac{2.157}{P} = \frac{2.157}{12} = .180 \text{ in.}$$

where P is the diametral pitch.

Set proper feeds and speeds on the machine. Start the mill spindle and raise the knee until the cutter just touches the gear blank. Set the knee micrometer collar to zero. A roughing cut of about .150 in. is recommended. This will leave .030 in. for finishing. Move the gear blank clear of the cutter and raise the knee .150 in. for roughing.

It is always a good idea to **verify indexing** by moving the gear blank up to the cutter until a small visible mark is made. Back away and index to the next tooth. Con-

tinue this process until **all tooth locations** have been marked and indexing has been verified (Figure 4). The gear blank should return to the starting point exactly. If it does not, you may have made an indexing error. This can now be corrected before a gear blank is ruined. If indexing is correct, make roughing cuts. Be sure to lock the index head spindle each time. Table feed trip dogs may be set to stop feed at the completion of each cut. A center rest may be used under the gear blank to increase rigidity.

After completing all roughing cuts, raise the knee the remaining amount for the finish cuts (Figure 5). Stay back from the full final depth until you have milled two adjacent teeth and made the tooth thickness measurement. After you have milled two adjacent teeth, deburr carefully and check tooth thickness with the gear tooth caliper. If you have stayed back from the full depth a few thousandths, the tooth thickness should be a small amount over size. Raise the knee to the final full depth; make the cuts on two adjacent teeth. Recheck thickness measurement. If the tooth thickness is correct, mill the remaining teeth. Burrs may be removed after the completed gear has been removed from the arbor.

SELF-TEST

1. What are two factors against cutting spur gears in the milling machine?
2. How many gear cutters are in a standard set?
3. Which cutter is used to cut a gear with 38 teeth?
4. Can a $14\frac{1}{2}$ degree pressure angle gear be in mesh with a 20 degree pressure angle gear?
5. A number 6 gear cutter has the correct tooth shape for a gear with how many teeth?
6. What information is marked on the side of gear cutters?
7. Why should the work and cutter be mounted close to the column?
8. How many holes should be located within the sector arms?
9. Why is the gear blank marked with the cutter prior to cutting the teeth?
10. When is a center rest used?

UNIT 4 GEAR INSPECTION AND MEASUREMENT

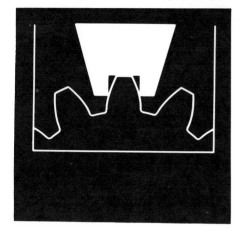

Gears, like any machined parts, must be measured to determine if dimensions are within tolerance. Gears are somewhat special in that dimensions are numerous and vary from gear to gear. Many gear measurements require the use of highly specialized measuring tools and techniques. In common spur gear cutting, gear measurement and inspection can be accomplished with common tools designed for this purpose. The purpose of this unit is to describe the common tools and their application in spur gear measurements.

OBJECTIVE

After completing this unit, you should be able to measure a spur gear using common tools.

METHODS OF GEAR MEASUREMENTS

Common methods of gear measurement include the **gear tooth vernier caliper, micrometer with two pins,** and the **optical comparator.**

Gear Tooth Vernier Caliper

The **gear tooth vernier caliper** is a combination vernier depth gage and vernier caliper. This tool is designed to measure the **thickness** of a gear tooth along a chord drawn through the two points where the pitch circle intersects the side of the tooth (Figure 1). In order to set the caliper jaws at this point, the depth gage on the gear tooth caliper must be set to the **chordal** or **corrected addendum.** This dimension is larger than the addendum. The required dimensions can be determined by the following calculations.

Calculating Chordal Tooth Thickness. To

determine the setting for the gear tooth caliper, it will be necessary to calculate several other dimensions first. Consider the following example. Calculate chordal tooth thickness for the following gear

Number of teeth $N = 12$
Diametral pitch $P = 6$
Outside diameter

$$D_0 = \frac{N + 2}{P} = \frac{12 + 2}{6} = \frac{14}{6} = 2.3333$$

Addendum

$$a = \frac{1}{P} = \frac{1}{6} = .1666 \text{ in.}$$

Pitch diameter

$$D = \frac{N}{P} = \frac{12}{6} = 2.000 \text{ in.}$$

Circular tooth thickness

$$t = \frac{1.5708}{P} = \frac{1.5708}{6} = .2168 \text{ in.}$$

Chordal addendum

$$a_c = a + \frac{t^2}{4D}$$
$$= .1666 + \frac{.2168^2}{4 \times 2}$$
$$= .1666 + \frac{.0685}{8} = .1751 \text{ in.}$$

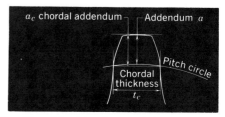

Figure 1.   Chordal addendum and chordal tooth thickness.

Figure 2. Measuring a spur gear with a gear tooth vernier caliper (Lane Community College).

Chordal tooth thickness

$$t_c = D \sin\left(\frac{90 \text{ deg.}}{N}\right)$$

$$= 2 \sin\left(\frac{90}{12}\right)$$

$$= 2 \sin 7.5 = 2(.1305) = .261 \text{ in.}$$

Measuring the Gear Tooth. Set the gear tooth caliper depth gage to the **chordal** or **corrected addendum** of .175 in. Rest the blade of the depth gage on top of the gear tooth (Figure 2). Use the vernier caliper to measure the chordal tooth thickness. This should be .261 in. If the outside diameter of the gear blank is undersized by .002 in., the depth gage setting should be **reduced by half this amount** or .001 in. This will assure that the tooth is being measured at the pitch diameter. If you are measuring a gear while still in the machine, be sure to **remove all burrs** on the teeth before making any measurements.

Micrometer and Pins

Another reliable method of gear measurement is by **micrometer and pins** (Figure 3). The diameter of the pin to use is found by the formula:

$$\text{Pin diameter} = 1.728/D$$

where D is the diametral pitch. The constant 1.728 is most commonly used for external spur gears. The

Figure 3. Measuring a spur gear with two pins and a micrometer (Lane Community College).

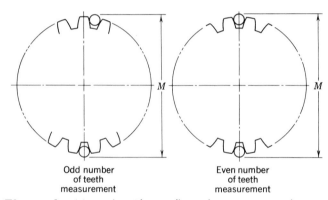

Odd number of teeth measurement	Even number of teeth measurement

Figure 4. Measuring of gear dimensions over two pins.

dimension M as measured across the pins (Figure 4) is found in the handbook depending on the pressure angle and number of teeth on the gear. Handbook tables for M dimension are given for a diametral pitch of 1. To apply the data to a specific gear, divide the table entry by the diametral pitch of the gear to be measured.

EXAMPLE

    Number of teeth 45
    Diametral pitch 10
    Pressure angle $14\frac{1}{2}$ degrees

$$\text{Pin diameter} = 1.728/10 = .1728 \text{ in.}$$

Measurement over pins M for a gear with a diametral pitch of 1 = 47.4437. Therefore,

$$M = 47.4437/10 = 4.7443 \text{ in.}$$

This calculated dimension assumes no backlash. However, in gear installations some backlash is required. If

specifications called for .005 in. backlash, the M dimension must be recalculated. Handbook tables show that for a 45 tooth gear, each .001 in. of tooth thickness reduction at the pitch circle reduces M by .0031. Since .005 in. backlash is required,

$$.005 \times .0031 = .0155$$

The measurement over the pins must be reduced by this amount.

$$M = 4.74437 - .0155 = 4.72887$$

This result would be the required dimension over the pins to obtain the required backlash of .005 in.

Optical Comparator

The optical comparator can also be used for gear measurement. The comparator projects a greatly magnified shadow or reflected image or the gear onto a glass screen (Figure 5). A transparent drawing of the gear to be measured is laid on the comparator screen and a direct comparison is made to the image of the gear being measured.

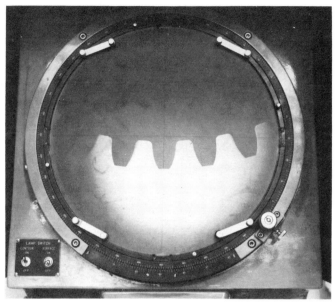

Figure 5. Using an optical comparator to check gear tooth dimensions (Lane Community College).

SELF-TEST

1. What are two common gear measurements performed by a machinist?
2. Which tooth thickness is measured by a gear tooth vernier caliper?
3. The vertical scale of a gear tooth vernier caliper is set to what dimension?
4. Which is larger, the chordal addendum or the standard addendum?
5. Which is larger, the chordal tooth thickness or the circular tooth thickness?

6. Name two ways of determining the chordal thickness of a gear tooth?
7. When a gear is measured with a micrometer and two pins, can any size pin be used?
8. How is the dimension determined when measuring over pins?
9. When a dimension is given for 1 diametral pitch but the gear measured is 12 diametral pitch, how is the measurement determined?
10. How is an optical comparator used in gear measurement?

SECTION M SHAPERS

The shaper cuts by passing a single point tool by the workpiece. The shaper cutting tool moves by reciprocating motion through a single axis while the workpiece moves past the tool either horizontally, vertically, or rotationally to the tool motion.

The shaper is considered by some to be an obsolete machine tool, and it is true that much of the shaper's work is now done on the milling machine. However, the shaper is a very versatile machine tool that can accomplish a wide variety of machining tasks. For this reason it is still a common sight in many machine shops.

SHAPER CAPABILITY Through numerous setups, the **horizontal shaper** (Figure 1) can accomplish a variety of machining tasks. These include:

Compound angles (Figure 2)
Dovetails (Figures 3 and 4)
Internal keyways (Figure 5)
Complex internal features (Figure 6)
Complex external features (Figure 7)

The **vertical shaper** or **slotter** (Figure 8) has a vertical ram and built-in rotary table. This machine tool functions much like its horizontal counterpart. The rotary table has two axes as well as rotary motion. The ram can be tilted 10 degrees from the vertical giving the machine additional capability for machining complex internal shapes. Hydraulic tracing attachments may also be used with the vertical shaper (Figure 9).

SHAPER SAFETY **The reciprocating motion of the shaper ram creates a significant hazard.** You must be careful around the machine while it is running. Also, you must caution others to stand well clear of the ram while it is in motion.

Be sure that the **stroke rate** and **length are in balance** and always engage the clutch slowly to bring the machine up to speed.

Large shapers eject large hot chips during heavy cuts. Portable safety screens should be used around the machine to restrain flying metal.

Be sure that all adjustment handles have been removed before starting the machine. Apply all the rules of good workholding techniques that you have already learned. **Always wear your safety glasses and use your common sense of safe shop practice.**

Figure 1. The horizontal shaper is a versatile machine tool capable of many motions. The model shown is a universal shaper (Courtesy of Cincinnati Incorporated).

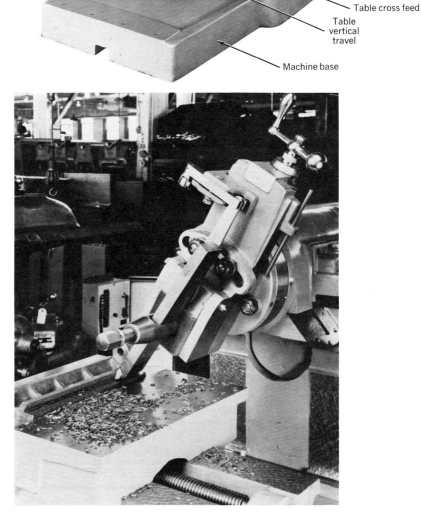

Figure 2. The workpiece in the universal shaper can be rotated about three axes to obtain compound angles on the workpiece (Courtesy of Cincinnati Incorporated).

Figure 3. The toolhead of the shaper can be readily swivelled to produce dovetails for machine assemblies. A toolslide is being machined.

Figure 4. An internal dovetail is being machined (Courtesy of Cincinnati Incorporated).

Figure 5. Making of internal keyways is an important ability of the shaper. This Kennedy keyway has to be held to close size tolerance to work effectively (Courtesy of Cincinnati Incorporated).

Figure 6. The dividing or indexing head in combination with the shaper can be used for making complex internal shapes (Courtesy of Cincinnati Incorporated).

Figure 7. A selection of complex parts on which the shaper was used with special tooling (Courtesy of Rockford Machine Tool Company).

Figure 8. A slotter being used for internal slotting in a casting (Courtesy of Rockford Machine Tool Company).

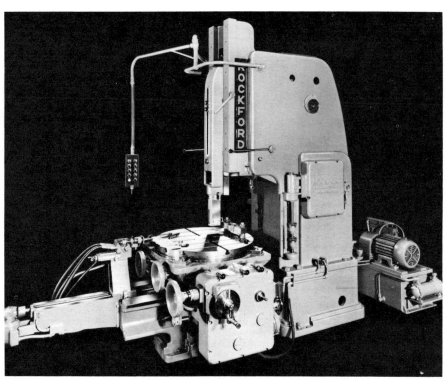

Figure 9. A slotter with a hydraulic tracer installed (Courtesy of Rockford Machine Tool Company).

PART 1 HORIZONTAL SHAPER

MAJOR PARTS

Before operating the shaper, you must know the names of the machine parts and their functions (Figure 10).

Base and Column

The **base** of the shaper (Figure 11) provides a platform for the main casting frequently known as the **column.** The column contains the drive mechanism and reservoirs for lubricants and hydraulic oil. The top of the column has dovetail ways that engage the ram.

Cross Rail

The **cross rail** assembly rides on a saddle that moves vertically on the face of the column. The cross rail contains the drive mechanism for the table. An apron is mounted on the cross rail and is moved horizontally by means of a lead screw.

Apron and Table

The **table** is attached to the **apron** and is equipped with T-slots for the attachment of vises, fixtures, and other tooling. The cutting action of the shaper exerts a substantial force on the table and apron assembly. To aid in support and increase rigidity, an **outrigger** is used to support the overhang of the table.

Shaper **tables** are either **plain** (Figure 11) or **universal.** The universal table may be rotated (Figure 12) in order to position the workpiece for machining angles.

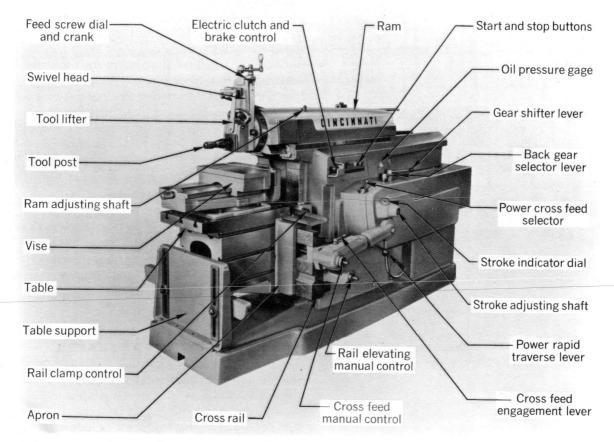

Figure 10. Detailed nomenclature of a plain horizontal shaper. Shapers are quite similar in location of basic controls despite drive differences (Courtesy of Cincinnati Incorporated).

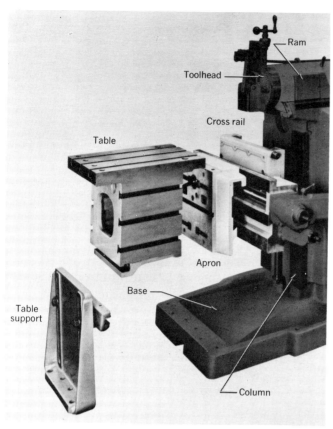

Figure 11. Components of the plain horizontal shaper table assembly (Courtesy of Cincinnati Incorporated).

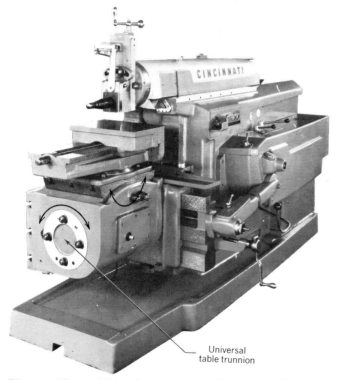

Figure 12. Additional workpiece motions are available on the universal shaper (Courtesy of Cincinnati Incorporated).

Figure 13. Shaper toolhead details (Lane Community College).

Ram

The **ram** engages the dovetail slide on the top of the shaper. Shaper rams are designed for strength and lightness so that they can stand up to the rapid reversals of direction during operation.

Toolhead

The **toolhead** is attached to the end of the ram and can be swiveled 180 degrees or more (Figure 13). The toolhead contains the toolslide with lead screw and micrometer collar. An apron attached to the toolslide contains the **clapper box, hinge pin,** and **toolpost** The function of the clapper box is to permit the tool to swing up as the ram returns on its back stroke. This prevents damage to the tool. Some shapers make use of a tool lifter that swings the tool up on the ram back stroke. A tool lifter must be employed when using carbide cutters.

SHAPER FEEDS

The vertical and horizontal travel of the table can be fed by hand or by power means. The toolslide feed is generally manual, but may also be powered on some machines. A rapid traverse feature permits rapid positioning of the table during machine setup or returning the table and workpiece to a starting point during machining.

WORKHOLDING ON THE SHAPER

The most common workholding method is the vise (Figure 14). Precision vises should be handled carefully and their jaws protected (Figure 15) if used to hold rough workpieces. A workpiece may be supported on parallels if necessary. This may require a **holddown wedge** (Figure 16) to insure that the workpiece is pressed firmly against the parallels.

Figure 14. Swivel base single screw shaper vise (Courtesy of Cincinnati Incorporated).

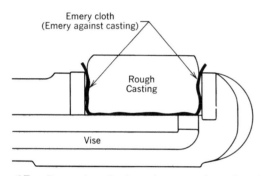

Figure 15. Protecting vise jaws from rough castings (Courtesy of Cincinnati Incorporated).

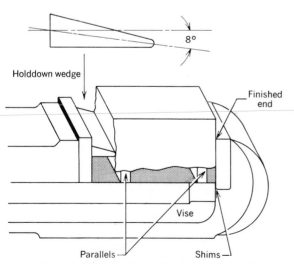

Figure 16. Holddown wedge for squaring to a finished surface (Courtesy of Cincinnati Incorporated).

Figure 17. Auxiliary workholding method to extend the usefulness of the vise (Courtesy of Rockford Machine Tool Company).

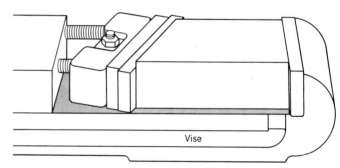

Figure 18. The double screw vise can hold workpieces that are not parallel (Courtesy of Cincinnati Incorporated).

Unlike milling machines, it is often necessary to direct cutting pressure against the movable vise jaw. To insure secure holding a shaper may have additional clamping for the movable jaw (Figure 17).

When the force of the cut is parallel to the vise jaws, sufficient pressure must be applied to securely hold the workpiece or it may be pushed from the vise. To overcome this problem, a double screw vise may be used (Figure 18). This type of vise is also used to hold tapered workpieces. Shaper vises may have serrated jaws to increase holding capability (Figure 19).

The T-slots permit direct mounting of workpieces to the top (Figure 20) and side (Figure 21) of the table. Be sure to follow the rules of safe clamping that you have

Figure 19. Multiple screw vise with serrated jaws has exceptional holding ability (Courtesy of Cincinnati Incorporated).

Figure 20. Use of stops and straps to make secure direct table clamping (Courtesy of Cincinnati Incorporated).

already learned. Workstops may also be used to restrain workpiece movement. Thin workpieces may be clamped by using **poppets** or **bunters** along with **toe dogs** (Figure 22).

Figure 21. The side of the table may also be used for direct attachment (Courtesy of Rockford Machine Tool Company).

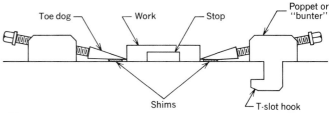

Figure 22. Using a bunter with toe dogs for a thin workpiece (Courtesy of Cincinnati Incorporated).

SHAPER CUTTING TOOLS

Common cutting tool materials include high speed steels and carbides. However, carbide tools may be less suited to the interrupted cutting action of the shaper. A tool lifter must be used to prevent chipping of the carbide tool during the return stroke of the ram.

High speed shaper cutters are much like single point lathe tools. Maximum cutting efficiency and tool life can only be realized if cutters are ground to established specifications (Figures 23 and 24).

TOOL HOLDING AND MOUNTING

Shaper toolholders (Figure 25) are most common. They permit the cutter to be set at various angles. Lathe toolholders should not be used (Figure 26) as the built-in rake

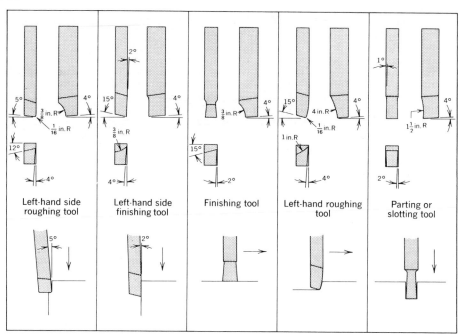

Figure 23. Shaper tool geometry for cutting low carbon steels (Courtesy of Cincinnati Incorporated).

Left-hand side roughing tool | Left-hand side finishing tool | Finishing tool | Left-hand roughing tool | Parting or slotting tool

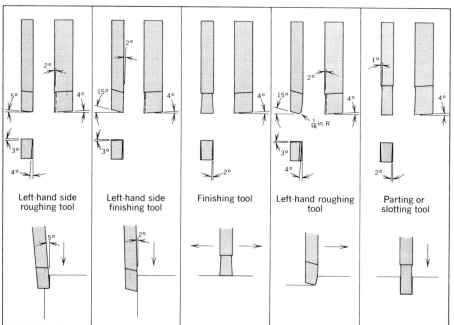

Figure 24. Shaper tool geometry for cutting cast iron (Courtesy of Cincinnati Incorporated).

Left-hand side roughing tool | Left-hand side finishing tool | Finishing tool | Left-hand roughing tool | Parting or slotting tool

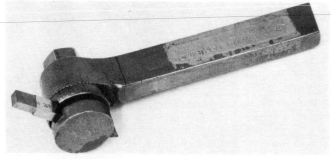

Figure 25. Toolholder can be set at various angles (Lane Community College).

causes the shaper cutter to dig into the work. This problem can be prevented by using a gooseneck tool that will permit the cutter to be pushed back and out of the workpiece if cutting forces become excessive. Extension toolholders (Figure 27) are used for internal machining.

When mounting tools, the same rules of rigidity apply as on the lathe. The tool slide, and cutter toolholder should not project more than is necessary from the tool post (Figure 28). This will maximize safety and rigidity.

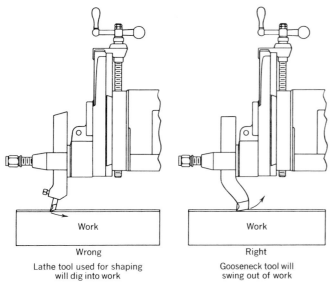

Wrong
Lathe tool used for shaping
will dig into work

Right
Gooseneck tool will
swing out of work

Figure 26. Using a gooseneck tool can avoid chatter (Courtesy of Cincinnati Incorporated).

Figure 27. Extension toolholder for internal shaping (Lane Community College).

Figure 28. Keep tool overhang short. Excessive overhang will result in chatter (Courtesy of Cincinnati Milacron).

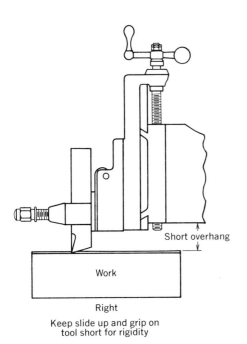

Short overhang

Work

Right
Keep slide up and grip on
tool short for rigidity

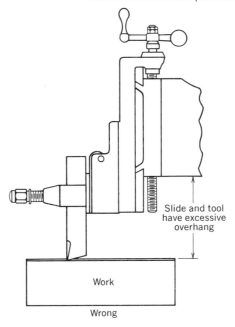

Slide and tool
have excessive
overhang

Work

Wrong

PART 2 FEEDS AND SPEEDS FOR SHAPING

SPEEDS

Cutting speeds in shaping are the same as in any other machining operation. The tool is passed through the work at a specified rate measured in surface feet per minute (SFPM). In shaping this is calculated by the formula

$$N = \frac{CS \times 7}{L}$$

where **N = number of ram strokes per minute, CS = cutting speed of the material being machined, L = length of the stroke, and 7 = shaper constant.**

EXAMPLE
Calculate speed for 10 in. of medium carbon steel at 60 SFPM.

$$N = \frac{CS \times 7}{L} = \frac{60 \times 7}{11} = \frac{420}{11} = 38.18$$

Note that 11 in. is used instead of 10 in. This takes into account ram **overtravel** before and after the cut. The tool must clear the work at the end of the cut and the clapper box must close fully before the tool contacts the work at the beginning of the cut. One-half inch should be allowed at both and for overtravel. In this example, set ram stroke rate at 38 strokes per minute.

FEEDS

The **roughing feedrate** should be **one-tenth of the cut depth.** This applies to deep cuts up to $\frac{1}{2}$ in. For **shallow cuts a feedrate of one-third to one-half depth of cut may be used.** Feeds for **finishing cuts** depend on the shape of the tool and should be set at a **rate about equal to three-quarters of the tool width.**

PART 3 USING THE SHAPER

LUBRICATING THE MACHINE

Like any machine tool, the shaper requires lubrication of its moving parts. Many shapers have automatic pressure fed lubrication systems. **Be sure to check the oil levels in the reservoirs.** On machines that are manually lubricated, check and oil all service points before operating.

LEARN CONTROLS AND THEIR FUNCTIONS

Familiarize yourself with all controls and adjustments (Figure 29). The transmission controls select the ram stroke rate. The indicator plate shows the corresponding lever settings (Figure 30). Stroke length is adjusted by engaging the crank at the proper position (Figure 31). Be sure that the clutch is disengaged before turning on the machine. All adjusting handles must be removed for safety.

Turn on the motor and slowly engage the clutch. Check and establish a suitable safety zone well clear of the reciprocating ram. Spend some time operating all the

Figure 29. Shaper controls (Lane Community College).

Figure 30. Stroke rate plate (Lane Community College).

Figure 32. Positioning the ram. On light machines this is done by releasing the ram and sliding it into position (Lane Community College).

machine controls until you are completely familiar with their functions.

SETTING UP THE SHAPER

The position of the ram must be set so that it will stroke at the right place relative to the position of the workpiece. This is done by unlocking the ram (Figure 32) and sliding it to the correct position. If you are indicating a vise (Figure 33), the stroke length should be adjusted so that the indicator will remain in contact with the vise jaw at each end of the ram travel. **Always run the ram slowly while indicating.** Universal tables may also have to be indicated for alignment during the machine setup.

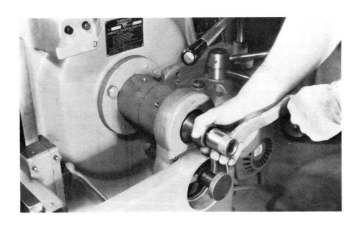

Figure 31. Adjusting the stroke length. A knurled ring unlocks the adjustment shaft (Lane Community College).

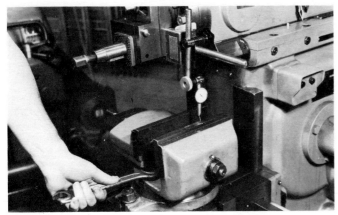

Figure 33. Indicating the shaper vise (Lane Community College).

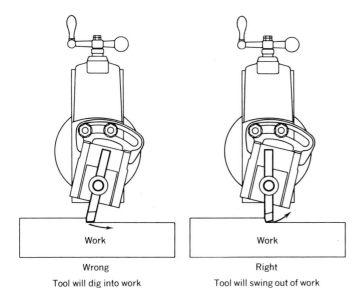

Work	Work
Wrong	Right
Tool will dig into work	Tool will swing out of work

Figure 34. On heavy cuts, leave room for the tool to escape (Courtesy of Cincinnati Incorporated).

Figure 35. Setting the feedrate with an adjustable eccentric (Lane Community College).

Figure 36. Setting and locking the depth of cut (Lane Community College).

Figure 37. Making the first cut (Lane Community College).

The cutter must be properly ground for the machining task. The toolholder should be positioned such that if the feed pressure becomes excessive, the tool will be pushed clear (Figure 34) of the workpiece instead of digging in.

Calculate the proper stroke rate and feed for the material you are machining. Set stroke length and **remember to add for overtravel at both ends.** Set correct feed on the adjustable eccentric selector (Figure 35). Start the ram well clear of the workpiece. Hand feed the table to bring the work up to the cutter. Depth of cut may be set on the ram toolhead slide (Figure 36).

Figure 38. Round bar forces reference surfaces together (Lane Community College).

Figure 40. Roughing out the V by hand contouring (Lane Community College).

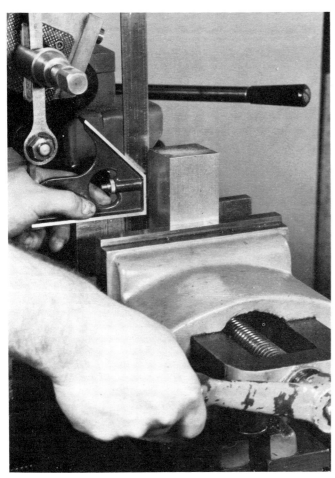

Figure 39. Setting a workpiece with the combination square (Lane Community College).

Figure 41. Setting the toolhead to 45 degrees (Lane Community College).

Allow the table to feed a short distance before the cutter begins cutting. This will give you time to check all factors of operation and setup without risk of damage to machine or part. If all is correct, continue the machining operation (Figure 37).

The workpiece is squared by the same sequence you learned in milling. A round piece of bar may be used to insure that the reference surface is pressed against the solid vise jaw (Figure 38). Ends may be machined by swiveling the vise and setting the part vertically square (Figure 39). Stroke length and rate will have to be recalculated. A long part may be squared by placing it out the end of the vise and using a slide tool.

Angular cutting such as a V-block can be done by roughing out the excess material while hand feeding (Figure 40). The toolhead is then set at the desired angle (Figure 41) and the cutter is fed by the tool slide (Figure 42). The workpiece should be placed end for end when machining the opposite side.

Figure 42. Finishing one side of the V. Turn the part end for end to finish the opposite side (Lane Community College).

Figure 43. (Courtesy of Cincinnati Incorporated).

SELF-TEST

1. Name the shaper features indicated in Figure 43.
2. What is the function of the clapper box on the toolhead?
3. Explain a holding method for securing thin parts to a shaper table.
4. You have a 15 in. long workpiece of pearlitic cast iron with free carbides that has a rated deep cutting speed of 12 SFPM. What number of strokes per minute would be right for this job?
5. You have a 4¼ in. long piece of medium carbon hot rolled steel with a shallow roughing speed of 60 SFPM. What number of strokes per minute would be right for this job?
6. For roughing cut, on shapers, what would be an expected feedrate to match a .450 in. depth of cut for deep roughing and a .090 in. cut for a shallow roughing cut, assuming

that the overall machining system is adequate for the jobs?
7. If you are making a .005 in. deep finishing cut on a large shaper in cast iron using a square nose finishing tool ½ in. wide, what feedrate would you set into the machine for making this cut?
8. How much additional ram travel should be allowed at both ends of the workpiece?
9. What specific, additional dial indicating should be done on a universal shaper?
10. Calculate the ram speed in strokes per minute for machining 4140 alloy steel. Assume a shallow roughing speed of 35 SPFM.
11. How does a piece of round stock aid in workholding when squaring a workpiece?

SECTION N GRINDING AND ABRASIVE MACHINING PROCESSES

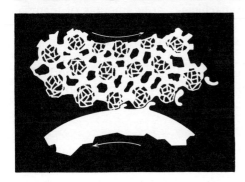

The common machining processes of drilling, turning, and milling generally produce a fairly large chip in comparison to those produced by the processes discussed in this section. **Abrasive materials** are the **cutting tools** in the machining processes called **grinding.** Grinding machines and grinding processes make up one of the most important areas in all machining.

Grinding processes are nonetheless metal cutting processes just like drilling, turning, and milling. However, grinding processes remove very small chips in very large numbers by the cutting action of many small individual **abrasive grains** (Figure 1). These abrasive grains are formed into a **grinding wheel** that is rotated against the workpiece at high speed. Each sharp corner of a grain cuts a small bit of material from the workpiece. When the corners become dull, heat and pressure break down the bonding material holding the grains in the grinding wheel. Dull grains are pulled from the wheel and new sharp grains are then exposed to the workpiece. Eventually, of course, the abrasive material wears completely from the grinding wheel, at which time it must be replaced. Abrasive materials are also coated on sheets and appear in the form of sandpaper or sanding belts and disks. They also appear as solid blocks such as sharpening or honing stones or deburring pellets.

In machining, grinding processes are often used as **finish machining processes.** The reason for this is that very small amounts of material may be removed from the workpiece. This is extremely useful in finish machining a

Figure 1. Large grains of silicon carbide (Courtesy of Exolon Company).

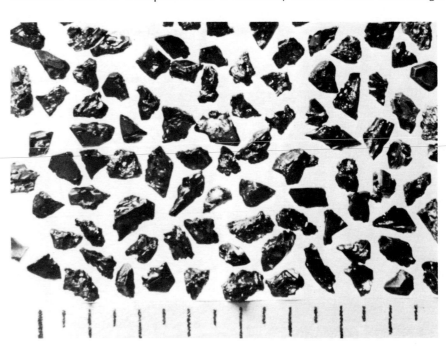

part to a high degree of dimensional accuracy. Furthermore, grinding processes result in **very smooth surface finishes** on the workpiece.

The abrasive materials that are the cutting tools in the grinding process are much harder than the equivalent materials used in common drills, lathe, and mill cutters. Therefore, these materials can be used to machine much harder materials than could ever be cut with high speed steel or even carbide. The grinding processes can be applied to finish machine metals that have been hardened by heat treatment. For example, bearing races are pre-machined to rough dimensions before heat treating. After hardening and tempering to exact specifications, they are finish machined by grinding.

Grinding processes are not necessarily limited to finish machining operations. In the process called **abrasive machining,** large amounts of material are roughed from the workpiece using only abrasives.

Grinding machines and grinding processes are essential to modern manufacturing industry. In this section, you will have the opportunity to study many of the types of grinding machines, other abrasive processes, and types of abrasives used. You will also set up and operate several common grinding machines found in your school shop.

TYPES OF GRINDING MACHINES

The versatility and wide application of the grinding processes have led to the development of many types of grinding machines. Your school shop will probably have two, three, or more of the common types. As a machinist, you should be familiar with the many types of these machine tools and the processes that they perform.

SURFACE GRINDERS

One of the most common grinding machines is the **surface grinder.** Types of surface grinders include:

1. Type I — Horizontal spindle with reciprocating table
2. Type II — Horizontal spindle with rotary table
3. Type III — Vertical spindle with either reciprocating or rotary table

Type I

This type of **surface grinder** (Figure 2) has the grinding wheel on a horizontal spindle. The **edge** of the wheel is presented to the workpiece. The workpiece, if of a ferrous material, is often held on a **magnetic chuck** and is moved back and forth under the rapidly rotating grinding wheel. The chuck may also

Figure 2. Principle of the type I surface grinder with alternative method of cross feeding motion (Courtesy of Bay State Abrasives, Dresser Industries, Inc.).

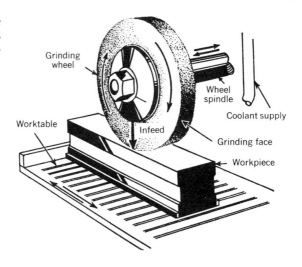

Figure 4. Grinding contours with the horizontal spindle surface grinder. The workpiece is directly under the wheel and the diamond-plated form dressing block is just in front of it (Courtesy of Engis Corporation).

Figure 3. Type I surface grinder (Courtesy of Boyar-Schultz Corp.).

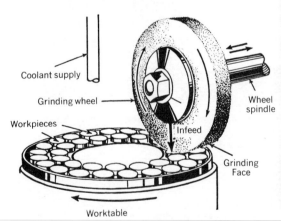

Figure 6. Horizontal spindle rotary table surface grinder (type II). With the workpiece centered on the chuck, the wheel will produce a concentric scratch pattern. The table can also be tilted, making it possible to grind a part thinner in the middle than at the rim or vice versa (Courtesy of Heald Machine Division/Cincinnati Milacron Company).

Figure 5. Principle of the type II surface grinder. Sometimes circular parts are centered on this grinder; the resulting concentric scratch pattern is excellent for metal-to-metal seals of mating parts (Courtesy of Bay State Abrasives, Dresser Industries, Inc.).

be moved in and out. Depth of cut is controlled by raising and lowering the wheel. Sizes of surface grinders range from a small machine that will grind an area up to 4 by 8 inches to large machines with the capacity to grind an area of 6 by 16 feet. The 6 by 12 inch machine is very common in machine shops (Figure 3). The surface grinder in general will produce a flat surface on the workpiece to a tolerance of less than .0002 in. By special shaping of the grinding wheel, contour surfaces may be ground (Figure 4).

Type II On the type II surface grinder, the **edge** of the wheel is also presented to the workpiece (Figure 5). Parts to be ground are mounted on a rotary table and run under the wheel (Figure 6). The table may also be tilted to provide special grinding geometry.

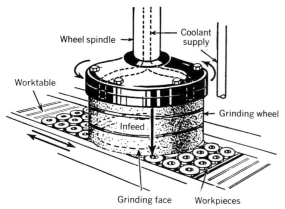

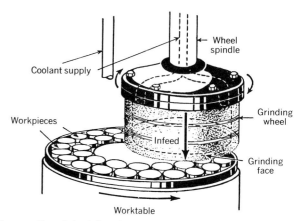

Figure 7. Principle of the type III surface grinder, which has a vertical spindle and a reciprocating table (Courtesy of Bay State Abrasives, Dresser Industries, Inc.).

Figure 8. Principle of the vertical spindle rotary grinder (Courtesy of Bay State Abrasives, Dresser Industries, Inc.).

Figure 9. A great variety of surfaces may be ground with an accessory spindle by dressing or tilting the wheel (Courtesy of Mattison Machine Works).

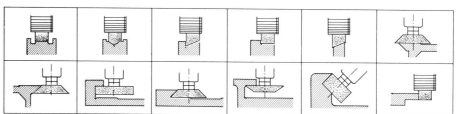

Figure 10. A large vertical spindle rotary table grinding machine (Courtesy of Mattison Machine Works).

Type III   The type III surface grinder has a vertical spindle and the **side (or end)** of the wheel is presented to the workpiece. The worktable may be reciprocating (Figure 7) or rotary (Figure 8). Accessory spindles and special wheel shaping (dressing) add to the versatility of this grinding machine (Figure 9). Vertical spindle grinding machines are often seen in large sizes (Figure 10).

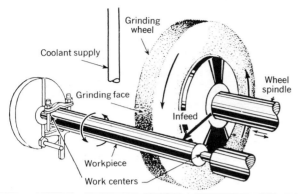

Figure 11. Principle of the cylindrical grinding machine showing the workpiece and wheel motions (Courtesy of Bay State Abrasives, Dresser Industries, Inc.).

Figure 12. Working area of a plain cylindrical grinder (Courtesy of Diamond Abrasives Corporation).

CYLINDRICAL GRINDERS

Whereas the surface grinders previously discussed are primarily used to grind flat surfaces, **cylindrical** or **cylinder grinders** are used to grind the diameters of round workpieces. Types of cylindrical grinders include:

1. Center type
2. Roll
3. Centerless
4. Internal cylindrical
5. Tool and cutter

Center Type

The center type cylindrical grinder, sometimes called a center grinder, grinds the outside diameter of a round workpiece that is mounted between centers (Figure 11). The workpiece is traversed past the grinding wheel while at the same time being rotated slowly in the opposite direction (Figure 12). By swiveling the table, tapers can be ground. This machine is also used for **plunge grinding** where the work and wheel are brought together without table traverse.

Steep tapers can be ground on the **universal cylindrical grinder** (Figure 13). Long slender workpieces can be ground using a steady rest (Figure 14).

The **angular type center grinder** (Figure 15) can grind into a shoulder (Figure 16), and can form cylindrical geometry by using special wheels (Figure 17).

Roll Type

Roll grinders are used to resurface large steel rolling mill rolls (Figure 18). Since these rolls are often very heavy, they are supported in bearings while in the grinding machine.

Centerless Grinders

Whereas in the center cylindrical grinder where the workpiece was supported between centers, the **centerless grinder** is used to grind parts that have no centers or that are too short to be supported between centers. Centerless grinders are frequently seen in production grinding operations where large numbers of parts must be quickly and accurately ground to close tolerance outside diameter dimensions.

Figure 13. A universal cylindrical grinder (Courtesy of Cincinnati Milacron).

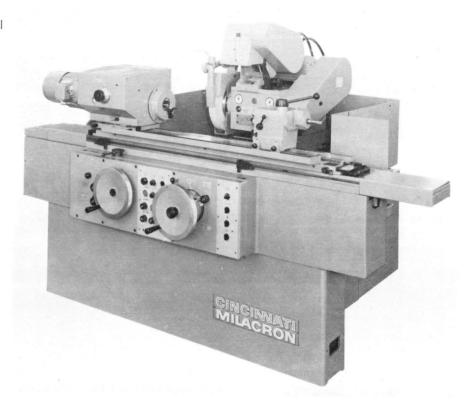

Figure 14. The use of a steady rest for grinding slender workpieces (Courtesy of Cincinnati Milacron).

The workpiece is fed between the **grinding wheel** and **regulating wheel** (Figure 19). The work rest located between the grinding and regulating wheel supports the workpiece. The regulating wheel is set at an angle causing the workpiece to be fed past the grinding wheel. Regulating wheel and grinding wheel turn in opposite directions causing the workpiece to turn as well. Parts are automatically ejected in centerless grinding, but may also be fed against

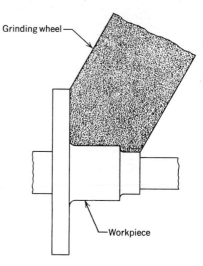

Figure 16. Typical application of the angular center type grinding machine showing angled grinding wheel finishing both diameter and shoulder.

Figure 15. Angular center type grinder with automatic control (Courtesy of Cincinnati Milacron).

Figure 17. Cylindrical form grinding (Courtesy of Bendix Automation and Measurement Division).

Figure 18. Roll grinding machine for grinding steel mill rolls (Courtesy of Landis Tool Div. Litton Industries).

Figure 19. Principle of the centerless grinder. The grinding wheel travels at normal speeds and the regulating wheel travels at a slower speed to control the rate of spin of the workpiece (Courtesy of Bay State Abrasives, Dresser Industries, Inc.).

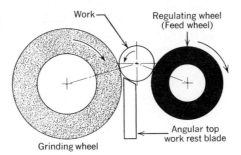

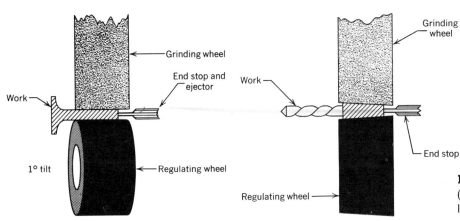

Figure 20. End feeding in the centerless grinder. The regulating wheel is set at a small tilt angle to keep the workpiece against the end stop (Courtesy of Bay State Abrasives, Dresser Industries, Inc.).

Figure 21. Centerless form grinding (Courtesy of Bay State Abrasives, Dresser Industries, Inc.).

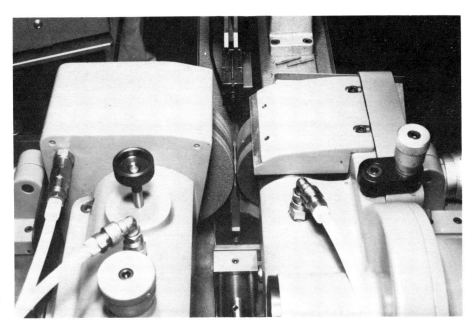

Figure 22. Centerless grinding both ends of a part.

a workstop (Figure 20). Centerless grinding is also suited to grinding **tapers** (Figure 21), parts with **different diameters** (Figure 22), and **threads** on such items as headless set screws. A typical example of a production centerless operation would be the outside diameter (O.D.) grinding of wrist pins for automobile engines.

Internal Cylindrical Grinders

Cylindrical grinding processes apply to internal (Figure 23) as well as external diameters. Internal grinding often uses a **mounted abrasive.** This is a grinding wheel with a built-in mounting shank (Figure 24). Internal grinding can be done on both concentric workpieces (Figure 25) and odd-shaped parts with special workholding techniques (Figure 26).

Tool and Cutter Grinder

The universal tool and cutter grinder is a type of cylindrical grinder. However, this machine can also accomplish certain types of surface grinding. The machine spindle can be tilted, swiveled, and several different shapes of grinding wheels may be used. Probably the primary application of the tool and cutter grinder is in the resharpening of milling cutters (Figures 27 and 28).

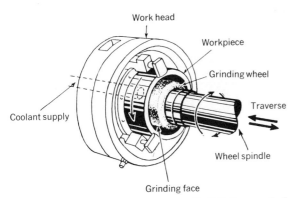

Figure 23. Principles of internal cylindrical grinding (Courtesy of Bay State Abrasives, Dresser Industries, Inc.).

Figure 24. An assortment of mounted wheels. (Courtesy of Bay State Abrasives, Dresser Industries, Inc.).

Figure 25. Internal cylindrical grinding (Courtesy of Heald Machine Division/Cincinnati Milacron Company).

Figure 26. Internal grinding is not limited to cylindrical parts. This automotive connecting rod is an example of odd configurations that can be ground internally (Courtesy of Heald Machine Division/Cincinnati Milacron Company).

Figure 27. Sharpening of a large brazed carbide tipped face mill with a diamond cup wheel (Courtesy of Cincinnati Milacron).

Figure 28. Sharpening a plain milling cutter held between centers on the cutter and tool grinder (Courtesy of Cincinnati Milacron).

641

Figure 29. Double disk production grinding machine with feed wheel to carry the parts between the two opposed disks for grinding. The parts then drop out at the bottom (Courtesy of Bendix Corporation).

Figure 30. Form type gear grinding machine (Courtesy of Ex-Cell-O Corporation).

MISCELLANEOUS GRINDING MACHINES

Other grinding machines include: the **disk grinder** (Figure 29) where parts are fed between the faces of two grinding wheels, and the **gear grinder** (Figure 30) used in gear finishing. Types of gear grinders include those that use form grinding wheels and those that generate the gear tooth shape in the same manner as a gear generator.

OTHER ABRASIVE PROCESSES

The grinding wheels used on the machines previously discussed generally operate at a very high rate of SFPM. Some abrasive processes use abrasive material applied to the workpiece at low rates of SFPM.

One type (Figure 31) uses **free running abrasive grains** circulated on a hardened steel plate to generate a flat surface on the workpiece. Related to this process is **lapping.** Abrasive grains are imbedded in the soft material of

Figure 31. Free abrasive grinding machine has a hard, water cooled plate on which the abrasive is fed in a slurry. The abrasive grains do not become embedded as they do in lapping. Hence, the grains always roll around under the workpieces (Courtesy of Speedfam Corporation).

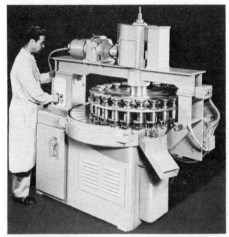

Figure 32. Lapping machine. The pressure plate on top holds the parts to be lapped by the abrasive embedded in the plate beneath (Courtesy of Lapmaster Division of Crane Packing Company).

Figure 33. Honing machine. Honing is a very popular method for finishing inside diameters of everything from bushings to cylinders of automobile engine blocks (Courtesy of Sunnen Products Company).

the **lapping plate.** Surfaces that are **extremely flat** can be generated by this method (Figure 32).

Parts such as engine cylinders may be finish machined by the **honing** process. The honing machine (Figure 33) can be used for both external and internal parts.

Figure 34. Superfinishing an automotive crank (Courtesy of Taft-Peirce Mfg. Co.).

Figure 35. This high production vibratory finisher shows the parts and abrasive coming from the vibrator to the front where the parts are unloaded; then the abrasive is returned to the vibrator by the conveyor (Courtesy of UltraMatic Equipment Co.).

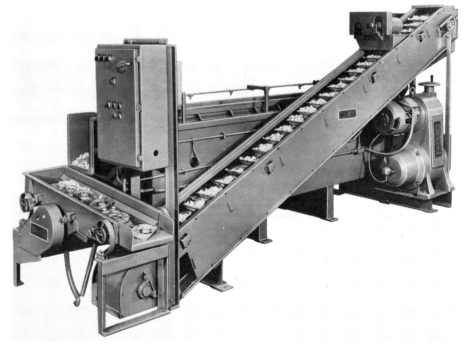

Superfinishing is another slow speed abrasive process. A formed abrasive pad (Figure 34) is held against the workpiece as it turns. A small side motion is also applied. The result is a highly finished accurate surface.

Removal of sharp edges left from almost all machining processes can be accomplished by **vibratory deburring** (Figure 35). The abrasive materials are in pellet form. Part and abrasive are vibrated together to remove burrs. This process can also be used to remove internal burrs that would be hard or impossible to reach from the outside.

Figure 36. Safety guard on a surface grinder (Courtesy of DoAll Company).

Figure 37. Making a ring test on a small wheel (Lane Community College).

Figure 38. Large grinding wheels can be slung for ring testing (Courtesy of DoAll Company).

GRINDING MACHINE SAFETY

Wheel Speed and Wheel Guards

The same general rules of safety apply to grinding machines as apply to any machine tools. An additional safety consideration is the **grinding wheel rotating at a high RPM. A grinding wheel can become cracked and if allowed to attain full speed, can fly apart ejecting large chunks of wheel from the machine at high velocity.**

To reduce the possible hazard from this, **wheel guards** (Figure 36) are used on almost every type of grinding machine, portable or otherwise. **Never operate any grinder without wheel guards in place.**

All grinding wheels are rated at specific maximum RPMs. Exceeding rated speeds can also cause a wheel to fly apart. **Always check rated speeds marked on the wheel blotter and never operate any grinding wheel beyond its maximum safe speed.**

Ring Testing a Grinding Wheel

A grinding wheel may be **ring tested** for possible cracks (Figure 37). Hold the wheel on your finger or on a small pin. Tap the wheel **gently** with a wood mallet or screwdriver handle. A good wheel will give off a clear ringing sound. A cracked wheel will sound dull and should be discarded immediately. Large grinding wheels may be ring tested while resting on the floor or while supported by a sling (Figure 38).

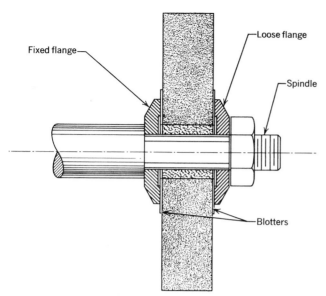

Figure 39. Typical set of flanges with flat rims and hollow centers with blotters separating the wheel and the flanges. Tightening the nut too much could spring the flanges and perhaps even crack the wheel.

Figure 40. Storing extra wheels at the machine on pegs is often convenient and practical. The main requirement is to keep the wheels separate or protected, and off the floor (Courtesy of DoAll Company).

Figure 41. Straight wheels are designed for grinding on the periphery. Never grind on the side. Cylinder wheels, cup wheels (both straight and flaring), and segments or segmental wheels (shown here without the holder) are all designed and safe for side grinding (Courtesy of Bay State Abrasives, Dresser Industries Inc.).

Mounting the Wheel and Starting the Machine   The wheel should be **ring tested** first and then fitted to the machine spindle. **It should fit snugly. Never force a wheel on the spindle. Blotters should be used on both sides** and should be larger than the flange diameter. Flanges should be **smooth** and the **spindle nut should not be overtightened** (Figure 39). **Stand** to one side clear of the wheel and start the machine. **Let the wheel run for one full minute with all guards in place.**

Handling and Storing Grinding Wheels

Grinding wheels should be **handled carefully** and **certainly never dropped.** Wheels may be stored in wheel racks or on a peg board (Figure 40) where they are separated from each other.

Operator Safety

Operator safety includes **wearing side shield safety glasses, removing rings and watches,** and securing loose clothing. When **side grinding, use only wheels designed for this purpose** (Figure 41). Always **approach the workpiece carefully. Never jam a grinding wheel.** The shock and sudden loading can chip or break the wheel. Turn off coolant a minute before stopping the wheel. Porous grinding wheels can collect coolant in the bottom half while at rest. Starting the machine can throw the wheel out of balance.

UNIT 1 SELECTION AND IDENTIFICATION OF GRINDING WHEELS

A 60 J8V

Selecting a grinding wheel is much like selecting any other cutting tool. Many of the same factors apply such as size and shape. However, in grinding wheels, additional factors influence the selection process. These include: **types of abrasives, grit, grade, structure,** and **bond** as well as the particular **grinding task** to be done. The purpose of this unit is to familiarize you with the identification of grinding wheels and to assist you in selecting the one that best fits your needs.

OBJECTIVES

After completing this unit, you should be able to:
1. List the five principal abrasives with their general areas of best use.
2. List the four principal bonds with the types of applications where they are most used.
3. Identify by type number and name, from unmarked sketches, or from actual wheels, the four most commonly used shapes of grinding wheels.
4. Interpret wheel shape and size markings together with the five basic symbols of a wheel specification into a description of the grinding wheel.
5. Given several standard, common grinding jobs, recommend the kind of abrasive, approximate grit size and grade, and bond.

SIZE AND SHAPE OF WHEELS

The standard coding system uses numbers 1 to 28 to indicate wheel size and shape. You should be familiar with five of the most common types.

Type 1 — Straight wheel (Figure 1)
Type 2 — Cylinder wheel (Figure 2)
Type 6 — Straight cup wheel (Figure 3)
Type 11 — Flaring cup wheel (Figure 4) with grinding faces on both face and wall
Type 12 — Shallow dish wheel (Figure 5)

STANDARD WHEEL MARKING SYSTEMS

A standard wheel marking system (Figure 6) is used for the purpose of identifying five major factors in grinding wheel selection.

1. Type of abrasive
2. Grit size
3. Grade or hardness
4. Structure
5. Bond

These factors are indicated on the grinding wheel blotter by a numeric and letter identification code. For example, a wheel marked:

$$\text{A 60 — J8V} \quad \text{(Figure 6)}$$

would indicate the following:

First Symbol—Type of Abrasive (A 60 — J8V)
Five major abrasives are in common use:

1. A — Aluminum oxide
2. C — Silicon carbide

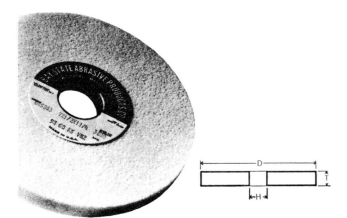

Figure 1. Straight or type 1 wheel, whose grinding face is the periphery. Usually comes with the grinding face at right angles to the sides, in what is sometimes called an "A" face (Courtesy of Bay State Abrasives, Dresser Industries, Inc.).

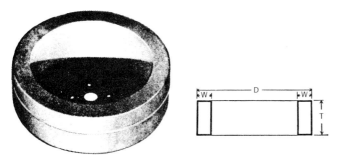

Figure 2. Cylinder or type 2 wheel, whose grinding face is the rim or wall end of the wheel. Has three dimensions – diameter, thickness, and wall thickness (Courtesy of Bay State Abrasives, Dresser Industries, Inc.).

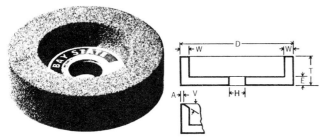

Figure 3. Straight cup or type 6 wheel, whose grinding face is the flat rim or wall end of the cup (Courtesy of Bay State Abrasives, Dresser Industries, Inc:).

3. D – Natural diamond
4. MD or SD – Manufactured or synthetic diamond
5. Cubic boron nitride

Aluminum oxide and silicon carbide are relatively inexpensive abrasives such that the entire grinding wheel can be made from the abrasive material.

Diamond and cubic boron nitride are relatively

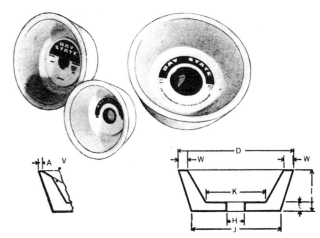

Figure 4. Flaring cup or type 11 wheel, whose grinding face is also the flat rim or wall of the cup. Note that the wall of the cup is tapered (Courtesy of Bay State Abrasives, Dresser Industries, Inc.).

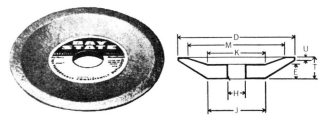

Figure 5. Dish or type 12 wheel, similar to type 11, but a narrow, straight peripheral grinding face in addition to the wall grinding face. Only wheel of those shown that is considered safe for both peripheral and wall or rim grinding (Courtesy of Bay State Abrasives, Dresser Industries, Inc.).

expensive abrasives and are only layered on a grinding wheel made from other materials. Diamond abrasive, because of its hardness, is widely used to grind extremely hard materials.

The selection of an abrasive will depend on the material to be ground and on what you know about their capabilities. General applications of the common abrasives are:

Most steels – Aluminum oxide
Tool and alloy steels – Boron nitride
Non-ferrous metals – Silicon carbide
Carbide – Diamond or green silicon carbide
Glass and non-metallic materials – Silicon carbide

Second Symbol—Grit Size   (A 60 — J8V)
Grit refers to the **size of the abrasive grains.** Grit size ranges from 4 to 8 (coarse) up to 500 or higher (fine). Grit numbering is derived from the screen openings used to sort the abrasive grains after manufacture. The fol-

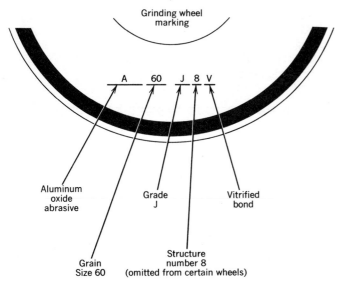

Grinding wheel
marking

A   60   J 8 V

Aluminum
oxide
abrasive

Grade
J

Vitrified
bond

Grain
Size 60

Structure
number 8
(omitted from certain wheels)

Figure 6. Wheel specification.

Weak holding power

Medium holding power

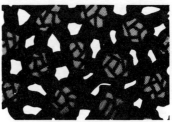

Strong holding power

Figure 7. Three sketches illustrating (from top down) a soft, a medium, and a hard wheel. This is the **grade** of the wheel. The white areas are voids with nothing but air; the black lines are the bond, and the others are the abrasive grain. The harder the wheel, the greater the proportion of bond and, usually, the smaller the voids (Courtesy of Bay State Abrasives, Dresser Industries, Inc.).

lowing approximate scale can be used to determine grit:

4	36	46	100	120	240	500

<—— Coarse——> <—Medium——> <—— Fine ——>

Selection of grit depends on the amount of stock to be removed and the surface finish requirements. Usually coarse grits are used for fast stock removal and on soft ductile materials. Fine grit is used for hard brittle materials. General usage calls for wheel grits ranging from 46 to 100.

Third Symbol—
Grade of Hardness (A 60 — J8V)

Grade or **hardness** (Figure 7) is a measure of the **bond strength** of the grinding wheel. The bond material holds the abrasive grains together in the wheel. The stronger the bond, the harder the wheel. Precision grinding wheels tend to be softer grades because it is necessary to have dull abrasive grains pulled from the wheel as soon as possible. This will expose new sharp grains to the workpiece. If this does not happen, the wheel will become glazed with dull abrasive. Cutting efficiency and surface finish will be poor. Later alphabet letters indicate harder grades. For example, F to G would be soft, where R to Z would be very hard.

Fourth Symbol—Structure (A 60 — J8V)

Structure, or the **spacing of the abrasive grains** in the wheel (Figure 8), is indicated by the numbers 1 (dense) to 15 (open). **Structure provides chip clearance** so that chips may be thrown from the wheel by centrifugal force or washed out by the grinding coolant. If this does

not happen the wheel becomes loaded with workpiece particles (Figure 9) and must be dressed.

Fifth Symbol—Bond (A 60 — J8V)

Bond is identified by letter according to the following:

V — Vitrified
B — Resinoid
R — Rubber
E — Shellac

Vitrified and resinoid bonds are the most common. Vitrified wheels are used for precision grinding. Resinoid wheels are used in rough grinding operations with high wheel speeds and heavy stock removal. Rubber and shellac are used more in special applications. Bonds also affect wheel speeds. Vitrified wheels are rated up to 6500 SFPM. Resinoid wheels are rated to 16,000 SFPM or higher.

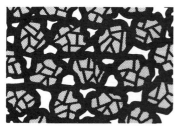

Dense spacing

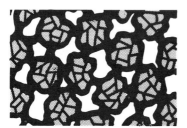

Medium spacing

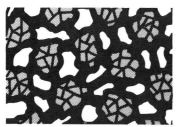

Open spacing

Figure 8. Three similar sketches showing structure. From the top down, dense, medium, and open structure or grain spacing. The proportions of bond, grain, and voids in all three sketches are about the same (Courtesy of Bay State Abrasives, Dresser Industries, Inc.).

OTHER FACTORS IN WHEEL SELECTION

Other factors in wheel selection include those that pertain to the workpiece material and the grinding machine. For example, a grinding machine with much horsepower can handle a harder grade wheel. Abrasive and bond selection depend on the severity of the grinding operation, as to whether loads on the wheel are light and constant or heavy and variable.

The area of contact is another consideration. Surface versus cylindrical grinding will affect grit and grade selection. Maximum wheel speeds depend on the type of bond. Grinding dry or with coolant will also affect the choice of grade.

Figure 9. The wheel at the left is called **loaded** with small bits of metal imbedded in its grinding facet. It is probably too dense in structure or perhaps has too fine an abrasive grain. Same wheel at the right has been dressed to remove all the loading (Courtesy of Desmond-Stephan Mfg. Co.).

SELF-TEST

1. Select the best abrasive for each of the following materials: bronze, steel, carbide, and high speed steel.
2. What are the three dimensions for grinding wheels?
3. What are the five shapes of grinding wheels?
4. What bond will withstand the highest RPM?
5. What is wheel grade?
6. List data on a A 14-Z3B and a C 14-J6V wheel.
7. Of a C 36-K8V and a C 25-H9V, which wheel is suitable for side grinding, which for peripheral grinding?
8. List data on a 32A 46-H8VBE wheel.

UNIT 2 TRUEING, DRESSING, AND BALANCING OF GRINDING WHEELS

A grinding wheel must run true with every point on its cutting surface concentric with the machine spindle. As it becomes loaded with workpiece material, it must be dressed to restore sharpness. It must also run in balance because of its great speed. These procedures of trueing, dressing, and balancing are important parts of grinding operations and the purpose of this unit is to describe and familiarize you with them.

OBJECTIVE

After completing this unit, you should be able to:
Describe trueing, dressing, and balancing of grinding wheels.

TRUEING AND DRESSING

When a new wheel is installed on the grinder, it must be **trued** before use. The cutting surface of a new wheel will run slightly out due to the clearance between the wheel bore and machine spindle (Figure 1). **Trueing** a wheel will bring every point on its cutting surface concentric with the machine spindle.

In most grinding operations, small chips of workpiece material become lodged in the cutting surface of the grinding wheel. These will impair the cutting efficiency and they must be removed at required intervals. This process is called **dressing** and is highly important to good results in grinding. Dressing is the process of **sharpening** a grinding wheel.

Both trueing and dressing remove a certain amount of material from the grinding wheel. **Wheels should be trued and dressed only enough to establish concentricity or to expose new sharp abrasive grains to the workpiece.**

Trueing and dressing can be hand operations when done on the pedestal grinder (Figure 2). A **star dresser** may be used (Figure 3), consisting of several star shaped metal wheels on a spindle. The dresser is applied to the rotating grinding wheel both to true the wheel and remove imbedded particles, thus restoring a sharp face.

Trueing and dressing on precision grinders is done with **single** (Figure 4) **or multiple point diamond dressers.** The **cluster dresser** (Figure 5) may be wide enough to

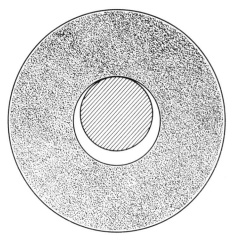

Figure 1. Sketch, exaggerated for effect, showing a grinding wheel on a spindle. Actually, the gap under the spindle may be only a few thousandths of an inch, but still enough to cause problems if the wheel is not trued to the center of the spindle.

Figure 2. Huntington dresser set up for dressing. The dresser has a hook or lug that fits over the workrest of the grinder (Courtesy of Norton Company).

Figure 3. Huntington type dresser (sometimes called a star) used for coarse wheels intended for rough grinding (Courtesy of Norton Company).

Figure 4. Single point diamond dresser. The most important precaution in using such a dresser is to turn the diamond often to avoid grinding flats on it. This diamond is pointing to the right (Courtesy of Desmond-Stephen Manufacturing Co.).

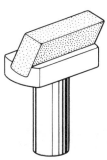

Figure 5. Cluster type dressers have come into use mostly because several smaller diamonds are cheaper than one large diamond (Courtesy of Desmond-Stephan Manufacturing Co.).

reach across the entire cutting surface of the wheel.

Dressers are always solidly mounted. The diamond and its holder are mounted on the grinder chuck so that they can be traversed across the cutting surface of the wheel. **The dresser must be positioned off center on the wheel on the outgoing rotation side** (Figure 6). This will preclude the dresser from getting caught and being pulled under the wheel. **Dressers are marked with arrows that are to be pointed in the same direction as wheel rotation.**

When trueing, lower the wheel head until the highest point on the wheel just begins to contact the dresser. Traverse the dresser across the wheel and feed down .001 in. after each pass. Each time, a bit more abrasive will be removed from the wheel. When the dresser is

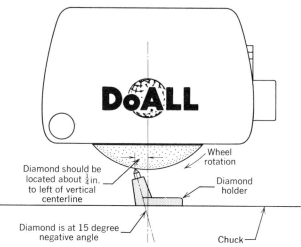

Figure 6. This is one of several ways of mounting a dresser on a surface grinder. The dresser with its diamond is spotted on the clean magnetic chuck. Note, that the diamond is slanted at a 15 degree angle and slightly past the vertical centerline of the wheel, (Courtesy of DoAll Company).

Figure 7. Built-in wheel dresser. Lever traverses dresser across wheel (Courtesy of DoAll Company).

Figure 8. Sometimes it is practical to use one grinding wheel to dress another. The abrasive wheel in the dresser is being used with a metal-bonded diamond wheel on the grinding machine (Courtesy of Norton Company).

Figure 9. Since the hole in the core of a diamond or CBN wheel is machined, it can be fitted to much closer tolerances (K & M Industrial Tool, Inc.).

cutting all around, the wheel has been fully trued. **Do not remove any more abrasive than is necessary to achieve concentric running of the cutting surface.** Trueing may be done dry, but is usually done with coolant. After trueing it may be desirable to break the sharp corners of the wheel leaving a small radius. This will prevent the sharp corners from leaving undesirable scratches on the workpiece.

After the wheel has been in use, the diamond will be used to remove imbedded workpiece particles and expose new sharp abrasive grains. This is the process of **dressing** and is done in the same way as trueing. The speed of traverse can influence the surface finish obtainable on the workpiece. **A slow dressing traverse will result in a finer dress and a better cutting surface for finish grinding. A fast dressing traverse will result in a coarser dress and a better cutting surface for rough grinding.** Grinding machines may have a built-in dresser with micrometer feed (Figure 7). Another grinding wheel can also be used as a dresser (Figure 8).

Because boron nitride and diamond abrasives are expensive, it would not be desirable to either true or dress these wheels excessively. The bore of a diamond wheel is machined so that it will closely fit the grinder spindle (Figure 9). When a diamond wheel is mounted it

may be adjusted to run true by using a dial indicator. The wheel is tapped lightly with a block of wood (Figure 10). If the diamond wheel cannot be adjusted within tolerance, it may be trued or dressed (Figure 11).

Radius and Form Dressing

Contours, radii, and other **special shapes** can be ground by forming the **reverse geometry** on the grinding wheel. Various methods are used for this. A **radius dresser** that

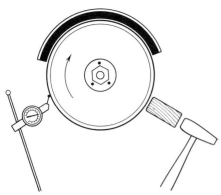

Figure 10. Runout on a diamond wheel is checked with a dial indicator and must be within .0005 in. for resinoid wheels or .00025 in. (half as much) for metal bonded wheels. Tapping a wooden block held against the wheel to shift the wheel on the spindle is often enough to bring it within limits. Otherwise, it will have to be trued (Courtesy of Precision Diamond Tool Co.).

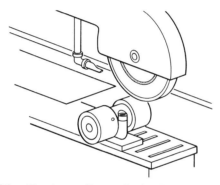

Figure 11. Trueing a diamond wheel, when necessary, is best done with a brake type trueing device, as shown. For resinoid wheels, the job may also be done by grinding a piece of low carbon steel (Courtesy of Precision Diamond Tool Co.).

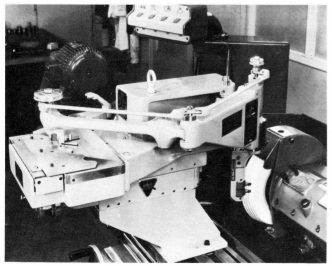

Figure 12. A dressing unit such as this can be set to dress practically any desired shape in a wheel. It is very versatile (Courtesy of Engis Co., Diamond Tool Division).

Figure 13. This is a crush roll, which literally crushes out the form in the wheel, instead of cutting it, as with diamond rolls or blocks (Courtesy of DoAll Company).

Figure 14. The crush roll must be mounted to provide support against considerable force, either as here on a center type cylindrical grinder, or on a surface grinder (Courtesy of Bendix Automation and Measurement Division).

swings the single point diamond in a preset arc is one method. The **wheel dressing pantograph** (Figure 12) can form dress a grinding wheel to almost any shape.

In **crush roll dressing** (Figure 13) the form is literally

Figure 16. This type of balancing device with overlapping wheels or disks is quite common. It has an advantage in that it need not be precisely leveled (Courtesy of Bay State Abrasives, Dresser Industries, Inc.).

Figure 15. Diamond-plated dressing block, intended for use on a surface grinder. The block is held flat on the magnetic chuck, and the wheel is traversed back and forth along it. The block is formed to the shape of the finished workpiece (Courtesy of Engis Co., Diamond Tool Division).

crushed into the wheel by a **carbide or diamond roll.** Crush dressing is used on both surface and cylindrical grinders. The roll must be solidly mounted to withstand the pressures involved (Figure 14). The **diamond dressing block** is another method used to form dress a wheel (Figure 15).

Figure 17. Balancing a wheel on two knife edges, as on this unit, is very accurate, because there is minimum friction. The course, the unit must be perfectly level and true. Otherwise, the wheel may roll from causes other than out-of-balance (Courtesy of Bay State Abrasives, Dresser Industries, Inc.).

BALANCING

Balancing may be required on large wheels (over 14 in. dia.) but is usually not required for smaller wheels. An out of balance wheel can cause variations in workpiece finish.

Wheels are balanced on the **overlapping disk balancing ways** (Figure 16) or **parallel ways** (Figure 17). **These tools must be set up exactly level.** The grinding wheel is mounted on a balancing arbor and placed on the ways. The heavy point will rotate to the lowest

position. By adjusting weights in the flanges (Figure 18), balance can be achieved. These techniques are static balance methods. Techniques used to balance a wheel while it is in **motion** are called **dynamic balance methods.**

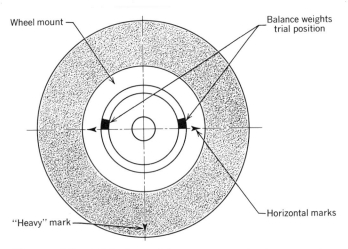

Figure 18. With the weights at some point between the vertical and the horizontal centerlines, the wheel should be in proper balance, stationary in any position. If not, one or two other balance weights should be used (Courtesy of Bay State Abrasives, Dresser Industries, Inc.).

SELF-TEST

1. What is meant by trueing a grinding wheel, and why is it important?
2. Explain the difference between dressing and trueing a wheel. How often should a wheel be dressed?
3. Define form dressing. Mention at least two methods of form dressing.
4. What is a star dresser?
5. Explain the placement of a single point dresser.
6. List the procedure in trueing an aluminum oxide or silicon carbide wheel after mounting.
7. Explain the essential differences between dressing a grinding wheel for roughing as against finishing.
8. Under what circumstances might it be necessary to true a diamond wheel and how is it done?
9. Generally, what determines whether a wheel needs to be balanced? Describe the procedure.

UNIT 3 GRINDING FLUIDS

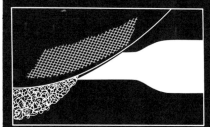

In grinding, a great deal of heat is generated from the friction between abrasive grains and the workpiece. Temperatures to 2000°F are not uncommon at the point where the grain is actually cutting. Even though much grinding is done with grinding fluids or coolants, the high speed of the grinding wheel creates enough of a fan effect to blow the coolant away from the contact area. The actual cutting process may then be occurring in a dry and hot environment. Nonetheless, coolants are almost essential in grinding. The purpose of this unit is to describe the purpose, types, application methods, and cleaning of grinding fluids.

OBJECTIVES

After completing this unit, you should be able to:
1. List reasons for using coolants.
2. List three types of coolants.
3. Describe methods and coolant application.
4. Describe methods of cleaning coolants.

PURPOSE OF GRINDING FLUIDS

Grinding fluids are the same as coolants. The terms are used interchangeably. Coolants are used to:

1. Reduce temperature in the workpiece, thus reducing warping.
2. Lubricate the contact area between wheel and work-

Figure 1. This is a very common method of flood coolant application. For the photograph, the volume of coolant has been reduced (Lane Community College).

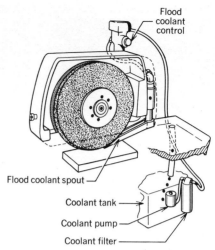

Figure 2. Fluid recirculates through the tank, piping, nozzle, and drains in flood grinding system (Courtesy of DoAll Company).

piece, thus aiding to prevent chips from sticking to the wheel.

3. Flush chips and abrasive, called swarf, from the workpiece.

4. Improve surface finish on the workpiece.

TYPES OF GRINDING FLUIDS

Water Soluble Chemical Types

This type of fluid has excellent lubricating and heat transfer characteristics. Various additives can be used to prevent rust, aid in cleaning, lubricate, and control bacterial growth in the coolant. Chemical fluids are used in heavy grinding jobs.

Water Soluble Oil Types

Like the chemical fluids, this type uses water as a base with a water soluble oil mixed in. The fluid is the common milky substance often seen in the machine shop. For grinding, this fluid is good for medium stock removal operations.

Straight Oils

Straight oils are unmatched for lubricating characteristics, but their heat transfer properties are not as good as water based coolants. Straight oils are used for heavy form grinding and thread grinding.

METHODS OF APPLICATION

Most grinding fluids are applied in a **flood stream** (Figure 1) by the machine coolant pump. The coolant is constantly recirculated and cleaned of **swarf** (Figure 2). The supply must be replenished from time to time with the

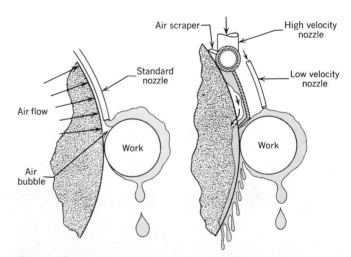

Figure 3. A specially designed nozzle like this helps to keep the fanlike effect of the rapidly rotating wheel from blowing coolant away from the wheel-work interface (Courtesy of Cincinnati Milacron, Products Division).

addition of water and additives. It is important to apply coolant **at the right place** (Figure 3). This is usually at **the immediate vicinity of the contact area.**

Air/mist coolant is another application method (Figure 4). Mist systems use much less liquid coolant volume. The rapidly evaporating mist provides good cooling in the contact area and the view of the workpiece is not obstructed as in flood applications.

Since the vitrified grinding wheel is porous, coolant may be applied **through the wheel** (Figure 5). Coolant is fed to a circular channel on the wheel, then through holes into the wheel, and ultimately out through the porous abrasive material. Centrifugal force keeps the coolant flowing outward. This method is very effective

Figure 4. Mist grinding fluid application is sometimes used on a normally dry grinder. The cooling effect is excellent, lubrication practically nil, but no recirculating system is required (Courtesy of DoAll Company).

Figure 5. Nozzle and flange design for through-the-wheel application. This allows coolant to filter through the wheel to the cutting area. It also sprays coolant over the inside of the wheel guard. (Courtesy of DoAll Company).

Figure 6. A settling tank. The two requirements for cleaning coolant by settling are that the tank be big enough to allow the coolant to remain still for enough time to allow the swarf to settle out, and that there always be enough coolant in the system. This also means that the tank must be kept clean; otherwise, dirty coolant is recirculated (Courtesy of The Carborundum Company).

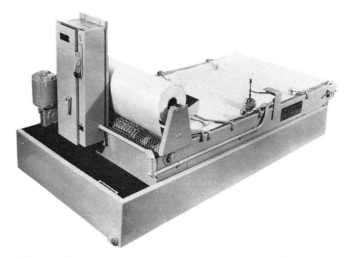

Figure 7. A widely used cleaning method is to let the fluid fall through filter fabric directly into a tank. Then, when the load on the fabric becomes heavy enough, it actuates a switch that pulls the loaded fabric into a waste container and also pulls a fresh section of fabric into place (Courtesy of The Carborundum Company).

for getting coolant to the contact area. However, the **fluid must be carefully cleaned** or swarf will plug the pores in the wheel. Fluid is also sprayed on the wheel guard and this must be kept clean to prevent dirty coolant from dripping on the workpiece.

CLEANING THE GRINDING FLUID

Coolant must be cleaned of swarf before returning it to the workpiece. If this is not done, swarf will be circulated

back through the contact area and result in surface finish problems on the workpiece. Many shops use centrally supplied coolant to all grinding machines. Cleaning of the fluid can be carefully done and monitored. Many grinding machines have a self-contained coolant system and a number of methods are used for coolant cleaning.

A fundamental technique is **settling.** Coolant is pumped to the settling tank where swarf settles out by gravity (Figure 6).

Since settling is slow, **filtering** may be used (Figure

Figure 8. The centrifugal unit on top spins at high speed to remove swarf from the fluid. Dirty fluid, already partly cleaned by settling, is pumped into the unit by the large hose from the tank and recirculated through the smaller hose and piping (Courtesy of Barrett Centrifugals).

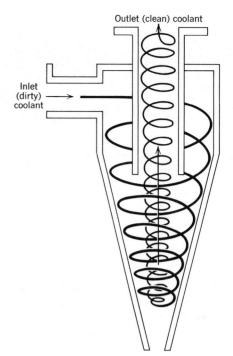

Figure 9. A cyclonic filter. The dirty coolant is fed in from the side, swirls around in the cone as the clean coolant goes out through the top, and the swarf through the bottom of the cone (Courtesy of Barnes Drill Co., Rockford, Ill.).

7). The filtering material is changed periodically. The type of filter used is limited as to the size of particles that can be trapped.

Other coolant cleaning methods include the **centrifugal separator** (Figure 8) where coolant is directed into a rapidly rotating centrifuge. Swarf is moved to the outside and clean coolant remains in the center.

The **cyclonic separator** (Figure 9) also uses centrifugal force. Clean coolant exits out the top while swarf goes to the bottom. The **magnetic separator** (Figure 10) will remove iron and steel grindings. A rotary magnetic drum rotates in the coolant and attracts the grindings, which are later scraped off and removed.

USING GRINDING FLUIDS

When using grinding fluids, be sure to check the following.

1. Maintain proper coolant level.
2. Maintain proper balance of water and additives.
3. Check for contamination by lubricating oils.
4. Make sure that coolant is supplied to the contact area in sufficient volume and at the right place.

Figure 10. This magnetic separator removes iron and steel chips from water soluble oils and cutting oils. The magnets are in the roll visible just past the electrical control box. Chips picked up by the roll are scraped off onto the slide and go down into the sludge box (Courtesy of Barnes Drill Co., Rockford, Ill.).

SELF-TEST

1. Explain the major functions of grinding fluids.
2. Where should the grinding fluid be applied?
3. What is mist coolant and how is it applied?

4. What are the major types of grinding fluids?
5. Describe methods of cleaning grinding fluids.

UNIT 4 HORIZONTAL SPINDLE RECIPROCATING TABLE SURFACE GRINDERS

The horizontal spindle reciprocating table surface grinder is probably the most common precision grinder found in the machine shop. The primary application of this machine is surface grinding. With accessories it can accomplish several other grinding tasks. The purpose of this unit is to familiarize you with the major parts of this machine, its controls and accessory capabilities.

OBJECTIVES

After completing this unit, you should be able to:
1. Name the components of the horizontal spindle surface grinder.
2. Define the functions of the various component parts of this grinder.
3. Name and describe the functions of at least two accessory devices used to increase the versatility of the surface grinder.

IDENTIFYING MACHINE PARTS AND THEIR FUNCTIONS

The **horizontal spindle reciprocating table surface grinder** (Figure 1), often simply called a **surface grinder,** presents the edge of the grinding wheel to the workpiece. The workpiece is mounted on a chuck, which in turn is mounted on a table that **reciprocates** back and forth under the wheel. Major parts of this grinding machine include the following.

Wheelhead

The **wheelhead** contains the spindle, bearings, and drive motor. This assembly is mounted on the downfeed slide.

Table with Chuck

The **table** supports the **chuck,** which is the primary workholding device on the grinder. The table reciprocates right and left to carry the workpiece under the grinding wheel. Table reciprocation may be done by hand or may be a powered function. On power fed tables, the length of stroke may be preset by positioning the feed reverse trips. The table is then reversed at the end of each stroke, causing it to feed in the opposite direction.

Saddle

The table is supported by the **saddle,** which moves in

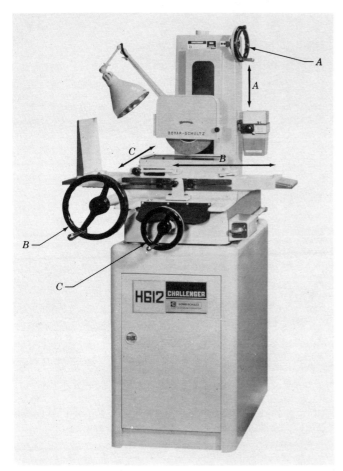

Figure 1. Surface grinder with direction and control of movements indicated by arrows. Wheel *A* controls downfeed *A*. Large wheel *B* controls table traverse *B*. Wheel *C* controls crossfeed *C* (Courtesy of Boyar-Schultz Corp.).

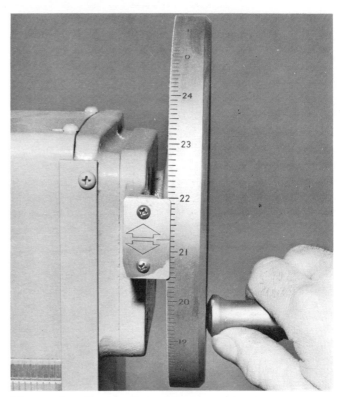

Figure 2. Closeup of downfeed handwheel. Moving from one mark to the next lowers or raises the grinding wheel .0001 in. (Courtesy of DoAll Company).

Figure 3. Same control wheel with slip ring set to zero. Now it is simpler for operator to down feed the grinding wheel as he grinds (Courtesy of DoAll Company).

and out in order to set the workpiece over after each reciprocation. This is also an automatic powered function on many grinders.

Controls

The **downfeed handwheel** (Figure 2) located on the wheelhead raises and lowers the wheel with reference to the workpiece. **Depth of cut is controlled by the downfeed.** The downfeed handwheel is graduated to **.0001 in. increments** and also has an **arrow indicating** the **direction of wheel feed.** The downfeed handwheel is equipped with a micrometer collar (Figure 3) that may be adjusted to zero at any point where the wheel just begins to cut the workpiece.

The **table feed crank** reciprocates the table back and forth. The **cross feed crank** moves the saddle in and out. The cross feed crank is graduated in .001 in. increments, permitting setover to be regulated so that the correct amount of overlap is obtained on each grinding pass.

Figure 4. Centerless grinding attachment mounted on surface grinder with an assortment of parts that can be ground on it (Courtesy of Unison Corporation).

Figure 5. Center type cylindrical attachment mounted on surface grinder. Attachment can be tilted for grinding a taper, as shown here, or set level for grinding a straight cylinder (Courtesy of Harig Mfg. Corp., Chicago, Ill.).

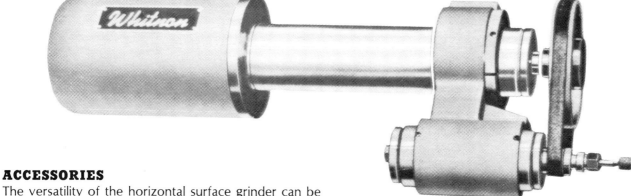

Figure 6. High speed spindle adds capability for internal grinding (Courtesy of Whitnon Spindle Division, Mite Corporation).

ACCESSORIES

The versatility of the horizontal surface grinder can be extended by the use of **accessory equipment.** Several of these pertain to workholding and will be discussed in the next unit. Accessories that increase the grinding capability of the machine include the following.

Centerless Attachment

Centerless grinding can be accomplished using the **centerless attachment** (Figure 4). Parts are held between rollers and the grinding wheel. Diameters up to 5 in. can be centerless ground using this attachment.

Center Type Cylindrical Attachment

Cylindrical grinding can be accomplished with this accessory (Figure 5). It can also be used to grind a flat on the workpiece.

High Speed Attachment

This attachment (Figure 6) is belt driven from the grinder spindle and can be used for **internal grinding.** A suitable method for holding the workpiece must be selected if this attachment is used on the surface grinder.

SELF-TEST

1. What is the function of the table?
2. What is the function of the saddle?
3. Explain the purpose of the downfeed hand crank, table, and saddle hand cranks.

4. Name two accessories for the horizontal surface grinder.
5. What is the discrimination of the downfeed hand crank graduations?

UNIT 5 WORKHOLDING ON THE SURFACE GRINDER

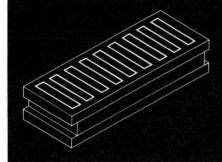

A fundamental consideration in any machining operation is **workholding.** Grinding machines are no exception. The workpiece must be safely and securely held, while permitting access by the grinding wheel. In machining operations like milling and turning, large chips are often removed by heavy cuts. This necessitates that the workpiece be restrained by stout clamps, vises, or chucks. In most common grinding, the amount of material that is removed from the workpiece on each pass of the wheel is quite small when compared to other machining operations. The workpiece must of course be securely held, but large clamps or heavy vises are usually not required. Special chucks designed for grinder workholding are in common use. These will usually meet a majority of common workholding requirements. The purpose of this unit is to describe the function and applications of these common grinder workholding devices.

OBJECTIVES

After completing this unit, you should be able to:
1. Describe the basic operating principle of common grinder chucks.
2. Explain care of grinder chucks.
3. Describe methods of holding odd-shaped, non-magnetic, and thin workpieces.

TYPES OF GRINDER CHUCKS

Magnetic Chucks
The most common workholding device for the surface grinder is the **magnetic chuck.** The two types are the **electro-magnet** (Figure 1) and the **permanent magnet** (Figure 2). Permanent magnet chucks are composed of a series of alternating plates consisting of powerful magnets. Since it is not possible to turn the magnetic field on and off with permanent magnets, the magnetic force is

mechanically conducted away from the workpiece so that it can be removed from the chuck.

The electro-magnet chuck is magnetized when electrically energized. The chuck remains magnetized as long as the power is applied. When power is removed, the chuck is demagnetized so that the workpiece can be removed. However, some residual magnetism often remains in the workpiece and can make removal from the chuck difficult. An electrical **demagnetization process** is used to remove any residual magnetism from the

Figure 1. Common type of magnetic chuck for reciprocating surface grinder. The guards at the back and left side are usually adjustable and help keep work from sliding off the chuck (Courtesy of DoAll Company).

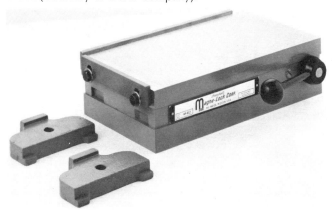

Figure 2. The permanent magnetic chuck looks about the same as any other chuck of the same shape and often is used where wiring would be inconvenient (Courtesy of Hitachi Magna-Lock Corp.).

Figure 3. Rotary magnetic chuck (Courtesy of M & M Precision Systems, Inc., Roto Grand®).

Figure 4. Magnetic sine chuck needed for grinding non-parallel surfaces (Courtesy of Hitachi Magna-Lock Corp.).

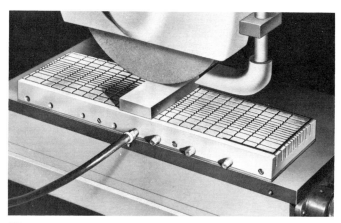

Figure 5. Vacuum chucks such as this one hold practically anything and are considered good for thin work (Courtesy of Thompson Vacuum Co., Inc.).

part. This is accomplished by a special switch and takes only a few seconds.

Magnetic chucks for surface grinders are usually rectangular. Those for rotary grinders are circular (Figure 3). Workpieces can be held on **magnetic sine chucks** for grinding angles or compound angles (Figure 4).

Vacuum Chucks

The **vacuum chuck** (Figure 5) is another tool popular for grinder workholding. By evacuating the air under the workpiece, the force of atmospheric pressure can be applied to hold the part on the chuck. This can be quite significant. On a chuck 6 by 12 inches, an atmospheric pressure of over 1000 pounds is applied to the workpiece if a good vacuum can be achieved. Vacuum chucks are also useful for holding thin workpieces.

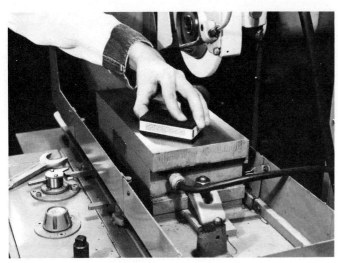

Figure 6. Periodic deburring of the chuck with a granite deburring stone like this, or with a fine grit oilstone, is a good practice (Courtesy of DoAll Company).

CARE OF GRINDER CHUCKS

Like much of the equipment found in the machine shop, **grinder chucks are precision tools** and deserve the same care and handling you would give your precision measuring instruments. With reasonable care they will maintain their accuracy over many years. Observe the following precautions when using grinder chucks:

1. Clean the chucking surface before mounting a workpiece.
2. Be sure that the workpiece is free from burrs.
3. On a magnetic chuck, be sure that small parts span as many magnetic poles as possible to insure maximum holding power.
4. Deburr the chucking surface from time to time (Figure 6).
5. Check the chucking surface with a dial indicator if the chuck has been removed and reinstalled on the machine or a new chuck is being used for the first time.

GRINDER CHUCKING SETUPS

Odd-Shaped Workpieces

A magnetic or vacuum chuck will exert the most reliable holding power on an odd-shaped workpiece if the area of contact can be maximized. Whenever possible, place the workpiece in such a manner that the largest surface area possible is on the chuck. Sometimes it is necessary to chuck on a smaller than desirable area (Figure 7). In these cases, the workpiece must be supported with **laminated parallels or vee-blocks** (Figure 8). These are especially designed for grinder work. Laminated accessories

Figure 7. Chuck setup for workpiece with projection on chucking side. Work is supported on laminated magnetic parallels (Courtesy of DoAll Company).

Figure 8. A set of magnetic parallels and vee-blocks can be very useful (Courtesy of Hitachi Magna-Lock Corp.).

are made with non-magnetic and steel inserts so that the lines of magnetic force will be conducted through to the workpiece. Odd-shaped workpieces may also be held by traditional machine tool workholding methods such as vises or clamps.

Non-magnetic Work

Non-magnetic materials may be held on a magnetic chuck by blocking the parts with **steel (magnetic) tooth clamps** (Figure 9). The comb-like teeth will keep a non-magnetic workpiece from sliding off the chuck. If you are using tooth clamps, be sure that they are lower than

Figure 9. Tooth clamps in use. Note that the toothed clamps are lower than the surface to be ground (Courtesy of DoAll Company).

the workpiece so that they will not come in contact with the grinding wheel.

Thin Workpieces

Thin material already warped or twisted will probably be pulled flat either on a magnetic or vacuum chuck. However, these workpieces may assume their original distorted shape after grinding and removal from the chuck.

Thin material can be successfully held and ground by using a **minimum amount of holding force.** One method of accomplishing this is by using double-backed tape with adhesive on both sides. One side of the tape is applied to the chuck while the other side holds the workpiece. This may be sufficient for light cuts. It may also be possible to shim under a warped thin workpiece with paper until one side has been ground true. The part may then be turned over and the true side placed on the chucking surface.

SELF-TEST

1. What are two common grinder chucks?
2. How is residual magnetism removed from a workpiece?
3. List three factors regarding the care of grinder chucks.
4. What are laminated accessories and how can they be used in grinder workholding?
5. Describe a method of holding thin workpieces.

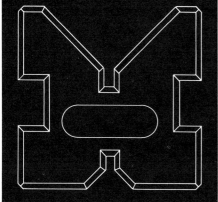

UNIT 6 USING THE SURFACE GRINDER

Using the surface grinder involves selecting and mounting the proper grinding wheel, grinding in the chuck if necessary, and using the proper combination of table and cross feeds. The surface grinder is a versatile and precision machine tool. Used correctly, it will finish your workpiece to a high degree of dimensional accuracy. The purpose of this unit is to describe the surface grinder and to familiarize you with its preparation, and with the grinding process required to finish a common grinding project.

OBJECTIVES

After completing this unit, you should be able to:

1. Prepare the surface grinder for a typical grinding job.
2. Check and grind in the chuck if necessary.
3. Finish grind a set of vee-blocks to required specifications.

GRINDING IN A MAGNETIC CHUCK

The first step in surface grinding is to **check,** and if necessary **grind in or true,** the chuck. Trueing the chuck is usually not necessary unless it has been removed and reinstalled or a new chuck is to be used for the first time. Any grinder chuck should be checked occasionally and if necessary trued by grinding a minimum amount from the chucking surface. To true a grinder chuck, the following procedure may be used.

1. Mount the chuck and align it in both table and saddle axes using a dial indicator.
2. Use the indicator to check the chucking surface to determine if trueing will be necessary.
3. If so, select and mount a proper wheel for this grinding task. A good choice would be an aluminum oxide, 46 grit, H grade, 8 structure with vitrified bond.
4. True and dress the wheel.
5. Mark the entire surface of the chuck with a thin coat of layout dye. This will indicate where the low spot is during grinding.
6. Magnetize the chuck.
7. Bring the wheel down to the chuck and use a feeler gage to set the wheel a few thousandths above the chucking surface.
8. Set the downfeed handwheel collar to zero.
9. Turn on wheel and coolant. Lower wheel the additional amount until it just contacts the chuck surface.
10. Using a fairly rapid table feed and slow cross feed, grind to a clean up condition on the chucking surface. Remove only enough material to clean the surface.
11. Demagnetize and check chucking surface with a dial indicator.
12. Remove any burrs with a stone.

GRINDING VEE-BLOCKS

The **vee-block** (Figure 1) is a common and useful machine shop tool. Precision types are finished machined by grinding after they have been rough machined and heat treated. Finish grinding of vee-blocks will provide you with a well-rounded surface grinding experience.

Refer to a working drawing (Figure 2) to determine dimensions and for planning the sequence of grinding operations.

Selecting the Wheel

For steel vee-blocks, the best abrasive will be aluminum oxide. Four suitable wheels for this task are:

1. 9A46-H8V
2. 9A60-K8V
3. 32A46-I8V
4. DA 46-J9V

Grinding Machine Setup

The following procedure may be used in setting up the grinding machine for vee-block grinding.

1. Select a suitable wheel.
2. Clean the spindle. Use a cloth to remove any grit or dirt from the spindle. If you lay tools and wheels on the chuck, cover it with a cloth for protection (Figure 3).
3. Ring test the grinding wheel (Figure 4).
4. Mount the wheel (Figure 5). The wheel should fit snugly and flanges should be the same size. Blotters will probably be attached to the wheel. If not, place a blotter between both flanges and the wheel.
5. Install spindle nut and tighten firmly. Do not overtighten (Figure 6).
6. Replace wheel guard (Figure 7).
7. Place the diamond dresser on the magnetic chuck in the proper position (Figure 8).
8. Dress the wheel, using coolant and a rapid cross feed (Figure 9).
9. Remove dresser and clean chucking surface (Figure 10).
10. Check chucking surface for nicks and burrs. Use a deburring stone if necessary (Figure 11).

Side and End Grinding Procedure

The vee-blocks should be match ground so that they are exactly the same dimensions when completed. The following procedural steps and illustrations will describe the process for side and end grinding.

1. Place the blocks with the large vee side up on the grinder chuck. Paper may be placed under the parts to protect the chucking surface during this initial grinding phase (Figure 12).
2. Magnetize the chuck mechanically or electrically depending on the type.
3. Lower the wheelhead until it is about an inch above the workpiece. Adjust table and saddle position so that blocks are centered.
4. Adjust table feed reverse trips so that the workpiece has about one inch of overtravel at each end of the table stroke (Figure 13).
5. Use a feeler gage or piece of paper and lower the wheelhead until it is a few thousandths above the surface to be ground.

Figure 1. Finished, hardened, and ground precision vee-block.

Figure 3. Cleaning the wheel spindle with a soft cloth (Lane Community College).

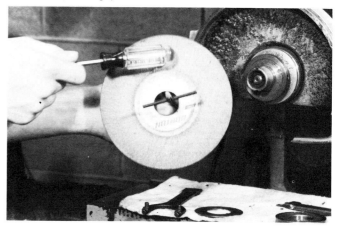

Figure 4. Ring testing the wheel (Lane Community College).

Figure 2. Dimensions and information for grinding the vee-block.

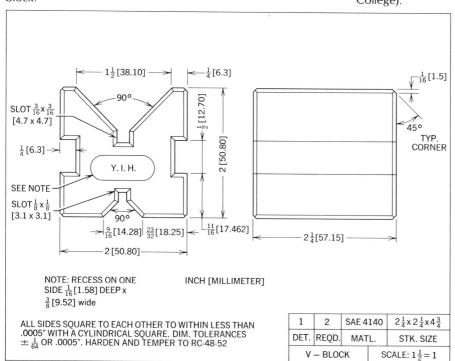

NOTE: RECESS ON ONE SIDE $\frac{1}{16}$ [1.58] DEEP x $\frac{3}{8}$ [9.52] wide   INCH [MILLIMETER]

ALL SIDES SQUARE TO EACH OTHER TO WITHIN LESS THAN .0005" WITH A CYLINDRICAL SQUARE. DIM. TOLERANCES $\pm \frac{1}{64}$ OR .0005". HARDEN AND TEMPER TO RC-48-52

1	2	SAE 4140	$2\frac{1}{4}$ x $2\frac{1}{4}$ x $4\frac{3}{4}$
DET.	REQD.	MATL.	STK. SIZE
V – BLOCK			SCALE: $1\frac{1}{2}$ = 1

Figure 5. Mounting the wheel, flange, and nut (Lane Community College).

Figure 8. Diamond dresser in the correct position. The camera angle does not show the location of the diamond clearly (Lane Community College).

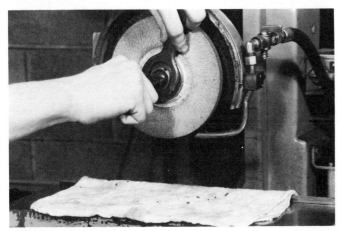

Figure 6. Tightening the nut with spanner wrenches (Lane Community College).

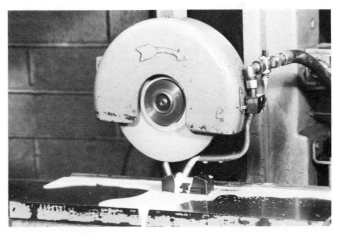

Figure 9. Dressing the wheel using coolant (Lane Community College).

Figure 7. The safety guard being replaced (Lane Community College).

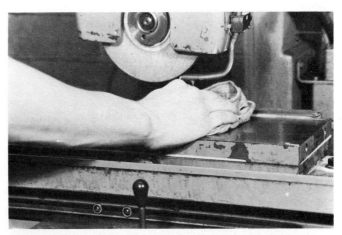

Figure 10. Cleaning the magnetic chuck with a cloth. The wheel must be completely stopped when this is done (Lane Community College).

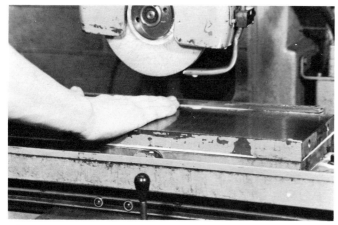

Figure 11. Checking for nicks or burrs on the magnetic chuck (Lane Community College).

Figure 12. The rough blocks in place with the large vee side up ready to be ground (Lane Community College).

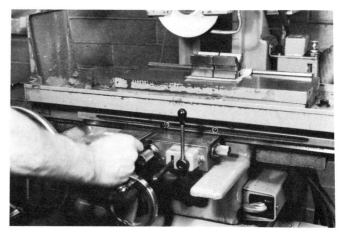

Figure 13. Setting the table stops (Lane Community College).

Figure 14. The coolant is turned on and an additional downfeed of .002 in. is made (Lane Community College).

6. Start the wheel and coolant. Start table cross feed and table feed. Carefully lower the wheel until it just begins to pick up the cut on the high point of the workpiece. Set the downfeed micrometer collar to zero at this point.

7. The amount to grind from the workpiece will depend on the amount of extra material left from the original machining. About .003 to .005 in. should be left for finish grinding on all surfaces. Downfeed about .002 in. per pass and grind to a clean up condition (Figure 14).

8. Turn the vee-blocks over and surface grind the small vee side (Figure 15).

9. The end of the block may be ground by clamping it to a precision angle plate (Figure 16). The block is adjusted into alignment using a test indicator. The end of the block should extend slightly beyond the angle plate.

10. Set the angle plate on the chuck and end grind the vee-block (Figure 17).

11. For grinding the remaining side, clamp the ground end to the angle plate leaving the side surface projecting above the angle plate (Figure 18). Grind **one** remaining side square to the end and square to the first surface ground in step 7.

12. End grind opposite ends (Figure 19). The vee-blocks may be set up on the magnetic chuck without further support.

13. Grind remaining sides leaving .003 to .005 in. for finishing (Figure 20).

Figure 15. The blocks are turned over and the opposite sides (small vee) are ground (Lane Community College).

Figure 18. The other two sides being ground square to the vee-block end that was previously ground (Lane Community College).

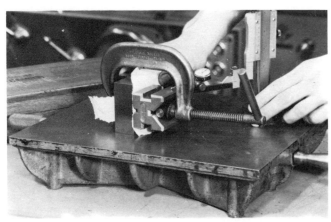

Figure 16. A ground side of the vee-block is clamped to a precision angle plate that is turned on its side and the top side of the vee-block is being leveled with a dial indicator that is mounted on a height gage (Lane Community College).

Figure 19. Grinding the opposite ends of both blocks in one setup to make them parallel (Lane Community College).

Figure 17. The precision angle plate and vee-block setup is turned with the vee-block end up on the magnetic chuck. The end of the vee-block is ground square to a ground side (Lane Community College).

Figure 20. The sides that have not been ground are also being ground in one setup to make them parallel to the other sides (Lane Community College).

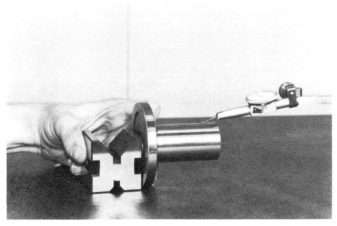

Figure 21. A vee-block now being checked for square on all sides using a precision cylindrical square, a dial indicator, and a height gage on a surface plate (Lane Community College).

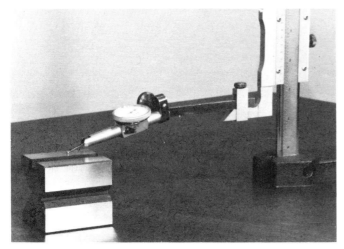

Figure 22. Dimensions being checked using a :0001 in. reading dial indicator on a height gage. Precision gage blocks may be used for comparison measurement for this operation (Lane Community College).

Figure 23. Setting up the magnetic vee-block to grind the angular surfaces on the large vees (Lane Community College).

Figure 24. The vee-blocks are repositioned and the other side of the large vees are being ground (Lane Community College).

14. Redress the wheel for finish grinding. Use a light cut of about .0002 in.
15. Check all sides and ends for squareness (Figure 21). Use a precision cylindrical square and vernier micrometer. Small errors can be corrected by further grinding if necessary. Paper shims may be used to achieve squareness.
16. Check all dimensions with a vernier micrometer (.0001 in. discrimination) or test indicator (Figure 22).
17. Finish grind all sides and ends to final dimensions. Both blocks can be match ground. Do not use any paper shims in the final grinding process.

Vee-Grinding

1. Grind one side of the large vee (Figure 23). Set the blocks in a magnetic vee-block and carefully align with table travel.
2. After grinding one side of the vee, reverse blocks and grind the other side (Figure 24) at the same cross slide setting. This will insure that the vee is centered on the blocks.
3. Repeat procedure for the remaining vee grooves.

SELF-TEST

Go to the surface grinder you will be using and familiarize yourself with the controls and tooling. If someone is using the machine, observe the operation for a time. Check the supply of grinding wheels and determine their possible uses by observing their color and by reading the printed symbol on the blotter.

UNIT 7 PROBLEMS AND SOLUTIONS IN SURFACE GRINDING

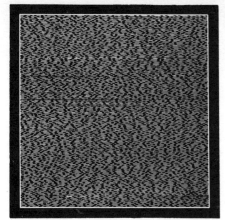

In any machining operation, there are many factors that can influence the final result. A good machinist knows what to look for; from experience, the machinist can identify a problem and implement a solution. The purpose of this unit is to help you identify common problems in surface grinding and recommend solutions.

OBJECTIVE

After completing this unit, you should be able to recognize the effects of common surface grinding problems and recommend solutions.

GENERAL CAUSES OF GRINDING PROBLEMS

Surface grinding problems can usually be attributed to the general factors of:

1. Machine condition
2. Machine operation

Machine Condition

Factors in machine condition include **spindle bearings, way lubrication,** the **overall weight and quality of the machine** and **machine location.**

All mechanical functions of the grinder must function properly for best grinding results. Spindle bearings must be tight and sliding components must be properly lubricated so they will slide smoothly. More massive grinding machines are generally more rigid and will produce better surface finishes than will lightweight machines.

External sources of vibration can affect a grinding machine. A grinder located close to a railroad track or punch press may pick up external vibrations that can show up as surface finish defects on the workpiece.

Operational Conditions

Conditions that are variable because of the way in which the machine is operated can also be the cause of grinding problems. These include **wheel selection, dressing technique, swarf in the coolant, loaded or glazed wheel,** and the **technique of the operator** in regard to table and cross feed.

SPECIFIC PROBLEMS AND SOLUTIONS IN SURFACE GRINDING (Table 1)

Effect — Chatter or vibration marks (Figure 1)

Cause — Interrupted cutting due to wheel balance, external vibrations, or a skipping wheel that is loaded or glazed

Solution — Rebalance wheel; redress wheel; relocate grinding machine and isolate from external vibration

Effect — Irregular scratches or fishtails (Figure 2)

Cause — Swarf in the coolant; swarf dripping from wheel guard; low coolant; sliding workpiece off a dirty chuck

Solution — Clean inside of wheel guard; clean coolant; clean chuck before removing workpiece; maintain coolant level

Effect — Discoloration of burning of workpiece (Figure 3)

Cause — Insufficient coolant; wheel too hard or too

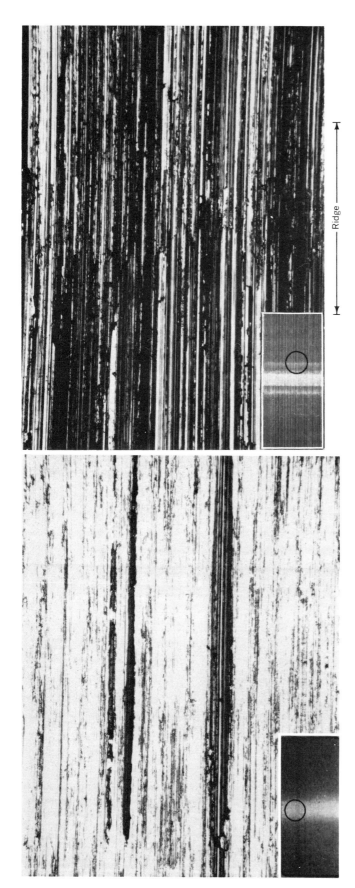

Figure 3. Discoloration or burning also enlarged 80 ×, with damaged area marked on inset (Courtesy of Surface Finishes, Inc.).

fine; concentration of heat because of too heavy cut in a small area

Solution — Speed up table travel; lighten depth of cut; increase coolant flow and volume for cooling

Effect — Work not parallel

Cause — Chuck out of line; chuck not ground in; chuck dirty or burred

Solution — Align chuck with dial indicator; follow grind in procedure; deburr and clean

Figure 2. Grinding marks or fishtails also enlarged 80 ×. Inset (enlarged 1.25 ×) shows the damaged area (Courtesy Surface Finishes, Inc.).

Table 1
Summary of Surface Grinding Defects and Possible Causes (Courtesy of DoAll Company)

Causes	Burning or Checking	Burnishing of Work	Chatter Marks	Scratches on Work	Wheel Glazing	Wheel Loading	Work Not Flat	Work Out of Parallel	Work Sliding on Chuck
Machine Operation									
Dirty coolant				x		x			
Insufficient coolant	x						x	x	
Wrong coolant					x	x			
Dirty or burred chuck				x			x	x	
Inadequate blocking									x
Poor chuck loading							x	x	x
Sliding work off chuck				x					
Dull diamond					x				
Too fine dress	x				x	x	x		
Too long a grinding stroke								x	
Loose dirt under guard				x					
Grinding Wheel									
Too fine grain size	x				x	x			
Too dense structure					x	x			
Too hard grade	x	x	x		x	x	x		
Too soft grade			x	x					
Machine Adjustment									
Chuck out of line								x	
Loose or cracked diamond				x			x	x	
No magnetism									x
Vibration			x						
Condition of Work									
Heat treat stresses							x		
Thin							x		

Effect — Workpiece not flat

Cause — Local overheating; internal stress relief; bent or twisted workpiece

Solution — Use minimum amount of chuck holding power; place workpiece on chuck bowed side up; turn workpiece over and shim with paper; take additional light cuts; reverse workpiece; remove and repeat procedure until flat

SELF-TEST

1. List two general factors that can be responsible for surface grinding problems.
2. Given the following problems, recommend appropriate solutions.
   a. Workpiece warps after removal from the chuck
   b. Surfaces out of parallel
   c. Cast iron burns
   d. Wheel skips
   e. Irregular scratches in the workpiece

UNIT 8 CENTER TYPE CYLINDRICAL GRINDERS

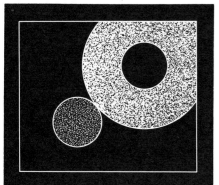

The center type cylindrical grinder, as its name implies, is used to grind cylinders or, more generally, the diameter of a round workpiece. The cylindrical grinder, like its horizontal counterpart, is a versatile machine tool capable of finish machining a round part to a high degree of dimensional accuracy. Various setups on the basic machine permit many different grinding tasks to be accomplished. The purpose of this unit is to familiarize you with the major part of this machine and its general capabilities.

OBJECTIVES

After completing this unit, you should be able to:
1. Identify the major parts of the cylindrical grinder.
2. Describe the various movements of the major parts.
3. Describe the general capabilities of this machine.

CYLINDRICAL GRINDING

The **cylindrical grinder** grinds the outside or inside diameter of a cylindrical (round) part. The abrasive wheel is brought into contact with the workpiece and is then traversed parallel (Figure 1) to the part thus reducing or increasing its diameter. In **cylindrical plunge grinding,** the wheel is brought into contact with the work but without traverse. In all cylindrical grinding, the workpiece is rotated opposite to the rotation of the abrasive wheel.

IDENTIFYING MACHINE PARTS AND THEIR FUNCTIONS

On the **center type cylindrical grinder,** the workpiece is mounted **between centers** much like it would be in the lathe. The **plain machine** (Figure 2) has a **fixed** wheelhead that cannot be swiveled, but only traversed. On the **universal machine** (Figure 3), the wheelhead and table may be swiveled for taper grinding. All possible motions are illustrated in Figure 4.

Major Parts of the Universal Center Type

Major parts of the machine include the **bed, slide, swivel table, headstock, footstock,** and **wheelhead.**

Bed.   The bed is the main structural component and is responsible for the rigidity of the machine tool. The bed

supports the slide, which in turn supports the swivel table.

Slide and Swivel Table.   The slide carries the swivel table and provides the **traverse motion** to carry the workpiece past the wheel. The swivel table is mounted on the slide and supports the head and foot stocks. Graduated scales are located on the swivel table for establishing taper angles.

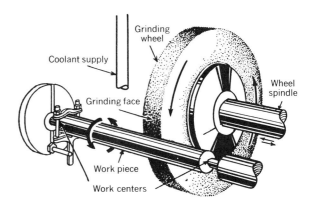

Figure 1.   Sketch of center type cylindrical grinder set up for traverse grinding. Note particularly the direction of travel of the grinding wheel and the workpiece, and the method of rotating the workpiece (Courtesy of Bay State Abrasives, Dresser Industries, Inc.).

Figure 2. Plain cylindrical grinder (Courtesy of Landis Tool Co., Division of Litton Industries).

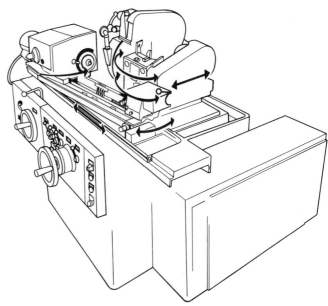

Figure 4. View of universal cylindrical grinder with arrows indicating the swiveling capabilities of the various major components (Courtesy of Cincinnati Milacron).

Figure 3. Modern universal cylindrical grinder (Courtesy of Landis Tool Co., Division of Litton Industries).

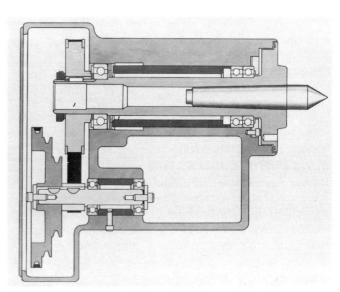

Headstock. The headstock (Figure 5) mounts on the swivel table and is used to support one end of the workpiece. The headstock also provides the rotating motion for the workpiece. The headstock spindle may be designed to accept a chuck or face plate. The headstock center is used when workpieces are mounted between center. Variable spindle speed selection is also available.

Footstock. The footstock (Figure 6) is also mounted on the swivel table and supports the opposite end of a workpiece mounted between centers. The footstock

Figure 5. Typical headstock of a center type cylindrical grinder with cutaway sketch (Courtesy of Landis Tool Co., Division of Litton Industries).

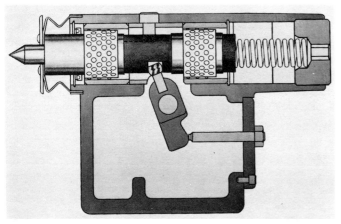

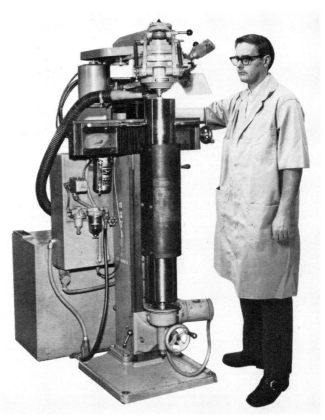

Figure 7. Center hole grinding machine (Courtesy of Bryant Grinder Corp.).

Figure 6. Typical footstock. The lever on top of the footstock retracts the work center so that the workpiece can be mounted on the grinder. The spring (right end of sketch) provides tension to hold the workpiece in place (Courtesy of Landis Tool Co., Division of Litton Industries).

center is spring loaded and is retracted by lever. This permits installation and removal of the workpiece. The footstock assembly is positioned on the swivel table at whatever points that will accommodate the length of the workpiece.

Wheelhead. The wheelhead, located at the back of the machine, contains the spindle, bearings, drive, and main motor.

WORKHOLDING AND CENTERHOLE GRINDING

The workpiece in center cylindrical grinding is most frequently mounted between the head-and footstock centers. This essentially provides a single point mounting on each end of the workpiece permitting maximum accuracy to be achieved in the grinding operation.

The **angle of center holes** in the workpiece is extremely important. The final result of a cylindrical

Figure 8. Closeup of center hole locating setup. Exact location of the center is a most critical step in the operation (Courtesy of Bryant Grinder Corp.).

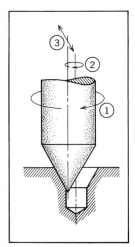

Figure 9. Sketch showing the motions of the grinding wheel in center hole grinding (Courtesy of Bryant Grinder Corp.).

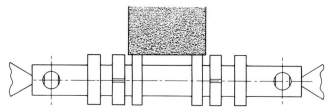

Figure 11. Sketch of traverse grinding with interrupted surfaces. Wheel should always be thick enough to span two surfaces or more at once (Courtesy of Cincinnati Milacron).

Figure 12. Multiple-diameter or form grinding. This is usually a plunge grinding operation with the form dressed in the wheel face (Courtesy of Cincinnati Milacron).

CAPABILITIES OF THE CENTER TYPE CYLINDRICAL GRINDER

Most common is **simple traverse grinding** (Figure 10). This may be done on interrupted surfaces (Figure 11) where the wheel should be thick enough to span two or more surfaces.

Multiple diameter form grinding (Figure 12) is a type of **plunge grinding** where the wheel may be **form dressed** to a desired shape. In **straight plunge grinding,** the wheel is brought into contact with the workpiece, but the workpiece is not traversed (Figure 13).

O.D. taper grinding (Figures 14 and 15) is done by swiveling the table. Steeper tapers may require that both table and wheelhead be swiveled in combination (Figure 16).

Angular shoulder grinding (Figure 17) and **angular plunge grinding** may require that the wheel be dressed at an appropriate angle (Figure 18).

Internal cylindrical grinding can be **straight** (Figure

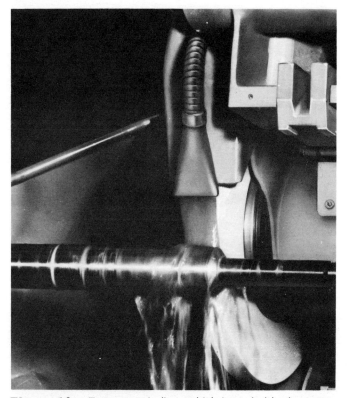

Figure 10. Traverse grinding, which is probably the most common type of cylindrical grinding (Courtesy of Cincinnati Milacron).

grinding job depends on this factor. Center holes in the workpiece are often precision ground to the correct geometry by a **center hole grinder** (Figure 7). **Location** of the center holes (Figure 8) and producing the **correct angle** (Figure 9) are **critical operations** in center hole grinding.

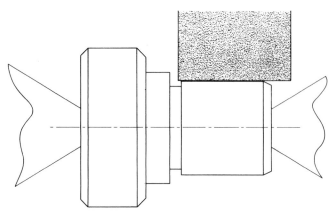

Figure 13. Straight plunge grinding, where the wheel is usually thicker than the length of the workpiece, except where the intent is to take a series of overlapping plunge cuts across a longer piece and finish with several traverses along the entire length (Courtesy of Cincinnati Milacron).

Figure 14. O.D. taper grinding, which may be done to produce a tapered finished workpiece or to straighten up a rough piece that was previously tapered (Courtesy of Cincinnati Milacron).

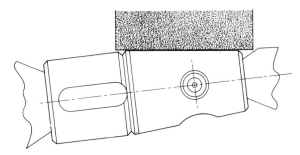

Figure 15. Taper grinding with the workpiece swiveled to the desired angle. For a steeper taper, the wheel might also have to be dressed at an angle less than 90 degrees (Courtesy of Cincinnati Milacron).

Figure 16. Steep taper grinding. Here the wheelhead has been swiveled to grind the workpiece taper (Courtesy of Cincinnati Milacron).

Figure 17. Angular-shoulder grinding. This is very often a production type operation, but it is shown here on a universal grinder (Courtesy of Cincinnati Milacron).

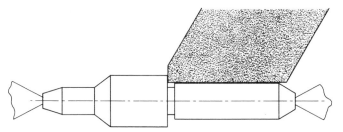

Figure 18. Angular plunge grinding with shoulder grinding. Note the dressing of the grinding wheel (Courtesy of Cincinnati Milacron).

Figure 19. Internal grinding, which requires a special high speed attachment that is mounted on the wheelhead so that it can be swung up out of the way when not in use. It also requires either a chuck or a face plate on the headstock (Courtesy of Cincinnati Milacron).

Figure 21. Backrest or steadyrest used to support a thin piece for grinding. If only one is used, as here, it is in the center of the workpiece. If more are used, it is always an odd number, and they are equally spaced along the workpiece (Courtesy of Cincinnati Milacron).

19) or **tapered** (Figure 20). The workpiece is held in a chuck or fixture so that the inside diameter can be accessed by the grinding wheel.

ACCESSORIES FOR CENTER TYPE GRINDERS

Accessories for center type cylindrical grinders include the **high speed internal attachment, headstock chucks, dressers,** and the **back** or **steady rest** for grinding slender workpieces (Figure 21).

Figure 20. I.D. taper grinding. This is the same sort of operation as shown in Figure 19, but with the workpiece swiveled at the required angle (Courtesy of Cincinnati Milacron).

SELF-TEST

1. Describe the basic principle of cylindrical grinding.
2. Describe two methods by which tapers may be ground.
3. What is the fundamental method of workholding on the center type grinder?
4. List the major movements on the universal center grinder.
5. How are workpiece center holes prepared and why are they important?

UNIT 9 USING THE CYLINDRICAL GRINDER

Using the cylindrical grinder involves many of the same steps that you learned in surface grinding. The cylindrical grinder is a versatile and precision machine tool. Used correctly, it will finish machine your workpiece to a high degree of dimensional accuracy. The purpose of this unit is to familiarize you with the preparation of the machine and the grinding process required to finish machine a typical cylindrical grinding project.

OBJECTIVES

After completing this unit, you should be able to:
1. Prepare the cylindrical grinder for a typical grinding job.
2. Finish grind a lathe mandrel to required specifications.

CYLINDRICAL GRINDING A LATHE MANDREL

A **lathe mandrel** is a common and useful machine shop tool. Precision mandrels are finished by cylindrical grinding after they have been rough machined and heat treated. Finish grinding the mandrel will provide you with a well-rounded experience in cylindrical grinding. Refer to a working drawing (Figure 1) to determine the required dimensions.

Selecting the Wheel

For a steel mandrel, the best abrasive will be aluminum oxide of 54 to 60 grit and a K, L, or M grade, and a somewhat dense structure.

Grinding Machine Setup

1. Set up the diamond dresser (Figure 2). Use the footstock center for height reference.
2. Dress the wheel with coolant. Use a rapid feed so that the wheel will dress for stock removal (Figure 3).
3. Place a parallel test bar between centers (Figure 4). Mount a dial indicator on the wheelhead, and set to zero at one end of the test bar.
4. Move the table 12 inches and read the indicator at the other end of the bar. The indicator should read .003 or a total of **.006 in. per foot** of taper (Figure 5).
5. Adjust swivel table to obtain correct amount of taper (Figure 6).
6. **Lubricate** the center hole in each end of the mandrel.
7. Place the dog on the mandrel and insert it between

Figure 2. Setting up the diamond for wheel dressing (Lane Community College).

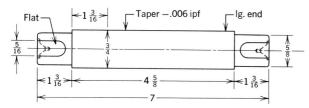

Figure 1. Sketch of tapered lathe mandrel.

Figure 3. Dressing the wheel with the coolant on (Lane Community College).

Figure 6. Adjusting the swivel table (Lane Community College).

Figure 4. Setting up the parallel test bar (Lane Community College).

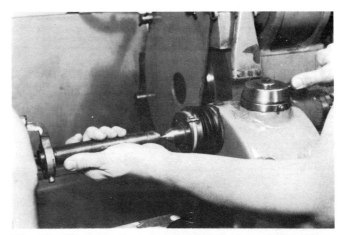

Figure 7. Clamping the footstock (Lane Community College).

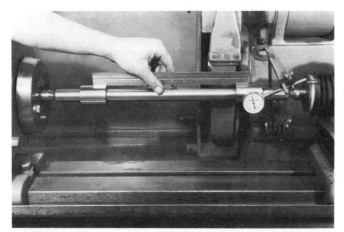

Figure 5. Second reading of the dial indicator (Lane Community College).

Figure 8. Checking the work dog clearance and drive pin contact (Lane Community College).

the head stock and footstock centers. Move the footstock up so that some tension is on the footstock center (Figure 7).

8. The dog must be free to turn and contact the drive pin (Figure 8).
9. The wheel must travel beyond the end of the work-

Figure 9. Adjusting the wheel overrun (Lane Community College).

Figure 10. Turning on the wheel (Lane Community College).

piece a distance equal to about one-third of the wheel thickness. This will insure that the ends of the mandrel are ground. Adjust stops to accommodate overtravel (Figure 9). Be sure that the wheel clears the dog.

Mandrel Grinding Procedure

1. Move the wheel close to the small end of the workpiece. You may use a feeler gage to position the wheel very close to the mandrel.

2. Turn on the wheel and headstock spindle. Adjust the workspeed.

3. Infeed wheel until it contacts the rotating mandrel. Sparks will begin to show (Figure 10).

4. Turn on coolant and table feed. Table traverse rate should be about **one-half** to **two-thirds** of the **wheel width** for each revolution of the workpiece.

5. Clean up grind two bands 4 inches apart at the same

Figure 11. Confirming taper (Lane Community College).

Figure 12. Measuring taper four inches down the part (Lane Community College).

infeed setting of the wheel. Stop machine and measure the diameters of the workpiece at these points to determine if the taper is correct. The difference should be .004. Adjust swivel table if necessary (Figures 11 and 12).

6. Rough and finish grind the mandrel to final size. The grinder may have an automatic infeed stop that will stop the infeed when final diameter is reached. On a manual machine, set infeed depth at about .001 to .002 per pass. **Remember that the diameter will be reduced by twice this amount (.002 to .004 in.)** The final pass should be about .0002, reducing the diameter by .0004 (Figure 13).

7. Check taper and diameter periodically. **Table traverse rate for finish pass should not exceed $\frac{1}{2}$ in. per revolution of the workpiece.** The grinding wheel may also wear to the extent that optimum SFPM will be affected. It may become necessary to reduce work speed to maintain the surface feet per minute rate that will produce an·acceptable result (Figure 14).

Figure 13. Grinding the mandrel to size (Lane Community College).

Figure 14. The finished mandrel (Lane Community College).

SELF-TEST

Your instructor will assign you a center type grinding project similar to the one you have just studied, which will involve setting up the machine from scratch, perhaps setting and checking a taper, starting up the grinder, and roughing and finishing the workpiece.

UNIT 10 UNIVERSAL TOOL AND CUTTER GRINDER

By now, you are well aware of the variety of cutting tools used in the machine shop. Like any cutting tools these become dull or occasionally broken during normal use. No production machine shop could function at peak efficiency unless it can keep all of its cutting tools sharp. The cutter and tool grinder is an essential tool for this purpose. In a large machine shop several cutter and tool grinders will be kept continuously busy sharpening and reconditioning a variety of cutting tools. At least one tool and cutter grinder is almost essential to any machine shop that expects its machinists to turn out quality work.

The operation of the cutter and tool grinder in a large machine shop is often delegated to specialists in tool grinding. These individuals may be assigned to the shop's tool making and tool grinding department. Even though tool grinding is a somewhat specialized area of machining, any well-rounded machinist should be familiar with the machines and processes used.

OBJECTIVES

After completing this unit, you should be able to:
1. Identify a cutter and tool grinder.
2. Briefly describe the function of this machine tool.
3. Under guidance from your instructor, sharpen common cutting tools.

The **tool and cutter grinder** is constructed much like a center type cylindrical grinder (Figure 1). It has the additional ability to swivel and tilt the wheelhead in two axes. This grinding machine may have a powered table traverse (Figure 2) and a power driven workhead, making possible cylindrical grinding.

CUTTER SHARPENING

The major application of the tool and cutter grinder is in **sharpening rotary milling cutters of all types.** Cutter sharpening requires an understanding of milling cutters and the grinding machine setups required to correctly produce cutting edge geometry.

Primary and Secondary Clearance Angles

In order to cut, a milling cutter must have **clearance** behind its cutting edge. The required clearance actually consists of **two angles** forming the **primary and secondary clearances.**

The surface immediately behind the cutting edge is called the **land.** The **angle** formed by the **land** and a **line tangent to the cutter at the tooth** tip creates the **primary clearance** (Figure 3). The **angle** between the **back of the land** and the **heel of the tooth** forms the **secondary clearance.**

Primary clearance is extremely important to the performance and life of a milling cutter. If this clearance is excessive, the cutting edge will be insufficiently supported and will chip from the pressure of the cut (Figure 4).

Primary and secondary clearance angles for cutters machining various materials are detailed in Table 1. When a milling cutter is sharpened, the **primary clearance is ground first.** The **secondary clearance is ground second** so that the width of the land may be brought to the recommended width. Land width will vary depending on the cutter diameter.

Measuring Clearance Angles

Two common methods are used to determine the clearance angle of a milling cutter. The **indicator drop**

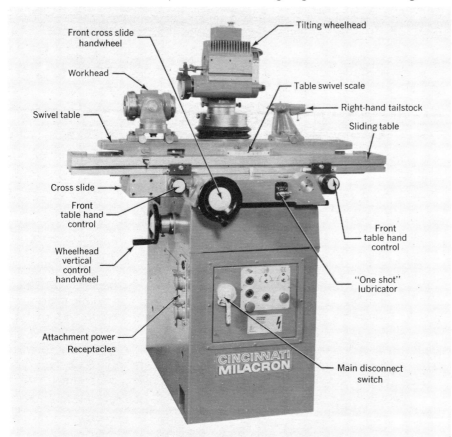

Labels: Front cross slide handwheel, Workhead, Swivel table, Cross slide, Front table hand control, Wheelhead vertical control handwheel, Attachment power Receptacles, Tilting wheelhead, Table swivel scale, Right-hand tailstock, Sliding table, Front table hand control, "One shot" lubricator, Main disconnect switch, CINCINNATI MILACRON

Figure 1. Components of the cutter and tool grinder (Courtesy of Cincinnati Milacron).

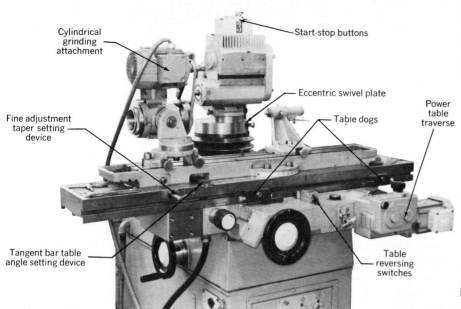

Cylindrical grinding attachment

Start-stop buttons

Eccentric swivel plate

Fine adjustment taper setting device

Table dogs

Power table traverse

Tangent bar table angle setting device

Table reversing switches

Figure 2. Cutter and tool grinder equipped with power table traverse and with a cylindrical grinding attachment mounted on the workhead (Industrial Plastics Products, Inc.).

Figure 4. This cutter was weakened by incorrect excessive clearance.

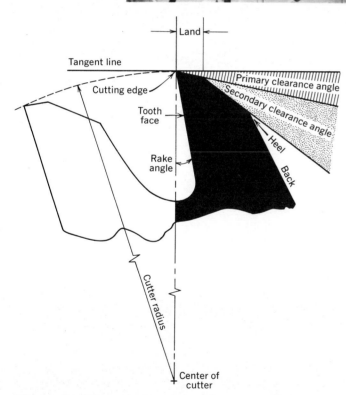

Land

Tangent line

Cutting edge

Tooth face

Rake angle

Primary clearance angle

Secondary clearance angle

Heel

Back

Cutter radius

Center of cutter

Figure 3. Primary and secondary clearance angles.

Table 1

Primary and Secondary Clearance Angles Suggested for High Speed Steel Cutters

Material	Primary Clearance (deg.)	Secondary Clearance (deg.)
Carbon steels	3–5	8–10
Gray cast iron	4–7	9–12
Bronze	4–7	7–12
Brasses and other copper alloys	5–8	10–13
Stainless steels	5–7	11–15
Titanium	8–12	14–18
Aluminum and magnesium alloys	10–12	15–17

method (Figure 5) uses a dial test indicator to measure the difference in height across the width of the land (Figure 6). This amount is expressed in terms of the angle formed by primary clearance (Table 2).

The **cutter clearance gage** (Figure 7) is somewhat more convenient as clearance angles can be measured directly in degrees.

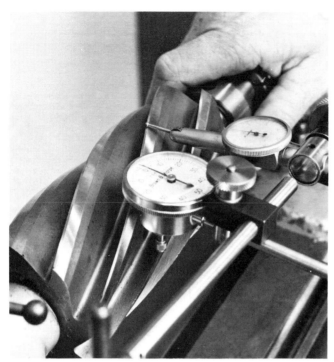

Figure 5. Setting up indicator for the indicator drop method of checking clearances (Lane Community College).

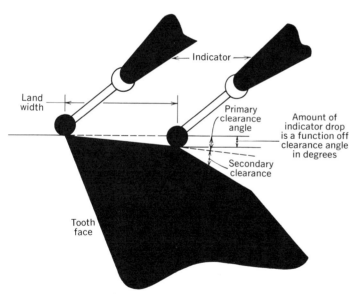

Figure 6. Measuring primary clearance by indicator drop.

Wheel Styles for Cutter Sharpening

Milling cutters may be sharpened with a **flaring cup wheel** or **straight wheel**. The flaring cup wheel will produce a **flat land** (Figure 8). A straight wheel will produce a **slight hollow grind** behind the cutting edge with curvature dependent on the diameter of the grinding wheel used. Form relieved cutters are sharpened with a **shallow dish** wheel.

Table 2
Indicator Drop Method of Determining Primary Clearance Angles

Diameter of Cutter (in.)	Average Range of Primary Clearance (deg.)	Indicator Drop for Range of Primary Clearance Shown		Radial Movement for Checking
		Minimum	Maximum	
$\frac{1}{16}$	20–25	.0018	.0027	.010
$\frac{1}{8}$	15–19	.0021	.0032	.015
$\frac{3}{16}$	12–16	.0020	.0034	.020
$\frac{1}{4}$	10–14	.0019	.0033	.020
$\frac{5}{16}$	10–13	.0020	.0033	.020
$\frac{7}{16}$	9–12	.0025	.0038	.025
$\frac{1}{2}$	9–12	.0027	.0040	.025
$\frac{5}{8}$	8–11	.0028	.0045	$\frac{1}{32}$
$\frac{7}{8}$	8–11	.0033	.0049	$\frac{1}{32}$
1	7–10	.0028	.0045	$\frac{1}{32}$
$1\frac{1}{4}$	6–9	.0025	.0042	$\frac{1}{32}$
$1\frac{1}{2}$	6–9	.0026	.0043	$\frac{1}{32}$
$1\frac{3}{4}$	6–9	.0027	.0044	$\frac{1}{32}$
2	6–9	.0028	.0045	$\frac{1}{32}$
$2\frac{1}{2}$	5–8	.0024	.0040	$\frac{1}{32}$
3	5–8	.0024	.0041	$\frac{1}{32}$
4	5–8	.0025	.0042	$\frac{1}{32}$
5	4–7	.0020	.0037	$\frac{1}{32}$
6	4–7	.0021	.0037	$\frac{1}{32}$
8	4–7	.0021	.0037	$\frac{1}{32}$

Workholding

Arbor driven milling cutters are held on a **grinding arbor** for sharpening (Figure 9). An expanding bushing arbor may also be used (Figure 10). **Shank cutters** like end mills are held in an **accessory spindle** or the **universal workhead**.

Toothrests

Since the cutter is free to turn on the grinding arbor, a provision must be made so that each tooth to be sharpened can be solidly rested. The **toothrest** is used for this purpose. Types of toothrests include the **plain design** (Figure 11) and the **micrometer adjustable type** (Figure 12). Various designs of toothrest **blades** are used (Figure 13) depending on the type of cutter to be sharpened. An **offset toothrest** is used for helical milling cutters (Figure 14).

Setting Up the Grinding Machine for Cutter Sharpening

The **centers** (Figure 15) are mounted on the swivel table so that they will accommodate the length of the cutter

Figure 7. Checking the primary relief of a stagger tooth milling cutter with a Starrett Cutter clearance gage (K & M Tool, Inc.).

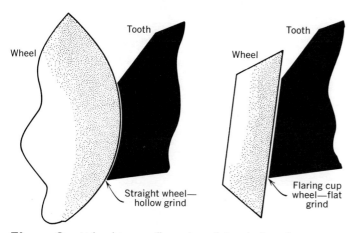

Figure 8. Wheel type will produce flat or hollow form.

Wheel — Tooth — Straight wheel—hollow grind

Wheel — Tooth — Flaring cup wheel—flat grind

Figure 9. Slitting saw being mounted on grinding arbor (Lane Community College).

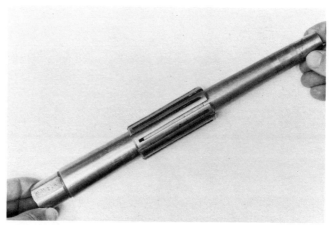

Figure 10. Adjustable grinding mandrel. The slotted bushing is moved along the mandrel to adjust for the I.D. of the tool to be mounted (Lane Community College).

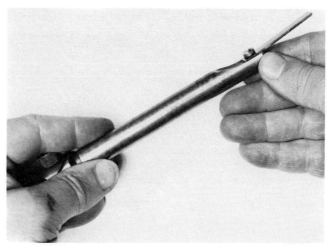

Figure 11. Plain type toothrest support (Lane Community College).

Figure 12. Micrometer type toothrest support. This example also has provision for spring loading of the finger to permit ratcheting of the cutter tooth, called a **flicker finger.**

Figure 15. Tailstock centers are basic to a large portion of cutter grinding (Industrial Plastics Products, Inc.).

Figure 13. Various designs of toothrest blades (Lane Community College).

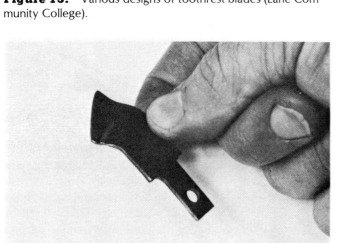

Figure 14. Offset toothrest blade for use in grinding helical milling cutters.

Figure 16. After checking the grinding arbor for runout on the centers at each end, the bezel should be zeroed and table alignment checked (Lane Community College).

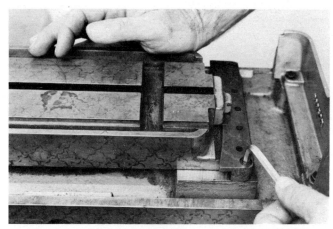

Figure 17. Adjusting and locking the swivel table in alignment (Lane Community College).

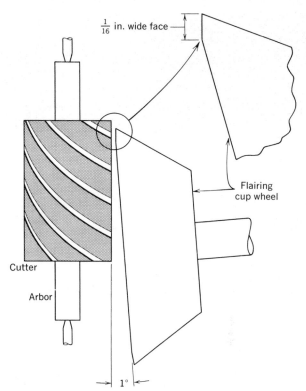

Figure 18. Wheel set at 1 degree to cutter and dressed to narrow land.

arbor. One center is spring loaded to facilitate installation and removal of the cutter arbor.

The arbor must be checked for **runout** and the table must be **aligned paralled** with the wheel head. Attach a dial indicator to the wheelhead (Figure 16) and use a parallel grinding arbor or test bar held between centers to determine table alignment. Make the necessary adjustments and lock the table in place (Figure 17).

CUTTER SHARPENING

Establishing Clearance Angles

The type of cutter to be sharpened will determine where the toothrest is to be mounted. For a straight tooth cutter such as a slitting saw, the toothrest will be mounted on the grinder table. When sharpening this type of cutter is is only necessary to rest each tooth solidly against the toothrest blade.

Since the toothrest is mounted to the table, clearance angles are established by **raising** the wheelhead above the center of the cutter. This will cause the grinding to occur back of the cutting edge thus establishing the correct clearance angle. The amount to raise the wheelhead (W_r) is calculated by the following formula:

$$W_r = \text{(sin of clearance angle) (radius of grinding wheel)}$$

Helical cutters, because of their helix angle, must be rotated during grinding so that each point on the tooth is presented to the grinding wheel. It would not be possible to rotate the cutter if the toothrest were mounted on the table. However, by mounting the toothrest on the wheelhead, the cutter tooth may be constantly kept in contact with the toothrest blade as the cutter rotates through its helix.

The clearance angle is established by **lowering** the wheelhead. This causes the toothrest to lower also and causes the cutter tooth to be rotated below cutter centerline. The grinding then occurs back of the cutting edge with the correct clearance angle. The amount to lower the wheel head (W_l) is calculated by the following formula:

$$W_l = \text{(sin of clearance angle) (radius of cutter)}$$

Flat Grinding a Plain Helical Milling Cutter

The following procedure may be used to sharpen a plain helical milling cutter.

1. Align the table.
2. Attach toothrest to wheelhead.
3. Set wheelhead at 89 degrees or so that the face of the flaring cup wheel will be set at a 1 degree angle to the cutter. Dress the wheel to a one-sixteenth in. wide face. This will insure that only the edge of the wheel will contact the cutter (Figure 18).
4. Lubricate the arbor centers and install arbor between centers.
5. Use the center gage and position grinder centers, wheel, and toothrest to the same height (Figure 19).
6. Rotate cutter firmly against the toothrest and recheck center height. Adjust if necessary (Figure 20).

Figure 19. Use the center gage to set wheel and toothrest blade height (Lane Community College).

Figure 20. Recheck tooth level and adjust toothrest blade to level if necessary (Lane Community College).

7. Calculate required wheelhead drop to determine primary clearance.
8. Lower wheelhead by this amount.
9. Approach the cutter carefully and grind a narrow land. Hold the cutter firmly against the toothrest as the table moves (Figure 21). Note the cross slide reading.
10. Move wheel back and rotate the cutter 180 degrees.
11. Approach cutter and grind according to the **same cross slide** setting noted in step 9.

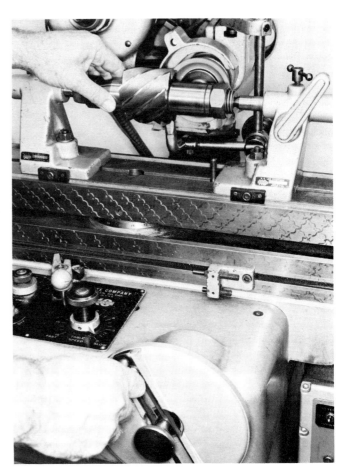

Figure 21. Make the grinding passes (Lane Community College).

Figure 22. The completed grind should have this appearance (K & M Tool, Inc.).

12. Measure cutter for taper with a micrometer. Correct table alignment and arbor runout if necessary. Taper should not exceed .001 in.
13. Grind all remaining teeth to a **spark-out condition** (Figure 22). Spark-out is when no more sparks are

Figure 23. Traverse the table while maintaining cutter contact with the support finger (K & M Tool, Inc.).

Figure 24. Grinding the primary relief (K & M Tool, Inc.).

visible from the wheel after grinding at a given setting.

14. Reset for secondary clearance.
15. Grind the secondary clearance.
16. Check the clearances by indicator drop or clearance gage.

Hollow Grinding a Plain Helical Mill

A straight wheel will produce the hollow grind form. The larger the wheel diameter, the less hollow will be ground. The same procedure will be used for setup as described in flat grinding. The wheel will be positioned perpendicular to the cutter (Figure 23). Since the toothrest is attached to the wheelhead, it will be necessary to lower the wheel to obtain the primary and secondary clearance.

Sharpening a Slitting Saw

For sharpening slitting saws, the toothrest is mounted on the swivel table since it is only necessary to hold the cutter in firm contact. Rotation of the cutter during the

grinding process is not necessary as it was for helical cutters. A **flicker type** toothrest is very useful in this operation. After one tooth is ground, the cutter is turned and the toothrest snaps aside indexing for the next tooth (Figure 24).

Stagger Tooth Cutters

The stagger tooth cutter is a helical cutter with the helix angle alternating direction on each tooth. The toothrest must be mounted on the wheelhead and must be **carefully centered** (Figure 25) so that the **primary clearance on each opposing helix will be concentric** (Figure 26).

An additional procedure is required to grind the side teeth of a stagger tooth cutter. Primary and secondary clearance are obtained by tilting the wheelhead (Figure 27).

Form Relieved Cutters

Form relieved cutters are designed to machine a specific form on the workpiece. Included in these are involute gear cutters, convex and concave milling cutters. **Form cutters are sharpened only on the face of the tooth** (Fig-

Figure 25. Grinding two successive teeth to check for centering of the toothrest (K & M Tool, Inc.).

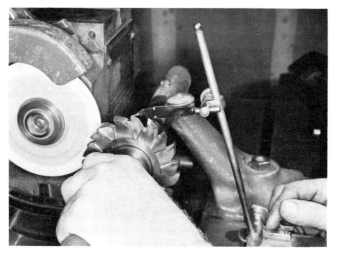

Figure 26. Checking for concentricity on the two teeth of opposite helix (K & M Tool, Inc.).

Figure 27. The workhead is given additional tilt to provide for secondary clearance (K & M Tool, Inc.).

Figure 28. The wheel is positioned relative to the face of the tooth (K & M Tool, Inc.).

ure 28) in order that the particular geometry be maintained. The grinding wheel must be properly dressed and positioned relative to the face of the tooth.

End Mills

End mills require sharpening both on the **side and end.** They may be held in a free turning **accessory spindle.** The spindle may be floated in an air bearing providing a high degree of concentricity and friction free movement. The accessory spindle can also be tilted away from the grinding wheel to facilitate the grinding procedure (Figure 29).

Grinding the primary and secondary clearances on the side of an end mill is much the same procedure as any plain helical cutter. Primary and secondary angles are specified in Table 3. The best practice is to sharpen from the shank end toward the tip (Figure 30). The toothrest will be mounted on the wheelhead and the wheelhead will be lowered to provide the proper clearances (Figure 31).

End Sharpening with the Universal Workhead.
The end of an end mill may be sharpened by using the **universal workhead.** If the end of the cutter has been damaged, it must be first cut off (Figure 32). The

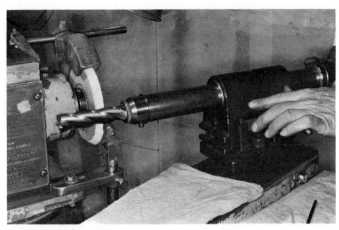

Figure 29. The fixture is rocked away from the wheel and the cutter is moved forward (K & M Tool, Inc.).

Table 3
Primary Clearance Angles for High Speed Steel End Mills

Workpiece Material	End Mill Diameter (in.)							
	$\frac{1}{8}$	$\frac{1}{4}$	$\frac{3}{8}$	$\frac{1}{2}$	$\frac{3}{4}$	1	$1\frac{1}{2}$	2
Carbon steels[a]	16°	12°	11°	10°	9°	8°	7°	6°
Nonferrous metals	19°	15°	13°	13°	12°	10°	8°	7°

[a] For tool steels, decrease indicated values about 20 percent. For secondary clearance angle, increase value by about $\frac{1}{3}$.

Figure 30. Passes are made with additional infeed until the primary relief is complete (K & M Tool, Inc.).

workhead spindle is tilted (Figure 33) to obtain the proper primary and secondary clearance (Figure 34).

Center Gashing. Center gashing is necessary to permit a center cutting end mill to make its own starting hole. A straight wheel is dressed to a sharp beveled edge. The cutter is then **gashed** (Figure 35) to center.

Figure 31. Correct appearance of the completed side grinding of the end mill (K & M Tool, Inc.).

Figure 32. Cutting off the damaged end (K & M Tool, Inc.).

After grinding each tooth, burrs may be removed with a suitable stone (Figure 36).

It should be noted that the gashing techniques shown present a **significant hazard**. The cutter is hand held with **fingers close to the high speed wheel.** Wrapping a cutter in a **rag also presents** a significant hazard near the revolving equipment. **You must be extremely careful if you are gashing end mills by this technique.** Until you become experienced, **ask your instructor for help** in performing this cutter grinding operation.

ADDITIONAL CAPABILITIES OF THE TOOL AND CUTTER GRINDER

Additional capabilities of this machine include sharpening of **reamers, taps, drills,** and **single point cutting tools.** The power driven workhead permits **cylindrical grinding** (Figure 37). The workpiece may be held in a **three jaw chuck** or **magnetic grinder chuck** (Figures 38 and 39).

Figure 33. Grinding the secondary clearance (K & M Tool, Inc.).

Figure 34. Appearance of the completed end grinding of the end mill.

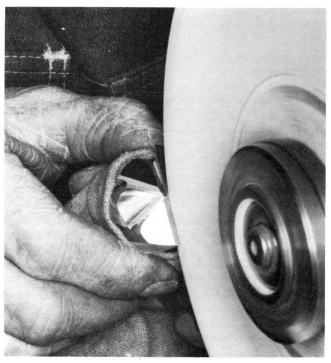

Figure 35. Grinding across the face of the tooth to center (K & M Tool, Inc.).

Figure 36. Remove the burrs. Note the completed appearance (K & M Tool, Inc.).

The **internal grinding attachment** permits **internal cylindrical grinding** (Figure 40). The swiveling capability of the workhead permits regrinding of **lathe centers** (Figure 41).

Figure 37.   Resizing the pilot portion of the counterbore by cylindrical grinding (Industrial Plastics Products, Inc.).

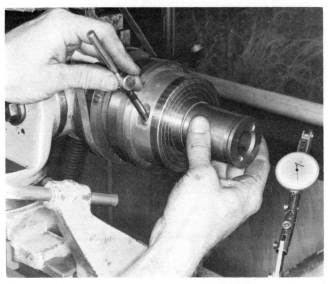

Figure 39.   A permanent magnet chuck is also very useful for cylindrical grinding (Industrial Plastics Products, Inc.).

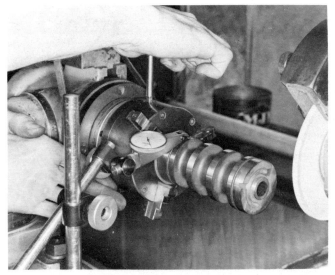

Figure 38.   Cylindrical grinding attachment being used with adjustable scroll chuck to set up part for cylindrical grinding (Industrial Plastics Products, Inc.).

Figure 40.   Internal grinding attachment set up for use with a mounted grinding wheel. Only the forward portion of the wheel is used; the rest is dressed away for clearance (Industrial Plastics Products, Inc.).

SELF-TEST

If your shop has a tool and cutter grinder, identify the major parts of the machine. Operate and familiarize yourself with the controls. Under guidance from your instructor, set up and sharpen common milling cutters.

Figure 41.   Another use for the cylindrical grinding attachment is the reconditioning of centers (Industrial Plastics Products, Inc.).

SECTION O
ADVANCED MACHINING PROCESSES

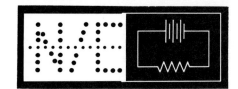

As the hardware of an advanced technology becomes more complex, new and visionary approaches to the processing of materials into useful products come into common use. This has been the trend in machining processes in recent years. Advanced methods of machine control as well as completely different methods of shaping materials have permitted the mechanical designer to proceed in directions that would have been totally impossible only a few years ago.

Parallel development in other technologies such as **electronics** and **computers** have made available to the machine tool designer methods and processes that can permit a machine tool to far exceed the capabilities of the most experienced machinist. Since these advanced technologies are constantly changing and expanding, the purpose of this section is to provide only an overview of two major areas:

1. **Numerical control of machine tools.**
2. **Electrical machining processes.**

As you proceed into further training and possibly to a career in machining, you may wish to concentrate your studies in these areas and specialize in them. Whatever path you might choose to follow, the fundamental knowledge and experience you have gained by studying the material presented in this text will prove to be invaluable.

PART 1 NUMERICAL CONTROL OF MACHINE TOOLS

Numerical control of machine tools is of major importance in modern machining technology. With numerical control **(N/C),** machining productivity is increased. This is an important consideration in an age where manufacturing is faced with rising costs. The N/C machine tool is helping to keep production costs down. Manufacturers have seen the value and versatility of these machines. They are appearing in machine shops of every size. Numerical control can be productively applied to almost any machining task. An individual beginning machinist training today does so in a numerical control environment.

As you begin a career in machining, N/C will play an ever increasing part. The field of N/C machining technology is constantly expanding. What was new in numerical control only a short time ago is becoming rapidly obsolete. The future of N/C today is solid, and in the future will present many areas for specialized study.

MACHINE CONTROL BY NUMERICAL INSTRUCTIONS

Numerical control is a method and a system of controlling a machine or process by instructions in the form of numbers. On a manually operated machine tool, the operator turns cranks in order to move milling machine tables or lathe cross slides and carriages. On the N/C machine tool, cranks are replaced by drive motors or hydraulic mechanisms. These are controlled from an external **machine control unit (MCU).**

Machine control functions previously provided by the operator are translated into **numeric instructions** that can be understood by the machine control unit. These control functions include **positioning tables** and **spindles, setting milling feedrates, setting spindle speeds, cycling drill press quills, changing cutting tools, and turning coolant on and off.**

N/C MACHINE TOOLS AND MACHINING CENTERS

A numerical control system can be added to an existing machine tool (Figure 1). This is called a **retrofit** and presents a less expensive way to gain N/C capability in the machine shop.

The many advantages of N/C have brought about extensive development of machine tools designed specifically for N/C operations. In conventional machining, a complex workpiece may have to be set up on several machine tools in order to complete all required machining tasks. The development of numerical control technology has brought about the concept of a **machining center** on which a wide variety of machining tasks can be accomplished on the same machine tool.

Vertical Spindle N/C Machining Centers

Vertical spindle N/C machining centers patterned after the vertical milling machine are very popular. The versatility of the vertical mill is mated to the advantages of numerical control. Vertical spindle machines may be equipped with an eight-position turret toolholder (Figure 2) or a drum or carousel toolholder containing many tools (Figure 3). Tool changing is numerically controlled. The vertical spindle design also includes large capacity multispindle milling machines such as the bridge type profiler (Figure 4) and the gantry type profiler (Figure 5). These machine tools permit several workpieces to be machined at the same time.

Horizontal Spindle N/C Machining Centers

Horizontal spindle N/C machining centers, patterned after the horizontal mill and horizontal boring machine, are also very popular and versatile. These machines may be equipped with side mounted tool carousels (Figure 6) or top mounted carousels (Figure 7). Tool changing is numerically controlled. The workpiece may be mounted on a rotary table, enabling both sides to be machined (Figure 8).

Large capacity horizontal spindle machines include the traveling column profiler (Figure 9). The machine tool shown is equipped with a conveyor system to remove chips. Horizontal multiple spindle profilers may be used to machine several workpieces at the same time (Figure 10).

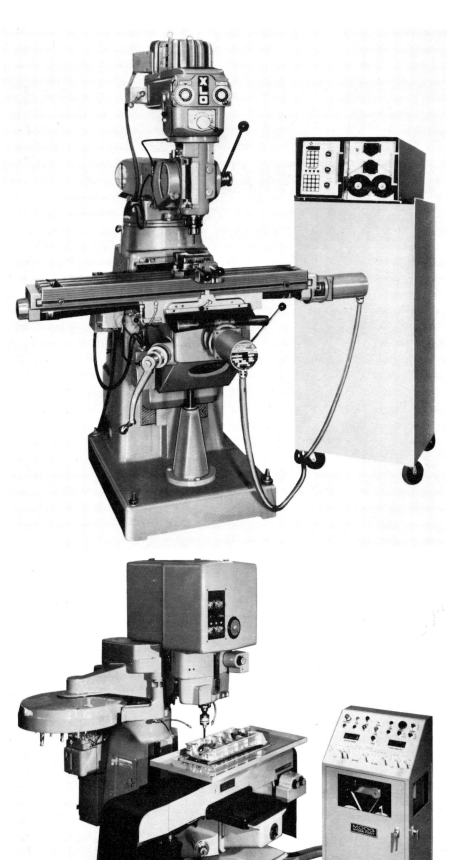

Figure 1. A numerical control system added to an existing milling machine (Courtesy of the Superior Electric Company).

Figure 2. Vertical spindle N/C milling machine with eight position turret toolholder (Courtesy of Cincinnati Milacron).

Figure 3. Vertical N/C milling machine with side mounted tool drum (Courtesy of Hydra-Point Division, Moog Inc.).

Figure 4. Bridge type multiple spindle N/C profiler (Courtesy of Cincinnati Milacron).

Figure 5. Gantry type multiple spindle N/C profiler (Courtesy of Cincinnati Milacron).

N/C Turning Centers

A sophisticated N/C lathe or turning center (Figure 11) may have numerically controlled turret toolholders for inside diameter turning (Figure 12). With the workpiece held in a chuck, a variety of cutting tools can be applied in the inside diameter turning loop (Figure 13). The outside diameter turret (Figure 14) operates in the outside diameter turning loop (Figure 15). Numerically controlled lathes are also used in shaft turning operations (Figure 16). The shaft turning loop requires use of a tailstock center (Figure 17).

ADVANTAGES OF NUMERICAL CONTROL MACHINING

Repeatability

The N/C machine tool can produce 1, 10, or 10,000 parts with unvarying accuracy. This is important to the production of duplicate parts that are within tolerance. A set of numeric instructions does not vary. The machine tool does not become fatigued or bored, as does the operator of its manually operated counterpart. The machine will repeat precisely during each machining

Figure 6. Horizontal spindle N/C machining center with side mounted tool drum (Courtesy of Cincinnati Milacron).

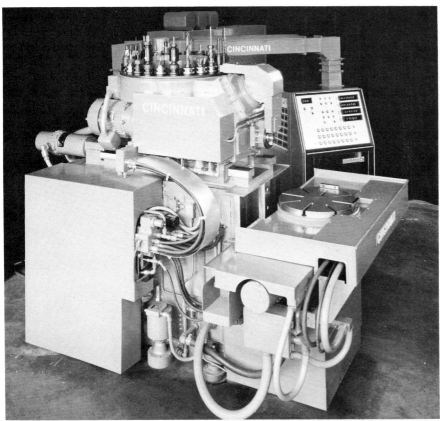

Figure 7. Horizontal spindle N/C machining center with top mounted tool drum (Courtesy of Cincinnati Milacron).

Figure 8. Rotary table on a horizontal spindle machining center (Courtesy of Cincinnati Milacron).

Figure 9. Traveling column N/C profiler with chip conveyor (Courtesy of Cincinnati Milacron).

Figure 10. Horizontal N/C profiler with three spindles (Courtesy of Cincinnati Milacron).

Figure 11. Dual turret N/C turning center (Courtesy of Cincinnati Milacron).

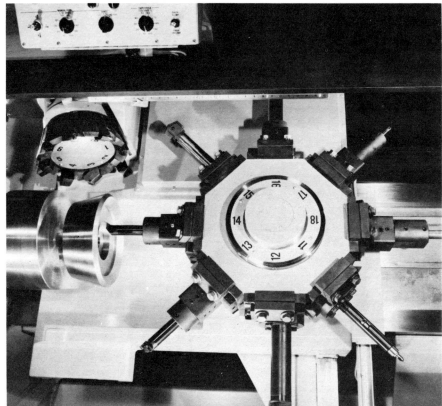

Figure 12. Inside and outside diameter N/C turning center turrets (Courtesy of Cincinnati Milacron).

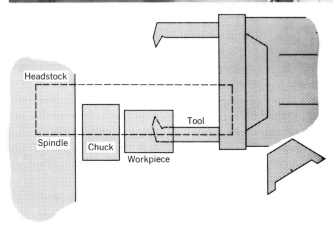

Figure 13. Inside diameter turning loop (Courtesy of Cincinnati Milacron).

Figure 14. Outside diameter turret on the N/C turning center (Courtesy of Cincinnati Milacron).

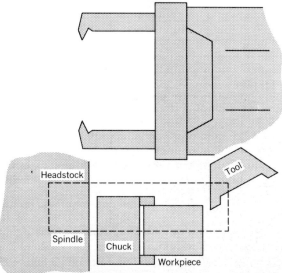

Figure 15. Outside diamter turning loop (Courtesy of Cincinnati Milacron).

Figure 16. Shaft turning on the N/C turning center (Courtesy of Cincinnati Milacron).

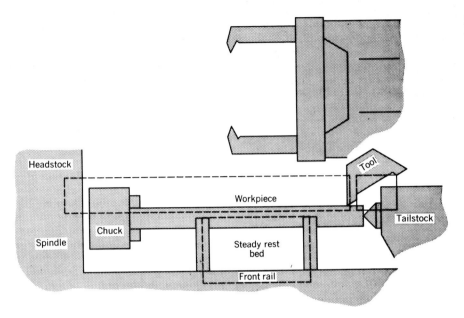

Figure 17. Shaft turning loop (Courtesy of Cincinnati Milacron).

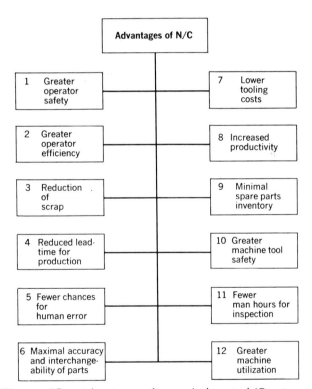

Figure 18. Advantages of numerical control (Courtesy of the Superior Electric Company).

cycle. Workpieces need only be removed and replaced with new stock. Except for downtime due to resharpening of cutting tools or routine maintenance, the N/C machine tool can function 24 hours a day, year round, if necessary. In this respect, it has a decided advantage over its manually controlled counterpart (Figure 18).

Versatility

The machining function of the N/C tool can easily be changed by inserting new programming. With computer control, N/C programs can be stored in computer memory and the machine tool can be operated directly. Tape N/C programs are permanent and can be stored for future use. A long production run can be stopped and a short run can be inserted. The machine tool can then be returned to its long run in a very short time.

Machining Capability

With the numerically controlled tool changer, the N/C machine tool or machining center can accomplish a wide variety of machining tasks. Tool changing may be a two-step operation where the drum is mounted on the side of the machine (Figure 19). The drum rotates the required tool into position, where it is pivoted down and grasped by the changing arm. The tool is then placed in the spindle (Figure 20). At the same time, the tool already in the spindle is returned to the pivot arm and replaced in the drum. Where the drum is on the top of the machine, the tool in the drum and the tool in the spindle are removed at the same time and exchanged (Figures 21a to 21d). Tools are secured in a self-releasing taper shank toolholder. The holder is secured in the machine by a locking mechanism contained within the spindle (Figure 22).

    Drilling (Figure 23) is a common N/C machining capability. Spindle speed, feedrate, and depth can be controlled from tape instructions. A **peck drilling** cycle can be used for deep hole or small hole drilling. When the peck drill cycle is initiated, the drill feeds part way

Figure 19. Pivoting presenter arm on a side mounted tool changer (Courtesy of Heald Machine Division/Cincinnati Milacron).

Figure 20. Tool changing arm (Courtesy of Heald Machine Division/Cincinnati Milacron).

into the workpiece, where it dwells for a short time. The drill is then automatically withdrawn in order to clear chips. The cycle is automatically repeated and the drill is permitted to feed further into the workpiece. The cycle continues until the final depth is reached. Dwell time during each **peck** can be varied manually.

Milling an enclosed feature or **pocket milling** (Figure 24) is another very common and useful machining capability. Spindle speed, milling feedrates, and direction and distance of the cuts are controlled from tape instructions.

Close tolerance boring (Figure 25) is frequently done on the N/C machine tool. Spindle speeds and bore feedrates are tape controlled. The boring bar may be withdrawn from the bore at the same feedrate used during boring. This reduces tool marks in the workpiece. Progressive boring bars may be used where close tolerances must be maintained. The hole is first bored with a roughing bar and finished with a finishing bar. Boring bars must be preset for correct diameter before they are used.

Tapping is another machining operation that is well suited to N/C operations. One method is leadscrew tapping (Figure 26). The leadscrew causes the machine spindle to feed or lead the same amount as the tap lead. Leadscrews are changed to correspond to different tap leads.

Probably the greatest machining capability of the N/C machine tool is that of **contouring or continuous path machining** (Figure 27). This includes circles, angles, and radius cuts, as well as irregular shapes in two or three dimensions. In fact, the N/C machine tool can produce shapes that would be quite impossible to machine by manual means. This capability has opened new avenues of study for the designer of mechanical hardware.

NUMERICAL CONTROL AND THE MACHINIST

The N/C machine tool, with its amazing capabilities, seldom requires a fully qualified machinist as an operator. In fact, the talent of the machinist would be wasted if time were spent changing workpieces on an N/C machine. Most N/C machine tools can be operated by a competent machine operator. However, the N/C operator has several important functions to perform (Figure 28). He must know the machine and its operating characteristics.

NUMERICAL CONTROL SYSTEMS

Closed Loop Systems

In a closed loop N/C system, a signal is fed back to the machine control unit confirming the specific instruction

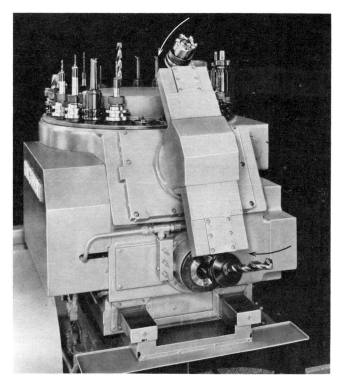

Figure 21. Tool changing sequence from a top mounted tool drum (Courtesy of Cincinnati Milacron).

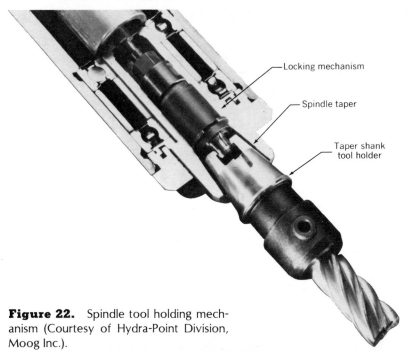

Locking mechanism

Spindle taper

Taper shank
tool holder

Figure 22. Spindle tool holding mechanism (Courtesy of Hydra-Point Division,
Moog Inc.).

Figure 25. N/C boring (Courtesy of Hydra-Point Division,
Moog Inc.).

Figure 23. N/C drilling (Courtesy of Hydra-Point Division,
Moog Inc.).

Figure 26. N/C leadscrew tapping (Courtesy of Hydra-
Point Division, Moog Inc.).

Figure 24. N/C pocket milling (Courtesy of Hydra-Point
Division, Moog Inc.).

Figure 27. Continuous path N/C machining (Yuba
College).

713

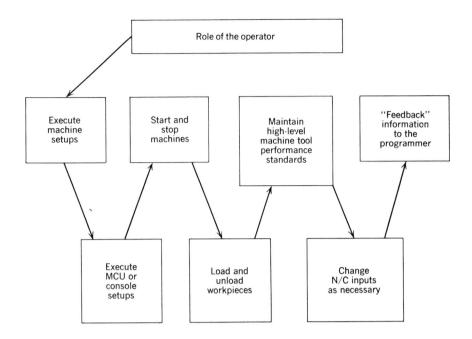

Figure 28. Role of the N/C machine tool operator (Courtesy of the Superior Electric Company).

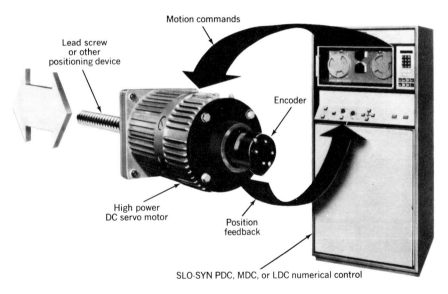

SLO-SYN PDC, MDC, or LDC numerical control

Figure 29. Closed loop N/C system (Courtesy of the Superior Electric Company).

(Figure 29). For example, if the MCU instructs a milling machine table to move 10 in., a signal would be fed back to the MCU from a sensor on the drive motor indicating that the table has moved the instructed distance. Closed loop provides the MCU with a check on the accuracy of machine movement.

Open Loop Systems

No feedback signal is used in an open loop N/C system. The open loop system may use an electric stepping motor to control the movement of machine components. The stepping motor is used on many numerical controls that are added to existing machine tools.

A stepping motor operates on a pulse of electric current supplied by the MCU. Each current pulse causes the motor rotor to turn or **step** a fraction of a revolution. When the motor is coupled to a mill table, lathe cross slide, or lathe leadscrew, it can act to move the screw specific amounts according to the number of pulses received from the MCU. Stepping motors are often designed to move machine tool tables a distance of .001 in. per pulse. They are reversible and can move a component in either direction.

NUMERICAL CONTROL AND THE COMPUTER

The computer is an important and valuable component of the modern numerical control system. The computer can do mathematics with great speed and accuracy. This

has made it a valuable tool in the N/C programming of complex machining operations. Mathematical computation necessary for continuous path machining would be difficult and time consuming if it had to be done by hand. The computer can accommodate this kind of calculation easily.

A computer can understand direct descriptions of workpiece geometry, machine control functions, and machining operations. This permits the N/C programmer to program much in the same way that he would verbally describe the machining task to be done. The computer can understand direct statements such as GO TO, MILL, DRILL, or BORE. These direct descriptions are translated by the computer into appropriate instructions for a specific N/C machine tool.

D N/C and C N/C

In **direct numerical control** or **D N/C,** central computers direct the operation of several N/C machines at the same time. Microelectronics has revolutionized computer technology such that individual N/C machine tools have their own self-contained **computer numerical controls,** or **C N/C.**

NUMERICAL CONTROL DIMENSIONING

The numerical control programmer studies a drawing of the workpiece and determines the direction and distance that the cutting tool must travel. The programmer then directs the machine movements along these paths by indicating the appropriate numerical instructions. In order to do this, the programmer must be able to define and identify the travel direction of a specific machine component. The programmer must also be able to differentiate travel directions of different machine components. This is the purpose of machine tool axis identifications and N/C dimensioning.

Machine Tool Axes
Basic Axes. The rectangular coordinate system consists of the two perpendicular axes of X and Y (Figure 30). The X and Y axes lie in the same plane and are known as coordinate axes. With the addition of a third axis, Z, that is perpendicular to the X-Y plane, a three-dimensional volume of space can be described and identified (Figure 31). The point at which the axes intersect is called the origin and has a numeric value of zero.

These notations are applied to N/C machine tools in order to identify the basic machine axes. The Z axis is always the spindle axis, even though the machine spindle may be horizontal or vertical. On a typical vertical spindle machine tool, such as a vertical mill, the spindle axis is Z. The X axis is the table and the Y axis is the saddle (Figure 32). The knee is in the Z axis.

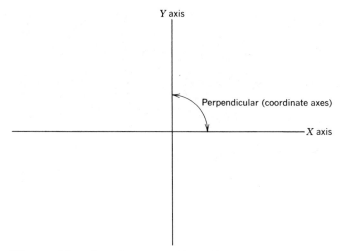

Figure 30. Coordinate axes X and Y.

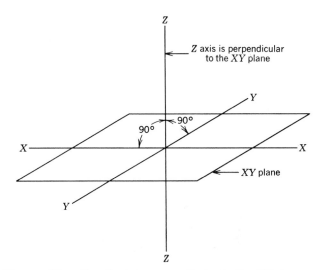

Figure 31. The Z axis is perpendicular to the XY plane.

On a horizontal spindle machine tool, Z remains the spindle axis while Y becomes vertical and X remains horizontal (Figure 33). The N/C lathe is also a horizontal spindle machine tool. The spindle axis is Z and the cross slide is X, or the horizontal axis perpendicular to Z (Figure 34). Since the lathe toolholder is not moved vertically, the Y axis is not used.

Rotational Axes. Rotational axes define numerically controlled motion around the X, Y, and Z basic axes. An N/C machine tool may have a rotary table or part indexer (Figure 35). These accessories may operate from tape instructions, rotationally around the basic axes. The direction of rotation, as well as the basic axes around which rotation occurs, must be identified. Rotational axes are identified as a, b, and c (Figure 36). Discussions about four and five axis N/C machine tools refer to the

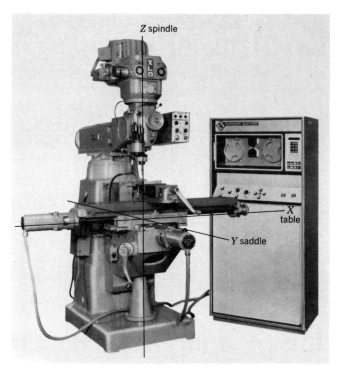

Figure 32. Basic axes of a vertical spindle N/C machine tool (Courtesy of the Superior Electric Company).

Figure 33. Basic axes of a horizontal spindle N/C machine tool (Courtesy of Cincinnati Milacron).

Figure 34. Basic axes of an N/C lathe (Courtesy of the Superior Electric Company).

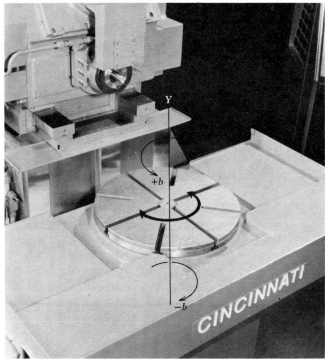

Figure 35. Rotational axis *b* defining rotary table motion (Courtesy of Cincinnati Milacron).

basic axes of *X, Y,* and *Z* and the rotational axes of *a, b,* and *c.*

Quadrants
The perpendicular coordinate axes *X* and *Y* form four quadrants (Figure 37). Quadrants are numbered in a counterclockwise direction beginning at the upper right. The point of axial intersection or origin has a numeric value of zero. All points to the right of zero along the *X* axis have positive value. All points to the left of zero have negative values. Points on the *Y* axis above zero are positive and points below zero are negative.

If the *X-Y* plane is horizontal, as it is on all vertical spindle machine tools, there is no geographic location of above and below zero. In this case, points from the origin away from you are positive, while points toward you from zero are negative.

Quadrant Point Values. Point values in the four quadrants are as follows.

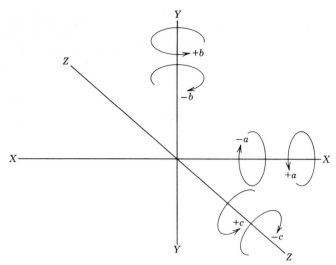

Figure 36. Rotational axes.

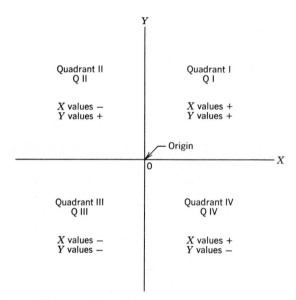

Figure 37. Quadrants formed by the X and Y coordinate axes.

Quadrant I: X positive, Y positive
Quadrant II: X negative, Y positive
Quadrant III: X negative, Y negative
Quadrant IV: X positive, Y negative

Directions of Machine Tool Spindle Travel

Understanding quadrant point values is important to the preparation of certain types of N/C tape instructions. The MCU must tell the machine tool spindle or worktable to move in a certain direction or to a specified location. This may be done by providing tape instructions that indicate positive and negative movement directions.

N/C programming is always done as if the tool were

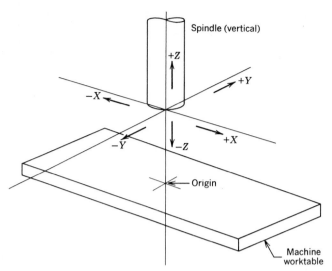

Figure 38. Directions of vertical spindle movement.

moving, even though the worktable is the moving component on a machine tool with a fixed spindle. The direction of spindle movement is expressed by noting its direction of travel along a specified axis (Figure 38). Spindle movement in the Z axis is also defined in terms of positive and negative directions. If the distance between the worktable and spindle is decreasing, the spindle is moving in a minus (−) Z direction. If the distance between worktable and spindle is increasing, the spindle is moving in a positive (+) Z direction.

Spindle Positioning by Incremental Measurement

Certain numerical control programs instruct the machine tool to position the spindle by incremental measurement. This means that the spindle measures the distance to its next location from the position at which it was last located. Incremental positioning requires positive and negative travel directions.

Example. A certain workpiece is to be drilled on an N/C machine tool positioning by incremental measurement. The workpiece is set up so that the spindle start point is over one corner and the edges of the part are parallel with the coordinate axes. The N/C program instructs the machine spindle to move in a +X direction a distance of 1 in. and in a +Y direction a distance of 4 in. (Figure 39). This will position the spindle over drilling location 1.

To reach the second location, the spindle moves in the +X direction an additional distance of 2 in. However, it must move in a −Y direction a distance of 1 in. to reach location 2. The machine uses location 1 as a new origin from which to measure its movement to location 2. After drilling is completed, it is desired to return the spindle to the start point. This requires a −X

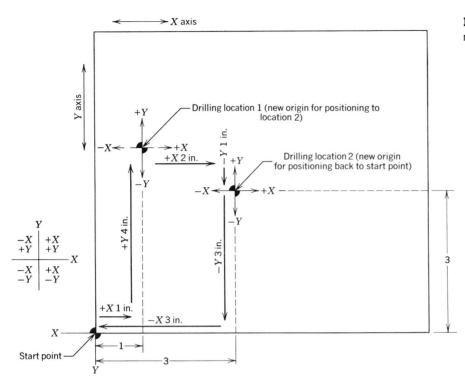

Figure 39. Positioning by incremental measurement.

move of 3 in. and a −Y move of 3 in. Once again, location 2 becomes a new origin from which to measure the distance back to the start point.

Spindle Positioning by Absolute or Coordinate Measurement

Other types of N/C machine tools position the spindle by absolute or coordinate measurement. Two systems are used.

With fixed zero absolute positioning, all measurements are taken from the same zero reference point located at the lower left corner of the workpiece or worktable. With fixed zero, the need for positive and negative moves is eliminated. For practical purposes, the spindle is always operating in Quadrant I, where all points have positive value. All points are specified as coordinate locations in terms of the distance from the coordinate axes.

Example. The same workpiece is to be drilled on a machine positioning by absolute measurement from fixed zero. Each drilling location is expressed as a dimension from the absolute zero point (Figure 40). Coordinate dimensions are measured parallel to the coordinate axes.

Drilling location 1 is at point (1X, 4Y) from zero. This is a coordinate location. Location 2 is at point (3X, 3Y) from zero. The N/C program instructs the spindle to position to coordinate location (1X, 4Y). After drilling the first hole, the spindle is instructed to position to location

2 at coordinate (3X, 3Y). Since this second location is measured from zero and not from the previous location, the machine positions to the new location without the need of movement in a negative direction. Return to the start point is accomplished by instructing the spindle to position to the coordinate location (0X, 0Y).

Some N/C machines permit any point to be established as absolute zero. This is known as **floating zero** and can be used to make certain programming easier.

Example. When drilling a symmetric pattern, it might be more convenient to start the program from a central location. Instead of starting the program over the corner of the part (Figure 41), the absolute zero point may be **floated** to a central location. Tool positioning to the hole locations is still done by specifying coordinate locations. However, holes are to be drilled in all four quadrants. This requires that positive and negative coordinate locations be specified.

When programming for an N/C machine using absolute positioning, drawing dimensions must be expressed in terms of absolute measure from an appropriate zero reference point.

Absolute positioning may be used on N/C machine tools that are designed to position with extreme accuracy. Many N/C machines can position their spindles or worktables within a few ten thousandths of an inch. Small errors that might be cumulative with incremental positioning do not pose a problem in absolute positioning.

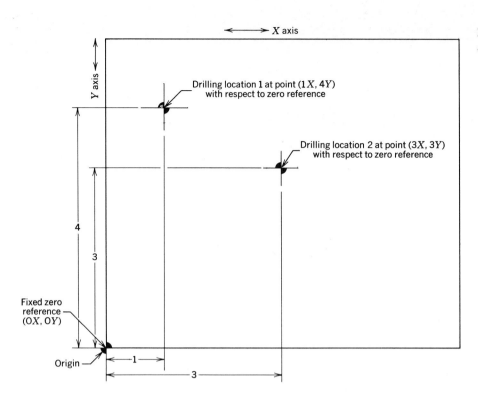

Figure 40. Positioning by fixed zero absolute or coordinate measurement.

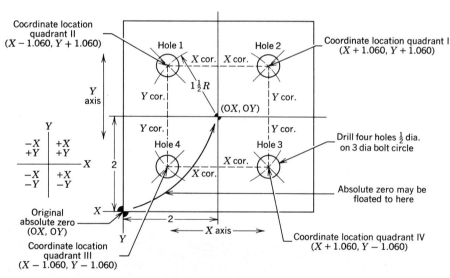

Figure 41. Positioning by floating zero absolute measurement.

N/C FROM PUNCHED TAPE

Once a control function has been translated into numeric form, the information must be provided to the machine tool. This can be done through a control medium such as punched cards, magnetic tape, or **punched tape.** Instructions are translated into numeric form and appear as specific patterns of holes punched into a tape. The tape is read by the tape reader in the machine control unit. The MCU then interprets the numerical information on the control tape and, through electric and mechanical means, controls components of the machine tool.

Punched tape has been a popular medium for communicating numeric instructions to a machine tool. It is likely that this method will be in use for some time even though the small computer is playing an ever increasing part in direct control of an N/C machine tool.

Tape Materials

N/C tape materials include paper or paper-plastic and aluminum-plastic laminates. Blank tape may be supplied in 1000 or 2000 ft. rolls, depending on thickness. The plastic and aluminum laminate materials are generally more durable than paper. They are more expensive, but

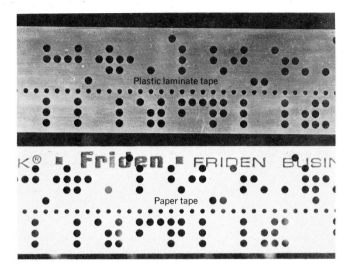

Figure 42.   Paper and plastic laminate tape materials.

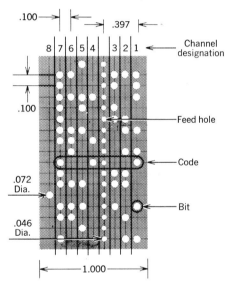

Figure 43.   Dimensions of N/C tape features (Courtesy of the Superior Electric Company).

they will withstand many trips through the tape reader without wear or damage. The plastic materials are also less subject to damage by oils and grease found around the machine and shop. Manufacturing tolerances are held closely (Figure 42) so that tape may be standardized between different manufacturers.

Paper tape is available in several different colors, including pink, yellow, and black. The color has no significance except that certain colors are more suitable for use in photoelectric tape readers. In these readers, light passes through the tape punches and activates photoelectric cells. A photoelectric tape reader using paper tape may require a black or dark color so that light will not pass through the tape material and activate improper photocells.

Figure 44.   Typewriter tape punch (California State University at Fresno).

Standard N/C tape is 1 in. wide and contains eight channels for information (Figure 43). A row of sprocket or feed holes also appears on the tape. These are necessary for transport through certain types of tape readers. The line of feed holes is punched off center to eliminate confusion as to how the tape is to be placed in the tape reader.

Tape Preparation

Control information is placed on the N/C tape by punching a specific pattern of holes. This is accomplished on a special typewriter tape punch machine (Figure 44). The typewriter keyboard operates in a similar manner as a standard typewriter. The tape punch typewriter has the same letters and numbers found on a standard typewriter. In addition, several extra symbols are included, as well as control keys for the tape punch.

The tape punch is activated as each typewriter key is depressed. This produces a pattern of holes in the tape that is unique to that typewriter symbol. As the tape is punched, a printed record is typed on paper in the typewriter carriage. The tape feed key (Figure 45) causes blank tape to feed through the punch. Feed holes are produced during this operation (Figure 46). Blank tape is run out to provide a leader that can be wound on the machine tool tape reader reels.

The typewriter tape punch also has a tape reading head. The reading head is not unlike the tape reader on the N/C machine tool. The function of the typewriter reader is to operate the typewriter from the punched tape. The reader is used to obtain a printed record of a punched tape. This is useful for verifying tape accuracy. After a tape has been prepared, it may be inserted in the typewriter reader (Figure 47). The tape will now activate

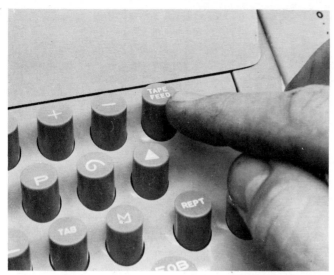

Figure 45. Tape feed key (California State University at Fresno).

Figure 47. Typewriter tape reader (California State University at Fresno).

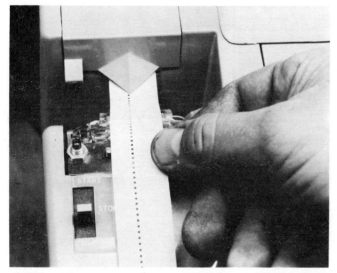

Figure 46. Blank tape with feed holes (California State University at Fresno).

the typewriter and a record of the information will be typed out. If there is an error in the tape information, it can be detected and corrected. The typewriter reader is also used to duplicate tapes.

Correcting Tape Errors. If an error in typing is made and detected at that time by the tape punch operator, a correction may be made by pressing the **delete** key. The delete key causes all seven rows on the tape to be punched out. The operator may then retype the correct information and continue with the remainder of the program.

If an error is not detected until the tape is com-

pleted and read back using the typewriter reader, a new tape will have to be produced. This can be done by inserting the incorrect tape in the reader and duplicating a new tape to the point of the error. The operator will, of course, have to watch the typed printout and stop the duplicating process when it reaches the last correct entry. The correct information is then typed from the keyboard. The incorrect information on the original tape is advanced through the reader by hand and the duplicating process is resumed.

Punched tape may also be corrected by inserting a splice at the appropriate point. This requires that the feed holes and tape perforations be precisely aligned.

Tape Code Systems

Standard systems of tape codes are used throughout industry. One system is the Electronics Industries Association code, known as EIA (Figure 48). Another system is the U.S.A. Standard Code for Information Interchange, known as ASCII (Figure 49). Note that each typewriter symbol has a specific pattern of holes in the tape. Typewriter keys such as "tab" and "carriage return" also produce a specific tape punch code. However, these codes do not produce a printed symbol.

Tape Readers

The tape reader is usually found in the machine control unit. The MCU may be attached to the machine tool, or

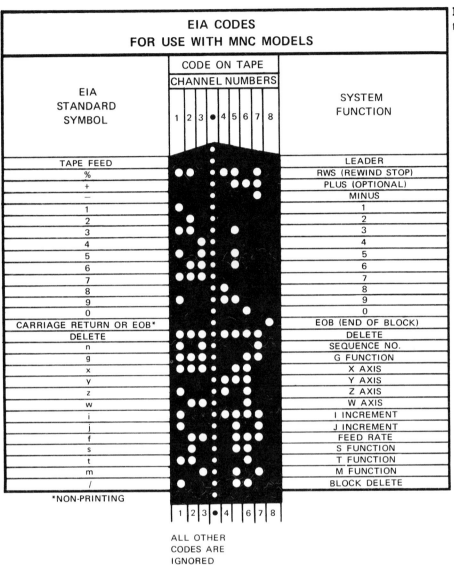

Figure 48. EIA tape codes (Courtesy of the Superior Electric Company).

it may be freestanding and connected to the machine by appropriate wiring. Tape readers may be electromechanical, photoelectric, or pneumatic. A tape reader consists of the tape reading head and tape transport system. The transport system includes the drive sprocket, tension arms, and tape reels. The tension arms maintain a taut tape as it passes by the reading head. In photoelectric tape readers, the tape may be transported through the reader by a pinch roll instead of by a drive sprocket.

Electromechanical Readers. The electromechanical reader uses electrical contacts that operate through the tape punches. Electromechanical readers are quite fast reading.

Photoelectric Readers. The photoelectric reader

(Figure 50) uses a concentrated light source that beams light through the tape punches. The light beam activates photoelectric cells. Photoelectric readers are fast reading and are used on numerical controls designed for continuous path machine tools. Continuous path machining may involve many small cuts to approximate a radius, angle, or irregular shape. Instructions for each move must be provided from tape instructions. If the machine tool has to wait for the tape reader to read a tape instruction, time will be lost, resulting in lowered productivity.

To reduce waiting time while instructions are read from the tape, the tape reader reads and stores one instruction ahead. The MCU may be equipped with a memory for this purpose. This is called a buffer storage. While the machine is performing its cut, the tape reader is reading and storing the next instruction. When the cut

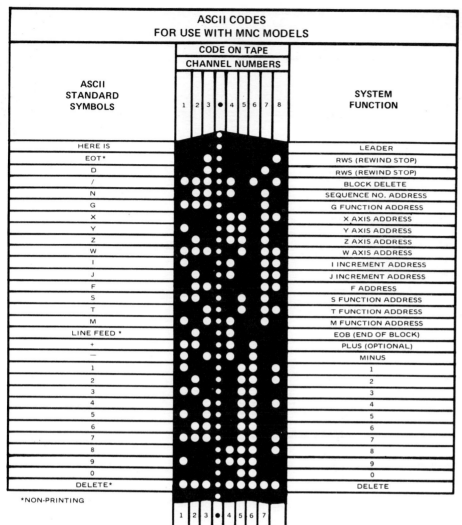

Figure 49. ASCII tape codes (Courtesy of the Superior Electric Company).

ASCII STANDARD SYMBOLS	CODE ON TAPE — CHANNEL NUMBERS	SYSTEM FUNCTION
HERE IS		LEADER
EOT*		RWS (REWIND STOP)
D		RWS (REWIND STOP)
/		BLOCK DELETE
N		SEQUENCE NO. ADDRESS
G		G FUNCTION ADDRESS
X		X AXIS ADDRESS
Y		Y AXIS ADDRESS
Z		Z AXIS ADDRESS
W		W AXIS ADDRESS
I		I INCREMENT ADDRESS
J		J INCREMENT ADDRESS
F		F ADDRESS
S		S FUNCTION ADDRESS
T		T FUNCTION ADDRESS
M		M FUNCTION ADDRESS
LINE FEED *		EOB (END OF BLOCK)
+		PLUS (OPTIONAL)
—		MINUS
1		1
2		2
3		3
4		4
5		5
6		6
7		7
8		8
9		9
0		0
DELETE*		DELETE

*NON-PRINTING

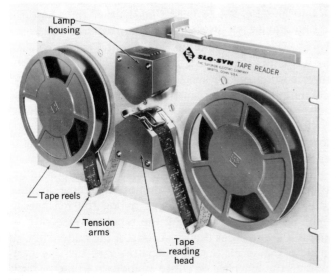

Figure 50. Photoelectric MCU tape reader (Courtesy of the Superior Electric Company).

is completed, the next instruction is instantly available from buffer storage. In this way, the machine does not have to wait for the tape reader to read the next instruction from the tape.

Pneumatic Readers. The pneumatic tape reader uses air flowing through the tape punches to activate electromechanical switches. Pneumatic readers are slower reading than the photoelectric or electromechanical types. They also depend on a precise alignment of the tape over the reader air jets.

OPERATING THE N/C MACHINE TOOL

Before operating the N/C machine tool from tape instructions, you must first become totally familiar with its manual operation. The N/C machine is somewhat different than its conventional counterpart in that control functions are accomplished from the MCU for both

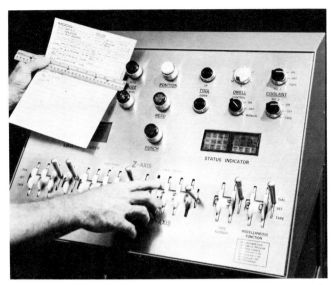

Figure 51. Entering positioning data on the MCU console (Courtesy of Hydra-Point Division, Moog Inc.).

Figure 52. Manually operated turret depth stop on an N/C milling machine (California State University at Fresno).

manual and tape operation. To protect yourself from injury and to protect an expensive machine tool from damage, it is most important to know ahead of time exactly what will happen when an MCU console control is actuated.

N/C Machine Safety

The same safety rules apply to N/C machine tools as apply to all machine tools. Always wear appropriate eye protection and short sleeves. Remove rings and watches before operating the machine. See that the workpiece is properly secured in a vise or by suitable clamps. Be sure that the cutter is clamped securely in its arbor or collet. Use proper speeds and feeds as you would for any machining task.

Manual Operation from the MCU Console

Many N/C machine tools, especially those that have been retrofitted with a numerical control system, may have some controls on the MCU console and other controls on the machine itself. Because of this, you must exercise additional caution when operating the machine manually.

The MCU console may have an emergency stop control that will stop worktable or spindle positioning in case a problem should develop during a cut. However, the emergency stop control may not stop spindle rotation. This may be a separate control attached to the machine tool and may be quite far removed from the MCU console.

When positioning the worktable or spindle man-

ually during the setup of the workpiece, be sure that the cutter and machine spindle are clear of vises and clamps before entering positioning data on the MCU console (Figure 51). Check clearances before lowering the quill on a vertical mill or drill press. It is good practice to set up the workpiece on a milling machine so that the quill must be lowered a small amount before beginning a milling cut. The quill should not be extended excessively as this will affect rigidity. If a problem should develop, the cutter can be quickly raised clear of the workpiece by actuating the quill up control on the MCU. However, if the setup has been made such that the quill is already in the full up position during milling, it cannot be raised clear of the workpiece. In case of a problem, the cutter, machine, or workpiece may be damaged.

If the N/C machine has a manually indexed turret to control quill travel (Figure 52), do not forget to index the turret at the appropriate points during the machining cycle. Be precise in adjusting the rapid traverse of the quill as it approaches the workpiece. If the cutter should run into the work during rapid traverse, damage can result to the machine or cutter in addition to the hazard of flying metal.

Figure 53. After punching a tape, obtain a printout using the typewriter reader (Courtesy of Hydra-Point Division, Moog Inc.).

Figure 54. Micrometer tool length gage (Courtesy of Hydra-Point Division, Moog Inc.).

Using the N/C Machine as a Conventional Tool

The N/C machine tool may be used as a substitute for its conventional counterpart. This will generally not be done in industry, since the reason for having the N/C machine is to realize its increased productivity and other advantages. However, in the school shop, the N/C machine tool may be used to supplement conventional machines. In fact, the accurate positioning of an N/C machine tool often makes it very effective for a routine machining task.

N/C Tape Operation

After a tape has been prepared, it should be read back at the typewriter tape punch to determine if any errors are present (Figure 53). The printout can be checked against the program manuscript. If the tape is correct, it should be verified by a ''dry run'' on the machine tool.

Be sure that the spindle and cutter are clear of all obstructions. On a milling machine this can be insured by moving the knee below the maximum extension of the spindle. Insert the tape in the MCU reader and observe the machine as it completes all programmed instructions. N/C machine tools will have a feature that permits tape blocks to be read one at a time. Each sequence can be initiated from the MCU. The machine will read and execute one tape block and stop. Positioning and miscellaneous functions can be observed and checked for accuracy. A dry tape run will safely verify the tape, thus preventing possible damage to the machine, cutter, or workpiece.

Gaging Tool Lengths for N/C

An N/C machining task often requires a number of different tools. For example, a drilling operation may require center drilling, drilling, and reaming. If the holes are through, the drill and reamer will have to extend from the tool holder the appropriate distance. Since the center drill is probably shorter, the machine spindle will have to extend further or the worktable raised accordingly.

In an industrial setting, an entire set of tools required for a specific job may be preset for length and stored for future use. When a machining job comes to the shop, the N/C machine operator obtains the complete set of preadjusted tools and places them in the machine tool changer or in a tool rack.

The tool length gage is used to measure the projection of cutting tools from their tool holders. Common length gages consist of a series of accurately spaced rings mounted on a column (Figure 54). The instrument is not unlike a precision height gage. Ring spacing is usually 1 in. A micrometer head with 1 in. travel spans the distance between the rings and can be placed at any desired height within the range of the gage. The cutting tool to be set is placed in its holder and the amount of projection is adjusted according to the job requirements. Tool length gages may also use dial indicators (Figure 55). This type of gage can be used to set boring bars and insert tooth cutters for specific diameters.

High discrimination electronic tool length gages are also used. These instruments are equipped with digital readouts (Figure 56). They can be used for tool length adjustments (Figure 57) and cutter diameter adjustments (Figure 58). One advantage of the electronic gage is its ability to read in inch and metric dimensions.

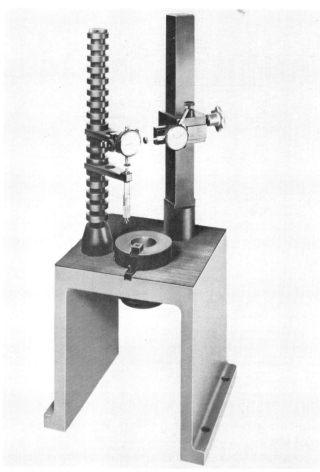

Figure 55. Dial indicator gage for adjusting length and diameter (Courtesy of Cincinnati Milacron).

Figure 57. Setting a tool length with the electronic gage (Courtesy of Cincinnati Milacron).

Figure 58. Setting an insert tooth milling cutter for diameter using the electronic gage (Courtesy of Cincinnati Milacron).

Figure 56. Electronic digital tool length gage (Courtesy of Cincinnati Milacron).

SELF-TEST

1. Identify the *X, Y,* and *Z* axes on the machine tool outlines (Figure 59).
2. Where might rotational axes be used?
3. An N/C instruction on a drill press instructs the spindle to move toward the workpiece. What is the axis and direction of travel?
4. The worktable on a vertical mill is moving the workpiece to the right of the operator. The saddle is stationary. What is the direction and axis of travel with reference to the machine spindle?
5. The tailstock of an N/C lathe is located in the _____ axis.
6. Name two common tape materials.
7. What are the advantages of the laminate materials?
8. What are the various functions of the typewriter tape punch?
9. Name two standard tape code systems.
10. Name three types of tape readers.
11. After you have punched a tape, what should you do before placing the tape in the machine tool for a dry run?
12. What is the purpose of a dry tape run?
13. What is an important precaution that must be considered when operating the machine tool from the MCU console?
14. What is the function of the tool length gage?
15. Name two types of tool length gages.

Figure 59.

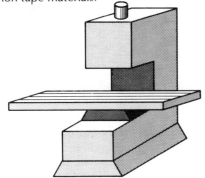
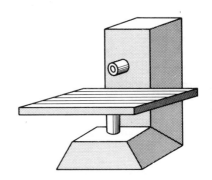
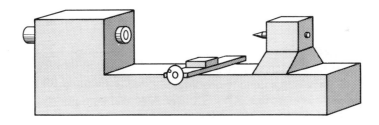

PART 2 ELECTRICAL MACHINING PROCESSES

The conventional machining processes of drilling, turning, milling, and grinding that have been discussed so far are those where a cutting tool is in direct contact with the workpiece. Since the cutting tool material is harder than the workpiece material, a chip of workpiece is machined away.

Space age technology has brought about a need for space age materials that are very difficult or in some

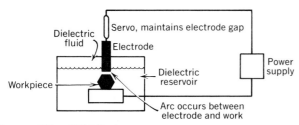

Figure 60.   EDM System

cases impossible to machine by conventional processes. Furthermore, space age designs call for machining of features in workpieces that would also be extremely difficult or impossible to accomplish by conventional methods.

The following electrical machining processes have not only helped to overcome difficulties in machining requirements, they have also permitted the designer greater latitude in applications of new materials to the increasingly complex hardware of an advancing technology.

The major electrical machining processes in widespread use include:

1. **EDM—Electrical Discharge Machining**
2. **ECM—Electro Chemical Machining**
3. **ELG—Electrolytic Grinding**

EDM—ELECTRICAL DISCHARGE MACHINING

Most of us have seen the results of an electrical short circuit. A visible arc, smoke, and often a definite eroding of any metal to which the arc was struck. This is the underlying principle of **electrical discharge machining,** or **EDM.** EDM is a process during which the workpiece is machined or eroded by high density electrical energy. In EDM machining, the spark erosion takes place in a non-conducting or **dielectric** fluid. The workpiece and EDM electrode are submerged in the dielectric, which is usually a light oil. The dielectric fluid will concentrate the arc energy and also flush away the material eroded from the workpiece.

The EDM System

The basic system (Figure 60) consists of a power supply dielectric reservoir, electrode, and workpiece. The power supply provides the electrical energy to the electrode. As the electrode approaches the workpiece, electrical pressure (voltage) is sufficiently high that current (amperage) will flow across the gap between electrode and work. When this occurs, a sufficient number of electrons impinge on the workpiece with sufficient force to dislodge small bits of material. A servo (slave) motor and

control system maintains the gap between electrode and work. By controlling the rate of arcing and the position of the electrode, a part may be electrical discharge machined to desired shape and dimensions.

Carbon in the form of graphite is a popular EDM electrode material. Graphite electrodes may be molded or machined to desired shapes. EDM electrodes designed for machining cavities in the workpiece will cut the same shape in the part as the shape of the electrode. Metal may also be used for EDM electrodes. In the wire cut EDM process the electrode is a slender wire.

A certain amount of electrode wear will occur during the EDM process. This can be minimized by proper selection of electrical polarity between electrode and work. EDM electrodes may also be preserved by machining in two or more stages. This involves use of a roughing and finishing electrode.

Advantages and Applications of EDM

Advantages of EDM include the ability to machine materials that would be difficult or impossible to cut by conventional methods. Complex geometry can be produced on the workpiece. Thin cross sections on a fragile workpiece can be shaped by this process. EDM is extremely useful for cavity machining related to die work. The wire cut EDM process coupled with numerical control for workpiece and electrode positioning can accomplish some amazing tasks. The following illustrations survey some of this capability.

1. Machining a turbine disk (Figure 61)
2. Blanking dies for watch parts (Figure 62)
3. Plastic mold for a squirrel cage fan (Figure 63)
4. Blanking punch and die set (Figure 64)

ECM—ELECTROCHEMICAL MACHINING

You are probably familiar with the process of plating or electrically depositing a metal such as chrome or zinc (galvinizing) on another metal. **Electrochemical machining,** or **ECM,** can be thought of as a **reverse** process. The workpiece material is removed by deplating from the workpiece to the electrode. A gap is maintained between work and electrode. The ECM process takes place in a conducting fluid medium, or **electrolyte.**

The ECM System

The basic ECM system (Figure 65) consists of a power supply, electrode, electrolyte circulation system, electrolyte cleaning system, and workpiece. The power supply provides the electrical energy. Current flows from the workpiece through the conducting electrolyte to the electrode. Electrolyte is circulated in the gap between workpiece and electrode at sufficient pressure and vol-

Figure 61. Machining a turbine disk by wire cut EDM (Courtesy of Japax Inc.).

Figure 62. Blanking dies for watch parts (Courtesy of Japax Inc.).

Figure 63. Plastic mold for squirrel cage fan (Courtesy of Japax Inc.).

Figure 64. Blanking punch and die set (Courtesy of Japax Inc.).

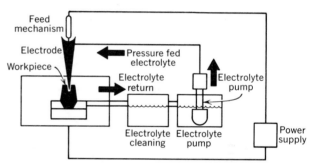

Figure 65. ECM System.

ume so that deplated workpiece material is flushed away. Deplated material is removed from the electrolyte in the cleaning system. ECM electrolytes include sodium hydroxide, sodium nitrate and sodium chloride in the form of salt water.

Advantages and Applications of ECM

Once again, the advantages of ECM include the ability to accomplish intricate shaping in hard to machine material. Good surface finishes can be obtained and ECM machining is burr free. Stresses that may be placed in the workpiece by the pressure of conventional machining processes are eliminated in the ECM process. Application of ECM include tool and die making and deburring.

ELG—ELECTROLYTIC GRINDING

Electrolytic grinding, or **ELG,** uses an abrasive wheel in which the bond is metal and can conduct electricity. Like

the ECM process, a conducting fluid or **electrolyte** flows between the abrasive wheel and the workpiece. Current flowing from the part through the electrolyte to the wheel deplates workpiece material. The abrasive grains in the grinding wheel are nonconducting and serve more to maintain the gap between wheel and work while at the same time cleaning oxides away so that the electrochemical process can continue efficiently.

The ELG System

The basic ELG system (Figure 66) consists of a power supply, metal bonded abrasive wheel (electrode), electrolyte circulating system, and workpiece. Electrical energy is provided by the power supply. Current flows from the work through the electrolyte to the wheel. Deplated workpiece material goes into solution in the electrolyte and the abrasive grains clean away oxides formed during the electrochemical process.

Advantages and Applications of ELG

Since the metal removal process in ELG is primarily **electrochemical** and not mechanical, as in conventional

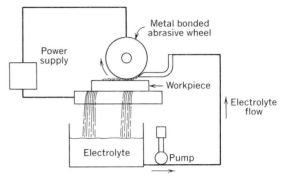

Figure 66. ELG System.

grinding, abrasive wheel life is greatly extended. Difficult material can be machined by the ELG process. ELG is burr free, which is very important in small precision parts. During conventional grinding, frictional heat may cause distortion in the workpiece. This problem is eliminated in ELG. A popular application of ELG is in carbide tool and cutter grinding. The process can be applied to all forms of grinding, including surface (Figure 67), cylindrical, plunge, internal, and form.

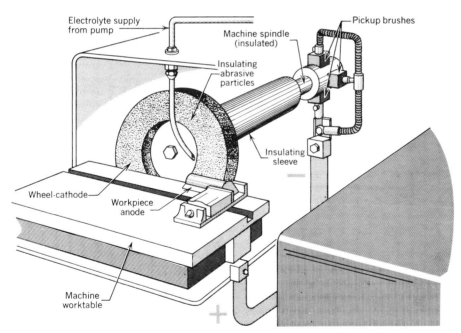

Figure 67. Electrolytic surface grinder (Courtesy of Hammond Machinery Builders Inc.).

SELF-TEST

1. What is EDM?
2. Where can EDM be applied in machining?
3. What is ECM and ELG?

4. Where can ECM and ELG be applied in machining?
5. Cite any advantages of these processes over conventional machining.

APPENDIX I
ANSWERS TO SELF-TESTS

SECTION A / PART 3 / SHOP SAFETY

SELF-TEST ANSWERS

1. Eye protection equipment.
2. Wear a safety goggle or full face shield. Prescription glasses may be made as safety glasses.
3. Shoes, short sleeves, short or properly secured hair, no rings and wristwatches, shop apron or shop coat with short sleeves.
4. Use of cutting fluids and vacuum dust collectors.
5. They may cause skin rashes or infections.
6. Bend knees and squat, lift with your legs, keeping your back straight.
7. Compressed air can propel chips through the air, implant dirt into skin, and possibly injure ear drums.
8. Good houskeeping includes cleaning up oil spills, keeping material off the floor, and keeping aisles clear of obstructions.
9. In the vertical position or with a person on each end.
10. Do I know how to operate this machine?
    What are the potential hazards involved?
    Are all guards in place?
    Are my procedures safe?
    Am I doing something I probably should not do?
    Have I made all proper adjustments and tightened all locking bolts and clamps?
    Is the workpiece secured properly?
    Do I have proper safety equipment?
    Do I know where the stop switch is?
    Do I think about safety in everything I do?

SECTION A / PART 4 / MECHANICAL HARDWARE

SELF-TEST ANSWERS

1. A bolt goes through parts being assembled and is tightened with a nut. A screw is used where a part is internally threaded and no nut is needed.
2. The minimum recommended thread engagement for a screw in an assembly is as much as the screw diameter; a better assembly will result when $1\frac{1}{2}$ times the screw diameter is used.
3. Class 2 threads are found on most screws, nuts, and bolts used in the manufacturing industry. Car and machine tools would be good examples.
4. Machine bolts are not machined to the precise dimensions of cap screws. Machine bolts have coarse threads where cap screws may have coarse or fine threads. Machine bolts have many uses in the construction industry, and cap screws are usually used in precision assemblies.
5. The formula is D = number of the machine screw times .013 in. plus .060 in. $D = 8 \times .013$ in. plus $.060 = 164$.
6. Set screws are used to secure gears or pulleys to shafts.
7. Stud bolts can be used instead of long bolts. Stud bolts are used to aid in the assembly of heavy parts by acting as guide pins.
8. Thread forming screws form threads by displacing material. Thread cutting screws produce threads by actually cutting grooves and making chips.
9. Castle nuts can be secured on a bolt with a cotter pin to prevent their accidental loosening.

10. Cap nuts are used because of their neat appearance. They also protect projecting threads from damage.
11. Flat washers protect the surface of parts from being marred by the tightening of screws or nuts. Flat washers also provide a larger contact area than nuts and screw heads to distribute the clamping pressure over a larger area.
12. A helical spring lock washer prevents the unplanned loosening of nut and bolt or screw assemblies. Spring lock washers will also provide for a limited amount of takeup when expansion or contraction takes place.
13. Internal-external tooth lock washers are used on oversized holes or to provide a large bearing surface.
14. Dowel pins are used to achieve accurate alignment between two or more parts.
15. Taper pins give accurate alignment to parts that have to be disassembled frequently.
16. Roll pins are used to align parts. Holes to receive roll pins do not have to be reamed, which is necessary for dowel pins and taper pins.
17. Retaining rings are used to hold bearings or seals in bearing housings or on shafts. Retaining rings have a spring action and are usually seated in grooves.
18. Keys transmit the driving force between a shaft and pulley.
19. Woodruff keys are used where only light loads are transmitted.
20. Gib head keys are used to transmit heavy loads. These keys are installed and removed from the same side of a hub and shaft assembly.

SECTION A / PART 5 / READING DRAWINGS

SELF-TEST ANSWERS

1. See Figure 57. (Page 30)

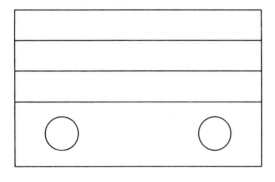

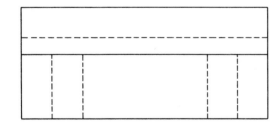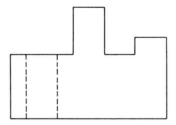

2. The tolerance of the hole is specified as ±.005. Therefore, the minimum size of the hole would be .750 − .005 or .745.
3. $2\frac{1}{4}$ in.
4. Since the slot conforms to standard tolerances, width is $\pm\frac{1}{64}$ of an inch.
5. $\frac{1}{8}$ in.
6. 6 in.
7. 1 in.
8. Drilling and reaming.
9. $\frac{1}{8}$ in. by 45 degrees.
10. Note 1 indicates that all sharp corners are to be broken, which means that all burrs and sharp edges left from machining are to be smoothed off.

SECTION B / UNIT 1 / WORKHOLDING FOR HAND OPERATIONS

SELF-TEST ANSWERS

1. The vise should be positioned so that a long piece may be held vertically in the jaws without interference from the workbench.
2. The solid base and the swivel-base types.
3. By the width of the jaws.
4. Pin vise or toolmaker vise.
5. Insert jaws are hardened and have diamond pattern or criss-cross serrations.
6. Copper, soft metal, or wood may be used to protect finishes from insert jaw serrations.
7. Vises used for sheet metal work have smooth, deep jaws.
8. Vises are used for holding work for assembly and disassembly; for filing, hacksawing, and bending light metal.
9. "Cheater" bars should never be used on the handle. The movable jaw slide bar should never be hammered upon, and excessive heat should never be applied to the jaws.
10. The vise should be taken apart, cleaned, and the screw and nut cleaned in solvent. A heavy grease should be packed on the screw and thrust collars before reassembly.

SECTION B / UNIT 2 / ARBOR AND SHOP PRESSES

SELF-TEST ANSWERS

1. To use the arbor press without instruction is unsafe for the operator; also very expensive equipment and materials may be damaged or ruined.
2. Arbor presses are hand powered and can be mechanical or hydraulic. Large power driven presses do not provide the "feel" needed when pressing delicate parts.
3. The arbor press is used for installing and removing mandrels, bushings, and ball bearings. The hydraulic shop press is also used for straightening and bending.
4. The shaft has seized or welded in the bore because it had not been lubricated with pressure lubricant.
5. A loose and rounded ram could cause a bushing to tilt or twist sideways while pressing and thus be ruined. In any case, the operator should always check to see if a bushing is going in straight. A pressing plug with a pilot would be helpful here.
6. No. Thirty tons would deform the extended end of the bushing. Just enough pressure should be applied to press in the bushing and when it contacts the press plate at the bottom, more pressure will be sensed. At that point it is time to stop.
7. Pressing on the inner race with the outer race supported will damage or break the bearing.
8. Ordinary shafts with press fits are not tapered but have the same dimension along the pressing length. Mandrels taper .006 in./ft, which causes them to tighten in the bore somewhere along their length.
9. The two most important steps, assuming that the dimensions are all correct, are to:
   a. Make sure the bore has a good chamfer and the bushing should also have a chamfer or "start."
   b. Apply high pressure lubricant to the bore and the bushing.
10. Five ways to avoid tool breakage and other problems when broaching keyways in the arbor press:
   a. Make sure the press ram is not loose and check to see that the proper hole in the press plate is under the work so that the broach has clearance to go through the work.
   b. Clean and lubricate the broach, especially the back edge between each cut.
   c. Do not use a broach on hard materials (over Rc 35).
   d. Use the right size bushing for the bore and broach.
   e. Make sure at least two teeth are continuously engaged in the work.

SECTION B / UNIT 3 / NONCUTTING HAND TOOLS

SELF-TEST ANSWERS

1. True.
2. The purpose of false jaws is to protect finished work from being damaged by the hard serrated jaws. Also, when gripping soft metals, "soft" jaws of leather or a softer metal are used.

3. False. C-clamps are used for heavy clamping work. Some heavy duty types can hold many hundreds of pounds.
4. False. This practice can quickly ruin good machinery so that the proper tool can never be used.
5. The principal advantage of the lever jawed wrench is its great holding power. Most types have hard serrated jaws and so should not be used on nuts and bolt heads.
6. No. Hammers used for layout work range from 4 to 10 ounces in weight. A smaller one should be used with a prick punch and for delicate work.
7. Soft hammers and mallets are made for this purpose. When setting down work in a drill press or milling machine vise, for instance, a lead hammer is best because it has no rebound.
8. The box type, either socket or end wrench, would be best as it provides contact on the six points of the capscrew, thus avoiding the damage and premature wear that would be caused by using an adjustable wrench.
9. The hard serrated jaws will damage machine parts. Pipe wrenches should be used on pipe and pipe fittings only.
10. Standard screwdrivers should have the right width blade to fit the screw head. They should be shaped correctly and, if worn, reground and shaped properly.

SECTION B / UNIT 4 / HACKSAWS

SELF-TEST ANSWERS

1. The kerf is the groove produced in the work by a saw blade.
2. The set on a saw blade is the width of the teeth that are bent out from the blade back.
3. The pitch of a hacksaw blade refers to the number of teeth per inch on a saw blade.
4. The first consideration in the selection of a saw blade is the kind of material being cut. For soft materials use a coarse tooth blade and for harder materials use a fine pitch blade. The second point to watch is that at least three teeth should be cutting at the same time.
5. The two basic kinds of saw blades are the all-hard blade and the flexible blade.
6. Generally a speed between 40 and 60 strokes per minute is suggested. It is best to use long and slow strokes utilizing the full length of the blade.
7. Excessive dulling of saw blades is caused by pressure on the saw blade on the return stroke, sawing too fast, letting the saw slide over the workpiece without any cutting pressure, or applying too much pressure.
8. Saw blades break if too much pressure is used or if the blade is not sufficiently tightened in the saw frame.
9. When the saw blade is used, the set wears and makes the kerf cut narrower with a used blade than the kerf cut with a new blade. If a cut started with a used blade can't be finished with that blade, but has to be completed with a new blade, the workpiece should be turned over and a new cut started from the opposite end of the original cut. A new blade, when used in a kerf started with a used blade, would lose its set immediately and start binding in the groove.
10. When a blade breaks, it shatters causing blade particles to fly quite a distance with the possibility of injuring someone. Should the blade break while sawing, it may catch the operator off balance and cause him to push his hand into the workpiece while following through with his sawing stroke. Serious cuts or abrasions can be the result of this action.

SECTION B / UNIT 5 / FILES AND OFF-HAND GRINDING

SELF-TEST ANSWERS

1. By its length, shape, cut, and coarseness.
2. Single cut, double cut, curved cut, and rasp.
3. Four out of these: rough, coarse, bastard, second cut, smooth, and dead smooth.
4. The double cut file.
5. To make it possible to file a flat surface by offsetting the tendency to rock a file. To compensate for the slight downward deflection when pressure is applied while filing. To concentrate pressure on fewer teeth for deeper penetration.
6. A blunt file has the same cross-sectional area from heel to point, where a tapered file is larger at the heel than at the point.
7. A mill file is thinner than a comparable size flat file.
8. A warding file is rectangular in shape and it tapers to a small point, making filing possible in narrow slots and grooves.

9. Swiss pattern files are more precise in construction; they are more slender and have teeth to the extreme edges.
10. Coarseness is identified by numbers from 00 fine to 6 coarse.
11. Where files touch each other, teeth break off or become dull.
12. Too much pressure will break teeth off a file. It also will cause pinning and scratching of the work surface.
13. Files in contact with each other, files rubbing over the work without any pressure being applied, filing too fast, or filing on hardened materials cause files to dull.
14. As a safety precaution; an unprotected tang can cause serious injury.
15. Measuring the workpiece for flatness and size assures the craftsman that the filing is done in the right place and that the filing is stopped before a piece is undersize. Measuring often is not a waste of time.
16. Touching a workpiece is just like lubricating the workpiece or the file so that it slips over the work without cutting. This also causes a file to dull quickly.
17. A soft workpiece requires a file with coarser teeth because there is less resistance to tooth penetration. A fine toothed file would clog up on soft materials. For harder materials use a fine toothed file in order to have more teeth making smaller chips.
18. The drawfiling stroke should be short enough that the file never slips over the end of the workpiece. Care should be taken that no hollow surface is created through too short of a stroke.
19. Pressure is only applied on the forward stroke, which is the cutting stroke.
20. Rotating a round file clockwise while filing makes the file cut better and improves the surface finish.
21. Wear eye protection, let wheel run at idle for a minute when first starting grinder, keep workrest close to wheel, keep wheel guards in place, keep wheel dressed, and use wheels of proper grit and grade.

SECTION B / UNIT 6 / HAND REAMERS

SELF-TEST ANSWERS

1. Hand reamers have a square on the shank and a long starting taper on the fluted end.
2. A reamer does its cutting on the tapered portion. A long taper will help in keeping a reamer aligned with the hole.
3. Spiral fluted reamers cut with a shearing action. They will also bridge over keyways and grooves without chattering.
4. The shank diameter is usually a few thousandths of an inch smaller than the nominal size of the reamer. This allows the reamer to pass through the hole without marring it.
5. Expansion reamers are useful to increase hole sizes by a very very small amount.
6. Expansion reamers can only be adjusted a small amount by moving a tapered internal plug. Adjustable reamers have a larger range of adjustments, from $\frac{1}{32}$ in. on small diameters to $\frac{5}{16}$ in. on large reamers. Adjustable reamers have removable blades. Size changes are made by moving these blades with nuts in external tapered slots.
7. Coolants are used to dissipate the heat generated by the reaming process, but in reaming coolants are more important in obtaining a high quality surface finish of the hole.
8. Reamers dull rapidly if they should be rotated backwards.
9. The hand reaming allowance is rather small, only between .001 and .005 in.

SECTION B / UNIT 7 / IDENTIFICATION AND USES OF TAPS

SELF-TEST ANSWERS

1. A set of taps consists of three taps with equal pitch diameters and major diameters with the difference being the number of chamfered threads on the cutting end. Serial taps have different pitch and major diameters within a nominal size designation. The smallest tap in the series is marked with a single ring on the shank near the square. The next larger tap has two rings on the shank and the tap that cuts the thread to its full size is marked with three rings.
2. Spiral pointed taps are used on through holes or blind holes with sufficient chip space at the bottom of a hole.
3. Fluteless spiral pointed taps are especially useful to tap holes in sheet metal or on soft, stringy materials where the thickness is no greater than one tap diameter.
4. Spiral fluted taps draw the chips out of the hole and are useful when tapping a hole that has a keyway in it bridged by the helical flutes.
5. Thread forming or fluteless taps do not produce chips because they don't cut threads. Their action can be compared to thread rolling in that material is being displaced in grooves to form ridges shaped in the precise form of a thread.

6. Taper pipe taps are identified by the taper of the body of the tap, which is $\frac{3}{4}$ inch per foot of length; also by the size marked on the shank.
7. Pulley taps and nut taps are both extended length hand taps. The pulley tap has a shank diameter equal to the nominal size of the thread tapped where a nut tap has a shank diameter slightly smaller than the minor diameter of the nut tapped.
8. When an Acme thread is cut, the tap is required to cut too much material in one pass. To obtain a quality thread, a roughing pass and then a finishing pass are needed.
9. Rake angles vary on tools depending on the kind of work material machined. In general, we can say that softer, more ductile materials require larger rake angles than do harder, less ductile materials.
10. Friction is reduced by back tapering, eccentric, or con-eccentric relief on the pitch diameter, concave groove land relief, making the tap in interrupted design, and in various surface treatments such as oxides and flash chrome plating.

SECTION B / UNIT 8 / TAPPING PROCEDURES

SELF-TEST ANSWERS

1. Taps are driven with tap wrenches or T-handle tap wrenches.
2. A hand tapper is a fixture used to hold a tap in precise alignment while hand tapping holes.
3. A tapping attachment is used when tapping holes in a machine or for production tapping.
4. The strength of a tapped hole is determined by the kind of material being tapped, the percentage of thread used, and the length or depth of thread engagement.
5. Holes should be tapped deep enough to provide 1 to $1\frac{1}{2}$ times the tap diameter of usable thread.
6. Tap drilled holes should be reamed when close control over the percentage of thread produced is necessary and when fine pitches of thread are produced, because a small change in tap drilled hole size would mean a large change in the percentage of thread cut.
7. Taps break because holes are drilled too shallow, chips are packed tight in the flutes, hard materials or hard spots are encountered, inadequate or the wrong kind of lubricant is used, or the cutting speed used is too great.
8. Tapped holes that are rough and torn are often caused by dull taps, chips clogging the flutes, insufficient lubrication, wrong kind of lubrication, or already rough holes being tapped.
9. Oversize tapped holes can be caused by a loose machine spindle or a worn tap holder, misaligned spindle, over-sized tap, a dull tap, chips packed in flutes, and buildup on cutting edges.
10. Broken taps can be removed by drilling them out after annealing the tap, or by using an electrical discharge machine to erode the tap.

SECTION B / UNIT 9 / THREAD CUTTING DIES AND THEIR USES

SELF-TEST ANSWERS

1. A die is used to cut external threads.
2. A die stock is used to hold the die when hand threading. A special die holder is used when machine threading.
3. The size of thread cut can only be changed a very small amount on round adjustable dies. Too much expansion or contraction may break the die.
4. The purpose of the guide is to align the die square to the workpiece to be threaded.
5. When assembling a two-piece die collet, be sure both die halves are marked with the same serial number and that the starting chamfer on the dies are toward the guide.
6. Hexagon rethreading dies are used to clean and recut slightly damaged or rusty threads. Only in emergencies should they be used to cut new threads.
7. The chamfer on the cutting end of a die distributes the cutting force over a number of threads and aids in starting the thread cutting operation.
8. Cutting fluids are very important in threading to achieve thread with a good surface finish, close tolerance, and to give long tool life.
9. Before a rod is threaded, it should be measured to assure its size is no larger than its nominal size. Preferably, it is .002 to .005 in. undersize.
10. The chamfer on a rod before threading makes it easy to start a die. It also protects the starting thread on a finished bolt.

SECTION C / UNIT 1 / SYSTEMS OF MEASUREMENT

SELF-TEST ANSWERS

1. To find in. knowing mm, multiply mm by .03937: $35 \times .03937 = 1.377$ in.
2. To find mm knowing in., multiply in. by 25.4: $.125 \times 25.4 = 3.17$ mm.
3. To find cm knowing in., multiply in. by 2.54: $6.273 \times 2.54 = 15.933$ cm.
4. To find mm knowing in., multiply in. by 25.4: $.050 \times 25.4 = 1.27$ mm.
5. 10 mm = 1 cm; therefore, to find cm knowing mm, divide mm by 10.
6. To find in. knowing mm, multiply mm by .03937: $.02 \times .03937 = .0008$ in. The tolerance would be $\pm .0008$ in.
7. SI refers to the International System of Units.
8. Conversions between metric and inch systems may be accomplished by mathematical procedures, conversion charts, and direct converting calculators.
9. The yard is presently defined in terms of the meter: $1 \text{ yard} = \dfrac{3600}{3937}$ meter.
10. Yes, by the use of appropriate conversion dials.

SECTION C / UNIT 2 / USING STEEL RULES

SELF-TEST ANSWERS

Fractional Inch Rules
Figure 22 $A = 1\frac{1}{4}$ in.
Figure 22 $B = 2\frac{1}{8}$ in.
Figure 22 $C = \frac{15}{16}$ in.
Figure 22 $D = 2\frac{5}{16}$ in.
Figure 22 $E = \frac{15}{32}$ in.
Figure 22 $F = 2\frac{25}{32}$ in.
Figure 22 $G = \frac{63}{64}$ in.
Figure 22 $H = 1\frac{59}{64}$ in.

Decimal Inch Rules
Figure 25 $A = \ \ .300$ in.
Figure 25 $B = \ \ .510$ in.
Figure 25 $C = 1.020$ in.
Figure 25 $D = 1.200$ in.
Figure 25 $E = 1.260$ in.

Metric Rules
Figure 28 $A = 11$ mm or 1.1 cm
Figure 28 $B = 27$ mm or 2.7 cm
Figure 28 $C = 52$ mm or 5.2 cm
Figure 28 $D = 7.5$ mm or .75 cm
Figure 28 $E = 20.5$ mm or 2.05 cm
Figure 28 $F = 45.5$ mm or 4.55 cm

SECTION C / UNIT 3 / USING VERNIER CALIPERS AND VERNIER DEPTH GAGES

SELF-TEST ANSWERS

Reading Inch
Vernier Calipers
Figure 11a. 1.304 in.
Figure 11b. .492 in.
Figure 11c. .532 in.
Figure 11d. .724 in.

Reading Metric
Vernier Calipers
Figure 13a. 20.26 mm
Figure 13b. 14.50 mm
Figure 13c. 29.84 mm
Figure 13d. 35.62 mm

Reading Inch
Vernier Depth Gages
Figure 17a. .943 in.
Figure 17b. 1.326 in
Figure 17c. 1.436 in.
Figure 17d. 3.768 in.

SECTION C / UNIT 4 / USING MICROMETER INSTRUMENTS

SELF-TEST ANSWERS

1. Anyone taking pride in his tools usually takes pride in his workmanship. The quality of a product produced depends to a large extent on the accuracy of the measuring tools used. A skilled craftsman protects his tools because he guarantees his product.
2. Moisture between the contact faces can cause corrosion.
3. Even small dust particles will change a dimension. Oil or grease attract small chips and dirt. All of these can cause incorrect readings.

4. A measuring tool is no more discriminatory than the smallest division marked on it. This means that a standard micrometer can discriminate to the nearest thousandth. A vernier scale on a micrometer will make it possible to discriminate a reading to one ten thousandths of an inch under controlled conditions.

5. The reliability of a micrometer depends on the inherent qualities built into it by its maker. Reliability also depends upon the skill of the user and the care the tool receives.

6. The sleeve is stationary in relation to the frame and is engraved with the main scale, which is divided into 40 equal spaces each equal to .025 in. The thimble is attached to the spindle and rotates with it. The thimble circumference is graduated with 25 equal divisions, each representing a value of .001 in.

7. There is less chance of accidentally moving the thimble when reading a micrometer while it is still in contact with the workpiece.

8. Measurement should be made at least twice. On critical measurements, checking the dimensions additional times will assure that the size measurement is correct.

9. As the temperature of a part is increased, the size of the part will increase. When a part is heated by the machining process, it should be permitted to cool down to room temperature before being measured.
   Holding a micrometer by the frame for an extended period of time will transfer body heat through the hand and affect the accuracy of the measurement taken.

10. The purpose of the ratchet stop or friction thimble is to enable equal pressure to be repeatedly applied between the measuring faces and the object being measured. Use of the ratchet stop or friction thimble will minimize individual differences in measuring pressure applied by different persons using the same micrometer.

Exercise Answers

Outside micrometer readings (Figures 39*a* to 39*e*):
   Figure 39*a*. .669 in.
   Figure 39*b*. .787 in.
   Figure 39*c*. .237 in.
   Figure 39*d*. .994 in.
   Figure 39*e*. .072 in.

Inside micrometer readings (Figures 46*a* to 46*e*):
   Figure 46*a*. 1.617
   Figure 46*b*. 2.000
   Figure 46*c*. 2.254
   Figure 46*d*. 2.562
   Figure 46*e*. 2.784

Depth micrometer readings (Figures 52*a* to 52*e*):
   Figure 52*a*. .535 in.
   Figure 52*b*. .815 in.
   Figure 52*c*. .732 in.
   Figure 52*d*. .535 in.
   Figure 52*e*. .647 in.

Metric micrometer readings (Figures 57*a* to 57*e*):
   Figure 57*a*. 21.21 mm
   Figure 57*b*. 13.27 mm
   Figure 57*c*. 9.94 mm
   Figure 57*d*. 5.59 mm
   Figure 57*e*. 4.08 mm

Vernier micrometer readings (Figures 59*a* to 59*e*):
   Figure 59*a*. .3749 in.
   Figure 59*b*. .5377 in.
   Figure 59*c*. .3123 in.
   Figure 59*d*. .2498 in.
   Figure 59*e*. .1255 in.

SECTION C / UNIT 5 / USING COMPARISON MEASURING INSTRUMENTS

SELF-TEST ANSWERS

1. Comparison measurement is measurement where an unknown dimension is compared to a known dimension. This often involves a transfer device that represents the unknown and is then transferred to the known where the reading can be determined.

2. Most comparison instruments do not have the capability to show measurement directly.

3. Cosine error is error incurred when misalignment exists between the axis of measurement and the axis of the measuring instrument.

4. Cosine error can be reduced by making sure that the axis of the measuring instrument is exactly in line with the axis of measurement.

5. Adjustable parallel (c).

6. Dial test indicator in conjunction with a height transfer micrometer. Height transfer measurements can also be accomplished with the test indicator and planer gage (f) and (n).

7. Optical comparator (p).

8. A combination square can be checked against a precision square or, if the actual amount of deviation is required, the cylindrical square or micrometer square can be used: (i), (j), and (l).
9. Telescoping gage and outside micrometer (b).
10. Thickness gage or, in the case of a thick shim or chock, the adjustable parallel: (c) and (e).

SECTION C / UNIT 6 / USING GAGE BLOCKS

SELF-TEST ANSWERS

1. The wringing interval in the space or interface between wrung gage blocks.
2. Wear blocks are made from very hard material such as tungsten carbide. Wear blocks are used in applications where direct contact with gage blocks might damage them.
3. If gage blocks should become heated or cooled above or below room temperature, normalizing is the process of returning them to room temperature.
4. AA grade — $\pm.000002$ in.
   A+   — $+.000004$ in.
              — $-.000002$ in.
   B   — Tolerance of B grade blocks is not specified.
5. The conditioning stone is a highly finished piece of granite or ceramic material and is used to remove burrs from the wringing surface of a gage block.
6. A microinch is one millionth of an inch. On surface finish it refers to the deviation of a surface from a uniform plane.
7. Gage block accuracy depends on the following factors:
   Extreme cleanliness
   No burrs
   Minimum use of the conditioning stone
   Leaving stacks assembled only for minimum amounts of time
   Cleaning before storage
   Application of gage block preservative

8.
```
  3.0213
   .1003
  ------
  2.9210
   .121
  ------
  2.800
   .800
  ------
  2.000
  2.000
  ------
  0.0000
```

9.
```
  1.9643
   .100   (Wear blocks 2 × .050)
  ------
  1.8643
   .1003
  ------
  1.7640
   .114
  ------
  1.6500
   .650
  ------
  1.0000
  1.000
  ------
  0.000
```

10. Gage blocks can be used: to check other measuring instruments, to set sine bars for angles, as precision height gages for layout, in direct gaging applications, and for setting machine and cutting tool positions.

SECTION C / UNIT 7 / USING ANGULAR MEASURING INSTRUMENTS

SELF-TEST ANSWERS

1. Plate protractor and machinist's combination set bevel protractor.
2. Five minutes of arc.
3. The sine bar becomes the hypotenuse of a right triangle. Angles are measured or established by elevating the bar a specified amount or calculating the amount of bar elevation, knowing the angle.
4. 50° (Figure 20)
5. 96° 15′ (Figure 21)

6. 34° 30′ (Figure 22)
7. 61° 45′ (Figure 23)
8. 56° 25′ (Figure 24)
9. Bar elevation = bar length × sine of angle desired
    = 5 in. × sin 37°
    = 5 × .6018
    = 3.0090 in.

10. Sine of the angle desired = elevation / bar length
    = 2.750 / 5
    Sin of angle = .550
    Angle = 33° 22′

SECTION C / UNIT 8 / TOLERANCES AND FITS

SELF-TEST ANSWERS

1. Tolerances are important because they control the size and therefore the ability of parts to fit together in complex assemblies.
2. Fractional dimensions $\pm\frac{1}{64}$ in.
   Two place decimals $\pm$.010 in.
   Three place decimals $\pm$.005 in.
   Four place decimals $\pm$.0005 in.
   Angles $\pm\frac{1}{2}$ degree
3. Straightness, roundness, flatness, perpendicularity, parallelism, concentricity, runout.
4. Typical press fit allowance is calculated by the formula: .0015 in. × the diameter of the part.
5. Shrink and expansion fits are accomplished by cooling (shrinking) or heating (expanding) the parts to be fitted together. After fitting in the shrunk or expanded state, the parts will securely hold together upon cooling or warming to ambient temperature.

SECTION D / UNIT 1 / SELECTION AND IDENTIFICATION OF STEELS

SELF-TEST ANSWERS

1. Carbon and alloy steels are designated by the numerical SAE or AISI system.
2. The three basic types of stainless steels are: martensitic (hardenable) and ferritic (nonhardenable), both magnetic and of the 400 series, and austenitic (nonmagnetic and nonhardenable, except by work hardening) of the 300 series.
3. The identification for each piece would be as follows:
    a. AISI C1020 CF is a soft, low carbon steel with a dull metallic luster surface finish. Use the observation test, spark test, and file test for hardness.
    b. AISI B1140 (G and P) is a medium carbon, resulfurized, free machining steel with a shiny finish. Use the observation test, spark test, and machinability test.
    c. AISI C4140 (G and P) is a chromium-molybdenum alloy, medium carbon content with a polished, shiny finish. Since an alloy steel would be harder than a similar carbon or low carbon content steel, a hardness test should be used such as the file or scratch test to compare with known samples. The machinability test would be useful as a comparison test.
    d. AISI 8620 HR is a tough low carbon steel used for carburizing purposes. A hardness test and a machinability test will immediately show the difference from low carbon hot rolled steel.
    e. AISI B1140 (ebony) is the same as the resulfurized steel in b, only the finish is different. The test would be the same as for b.
    f. AISI D1040 is a medium carbon steel. The spark test would be useful here as well as the hardness and machinability tests.
4. A magnetic test can quickly determine whether it is a ferrous metal or perhaps a nickel. If the metal is white in color, a spark test will be needed to determine whether it is a nickel casting or one of white cast iron, since they are similar in appearance. If a small piece can be broken off, the fracture will show whether it is white or grey cast iron. Grey cast iron will leave a black smudge on the finger. If it is cast steel, it will be more ductile than cast iron and a spark test should reveal a smaller carbon content.

5. O1 refers to an alloy type oil hardening (oil quench) tool steel. W1 refers to a water hardening (water quench) tool steel.
6. The 40 in. long, $2\frac{7}{16}$ in. diameter shaft weighs 1.322 lbs/in. The cost is $.30/lb.
   $1.322 \times 40 \times .30 = \$15.86$ cost of the shaft.
7. a. No.
   b. Hardened tool steel or case hardened steel.
8. Austenitic (having a face centered cubic unit cell in its lattice structure). Examples are chromium, nickel, stainless steel, and high manganese alloy steel.
9. Nickel is a nonferrous metal that has magnetic properties. Some alloy combinations of nonferrous metals make strong permanent magnets; for example, the well-known Alnico magnet, an alloy of aluminum, nickel and cobalt.
10. Some properties of steel to be kept in mind when ordering or planning for a job would be:
    Strength
    Machinability
    Hardenability
    Weldability (if welding is involved)
    Fatigue resistance
    Corrosion resistance (especially if the piece is to be exposed to a corrosive atmosphere)

SECTION D / UNIT 2 / SELECTION AND IDENTIFICATION OF NONFERROUS METALS

SELF-TEST ANSWERS

1. Since aluminum is about one-third lighter than steel, it is used extensively in aircraft. It also forms an oxide on the surface that resists further corrosion. The initial cost is much greater. Higher strength aluminum alloys cannot be welded.
2. The letter "H" following the four digit number always designates strain on work hardening. The letter "T" refers to heat treatment.
3. Magnesium weighs approximately one-third less than aluminum and is approximately one-quarter the weight of steel. Magnesium will burn in air when finely divided.
4. Copper is most extensively used in the electrical industries because of its low resistance to the passage of current when it is unalloyed with other metals. Copper can be strain hardened or work hardened and certain alloys may be hardened by a solution heat treat and aging process.
5. Bronze is basically copper and tin. Brass is basically copper and zinc.
6. Nickel is used to electroplate surfaces of metals for corrosion resistance, and as an alloying element with steels and nonferrous metals.
7. All three resist deterioration from corrosion.
8. Alloy.
9. Tin, lead, and cadmium.
10. Die cast metals, sometimes called "pot metal."

SECTION D / UNIT 3 / HARDENING, CASE HARDENING, AND TEMPERING

SELF-TEST ANSWERS

1. No hardening would result as 1200°F (649°C) is less than the lower critical point and no dissolving of carbon has taken place.
2. There would be almost no change. For all practical purposes in the shop these low carbon steels are not considered hardenable.
3. They are shallow hardening, and liable to distortion and quench cracking because of the severity of the water quench.
4. Air and oil hardening steels are not so subject to distortion and cracking as W1 steels and are deep hardening.
5. 1450°F (788°C). 50°F (10°C) above the upper critical limit.

6. Tempering is done to remove the internal stresses in hard martensite, which is very brittle. The temperature used gives the best compromise between hardness and toughness or ductility.
7. Tempering temperature should be specified according to the hardness, strength, and ductility desired. Mechanical properties charts give this data.
8. 525°F (274°C). Purple.
9. 600°F (315°C). It would be too soft for any cutting tool.
10. Immediately. If you let it set for any length of time, it may crack from internal stresses.
11. The low carbon steel core does not harden when quenched from 1650°F (899°C), so it remains soft and tough, but the case becomes very hard. No tempering is therefore required as the piece is not brittle all the way through as a fully hardened carbon steel would be.
12. A deep case can be made by pack carburizing or by a liquid bath carburizing. A relatively deep case is often applied by nitriding or by similar procedures.
13. No. The base material must contain sufficient carbon to harden by itself without adding more for surface hardening.
14. Three methods of introducing carbon into heated steel are roll, pack, and liquid carburizing.
15. Nitriding.
16. Electric, gas, oil fired, and pot furnaces.
17. The surface decarburizes or loses surface carbon to the atmosphere as it combines with oxygen to form carbon dioxide.
18. Dispersion of carbon atoms in the solid solution of austenite may be incomplete and little or no hardening in the quench takes place as a result. Also, the center of a thick section takes more time to come to the austenitizing temperature.
19. Circulation or agitation breaks down the vapor barrier. This action allows the quench to proceed at a more rapid rate.
20. By furnace.
21. They run from the surface toward the center of the piece. The fractured surfaces usually appear blackened. The surfaces have a fine crystalline structure.
22. a. Overheating.
    b. Wrong quench.
    c. Wrong selection of steel.
    d. Poor design.
    e. Time delays between quench and tempering.
    f. Wrong angle into the quench.
    g. Not enough material to grind off decarburization.
23. a. Controlled atmosphere furnace.
    b. Wrapping the piece in stainless steel foil.
    c. Covering with cast iron chips.
24. Changes in hardness of the surface area and the development of high internal stresses during grinding.
25. An air hardening tool steel should be used when distortion must be kept to a minimum.

SECTION D / UNIT 4 / ANNEALING, NORMALIZING, AND STRESS RELIEVING

SELF-TEST ANSWERS

1. Medium carbon steels that are not uniform, have hardened areas from welding, or prior heat treating need to be normalized so they can be machined. Forgings, castings, and tool steel in the as-rolled condition are normalized before any further heat treatments or machining is done.
2. 1550°F (843°C). 50°F (10°C) above the upper critical limit.
3. The spheroidization temperature is quite close to the lower critical temperature line, about 1300°F (704°C).
4. The full anneal brings carbon steel to its softest condition as all the grains are reformed (recrystallized), and any hard carbide structures become soft pearlite as it slowly cools. Stress relieving will only recrystallize distorted ferrite grains and not the hard carbide structures or pearlite grains.
5. Stress relieving should be used on severely cold worked steels or for weldments.
6. High carbon steels (.8 to 1.7 percent C).
7. Process annealing is used by the sheet and wire industry and is essentially the same as stress relieving.
8. In still air.

9. Very slowly. Packed in insulating material or cooled in a furnace.
10. Low carbon steels tend to become gummy when spheroidized so the machinability is worse than in the as-rolled condition. Spheroidization sometimes is desirable when stress relieving weldments on low carbon steels.

SECTION D / UNIT 5 / ROCKWELL AND BRINELL HARDNESS TESTERS

SELF-TEST ANSWERS

1. Resistance to penetration is the one category that is utilized by the Rockwell and Brinell testers. The depth of penetration is measured when the major load is removed on the Rockwell tester and the diameter of the impression is measured to determine a Brinell hardness number.
2. As the hardness of a metal increases, the strength increases.
3. The "A" scale and a Brale marked "A" with a major load of 60 kgf should be used to test a tungsten carbide block.
4. It would become deformed or flattened and give an incorrect reading.
5. No. The Brale used with the Rockwell superficial tester is always marked or prefixed with the letter "N."
6. False. The ball penetrator is the same for all the scales using the same diameter ball.
7. The diamond spot anvil is used for superficial testing on the Rockwell tester. When used, it does not become indented, as is the case when using the spot anvil.
8. Roughness will give less accurate results than would a smooth surface.
9. The surface "skin" would be softer than the interior of the decarburized part.
10. A curved surface will give inaccurate readings.
11. A 3000 kg weight would be used to test steel specimens on the Brinell tester.
12. A 10 mm steel ball is usually used on the Brinell tester.

SECTION E / UNIT 1 / BASIC SEMIPRECISION LAYOUT PRACTICE

SELF-TEST ANSWERS

1. The workpiece should have all sharp edges removed by grinding or filing. A thin, even coat of layout dye should be applied.
2. The towel will prevent spilling layout dye on the layout plate or layout table.
3. The punch should be tilted so that it is easier to see when the point is located on the scribe mark. It should then be moved to the upright position before it is tapped with the layout hammer.
4. The combination square can be positioned on the rule for measurements. The square head acts as a positive reference point for measurements. The rule may be removed and used as a straight edge for scribing.
5. The divider should be adjusted until you feel the tip drop into rule engraving.

SECTION E / UNIT 2 / BASIC PRECISION LAYOUT PRACTICE

SELF-TEST ANSWERS

1. (Figure 32) Inch — 5.030 in. Metric — 127.76 mm
2. (Figure 33) Inch — 8.694 in. Metric — 220.82 mm
3. (Figure 34) Inch — 5.917 in. Metric — 150.30 mm
4. (Figure 35) Inch — 4.086 in.
5. (Figure 36) Inch — 1.456 in.
6. Zero reference is checked by bringing the scriber to rest on the reference surface and then checking the alignment of the beam and vernier zero lines.
7. The position of the vernier scale may be adjusted on height gages with this feature.
8. By turning the workpiece 90 degrees.
9. 10 to 72 in.
10. The sine bar.

SECTION F / UNIT 1 / USING RECIPROCATING AND HORIZONTAL BAND CUTOFF MACHINES

SELF-TEST ANSWERS

1. Raker, wave, and straight.
2. Workpiece material, cross section shape, and thickness.
3. On the back stroke.
4. The tooth offset on either side of the blade. Set provides clearance for the back of the blade.
5. Standard skip and hook.
6. Cutoff material can bind the blade and destroy the set.
7. The horizontal band saw.
8. Cooling, lubrication, and chip removal.
9. Scoring and possible blade breakage.
10. The workpiece must be turned over and a new cut started.

SECTION F / UNIT 2 / ABRASIVE AND COLD SAWS

SELF-TEST ANSWERS

1. Probably not.
2. Fast cutting and they can be used to cut nonmetallic materials.
3. Aluminum oxide, silicon carbide, and diamond.
4. Shellac, resinoid, and rubber.
5. Length tolerance of cutoff stock can be held very close.

SECTION F / UNIT 3 / PREPARING TO USE THE VERTICAL BAND MACHINE

SELF-TEST ANSWERS

1. The ends of the blade should be ground with the teeth opposed. This will insure that the ends of the blade are square.
2. The blade ends are placed in the welder with the teeth pointed in. The ends must contact squarely in the gap between the jaws. The welder must be adjusted for the band width to be welded. You should wear eye protection and stand to one side during the welding operation. The weld will occur when the weld lever is depressed.
3. The weld is ground on the grinding wheel attached to the welder. Grind the weld on both sides of the band until the band fits the thickness gage. Be careful not to grind the saw teeth.
4. The guides support the band. This is essential to straight cutting.
5. Band guides must fully support the band except for the teeth. A wide guide used on a narrow band will destroy the saw set as soon as the machine is started.
6. The guide setting gage is used to adjust the band guides.
7. Annealing is the process of softening the band weld in order to improve strength qualities.
8. The band should be clamped in the annealing jaws with the teeth pointed out. A small amount of compression should be placed on the movable welder jaw prior to clamping the band. The correct annealing color is dull red. As soon as this color is reached, the anneal switch should be released and then operated briefly several times to slow the cooling rate of the weld.
9. Band tracking is the position of the band as it runs on the idler wheels.
10. Band tracking is adjusted by tilting the idler wheels until the band just touches the backup bearing.

SECTION F / UNIT 4 / USING THE VERTICAL BAND MACHINE

SELF-TEST ANSWERS

1. The three sets are straight, wave, and raker. Straight set may be used for thin material, wave for material with a variable cross section, and raker for general purpose sawing.

2. Scalloped and wavy edged bands might be used on nonmetallic material where blade teeth would tear the material being cut.
3. Band velocity is measured in feet per minute.
4. The variable speed pulley is designed so that the pulley flanges may be moved toward and away from each other. This permits the belt position to be varied, resulting in speed changes.
5. The job selector provides information about recommended saw velocity, saw pitch, power feed, saw set, and temper. Band filing information is also indicated.
6. Speed range is selected by shifting the transmission.
7. Speed range shift must be done with the band speed set at the lowest setting.
8. The upper guidepost must be adjusted so that it is as close to the workpiece as possible.
9. Band pitch must be correct for the thickness of material to be cut. Generally, a fine pitch will be used on thin material. Cutting a thick workpiece with a fine pitch band will clog saw teeth and reduce cutting efficiency.
10. Band set must be adequate for the thickness of the blade used in a contour cut. If set is insufficient, the blade may not be able to cut the desired radius.

SECTION G / UNIT 1 / THE DRILL PRESS

SELF-TEST ANSWERS

1. a. The sensitive, upright, and radial-arm drill presses are the three basic types. The sensitive drill press is made for light duty work and it provides the operator with a sense or "feel" of the feed on the drill. The upright is a similar, but heavy duty, drill press equipped with power feed. The radial-arm drill press allows the operator to position the drill over the work where he needs it, rather than to position the work under the drill as with other drill presses.
   b. The sensitive, upright, and radial-arm drill presses all perform much the same functions of drilling, reaming, counterboring, countersinking, spot facing, and tapping, but the upright and radial machines do heavier and larger jobs. The radial-arm drill can support large, heavy castings and work can be done on them without the workpiece being moved.

2. Sensitive drill press

a	Spindle	f	Base	3. Radial drill press			
g	Quill lock handle	c	Power feed		b	Column	
e	Column	j	Motor		c	Radial arm	
l	Switch	d	Variable speed control		a	Spindle	
b	Depth Stop	k	Table lift crank		d	Base	
n	Head	i	Quill return spring		e	Drill head	
o	Table	m	Guard				
h	Table lock						

SECTION G / UNIT 2 / DRILLING TOOLS

SELF-TEST ANSWERS

1.

t	Web
u	Margin
d	Drill point angle
p	Cutting lip
k	Flute
o	Body
e	Lip relief angle
g	Land
b	Chisel edge angle
j	Body clearance
i	Helix angle
y	Axis of drill
n	Shank length
c	Tang
x	Taper shank
w	Straight shank

2.

	Decimal Diameter	Fractional Size	Number Size	Letter Size	Metric Size
a	.0781	$\frac{5}{64}$			
b	.1495		25		
c	.272			I	
d	.159		21		
e	.1969				5
f	.323			P	
g	.3125	$\frac{5}{16}$			
h	.4375	$\frac{7}{16}$			
i	.201		7		
j	.1875	$\frac{3}{16}$			

SECTION G / UNIT 4 / WORK LOCATING AND HOLDING DEVICES ON DRILLING MACHINES

SELF-TEST ANSWERS

1. The purpose for using workholding devices is to keep the workpiece rigid, from turning with the drill, and for operator safety.
2. Included in a list of workholding devices would be strap clamps, T-bolts, and step blocks. Also used are C-clamps, V-blocks, vises, jigs and fixtures, and angle plates.
3. Parallels are mostly used to raise workpieces off the drill press table or to lift the workpiece higher in a vise, thus providing a space for the drill breakthrough. They are made of hardened steel so care should be exercised in their use.
4. Thin limber materials tend to be sprung downward from the force of drilling until drill breakthrough begins. The drill then ''grabs'' as the material springs upward and a broken drill is often the result. This can be avoided by placing the support or parallels as near the drill as possible.
5. Angle drilling is done by tilting a drill press table (not all types tilt), or by using an angular vise. If no means of setting the exact angle is provided, a protractor head with level may be used.
6. Vee-blocks are suited to hold round stock for drilling. The most frequent use of vee-blocks is for cross drilling holes in shafts, although many other setups are used.
7. The wiggler is used for locating a center punch mark under the center axis of a drill spindle.
8. Some odd-shaped workpieces, such as gears with extending hubs that need holes drilled for set screws, might be difficult to set up without an angle plate.
9. One of the difficulties with hand tapping is the tendency for taps to start crooked or misaligned with the tap drilled hole. Starting a tap by hand in a drill press with the same set up as used for the tap drilling assures a perfect alignment.
10. Since jigs and fixtures are mostly used for production manufacturing, small machine shops rarely have a use for them.

SECTION G / UNIT 5 / OPERATING DRILLING MACHINES

SELF-TEST ANSWERS

1. The three considerations would be speeds, feeds, and coolants.
2. The RPMs of the drills would be:
   a. $\frac{1}{4}$ in. diameter is 1440 RPM.   c. $\frac{3}{4}$ in. diameter is 480 RPM.   e. $1\frac{1}{2}$ in. diameter is 240 RPM.
   b. 2 in. diameter is 180 RPM. $\frac{3}{8}$ in. diameter is 960 RPM.
3. Worn margins and outer corners broken down. The drill can be ground back to its full size and resharpened.
4. The operator will increase the feed in order to produce a chip. This increased feed is often greater than the drill can stand without breaking.
5. The feed is about right when the chip rolls into a close helix. Long, stringy chips can indicate too much feed.
6. Feeds are designated by a small measured advance movement of the drill for each revolution. A .001 in. feed for a $\frac{1}{8}$ in. diameter drill, for example, would move the drill .001 in. into the work for every turn of the drill.
7. The water soluble oil types and the cutting oils, both animal and mineral.
8. Besides having the correct cutting speed, a sulfurized oil based cutting fluid helps to reduce friction and cool the cutting edge.
9. Drill ''jamming'' can be avoided by a ''pecking'' procedure. The operator drills a small amount and pulls out the drill to remove the chips. This is repeated until the hole is finished.
10. The depth stop is used to limit the travel of the drill so it will not go on into the table or vise. The depth of blind holes is preset and drilled. Countersink and counterbore depths are set so that several can be easily made the same.

SECTION G / UNIT 6 / COUNTERSINKING AND COUNTERBORING

SELF-TEST ANSWERS

1. Countersinks are used to chamfer holes and to provide tapered holes for flat head fasteners such as screws and rivets.

2. Countersink angles vary to match the angles of different flat head fasteners or different taper hole requirements.
3. A center drill is used to make a 60 degree countersunk hole in workpieces for lathes and grinders.
4. A counterbore makes a cylindrical recess concentric with a smaller hole so that a hex head bolt or socket head cap screw can be flush mounted with the surface of a workpiece.
5. The pilot diameter should always be a few thousandths of an inch smaller than the hole, but not more than .005 in.
6. Lubrication of the pilot prevents metal to metal contact between it and the hole. It will also prevent the scoring of the hole surface.
7. A general rule is to use approximately one-third of the cutting speed when counterboring as when using a twist drill with the same diameter.
8. Feeds and speeds when counterboring are controlled to a large extent by the condition of the equipment, the available power, and the material being counterbored.
9. Spotfacing is performed with a counterbore. It makes a flat bearing surface, square with a hole to seat a nut, washer, or bolt head.
10. Counterboring requires a rigid setup with the workpiece being securely fastened and provisions made to allow the pilot to protrude below the bottom surface of the workpiece.

SECTION G / UNIT 7 / REAMING IN THE DRILL PRESS

SELF-TEST ANSWERS

1. Machine reamers are identified by the design of the shank, either a straight or tapered shank and usually a 45 degree chamfer on the cutting end.
2. A chucking reamer is a finishing reamer, the fluted part is cylindrical, and the lands are relieved. A rose reamer is a roughing reamer. It can remove a considerable amount of material. The body has a slight back taper and no relief on the lands. All cutting takes place on the chamfered end.
3. A jobbers reamer is a finishing reamer like a chucking reamer but it has a longer fluted body.
4. Shell reamers are more economical to produce than solid reamers, especially in larger sizes.
5. An accurate hole size cannot be obtained without a high quality surface finish.
6. As a general rule the cutting speed used to ream a hole is about one-third to one-half of the speed used to drill a hole of the same size in the same material.
7. The feed rate, when reaming as compared to drilling the same material, is approximately two to three times as great. As an example, for a 1 in. drill the feed rate is about .010 to .015 in. per revolution. A 1 in. reamer would have a feed rate of between .020 and .030 in.
8. The reaming allowance for a $\frac{1}{2}$ in. diameter hole would be $\frac{1}{64}$ in.
9. Coolants cool the tool and workpiece and act as lubricants.
10. Chatter may be eliminated by reducing the speed, increasing the feed, or using a piloted reamer.
11. Oversized holes may be caused by a bent reamer shank or buildup on the cutting edges. Check also if there is a sufficient amount and if the correct kind of coolant is being used.
12. Bell-mouthed holes are usually caused by a misaligned reamer and workpiece setup. Piloted reamers, bushings, or a floating holder may correct this problem.
13. Surface finish can be improved by decreasing the feed and checking the reaming allowance. Too much or not enough material will cause poor finish. Use a large volume of coolant.
14. Carbide tipped reamers are recommended for long production runs where highly abrasive materials are reamed.
15. Cemented carbides are very hard, but also very brittle. The slightest amount of chatter or vibration may chip the cutting edges.

SECTION H / UNIT 1 / THE ENGINE LATHE

SELF-TEST ANSWERS

1. Fine chips, filings, and grindings form an abrasive sludge that wears and scores the sliding surfaces. Frequent cleaning will help to prevent damage to the machine.
2. Heavier chips should be removed with a brush; never use an air jet. The ways should then be wiped clean with a cloth and lightly oiled.
3. Since most nicks come from dropping chucks and heavy workpieces on the lathe, a lathe board used every time a chuck is changed or heavy work is installed will prevent much of this. A tool board will help keep tools such as files from being laid across the ways.

4. Once daily.
5. No. The oil on the ways may have collected dirt or grit from the air to form an abrasive mixture. The ways should first be cleaned and oiled.
6. The chips should be cleaned from the lathe and swept up on the surrounding floor area. The lathe ways and slides should be wiped and oiled.
7. Straight gibs and tapered gibs.
8. The gib on the cross slide should be adjusted so it will have a slight drag, but the compound should be set up fairly tight when it is not being used.

SECTION H / UNIT 2 / TOOLHOLDERS AND TOOL HOLDING FOR THE LATHE

SELF-TEST ANSWERS

1. A toolholder is needed to rigidly support and hold a cutting tool during the actual cutting operation. The cutting tool is often only a small piece of high speed steel or other cutting material that has to be clamped in a much larger toolholder in order to be usable.
2. On a left-hand toolholder, when viewed from above, the cutting tool end is bent to the right.
3. For high speed tools the square tool bit hole is angled upward in relation to the base of the toolholder, where it is parallel to the base for carbide tools.
4. Turning close to the chuck is usually best accomplished with a left-hand toolholder.
5. Tool height adjustments on a standard type toolholder are made by swiveling the rocker in the tool post ring.
6. Quick-change toolholders are adjusted for height with a micrometer collar.
7. Tool height on turret toolholders is adjusted by placing shims under the tool.
8. Toolholder overhang affects the rigidity of a setup; too much overhang may cause chatter.
9. The difference between a standard type toolholder and a quick-change type toolholder is in the speed with which tools can be interchanged. The tools are usually fastened more securely in a quick-change toolholder and height adjustments on a quick-change toolholder do not change the effective back rake angle of the cutting tool.
10. Drilling machine tools are used in a lathe tailstock.
11. The lathe tailstock is bored with a Morse taper hole to hold Morse taper shank tools.
12. When a series of repeat tailstock operations are to be performed on several different workpieces, a tailstock turret should be used.

SECTION H / UNIT 3 / CUTTING TOOLS FOR THE LATHE

SELF-TEST ANSWERS

1. High speed steel is easily shaped into the desired shape of cutting tool. It produces better finishes on low speed machines and on soft metals.
2. Its geometrical form: the side and back rake, front and side relief angles, and chip breakers.
3. Unlike single point tools, form tools produce their shape by plunging directly into the work.
4. When a "chip trap" is formed by improper grinding on a tool, the chip is not able to clear the tool; this prevents a smooth flow across the face of the tool. The result is tearing of the surface on the workpiece and a possible broken tool.
5. Some tool holders provide a built-in back rake of about 16 degrees; to this is added any back rake on the tool to make a total back rake that is excessive.
6. A zero rake should be used for threading tools. A zero to slightly negative back rake should be used for plastics and brass, since they tend to "dig in."
7. The side relief allows the tool to feed into the work material. The end relief angle keeps the tool end from rubbing on the work.
8. The side rake directs the chip flow away from the cut and it also provides for a keen cutting edge. The back rake promotes smooth chip flow and good finishes.
9. The angles can be checked with a tool grinding gage, a protractor, or an optical comparator.
10. Long, stringy chips or those that become snarled on workpieces, tool post, chuck or lathe dog are hazardous to the operator. Chip breakers and correct feeds can produce an ideal chip that does not fly off but will simply drop to the chip pan and is easily handled.

11. Chips can be broken up by using coarse feeds and maximum depth of cuts for roughing cuts and by using tools with chipbreakers on them.
12. Overheating a tool causes small cracks to form on the edge. When a stress is applied, as in a roughing cut, the tool end may break off.

SECTION H / UNIT 4 / LATHE SPINDLE TOOLING

SELF-TEST ANSWERS

1. The lathe spindle is a hollow shaft that can have one of three mounting devices machined on the spindle nose. It has an internal Morse taper that will accommodate centers or collets.
2. The spindle nose types are the threaded, long taper key drive, and the camlock.
3. The independent chuck is a four-jaw chuck in which each jaw can move separately and independently of the others. It is used to hold odd-shaped workpieces.
4. The universal chuck is most often a three-jaw chuck although they are made with more or less jaws. Each jaw moves in or out by the same amount when the chuck wrench is turned. They are used to hold and quickly center round stock.
5. Combination chucks and Adjust-Tru three-jaw chucks.
6. A drive plate.
7. The live center is made of soft steel so it can be turned to true it up if necessary. It is made with a Morse taper to fit the spindle taper or special sleeve if needed.
8. A hardened drive center is serrated so it will turn the work between centers, but only light cuts can be taken. Face drives use a number of driving pins that dig into the work and are hydraulically compensated for irregularities.
9. Workpieces and fixtures are mounted on face plates. These are identified by their heavy construction and the T slots. Drive plates have only slots.
10. Collet chucks are very accurate workholding devices. Spring collets are limited to smaller material and to specific sizes.

SECTION H / UNIT 5 / OPERATING THE MACHINE CONTROLS

SELF-TEST ANSWERS

1. Very low speeds are made possible by disengaging the spindle by pulling out the lockpin and engaging the back gear.
2. The varidrive is changed while the motor is running, but the back gear lever is only shifted with the motor off.
3. Levers that are located on the headstock can be shifted in various arrangements to select speeds.
4. The feed reverse lever.
5. These levers are used for selecting feeds or threads per inch for threading.
6. The quick approach and return of the tool; this is used for delicate work and when approaching a shoulder or chuck jaw.
7. Since the cross feed is geared differently (about one-third of the longitudinal feed), the outside diameter would have a coarser finish than the face.
8. The half-nut lever is used only for threading.
9. They are graduated in English units. Some metric conversion collars are being made and used that read in both English and metric units at the same time.
10. You can test with a rule and a given slide movement such as .125 or .250 in. If the slide moves one-half that distance, the lathe is calibrated for double depth and reads the same amount as that taken off the diameter.

SECTION H / UNIT 6 / FACING AND CENTER DRILLING

SELF-TEST ANSWERS

1. A lathe board is placed on the ways under the chuck and the chuck is removed, since it is the wrong chuck to hold rectangular work. The mating parts of an independent chuck and the lathe spindle are cleaned and the chuck is mounted. The part is roughly centered in the jaws and adjusted to center by using the back of a toolholder or a dial indicator.

2. The tool should be on the center of the lathe axis.
3. No. The resultant facing feed would be approximately 0.3 to 0.5 $\times$ .012 in., which would be a finishing feed.
4. The compound must be swung to either 30 or 90 degrees so that the tool can be fed into the face of the work by a measured amount. A depth micrometer or a micrometer caliper can be used to check the trial finish cut. A right-hand facing tool is used for shaft ends. It is different from a turning tool in that its point is only a 58 degree included angle to fit in the narrow space between the shaft face and the center.
6. $\text{RPM} = \dfrac{300 \times 4}{4} = 300$.
7. Center drilling is done to prepare work for turning between centers and for spotting workpieces for drilling in the lathe.
8. Round stock is laid out with a center head and square or rectangular with diagonal lines. Stock can be held vertically in a vise or angle plates and vee-blocks for center drilling in a drill press.
9. Center drills are broken as a result of feeding the drill too fast and having the lathe speed too slow. Other causes result from having the tailstock off center, the work off center in a steady rest, or lack of cutting oil.
10. The sharp edge provides a poor bearing surface and soon wears out of round, causing machining problems such as chatter.

SECTION H / UNIT 7 / TURNING BETWEEN CENTERS

SELF-TEST ANSWERS

1. A shaft between centers can be turned end for end without loss of concentricity and it can be removed from the lathe and returned without loss of synchronization between thread and tool. Cutting off between centers is not done as it would break the parting tool and ruin the work. Steady rest work is not done with work mounted in a center in the headstock spindle.
2. The other method is where the workpiece is held in a chuck on one end and in the tailstock center on the other end.
3. Coarser feeds, deeper cuts, and smaller rake angles all tend to increase chip curl. Chip breakers also make the chip curl.
4. Dead centers are hardened 60 degree centers that do not rotate with the work but require high pressure lubricant. Ball bearing centers turn with work and do not require lubricant. Pipe centers turn with the work and are used to support tubular material.
5. With no end play in the workpiece and the bent tail of the lathe dog free to click against the sides of the slot.
6. Because of expansion of the workpiece from the heat of machining, it tightens on the center, thus causing more friction and more heat. This could ruin the center.
7. Excess overhang promotes lack of rigidity. This causes chatter and tool breakage.
8. $\text{RPM} = \dfrac{90 \times 4}{1\frac{1}{2}} = 360 \div \dfrac{3}{2} = 360 \times \dfrac{2}{3} = 240 \quad \text{or} \quad \dfrac{360}{1.5} = 240$
9. The spacing would be .010 in. as the tool moves that amount for each revolution of the spindle.
10. The feed rate for roughing should be $\frac{1}{5}$ to $\frac{1}{10}$ as much as the depth of cut. This should be limited to what the tool, workpiece, or machine can stand without undue stress.
11. For most purposes where liberal tolerances are allowed, .015 to .030 in. can be left for finishing. When closer tolerances are required, two finish cuts are taken with .005 to .010 in. left for the last finish cut.
12. After roughing is completed, .015 to .030 in. is left for finishing. The diameter of the workpiece is checked with a micrometer and the remaining amount is dialed on the cross feed micrometer collar. A short trial cut is taken and the lathe is stopped. This diameter is again checked. If the diameter is within tolerance, the finish cut is taken.

SECTION H / UNIT 8 / ALIGNMENT OF THE LATHE CENTERS

SELF-TEST ANSWERS

1. The workpiece becomes tapered.
2. The workpiece is tapered with the small end at the tailstock.
3. By the witness mark on the tailstock, by using a test bar, and by taking a light cut on a workpiece and measuring.
4. The dial indicator.
5. With a micrometer. The tailstock is set over with a dial indicator.

SECTION H / UNIT 9 / DRILLING, BORING, REAMING, KNURLING, RECESSING, PARTING, AND TAPPING IN THE LATHE

SELF-TEST ANSWERS

1. Drilled holes are not sufficiently accurate for bores in machine parts as they would be loose on the shaft and would not run true.
2. The workpiece is center spotted with a center drill at the correct RPM and, if the hole is to be more than a $\frac{3}{8}$ in. diameter, a pilot drill is put through. Cutting oil is used. The final size drill is put through at a slower speed.
3. The chief advantage of boring in the lathe is the bore runs true with the center line of the lathe and the outside of the workpiece, if the workpiece has been set up to run true (with no runout). This is not always possible when reaming bores that have been drilled, since the reamer follows the eccentricity or runout of the bore.
4. Ways to eliminate chatter in a boring bar are:
    a. Shorten the bar overhang, if possible.
    b. Reduce the spindle speed.
    c. Make sure the tool is on center.
    d. Use as large a diameter bar as possible without binding in the bore.
    e. Reduce the nose radius on the tool.
    f. Apply cutting oil to the bore.
    g. Use tuned or solid carbide boring bars.
5. Through boring is making a bore the same diameter all the way through the part. Counterboring is making two or more diameters in the same bore, usually with 90 degree or square internal shoulders. Blind holes are bores that do not go all the way through.
6. Grooves and thread relief are made in bores by means of specially shaped or ground tools in a boring bar.
7. A floating reamer holder will help to eliminate the bell mouth, but it does not remove the runout.
8. Hand reamers produce a better finish than machine reaming.
9. Cutting speeds for reaming are *one-half* that used for drilling; feeds used for reaming are *twice* that used for drilling.
10. Large internal threads are produced with a boring tool. Heavy forces are needed to turn large hand taps, so it is not advisable to use large taps in a lathe.
11. A tap drill can be used as a reamer by first drilling with a drill that is $\frac{1}{32}$ to $\frac{1}{16}$ in. undersized. This procedure assures a more accurate hole size by drilling.
12. A spiral point tap works best for power tapping.
13. The variations in pitch of the hand cut threads would cause the micrometer collar to give erroneous readings. A screw used for this purpose and for most machine parts must be threaded with a tool guided by the leadscrew on the lathe.
14. Thread relief and external grooves are produced by specially ground tools that are similar to internal grooving tools except that they have less end relief. Parting tools are often used for making external grooves.
15. Parting tools tend to seize in the work, especially with deep cuts or heavy feeds. Without cutting oil seizing is almost sure to follow with the possibility of a broken parting tool and misaligned or damaged work.
16. You can avoid chatter when cutting off with a parting tool by maintaining a rigid setup and keeping enough feed to produce a continuous chip, if possible.
17. Knurling is used to improve the appearance of a part, to provide a good gripping surface, and to increase the diameter of a part for press fits.
18. Ordinary knurls make a straight or diamond pattern impression by displacing the metal with high pressures.
19. When knurls produce a double impression, they can be readjusted up or down and moved to a new position. Angling the toolholder 5 degrees may help.
20. You can avoid producing a flaking knurled surface by stopping the knurling process when the diamond points are almost sharp. Also use a lubricant while knurling.

SECTION H / UNIT 10 / SIXTY DEGREE THREAD INFORMATION AND CALCULATIONS

SELF-TEST ANSWERS

1. The sharp V thread can be easily damaged while handling if it is dropped or allowed to strike against a hard surface.

2. The pitch is the distance between a point on a screw thread to a corresponding point on the next thread measured parallel to the axis. "Threads per inch" is the number of threads in one inch.
3. American National Standard and Unified Standard threads both have the 60 degree included angle and are both based on the inch measure with similar pitch series. The depth of the thread and the classes of thread fits are different in the two systems.
4. To allow for tolerancing of external and internal threads to promote standardization and interchangeability of parts.
5. This describes a diameter of $\frac{1}{2}$ in. 20 threads per inch, and Unified coarse series external thread with a class 2 thread tolerance.
6. The flat on the end of the tool for 20 threads per inch should be P = .050 × .125 = .006 in. for American National threads and for Unified threads.
7. The compound at 30° will move in .708/20 = .0354 in. for Unified threads.
   The compound will move in .75/20 = .0375 in. for American National threads.
8. The fit of the thread refers to classes of fits and tolerances, while percent of thread refers to the actual minor diameter of an internal thread, a 100 percent thread being full depth internal threads.
9. The Systéme International (SI) thread and the British Standard ISO Metric Screw Threads are two metric thread systems in use.
10. In metric tolerance symbols, smaller numbers refer to smaller tolerances.

SECTION H / UNIT 11 / CUTTING UNIFIED EXTERNAL THREADS

SELF-TEST ANSWERS

1. A series of cuts are made in the same groove with a single point tool by keeping the same ratio and relative position of the tool on each pass. The quick-change gearbox allows choices of various pitches or leads.
2. The chips are less likely to bind and tear off when feeding in with the compound set at 29 degrees and the tool is less likely to break.
3. The 60 degree angle on the tool is checked with a center gage or optical comparator.
4. The number of threads per inch can be checked with a screw pitch gage or by using a rule and counting the threads in one inch.
5. A center gage is used to align the tool to the work.
6. No. The carriage is moved by the thread on the leadscrew when the half-nuts are engaging it.
7. Even numbered threads may be engaged on the half-nuts at any line and odd numbered threads at any numbered line. It would be best to use the same line every time for fractional numbered threads.
8. The spindle should be turning slow enough for the operator to maintain control of the threading operation, about one-fourth turning speeds usually.
9. The leadscrew rotation is reversed, which causes the cut to be made from the left to the right. The compound is set at 29 degrees to the left. The threading tool and lathe settings are set up in the same way as for cutting right-hand threads.
10. Picking up the thread or resetting the tool is a procedure that is used to position a tool to existing threads.

SECTION H / UNIT 12 / CUTTING UNIFIED INTERNAL THREADS

SELF-TEST ANSWERS

1. The minor diameter of the thread.
2. By varying the bore size, usually larger than the minor diameter. This is done to make tapping easier.
3. 75 percent.
4. A drill just under the tap drill size should first be used; thus the tap drill acts as a reamer.
5. $.500 - \left(\dfrac{.65}{13} \times 2 \times .6 \right) = .440$
   Since the nearest fractional drill size is $\frac{7}{16}$ in. = .4375, the tap drill for 60% threads is $\frac{7}{16}$ in.
6. Large internal threads of various forms can be made, and the threads are concentric to the axis of the work.
7. To the left of the operator.
8. A screw pitch gage should be used.

9. Boring bar and tool deflection cause the threads to be undersize from the calculations and settings on the micrometer collars.
10. The minor diameter equals $D - (P \times .541 \times 2)$.
   $\frac{1}{8}$ in. $= .125$ in.
   $d = 1$ in. $- (.125 \times .541 \times 2) = .8648$ or $.865$ in.

SECTION H / UNIT 13 / TAPER TURNING, TAPER BORING, AND FORMING

SELF-TEST ANSWERS

1. Steep tapers are quick release tapers and slight tapers are self-holding tapers.
2. Tapers are expressed in taper per foot, taper per inch, and by angles.
3. Tapers are turned by hand feeding the compound slide, by offsetting the tailstock and turning between centers, or by using a taper attachment. A fourth method is to use a tool that is set to the desired angle and form cut the taper.
4. No. The angle on the workpiece would be the included angle, which is twice that on the compound setting. The angle on the compound swivel base is the angle with the work centerline.
5. The reading at the lathe centerline index would be 55 degrees, which is the complementary angle.
6. Offset $= \dfrac{10 \times (1.125 - .75)}{2 \times 3} = \dfrac{3.75}{6} = .625$ in.
7. Four methods of measuring the offset on the tailstock are centers and a rule, witness marks and a rule, the dial indicator, and toolholder-micrometer dial.
8. The two types of taper attachments are the plain and the telescopic. Internal and external and slight to fairly steep tapers can be made. Centers remain in line, and power feed is used for good finishes.
9. The taper plug gage and the taper gage are the simplest and most practical means to check a taper. Four methods of measuring tapers are the plug and ring gages; using a micrometer on layout lines; using a micrometer with precision parallels and drill rod on a surface plate; and using a sine bar, gage block, and a dial indicator.
10. Chamfers, V-grooves, and very short tapers may be made by the form tool method.

SECTION H / UNIT 14 / USING STEADY AND FOLLOWER RESTS IN THE LATHE

SELF-TEST ANSWERS

1. When workpieces extend from the chuck more than four or five workpiece diameters and are unsupported by a dead center; when workpieces are long and slender.
2. Since they are useful for supporting long workpieces, heavier cuts can be taken or operations such as turning, threading, and grooving may be performed without chattering. Internal operations such as boring may be done on long workpieces.
3. The steady rest is placed near the tailstock end of the shaft, which is supported in a dead center. The steady rest is clamped to the lathe bed and the lower jaws are adjusted to the shaft finger tight. The upper half of the frame is closed and the top jaw is adjusted with some clearance. The jaws are locked and lubricant is applied.
4. The jaws should be readjusted when the shaft heats up from friction in order to avoid scoring. Also soft materials are sometimes used on the jaws to protect finishes.
5. A center punch mark is placed in the center of the end of the shaft. The lower two jaws on the steady rest are adjusted until the center punch mark aligns with the point of the dead center.
6. No.
7. No. When the surface is rough, a bearing spot must be turned for the steady rest jaws.
8. By using a cat head.
9. A follower rest.
10. The shaft is purposely made one or two inches longer and an undercut is machined on the end to clear the follower rest jaws.

SECTION H / UNIT 15 / ADDITIONAL THREAD FORMS

SELF-TEST ANSWERS

1. Translating type screws are mostly used for imparting motion or power and to position mechanical parts.
2. Square, modified square, Acme, stub Acme, and Buttress are five basic translating thread forms.
3. Since the pitch for 4 TPI would be .250 in., the depth of thread would be P/2 = .250/2 = .125 in.
4. Since the pitch for 4 TPI would be .250 in., the depth of the Acme thread would be .5P + .010 in. or .5 × .250 in. + .010 in. = .135 in.
5. General purpose Acme threads bear on the flanks and centralizing Acme threads bear at the major diameter.
6. 29 degrees.
7. The general use for stub Acme threads is where a coarse pitch thread with a shallow depth is required.
8. The modified square thread.
9. The Acme thread form.
10. Buttress threads are used where great forces or pressures are exerted in one direction.
11. .375 in.
12. The distance from a point on one thread to a corresponding point on the next.
13. The distance the nut travels in one revolution.
14. Single lead.
15. a. Accurately slotted face plate.   c. Using the thread chasing dial.
    b. Indexing a gear on the drive train.   d. The compound rest method.
16. They provide rapid traverse, are more efficient, have a larger minor diameter and are stronger, furnish more bearing surface area than a single thread.
17. Most kinds. Sharp-V, American national, Unified, metric, buttress, square, and acme can be made multiple lead, either in right- or left-hand threads.
18. You can determine the number of leads by counting the number of starting grooves at the end of a bolt or screw.
19. Roughing of coarse threads may move the tool slightly. If one thread has already been finished, there is no more allowance for adjustment. Finishing both threads consecutively, however, gives a much greater assurance that the setup will not move.
20. Lighter cuts should be taken to keep from tearing the threads.

SECTION H / UNIT 16 / CUTTING ACME THREADS ON THE LATHE

SELF-TEST ANSWERS

1. The thread angle.
2. The included angle, the relief angle, and the flat on the end of the tool.
3. Coarse threading on a lathe imposes heavy loads on these parts. Lubrication prior to threading helps to reduce excess wear.
4. The compound is usually set at $14\frac{1}{2}$ degrees. Some machinists prefer to set the compound at 90 degrees.
5. $P = \frac{1}{6} = .1666$ in.; depth — .5P + .010 in. = .93 in.
6. The tool is aligned by using the Acme tool gage. Refer to Figure 6.
7. $P = .1666$ in.; minor diameter = .750 in. − .1666 in. = .583 in.
8. With an Acme tap set.
9. An Acme thread plug gage.
10. Light finishing cuts with a honed tool and a good grade of sulfurized cutting oil will help make good thread finishes. A rigid setup and low speeds will also help.

SECTION H / UNIT 17 / USING CARBIDES AND OTHER TOOL
MATERIALS ON THE LATHE

SELF-TEST ANSWERS

1. Tungsten carbide and cobalt.
2. Decreased hardness and increased toughness.

3. Edge or flank wear is considered normal wear.
4. Yes, if it is set at 90 degrees to the axis of the work.
5. No. The cutting edge engagement length is greater than the depth of cut.
6. Antiweld, anticratering for machining steels.
7. Higher red hardness.
8. Increasing the nose radius will give good finishes even with an increased feed rate.
9. Tools are stronger.
10. Chatter may develop between tool and work.
11. Relief is ground just below the cutting edges of the carbide and clearance is ground primarily on the shank of the tool.
12. Aluminum oxide.
13. When considerable wear is evident on carbide tools. Equipment and setups must be very rigid for ceramics.
14. C-2
15. C-5
16. 44-A
17. C-7
18. The stock removal rate is low but very high finishes are obtained with these tools.
19. Very high tool life on some abrasive, difficult to machine materials.
20. Only silicon carbide (or diamond) wheels may be used for grinding carbide tools. The shank is made of steel, however, and clearance may be ground first on an aluminum oxide wheel.

SECTION I / UNIT 1 / THE VERTICAL SPINDLE MILLING MACHINE

SELF-TEST ANSWERS

1. The column, knee, saddle, table, ram, and toolhead.
2. The table traverse handwheel and the table power feed.
3. The cross traverse handwheel.
4. The quill feed hand lever and handwheel.
5. The table clamp locks the table rigidly and keeps it from moving while other table axes are in movement.
6. The spindle brake locks the spindle while tool changes are being made.
7. The spindle has to stop before speed changes from high to low are made.
8. The ram movement increases the working capacity of the toolhead.
9. Loose machine movements are adjusted with the slide gibs.
10. The quill clamp is tightened to lock the quill rigidly while milling.

SECTION I / UNIT 2 / CUTTING TOOLS AND CUTTER HOLDERS FOR THE VERTICAL MILLING MACHINE

SELF-TEST ANSWERS

1. When viewed from the cutting end, a right-hand cut end mill will rotate counterclockwise.
2. An end mill has to have center cutting teeth to be used for plunge cutting.
3. End mills for aluminum usually have a fast helix angle and also highly polished flutes and cutting edges.
4. Carbide end mills are very effective when milling abrasive or hard materials.
5. Roughing mills are used to remove large amounts of material.
6. Tapered end mills are mostly used in mold or die making to obtain precisely tapered sides on workpieces.
7. Carbide insert tools are used because new cutting edges are easily exposed. They are available in grades to cut most materials and they are very efficient cutting tools.
8. Straight shank mills are held in collets or adapters.
9. Shell end mills are mounted on shell mill arbors.
10. Quick change toolholders make presetting of a number of tools possible and tools can be changed with a minimum loss of time.

SECTION I / UNIT 3 / SETUPS ON THE VERTICAL MILLING MACHINE

SELF-TEST ANSWERS

1. Workpieces can be aligned on a machine table by measuring their distance from the edge of the table, by locating against stops in the T-slots, or by indicating the workpiece side.
2. To align a vise on a machine table, the solid vise jaw needs to be indicated.
3. Toolhead alignment is checked when it is important that machining takes place square to the machine table.
4. When the knee clamping bolts are loose, the weight of the knee makes it sag. But when the knee clamps are tightened, the knee is pulled into its normal position in relation to the column.
5. When the toolhead clamping bolts are tightened, it usually produces a small change in the toolhead position.
6. A machine spindle can be located over the edge of a workpiece with an edge finder or with the aid of dial indicator.
7. The spindle axis is one-half of the tip diameter away from the workpiece edge when the tip walks off sideways.
8. An offset edge finder works best at 600 to 800 RPM.
9. To eliminate the effect of backlash, always position from the same direction.
10. The center of a hole is located with a dial indicator mounted in the machine spindle.

SECTION I / UNIT 4 / FEEDS AND SPEEDS FOR END MILLING

SELF-TEST ANSWERS

1. Lower cutting speeds are used to machine hard materials, tough materials, abrasive material, on heavy cuts, and to get maximum tool life.
2. Higher cutting speeds are used to machine softer materials, to obtain good surface finishes, with small diameter cutters, for light cuts, on frail workpieces and on frail setups.
3. The calculated RPM is a starting point and may change depending on conditions illustrated in the answers to Problems 1 and 2.
4. Cutting fluids are used with HSS cutters except on materials such as cast iron, brass, and many nonmetallic materials.
5. Cutting with carbide cutters is performed without a cutting fluid, unless a steady stream of fluid can be maintained at the cutting edge of the tool.
6. The thickness of the chips affects the tool life of the cutter. Very thin chips dull a cutting edge quickly. Too thick chips cause tool breakage or the chipping of the cutting edge.
7. The depth of cut for an end mill should not exceed one-half of the diameter of the cutter.
8. Limitations on the depth of cut for an end mill are the amount of material to be removed, the power available, and the rigidity of the tool and setup.
9. The RPM for a $\frac{3}{4}$ in. diameter end mill to cut brass is:

$$RPM = \frac{CS\ 4}{D} = \frac{200 \times 4}{\frac{3}{4}} = 1067\ RPM$$

10. The feedrate for a two flute, $\frac{1}{4}$ in. diameter carbide end mill in medium alloy steel is:

$$feedrate = f \times RPM \times n$$
$$f = .0005$$
$$RPM = \frac{CS \times 4}{D} = \frac{150 \times 4}{\frac{1}{4}} = 2400$$
$$n = 2$$
$$Feedrate = .0005 \times 2400 \times 2 = 2.4\ IPM$$

SECTION I / UNIT 5 / VERTICAL MILLING MACHINE OPERATIONS

SELF-TEST ANSWERS

1. Accurate centering of a cutter over a shaft is done with the machine dials.

2. The feed direction against the cutter rotation assures positive dimensional movement. It also prevents the workpiece from being pulled into the cutter because of any backlash in the machine.
3. End mills can work themselves out of a split collet if the cut is too heavy or when the cutter gets dull.
4. Angular cuts can be made by tilting the workpiece or by tilting the workhead.
5. Circular slots can be milled by using a rotary table or an index head.
6. Squares, hexagons, or other shapes that require surfaces at precise angles to each other are made by using a dividing head.
7. Square holes or other internal hole shapes can be made by using a vertical shaping attachment.
8. With a right angle milling attachment, milling cuts can be made in very inaccessible places.
9. Layout lines are used as guides to indicate where machining should take place. Layouts should be made prior to machining any reference surfaces away.
10. A T-slot cutter only enlarges the bottom part of a groove. The groove has to be made before a T-slot cutter can be used.

SECTION I / UNIT 6 / USING THE OFFSET BORING HEAD

SELF-TEST ANSWERS

1. An offset boring head is used to produce standard and nonstandard size holes at precisely controllable hole locations.
2. Parallels raise the workpiece off the table or other workholding device to allow through holes to be bored.
3. Unless the locking screw is tightened after toolslide adjustments are made, the toolslide will move during the cutting operation, resulting in a tapered or odd-sized hole.
4. The toolslide has a number of holes so that the boring tool can be held in different positions in relation to the spindle axis for different size bores.
5. It is important that you know if one graduation is one-thousandth of an inch or two-thousandths of an inch in hole size change.
6. The best boring tool to use is the one with the largest diameter that can be used and the one with the shortest shank.
7. It is very important that the cutting edge of the boring tool is on the centerline of the axis of the toolslide. Only in this position are the rake and clearance angles correct as ground on the tool.
8. The hole size obtained for given amount of depth of cut can change depending on the sharpness of the tool, the amount of tool overhang (boring bar length), and the amount of feed per revolution.
9. Boring tool deflection changes when the tool gets dull, the depth of cut increases or decreases, or the feed is changed.
10. The cutting speed is determined by the kind of tool material and the kind of work material, but boring vibrations set up through an unbalanced cutting tool or a very long boring bar may require a smaller than calculated RPM.

SECTION J / UNIT 2 / TYPES OF SPINDLES, ARBORS, AND ADAPTORS

SELF-TEST ANSWERS

1. Face mills over 6 in. in diameter.
2. The two classes of taper are self-holding, with a small included angle, and self-releasing, with a steep taper.
3. $3\frac{1}{2}$ IPF.
4. Where small diameter cutters are used, on light cuts, and where little clearance is available.
5. A Style C arbor is a shell end mill arbor.
6. To increase the range of cutters that can be used on a milling machine with a given size spindle socket.
7. Spacing collars are used to take up the space between the cutter and the end of the arbor. They are also used to space straddle milling cutters. Bearing collars ride in the arbor support bearing; they provide support for the outer end of the arbor. Spacing and bearing collars are precision accessories and should be protected against nicks and burrs.
8. Dirt or burrs between collars can cause cutter runout and inaccurate machining.
9. Your instructor will show you how to adjust bearing clearance. Check to see that the oil reservoir is full or that sufficient oil is applied to keep the arbor bearing well lubricated during milling.
10. Quick-change tooling systems save time as many different tools can be setup and quickly inserted in the machine.

SECTION J / UNIT 3 / ARBOR-DRIVEN MILLING CUTTERS

SELF-TEST ANSWERS

1. Profile sharpened cutters and form relieved cutters.
2. Light duty plain milling cutters have many teeth. They are used for finishing operations. Heavy duty plain mills have few but coarse teeth, designed for heavy cuts.
3. Plain milling cutters do not have side cutting teeth. This would cause extreme rubbing if used to mill steps or grooves. Plain milling cutters should be wider than the flat surface they are machining.
4. Side milling cutters, having side cutting teeth, are used when grooves are machined.
5. Straight tooth side mills are used only to mill shallow grooves because of their limited chip space between the teeth and their tendency to chatter. Stagger tooth mills have a smoother cutting action because of the alternate helical teeth; more chip clearance allows deeper cuts.
6. Half side milling cutters are efficiently used when straddle milling.
7. Metal slitting saws are used in slotting or cut off operations.
8. Gear tooth cutters and corner rounding cutters.
9. To mill V-notches, dovetails, or chamfers.
10. A right-hand cutter rotates counterclockwise when viewed from the outside end.

SECTION J / UNIT 4 / WORKHOLDING METHODS AND STANDARD SETUPS

SELF-TEST ANSWERS

1. A clamping bolt should be close to the workpiece and a greater distance away from the support block.
2. Finished surfaces should be protected with shims from being marked by clamps or rough vise jaws.
3. Screwjacks are used to support workpieces or to support the end of a clamp.
4. A stop block prevents a workpiece from being moved by cutting pressure.
5. Quick action jaws are two independent jaws mounted anywhere on a machine table to form a custom vise.
6. Swivel vise has one movement in a horizontal plane, where a universal vise swivels both horizontally and vertically.
7. All-steel vises are used to hold rough workpieces such as castings or forgings.
8. A rotary table is used to mill gears, circular grooves, or for angular indexing.
9. A dividing head is used to divide accurately the circumference of a workpiece into any number of equal divisions.
10. A fixture is used when a great number of pieces have to be machined in exactly the same way, and when the cost of making the fixture can be justified in savings resulting from its use.

SECTION J / UNIT 5 / FEEDS AND SPEEDS FOR HORIZONTAL MILLING

SELF-TEST ANSWERS

1. Cutting speed is the distance a cutting edge of a tool travels in one minute. It is expressed in feet per minute (FPM).
2. Starting a cut at the low end of the speed range will save the cutter from overheating.
3. Carbide tools are operated at two to six times the speed of HSS tools. If a HSS tool is 100 FPM, the carbide tool would be 200 to 600 FPM.
4. Too low a cutting speed is inefficient because a cutter can do more work in a given time period.
5. The feedrate on a milling machine is given in inches per minute (IPM).
6. The feedrate is the product of RPM times the number of teeth of the cutter times the feed per tooth.
7. Feed per revolution does not consider the number of teeth on different cutters.
8. Too low a feedrate causes the cutter to rub and scrape the surface of the work instead of cut. Because of the high friction, the tool will dull quickly.
9. $\text{RPM} = \dfrac{\text{CS} \times 4}{\text{D}} = \dfrac{60 \times 4}{3} = 80 \text{ RPM}.$
10. $\text{RPM} = \dfrac{\text{CS} \times 4}{\text{D}} = \dfrac{150 \times 4}{4} = 150 \text{ RPM}.$

Feed per tooth = .003 in.

Number of teeth = 5

Feedrate = RPM × feed per tooth × number of teeth = 150 × .003 × 5 = 2.25 = $2\frac{1}{4}$ IPM.

SECTION J / UNIT 6 / MACHINE SETUP AND TECHNIQUES FOR PLAIN MILLING

SELF-TEST ANSWERS

1. Because the movable jaw is not solidly held. It can move and swivel slightly to align itself with the work to some extent.
2. The dial indicator is more accurate. It will show you the amount of misalignment when you make adjustments, you can see when alignment is achieved.
3. Keys are designed to align a vise or other attachments with the T-slots on a machine table.
4. No, indicating the table from the column only measures the table sliding in its ways, but it does not show if it travels parallel to the column.
5. Yes, if possible the cutting tool pressure should be against the solid jaw. This makes the most rigid setup.
6. The smallest diameter cutter that will do the job will be the most efficient, because it requires a shorter movement to have the workpiece move clear of the cutter.
7. In conventional milling, the cutting pressure is against the feed direction and also up, where in climb milling the cutting pressure is down and the cutter tends to pull the workpiece under itself.
8. A good depth for a finish cut is .015 to .030 in. Less than .010 in. makes the cutter rub, which causes rapid wear.
9. Cutting vibrations and cutting pressures may make the table move when it should be rigidly clamped.
10. When a revolving cutter is moved over a just machined surface, it will leave tool marks.

SECTION J / UNIT 7 / USING SIDE MILLING CUTTERS

SELF-TEST ANSWERS

1. Full side milling cutters are used to cut slots and grooves and where contact on both sides of the cutter is made.
2. Half side milling cutters make contact on one side only, as in straddle milling where a left-hand and a right-hand cutter are combined to cut a workpiece to length.
3. The best cutter is the one with the smallest diameter that will work, considering the clearance needed under the arbor support.
4. Usually a groove is wider than the cutter.
5. A layout shows the machinist where the machining is to take place. It helps in preventing errors.
6. Accurate positioning is done with the help of a paper feeler strip. Often adequate accuracy is achieved by using a steel rule or by aligning by sight with the layout lines.
7. If a workpiece is measured while it is clamped in the machine, additional cuts can be made without additional setups being made.
8. Shims and spacers control workpiece width in straddle milling operations.
9. The diameters of the individual cutters determine the relationship of the depth of the steps in gang milling.
10. Interlocking side mills are used to cut slots over 1 in. wide and also when precise slot width is to be produced.

SECTION K / UNIT 1 / SETUP AND OPERATION OF INDEXING HEADS AND ROTARY TABLES

SELF-TEST ANSWERS

1. When accurate spacings are made as with gears, splines, keyways, or precise angular spacings.
2. The use of a worm and worm wheel unit.
3. To make the spindle freewheeling and when direct indexing.
4. For direct indexing.
5. The most common ratio is 40:1.
6. Different hole circles are used to make precise partial revolutions with the index crank.

7. The sector arms are set to the number of holes that the index crank is to move. They eliminate the counting of these holes for each spacing.
8. The spindle lock is tightened after each indexing operation and before a cut is made to prevent any rotary movement of the spindle.
9. With the use of high number index plates or with a wide range divider.
10. When the rotation of the index crank is reversed, the backlash between the worm and worm wheel affects the accuracy of the spacing.

SECTION K / UNIT 2 / DIRECT AND SIMPLE INDEXING

SELF-TEST ANSWERS

1. Direct indexing is performed from index holes on the spindle nose. Simple indexing uses the worm and worm wheel drive and the side index plate.
2. Use a marking pen or layout dye to mark the holes to be used in direct indexing.
3. Twenty-four index holes let you make equal divisions of 2, 3, 4, 6, 8, 12, and 24 parts.
4. The sector arms can be adjusted so that the number of holes to be indexed plus one are between the beveled edges.
5. For the highest degree of accuracy use the largest possible hole circle.
6. $\frac{40}{6} = \frac{20}{3} = 6\frac{2}{3}$ turns. Use the 57 hole circle for the $\frac{2}{3}$ turn. $\frac{2}{3} \times \frac{19}{19} = \frac{38}{57}$. The fraction is 38 holes in the 57 hole circle.
7. $\frac{40}{15} = \frac{8}{3} = 2\frac{2}{3}$ turns. Use the same hole circle as for Problem 6 above. Two turns and $\frac{38}{57}$ turn.
8. $\frac{40}{25} = \frac{8}{5} = 1\frac{3}{5}$ turns. $\frac{3}{5} \times \frac{6}{6} = \frac{18}{30}$. One turn and 18 holes in the 30 hole circle.
9. $\frac{40}{47}$. There is a 47 hole circle, so use 40 holes in the 47 hole circle.
10. $\frac{40}{64} = \frac{5}{8}$ turns. The only hole circle divisible by 8 is 24. So, $\frac{5}{8} \times \frac{3}{3} = \frac{15}{24}$. = 15 holes in the 24 hole circle.

SECTION K / UNIT 3 / ANGULAR INDEXING

SELF-TEST ANSWERS

1. 15 degrees.
2. Three holes
3. Nine degrees.
4. All those hole circles are divisible by 9.
5. $\frac{17}{9} = 1\frac{8}{9}$ turn of the index crank.
6. 30 min or $\frac{1}{2}$ degrees.
7. 15 min or $\frac{1}{4}$ degrees.
8. 10 min or $\frac{1}{6}$ degrees.
9. 540 min.
10. Converting 54°30′ into minutes = 3270 min.
$$\frac{\text{Required minutes}}{540} = \frac{3270}{540} = 6\frac{30}{540} = 6\frac{3}{54} = 6 \text{ turns}$$
and 3 holes in the 54 hole circle.

SECTION L / UNIT 1 / INTRODUCTION TO GEARS

SELF-TEST ANSWERS

1. Spur gears and helical gears.
2. Helical gears run more smoothly than spur gears because more than one tooth is in mesh at all times. Helical gears, however, generate axial thrust that has to be offset with thrust bearings.
3. The pinion in mesh with an internal gear rotates in the same direction as the gear.
4. The shafts will be at 90 degrees to each other.
5. 50:1.
6. No, a single start worm can only be replaced with a single start worm. To change the gear ratio, the number of teeth in the gear need to be changed.
7. Hardened steel.
8. Nonmetallic materials.
9. By making the pinion harder than the gear.
10. Nonferrous materials.

SECTION L / UNIT 2 / SPUR GEAR TERMS AND CALCULATIONS

SELF-TEST ANSWERS

1. Pressure angles on gears vary from $14\frac{1}{2}$ to 20 to 25 degrees.
2. Larger pressure angles make stronger teeth. They also allow gears to be made with fewer teeth.
3. $C = \dfrac{N_1 + N_2}{2P} = \dfrac{20 \times 30}{2 \times 10} = \dfrac{50}{20} = 2.500$ in.
4. $C = \dfrac{D_1 + D_2}{2} = \dfrac{3.500 + 2.500}{2} = \dfrac{6.000}{2} = 3.000$ in.
5. The whole depth of a tooth is how deep a tooth is cut. The working depth gives the distance the teeth from one gear enter the opposing gear in meshing.
6. The addendum is above the pitch diameter and the dedendum is below the pitch diameter of a gear.

7. $D_o = \dfrac{N + 2}{P} = \dfrac{50 + 2}{5} = \dfrac{52}{5} = 10.400$ in.

   $t = \dfrac{1.5708}{P} = \dfrac{1.5708}{5} = .314$ in.

8. $P = \dfrac{N}{D} = \dfrac{36}{3} = 12$

9. $D_o = \dfrac{N + 2}{P} = \dfrac{40 + 2}{8} = \dfrac{42}{8} = 5.250$ in.

   $h_t = \dfrac{2.250}{P} = \dfrac{2.250}{8} = .2812$ in.

   $D = \dfrac{N}{P} = \dfrac{40}{8} = 5.000$ in.

   $b = \dfrac{1.250}{P} = \dfrac{1.250}{8} = .1562$ in.

10. $D_o = \dfrac{N + 2}{P} = \dfrac{48 + 2}{6} = \dfrac{50}{6} = 8.3333$ in.

    $c = \dfrac{.157}{P} = \dfrac{.157}{6} = .0261$ in.

    $h_t = \dfrac{2.157}{P} = \dfrac{2.157}{6} = .3595$ in.

    $t = \dfrac{1.5708}{P} = \dfrac{1.5708}{8} = .2618$ in.

    $D = \dfrac{N}{P} = \dfrac{48}{6} = 8.000$ in.

SECTION L / UNIT 3 / CUTTING A SPUR GEAR

SELF-TEST ANSWERS

1. Gears cut on a milling machine lack a high degree of accuracy and are expensive to make.
2. Eight.
3. No. 3.
4. No, the tooth profile differs with different pressure angles.
5. For a 17 tooth gear.
6. The number of the cutter, the diametral pitch, the number of teeth the cutter can cut, the pressure angle, and the whole depth of tooth.
7. To get a setup as rigid as possible.
8. The number of holes to be indexed plus one.
9. To check the correctness of the number of spaces required.
10. A center rest is used under gear blanks, mandrels, or shafts to help prevent chatter and deflection.

SECTION L / UNIT 4 / GEAR INSPECTION AND MEASUREMENT

SELF-TEST ANSWERS

1. Gear measurements with a gear tooth vernier caliper and with a micrometer over two wires or pins.
2. The chordal tooth thickness.
3. The chordal addendum.
4. The chordal addendum.
5. The circular thickness.

6. By calculation or from *Machinery's Handbook* tables.
7. No, the pin sizes are specifically calculated for each differing diametral pitch.
8. By consulting a *Machinery's Handbook* table.
9. The dimension given is divided by the diametral pitch used; in this question, the divisor is 12.
10. The optical comparator magnifies the gear tooth profile and projects it on a screen. On the screen there is also a transparent drawing with the tooth profile; by aligning the shadow with the drawn profile, any variation between the two can be seen and measured.

SECTION M / SHAPERS

SELF-TEST ANSWERS

1. *A.* Tilt table   *F.* Stroke adjusting shaft
   B. Apron   *G.* Ram
   C. Cross rail   *H.* Ram adjusting shaft
   D. Crossfeed engagement lever   *I.* Tool (swivel) head
   E. Rail elevating crank   *J.* Tool lifter
2. It permits the cutting tool to tilt up on the return (feeding) stroke of the ram without damaging the cutting edge.
3. The use of a stop to arrest end motion and poppets or bunters and toe dogs to secure the part down to the table.
4. $\dfrac{CS \times 7}{L} = \dfrac{12 \times 7}{15 + 1} = \dfrac{84}{16} = 5.25$ strokes per minute.
5. $\dfrac{CS \times 7}{L} = \dfrac{60 \times 7}{4\frac{1}{4} + \frac{3}{4}} = \dfrac{420}{5} = 84$ strokes per minute.
6. Deep roughing = depth $\times$ 10 percent = .450 $\times$ .10 = .045 in.; shallow roughing = depth $\times$ $\frac{1}{3}$ to $\frac{1}{2}$ = .100 $\times$ .33 to .5 = .033 to .050 in.
7. Finishing feed with square nose finishing tool = approximately three-quarter tool width. $\frac{1}{2} \times \frac{3}{4}$ = .50 $\times$ .75 = .375 in. desired feedrate.
8. At least $\frac{1}{2}$ in. before the cut and $\frac{1}{4}$ in. after (unless you are working to a shoulder).
9. The table should be indicated in the crossfeed direction. The tilt plate should be indicated (if that side is up).
10. $\dfrac{CS \times 7}{L} = \dfrac{35 \times 7}{L + 1} = \dfrac{245}{6.5} = 37.6$ strokes per minute.
11. The line contact provided by the round bar forces the reference surface into full contact with the solid jaw of the vise.

SECTION N / UNIT 1 / SELECTION AND IDENTIFICATION OF GRINDING WHEELS

SELF-TEST ANSWERS

1. Bronze — silicon carbide; steel — aluminum oxide; carbide — diamond; high speed steel — aluminum oxide.
2. Outside diameter, spindle bore, wall thickness.
3. Straight, cylinder, straight cup, flaring cup, shallow dish.
4. Resinoid.
5. Grade refers to the strength of the wheel bond. Stronger bonds are harder wheels, softer grades are weaker bonds.
6. For A 14-Z3B: Aluminum oxide, 14 grit (coarse), Z grade (very hard), 3 structure (medium), B bond (resinoid).
   For C 14-J6V: Silicon carbide, 14 grit (coarse), J grade (medium), 6 structure (medium toward dense), V bond (vitrified).
7. C 36-K8V for peripheral (harder and denser); C 25-H9V for side grinding (coarser).
8. 32A 46-H8VBE: Aluminum oxide (32 indicates a specific kind), 46 grit (medium toward coarse), H grade (soft), V bond (vitrified, BE indicating a specific type).

SECTION N / UNIT 2 / TRUEING, DRESSING, AND BALANCING OF GRINDING WHEELS

SELF-TEST ANSWERS

1. Trueing a grinding wheel means making the OD of the wheel concentric with the center of the spindle after the wheel is mounted. This means that the wheel will be a little out-of-round with its own center. On aluminum oxide wheels and silicon carbide wheels this usually means dressing abrasive grain off the periphery of the wheel. On diamond wheels the adjustment is made as close as possible by tapping the wheel into place. Trueing is needed to insure a good finish on the workpiece.

2. Trueing is a dimensional job, making the wheel's OD concentric with the machine's spindle. Dressing is resharpening the wheel by removing dull grain and bits of work material. Wheels should be dressed when the grain becomes dulled or loaded (filled with bits of metal), and also when you change from roughing to finishing or back to roughing.

3. Form dressing is simply shaping the grinding surface of a wheel to produce something other than a flat surface on the workpiece. It can be done by crush roll, diamond-plated form block or roll, or single point diamond tools mounted so that it can accurately generate a shape in the wheel face by following a pattern.

4. A star dresser consists of several star-shaped metal wheels on a spindle. When applied to the grinding wheel, the star wheels rotate and dress material from the abrasive wheel. Star dressers are most frequently used on pedestal grinders for wheel dressing.

5. The diamond dresser must be placed such that the angle tilts in the direction of wheel rotation and the dresser must be placed a little past the vertical centerline of the wheel on the outgoing rotation side.

6. The steps in trueing a wheel are:
   a. Assuming the diamond is properly placed, adjust the wheel so that the diamond is touching the high point of the wheel.
   b. Turn on the coolant (if possible) and start the wheel, allowing it to run for about a minute before starting to true the wheel.
   c. Use light infeed, .001 in. or less per pass across the wheel. For trueing, the speed of traverse does not matter.
   d. If dressing is done dry, stop traversing after every three or four passes to allow the diamond to cool.
   e. Continue trueing only until the diamond is contacting the complete grinding surface of the wheel. Going further wastes abrasive, and stopping short of that point means there is still a low point on the grinding surface of the wheel.

7. For roughing, you want the grinding surface to be as sharp and open as possible, so you take quick passes across the wheel. For finish grinding, the passes are slower, not so deep, and you probably will finish with two or three passes without any downfeed or infeed at all.

8. Assuming that bearings and other machine components are running true, if diamond wheel runout is still too much, the wheel must be trued. This can be done with a brake trueing device or, in the case of a resinoid-bonded diamond wheel, by grinding a piece of low carbon steel.

9. Generally, any wheel 12 in. or over in diameter should be balanced the first time it is mounted, particularly when it is mounted on flanges, and any other time it is remounted. If there is a pattern of recurring marks on the finish of the workpiece, then rebalancing may be in order also.

SECTION N / UNIT 3 / GRINDING FLUIDS

SELF-TEST ANSWERS

1. Cool, lubricate, and clean the surface being ground.
2. In the immediate area of grinding wheel contact on the workpiece.
3. Mist coolant is coolant mixed with air. It is applied in an air jet mist form.
4. Water soluble chemicals, water soluble oils, straight oils.
5. Settling, filtering, centrifuging, magnetic.

SECTION N / UNIT 4 / HORIZONTAL SPINDLE RECIPROCATING TABLE SURFACE GRINDERS

SELF-TEST ANSWERS

1. The table supports the work chuck and carries both back and forth under the grinding wheel.
2. The saddle supports the table and moves it in and out so that the workpiece may be set over for the next grinding pass.
3. The downfeed hand crank raises and lowers the wheel so that depth of cut may be set. The table hand crank reciprocates the table and the saddle crank moves the saddle and table in and out.
4. High speed internal attachment, centerless attachment.
5. The downfeed hand crank discriminates to .0001 in.

SECTION N / UNIT 5 / WORKHOLDING ON THE SURFACE GRINDER

SELF-TEST ANSWERS

1. Magnetic and vacuum.
2. By electrical demagnetism. The electro-magnetic field is cycled on and off.
3. Chuck must be free of burrs; chucking surface must be ground in if necessary; surface must be clean before locating workpiece.
4. Laminated accessories include parallels and vee-blocks, made with alternating layers of steel and non-magnetic aluminum. They are used as accessory workholding devices on magnetic chucks.
5. Thin workpieces may be held on double-backed tape and may be supported with paper shims if neccesary.

SECTION N / UNIT 7 / PROBLEMS AND SOLUTIONS IN SURFACE GRINDING

SELF-TEST ANSWERS

1. Machine condition and machine operation.
2. a. Minimize chucking force, shim workpiece until one side has been ground true.
   b. Realign chuck, grind in chucking surface, clean and deburr chuck.
   c. Increase coolant, use less depth of cut, increase rate of table travel.
   d. Redress wheel, rebalance wheel, eliminate cause of external vibration.
   e. Swarf in the coolant, check filtering and dirty coolant dripping from wheel guard.

SECTION N / UNIT 8 / CENTER-TYPE CYLINDRICAL GRINDERS
SELF-TEST ANSWERS

1. In cylindrical grinding, the wheel contacts the inside or outside diameter of a cylindrical workpiece rotating slowly in the opposite direction to wheel rotation.
2. Tapers may be ground by adjusting the swivel table angle and the angle of the wheelhead on the universal cylindrical grinder.
3. Holding between centers.
4. Table traverse, table swivel, spindle rotation, wheelhead swivel, wheelhead movement in and out for depth of cut.
5. Center holes can be prepared on the center hole grinder. Thay are important because the accuracy of the cylindrical grinding task depends on their location and geometry.

SECTION O / PART 1 / NUMERICAL CONTROL OF MACHINE TOOLS

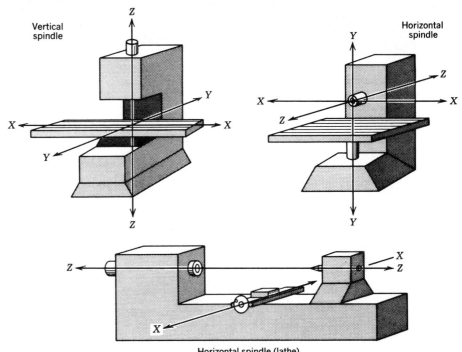

Figure 59.

SELF-TEST ANSWERS

1. See Figure 59.
2. Rotational axes might be used to define the motion of a rotary table or part indexer that operates rotationally around one of the basic axes.
3. -Z axis.
4. -X axis, with respect to the spindle. As the worktable moves right, the apparent spindle motion is left or in a -X direction.
5. Z.
6. Paper and plastic laminates.
7. More durable and less subject to damage and wear in the tape reader.
8. Preparation of new tapes, tape duplication, error correction, and typed records of tape information.
9. EIA and ASCII.
10. Electromechanical, photoelectric, and pneumatic.
11. After the tape has been punched, a printout should be obtained and checked against the program manuscript.
12. The dry tape run will verify the accuracy of the tape and prevent possible damage to the machine tool.
13. Be sure that the spindle and cutter are clear of all obstructions before positioning the worktable.
14. The tool length gage is used to adjust tool lengths as well as diameters on boring bars and insert cutters.
15. Micrometers and dial indicator types, electronic digital types.

SECTION O / PART 2 / ELECTRICAL MACHINING PROCESSES

SELF-TEST ANSWERS

1. EDM is electrical discharge machining where workpiece material is removed by spark erosion.
2. EDM can be applied in hard to machine materials, and in complex geometry that would be difficult or impossible to machine by conventional methods.
3. ECM is electrochemical machining. ELG is electrolytic grinding. Workpiece material is removed by electrochemical deplating action.

4. ECM and ELG can be used on difficult-to-machine materials and where burr free machining is an advantage, such as very small precision parts.
5. Electrical processes can be used to advantage on hard-to-machine material, for producing very complex geometry, where burr free parts are an advantage, cutter sharpening to preserve abrasive wheel life.

APPENDIX II
GENERAL TABLES

Table 1

Decimal Equivalents of Fractional Inches

FRACTION INCH			DECIMAL INCH	DECIMAL MILLI-METERS	FRACTION INCH			DECIMAL INCH	DECIMAL MILLI-METERS
		1/64	.015625	0.39688			33/64	.515625	13.09690
	1/32		.03125	0.79375		17/32		.53125	13.49378
		3/64	.046875	1.19063			35/64	.546875	13.89065
1/16			.0625	1.58750	9/16			.5625	14.28753
		5/64	.078125	1.98438			37/64	.578125	14.68440
	3/32		.09375	2.38125		19/32		.59375	15.08128
		7/64	.109375	2.77813			39/64	.609375	15.47816
1/8			.1250	3.17501	5/8			.6250	15.87503
		9/64	.140625	3.57188			41/64	.640625	16.27191
	5/32		.15625	3.96876		21/32		.65625	16.66878
		11/64	.171875	4.36563			43/64	.671875	17.06566
3/16			.1875	4.76251	11/16			.6875	17.46253
		13/64	.203125	5.15939			45/64	.703125	17.85941
	7/32		.21875	5.55626		23/32		.71875	18.25629
		15/64	.234375	5.95314			47/64	.734375	18.65316
1/4			.2500	6.35001	3/4			.7500	19.05004
		17/64	.265625	6.74689			49/64	.765625	19.44691
	9/32		.28125	7.14376		25/32		.78125	19.84379
		19/64	.296875	7.54064			51/64	.796875	20.24067
5/16			.3125	7.93752	13/16			.8125	20.63754
		21/64	.328125	8.33439			53/64	.828125	21.03442
	11/32		.34375	8.73127		27/32		.84375	21.43129
		23/64	.359375	9.12814			55/64	.859375	21.82817
3/8			.3750	9.52502	7/8			.8750	22.22504
		25/64	.390625	9.92189			57/64	.890625	22.62192
	13/32		.40625	10.31877		29/32		.90625	23.01880
		27/64	.421875	10.71565			59/64	.921875	23.41567
7/16			.4375	11.11252	15/16			.9375	23.81255
		29/64	.453125	11.50940			61/64	.953125	24.20942
	15/32		.46875	11.90627		31/32		.96875	24.60630
		31/64	.484375	12.30315			63/64	.984375	25.00318
1/2			.5000	12.70003	1			1.0000	25.40005

Table 2
Inch/Metric Conversion Table

Drill No. or Letter	Inch	mm
	.001	0,0254
	.002	0,0508
	.003	0,0762
	.004	0,1016
	.005	0,1270
	.006	0,1524
	.007	0,1778
	.008	0,2032
	.009	0,2286
	.010	0,2540
	.011	0,2794
	.012	0,3048
80 .0135	.013	0,3302
79 .0145	.014	0,3556
	.015	0,3810
1/64	.0156	0,3969
78	.016	0,4064
	.017	0,4318
77	.018	0,4572
	.019	0,4826
76	.020	0,5080
75	.021	0,5334
74 .0225	.022	0,5588
	.023	0,5842
73	.024	0,6096
72	.025	0,6350
71	.026	0,6604
	.027	0,6858
70	.028	0,7112
69 .0292	.029	0,7366
	.030	0,7620
68	.031	0,7874
1/32	.0312	0,7937
67	.032	0,8128
66	.033	0,8382
	.034	0,8636
65	.035	0,8890
64	.036	0,9144
63	.037	0,9398
62	.038	0,9652
61	.039	0,9906
	.0394	1,0000
60	.040	1,0160
59	.041	1,0414
58	.042	1,0668
57	.043	1,0922
	.044	1,1176
	.045	1,1430
56 .0465	.046	1,1684
3/64	.0469	1,1906
	.047	1,1938
	.048	1,2192
	.049	1,2446
	.050	1,2700
	.051	1,2954
55	.052	1,3208
	.053	1,3462
	.054	1,3716
54	.055	1,3970
	.056	1,4224
	.057	1,4478
	.058	1,4732
	.059	1,4986
53 .0595	.060	1,5240
	.061	1,5494
	.062	1,5748
1/16	.0625	1,5875
	.063	1,6002
52 .0635	.064	1,6256
	.065	1,6510
	.066	1,6764
51	.067	1,7018
	.068	1,7272
	.069	1,7526
50	.070	1,7780
	.071	1,8034
	.072	1,8288
49	.073	1,8542
	.074	1,8796
	.075	1,9050
48	.076	1,9304
	.077	1,9558
47 .0785	.078	1,9812
5/64	.0781	1,9844
	.0787	2,0000
	.079	2,0066
	.080	2,0320
46	.081	2,0574
45	.082	2,0828
	.083	2,1082
	.084	2,1336
	.085	2,1590
44	.086	2,1844
	.087	2,2098
	.088	2,2352
43	.089	2,2606
	.090	2,2860
	.091	2,3114
	.092	2,3368
42 .0935	.093	2,3622
3/32	.0937	2,3812
	.094	2,3876
	.095	2,4130
41	.096	2,4384
	.097	2,4638
40	.098	2,4892
	.099	2,5146
39 .0995	.100	2,5400

Drill No. or Letter	Inch	mm
38 .1015	.101	2,5654
	.102	2,5908
	.103	2,6162
37	.104	2,6416
	.105	2,6670
36 .1065	.106	2,6924
	.107	2,7178
	.108	2,7432
	.109	2,7686
7/64	.1094	2,7781
35	.110	2,7940
34	.111	2,8194
	.112	2,8448
33	.113	2,8702
	.114	2,8956
	.115	2,9210
32	.116	2,9464
	.117	2,9718
	.118	2,9972
	.1181	3,0000
	.119	3,0226
31	.120	3,0480
	.121	3,0734
	.122	3,0988
	.123	3,1242
	.124	3,1496
1/8	.125	3,1750
	.126	3,2004
	.127	3,2258
30 .1285	.128	3,2512
	.129	3,2766
	.130	3,3020
	.131	3,3274
	.132	3,3528
	.133	3,3782
	.134	3,4036
	.135	3,4290
29	.136	3,4544
	.137	3,4798
	.138	3,5052
	.139	3,5306
28 .1405	.140	3,5560
9/64	.1406	3,5719
	.141	3,5814
	.142	3,6068
	.143	3,6322
27	.144	3,6576
	.145	3,6830
	.146	3,7084
26	.147	3,7338
	.148	3,7592
25 .1495	.149	3,7846
	.150	3,8100
	.151	3,8354
24	.152	3,8608
	.153	3,8862
23	.154	3,9116
	.155	3,9370
	.156	3,9624
5/32	.1562	3,9687
22	.157	3,9878
	.1575	4,0000
	.158	4,0132
21	.159	4,0386
	.160	4,0640
20	.161	4,0894
	.162	4,1148
	.163	4,1402
	.164	4,1656
	.165	4,1910
19	.166	4,2164
	.167	4,2418
	.168	4,2672
	.169	4,2926
18 .1635	.170	4,3180
	.171	4,3434
11/64	.1719	4,3656
	.172	4,3688
17	.173	4,3942
	.174	4,4196
	.175	4,4450
	.176	4,4704
16	.177	4,4958
	.178	4,5212
	.179	4,5466
15	.180	4,5720
	.181	4,5974
14	.182	4,6228
	.183	4,6482
	.184	4,6736
13	.185	4,6990
	.186	4,7244
	.187	4,7498
3/16	.1875	4,7625
	.188	4,7752
12	.189	4,8006
	.190	4,8260
11	.191	4,8514
	.192	4,8768
10 .1935	.193	4,9022
	.194	4,9276
	.195	4,9530
9	.196	4,9784
	.1969	5,0000
	.197	5,0038
	.198	5,0292
	.199	5,0546
8	.200	5,0800

Drill No. or Letter	Inch	mm
7	.201	5,1054
	.202	5,1308
	.203	5,1562
13/64	.2031	5,1594
6	.204	5,1816
5 .2055	.205	5,2070
	.206	5,2324
	.207	5,2578
	.208	5,2832
4	.209	5,3086
	.210	5,3340
	.211	5,3594
	.212	5,3848
3	.213	5,4102
	.214	5,4356
	.215	5,4610
	.216	5,4864
	.217	5,5118
	.218	5,5372
7/32	.2187	5,5562
	.219	5,5626
	.220	5,5880
2	.221	5,6134
	.222	5,6388
	.223	5,6642
	.224	5,6896
	.225	5,7150
	.226	5,7404
	.227	5,7658
1	.228	5,7912
	.229	5,8166
	.230	5,8420
	.231	5,8674
	.232	5,8928
	.233	5,9182
A	.234	5,9436
15/64	.2344	5,9531
	.235	5,9690
	.236	5,9944
	.2362	6,0000
	.237	6,0198
B	.238	6 0452
	.239	6,0706
	.240	6,0960
	.241	6,1214
C	.242	6,1468
	.243	6,1722
	.244	6,1976
	.245	6,2230
D	.246	6,2484
	.247	6,2738
	.248	6,2992
	.249	6,3246
E 1/4	.250	6,3500
	.251	6,3754
	.252	6,4008
	.253	6,4262
	.254	6,4516
	.255	6,4770
	.256	6,5024
F	.257	6,5278
	.258	6,5532
	.259	6,5786
	.260	6,6040
G	.261	6,6294
	.262	6,6548
	.263	6,6802
	.264	6,7056
	.265	6,7310
17/64	.2656	6,7469
H	.266	6,7564
	.267	6,7818
	.268	6,8072
	.269	6,8326
	.270	6,8580
	.271	6,8834
I	.272	6,9088
	.273	6,9342
	.274	6,9596
	.275	6,9850
	.2756	7,0000
	.276	7,0104
J	.277	7,0358
	.278	7,0612
	.279	7,0866
	.280	7,1120
K	.281	7,1374
9/32	.2812	7,1437
	.282	7,1628
	.283	7,1882
	.284	7,2136
	.285	7,2390
	.286	7,2644
	.287	7,2898
	.288	7,3152
	.289	7,3406
L	.290	7,3660
	.291	7,3914
	.292	7,4168
	.293	7,4422
	.294	7,4676
M	.295	7,4930
	.296	7,5184
19/64	.2969	7,5406
	.297	7,5438
	.298	7,5692
	.299	7,5946
	.300	7,6200

Drill No. or Letter	Inch	mm
	.301	7,6454
N	.302	7,6708
	.303	7,6962
	.304	7,7216
	.305	7,7470
	.306	7,7724
	.307	7,7978
	.308	7,8232
	.309	7,8486
	.310	7,8740
	.311	7,8994
	.312	7,9248
5/16	.3125	7,9375
	.313	7,9502
	.314	7,9756
	.3150	8,0000
	.315	8,0010
O	.316	8,0264
	.317	8,0518
	.318	8,0772
	.319	8,1026
	.320	8,1280
	.321	8,1534
	.322	8,1788
P	.323	8,2042
	.324	8,2296
	.325	8,2550
	.326	8,2804
	.327	8,3058
	.328	8,3312
21/64	.3281	8,3344
	.329	8,3566
	.330	8,3820
	.331	8,4074
Q	.332	8,4328
	.333	8,4582
	.334	8,4836
	.335	8,5090
	.336	8,5344
	.337	8,5598
	.338	8,5852
R	.339	8,6106
	.340	8,6360
	.341	8,6614
	.342	8,6868
	.343	8,7122
11/32	.3437	8,7312
	.344	8,7376
	.345	8,7630
	.346	8,7884
	.347	8,8138
S	.348	8,8392
	.349	8,8646
	.350	8,8900
	.351	8,9154
	.352	8,9408
	.353	8,9662
	.354	8,9916
	.3543	9,0000
	.355	9,0170
	.356	9,0424
	.357	9,0678
T	.358	9,0932
	.359	9,1186
23/64	.3594	9,1281
	.360	9,1440
	.361	9,1694
	.362	9,1948
	.363	9,2202
	.364	9,2456
	.365	9,2710
	.366	9,2964
	.367	9,3218
U	.368	9,3472
	.369	9,3726
	.370	9,3980
	.371	9,4234
	.372	9,4488
	.373	9,4742
	.374	9,4996
3/8	.375	9,5250
	.376	9,5504
V	.377	9,5758
	.378	9,6012
	.379	9,6266
	.380	9,6520
	.381	9,6774
	.382	9,7028
	.383	9,7282
	.384	9,7536
	.385	9,7790
W	.386	9,8044
	.387	9,8298
	.388	9,8552
	.389	9,8806
	.390	9,9060
25/64	.3906	9,9219
	.391	9,9314
	.392	9,9568
	.393	9,9822
	.3937	10,0000
	.394	10,0076
	.395	10,0330
	.396	10,0584
X	.397	10,0838
	.398	10,1092
	.399	10,1346
	.400	10,1600

Drill No. or Letter	Inch	mm
	.401	10,1854
	.402	10,2108
	.403	10,2362
Y	.404	10,2616
	.405	10,2870
	.406	10,3124
13/32	.4062	10,3187
	.407	10,3378
	.408	10,3632
	.409	10,3886
	.410	10,4140
	.411	10,4394
	.412	10,4648
Z	.413	10,4902
	.414	10,5156
	.415	10,5410
	.416	10,5664
	.417	10,5918
	.418	10,6172
	.419	10,6426
	.420	10,6680
	.421	10,6934
27/64	.4219	10,7156
	.422	10,7188
	.423	10,7442
	.424	10,7696
	.425	10,7950
	.426	10,8204
	.427	10,8458
	.428	10,8712
	.429	10,8966
	.430	10,9220
	.431	10,9474
	.432	10,9728
	.433	10,9982
	.4331	11,0000
	.434	11,0236
	.435	11,0490
	.436	11,0744
	.437	11,0998
7/16	.4375	11,1125
	.438	11,1252
	.439	11,1506
	.440	11,1760
	.441	11,2014
	.442	11,2268
	.443	11,2522
	.444	11,2776
	.445	11,3030
	.446	11,3284
	.447	11,3538
	.448	11,3792
	.449	11,4046
	.450	11,4300
	.451	11,4554
	.452	11,4808
	.453	11,5062
29/64	.4531	11,5094
	.454	11,5316
	.455	11,5570
	.456	11,5824
	.457	11,6078
	.458	11,6332
	.459	11,6586
	.460	11,6840
	.461	11,7094
	.462	11,7348
	.463	11,7602
	.464	11,7856
	.465	11,8110
	.466	11,8364
	.467	11,8618
	.468	11,8872
15/32	.4687	11,9062
	.469	11,9126
	.470	11,9380
	.471	11,9634
	.472	11,9888
	.4724	12,0000
	.473	12,0142
	.474	12,0396
	.475	12,0650
	.476	12,0904
	.477	12,1158
	.478	12,1412
	.479	12,1666
	.480	12,1920
	.481	12,2174
	.482	12,2428
	.483	12,2682
	.484	12,2936
31/64	.4844	12,3031
	.485	12,3190
	.486	12,3444
	.487	12,3698
	.488	12,3952
	.489	12,4206
	.490	12,4460
	.491	12,4714
	.492	12,4968
	.493	12,5222
	.494	12,5476
	.495	12,5730
	.496	12,5984
	.497	12,6238
	.498	12,6492
	.499	12,6746
1/2	.500	12,7000

Source. Courtesy of the Standard Gage Company.

Table 2 Continued

Frac	Inch	mm
	.501	12,7254
	.502	12,7508
	.503	12,7762
	.504	12,8016
	.505	12,8270
	.506	12,8524
	.507	12,8778
	.508	12,9032
	.509	12,9286
	.510	12,9540
	.511	12,9794
	.5118	13,0000
	.512	13,0048
	.513	13,0302
	.514	13,0556
	.515	13,0810
33/64	.5156	13,0968
	.516	13,1064
	.517	13,1318
	.518	13,1572
	.519	13,1826
	.520	13,2080
	.521	13,2334
	.522	13,2588
	.523	13,2842
	.524	13,3096
	.525	13,3350
	.526	13,3604
	.527	13,3858
	.528	13,4112
	.529	13,4366
	.530	13,4620
	.531	13,4874
17/32	.5312	13,4937
	.532	13,5128
	.533	13,5382
	.534	13,5636
	.535	13,5890
	.536	13,6144
	.537	13,6398
	.538	13,6652
	.539	13,6906
	.540	13,7160
	.541	13,7414
	.542	13,7668
	.543	13,7922
	.544	13,8176
	.545	13,8430
	.546	13,8684
35/64	.5469	13,8906
	.547	13,8938
	.548	13,9192
	.549	13,9446
	.550	13,9700
	.551	13,9954
	.5512	14,0000
	.552	14,0208
	.553	14,0462
	.554	14,0716
	.555	14,0970
	.556	14,1224
	.557	14,1478
	.558	14,1732
	.559	14,1986
	.560	14,2240
	.561	14,2494
	.562	14,2748
9/16	.5625	14,2875
	.563	14,3002
	.564	14,3256
	.565	14,3510
	.566	14,3764
	.567	14,4018
	.568	14,4272
	.569	14,4526
	.570	14,4780
	.571	14,5034
	.572	14,5288
	.573	14,5542
	.574	14,5796
	.575	14,6050
	.576	14,6304
	.577	14,6558
	.578	14,6812
37/64	.5781	14,6844
	.579	14,7066
	.580	14,7320
	.581	14,7574
	.582	14,7828
	.583	14,8082
	.584	14,8336
	.585	14,8590
	.586	14,8844
	.587	14,9098
	.588	14,9352
	.589	14,9606
	.590	14,9860
	.5906	15,0000
	.591	15,0114
	.592	15,0368
	.593	15,0622
19/32	.5937	15,0812
	.594	15,0876
	.595	15,1130
	.596	15,1384
	.597	15,1638
	.598	15,1892
	.599	15,2146

Frac	Inch	mm
	.600	15,2400
	.601	15,2654
	.602	15,2908
	.603	15,3162
	.604	15,3416
	.605	15,3670
	.606	15,3924
	.607	15,4178
	.608	15,4432
	.609	15,4686
39/64	.6094	15,4781
	.610	15,4940
	.611	15,5194
	.612	15,5448
	.613	15,5702
	.614	15,5956
	.615	15,6210
	.616	15,6464
	.617	15,6718
	.618	15,6972
	.619	15,7226
	.620	15,7480
	.621	15,7734
	.622	15,7988
	.623	15,8242
	.624	15,8496
5/8	.625	15,8750
	.626	15,9004
	.627	15,9258
	.628	15,9512
	.629	15,9766
	.6299	16,0000
	.630	16,0020
	.631	16,0274
	.632	16,0528
	.633	16,0782
	.634	16,1036
	.635	16,1290
	.636	16,1544
	.637	16,1798
	.638	16,2052
	.639	16,2306
	.640	16,2560
41/64	.6406	16,2719
	.641	16,2814
	.642	16,3068
	.643	16,3322
	.644	16,3576
	.645	16,3830
	.646	16,4084
	.647	16,4338
	.648	16,4592
	.649	16,4846
	.650	16,5100
	.651	16,5354
	.652	16,5608
	.653	16,5862
	.654	16,6116
	.655	16,6370
21/32	.6562	16,6687
	.656	16,6624
	.657	16,6878
	.658	16,7132
	.659	16,7386
	.660	16,7640
	.661	16,7894
	.662	16,8148
	.663	16,8402
	.664	16,8656
	.665	16,8910
	.666	16,9164
	.667	16,9418
	.668	16,9672
	.669	16,9926
	.6693	17,0000
	.670	17,0180
	.671	17,0434
43/64	.6719	17,0656
	.672	17,0688
	.673	17,0942
	.674	17,1196
	.675	17,1450
	.676	17,1704
	.677	17,1958
	.678	17,2212
	.679	17,2466
	.680	17,2720
	.681	17,2974
	.682	17,3228
	.683	17,3482
	.684	17,3736
	.685	17,3990
	.686	17,4244
	.687	17,4498
11/16	.6875	17,4625
	.688	17,4752
	.689	17,5006
	.690	17,5260
	.691	17,5514
	.692	17,5768
	.693	17,6022
	.694	17,6276
	.695	17,6530
	.696	17,6784
	.697	17,7038
	.698	17,7292
	.699	17,7546
	.700	17,7800

Frac	Inch	mm
	.701	17,8054
	.702	17,8308
	.703	17,8562
45/64	.7031	17,8594
	.704	17,8816
	.705	17,9070
	.706	17,9324
	.707	17,9578
	.708	17,9832
	.7087	18,0000
	.709	18,0086
	.710	18,0340
	.711	18,0594
	.712	18,0848
	.713	18,1102
	.714	18,1356
	.715	18,1610
	.716	18,1864
	.717	18,2118
	.718	18,2372
23/32	.7187	18,2562
	.719	18,2626
	.720	18,2880
	.721	18,3134
	.722	18,3388
	.723	18,3642
	.724	18,3896
	.725	18,4150
	.726	18,4404
	.727	18,4658
	.728	18,4912
	.729	18,5166
	.730	18,5420
	.731	18,5674
	.732	18,5928
	.733	18,6182
	.734	18,6436
47/64	.7344	18,6532
	.735	18,6690
	.736	18,6944
	.737	18,7198
	.738	18,7452
	.739	18,7706
	.740	18,7960
	.741	18,8214
	.742	18,8468
	.743	18,8722
	.744	18,8976
	.745	18,9230
	.746	18,9484
	.747	18,9738
	.748	18,9992
	.7480	19,0000
	.749	19,0246
3/4	.750	19,0500
	.751	19,0754
	.752	19,1008
	.753	19,1262
	.754	19,1516
	.755	19,1770
	.756	19,2024
	.757	19,2278
	.758	19,2532
	.759	19,2786
	.760	19,3040
	.761	19,3294
	.762	19,3548
	.763	19,3802
	.764	19,4056
	.765	19,4310
49/64	.7656	19,4469
	.766	19,4564
	.767	19,4818
	.768	19,5072
	.769	19,5326
	.770	19,5580
	.771	19,5834
	.772	19,6088
	.773	19,6342
	.774	19,6596
	.775	19,6850
	.776	19,7104
	.777	19,7358
	.778	19,7612
	.779	19,7866
	.780	19,8120
	.781	19,8374
25/32	.7812	19,8433
	.782	19,8628
	.783	19,8882
	.784	19,9136
	.785	19,9390
	.786	19,9644
	.787	19,9898
	.7874	20,0000
	.788	20,0152
	.789	20,0406
	.790	20,0660
	.791	20,0914
	.792	20,1168
	.793	20,1422
	.794	20,1676
	.795	20,1930
	.796	20,2184
51/64	.7969	20,2402
	.797	20,2438
	.798	20,2692
	.799	20,2946

Frac	Inch	mm
	.800	20,3200
	.801	20,3454
	.802	20,3708
	.803	20,3962
	.804	20,4216
	.805	20,4470
	.806	20,4724
	.807	20,4978
	.808	20,5232
	.809	20,5486
	.810	20,5740
	.811	20,5994
	.812	20,6248
13/16	.8125	20,6375
	.813	20,6502
	.814	20,6756
	.815	20,7010
	.816	20,7264
	.817	20,7518
	.818	20,7772
	.819	20,8026
	.820	20,8280
	.821	20,8534
	.822	20,8788
	.823	20,9042
	.824	20,9296
	.825	20,9550
	.826	20,9804
	.8268	21,0000
	.827	21,0058
	.828	21,0312
53/64	.8281	21,0344
	.829	21,0566
	.830	21,0820
	.831	21,1074
	.832	21,1328
	.833	21,1582
	.834	21,1836
	.835	21,2090
	.836	21,2344
	.837	21,2598
	.838	21,2852
	.839	21,3106
	.840	21,3360
	.841	21,3614
	.842	21,3868
	.843	21,4122
27/32	.8437	21,4312
	.844	21,4376
	.845	21,4630
	.846	21,4884
	.847	21,5138
	.848	21,5392
	.849	21,5646
	.850	21,5900
	.851	21,6154
	.852	21,6408
	.853	21,6662
	.854	21,6916
	.855	21,7170
	.856	21,7424
	.857	21,7678
	.858	21,7932
	.859	21,8186
55/64	.8594	21,8281
	.860	21,8440
	.861	21,8694
	.862	21,8948
	.863	21,9202
	.864	21,9456
	.865	21,9710
	.866	21,9964
	.8661	22,0000
	.867	22,0218
	.868	22,0472
	.869	22,0726
	.870	22,0980
	.871	22,1234
	.872	22,1488
	.873	22,1742
	.874	22,1996
7/8	.875	22,2250
	.876	22,2504
	.877	22,2758
	.878	22,3012
	.879	22,3266
	.880	22,3520
	.881	22,3774
	.882	22,4028
	.883	22,4282
	.884	22,4536
	.885	22,4790
	.886	22,5044
	.887	22,5298
	.888	22,5552
	.889	22,5806
	.890	22,6060
57/64	.8906	22,6219
	.891	22,6314
	.892	22,6568
	.893	22,6822
	.894	22,7076
	.895	22,7330
	.896	22,7584
	.897	22,7838
	.898	22,8092
	.899	22,8346
	.900	22,8600

Frac	Inch	mm
	.901	22,8854
	.902	22,9108
	.903	22,9362
	.904	22,9616
	.905	22,9870
	.9055	23,0000
	.906	23,0124
29/32	.9062	23,0187
	.907	23,0378
	.908	23,0632
	.909	23,0886
	.910	23,1140
	.911	23,1394
	.912	23,1648
	.913	23,1902
	.914	23,2156
	.915	23,2410
	.916	23,2664
	.917	23,2918
	.918	23,3172
	.919	23,3426
	.920	23,3680
	.921	23,3934
59/64	.9219	23,4156
	.922	23,4188
	.923	23,4442
	.924	23,4696
	.925	23,4950
	.926	23,5204
	.927	23,5458
	.928	23,5712
	.929	23,5966
	.930	23,6220
	.931	23,6474
	.932	23,6728
	.933	23,6982
	.934	23,7236
	.935	23,7490
	.936	23,7744
	.937	23,7998
15/16	.9375	23,8125
	.938	23,8252
	.939	23,8506
	.940	23,8760
	.941	23,9014
	.942	23,9268
	.943	23,9522
	.944	23,9776
	.9449	24,0000
	.945	24,0030
	.946	24,0284
	.947	24,0538
	.948	24,0792
	.949	24,1046
	.950	24,1300
	.951	24,1554
	.952	24,1808
	.953	24,2062
61/64	.9531	24,2094
	.954	24,2316
	.955	24,2570
	.956	24,2824
	.957	24,3078
	.958	24,3332
	.959	24,3586
	.960	24,3840
	.961	24,4094
	.962	24,4348
	.963	24,4602
	.964	24,4856
	.965	24,5110
	.966	24,5364
	.967	24,5618
	.968	24,5872
31/32	.9687	24,6062
	.969	24,6126
	.970	24,6380
	.971	24,6634
	.972	24,6888
	.973	24,7142
	.974	24,7396
	.975	24,7650
	.976	24,7904
	.977	24,8158
	.978	24,8412
	.979	24,8666
	.980	24,8920
	.981	24,9174
	.982	24,9428
	.983	24,9682
	.984	24,9936
63/64	.9844	25,0000
	.985	25,0190
	.986	25,0444
	.987	25,0698
	.988	25,0952
	.989	25,1206
	.990	25,1460
	.991	25,1714
	.992	25,1968
	.993	25,2222
	.994	25,2476
	.995	25,2730
	.996	25,2984
	.997	25,3238
	.998	25,3492
	.999	25,3746
	1.000	25,4000

Table 3
Tap Drill Sizes

Tap	Tap Drill	Decimal Equivalent of Tap Drill	Tap	Tap Drill	Decimal Equivalent of Tap Drill	Tap	Tap Drill	Decimal Equivalent of Tap Drill
0-80	56	.0465		28	.1405		Q	.3320
	3/64	.0469		9/64	.1406		R	.3390
1-64	54	.0550	10-24	27	.1440	7/16-14	T	.3580
	53	.0595		26	.1470		23/64	.3594
1-72	53	.0595		25	.1495		U	.3680
	1/16	.0625		24	.1520		3/8	.3750
2-56	51	.0670		23	.1540		V	.3770
	50	.0700		5/32	.1563	7/16-20	W	.3860
	49	.0730		22	.1570		25/64	.3906
2-64	50	.0700	10-32	5/32	.1563		X	.3970
	49	.0730		22	.1570	1/2-13	27/64	.4219
3-48	48	.0760		21	.1590		7/16	.4375
	5/64	.0781		20	.1610	1/2-20	29/64	.4531
	47	.0785		19	.1660	9/16-12	15/32	.4688
	46	.0810	12-24	11/64	.1719		31/64	.4844
	45	.0820		17	.1730	9/16-18	1/2	.500
3-56	46	.0810		16	.1770		33/64	.5156
	45	.0820		15	.1800	5/8-11	17/32	.5313
	44	.0860		14	.1820		35/64	.5469
4-40	44	.0860	12-28	16	.1770	5/8-18	9/16	.5625
	43	.0890		15	.1800		37/64	.5781
	42	.0935		14	.1820	3/4-10	41/64	.6406
	3/32	.0938		13	.1850		21/32	.6563
4-48	42	.0935		3/16	.1875	3/4-16	11/16	.6875
	3/32	.0938	1/4-20	9	.1960	7/8-9	49/64	.7656
	41	.0960		8	.1990		25/32	.7812
5-40	40	.0980		7	.2010	7/8-14	51/64	.7969
	39	.0995		13/64	2031		13/16	.8125
	38	.1015		6	.2040	1"-8	55/64	.8594
	37	.1040		5	.2055		7/8	.875
5-44	38	.1015		4	.2090		57/64	.8906
	37	.1040	1/4-28	3	.2130		29/32	.9063
	36	.1065		7/32	.2188	1-12	29/32	.9063
6-32	37	.1040		2	.2210		59/64	.9219
	36	.1065	5/16-18	F	.2570		15/16	.9375
	7/64	.1094		G	.2610	1-14	59/64	.9219
	35	.1100		17/64	.2656		15/16	.9375
	34	.1110		H	.2660	1 1/8-7	31/32	.9688
	33	.1130	5/16-24	H	.2660		63/64	.9844
6-40	34	.1110		I	.2720		1"	1.0000
	33	.1130		J	.2770			
	32	.1160	3/8-16	5/16	.3125			
8-32	29	.1360		O	.3160			
	28	.1405		P	.3230			
8-36	29	.1360	3/8-24	21/64	.3281			

Table 3 Continued
Tap Drill Sizes

Tap	Tap Drill	Decimal Equivalent of Tap Drill
	$1\frac{1}{64}$	1.0156
$1\frac{1}{8}$-12	$1\frac{1}{32}$	1.0313
	$1\frac{3}{64}$	1.0469
$1\frac{1}{4}$-7	$1\frac{3}{32}$	1.0938
	$1\frac{7}{64}$	1.1094
	$1\frac{1}{8}$	1.1250
$1\frac{1}{4}$-12	$1\frac{5}{32}$	1.1563
	$1\frac{11}{64}$	1.1719
$1\frac{3}{8}$-6	$1\frac{3}{16}$	1.1875
	$1\frac{13}{64}$	1.2031
	$1\frac{7}{32}$	1.2188
	$1\frac{15}{64}$	1.2344
$1\frac{3}{8}$-12	$1\frac{9}{32}$	1.2813
	$1\frac{19}{64}$	1.2969
$1\frac{1}{2}$-6	$1\frac{5}{16}$	1.3125
	$1\frac{21}{64}$	1.3281
	$1\frac{11}{32}$	1.3438
	$1\frac{23}{64}$	1.3594
$1\frac{1}{2}$-12	$1\frac{13}{32}$	1.4063
	$1\frac{27}{64}$	1.4219

Pipe (American Standard)
For use with Taper Pipe Taps.

Nominal Pipe Size Inches	Threads per Inch	Tap Drill Size
$\frac{1}{16}$	. .	R
$\frac{1}{8}$	27	$\frac{11}{32}$
$\frac{1}{4}$	18	$\frac{7}{16}$
$\frac{3}{8}$	18	$\frac{37}{64}$
$\frac{1}{2}$	14	$\frac{23}{32}$
$\frac{3}{4}$	14	$\frac{59}{64}$
1	$11\frac{1}{2}$	$1\frac{5}{32}$
$1\frac{1}{4}$	$11\frac{1}{2}$	$1\frac{1}{2}$
$1\frac{1}{2}$	$11\frac{1}{2}$	$1\frac{47}{64}$
2	$11\frac{1}{2}$	$2\frac{7}{32}$
$2\frac{1}{2}$	8	$2\frac{5}{8}$
3	8	$3\frac{1}{4}$
$3\frac{1}{2}$	8	$3\frac{3}{4}$
4	8	$4\frac{1}{4}$

Table 4
Wire Gages and Metric Equivalents

Gage No.	American or Brown & Sharpe's (in.)	(mm)	Gage No.	American or Brown & Sharpe's (in.)	(mm)
000000	.5800	14.732	21	.02846	.723
00000	.5165	13.119			
0000	.4600	11.684	22	.02535	.644
000	.4096	10.404	23	.02257	.573
00	.3648	9.266	24	.02010	.511
0	.3249	8.252	25	.01790	.455
			26	.01594	.405
1	.2893	7.348	27	.01420	.361
2	.2576	6.543	28	.01264	.321
3	.2294	5.827			
4	.2043	5.189	29	.01126	.286
5	.1819	4.620	30	.01003	.255
6	.1620	4.115	31	.008928	.227
7	.1443	3.665	32	.007950	.202
			33	.007080	.180
8	.1285	3.264	34	.006305	.160
9	.1144	2.906	35	.005615	.143
10	.1019	2.588			
11	.09074	2.305	36	.005000	.127
12	.08081	2.053	37	.004453	.113
13	.07196	1.828	38	.003965	.101
14	.06408	1.628	39	.003531	.090
			40	.003145	.080
15	.05707	1.450	41	.002800	.071
16	.05082	1.291	42	.002494	.063
17	.04526	1.150			
18	.04030	1.024	43	.002221	.056
19	.03589	.912	44	.001978	.050
20	.03196	.812			

Table 5A
Tapers

Useful Information on Tapers
Amount of Taper
Length Tapered Portion (in.)

Taper Per Foot	1/32	1/16	1/8	3/16	1/4	5/16	3/8	7/16	1/2	9/16	5/8	11/16	3/4	13/16
1/16	.0002	.0003	.0007	.0010	.0013	.0016	.0020	.0023	.0026	.0029	.0033	.0036	.0039	.0042
3/32	.0002	.0005	.0010	.0015	.0020	.0024	.0029	.0034	.0039	.0044	.0049	.0054	.0059	.0063
1/8	.0003	.0007	.0013	.0020	.0026	.0033	.0039	.0046	.0052	.0059	.0065	.0072	.0078	.0085
1/4	.0007	.0013	.0026	.0039	.0052	.0065	.0078	.0091	.0104	.0117	.0130	.0143	.0156	.0169
3/8	.0010	.0020	.0039	.0059	.0078	.0098	.0117	.0137	.0156	.0176	.0195	.0215	.0234	.0254
1/2	.0013	.0026	.0052	.0078	.0104	.0130	.0156	.0182	.0208	.0234	.0260	.0286	.0312	.0339
5/8	.0016	.0033	.0065	.0098	.0130	.0163	.0195	.0228	.0260	.0293	.0326	.0358	.0391	.0423
3/4	.0020	.0039	.0078	.0117	.0156	.0195	.0234	.0273	.0312	.0352	.0391	.0430	.0469	.0508
1	.0026	.0052	.0104	.0156	.0208	.0260	.0312	.0365	.0417	.0469	.0521	.0573	.0625	.0677
1 1/4	.0063	.0065	.0130	.0195	.0260	.0326	.0391	.0456	.0521	.0586	.0651	.0716	.0781	.0846

Amount of Taper
Length Tapered Portion (in.)

Taper Per Foot	7/8	15/16	1	2	3	4	5	6	7	8	9	10	11	12
1/16	.0046	.0049	.0052	.0104	.0156	.0208	.0260	.0312	.0365	.0417	.0469	.0521	.0573	.0625
3/32	.0068	.0073	.0078	.0156	.0234	.0312	.0391	.0469	.0547	.0625	.0703	.0781	.0859	.0937
1/8	.0091	.0098	.0104	.0208	.0312	.0417	.0521	.0625	.0729	.0833	.0937	.1042	.1146	.1250
1/4	.0182	.0195	.0208	.0417	.0625	.0833	.1042	.1250	.1458	.1667	.1875	.2083	.2292	.2500
3/8	.0273	.0293	.0312	.0625	.0937	.1250	.1562	.1875	.2187	.2500	.2812	.3125	.3437	.3750
1/2	.0365	.0391	.0417	.0833	.1250	.1667	.2083	.2500	.2917	.3333	.3750	.4167	.4583	.5000
5/8	.0456	.0488	.0521	.1042	.1562	.2083	.2604	.3125	.3646	.4167	.4687	.5208	.5729	.6250
3/4	.0547	.0586	.0625	.1250	.1875	.2500	.3125	.3750	.4375	.5000	.5625	.6250	.6875	.7500
1	.0729	.0781	.0833	.1667	.2500	.3333	.4167	.5000	.5833	.6667	.7500	.8333	.9167	1.0000
1 1/4	.0911	.0977	.1042	.2083	.3125	.4167	.5208	.6250	.7292	.8333	.9375	1.0417	1.1458	1.2500

Amount of Taper
Length Tapered Portion (in.)

Taper Per Foot	13	14	15	16	17	18	19	20	21	22	23	24		
1/16	.0677	.0729	.0781	.0833	.0885	.0937	.0990	.1042	.1094	.1146	.1198	.1250	. . .	. . .
3/32	.1016	.1094	.1172	.1250	.1328	.1406	.1484	.1562	.1641	.1719	.1797	.1875	. . .	. . .
1/8	.1354	.1458	.1562	.1667	.1771	.1875	.1979	.2083	.2187	.2292	.2396	.2500	. . .	. . .
1/4	.2708	.2917	.3125	.3333	.3542	.3750	.3958	.4167	.4375	.4583	.4792	.5000	. . .	. . .
3/8	.4062	.4375	.4687	.5000	.5312	.5625	.5937	.6250	.6562	.6875	.7187	.7500	. . .	. . .
1/2	.5417	.5833	.6250	.6667	.7083	.7500	.7917	.8333	.8750	.9167	.9583	1.0000	. . .	. . .
5/8	.6771	.7292	.7812	.8333	.8854	.9375	.9896	1.0417	1.0937	1.1458	1.1979	1.2500	. . .	. . .
3/4	.8125	.8750	.9375	1.0000	1.0625	1.1250	1.1875	1.2500	1.3125	1.3750	1.4375	1.5000	. . .	. . .
1	1.0833	1.1667	1.2500	1.3333	1.4167	1.5000	1.5833	1.6667	1.7500	1.8333	1.9167	2.0000	. . .	. . .
1 1/4	1.3542	1.4583	1.5625	1.6667	1.7708	1.8750	1.9792	2.0833	2.1875	2.2917	2.3958	2.5000	. . .	. . .

Table 5B
Tapers and Angles

Taper per Foot	Included Angle			Angle with Center Line			Taper per Inch	Taper per Inch from Center Line
	Deg.	Min.	Sec.	Deg.	Min.	Sec.		
$\frac{1}{8}$	0	35	47	0	17	54	.010416	.005208
$\frac{3}{16}$	0	53	44	0	26	52	.015625	.007812
$\frac{1}{4}$	1	11	38	0	35	49	.020833	.010416
$\frac{5}{16}$	1	29	31	0	44	46	.026042	.013021
$\frac{3}{8}$	1	47	25	0	53	42	.031250	.015625
$\frac{7}{16}$	2	5	18	1	2	39	.036458	.018229
$\frac{1}{2}$	2	23	12	1	11	36	.041667	.020833
$\frac{9}{16}$	2	41	7	1	20	34	.046875	.023438
$\frac{5}{8}$	2	59	3	1	29	31	.052084	.026042
$\frac{11}{16}$	3	16	56	1	38	28	.057292	028646
$\frac{3}{4}$	3	34	48	1	47	24	.062500	.031250
$\frac{13}{16}$	3	52	42	1	56	21	.067708	.033854
$\frac{7}{8}$	4	10	32	2	5	16	.072917	.036456
$\frac{15}{16}$	4	28	26	2	14	13	.078125	.039063
1	4	46	19	2	23	10	.083330	.041667
$1\frac{1}{4}$	5	57	45	2	58	53	.104166	.052084
$1\frac{1}{2}$	7	9	10	3	34	35	.125000	.062500
$1\frac{3}{4}$	8	20	28	4	10	14	.145833	.072917
2	9	31	37	4	45	49	.166666	.083332
$2\frac{1}{2}$	11	53	38	5	56	49	.208333	.104166
3	14	2	0	7	1	0	.250000	.125000
$3\frac{1}{2}$	16	35	39	8	17	49	.291666	.145833
4	18	55	31	9	27	44	.333333	.166666
$4\frac{1}{2}$	21	14	20	10	37	10	.375000	.187500
5	23	32	12	11	46	6	.416666	.208333
6	28	4	20	14	2	10	.500000	.250000

Table 6
General Measurements

Measurement Rules

Length

Side of square of equal periphery as circle = diameter × 0.7854.

Diameter of circle of equal periphery as square = side × 1.2732.

Length of arc = number of degrees × diameter × 0.008727

Area

Triangle = base × half perpendicular height.

Parallelogram = base × perpendicular.

Trapezoid = half the sum of the parallel sides × perpendicular height.

Trapezium, divide two triangles and find area of the triangles.

Parabola = base × $\frac{2}{3}$ height.

Ellipse = long diameter × short diameter × 0.7854.

Regular polygon = sum of sides × half perpendicular distance from center to sides.

Surface of cylinder = circumference × length + area of two ends.

Surface of pyramid or cone = circumference of base × $\frac{1}{2}$ of the slant height + area of the base.

Surface of a frustrum of a regular right pyramid or cone = sum of peripheries or circumferences of the two ends × half slant height + area of both ends.

Area of rectangle = length × breadth.

Table 6 Continued

General Information

To find the circumference of a circle, multiply diameter by 3.1416.

To find diameter of a circle, multiply circumference by .31831.

To find area of a circle, multiply square of radius by 3.1416.

Area of rectangle: Length multiplied by breadth. Doubling the diameter of a circle increases its area four times.

To find area of a triangle, multiply base by $\frac{1}{2}$ perpendicular height.

To find side of square inscribed in a circle, multiply diameter by 0.7071, or multiply circumference by 0.2251, or divide circumference by 4.4428.

To find diameter of circle circumscribing a square, multiply one side by 1.4142.

A side multiplied by 4.4428 equals circumference of its circumscribing circle.

A side multiplied by 1.128 equals diameter of a circle of equal area.

A side multiplied by 3.547 equals circumference of a circle of equal area.

Equivalent Measures

Measures of Length

1 Meter =

39.37	inches
3.28083	feet
1.09361	yards
1000.	millimeters
100.	centimeters
10.	decimeters
0.001	kilometers

1 Centimeter =

0.3937	inch
0.0328083	foot
10.	millimeters
0.01	meters

1 Millimeter =

39.370	mils
0.03937	inch (or $\frac{1}{25}$ inch nearly)
0.001	meter

Kilometer =

3280.83	feet
1093.61	yards
0.62137	mile
1000.	meters

Mil =

0.001	inch
0.02540	millimeter
0.00254	centimeter

1 Inch =

1000.	mils
0.0833	foot
0.02777	yard
25.40	millimeters
2.540	centimeters

1 Foot =

12.	inches
1.33333	yard
0.0001893	miles
0.30480	meter
30.480	centimeters

1 Yard =

36.	inches
3.	feet
0.0005681	mile
0.914402	meter

1 Mile =

63360.	inches
5280.	feet
1760.	yards
320.	rods
8.	furlongs
1609.35	meters
1.60935	kilometers

Measures of Volume and Capacity

1 Cubic Meter =

61023.4	cubic in.
35.3145	cubic feet
1.30794	cubic yd
1000.	liters
264.170	gallons U.S. liquid = 231 cubic in.

1 Cubic decimeter =

61.0234	cubic in.
0.0353145	cubic foot
0.26417	U.S. liquid gallon
1000.	cubic centimeters
0.001	cubic meter

1 Cubic Centimeter =

0.0000353	cubic foot
0.0610234	cubic inch
1000.0	cubic millimeters
0.001	liter

1 Cubic millimeter =

0.00006 1023	cubic inch
0.0000000353	cubic foot
0.001	cubic centimeter

1 Liter =

1.	cubic decimeter
61.0234	cubic inches
0.353145	cubic foot
1000.	cubic centimeters or centiliters
0.001	cubic meter
0.26417	U.S. gallon liquid
1.0567	U.S. quart
2.202	lbs. of water at 62 degrees Fahrenheit

1 Cubic Yard =

46656.	cubic inches
27.	cubic feet
0.76456	cubic meter

1 Cubic foot =

1728.	cubic inches
0.03703703	cubic yard
28.317	cubic decimeters or liters
0.028317	cubic meter
7.4805	gallons

1 Cubic inch =

16.3872 cubic centimeters

1 Gallon (British) =

4.54374 liters

1 Gallon (U.S.) =

3.78543 liters

Measures of Weight

1 Gram =

15.432	grains
0.022046	lb (avoir.)
0.3527	oz (avoir.)

1 Kilogram =

1000.	grams
2.20462	lb (avoir.)
35.2739	oz (avoir.)

1 Metric ton =

2204.62	pounds
0.984206	ton of 2240 pounds
22.0462	cwt
1.10231	ton of 2000 pounds
1000.	kilograms

1 Gram =

0.064799 grains

1 Ounce =

437.5	grains
0.0625	pounds
28.3496	grams

1 Pound =

7000.	grains
16.	ounces
453.593	grams
0.453593	kilograms

1 Ton (2240 pounds) =

1.01605	metric tons
1016.05	kilograms

Table 7
Density and Melting Points for Metals and
Other Materials

Density or Specific Gravity of Metals and Alloys

Material	Specific Gravity	Weight in Lb. Cu. Ft.	Weight in Lb. Cu. In.	Cu. In. in One Lb.
Aluminum Cast	2.569	160.	.093	10.80
Aluminum Wrought	2.681	167.	.097	10.35
Aluminum Bronze	7.787	485.	.281	3.56
Antimony	6.712	418.	.242	4.13
Arsenic	5.748	358.	.207	4.83
Bismuth	9.827	612.	.354	2.82
Benedict nickel	8.691	542.6	.3140	3.19
Gold (pure)	19.316	1203.	.696	1.44
Standard 22 carat fine	17.502	1090.	.631	1.59
Iron — cast	6.904	430.	.249	4.02
	7.386	499.	.266	3.76
	7.209	464.	.260	3.85
Iron — wrought	7.547	470.	.272	3.56
	7.803	486.	.281	3.68
	7.707	480.	.278	3.60
Lead — cast	11.368	708.	.410	2.44
Lead sheet	11.432	712.	.412	2.43
Manganese	8.012	499.	.289	2.46
Nickel — cast	8.285	516.	.299	3.35
Nickel rolled	8.687	541.	.313	3.19
Platinum	21.516	1340.	.775	1.29
Silver	10.517	655.	.379	2.64
Steel	7.820	487.	.282	3.55
	7.916	493.	.285	3.51
	7.868	490.	.284	3.53
Tin	7.418	462.	.267	3.74
White metal (Babbitt's)	7.322	456.	.264	3.79
Zinc — cast	6.872	428.	.248	4.05
Zinc sheet	7.209	449.	.260	3.84

Approximate Melting Points of Metals and Various Substances

Solid	Degrees Centigrade	Degrees Fahrenheit
Alloy — 3 Lead, 2 Tin, 5 Bismuth	100	212
Alloy — 1 Lead 1½ Tin	200	392
Alloy — 1 Lead 1 Tin	215	419
Aluminum	657.3	1215
Antimony	430 to 630	806 to 1166
Bismuth	269.2	517
Brass	1030	1886
Bronze	920	1688
Cadmium	320	608
Chromium	1487 to 1515	2709 to 2749
Cobalt	1463 to 1500	2665 to 2732
Copper	1054 to 1084	1929 to 1893
Gold	1045 to 1064	1913 to 1947
Iridium	1950 to 2500	3542 to 4532
Iron — Cast Gray	1220 to 1530	2228 to 2786
Iron — Cast White	1050 to 1135	1922 to 2075
Iron — Wrought	1500 to 1600	2732 to 1912
Lead	327	620
Magnesium	750	1382
Manganese	1207 to 1245	2205 to 2273
Mercury	−39.7	−39.5
Nickel	1435	2615
Osmium	2500	4532
Palladium	1546 to 1900	2815 to 3452
Platinum	1753 to 1780	3187 to 3276
Potassium	62	144
Rhodium	2000	3632
Ruthenium	2000+	3632
Silver	960	1760
Sodium	79 to 95	174.2 to 203
Steel	1300 to 1378	2372 to 2532
Steel — Hard	1410	2570
Steel — Mild	1475	2687
Tin	232	449
Titanium	1700	3092
Tungsten	3000	5432
Vanadium	1775	3227
Zinc	419	786
Phosphorous	44.4	112
Calcium	760	1400

Table 8

Right Triangle Solution Formulas

∠A	∠B	Side a	Side b	Side c
$\sin A = \dfrac{a}{c}$		$a = c \times \sin A$		$c = \dfrac{a}{\sin A}$
$\cos A = \dfrac{b}{c}$			$b = c \times \cos A$	$c = \dfrac{b}{\cos A}$
$\tan A = \dfrac{a}{b}$		$a = b \times \tan A$	$b = \dfrac{a}{\tan A}$	
$\cot A = \dfrac{b}{a}$		$a = \dfrac{b}{\cot A}$	$b = a \times \cot A$	
$\sec A = \dfrac{c}{b}$			$b = \dfrac{c}{\sec A}$	$c = b \times \sec A$
$\csc A = \dfrac{c}{a}$		$a = \dfrac{c}{\csc A}$		$c = a \times \csc A$
	$\sin B = \dfrac{b}{c}$		$b = c \times \sin B$	$c = \dfrac{b}{\sin B}$
	$\cos B = \dfrac{a}{c}$	$a = c \times \cos B$		$c = \dfrac{a}{\cos B}$
	$\tan B = \dfrac{b}{a}$	$a = \dfrac{b}{\tan B}$	$b = a \times \tan B$	
	$\cot B = \dfrac{a}{b}$		$b = \dfrac{a}{\cot B}$	
	$\sec B = \dfrac{c}{a}$	$a = \dfrac{c}{\sec B}$		$c = a \times \sec B$
	$\csc B = \dfrac{c}{b}$		$b = \dfrac{c}{\csc B}$	$c = b \csc B$

Table 9

Natural Trigonometric Functions

	0°						1°						2°						3°						
′	sin	cos	tan	cot	sec	cosec	sin	cos	tan	cot	sec	cosec	sin	cos	tan	cot	sec	cosec	sin	cos	tan	cot	sec	cosec	′
0	.00000	1.0000	.00000	Infinite	1.0000	Infinite	.01745	.99985	.01745	57.290	1.0001	57.299	.03490	.99939	.03492	28.636	1.0006	28.654	.05234	.99863	.05241	19.081	1.0014	19.107	60
1	.00029	.0000	.00029	3437.7	.0000	3437.7	.01774	.99984	.01775	56.350	.0001	56.359	.03519	.99938	.03521	28.399	.0006	28.417	.05263	.99861	.05270	18.975	.0014	19.002	59
2	.00058	.0000	.00058	1718.9	.0000	1718.9	.01803	.99984	.01804	55.441	.0001	55.450	.03548	.99937	.03550	28.166	.0006	28.184	.05292	.99860	.05299	18.871	.0014	18.897	58
3	.00087	.0000	.00087	1145.9	.0000	1145.9	.01832	.99983	.01833	54.561	.0002	54.570	.03577	.99936	.03579	27.937	.0006	27.955	.05321	.99858	.05328	18.768	.0014	18.794	57
4	.00116	.0000	.00116	859.44	.0000	859.44	.01861	.99983	.01862	53.708	.0002	53.718	.03606	.99935	.03608	27.712	.0006	27.730	.05350	.99857	.05357	18.665	.0014	18.692	56
5	.00145	1.0000	.00145	687.55	.0000	687.55	.01891	.99982	.01891	52.882	.0002	52.891	.03635	.99934	.03638	27.490	.0007	27.508	.05379	.99855	.05387	18.564	.0014	18.591	55
6	.00174	.0000	.00174	572.96	.0000	572.96	.01920	.99981	.01920	52.081	.0002	52.090	.03664	.99933	.03667	27.271	.0007	27.290	.05408	.99854	.05416	18.464	.0015	18.491	54
7	.00204	.0000	.00204	491.11	.0000	491.11	.01949	.99981	.01949	51.303	.0002	51.313	.03693	.99932	.03696	27.056	.0007	27.075	.05437	.99852	.05445	18.365	.0015	18.393	53
8	.00233	.0000	.00233	429.72	.0000	429.72	.01978	.99980	.01978	50.548	.0002	50.558	.03722	.99931	.03725	26.845	.0007	26.864	.05466	.99850	.05474	18.268	.0015	18.295	52
9	.00262	.0000	.00262	381.97	.0000	381.97	.02007	.99980	.02007	49.816	.0002	49.826	.03751	.99930	.03754	26.637	.0007	26.655	.05495	.99849	.05503	18.171	.0015	18.198	51
10	.00291	0.99999	.00291	343.77	.0000	343.77	.02036	.99979	.02036	49.104	.0002	49.114	.03781	.99928	.03783	26.432	.0007	26.450	.05524	.99847	.05532	18.075	.0015	18.103	50
11	.00320	.99999	.00320	312.52	.0000	312.52	.02065	.99979	.02066	48.412	.0002	48.422	.03810	.99927	.03812	26.230	.0007	26.249	.05553	.99846	.05562	17.980	.0015	18.008	49
12	.00349	.99999	.00349	286.48	.0000	286.48	.02094	.99978	.02095	47.739	.0002	47.750	.03839	.99926	.03842	26.031	.0007	26.050	.05582	.99844	.05591	17.886	.0016	17.914	48
13	.00378	.99999	.00378	264.44	.0000	264.44	.02123	.99977	.02124	47.085	.0002	47.096	.03868	.99925	.03871	25.835	.0007	25.854	.05611	.99842	.05620	17.793	.0016	17.821	47
14	.00407	.99999	.00407	245.55	.0000	245.55	.02152	.99977	.02153	46.449	.0002	46.460	.03897	.99924	.03900	25.642	.0008	25.661	.05640	.99841	.05649	17.701	.0016	17.730	46
15	.00436	.99999	.00436	229.18	.0000	229.18	.02181	.99976	.02182	45.829	.0002	45.840	.03926	.99923	.03929	25.452	.0008	25.471	.05669	.99839	.05678	17.610	.0016	17.639	45
16	.00465	.99999	.00465	214.86	.0000	214.86	.02210	.99975	.02211	45.226	.0002	45.237	.03955	.99922	.03958	25.264	.0008	25.284	.05698	.99837	.05707	17.520	.0016	17.549	44
17	.00494	.99999	.00494	202.22	.0000	202.22	.02240	.99975	.02240	44.638	.0002	44.650	.03984	.99921	.03987	25.080	.0008	25.100	.05727	.99836	.05737	17.431	.0016	17.460	43
18	.00524	.99999	.00524	190.98	.0000	190.99	.02269	.99974	.02269	44.066	.0002	44.077	.04013	.99919	.04016	24.898	.0008	24.918	.05756	.99834	.05766	17.343	.0017	17.372	42
19	.00553	.99998	.00553	180.93	.0000	180.93	.02298	.99974	.02298	43.508	.0003	43.520	.04042	.99918	.04045	24.718	.0008	24.739	.05785	.99832	.05795	17.256	.0017	17.285	41
20	.00582	.99998	.00582	171.88	.0000	171.89	.02326	.99973	.02327	42.964	.0003	42.976	.04071	.99917	.04075	24.542	.0008	24.562	.05814	.99831	.05824	17.169	.0017	17.198	40
21	.00611	.99998	.00611	163.70	.0000	163.70	.02356	.99972	.02357	42.433	.0003	42.445	.04100	.99916	.04104	24.367	.0008	24.388	.05843	.99829	.05853	17.084	.0017	17.113	39
22	.00640	.99998	.00640	156.26	.0000	156.26	.02385	.99971	.02386	41.916	.0003	41.928	.04129	.99915	.04133	24.196	.0008	24.216	.05872	.99827	.05883	16.999	.0017	17.028	38
23	.00669	.99998	.00669	149.46	.0000	149.47	.02414	.99971	.02415	41.410	.0003	41.423	.04158	.99913	.04162	24.026	.0009	24.047	.05902	.99826	.05912	16.915	.0017	16.944	37
24	.00698	.99997	.00698	143.24	.0000	143.24	.02443	.99970	.02444	40.917	.0003	40.930	.04187	.99912	.04191	23.859	.0009	23.880	.05931	.99824	.05941	16.832	.0018	16.861	36
25	.00727	.99997	.00727	137.51	.0000	137.51	.02472	.99969	.02473	40.436	.0003	40.448	.04217	.99911	.04220	23.694	.0009	23.716	.05960	.99822	.05970	16.750	.0018	16.779	35
26	.00756	.99997	.00756	132.22	.0000	132.22	.02501	.99969	.02502	39.965	.0003	39.978	.04246	.99910	.04249	23.532	.0009	23.553	.05989	.99820	.05999	16.668	.0018	16.698	34
27	.00785	.99997	.00785	127.32	.0000	127.32	.02530	.99968	.02531	39.506	.0003	39.518	.04275	.99908	.04279	23.372	.0009	23.393	.06018	.99819	.06029	16.587	.0018	16.617	33
28	.00814	.99997	.00814	122.77	.0000	122.78	.02559	.99967	.02560	39.057	.0003	39.069	.04304	.99907	.04308	23.214	.0009	23.235	.06047	.99817	.06058	16.507	.0018	16.538	32
29	.00843	.99996	.00844	118.54	.0000	118.54	.02589	.99966	.02589	38.618	.0003	38.631	.04333	.99906	.04337	23.058	.0009	23.079	.06076	.99815	.06087	16.428	.0018	16.459	31
30	.00873	.99996	.00873	114.59	.0000	114.59	.02618	.99966	.02618	38.188	.0003	38.201	.04362	.99905	.04366	22.904	.0009	22.925	.06105	.99813	.06116	16.350	.0019	16.380	30
31	.00902	.99996	.00902	110.89	.0000	110.90	.02647	.99965	.02648	37.769	.0003	37.782	.04391	.99903	.04395	22.752	.0010	22.774	.06134	.99812	.06145	16.272	.0019	16.303	29
32	.00931	.99996	.00931	107.43	.0000	107.43	.02676	.99964	.02677	37.358	.0003	37.371	.04420	.99902	.04424	22.602	.0010	22.624	.06163	.99810	.06175	16.195	.0019	16.226	28
33	.00960	.99995	.00960	104.17	.0000	104.17	.02705	.99963	.02706	36.956	.0004	36.969	.04449	.99901	.04453	22.454	.0010	22.476	.06192	.99808	.06204	16.119	.0019	16.150	27
34	.00989	.99995	.00989	101.11	.0000	101.11	.02734	.99963	.02735	36.563	.0004	36.576	.04478	.99900	.04483	22.308	.0010	22.330	.06221	.99806	.06233	16.043	.0019	16.075	26
35	.01018	.99995	.01018	98.218	.0000	98.223	.02763	.99962	.02764	36.177	.0004	36.191	.04507	.99898	.04512	22.164	.0010	22.186	.06250	.99804	.06262	15.969	.0019	16.000	25
36	.01047	.99994	.01047	95.489	.0000	95.495	.02792	.99961	.02793	35.800	.0004	35.814	.04536	.99897	.04541	22.022	.0010	22.044	.06279	.99803	.06291	15.894	.0020	15.926	24
37	.01076	.99994	.01076	92.908	.0000	92.914	.02821	.99960	.02822	35.431	.0004	35.445	.04565	.99896	.04570	21.881	.0010	21.904	.06308	.99801	.06321	15.821	.0020	15.853	23
38	.01105	.99994	.01105	90.463	.0001	90.469	.02850	.99959	.02851	35.069	.0004	35.084	.04594	.99894	.04599	21.742	.0010	21.765	.06337	.99799	.06350	15.748	.0020	15.780	22
39	.01134	.99993	.01134	88.143	.0001	88.149	.02879	.99958	.02880	34.715	.0004	34.729	.04623	.99893	.04628	21.606	.0011	21.629	.06366	.99797	.06379	15.676	.0020	15.708	21
40	.01163	.99993	.01164	85.940	.0001	85.946	.02908	.99958	.02910	34.368	.0004	34.382	.04652	.99892	.04657	21.470	.0011	21.494	.06395	.99795	.06408	15.605	.0020	15.637	20
41	.01193	.99993	.01193	83.843	.0001	83.849	.02937	.99957	.02939	34.027	.0004	34.042	.04681	.99890	.04687	21.337	.0011	21.360	.06424	.99793	.06437	15.534	.0021	15.566	19
42	.01222	.99992	.01222	81.847	.0001	81.853	.02967	.99956	.02968	33.693	.0004	33.708	.04711	.99889	.04716	21.205	.0011	21.228	.06453	.99791	.06467	15.464	.0021	15.496	18
43	.01251	.99992	.01251	79.943	.0001	79.950	.02996	.99955	.02997	33.366	.0004	33.381	.04740	.99888	.04745	21.075	.0011	21.098	.06482	.99790	.06496	15.394	.0021	15.427	17
44	.01280	.99992	.01280	78.126	.0001	78.133	.03025	.99954	.03026	33.045	.0004	33.060	.04769	.99886	.94774	20.946	.0011	20.970	.06511	.99788	.06525	15.325	.0021	15.358	16
45	.01309	.99991	.01309	76.390	.0001	76.396	.03054	.99953	.03055	32.730	.0005	32.745	.04798	.99885	.04803	20.819	.0011	20.843	.06540	.99786	.06554	15.257	.0021	15.290	15
46	.01338	.99991	.01338	74.729	.0001	74.736	.03083	.99952	.03084	32.421	.0005	32.437	.04827	.99883	.04832	20.693	.0012	20.717	.06569	.99784	.06583	15.189	.0022	15.222	14
47	.01367	.99991	.01367	73.139	.0001	73.146	.03112	.99951	.03113	32.118	.0005	32.134	.04856	.99882	.04862	20.569	.0012	20.593	.06598	.99782	.06613	15.122	.0022	15.155	13
48	.01396	.99990	.01396	71.615	.0001	71.622	.03141	.99951	.03143	31.820	.0005	31.836	.04885	.99881	.04891	20.446	.0012	20.471	.06627	.99780	.06642	15.056	.0022	15.089	12
49	.01425	.99990	.01425	70.153	.0001	70.160	.03170	.99950	.03172	31.528	.0005	31.544	.04914	.99879	.04920	20.325	.0012	20.350	.06656	.99778	.06671	14.990	.0022	15.023	11
50	.01454	.99989	.01454	68.750	.0001	68.757	.03199	.99949	.03201	31.241	.0005	31.257	.04943	.99878	.04949	20.205	.0012	20.230	.06685	.99776	.06700	14.924	.0022	14.958	10
51	.01483	.99989	.01484	67.402	.0001	67.409	.03228	.99948	.03230	30.960	.0005	30.976	.04972	.99876	.04978	20.087	.0012	20.112	.06714	.99774	.06730	14.860	.0023	14.893	9
52	.01512	.99988	.01513	66.105	.0001	66.113	.03257	.99947	.03259	30.683	.0005	30.699	.05001	.99875	.05007	19.970	.0012	19.995	.06743	.99772	.06759	14.795	.0023	14.829	8
53	.01542	.99988	.01542	64.858	.0001	64.866	.03286	.99946	.03288	30.411	.0005	30.428	.05030	.99873	.05037	19.854	.0013	19.880	.06772	.99770	.06788	14.732	.0023	14.765	7
54	.01571	.99988	.01571	63.657	.0001	63.664	.03315	.99945	.03317	30.145	.0005	30.161	.05059	.99872	.05066	19.740	.0013	19.766	.06801	.99768	.06817	14.668	.0023	14.702	6
55	.01600	.99987	.01600	62.499	.0001	62.507	.03344	.99944	.03346	29.882	.0005	29.899	.05088	.99870	.05095	19.627	.0013	19.653	.06830	.99766	.06846	14.606	.0023	14.640	5
56	.01629	.99987	.01629	61.383	.0001	61.391	.03374	.99943	.03375	29.624	.0006	29.641	.05117	.99869	.05124	19.515	.0013	19.541	.06859	.99764	.06876	14.544	.0024	14.578	4
57	.01658	.99987	.01658	60.306	.0001	60.314	.03403	.99942	.03405	29.371	.0006	29.388	.05146	.99867	.05153	19.405	.0013	19.431	.06888	.99762	.06905	14.482	.0024	14.517	3
58	.01687	.99986	.01687	59.266	.0001	59.274	.03432	.99941	.03434	29.122	.0006	29.139	.05175	.99866	.05182	19.296	.0013	19.322	.06918	.99760	.06934	14.421	.0024	14.456	2
59	.01716	.99985	.01716	58.261	.0001	58.270	.03461	.99940	.03463	28.877	.0006	28.894	.05204	.99864	.05212	19.188	.0013	19.214	.06947	.99758	.06963	14.361	.0024	14.395	1
60	.01745	.99985	.01745	57.290	.0001	57.299	.03490	.99939	.03492	28.636	.0006	28.654	.05234	.99863	.05241	19.081	.0014	19.107	.06976	.99756	06993	14.301	.0024	14.335	0
′	cos	sin	cot	tan	cosec	sec	cos	sin	cot	tan	cosec	sec	cos	sin	cot	tan	cosec	sec	cos	sin	cot	tan	cosec	sec	′
	89°						88°						87°						86°						

Source. (Courtesy of Bethlehem Steel.)

778 APPENDIX II GENERAL TABLES

	4°						5°					
′	sin	cos	tan	cot	sec	cosec	sin	cos	tan	cot	sec	cosec
0	.06976	.99756	.06993	14.301	1.0024	14.335	.08715	.99619	.08749	11.430	1.0038	11.474
1	.07005	.99754	.07022	14.241	.0025	14.276	.08744	.99617	.08778	11.392	.0038	11.436
2	.07034	.99752	.07051	14.182	.0025	14.217	.08773	.99614	.08807	11.354	.0039	11.398
3	.07063	.99750	.07080	14.123	.0025	14.159	.08802	.99612	.08837	11.316	.0039	11.360
4	.07092	.99748	.07110	14.065	.0025	14.101	.08831	.99609	.08866	11.279	.0039	11.323
5	.07121	.99746	.07139	14.008	.0025	14.043	.08860	.99607	.08895	11.242	.0039	11.286
6	.07150	.99744	.07168	13.951	.0026	13.986	.08889	.99604	.08925	11.205	.0040	11.249
7	.07179	.99742	.07197	13.894	.0026	13.930	.08918	.99601	.08954	11.168	.0040	11.213
8	.07208	.99740	.07226	13.838	.0026	13.874	.08947	.99599	.08983	11.132	.0040	11.176
9	.07237	.99738	.07256	13.782	.0026	13.818	.08976	.99596	.09013	11.095	.0040	11.140
10	.07266	.99736	.07285	13.727	.0026	13.763	.09005	.99594	.09042	11.059	.0041	11.104
11	.07295	.99733	.07314	13.672	.0027	13.708	.09034	.99591	.09071	11.024	.0041	11.069
12	.07324	.99731	.07343	13.617	.0027	13.654	.09063	.99588	.09101	10.988	.0041	11.033
13	.07353	.99729	.07373	13.563	.0027	13.600	.09092	.99586	.09130	10.953	.0041	10.998
14	.07382	.99727	.07402	13.510	.0027	13.547	.09121	.99583	.09159	10.918	.0042	10.963
15	.07411	.99725	.07431	13.457	.0027	13.494	.09150	.99580	.09189	10.883	.0042	10.929
16	.07440	.99723	.07460	13.404	.0028	13.441	.09179	.99578	.09218	10.848	.0042	10.894
17	.07469	.99721	.07490	13.351	.0028	13.389	.09208	.99575	.09247	10.814	.0043	10.860
18	.07498	.99718	.07519	13.299	.0028	13.337	.09237	.99572	.09277	10.780	.0043	10.826
19	.07527	.99716	.07548	13.248	.0028	13.286	.09266	.99570	.09306	10.746	.0043	10.792
20	.07556	.99714	.07577	13.917	.0029	13.235	.09295	.99567	.09335	10.712	.0043	10.758
21	.07585	.99712	.07607	13.146	.0029	13.184	.09324	.99564	.09365	10.678	.0044	10.725
22	.07614	.99710	.07636	13.096	.0029	13.134	.09353	.99562	.09394	10.645	.0044	10.692
23	.07643	.99707	.07665	13.046	.0029	13.084	.09382	.99559	.09423	10.612	.0044	10.659
24	.07672	.99705	.07694	12.996	.0029	13.034	.09411	.99556	.09453	10.579	.0044	10.626
25	.07701	.99703	.07724	12.947	.0030	12.985	.09440	.99553	.09482	10.546	.0045	10.593
26	.07730	.99701	.07753	12.898	.0030	12.937	.09469	.99551	.09511	10.514	.0045	10.561
27	.07759	.99698	.07782	12.849	.0030	12.888	.09498	.99548	.09541	10.481	.0045	10.529
28	.07788	.99696	.07812	12.801	.0030	12.840	.09527	.99545	.09570	10.449	.0046	10.497
29	.07817	.99694	.07841	12.754	.0031	12.793	.09556	.99542	.09599	10.417	.0046	10.465
30	.07846	.99692	.07870	12.706	.0031	12.745	.09584	.99540	.09629	10.385	.0046	10.433
31	.07875	.99689	.07899	12.659	.0031	12.698	.09613	.99537	.09658	10.354	.0046	10.402
32	.07904	.99687	.07929	12.612	.0031	12.652	.09642	.99534	.09688	10.322	.0047	10.371
33	.07933	.99685	.07958	12.566	.0032	12.606	.09671	.99531	.09717	10.291	.0047	10.340
34	.07962	.99682	.07987	12.520	.0032	12.560	.09700	.99528	.09746	10.260	.0047	10.309
35	.07991	.99680	.08016	12.474	.0032	12.514	.09729	.99525	.09776	10.229	.0048	10.278
36	.08020	.99678	.08046	12.429	.0032	12.469	.09758	.99523	.09805	10.199	.0048	10.248
37	.08049	.99675	.08075	12.384	.0032	12.424	.09787	.99520	.09834	10.168	.0048	10.217
38	.08078	.99673	.08104	12.339	.0033	12.379	.09816	.99517	.09864	10.138	.0048	10.187
39	.08107	.99671	.08134	12.295	.0033	12.335	.09845	.99514	.09893	10.108	.0049	10.157
40	.08136	.99668	.08163	12.250	.0033	12.291	.09874	.99511	.09922	10.078	.0049	10.127
41	.08165	.99666	.08192	12.207	.0033	12.248	.09903	.99508	.09952	10.048	.0049	10.098
42	.08194	.99664	.08221	12.163	.0034	12.204	.09932	.99505	.09981	10.019	.0050	10.068
43	.08223	.99661	.08251	12.120	.0034	12.161	.09961	.99503	.10011	9.9893	.0050	10.039
44	.08252	.99659	.08280	12.077	.0034	12.118	.09990	.99500	.10040	9.9601	.0050	10.010
45	.08281	.99656	.08309	12.035	.0034	12.076	.10019	.99497	.10069	9.9310	.0050	9.9812
46	.08310	.99654	.08339	11.992	.0035	12.034	.10048	.99494	.10099	9.9021	.0051	9.9525
47	.08339	.99652	.08368	11.950	.0035	11.992	.10077	.99491	.10128	9.8734	.0051	9.9239
48	.08368	.99649	.08397	11.909	.0035	11.950	.10106	.99488	.10158	9.8448	.0051	9.8955
49	.08397	.99647	.08426	11.867	.0035	11.909	.10134	.99485	.10187	9.8164	.0052	9.8672
50	.08426	.99644	.08456	11.826	.0036	11.868	.10163	.99482	.10216	9.7882	.0052	9.8391
51	.08455	.99642	.08485	11.785	.0036	11.828	.10192	.99479	.10246	9.7601	.0052	9.8112
52	.08484	.99639	.08514	11.745	.0036	11.787	.10221	.99476	.10275	9.7322	.0053	9.7834
53	.08513	.99637	.08544	11.704	.0036	11.747	.10250	.99473	.10305	9.7044	.0053	9.7558
54	.08542	.99634	.08573	11.664	.0037	11.707	.10279	.99470	.10334	9.6768	.0053	9.7283
55	.08571	.99632	.08602	11.625	.0037	11.668	.10308	.99467	.10363	9.6493	.0053	9.7010
56	.08600	.99629	.08632	11.585	.0037	11.628	.10337	.99464	.10393	9.6220	.0054	9.6739
57	.08629	.99627	.08661	11.546	.0037	11.589	.10366	.99461	.10422	9.5949	.0054	9.6469
58	.08658	.99624	.08690	11.507	.0038	11.550	.10395	.99458	.10452	9.5679	.0054	9.6200
59	.08687	.99622	.08719	11.468	.0038	11.512	.10424	.99455	.10481	9.5411	.0055	9.5933
60	.08715	.99619	.08749	11.430	.0038	11.474	.10453	.99452	.10510	9.5144	.0055	9.5668
′	cos	sin	cot	tan	cosec	sec	cos	sin	cot	tan	cosec	sec
	85°						84°					

6°						7°						
sin	cos	tan	cot	sec	cosec	sin	cos	tan	cot	sec	cosec	′
.10453	.99452	.10510	9.5144	1.0055	9.5668	.12187	.99255	.12278	8.1443	1.0075	8.2055	60
.10482	.99449	.10540	.4878	.0055	.5404	.12216	.99251	.12308	.1248	.0075	.1861	59
.10511	.99446	.10569	.4614	.0056	.5141	.12245	.99247	.12337	.1053	.0076	.1668	58
.10540	.99443	.10599	.4351	.0056	.4880	.12273	.99244	.12367	.0860	.0076	.1476	57
.10568	.99440	.10628	.4090	.0056	.4620	.12302	.99240	.12396	.0667	.0076	.1285	56
.10597	.99437	.10657	9.3831	.0057	9.4362	.12331	.99237	.12426	8.0476	.0077	8.1094	55
.10626	.99434	.10687	.3572	.0057	.4105	.12360	.99233	.12456	.0285	.0077	.0905	54
.10655	.99431	.10716	.3315	.0057	.3850	.12389	.99229	.12485	.0095	.0078	.0717	53
.10684	.99428	.10746	.3060	.0057	.3596	.12418	.99226	.12515	7.9906	.0078	.0529	52
.10713	.99424	.10775	.2806	.0058	.3343	.12447	.99222	.12544	.9717	.0078	.0342	51
.10742	.99421	.10805	9.2553	.0058	9.3092	.12476	.99219	.12574	7.9530	.0079	8.0156	50
.10771	.99418	.10834	.2302	.0058	.2842	.12504	.99215	.12603	.9344	.0079	7.9971	49
.10800	.99415	.10863	.2051	.0059	.2593	.12533	.99211	.12633	.9158	.0079	.9787	48
.10829	.99412	.10893	.1803	.0059	.2346	.12562	.99208	.12662	.8973	.0080	.9604	47
.10858	.99409	.10922	.1555	.0059	.2100	.12591	.99204	.12692	.8789	.0080	.9421	46
.10887	.99406	.10952	9.1309	.0060	9.1855	.12620	.99200	.12722	7.8606	.0080	7.9240	45
.10916	.99402	.10981	.1064	.0060	.1612	.12649	.99197	.12751	.8424	.0081	.9059	44
.10944	.99399	.11011	.0821	.0060	.1370	.12678	.99193	.12781	.8243	.0081	.8879	43
.10973	.99396	.11040	.0579	.0061	.1129	.12706	.99189	.12810	.8062	.0082	.8700	42
.11002	.99393	.11069	.0338	.0061	.0890	.12735	.99186	.12840	.7882	.0082	.8522	41
.11031	.99390	.11099	9.0098	.0061	9.0651	.12764	.99182	.12869	7.7703	.0082	7.8344	40
.11060	.99386	.11128	8.9860	.0062	.0414	.12793	.99178	.12899	.7525	.0083	.8168	39
.11089	.99383	.11158	.9623	.0062	.0179	.12822	.99174	.12928	.7348	.0083	.7992	38
.11118	.99380	.11187	.9387	.0062	8.9944	.12851	.99171	.12958	.7171	.0084	.7817	37
.11147	.99377	.11217	.9152	.0063	.9711	.12879	.99167	.12988	.6996	.0084	.7642	36
.11176	.99373	.11246	8.8918	.0063	8.9479	.12908	.99163	.13017	7.6821	.0084	7.7469	35
.11205	.99370	.11276	.8686	.0063	.9248	.12937	.99160	.13047	.6646	.0085	.7296	34
.11234	.99367	.11305	.8455	.0064	.9018	.12966	.99156	.13076	.6473	.0085	.7124	33
.11262	.99364	.11335	.8225	.0064	.8790	.12995	.99152	.13106	.6300	.0085	.6953	32
.11291	.99360	.11364	.7996	.0064	.8563	.13024	.99148	.13136	.6129	.0086	.6783	31
.11320	.99357	.11393	8.7769	.0065	8.8337	.13053	.99144	.13165	7.5957	.0086	7.6613	30
.11349	.99354	.11423	.7542	.0065	.8112	.13081	.99141	.13195	.5787	.0087	.6444	29
.11378	.99350	.11452	.7317	.0065	.7888	.13110	.99137	.13224	.5617	.0087	.6276	28
.11407	.99347	.11482	.7093	.0066	.7665	.13139	.99133	.13254	.5449	.0087	.6108	27
.11436	.99344	.11511	.6870	.0066	.7444	.13168	.99129	.13284	.5280	.0088	.5942	26
.11465	.99341	.11541	8.6648	.0066	8.7223	.13197	.99125	.13313	7.5113	.0088	7.5776	25
.11494	.99337	.11570	.6427	.0067	.7004	.13226	.99121	.13343	.4946	.0089	.5611	24
.11523	.99334	.11600	.6208	.0067	.6786	.13254	.99118	.13372	.4780	.0089	.5446	23
.11551	.99330	.11629	.5989	.0067	.6569	.13283	.99114	.13402	.4615	.0089	.5282	22
.11580	.99327	.11659	.5772	.0068	.6353	.13312	.99110	.13432	.4451	.0090	.5119	21
.11609	.99324	.11688	8.5555	.0068	8.6138	.13341	.99106	.13461	7.4287	.0090	7.4957	20
.11638	.99320	.11718	.5340	.0068	.5924	.13370	.99102	.13491	.4124	.0090	.4795	19
.11667	.99317	.11747	.5126	.0069	.5711	.13399	.99098	.13520	.3961	.0091	.4634	18
.11696	.99314	.11777	.4913	.0069	.5499	.13427	.99094	.13550	.3800	.0091	.4474	17
.11725	.99310	.11806	.4701	.0069	.5289	.13456	.99090	.13580	.3639	.0092	.4315	16
.11754	.99307	.11836	8.4489	.0070	8.5079	.13485	.99086	.13609	7.3479	.0092	7.4156	15
.11783	.99303	.11865	.4279	.0070	.4871	.13514	.99083	.13639	.3319	.0092	.3998	14
.11811	.99300	.11895	.4070	.0070	.4663	.13543	.99079	.13669	.3160	.0093	.3840	13
.11840	.99296	.11924	.3862	.0071	.4457	.13571	.99075	.13698	.3002	.0093	.3683	12
.11869	.99293	.11954	.3655	.0071	.4251	.13600	.99071	.13728	.2844	.0094	.3527	11
.11898	.99290	.11983	8.3449	.0071	8.4046	.13629	.99067	.13757	7.2687	.0094	7.3372	10
.11927	.99286	.12013	.3244	.0072	.3843	.13658	.99063	.13787	.2531	.0094	.3217	9
.11956	.99283	.12042	.3040	.0072	.3640	.13687	.99059	.13817	.2375	.0095	.3063	8
.11985	.99279	.12072	.2837	.0073	.3439	.13716	.99055	.13846	.2220	.0095	.2909	7
.12014	.99276	.12101	.2635	.0073	.3238	.13744	.99051	.13876	.2066	.0096	.2757	6
.12042	.99272	.12131	8.2434	.0073	8.3039	.13773	.99047	.13906	7.1912	.0096	7.2604	5
.12071	.99269	.12160	.2234	.0074	.2840	.13802	.99043	.13935	.1759	.0097	.2453	4
.12100	.99265	.12190	.2035	.0074	.2642	.13831	.99039	.13965	.1607	.0097	.2302	3
.12129	.99262	.12219	.1837	.0074	.2446	.13860	.99035	.13995	.1455	.0097	.2152	2
.12158	.99258	.12249	.1640	.0075	.2250	.13888	.99031	.14024	.1304	.0098	.2002	1
.12187	.99255	.12278	8.1443	.0075	8.2055	.13917	.99027	.14054	7.1154	.0098	7.1853	0
cos	sin	cot	tan	cosec	sec	cos	sin	cot	tan	cosec	sec	′
83°						82°						

	8°						9°						10°						11°						
′	sin	cos	tan	cot	sec	cosec	sin	cos	tan	cot	sec	cosec	sin	cos	tan	cot	sec	cosec	sin	cos	tan	cot	sec	cosec	′
0	.13917	.99027	.14054	7.1154	1.0098	7.1853	.15643	.98769	.15838	6.3137	1.0215	6.3924	.17365	.98481	.17633	5.6713	1.0154	5.7588	.19081	.98163	.19438	5.1445	1.0187	5.2408	60
1	.13946	.99023	.14084	.1004	.0099	.1704	.15672	.98764	.15868	.3019	.0125	.3807	.17393	.98476	.17663	.6616	.0155	.7493	.19109	.98157	.19468	.1366	.0188	.2330	59
2	.13975	.99019	.14113	.0854	.0099	.1557	.15701	.98760	.15898	.2901	.0125	.3690	.17422	.98471	.17693	.6520	.0155	.7398	.19138	.98152	.19498	.1286	.0188	.2252	58
3	.14004	.99015	.14143	.0706	.0099	.1409	.15730	.98755	.15928	.2783	.0126	.3574	.17451	.98465	.17723	.6425	.0156	.7304	.19166	.98146	.19529	.1207	.0189	.2174	57
4	.14032	.99010	.14173	.0558	.0100	.1263	.15758	.98750	.15958	.2665	.0126	.3458	.17479	.98460	.17753	.6329	.0156	.7210	.19195	.98140	.19559	.1128	.0189	.2097	56
5	.14061	.99006	.14202	7.0410	.0100	7.1117	.15787	.98746	.15987	6.2548	.0127	6.3343	.17508	.98455	.17783	5.6234	.0157	5.7117	.19224	.98135	.19589	5.1049	.0190	5.2019	55
6	.14090	.99002	.14232	.0264	.0101	.0972	.15816	.98741	.16017	.2432	.0217	.3228	.17537	.98450	.17813	.6140	.0157	.7023	.19252	.98129	.19619	.0970	.0191	.1942	54
7	.14119	.98998	.14262	.0117	.0101	.0827	.15844	.98737	.16047	.2316	.0128	.3113	.17565	.98445	.17843	.6045	.0158	.6930	.19281	.98124	.19649	.0892	.0191	.1865	53
8	.14148	.98994	.14291	6.9972	.0102	.0683	.15873	.98732	.16077	.2200	.0128	.2999	.17594	.98440	.17873	.5951	.0158	.6838	.19309	.98118	.19680	.0814	.0192	.1788	52
9	.14176	.98990	.14321	.9827	.0102	.0539	.15902	.98727	.16107	.2085	.0129	.2885	.17622	.98435	.17903	.5857	.0159	.6745	.19338	.98112	.19710	.0736	.0192	.1712	51
10	.14205	.98986	.14351	6.9682	.0102	7.0396	.15931	.98723	.16137	6.1970	.0129	6.2772	.17651	.98430	.17933	5.5764	.0159	5.6653	.19366	.98107	.19740	5.0658	.0193	5.1636	50
11	.14234	.98982	.14380	.9538	.0103	.0254	.15959	.98718	.16167	.1856	.0130	.2659	.17680	.98425	.17963	.5670	.0160	.6561	.19395	.98101	.19770	.0581	.0193	.1560	49
12	.14263	.98978	.14410	.9395	.0103	.0112	.15988	.98714	.16196	.1742	.0130	.2546	.17708	.98419	.17993	.5578	.0160	.6470	.19423	.98095	.19800	.0504	.0194	.1484	48
13	.14292	.98973	.14440	.9252	.0104	6.9971	.16017	.98709	.16226	.1628	.0131	.2434	.17737	.98414	.18023	.5485	.0161	.6379	.19452	.98090	.19831	.0427	.0195	.1409	47
14	.14320	.98969	.14470	.9110	.0104	.9830	.16045	.98704	.16256	.1515	.0131	.2322	.17766	.98409	.18053	.5393	.0162	.6288	.19480	.98084	.19861	.0350	.0195	.1333	46
15	.14349	.98965	.14499	6.8969	.0104	6.9690	.16074	.98700	.16286	6.1402	.0132	6.2211	.17794	.98404	.18083	5.5301	.0162	5.6197	.19509	.98078	.19891	5.0273	.0196	5.1258	45
16	.14378	.98961	.14529	.8828	.0105	.9550	.16103	.98695	.16316	.1290	.0132	.2100	.17823	.98399	.18113	.5209	.0163	.6107	.19537	.98073	.19921	.0197	.0196	.1183	44
17	.14407	.98957	.14559	.8687	.0105	.9411	.16132	.98690	.16346	.1178	.0133	.1990	.17852	.98394	.18143	.5117	.0163	.6017	.19566	.98067	.19952	.0121	.0197	.1109	43
18	.14436	.98952	.14588	.8547	.0106	.9273	.16160	.98685	.16376	.1066	.0133	.1880	.17880	.98388	.18173	.5026	.0164	.5928	.19595	.98061	.19982	.0045	.0198	.1034	42
19	.14464	.98948	.14618	.8408	.0106	.9135	.16189	.98681	.16405	.0955	.0134	.1770	.17909	.98383	.18203	.4936	.0164	.5838	.19623	.98056	.20012	4.9969	.0198	.0960	41
20	.14493	.98944	.14648	6.8269	.0107	6.8998	.16218	.98676	.16435	6.0844	.0134	6.1661	.17937	.98378	.18233	5.4845	.0165	5.5749	.19652	.98050	.20042	4.9894	.0199	5.0886	40
21	.14522	.98940	.14677	.8131	.0107	.8861	.16246	.98671	.16465	.0734	.0135	.1552	.17966	.98373	.18263	.4755	.0165	.5660	.19680	.98044	.20073	.9819	.0199	.0812	39
22	.14551	.98936	.14707	.7993	.0107	.8725	.16275	.98667	.16495	.0624	.0135	.1443	.17995	.98368	.18293	.4665	.0166	.5572	.19709	.98039	.20103	.9744	.0200	.0739	38
23	.14579	.98931	.14737	.7856	.0108	.8589	.16304	.98662	.16525	.0514	.0136	.1335	.18023	.98362	.18323	.4575	.0166	.5484	.19737	.98033	.20133	.9669	.0201	.0666	37
24	.14608	.98927	.14767	.7720	.0108	.8454	.16333	.98657	.16555	.0405	.0136	.1227	.18052	.98357	.18353	.4486	.0167	.5396	.19766	.98027	.20163	.9594	.0201	.0593	36
25	.14637	.98923	.14796	6.7584	.0109	6.8320	.16361	.98652	.16585	6.0296	.0136	6.1120	.18080	.98352	.18383	5.4396	.0167	5.5308	.19794	.98021	.20194	4.9520	.0202	5.0520	35
26	.14666	.98919	.14826	.7448	.0109	.8185	.16390	.98648	.16615	.0188	.0137	.1013	.18109	.98347	.18413	.4308	.0168	.5221	.19823	.98016	.20224	.9446	.0202	.0447	34
27	.14695	.98914	.14856	.7313	.0110	.8052	.16419	.98643	.16644	.0080	.0137	.0906	.18138	.98341	.18444	.4219	.0169	.5134	.19851	.98010	.20254	.9372	.0203	.0375	33
28	.14723	.98910	.14886	.7179	.0110	.7919	.16447	.98638	.16674	5.9972	.0138	.0800	.18166	.98336	.18474	.4131	.0169	.5047	.19880	.98004	.20285	.9298	.0204	.0302	32
29	.14752	.98906	.14915	.7045	.0111	.7787	.16476	.98633	.16704	.9865	.0138	.0694	.18195	.98331	.18504	.4043	.0170	.4960	.19908	.97998	.20315	.9225	.0204	.0230	31
30	.14781	.98901	.14945	6.6911	.0111	6.7655	.16505	.98628	.16734	5.9758	.0139	6.0588	.18223	.98325	.18534	5.3955	.0170	5.4874	.19937	.97992	.20345	4.9151	.0205	5.0158	30
31	.14810	.98897	.14975	.6779	.0111	.7523	.16533	.98624	.16764	.9651	.9139	.0483	.18252	.98320	.18564	.3868	.0171	.4788	.19965	.97987	.20375	.9078	.0205	.0087	29
32	.14838	.98893	.15004	.6646	.0112	.7392	.16562	.98619	.16794	.9545	.9140	.0379	.18281	.98315	.18594	.3780	.0171	.4702	.19994	.97981	.20406	.9006	.0206	.0015	28
33	.14867	.98889	.15034	.6514	.0112	.7262	.16591	.98614	.16824	.9439	.0140	.0274	.18309	.98309	.18624	.3694	.0172	.4617	.20022	.97975	.20436	.8933	.0207	4.9944	27
34	.14896	.98884	.15064	.6383	.0113	.7132	.16619	.98609	.16854	.9333	.0141	.0170	.18338	.98304	.18654	.3607	.0172	.4532	.20051	.97969	.20466	.8860	.0207	.9873	26
35	.14925	.98880	.15094	6.6252	.0113	6.7003	.16648	.98604	.16884	5.9228	.0141	6.0066	.18366	.98299	.18684	5.3521	.0173	5.4447	.20079	.97963	.20497	4.8788	0208	4.9802	25
36	.14953	.98876	.15123	.6122	.0114	.6874	.16677	.98600	.16914	.9123	.0142	5.9963	.18395	.98293	.18714	.3434	.0174	.4362	.20108	.97957	.20527	.8716	.0208	.9732	24
37	.14982	.98871	.15153	.5992	.0114	.6745	.16705	.98595	.16944	.9019	.0142	.9860	.18424	.98288	.18745	.3349	.0174	.4278	.20136	.97952	.20557	.8644	.0209	.9661	23
38	.15011	.98867	.15183	.5863	.0115	.6617	.16734	.98590	.16973	.8915	.0143	.9758	.18452	.98283	.18775	.3263	.0175	.4194	.20165	.97946	.20588	.8573	.0210	.9591	22
39	.15050	.98862	.15213	.5734	.0115	.6490	.16763	.98585	.17003	.8811	.0143	.9655	.18481	.98277	.18805	.3178	.0175	.4110	.20193	.97940	.20618	.8501	.0210	.9521	21
40	.15068	.98858	.15243	6.5605	.0115	6.6363	.16791	.98580	.17033	5.8708	.0144	5.9554	.18509	.98272	.18835	5.3093	.0176	5.4026	.20222	.97934	.20648	4.8430	.0211	4.9452	20
41	.15097	.98854	.15272	.5478	.0116	.6237	.16820	.98575	.17063	.8605	.0144	.9452	.18538	.98267	.18865	.3008	.0176	.3943	.20250	.97928	.20679	.8359	.0211	.9382	19
42	.15126	.98849	.15302	.5350	.0116	.6111	.16849	.98570	.17093	.8502	.0145	.9351	.18567	.98261	.18895	.2923	.0177	.3860	.20279	.97922	.20709	.8288	.0212	.9313	18
43	.15155	.98845	.15332	.5223	.0117	.5985	.16878	.98565	.17123	.8400	.0145	.9250	.18595	.98256	.18925	.2839	.0177	.3777	.20307	.97916	.20739	.8217	.0213	.9243	17
44	.15183	.98840	.15362	.5097	.0117	.5860	.16906	.98560	.17153	.8298	.0146	.9150	.18624	.98250	.18955	.2755	.0178	.3695	.20336	.97910	.20770	.8147	.0213	.9175	16
45	.15212	.98836	.15391	6.4971	.0118	6.5736	.16935	.98556	.17183	5.8196	.0146	5.9049	.18652	.98245	.18985	5.2671	.0179	5.3612	.20364	.97904	.20800	4.8077	.0214	4.9106	15
46	.15241	.98832	.15421	.4845	.0118	.5612	.16964	.98551	.17213	.8095	.0147	.8950	.18681	.98240	.19016	.2588	.0179	.3530	.20393	.97899	.20830	.8007	.0215	.9037	14
47	.15270	.98827	.15451	.4720	.0119	.5488	.16992	.98546	.17243	.7994	.0147	.8850	.18709	.98234	.19046	.2505	.0180	.3449	.20421	.97893	.20861	.7937	.0215	.8969	13
48	.15298	.98823	.15481	.4596	.0119	.5365	.17021	.98541	.17273	.7894	.0148	.8751	.18738	.98229	.19076	.2422	.0180	.3367	.20450	.97887	.20891	.7867	.0216	.8901	12
49	.15328	.98818	.15511	.4472	.0119	.5243	.17050	.98536	.17303	.7794	.0148	.8652	.18767	.98223	.19106	.2339	.0181	.3286	.20478	.97881	.20921	.7798	.0216	.8833	11
50	.15356	.98814	.15540	6.4348	.0120	6.5121	.17078	.98531	.17333	5.7694	.0149	5.8554	.18795	.98218	.19136	5.2257	.0181	5.3205	.20506	.97875	.20952	4.7728	.0217	4.8765	10
51	.15385	.98809	.15570	.4225	.0120	.4999	.17107	.98526	.17363	.7594	.0150	.8456	.18824	.98212	.19166	.2174	.0182	.3124	.20535	.97869	.20982	.7659	.0218	.8967	9
52	.15413	.98805	.15600	.4103	.0121	.4878	.17136	.98521	.17393	.7495	.0150	.8358	.18852	.98207	.19197	.2092	.0182	.3044	.20563	.97863	.21012	.7591	.0218	.8630	8
53	.15442	.98800	.15630	.3980	.0121	.4757	.17164	.98516	.17423	.7396	.0151	.8261	.18881	.98201	.19227	.2011	.0183	.2963	.20592	.97857	.21043	.7522	.0219	.8563	7
54	.15471	.98796	.15659	.3859	.0122	.4637	.17193	.98511	.17453	.7297	.0151	.8163	.18909	.98196	.19257	.1929	.0184	.2883	.20620	.97851	.21073	.7453	.0220	.8496	6
55	.15500	.98791	.15689	6.3737	.0122	6.4517	.17221	.98506	.17483	5.7199	.0152	5.8067	.18938	.98190	.19287	5.1848	.0184	5.2803	.20649	.97845	.21104	4.7385	.0220	4.8429	5
56	.15528	.98787	.15719	.3616	.0123	.4398	.17250	.98501	.17513	.7101	.0152	.7970	.18967	.98185	.19317	.1767	.0185	.2724	.20677	.97839	.21134	.7317	.0221	.8362	4
57	.15557	.98782	.15749	.3496	.0123	.4279	.17279	.98496	.17543	.7004	.0153	.7874	.18995	.98179	.19347	.1686	.0185	.2645	.20706	.97833	.21164	.7249	.0221	.8296	3
58	.15586	.98778	.15779	.3376	.0124	.4160	.17307	.98491	.17573	.6906	.0153	.7778	.19024	.98174	.19378	.1606	.0186	.2566	.20734	.97827	.21195	.7181	.0222	.8229	2
59	.15615	.98773	.15809	.3257	.0124	.4042	.17336	.98486	.17603	.6809	.0154	.7683	.19052	.98168	.19408	.1525	.0186	.2487	.20763	.97821	.21225	.7114	.0223	.8163	1
60	.15643	.98769	.15838	6.3137	.0125	6.3924	.17365	.98481	.17633	5.6713	.0154	5.7588	.19081	.98163	.19438	5.1445	.0187	5.2408	.20791	.97815	.21256	4.7046	.0223	4.8097	0
′	cos	sin	cot	tan	cosec	sec	cos	sin	cot	tan	cosec	sec	cos	sin	cot	tan	cosec	sec	cos	sin	cot	tan	cosec	sec	′
	81°						80°						79°						78°						

	12°						13°						14°						15°						
′	sin	cos	tan	cot	sec	cosec	sin	cos	tan	cot	sec	cosec	sin	cos	tan	cot	sec	cosec	sin	cos	tan	cot	sec	cosec	′
0	.20791	.97815	.21256	4.7046	1.0223	4.8097	.22495	.97437	.23087	4.3315	1.0263	4.4454	.24192	.97029	.24933	4.0108	1.0306	4.1336	.25882	.96592	.26795	3.7320	1.0353	3.8637	60
1	.20820	.97809	.21286	.6979	.0224	.8032	.22523	.97430	.23117	.3257	.0264	.4398	.24220	.97022	.24964	.0058	.0307	.1287	.25910	.96585	.26826	.7277	.0353	.8595	59
2	.20848	.97803	.21316	.6912	.0225	.7966	.22552	.97424	.23148	.3200	.0264	.4342	.24249	.97015	.24995	.0009	.0308	.1239	.25938	.96577	.26857	.7234	.0354	.8553	58
3	.20876	.97797	.21347	.6845	.0225	.7901	.22580	.97417	.23179	.3143	.0265	.4287	.24277	.97008	.25025	3.9959	.0308	.1191	.25966	.96570	.26888	.7191	.0355	.8512	57
4	.20905	.97790	.21377	.6778	.0226	.7835	.22608	.97411	.23209	.3086	.0266	.4231	.24305	.97001	.25056	.9910	.0309	.1144	.25994	.96562	.26920	.7147	.0356	.8470	56
5	.20933	.97784	.21408	4.6712	.0226	4.7770	.22637	.97404	.23240	4.3029	.0266	4.4176	.24333	.96994	.25087	3.9861	.0310	4.1096	.26022	.96555	.26951	3.7104	.0357	3.8428	55
6	.20962	.97778	.21438	.6646	.0227	.7706	.22665	.97398	.23270	.2972	.0267	.4121	.24361	.96987	.25118	.9812	.0311	.1048	.26050	.96547	.26982	.7062	.0358	.8387	54
7	.20990	.97772	.21468	.6580	.0228	.7641	.22693	.97391	.23301	.2916	.0268	.4065	.24390	.96980	.25149	.9763	.0311	.1001	.26078	.96540	.27013	.7019	.0358	.8346	53
8	.21019	.97766	.21499	.6514	.0228	.7576	.22722	.97384	.23332	.2859	.0268	.4011	.24418	.96973	.25180	.9714	.0312	.0953	.26107	.96532	.27044	.6976	.0359	.8304	52
9	.21047	.97760	.21529	.6448	.0229	.7512	.22750	.97378	.23363	.2803	.0269	.3956	.24446	.96966	.25211	.9665	.0313	.0906	.26135	.96524	.27076	.6933	.0360	.8263	51
10	.21076	.97754	.21560	4.6382	.0230	4.7448	.22778	.97371	.23393	4.2747	.0270	4.3901	.24474	.96959	.25242	3.9616	.0314	4.0859	.26163	.96517	.27107	3.6891	.0361	3.8222	50
11	.21104	.97748	.21590	.6317	.0230	.7384	.22807	.97364	.23424	.2691	.0271	.3847	.24502	.96952	.25273	.9568	.0314	.0812	.26191	.96509	.27138	.6848	.0362	.8181	49
12	.21132	.97741	.21621	.6252	.0231	.7320	.22835	.97358	.23455	.2635	.0271	.3792	.24531	.96944	.25304	.9520	.0315	.0765	.26219	.96502	.27169	.6806	.0362	.8140	48
13	.21161	.97735	.21651	.6187	.0232	.7257	.22863	.97351	.23485	.2579	.0272	.3738	.24559	.96937	.25335	.9471	.0316	.0718	.26247	.96494	.27201	.6764	.0363	.8100	47
14	.21189	.97729	.21682	.6122	.0232	.7193	.22892	.97344	.23516	.2524	.0273	.3684	.24587	.96930	.25366	.9423	.0317	.0672	.26275	.96486	.27232	.6722	.0364	.8059	46
15	.21218	.97723	.21712	4.6057	.0233	4.7130	.22920	.97338	.23547	4.2468	.0273	4.3630	.24615	.96923	.25397	3.9375	.0317	4.0625	.26303	.96479	.27263	3.6679	.0365	3.8018	45
16	.21246	.97717	.21742	.5993	.0234	.7067	.22948	.97331	.23577	.2413	.0274	.3576	.24643	.96916	.25428	.9327	.0318	.0579	.26331	.96471	.27294	.6637	.0366	.7978	44
17	.21275	.97711	.21773	.5928	.0234	.7004	.22977	.97324	.23608	.2358	.0275	.3522	.24672	.96909	.25459	.9279	.0319	.0532	.26359	.96463	.27326	.6596	.0367	.7937	43
18	.21303	.97704	.21803	.5864	.0235	.6942	.23005	.97318	.23639	.2303	.0276	.3469	.24700	.96901	.25490	.9231	.0320	.0486	.26387	.96456	.27357	.6554	.0367	.7897	42
19	.21331	.97698	.21834	.5800	.0235	.6879	.23033	.97311	.23670	.2248	.0276	.3415	.24728	.96894	.25521	.9184	.0320	.0440	.26415	.96448	.27388	.6512	.0368	.7857	41
20	.21360	.97692	.21864	4.5736	.0236	4.6817	.23061	.97304	.23700	4.2193	.0277	4.3362	.24756	.96887	.25552	3.9136	.0321	4.0394	.26443	.96440	.27419	3.6470	.0369	3.7816	40
21	.21388	.97686	.21895	.5673	.0237	.6754	.23090	.97298	.23731	.2139	.0278	.3309	.24784	.96880	.25583	.9089	.0322	.0348	.26471	.96433	.27451	.6429	.0370	.7776	39
22	.21417	.97680	.21925	.5609	.0237	.6692	.23118	.97291	.23762	.2084	.0278	.3256	.24813	.96873	.25614	.9042	.0323	.0302	.26499	.96425	.27482	.6387	.0371	.7736	38
23	.21445	.97673	.21956	.5546	.0238	.6631	.23146	.97284	.23793	.2030	.0279	.3203	.24841	.96865	.25645	.8994	.0323	.0256	.26527	.96417	.27513	.6346	.0371	.7697	37
24	.21473	.97667	.21986	.5483	.0239	.6569	.23175	.97277	.23823	.1976	.0280	.3150	.24869	.96858	.25676	.8947	.0324	.0211	.26556	.96409	.27544	.6305	.0372	.7657	36
25	.21502	.97661	.22017	4.5420	.0239	4.6507	.23202	.97271	.23854	4.1921	.0280	4.3098	.24897	.96851	.25707	3.8900	.0325	4.0165	.26584	.96402	.27576	3.6263	.0373	3.7617	35
26	.21530	.97655	.22047	.5357	.0240	.6446	.23231	.97264	.23885	.1867	.0281	.3045	.24925	.96844	.25738	.8853	.0326	.0120	.26612	.96394	.27607	.6222	.0374	.7577	34
27	.21559	.97648	.22078	.5294	.0241	.6385	.23260	.97257	.23916	.1814	.0282	.2993	.24953	.96836	.25769	.8807	.0327	.0074	.26640	.96386	.27638	.6181	.0375	.7538	33
28	.21587	.97642	.22108	.5232	.0241	.6324	.23288	.97250	.23946	.1760	.0283	.2941	.24982	.96829	.25800	.8760	.0327	.0029	.26668	.96378	.27670	.6140	.0376	.7498	32
29	.21615	.97636	.22139	.5169	.0242	.6263	.23316	.97244	.23977	.1706	.0283	.2838	.25010	.96822	.25831	.8713	.0328	3.9984	.26696	.96371	.27701	.6100	.0376	.7459	31
30	.21644	.97630	.22169	4.5107	.0243	4.6201	.23344	.97237	.24008	4.1653	.0284	4.2836	.25038	.96815	.25862	3.8667	.0329	3.9939	.26724	.96363	.27732	3.6059	.0377	3.7420	30
31	.21672	.97623	.22200	.5045	.0243	.6142	.23373	.97230	.24039	.1600	.0285	.2785	.25066	.96807	.25893	.8621	.0330	.9894	.26752	.96355	.27764	.6018	.0378	.7380	29
32	.21701	.97617	.22230	.4983	.0244	.6081	.23401	.97223	.24069	.1546	.0285	.2733	.25094	.96800	.25924	.8574	.0330	.9850	.26780	.96347	.27795	.5977	.0379	.7341	28
33	.21729	.97611	.22261	.4921	.0245	.6021	.23429	.97216	.24100	.1493	.0286	.2681	.25122	.96793	.25955	.8528	.0331	.9805	.26808	.96340	.27826	.5937	.0380	.7302	27
34	.21757	.97604	.22291	.4860	.0245	.5961	.23458	.97210	.24131	.1440	.0287	.2630	.25151	.96785	.25986	.8482	.0332	.97[illegible]	.26836	.96332	.27858	.5896	.0381	.7263	26
35	.21786	.97598	.22322	4.4799	.0246	4.5901	.23486	.97203	.24162	4.1388	.0288	4.2579	.25179	.96778	.26017	3.8436	.0333	3.9716	.26864	.96324	.27889	3.5856	.0382	3.7224	25
36	.21814	.97592	.22353	.4737	.0247	.5841	.23514	.97196	.24192	.1335	.0288	.2527	.25207	.96771	.26048	.8390	.0334	.9672	.26892	.96316	.27920	.5816	.0382	.7186	24
37	.21843	.97575	.22383	.4676	.0247	.5782	.23542	.97189	.24223	.1282	.0289	.2476	.25235	.96763	.26079	.8345	.0334	.9627	.26920	.96308	.27952	.5776	.0383	.7147	23
38	.21871	.97579	.22414	.4615	.0248	.5722	.23571	.97182	.24254	.1230	.0290	.2425	.25263	.96756	.26110	.8299	.0335	.9583	.26948	.96301	.27983	.5736	.0384	.7108	22
39	.21899	.97573	.22444	.4555	.0249	.5663	.23599	.97175	.24285	.1178	.0291	.2375	.25291	.96749	.26141	.8254	.0336	.9539	.26976	.96293	.28014	.5696	.0385	.7070	21
40	.21928	.97566	.22475	4.4494	.0249	4.5604	.23627	.97169	.24316	4.1126	.0291	4.2324	.25319	.96741	.26172	3.8208	.0337	3.9495	.27004	.96285	.28046	3.5656	.0386	3.7031	20
41	.21956	.97560	.22505	.4434	.0250	.5545	.23655	.97162	.24346	.1073	.0292	.2273	.25348	.96734	.26203	.8163	.0338	.9451	.27032	.96277	.28077	.5616	.0387	.6993	19
42	.21985	.97553	.22536	.4373	.0251	.5486	.23684	.97155	.24377	.1022	.0293	.2223	.25376	.96727	.26234	.8118	.0338	.9408	.27060	.96269	.28109	.5576	.0387	.6955	18
43	.22013	.97547	.22566	.4313	.0251	.5428	.23712	.97148	.24408	.0970	.0293	.2173	.25404	.96719	.26266	.8073	.0339	.9364	.27088	.96261	.28140	.5536	.0388	.6917	17
44	.22041	.97541	.22597	.4253	.0252	.5369	.23740	.97141	.24439	.0918	.0294	.2122	.25432	.96712	.26297	.8027	.0340	.9320	.27116	.96253	.28171	.5497	.0389	.6878	16
45	.22070	.97534	.22628	4.4194	.0253	4.5311	.23768	.97134	.24470	4.0867	.0295	4.2072	.25460	.96704	.26328	3.7983	.0341	3.9277	.27144	.96245	.28203	3.5457	.0390	3.6840	15
46	.22098	.97528	.22658	.4134	.0253	.5253	.23797	.97127	.24501	.0815	.0296	.2022	.25488	.96697	.26359	.7938	.0341	.9234	.27172	.96238	.28234	.5418	.0391	.6802	14
47	.22126	.97521	.22689	.4074	.0254	.5195	.23825	.97120	.24531	.0764	.0296	.1972	.25516	.96690	.26390	.7893	.0342	.9190	.27200	.96230	.28266	.5378	.0392	.6765	13
48	.22155	.97515	.22719	.4015	.0255	.5137	.23853	.97113	.24562	.0713	.0297	.1923	.25544	.96682	.26421	.7848	.0343	.9147	.27228	.96222	.28297	.5339	.0393	.6727	12
49	.22183	.97508	.22750	.3956	.0255	.5079	.23881	.97106	.24593	.0662	.0298	.1873	.25573	.96675	.26452	.7804	.0344	.9104	.27256	.96214	.28328	.5300	.0393	.6689	11
50	.22211	.97502	.22781	4.3897	.0256	4.5021	.23910	.97099	.24624	4.0611	.0299	4.1824	.25601	.96667	.26483	3.7759	.0345	3.9061	.27284	.96206	.28360	3.5261	.0394	3.6651	10
51	.22240	.97495	.22811	.3838	.0257	.4964	.23938	.97092	.24655	.0560	.0299	.1774	.25629	.96660	.26514	.7715	.0345	.9018	.27312	.96198	.28391	.5222	.0395	.6614	9
52	.22268	.97489	.22842	.3779	.0257	.4907	.23966	.97086	.24686	.0509	.0300	.1725	.25657	.96652	.26546	.7671	.0346	.8976	.27340	.96190	.28423	.5183	.0396	.6576	8
53	.22297	.97483	.22872	.3721	.0258	.4850	.23994	.97079	.24717	.0458	.0301	.1676	.25685	.96645	.26577	.7627	.0347	.8933	.27368	.96182	.28454	.5144	.0397	.6539	7
54	.22325	.97476	.22903	.3662	.0259	.4793	.24023	.97072	.24747	.0408	.0302	.1627	.25713	.96638	.26608	.7583	.0348	.8890	.27396	.96174	.28486	.5105	.0398	.6502	6
55	.22353	.97470	.22934	4.3604	.0260	4.4736	.24051	.97065	.24778	4.0358	.0302	4.1578	.25741	.96630	.26639	3.7539	.0349	3.8848	.27424	.96166	.28517	3.5066	.0399	3.6464	5
56	.22382	.97463	.22964	.3546	.0260	.4679	.24079	.97058	.24809	.0307	.0303	.1529	.25769	.96623	.26670	.7495	.0349	.8805	.27452	.96158	.28549	.5028	.0399	.6427	4
57	.22410	.97457	.22995	.3488	.0261	.4623	.24107	.97051	.24840	.0257	.0304	.1481	.25798	.96615	.26701	.7451	.0350	.8763	.27480	.96150	.28580	.4989	.0400	.6390	3
58	.22438	.97450	.23025	.3430	.0262	.4566	.24136	.97044	.24871	.0207	.0305	.1432	.25826	.96608	.26732	.7407	.0351	.8721	.27508	.96142	.28611	.4951	.0401	.6353	2
59	.22467	.97443	.23056	.3372	.0262	.4510	.24164	.97037	.24902	.0157	.0305	.1384	.25854	.96600	.26764	.7364	.0352	.8679	.27536	.96134	.28643	.4912	.0402	.6316	1
60	.22495	.97437	.23087	4.3315	.0263	4.4454	.24192	.97029	.24933	4.0108	.0306	4.1336	.25882	.96592	.26795	3.7320	.0353	3.8637	.27564	.96126	.28674	3.4874	.0403	3.6279	0
′	cos	sin	cot	tan	cosec	sec	cos	sin	cot	tan	cosec	sec	cos	sin	cot	tan	cosec	sec	cos	sin	cot	tan	cosec	sec	′
	77°						76°						75°						74°						

	16°						17°						18°						19°						
′	sin	cos	tan	cot	sec	cosec	sin	cos	tan	cot	sec	cosec	sin	cos	tan	cot	sec	cosec	sin	cos	tan	cot	sec	cosec	′
0	.27564	.96126	.28674	3.4874	1.0403	3.6279	.29237	.95630	.30573	3.2708	1.0457	3.4203	.30902	.95106	.32492	3.0777	1.0515	3.2361	.32557	.94552	.34433	2.9042	1.0576	3.0715	60
1	.27592	.96118	.28706	.4836	.0404	.6243	.29265	.95622	.30605	.2674	.0458	.4170	.30929	.95097	.32524	.0746	.0516	.2332	.32584	.94542	.34465	.9015	.0577	.0690	59
2	.27620	.96110	.28737	.4798	.0405	.6206	.29293	.95613	.30637	.2640	.0459	.4138	.30957	.95088	.32556	.0716	.0517	.2303	.32612	.94533	.34498	.8987	.0578	.0664	58
3	.27648	.96102	.28769	.4760	.0406	.6169	.29321	.95605	.30668	.2607	.0460	.4106	.30985	.95079	.32588	.0686	.0518	.2274	.32639	.94523	.34530	.8960	.0579	.0638	57
4	.27675	.96094	.28800	.4722	.0406	.6133	.29348	.95596	.30700	.2573	.0461	.4073	.31012	.95070	.32621	.0655	.0519	.2245	.32667	.94514	.34563	.8933	.0580	.0612	56
5	.27703	.96086	.28832	3.4684	.0407	3.6096	.29376	.95588	.30732	3.2539	.0461	3.4041	.31040	.95061	.32653	3.0625	.0520	3.2216	.32694	.94504	.34595	2.8905	.0581	3.0586	55
6	.27731	.96078	.28863	.4646	.0408	.6060	.29404	.95579	.30764	.2505	.0462	.4009	.31068	.95051	.32685	.0595	.0521	.2188	.32722	.94495	.34628	.8878	.0582	.0561	54
7	.27759	.96070	.28895	.4608	.0409	.6024	.29432	.95571	.30796	.2472	.0463	.3977	.31095	.95042	.32717	.0565	.0522	.2159	.32749	.94485	.34661	.8851	.0584	.0535	53
8	.27787	.96062	.28926	.4570	.0410	.5987	.29460	.95562	.30828	.2438	.0464	.3945	.31123	.95033	.32749	.0535	.0523	.2131	.32777	.94476	.34693	.8824	.0585	.0509	52
9	.27815	.96054	.28958	.4533	.0411	.5951	.29487	.95554	.30859	.2405	.0465	.3913	.31150	.95024	.32782	.0505	.0524	.2102	.32804	.94466	.34726	.8797	.0586	.0484	51
10	.27843	.96045	.28990	3.4495	.0412	3.5915	.29515	.95545	.30891	3.2371	.0466	3.3881	.31178	.95015	.32814	3.0475	.0525	3.2074	.32832	.94457	.34758	2.8770	.0587	3.0458	50
11	.27871	.96037	.29021	.4458	.0413	.5879	.29543	.95536	.30923	.2338	.0467	.3849	.31206	.95006	.32846	.0445	.0526	.2045	.32859	.94447	.34791	.8743	.0588	.0433	49
12	.27899	.96029	.29053	.4420	.0413	.5843	.29571	.95528	.30955	.2305	.0468	.3817	.31233	.94997	.32878	.0415	.0527	.2017	.32887	.94438	.34824	.8716	.0589	.0407	48
13	.27927	.96021	.29084	.4383	.0414	.5807	.29598	.95519	.30987	.2271	.0469	.3785	.31261	.94988	.32910	.0385	.0528	.1989	.32914	.94428	.34856	.8689	.0590	.0382	47
14	.27955	.96013	.29116	.4346	.0415	.5772	.29626	.95511	.31019	.2238	.0470	.3754	.31289	.94979	.32943	.0356	.0529	.1960	.32942	.94418	.34889	.8662	.0591	.0357	46
15	.27983	.96005	.29147	3.4308	.0416	3.5736	.29654	.95502	.31051	3.2205	.0471	3.3722	.31316	.94970	.32975	3.0326	.0530	3.1932	.32969	.94409	.34921	2.8636	.0592	3.0331	45
16	.28011	.95997	.29179	.4271	.0417	.5700	.29682	.95493	.31083	.2172	.0472	.3690	.31344	.94961	.33007	.0296	.0531	.1904	.32996	.94399	.34954	.8609	.0593	.0306	44
17	.28039	.95989	.29210	.4234	.0418	.5665	.29710	.95485	.31115	.2139	.0473	.3659	.31372	.94952	.33039	.0267	.0532	.1876	.33024	.94390	.34987	.8582	.0594	.0281	43
18	.28067	.95980	.29242	.4197	.0419	.5629	.29737	.95476	.31146	.2106	.0474	.3627	.31399	.94942	.33072	.0237	.0533	.1848	.33051	.94380	.35019	.8555	.0595	.0256	42
19	.28094	.95972	.29274	.4160	.0420	.5594	.29765	.95467	.31178	.2073	.0475	.3596	.31427	.94933	.33104	.0208	.0534	.1820	.33079	.94370	.35052	.8529	.0596	.0231	41
20	.28122	.95964	.29305	3.4124	.0420	3.5559	.29793	.95459	.31210	3.2041	.0476	3.3565	.31454	.94924	.33136	3.0178	.0535	3.1792	.33106	.94361	.35085	2.8502	.0598	3.0206	40
21	.28150	.95956	.29337	.4087	.0421	.5523	.29821	.95450	.31242	.2008	.0477	.3534	.31482	.94915	.33169	.0149	.0536	.1764	.33134	.94351	.35117	.8476	.0599	.0181	39
22	.28178	.95948	.29368	.4050	.0422	.5488	.29848	.95441	.31274	.1975	.0478	.3502	.31510	.94906	.33201	.0120	.0537	.1736	.33161	.94341	.35150	.8449	.0600	.0156	38
23	.28206	.95940	.29400	.4014	.0423	.5453	.29876	.95433	.31306	.1942	.0478	.3471	.31537	.94897	.33233	.0090	.0528	.1708	.33189	.94332	.35183	.8423	.0601	.0131	37
24	.28234	.95931	.29432	.3977	.0424	.5418	.29904	.95424	.31338	.1910	.0479	.3440	.31565	.94888	.33265	.0061	.0539	.1681	.33216	.94322	.35215	.8396	.0602	.0106	36
25	.28262	.95923	.29463	3.3941	.0425	3.5383	.29932	.95415	.31370	3.1877	.0480	3.3409	.31592	.94878	.33298	3.0032	.0540	3.1653	.33243	.94313	.35248	2.8370	.0603	3.0081	35
26	.28290	.95915	.29495	.3904	.0426	.5348	.29959	.95407	.31402	.1845	.0481	.3378	.31620	.94869	.33330	.0003	.0541	.1625	.33271	.94303	.35281	.8344	.0604	.0056	34
27	.28318	.95907	.29526	.3868	.0427	.5313	.29987	.95398	.31434	.1813	.0482	.3347	.31648	.94860	.33362	2.9974	.0542	.1598	.33298	.94293	.35314	.8318	.0605	.0031	33
28	.28346	.95898	.29558	.3832	.0428	.5279	.30015	.95389	.31466	.1780	.0483	.3316	.31675	.94851	.33395	.9945	.0543	.1570	.33326	.94283	.35346	.8291	.0606	.0007	32
29	.28374	.95890	.29590	.3795	.0428	.5244	.30043	.95380	.31498	.1748	.0484	.3286	.31703	.94841	.33427	.9916	.0544	.1543	.33353	.94274	.35379	.8265	.0607	2.9982	31
30	.28401	.95882	.29621	3.3759	.0429	3.5209	.30070	.95372	.31530	3.1716	.0485	3.3255	.31730	.94832	.33459	2.9887	.0545	3.1515	.33381	.94264	.35412	2.8239	.0608	2.9957	30
31	.28429	.95874	.29653	.3723	.0430	.5175	.30098	.95363	.31562	.1684	.0486	.3224	.31758	.94823	.33492	.9858	.0546	.1488	.33408	.94254	.35445	.8213	.0609	.9933	29
32	.28457	.95865	.29685	.3687	.0431	.5140	.30126	.95354	.31594	.1652	.0487	.3194	.31786	.94814	.33524	.9829	.0547	.1461	.33435	.94245	.35477	.8187	.0611	.9908	28
33	.28485	.95857	.29716	.3651	.0432	.5106	.30154	.95345	.31626	.1620	.0488	.3163	.31813	.94805	.33557	.9800	.0548	.1433	.33463	.94235	.35510	.8161	.0612	.9884	27
34	.28513	.95849	.29748	.3616	.0433	.5072	.30181	.95337	.31658	.1588	.0489	.3133	.31841	.94795	.33589	.9772	.0549	.1406	.33490	.94225	.35543	.8135	.0613	.9859	26
35	.28541	.95840	.29780	3.3580	.0434	3.5037	.30209	.95328	.31690	3.1556	.0490	3.3102	.31868	.94786	.33621	2.9743	.0550	3.1379	.33518	.94215	.35576	2.8109	.0614	2.9835	25
36	.28569	.95832	.29811	.3544	.0435	.5003	.30237	.95319	.31722	.1524	.0491	.3072	.31896	.94777	.33654	.9714	.0551	.1352	.33545	.94206	.35608	.8083	.0615	.9810	24
37	.28597	.95824	.29843	.3509	.0436	.4969	.30265	.95310	.31754	.1492	.0492	.3042	.31923	.94767	.33686	.9686	.0552	.1325	.33572	.94196	.35641	.8057	.0616	.9786	23
38	.28624	.95816	.29875	.3473	.0437	.4935	.30292	.95301	.31786	.1460	.0493	.3011	.31951	.94758	.33718	.9657	.0553	.1298	.33600	.94186	.35674	.8032	.0617	.9762	22
39	.28652	.95807	.29906	.3438	.0438	.4901	.30320	.95293	.31818	.1429	.0494	.2981	.31978	.94749	.33751	.9629	.0554	.1271	.33627	.94176	.35707	.8006	.0618	.9738	21
40	.28680	.95799	.29938	3.3402	.0438	3.4867	.30348	.95284	.31850	3.1397	.0495	3.2951	.32006	.94740	.33783	2.9600	.0555	3.1244	.33655	.94167	.35739	2.7980	.0619	2.9713	20
41	.28708	.95791	.29970	.3367	.0439	.4833	.30375	.95275	.31882	.1366	.0496	.2921	.32034	.94730	.33816	.9572	.0556	.1217	.33682	.94157	.35772	.7954	.0620	.9689	19
42	.28736	.95782	.30001	.3332	.0440	.4799	.30403	.95266	.31914	.1334	.0497	.2891	.32061	.94721	.33848	.9544	.0557	.1190	.33709	.94147	.35805	.7929	.0622	.9665	18
43	.28764	.95774	.30033	.3296	.0441	.4766	.30431	.95257	.31946	.1303	.0498	.2861	.32089	.94712	.33880	.9515	.0558	.1163	.33737	.94137	.35838	.7903	.0623	.9641	17
44	.28792	.95765	.30065	.3261	.0442	.4732	.30459	.95248	.31978	.1271	.0499	.2831	.32116	.94702	.33913	.9487	.0559	.1137	.33764	.94127	.35871	.7878	.0624	.9617	16
45	.28820	.95757	.30096	3.3226	.0443	3.4698	.30486	.95239	.32010	3.1240	.0500	3.2801	.32144	.94693	.33945	2.9459	.0560	3.1110	.33792	.94118	.35904	2.7852	.0625	2.9593	15
46	.28847	.95749	.30128	.3191	.0444	.4665	.30514	.95231	.32042	.1209	.0501	.2772	.32171	.94684	.33978	.9431	.0561	.1083	.33819	.94108	.35936	.7827	.0626	.9569	14
47	.28875	.95740	.30160	.3156	.0445	.4632	.30542	.95222	.32074	.1177	.0502	.2742	.32199	.94674	.34010	.9403	.0562	.1057	.33846	.94098	.35969	.7801	.0627	.9545	13
48	.28903	.95732	.30192	.3121	.0446	.4598	.30569	.95213	.32106	.1146	.0503	.2712	.32226	.94665	.34043	.9375	.0563	.1030	.33874	.94088	.36002	.7776	.0628	.9521	12
49	.28931	.95723	.30223	.3087	.0447	.4565	.30597	.95204	.32138	.1115	.0504	.2683	.32254	.94655	.34075	.9347	.0565	.1004	.33901	.94078	.36035	.7751	.0629	.9497	11
50	.28959	.95715	.30255	3.3052	.0448	3.4532	.30625	.95195	.32171	3.1084	.0505	3.2653	.32282	.94646	.34108	2.9319	.0566	3.0977	.33928	.94068	.36068	2.7725	.0630	2.9474	10
51	.28987	.95707	.30287	.3017	.0448	.4498	.30653	.95186	.32203	.1053	.0506	.2624	.32309	.94637	.34140	.9291	.0567	.0951	.33956	.94058	.36101	.7700	.0632	.9450	9
52	.29014	.95698	.30319	.2983	.0449	.4465	.30680	.95177	.32235	.1022	.0507	.2594	.32337	.94627	.34173	.9263	.0568	.0925	.33983	.94049	.36134	.7675	.0633	.9426	8
53	.29042	.95690	.30350	.2948	.0450	.4432	.30708	.95168	.32267	.0991	.0508	.2565	.32364	.94618	.34205	.9235	.0569	.0898	.34011	.94039	.36167	.7650	.0634	.9402	7
54	.29070	.95681	.30382	.2914	.0451	.4399	.30736	.95159	.32299	.0960	.0509	.2535	.32392	.94608	.34238	.9208	.0570	.0872	.34038	.94029	.36199	.7625	.0635	.9379	6
55	.29098	.95673	.30414	3.2879	.0452	3.4366	.30763	.95150	.32331	3.0930	.0510	3.2506	.32419	.94599	.34270	2.9180	.0571	3.0846	.34065	.94019	.36232	2.7600	.0636	2.9355	5
56	.29126	.95664	.30446	.2845	.0453	.4334	.30791	.95141	.32363	.0899	.0511	.2477	.32447	.94590	.34303	.9152	.0572	.0820	.34093	.94009	.36265	.7575	.0637	.9332	4
57	.29154	.95656	.30478	.2811	.0454	.4301	.30819	.95132	.32395	.0868	.0512	.2448	.32474	.94580	.34335	.9125	.0573	.0793	.34120	.93999	.36298	.7550	.0638	.9308	3
58	.29181	.95647	.30509	.2777	.0455	.4268	.30846	.95124	.32428	.0838	.0513	.2419	.32502	.94571	.34368	.9097	.0574	.0767	.34147	.93989	.36331	.7525	.0639	.9285	2
59	.29209	.95639	.30541	.2742	.0456	.4236	.30874	.95115	.32460	.0807	.0514	.2390	.32529	.94561	.34400	.9069	.0575	.0741	.34175	.93979	.36364	.7500	.0641	.9261	1
60	.29237	.95630	.30573	3.2708	.0457	3.4203	.30902	.95106	.32492	3.0777	.0515	3.2361	.32557	.94552	.34433	2.9042	.0576	3.0715	.34202	.93969	.36397	2.7475	.0642	2.9238	0
′	cos	sin	cot	tan	cosec	sec	cos	sin	cot	tan	cosec	sec	cos	sin	cot	tan	cosec	sec	cos	sin	cot	tan	cosec	sec	′
	73°						72°						71°						70°						

	20°						21°						22°						23°						
′	sin	cos	tan	cot	sec	cosec	sin	cos	tan	cot	sec	cosec	sin	cos	tan	cot	sec	cosec	sin	cos	tan	cot	sec	cosec	′
0	.34202	.93969	.36397	2.7475	1.0642	2.9238	.35837	.93358	.38386	2.6051	1.0711	2.7904	.37461	.92718	.40403	2.4751	1.0785	2.6695	.39073	.92050	.42447	2.3558	1.0864	2.5593	60
1	.34229	.93959	.36430	.7450	.0643	.9215	.35864	.93348	.38420	.6028	.0713	.7883	.37488	.92707	.40436	.4730	.0787	.6675	.39100	.92039	.42482	.3539	.0865	.5575	59
2	.34257	.93949	.36463	.7425	.0644	.9191	.35891	.93337	.38453	.6006	.0714	.7862	.37514	.92696	.40470	.4709	.0788	.6656	.39126	.92028	.42516	.3520	.0866	.5558	58
3	.34284	.93939	.36496	.7400	.0645	.9168	.35918	.93327	.38486	.5983	.0715	.7841	.37541	.92686	.40504	.4689	.0789	.6637	.39153	.92016	.42550	.3501	.0868	.5540	57
4	.34311	.93929	.36529	.7376	.0646	.9145	.35945	.93316	.38520	.5960	.0716	.7820	.37568	.92675	.40538	.4668	.0790	.6618	.39180	.92005	.42585	.3482	.0869	.5523	56
5	.34339	.93919	.36562	2.7351	.0647	2.9122	.35972	.93306	.38553	2.5938	.0717	2.7799	.37595	.92664	.40572	2.4647	.0792	2.6599	.39207	.91993	.42619	2.3463	.0870	2.5506	55
6	.34366	.93909	.36595	.7326	.0648	.9098	.36000	.93295	.38587	.5916	.0719	.7778	.37622	.92653	.40606	.4627	.0793	.6580	.39234	.91982	.42654	.3445	.0872	.5488	54
7	.34393	.93899	.36628	.7302	.0650	.9075	.36027	.93285	.38620	.5893	.0720	.7757	.37649	.92642	.40640	.4606	.0794	.6561	.39260	.91971	.42688	.3426	.0873	.5471	53
8	.34421	.93889	.36661	.7277	.0651	.9052	.36054	.93274	.38654	.5871	.0721	.7736	.37676	.92631	.40673	.4586	.0795	.6542	.39287	.91959	.42722	.3407	.0874	.5453	52
9	.34448	.93879	.36694	.7252	.0652	.9029	.36081	.93264	.38687	.5848	.0722	.7715	.37703	.92620	.40707	.4565	.0797	.6523	.39314	.91948	.42757	.3388	.0876	.5436	51
10	.34475	.93869	.36727	2.7228	.0653	2.9006	.36108	.93253	.38720	2.5826	.0723	2.7694	.37730	.92609	.40741	2.4545	.0798	2.6504	.39341	.91936	.42791	2.3369	.0877	2.5419	50
11	.34502	.93859	36760	.7204	.0654	.8983	.36135	.93243	.38754	.5804	.0725	.7674	.37757	.92598	.40775	.4525	.0799	.6485	.39367	.91925	.42826	.3350	.0878	.5402	49
12	.34530	.93849	.36793	.7179	.0655	.8960	.36162	.93232	.38787	.5781	.0726	.7653	.37784	.92587	.40809	.4504	.0801	.6466	.39394	.91913	.42860	.3332	.0880	.5384	48
13	.34557	.93839	.36826	.7155	.0656	.8937	.36189	.93222	.38821	.5759	.0727	.7632	.37811	.92576	.40843	.4484	.0802	.6447	.39421	.91902	.42894	.3313	.0881	.5367	47
14	.34584	.93829	.36859	.7130	.0658	.8915	.36217	.93211	.38854	.5737	.0728	.7611	.37838	.92565	.40877	.4463	.0803	.6428	.39448	.91891	.42929	.3294	.0882	.5350	46
15	.34612	.93819	.36892	2.7106	.0659	2.8892	.36244	.93201	.38888	2.5715	.0729	2.7591	.37865	.92554	.40911	2.4443	.0804	2.6410	.39474	.91879	.42963	2.3276	.0884	2.5333	45
16	.34639	.93809	.36925	.7082	.0660	.8869	.36271	.93190	.38921	.5693	.0731	.7570	.37892	.92543	.40945	.4423	.0806	.6391	.39501	.91868	.42998	.3257	.0885	.5316	44
17	.34666	.93799	.36958	.7058	.0661	.8846	.36298	.93180	.38955	.5671	.0732	.7550	.37919	.92532	.40979	.4403	.0807	.6372	.39528	.91856	.43032	.3238	.0886	.5299	43
18	.34693	.93789	.36991	.7033	.0662	.8824	.36325	.93169	.38988	.5649	.0733	.7529	.37946	.92521	.41013	.4382	.0808	.6353	.39554	.91845	.43067	.3220	.0888	.5281	42
19	.34721	.93779	.37024	.7009	.0663	.8801	.36352	.93158	.39022	.5627	.0734	.7509	.37972	.92510	.41047	.4362	.0810	.6335	.39581	.91833	.43101	.3201	.0889	.5264	41
20	.34748	.93769	.37057	2.6985	.0664	2.8778	.36379	.93148	.39055	2.5605	.0736	2.7488	.37999	.92499	.41081	2.4342	.0811	2.6316	.39608	.91822	.43136	2.3183	.0891	2.5247	40
21	.34775	.93758	.37090	.6961	.0666	.8756	.36406	.93137	.39089	.5583	.0737	.7468	.38026	.92488	.41115	.4322	.0812	.6297	.39635	.91810	.43170	.3164	.0892	.5230	39
22	.34803	.93748	.37123	.6937	.0667	.8733	.36433	.93127	.39122	.5561	.0738	.7447	.38053	.92477	.41149	.4302	.0813	.6279	.39661	.91798	.43205	.3145	.0893	.5213	38
23	.34830	.93738	.37156	.6913	.0668	.8711	.36460	.93116	.39156	.5539	.0739	.7427	.38080	.92466	.41183	.4282	.0815	.6260	.39688	.91787	.43239	.3127	.0895	.5196	37
24	.34857	.93728	.37190	.6889	.0669	.8688	.36488	.93105	.39189	.5517	.0740	.7406	.38107	.92455	.41217	.4262	.0816	.6242	.39715	.91775	.43274	.3109	.0896	.5179	36
25	.34884	.93718	.37223	2.6865	.0670	2.8666	.36515	.93095	.39223	2.5495	.0742	2.7386	.38134	.92443	.41251	2.4242	.0817	2.6223	.39741	.91764	.43308	2.3090	.0897	2.5163	35
26	.34912	.93708	.37256	.6841	.0671	.8644	.36542	.93084	.39257	.5473	.0743	.7366	.38161	.92432	.41285	.4222	.0819	.6205	.39768	.91752	.43343	.3072	.0899	.5146	34
27	.34939	.93698	.37289	.6817	.0673	.8621	.36569	.93074	.39290	.5451	.0744	.7346	.38188	.92421	.41319	.4202	.0820	.6186	.39795	.91741	.43377	.3053	.0900	.5129	33
28	.34966	.93687	.37322	.6794	.0674	.8599	.36596	.93063	.39324	.5430	.0745	.7325	.38214	.92410	.41353	.4182	.0821	.6168	.39821	.91729	.43412	.3035	.0902	.5112	32
29	.34993	.93677	.37355	.6770	.0675	.8577	.36623	.93052	.39357	.5408	.0747	.7305	.38241	.92399	.41387	.4162	.0823	.6150	.39848	.91718	.43447	.3017	.0903	.5095	31
30	.35021	.93667	.37388	2.6746	.0676	2.8554	.36650	.93042	.39391	2.5386	.0748	2.7285	.38268	.92388	.41421	2.4142	.0824	2.6131	.39875	.91706	.43481	2.2998	.0904	2.5078	30
31	.35048	.93657	.37422	.6722	.0677	.8532	.36677	.93031	.39425	.5365	.0749	.7265	.38295	.92377	.41455	.4122	.0825	.6113	.39901	.91694	.43516	.2980	.0906	.5062	29
32	.35075	.93647	.37455	.6699	.0678	.8510	.36704	.93020	39458	.5343	.0750	.7245	.38322	.92366	.41489	.4102	.0826	.6095	.39928	.91683	.43550	.2962	.0907	.5045	28
33	.35102	.93637	.37488	.6675	.0679	.8488	.36731	.93010	.39492	.5322	.0751	.7225	.38349	.92354	.41524	.4083	.0828	.6076	.39955	.91671	.43585	.2944	.0908	.5028	27
34	.35130	.93626	.37521	.6652	.0681	.8466	.36758	.92999	.39525	.5300	.0753	.7205	.38376	.92343	.41558	.4063	.0829	.6058	.39981	.91659	.43620	.2925	.0910	.5011	26
35	.35157	.93616	.37554	2.6628	.0682	2.8444	.36785	.92988	.39559	2.5278	.0754	2.7185	.38403	.92332	.41592	2.4043	.0830	2.6040	.40008	.91648	.43654	2.2907	.0911	2.4995	25
36	.35184	.93606	.37587	.6604	.0683	.8422	.36812	.92978	.39593	.5257	.0755	.7165	.38429	.92321	.41626	.4023	.0832	.6022	.40035	.91636	.43689	.2889	.0913	.4978	24
37	.35211	.93596	.37621	.6581	.0684	.8400	.36839	.92967	.39626	.5236	.0756	.7145	.38456	.92310	.41660	.4004	.0833	.6003	.40061	.91625	.43723	.2871	.0914	.4961	23
38	.35239	.93585	.37654	.6558	.0685	.8378	.36866	.92956	.39660	.5214	.0758	.7125	.38483	.92299	.41694	.3984	.0834	.5985	.40088	.91613	.43758	.2853	.0915	.4945	22
39	.35266	.93575	.37687	.6534	.0686	.8356	.36893	.92945	.39694	.5193	.0759	.7105	.38510	.92287	.41728	.3964	.0836	.5967	.40115	.91601	.43793	.2835	.0917	.4928	21
40	.35293	.93565	.37720	2.6511	.0688	2.8334	.36921	.92935	.39727	2.5171	.0760	2.7085	.38537	.92276	.41762	2.3945	.0837	2.5949	.40141	.91590	.43827	2.2817	.0918	2.4912	20
41	.35320	.93555	.37754	.6487	.0689	.8312	.36948	.92924	.39761	.5150	.0761	.7065	.38564	.92265	.41797	.3925	.0838	.5931	.40168	.91578	.43862	.2799	.0920	.4895	19
42	.35347	.93544	.37787	.6464	.0690	.8290	.36975	.92913	.39795	.5129	.0763	.7045	.38591	.92254	.41831	.3906	.0840	.5913	.40195	.91566	.43897	.2781	.0921	.4879	18
43	.35375	.93534	.37820	.6441	.0691	.8269	.37002	.92902	.39828	.5108	.0764	.7026	.38617	.92242	.41865	.3886	.0841	.5895	.40221	.91554	.43932	.2763	.0922	.4862	17
44	.35402	.93524	.37853	.6418	.0692	.8247	.37029	.92892	.39862	.5086	.0765	.7006	.38644	.92231	.41899	.3867	.0842	.5877	.40248	.91543	.43966	.2745	.0924	.4846	16
45	.35429	.93513	.37887	2.6394	.0694	2.8225	.37056	.92881	.39896	2.5065	.0766	2.6986	.38671	.92220	.41933	2.3847	.0844	2.5958	.40205	.91531	.44001	2.2727	.0925	2.4829	15
46	.35456	.93503	.37920	.6371	.0695	.8204	.37083	.92870	.39930	.5044	.0768	.6967	.38698	.92209	.41968	.3828	.0845	.5841	.40301	.91519	.44036	.2709	.0927	.4813	14
47	.35483	.93493	.37953	.6348	.0696	.8182	.37110	.92859	.39963	.5023	.0769	.6947	.38725	.92197	.42002	.3808	.0846	.5823	.40328	.91508	.44070	.2691	.0928	.4797	13
48	.35511	.93482	.37986	.6325	.0697	.8160	.37137	.92848	.39997	.5002	.0770	.6927	.38751	.92186	.42036	.3789	.0847	.5805	.40354	.91496	.44105	.2673	.0929	.4780	12
49	.35538	.93472	.38020	.6302	.0698	.8139	.37164	.92838	.40031	.4981	.0771	.6908	.38778	.92105	.42070	.3770	.0849	.5787	.40381	.91484	.44140	.2655	.0931	.4764	11
50	.35565	.93462	.38053	2.6279	.0699	2.8117	.37191	.92827	.40065	2.4960	.0773	2.6888	.38805	.92164	.42105	2.3750	.0850	2.5770	.40408	.91472	.44175	2.2637	.0932	2.4748	10
51	.35592	.93451	.38086	.6256	.0701	.8096	.37218	.92816	.40098	.4939	.0774	.6869	.38832	.92152	.42139	.3731	.0851	.5752	.40434	.91461	.44209	.2619	.0934	.4731	9
52	.35619	.93441	.38120	.6233	.0702	.8074	.37245	.92805	.40132	.4918	.0775	.6849	.38859	.92141	.42173	.3712	.0853	.5734	.40461	.91449	.44244	.2602	.0935	.4715	8
53	.35647	.93431	.38153	.6210	.0703	.8053	.37272	.92794	.40166	.4897	.0776	.6830	.38886	.92130	.42207	.3692	.0854	.5716	.40487	.91437	.44279	.2584	.0936	.4699	7
54	.35674	.93420	.38186	.6187	.0704	.8032	.37299	.92784	.40200	.4876	.0778	.6810	.38912	.92118	.42242	.3673	.0855	.5699	.40514	.91425	.44314	.2566	.0938	.4683	6
55	.35701	.93410	.38220	2.6164	.0705	2.8010	.37326	.92773	.40233	2.4855	.0779	2.6791	.38939	.92107	.42276	2.3654	.0857	2.5681	.40541	.91414	.44349	2.2548	.0939	2.4666	5
56	.35728	.93400	.38253	.6142	.0707	.7989	.37353	.92762	.40267	.4834	.0780	.6772	.38966	.92096	.42310	.3635	.0858	.5663	.40567	.91402	.44383	.2531	.0941	.4650	4
57	.35755	.93389	.38286	.6119	.0708	.7968	.37380	.92751	.40301	.4813	.0781	.6752	.38993	.92084	.42344	.3616	.0859	.5646	.40594	.91390	.44418	.2513	.0942	.4634	3
58	.35782	.93379	.38320	.6096	.0709	.7947	.37407	.92740	.40335	.4792	.0783	.6733	.39019	.92073	.42379	.3597	.0861	.5628	.40620	.91378	.44453	.2495	.0943	.4618	2
59	.35810	.93368	.38353	.6073	.0710	.7925	.37434	.92729	.40369	.4772	.0784	.6714	.39046	.92062	.42413	.3577	.0862	.5610	.40647	.91366	.44488	.2478	.0945	.4602	1
60	.35837	.93358	.38386	2.6051	.0711	2.7904	.37461	.92718	.40403	2.4751	.0785	2.6695	.39073	.92050	.42447	2.3558	.0864	2.5593	.40674	.91354	.44523	2.2460	.0946	2.4586	0
′	cos	sin	cot	tan	cosec	sec	cos	sin	cot	tan	cosec	sec	cos	sin	cot	tan	cosec	sec	cos	sin	cot	tan	cosec	sec	′
	69°						68°						67°						66°						

	24°						25°						26°						27°						
′	sin	cos	tan	cot	sec	cosec	sin	cos	tan	cot	sec	cosec	sin	cos	tan	cot	sec	cosec	sin	cos	tan	cot	sec	cosec	′
0	.40674	.91354	.44523	2.2460	1.0946	2.4586	.42262	.90631	.46631	2.1445	1.1034	2.3662	.43837	.89879	.48773	2.0503	1.1126	2.2812	.45399	.89101	.50952	1.9626	1.1223	2.2027	60
1	.40700	.91343	.44558	.2443	.0948	.4570	.42288	.90618	.46666	.1429	.1035	.3647	.43863	.89867	.48809	.0488	.1127	.2798	.45425	.89087	.50989	.9612	.1225	.2014	59
2	.40727	.91331	.44593	.2425	.0949	.4554	.42314	.90606	.46702	.1412	.1037	.3632	.43889	.89854	.48845	.0473	.1129	.2784	.45451	.89074	.51026	.9598	.1226	.2002	58
3	.40753	.91319	.44627	.2408	.0951	.4538	.42341	.90594	.46737	.1396	.1038	.3618	.43915	.89841	.48881	.0458	.1131	.2771	.45477	.89061	.51062	.9584	.1228	.1989	57
4	.40780	.91307	.44662	.2390	.0952	.4522	.42367	.90581	.46772	.1380	.1040	.3603	.43942	.89828	.48917	.0443	.1132	.2757	.45503	.89048	.51099	.9570	.1230	.1977	56
5	.40806	.91295	.44697	2.2373	.0953	2.4506	.42394	.90569	.46808	2.1364	.1041	2.3588	.43968	.89815	.48953	2.0427	.1134	2.2744	.45528	.89034	.51136	1.9556	.1231	2.1964	55
6	.40833	.91283	.44732	.2355	.0955	.4490	.42420	.90557	.46843	.1348	.1043	.3574	.43994	.89803	.48989	.0412	.1135	.2730	.45554	.89021	.51172	.9542	.1233	.1952	54
7	.40860	.91271	.44767	.2338	.0956	.4474	.42446	.90544	.46879	.1331	.1044	.3559	.44020	.89790	.49025	.0397	.1137	.2717	.45580	.89008	.51209	.9528	.1235	.1939	53
8	.40886	.91260	.44802	.2320	.0958	.4458	.42473	.90532	.46914	.1315	.1046	.3544	.44046	.89777	.49062	.0382	.1139	.2703	.45606	.88995	.51246	.9514	.1237	.1927	52
9	.40913	.91248	.44837	.2303	.0959	.4442	.42499	.90520	.46950	.1299	.1047	.3530	.44072	.89764	.49098	.0367	.1140	.2690	.45632	.88981	.51283	.9500	.1238	.1914	51
10	.40939	.91236	.44872	2.2286	.0961	2.4426	.42525	.90507	.46985	2.1283	.1049	2.3515	.44098	.89751	.49134	2.0352	.1142	2.2676	.45658	.88968	.51319	1.9486	.1240	2.1902	50
11	.40966	.91224	.44907	.2268	.0962	.4418	.42552	.90495	.47021	.1267	.1050	.3501	.44124	.89739	.49170	.0338	.1143	.2663	.45684	.88955	.51356	.9472	.1242	.1889	49
12	.40992	.91212	.44942	.2251	.0963	.4395	.42578	.90483	.47056	.1251	.1052	.3486	.44150	.89726	.49206	.0323	.1145	.2650	.45710	.88942	.51393	.9458	.1243	.1877	48
13	.41019	.91200	.44977	.2234	.0965	.4379	.42604	.90470	.47092	.1235	.1053	.3472	.44177	.89713	.49242	.0308	.1147	.2636	.45736	.88928	.51430	.9444	.1245	.1865	47
14	.41045	.91188	.45012	.2216	.0966	.4363	.42630	.90458	.47127	.1219	.1055	.3457	.44203	.89700	.49278	.0293	.1148	.2623	.45761	.88915	.51466	.9430	.1247	.1852	46
15	.41072	.91176	.45047	2.2199	.0968	2.4347	.42657	.90445	.47163	2.1203	.1056	2.3443	.44229	.89687	.49314	2.0278	.1150	2.2610	.45787	.88902	.51503	1.9416	.1248	2.1840	45
16	.41098	.91164	.45082	.2182	.0969	.4332	.42683	.90433	.47199	.1187	.1058	.3428	.44255	.89674	.49351	.0263	.1151	.2596	.45813	.88888	.51540	.9402	.1250	.1828	44
17	.41125	.91152	.45117	.2165	.0971	.4316	.42709	.90421	.47234	.1171	.1059	.3414	.44281	.89661	.49387	.0248	.1153	.2583	.45839	.88875	.51577	.9388	.1252	.1815	43
18	.41151	.91140	.45152	.2147	.0972	.4300	.42736	.90408	.47270	.1155	.1061	.3399	.44307	.89649	.49423	.0233	.1155	.2570	.45865	.88862	.51614	.9375	.1253	.1803	42
19	.41178	.91128	.45187	.2130	.0973	.4285	.42762	.90396	.47305	.1139	.1062	.3385	.44333	.89636	.49459	.0219	.1156	.2556	.45891	.88848	.51651	.9361	.1255	.1791	41
20	.41204	.91116	.45222	2.2113	.0975	2.4269	.42788	.90383	.47341	2.1123	.1064	2.3371	.44359	.89623	.49495	2.0204	.1158	2.2543	.45917	.88835	.51687	1.9347	.1257	2.1778	40
21	.41231	.91104	.45257	.2096	.0976	.4254	.42815	.90371	.47376	.1107	.1065	.3356	.44385	.89610	.49532	.0189	.1159	.2530	.45942	.88822	.51724	.9333	.1258	.1766	39
22	.41257	.91092	.45292	.2079	.0978	.4238	.42841	.90358	.47412	.1092	.1067	.3342	.44411	.89597	.49568	.0174	.1161	.2517	.45968	.88808	.51761	.9319	.1260	.1754	38
23	.41284	.91080	.45327	.2062	.0979	.4222	.42867	.90346	.47448	.1076	.1068	.3328	.44437	.89584	.49604	.0159	.1163	.2503	.45994	.88795	.51798	.9306	.1262	.1742	37
24	.41310	.91068	.45362	.2045	.0981	.4207	.42893	.90333	.47483	.1060	.1070	.3313	.44463	.89571	.49640	.0145	.1164	.2490	.46020	.88781	.51835	.9292	.1264	.1730	36
25	.41337	.91056	.45397	2.2028	.0982	2.4191	42920	.90321	.47519	2.1044	.1072	2.3299	.44489	.89558	.49677	2.0130	.1166	2.2477	.46046	.88768	.51872	1.9278	.1265	2.1717	35
26	.41363	.91044	.45432	.2011	.0984	.4176	.42946	.90308	.47555	.1028	.1073	.3285	.44516	.89545	.49713	.0115	.1167	.2464	.46072	.88755	.51909	.9264	.1267	.1705	34
27	.41390	.91032	.45467	.1994	.0985	.4160	.42972	.90296	.47590	.1013	.1075	.3271	.44542	.89532	.49749	.0101	.1169	.2451	.46097	.88741	.51946	.9251	.1269	.1693	33
28	.41416	.91020	.45502	.1977	.0986	.4145	.42998	.90283	.47626	.0997	.1076	.3256	.44568	.89519	.49785	.0086	.1171	.2438	.46123	.88728	.51983	.9237	.1270	.1681	32
29	.41443	.91008	.45537	.1960	.0988	.4130	.43025	.90271	.47662	.0981	.1078	.3242	.44594	.89506	.49822	.0071	.1172	.2425	.46149	.88714	.52020	.9223	.1272	.1669	31
30	.41469	.90996	.45573	2.1943	.0989	2.4114	.43051	.90258	.47697	2.0965	.1079	2.3228	.44620	.89493	.49858	2.0057	.1174	2.2411	.46175	.88701	.52057	1.9210	.1274	2.1657	30
31	.41496	.90984	.45608	.1926	.0991	.4099	.43077	.90246	.47733	.0950	.1081	.3214	.44646	.89480	.49894	.0042	.1176	.2398	.46201	.88688	.52094	.9196	.1275	.1645	29
32	.41522	.90972	.45643	.1909	.0992	.4083	.43104	.90233	.47769	.0934	.1082	.3200	.44672	.89467	.49931	.0028	.1177	.2385	.46226	.88674	.52131	.9182	.1277	.1633	28
33	.41549	.90960	.45678	.1892	.0994	.4068	.43130	.90221	.47805	.0918	.1084	.3186	.44698	.89454	.49967	.0013	.1179	.2372	.46252	.88661	.52168	.9169	.1279	.1620	27
34	.41575	.90948	.45713	.1875	.0995	.4053	.43156	.90208	.47840	.0903	.1085	.3172	.44724	.89441	.50003	1.9998	.1180	.2359	.46278	.88647	.52205	.9155	.1281	.1608	26
35	.41602	.90936	.45748	2.1859	.0997	2.4037	.43182	.90196	.47876	2.0887	.1087	2.3158	.44750	.89428	.50040	1.9984	.1182	2.2346	.46304	.88634	.52242	1.9142	.1282	2.1596	25
36	.41628	.90924	.45783	.1842	.0998	.4022	.43208	.90183	.47912	.0872	.1088	.3143	.44776	.89415	.50076	.9969	.1184	.2333	.46330	.88620	.52279	.9128	.1284	.1584	24
37	.41654	.90911	.45819	.1825	.1000	.4007	.43235	.90171	.47948	.0856	.1090	.3129	.44802	.89402	.50113	.9955	.1185	.2320	.46355	.88607	.52316	.9115	.1286	.1572	23
38	.41681	.90899	.45854	.1808	.1001	.3992	.43261	.90158	.47983	.0840	.1092	.3115	.44828	.89389	.50149	.9940	.1187	.2307	.46381	.88593	.52353	.9101	.1287	.1560	22
39	.41707	.90887	.45889	.1792	.1003	.3976	.43287	.90145	.48019	.0825	.1093	.3101	.44854	.89376	.50185	.9926	.1189	.2294	.46407	.88580	.52390	.9088	.1289	.1548	21
40	.41734	.90875	.45924	2.1775	.1004	2.3961	.43313	.90133	.48055	2.0809	.1095	2.3087	.44880	.89363	.50222	1.9912	.1190	2.2282	.46433	.88566	.52427	1.9074	.1291	2.1536	20
41	.41760	.90863	.45960	.1758	.1005	.3946	.43340	.90120	.48091	.0794	.1096	.3073	.44906	.89350	.50258	.9897	.1192	.2269	.46458	.88553	.52464	.9061	.1293	.1525	19
42	.41787	.90851	.45995	.1741	.1007	.3931	.43366	.90108	.48127	.0778	.1098	.3059	.44932	.89337	.50295	.9883	.1193	.2256	.46484	.88539	.52501	.9047	.1294	.1513	18
43	.41813	.90839	.46030	.1725	.1008	.3916	.43392	.90095	.48162	.0763	.1099	.3046	.44958	.89324	.50331	.9868	.1195	.2243	.46510	.88526	.52538	.9034	.1296	.1501	17
44	.41839	.90826	.46065	.1708	.1010	.3901	.43418	.90082	.48198	.0747	.1101	.3032	.44984	.89311	.50368	.9854	.1197	.2230	.46536	.88512	.52575	.9020	.1298	.1489	16
45	.41866	.90814	.46101	2.1692	.1011	2.3886	.43444	.90070	.48234	2.0732	.1102	2.3018	.45010	.89298	.50404	1.9840	.1198	2.2217	.46561	.88499	.52612	1.9007	.1299	2.1477	15
46	.41892	.90812	.46136	.1675	.1013	.3871	.43471	.90057	.48270	.0717	.1104	.3004	.45036	.89285	.50441	.9825	.1200	.2204	.46587	.88485	.52650	.8993	.1301	.1465	14
47	.41919	.90790	.46171	.1658	.1014	.3856	.43497	.90044	.48306	.0701	.1106	.2990	.45062	.89272	.50477	.9811	.1202	.2192	.46613	.88472	.52687	.8980	.1303	.1453	13
48	.41945	.90778	.46206	.1642	.1016	.3841	.43523	.90032	.48342	.0686	.1107	.2976	.45088	.89258	.50514	.9797	.1203	.2179	.46639	.88458	.52724	.8967	.1305	.1441	12
49	.41972	.90765	.46242	.1625	.1017	.3826	.43549	.90019	.48378	.0671	.1109	.2962	.45114	.89245	.50550	.9782	.1205	.2166	.46664	.88444	.52761	.8953	.1306	.1430	11
50	.41998	.90753	.46277	2.1609	.1019	2.3811	.43575	.90006	.48414	2.0655	.1110	2.2949	.45140	.89232	.50587	1.9768	.1207	2.2153	.46690	.88431	.52798	1.8940	.1308	2.1418	10
51	.42024	.90741	.46312	.1592	.1020	.3796	.43602	.89994	.48449	.0640	.1112	.2935	.45166	.89219	.50623	.9754	.1208	.2141	.46716	.88417	.52836	.8927	.1310	.1406	9
52	.42051	.90729	.46348	.1576	.1022	.3781	.43628	.89981	.48485	.0625	.1113	.2921	.45191	.89206	.50660	.9739	.1210	.2128	.46741	.88404	.52873	.8913	.1312	.1394	8
53	.42077	.90717	.46383	.1559	.1023	.3766	.43654	.89968	.48521	.0609	.1115	.2907	.45217	.89193	.50696	.9725	.1212	.2115	.46767	.88390	.52910	.8900	.1313	.1382	7
54	.42103	.90704	.46418	.1543	.1025	.3751	.43680	.89956	.48557	.0594	.1116	.2894	.45243	.89180	.50733	.9711	.1213	.2103	.46793	.88376	.52947	.8887	.1315	.1371	6
55	.42130	.90692	.46454	2.1527	.1026	2.3736	.43706	.89943	.48593	2.0579	.1118	2.2880	.45269	.89166	.50769	1.9697	.1215	2.2090	.46819	.88363	.52984	1.8873	.1317	2.1359	5
56	.42156	.90680	.46489	.1510	.1028	.3721	.43732	.89930	.48629	.0564	.1120	.2866	.45295	.89153	.50806	.9683	.1217	.2077	.46844	.88349	.53022	.8860	.1319	.1347	4
57	.42183	.90668	.46524	.1494	.1029	.3706	.43759	.89918	.48665	.0548	.1121	.2853	.45321	.89140	.50843	.9668	.1218	.2065	.46870	.88336	.53059	.8847	.1320	.1335	3
58	.42209	.90655	.46560	.1478	.1031	.3691	.43785	.89905	.48701	.0533	.1123	.2839	.45347	.89127	.50879	.9654	.1220	.2052	.46896	.88322	.53096	.8834	.1322	.1324	2
59	.42235	.90643	.46595	.1461	.1032	.3677	.43811	.89892	.48737	.0518	.1124	.2825	.45373	.89114	.50916	.9640	.1222	.2039	.46921	.88308	.53134	.8820	.1324	.1312	1
60	.42262	.90631	.46631	2.1445	.1034	2.3662	.43837	.89879	.48773	2.0503	.1126	2.2812	.45399	.89101	.50952	1.9626	.1223	2.2027	.46947	.88295	.53171	1.8807	.1326	2.1300	0
′	cos	sin	cot	tan	cosec	sec	cos	sin	cot	tan	cosec	sec	cos	sin	cot	tan	cosec	sec	cos	sin	cot	tan	cosec	sec	′
	65°						64°						63°						62°						

	28°						29°						30°						31°						
′	sin	cos	tan	cot	sec	cosec	sin	cos	tan	cot	sec	cosec	sin	cos	tan	cot	sec	cosec	sin	cos	tan	cot	sec	cosec	′
0	.46947	.88295	.53171	1.8807	1.1326	2.1300	.48481	.87462	.55431	1.8040	1.1433	2.0627	.50000	.86603	.57735	1.7320	1.1547	2.0000	.51504	.85717	.60086	1.6643	1.1666	1.9416	60
1	.46973	.88281	.53208	.8794	.1327	.1289	.48506	.87448	.55469	.8028	.1435	.0616	.50025	.86588	.57774	.7309	.1549	1.9990	.51529	.85702	.60126	.6632	.1668	.9407	59
2	.46998	.88267	.53245	.8781	.1329	.1277	.48532	.87434	.55507	.8016	.1437	.0605	.50050	.86573	.57813	.7297	.1551	.9980	.51554	.85687	.60165	.6621	.1670	.9397	58
3	.47024	.88254	.53283	.8768	.1331	.1266	.48557	.87420	.55545	.8003	.1439	.0594	.50075	.86559	.57851	.7286	.1553	.9970	.51578	.85672	.60205	.6610	.1672	.9388	57
4	.47050	.88240	.53320	.8754	.1333	.1254	.48583	.87405	.55583	.7991	.1441	.0583	.50101	.86544	.57890	.7274	.1555	.9960	.51603	.85657	.60244	.6599	.1674	.9378	56
5	.47075	.88226	.53358	1.8741	.1334	2.1242	.48608	.87391	.55621	1.7979	.1443	2.0573	.50126	.86530	.57929	1.7262	.1557	1.9950	.51628	.85642	.60284	1.6588	.1676	1.9369	55
6	.47101	.88213	.53395	.8728	.1336	.1231	.48633	.87377	.55659	.7966	.1445	.0562	.50151	.86515	.57968	.7251	.1559	.9940	.51653	.85627	.60324	.6577	.1678	.9360	54
7	.47127	.88199	.53432	.8715	.1338	.1219	.48659	.87363	.55697	.7954	.1446	.0551	.50176	.86500	.58007	.7239	.1561	.9930	.51678	.85612	.60363	.6566	.1681	.9350	53
8	.47152	.88185	.53470	.8702	.1340	.1208	.48684	.87349	.55735	.7942	.1448	.0540	.50201	.86486	.58046	.7228	.1562	.9920	.51703	.85597	.60403	.6555	.1683	.9341	52
9	.47178	.88171	.53507	.8689	.1341	.1196	.48710	.87335	.55774	.7930	.1450	.0530	.50226	.86471	.58085	.7216	.1564	.9910	.51728	.85582	.60443	.6544	.1685	.9332	51
10	.47204	.88158	.53545	1.8676	.1343	2.1185	.48735	.87320	.55812	1.7917	.1452	2.0519	.50252	.86457	.58123	1.7205	.1566	1.9900	.51753	.85566	.60483	1.6534	.1687	1.9322	50
11	.47229	.88144	.53582	.8663	.1345	.1173	.48760	.87306	.55850	.7905	.1454	.0508	.50277	.86442	.58162	.7193	.1568	.9890	.51778	.85551	.60522	.6523	.1689	.9313	49
12	.47255	.88130	.53619	.8650	.1347	.1162	.48786	.87292	.55888	.7893	.1456	.0498	.50302	.86427	.58201	.7182	.1570	.9880	.51803	.85536	.60562	.6512	.1691	.9304	48
13	.47281	.88117	.53657	.8637	.1349	.1150	.48811	.87278	.55926	.7881	.1458	.0487	.50327	.86413	.58240	.7170	.1572	.9870	.51827	.85521	.60602	.6501	.1693	.9295	47
14	.47306	.88103	.53694	.8624	.1350	.1139	.48837	.87264	.55964	.7868	.1459	.0476	.50352	.86398	.58279	.7159	.1574	.9860	.51852	.85506	.60642	.6490	.1695	.9285	46
15	.47332	.88089	.53732	1.8611	.1352	2.1127	.48862	.87250	.56003	1.7856	.1461	2.0466	.50377	.86383	.58318	1.7147	.1576	1.9850	.51877	.85491	.60681	1.6479	.1697	1.9276	45
16	.47357	.88075	.53769	.8598	.1354	.1116	.48887	.87235	.56041	.7844	.1463	.0455	.50402	.86369	.58357	.7136	.1578	.9840	.51902	.85476	.60721	.6469	.1699	.9267	44
17	.47383	.88061	.53807	.8585	.1356	.1104	.48913	.87221	.56079	.7832	.1465	.0444	.50428	.86354	.58396	.7124	.1580	.9830	.51927	.85461	.60761	.6458	.1701	.9258	43
18	.47409	.88048	.53844	.8572	.1357	.1093	.48938	.87207	.56117	.7820	.1467	.0434	.50453	.86339	.58435	.7113	.1582	.9820	.51952	.85446	.60801	.6447	.1703	.9248	42
19	.47434	.88034	.53882	.8559	.1359	.1082	.48964	.87193	.56156	.7808	.1469	.0423	.50478	.86325	.58474	.7101	.1584	.9811	.51977	.85431	.60841	.6436	.1705	.9239	41
20	.47460	.88020	.53919	1.8546	.1361	2.1070	.48989	.87178	.56194	1.7795	.1471	2.0413	.50503	.86310	.58513	1.7090	.1586	1.9801	.52002	.85416	.60881	1.6425	.1707	1.9230	40
21	.47486	.88006	.53957	.8533	.1363	.1059	.49014	.87164	.56232	.7783	.1473	.0402	.50528	.86295	.58552	.7079	.1588	.9791	.52026	.85400	.60920	.6415	.1709	.9221	39
22	.47511	.87992	.53995	.8520	.1365	.1048	.49040	.87150	.56270	.7771	.1474	.0392	.50553	.86281	.58591	.7067	.1590	.9781	.52051	.85385	.60960	.6404	.1712	.9212	38
23	.47537	.87979	.54032	.8507	.1366	.1036	.49065	.87136	.56309	.7759	.1476	.0381	.50578	.86266	.58630	.7056	.1592	.9771	.52076	.85370	.61000	.6393	.1714	.9203	37
24	.47562	.87965	.54070	.8495	.1368	.1025	.49090	.87121	.56347	.7747	.1478	.0370	.50603	.86251	.58670	.7044	.1594	.9761	.52101	.85355	.61040	.6383	.1716	.9193	36
25	.47588	.87951	.54107	1.8482	.1370	2.1014	.49116	.87107	.56385	1.7735	.1480	2.0360	.50628	.86237	.58709	1.7033	.1596	1.9752	.52126	.85340	.61080	1.6372	.1718	1.9184	35
26	.47613	.87937	.54145	.8469	.1372	.1002	.49141	.87093	.56424	.7723	.1482	.0349	.50653	.86222	.58748	.7022	.1598	.9742	.52151	.85325	.61120	.6361	.1720	.9175	34
27	.47639	.87923	.54183	.8456	.1373	.0991	.49166	.87078	.56462	.7711	.1484	.0339	.50679	.86207	.58787	.7010	.1600	.9732	.52175	.85309	.61160	.6350	.1722	.9166	33
28	.47665	.87909	.54220	.8443	.1375	.0980	.49192	.87064	.56500	.7699	.1486	.0329	.50704	.86192	.58826	.6999	.1602	.9722	.52200	.85294	.61200	.6340	.1724	.9157	32
29	.47690	.87895	.54258	.8430	.1377	.0969	.49217	.87050	.56539	.7687	.1488	.0318	.50729	.86178	.58865	.6988	.1604	.9713	.52225	.85279	.61240	.6329	.1726	.9148	31
30	.47716	.87882	.54295	1.8418	.1379	2.0957	.49242	.87035	.56577	1.7675	.1489	2.0308	.50754	.86163	.58904	1.6977	.1606	1.9703	.52250	.85264	.61280	1.6318	.1728	1.9139	30
31	.47741	.87868	.54333	.8405	.1381	.0946	.49268	.87021	.56616	.7663	.1491	.0297	.50779	.86148	.58944	.6965	.1608	.9693	.52275	.85249	.61320	.6308	.1730	.9130	29
32	.47767	.87854	.54371	.8392	.1382	.0935	.49293	.87007	.56654	.7651	.1493	.0287	.50804	.86133	.58983	.6954	.1610	.9683	.52299	.85234	.61360	.6297	.1732	.9121	28
33	.47792	.87840	.54409	.8379	.1384	.0924	.49318	.86992	.56692	.7639	.1495	.0276	.50829	.86118	.59022	.6943	.1612	.9674	.52324	.85218	.61400	.6286	.1734	.9112	27
34	.47818	.87826	.54446	.8367	.1386	.0912	.49343	.86978	.56731	.7627	.1497	.0266	.50854	.86104	.59061	.6931	.1614	.9664	.52349	.85203	.61440	.6276	.1737	.9102	26
35	.47844	.87812	.54484	1.8354	.1388	2.0901	.49369	.86964	.56769	1.7615	.1499	2.0256	.50879	.86089	.59100	1.6920	.1616	1.9654	.52374	.85188	.61480	1.6265	.1739	1.9093	25
36	.47869	.87798	.54522	.8341	.1390	.0890	.49394	.86949	.56808	.7603	.1501	.0245	.50904	.86074	.59140	.6909	.1618	.9645	.52398	.85173	.61520	.6255	.1741	.9084	24
37	.47895	.87784	.54559	.8329	.1391	.0879	.49419	.86935	.56846	.7591	.1503	.0235	.50929	.86059	.59179	.6898	.1620	.9635	.52423	.85157	.61560	.6244	.1743	.9075	23
38	.47920	.87770	.54597	.8316	.1393	.0868	.49445	.86921	.56885	.7579	.1505	.0224	.50954	.86044	.59218	.6887	.1622	.9625	.52448	.85142	.61601	.6233	.1745	.9066	22
39	.47946	.87756	.54635	.8303	.1395	.0857	.49470	.86906	.56923	.7567	.1507	.0214	.50979	.86030	.59258	.6875	.1624	.9616	.52473	.85127	.61641	.6223	.1747	.9057	21
40	.47971	.87742	.54673	1.8291	.1397	2.0846	.49495	.86892	.56962	1.7555	.1508	2.0204	.51004	.86015	.59297	1.6864	.1626	1.9606	.52498	.85112	.61681	1.6212	.1749	1.9048	20
41	.47997	.87728	.54711	.8278	.1399	.0835	.49521	.86877	.57000	.7544	.1510	.0194	.51029	.86000	.59336	.6853	.1628	.9596	.52522	.85096	.61721	.6202	.1751	.9039	19
42	.48022	.87715	.54748	.8265	.1401	.0824	.49546	.86863	.57039	.7532	.1512	.0183	.51054	.85985	.59376	.6842	.1630	.9587	.52547	.85081	.61761	.6191	.1753	.9030	18
43	.48048	.87701	.54786	.8253	.1402	.0812	.49571	.86849	.57077	.7520	.1514	.0173	.51079	.85970	.59415	.6831	.1632	.9577	.52572	.85066	.61801	.6181	.1756	.9021	17
44	.48073	.87687	.54824	.8240	.1404	.0801	.49596	.86834	.57116	.7508	.1516	.0163	.51104	.85955	.59454	.6820	.1634	.9568	.52597	.85050	.61842	.6170	.1758	.9013	16
45	.48099	.87673	.54862	1.8227	.1406	2.0790	.49622	.86820	.57155	1.7496	.1518	2.0152	.51129	.85941	.59494	1.6808	.1636	1.9558	.52621	.85735	.61882	1.6160	.1760	1.9004	15
46	.48124	.87659	.54900	.8215	.1408	.0779	.49647	.86805	.57193	.7484	.1520	.0142	.51154	.85926	.59533	.6797	.1638	.9549	.52646	.85020	.61922	.6149	.1762	.8995	14
47	.48150	.87645	.54937	.8202	.1410	.0768	.49672	.86791	.57232	.7473	.1522	.0132	.51179	.85911	.59572	.6786	.1640	.9539	.52671	.85004	.61962	.6139	.1764	.8986	13
48	.48175	.87631	.54975	.8190	.1411	.0757	.49697	.86776	.57270	.7461	.1524	.0122	.51204	.85896	.59612	.6775	.1642	.9530	.52695	.84989	.62003	.6128	.1766	.8977	12
49	.48201	.87617	.55013	.8177	.1413	.0746	.49723	.86762	.57309	.7449	.1526	.0111	.51229	.85881	.59651	.6764	.1644	.9520	.52720	.84974	.62043	.6118	.1768	.8968	11
50	.48226	.87603	.55051	1.8165	.1415	2.0735	.49748	.86748	.57348	1.7437	.1528	2.0101	.51254	.85866	.59691	1.6753	.1646	1.9510	.52745	.84959	.62083	1.6107	.1770	1.8959	10
51	.48252	.87588	.55089	.8152	.1417	.0725	.49773	.86733	.57386	.7426	.1530	.0091	.51279	.85851	.59730	.6742	.1648	.9501	.52770	.84943	.62123	.6097	.1772	.8950	9
52	.48277	.87574	.55127	.8140	.1419	.0714	.49798	.86719	.57425	.7414	.1531	.0081	.51304	.85836	.59770	.6731	.1650	.9491	.52794	.84928	.62164	.6086	.1775	.8941	8
53	.48303	.87560	.55165	.8127	.1421	.0703	.49823	.86704	.57464	.7402	.1533	.0071	.51329	.85821	.59809	.6720	.1652	.9482	.52819	.84912	.62204	.6076	.1777	.8932	7
54	.48328	.87546	.55203	.8115	.1422	.0692	.49849	.86690	.57502	.7390	.1535	.0061	.51354	.85806	.59849	.6709	.1654	.9473	.52844	.84897	.62244	.6066	.1779	.8924	6
55	.48354	.87532	.55241	1.8102	.1424	2.0681	.49874	.86675	.57541	1.7379	.1537	2.0050	.51379	.85791	.59888	1.6698	.1656	1.9463	.52868	.84882	.62285	1.6055	.1781	1.8915	5
56	.48379	.87518	.55279	.8090	.1426	.0670	.49899	.86661	.57580	.7367	.1539	.0040	.51404	.85777	.59928	.6687	.1658	.9454	.52893	.84866	.62325	.6045	.1783	.8906	4
57	.48405	.87504	.55317	.8078	.1428	.0659	.49924	.86646	.57619	.7355	.1541	.0030	.51429	.85762	.59967	.6676	.1660	.9444	.52918	.84851	.62366	.6034	.1785	.8897	3
58	.48430	.87490	.55355	.8065	.1430	.0648	.49950	.86632	.57657	.7344	.1543	.0020	.51454	.85747	.60007	.6665	.1662	.9435	.52942	.84836	.62406	.6024	.1787	.8888	2
59	.48455	.87476	.55393	.8053	.1432	.0637	.49975	.86617	.57696	.7332	.1545	.0010	.51479	.85732	.60046	.6654	.1664	.9425	.52967	.84820	.62446	.6014	.1790	.8879	1
60	.48481	.87462	.55431	1.8040	.1433	2.0627	.50000	.86603	.57735	1.7320	.1547	2.0000	.51504	.85717	.60086	1.6643	.1666	1.9416	.52992	.84805	.62487	1.6003	.1792	1.8871	0
′	cos	sin	cot	tan	cosec	sec	cos	sin	cot	tan	cosec	sec	cos	sin	cot	tan	cosec	sec	cos	sin	cot	tan	cosec	sec	′
	61°						60°						59°						58°						

	32°						33°						34°						35°						
′	sin	cos	tan	cot	sec	cosec	sin	cos	tan	cot	sec	cosec	sin	cos	tan	cot	sec	cosec	sin	cos	tan	cot	sec	cosec	′
0	.52992	.84805	.62487	1.6003	1.1792	1.8871	.54464	.83867	.64941	1.5399	1.1924	1.8361	.55919	.82904	.67451	1.4826	1.2062	1.7883	.57358	.81915	.70021	1.4281	1.2208	1.7434	60
1	.53016	.84789	.62527	.5993	.1794	.8862	.54488	.83851	.64982	.5389	.1926	.8352	.55943	.82887	.67493	.4816	.2064	.7875	.57381	.81898	.70064	.4273	.2210	.7427	59
2	.53041	.84774	.62568	.5983	.1796	.8853	.54513	.83835	.65023	.5379	.1928	.8344	.55967	.82871	.67535	.4807	.2067	.7867	.57405	.81882	.70107	.4264	.2213	.7420	58
3	.53066	.84758	.62608	.5972	.1798	.8844	.54537	.83819	.65065	.5369	.1930	.8336	.55992	.82855	.67578	.4798	.2069	.7860	.57429	.81865	.70151	.4255	.2215	.7413	57
4	.53090	.84743	.62649	.5962	.1800	.8836	.54561	.83804	.65106	.5359	.1933	.8328	.56016	.82839	.67620	.4788	.2072	.7852	.57453	.81848	.70194	.4246	.2218	.7405	56
5	.53115	.84728	.62689	1.5952	.1802	1.8827	.54586	.83788	.65148	1.5350	.1935	1.8320	.56040	.82822	.67663	1.4779	.2074	1.7844	.57477	.81832	.70238	1.4237	.2220	1.7398	55
6	.53140	.84712	.62730	.5941	.1805	.8818	.54610	.83772	.65189	.5340	.1937	.8311	.56064	.82806	.67705	.4770	.2076	.7837	.57500	.81815	.70281	.4228	.2223	.7391	54
7	.53164	.84697	.62770	.5931	.1807	.8809	.54634	.83756	.65231	.5330	.1939	.8303	.56088	.82790	.67747	.4761	.2079	.7829	.57524	.81798	.70325	.4220	.2225	.7384	53
8	.53189	.84681	.62811	.5921	.1809	.8801	.54659	.83740	.65272	.5320	.1942	.8295	.56112	.82773	.67790	.4751	.2081	.7821	.57548	.81781	.70368	.4211	.2228	.7377	52
9	.53214	.84666	.62851	.5910	.1811	.8792	.54683	.83724	.65314	.5311	.1944	.8287	.56136	.82757	.67832	.4742	.2083	.7814	.57572	.81765	.70412	.4202	.2230	.7369	51
10	.53238	.84650	.62892	1.5900	.1813	1.8783	.54708	.83708	.65355	1.5301	.1946	1.8279	.56160	.82741	.67875	1.4733	.2086	1.7806	.57596	.81748	.70455	1.4193	.2233	1.7362	50
11	.53263	.84635	.62933	.5890	.1815	.8775	.54732	.83692	.65397	.5291	.1948	.8271	.56184	.82724	.67917	.4724	.2088	.7798	.57619	.81731	.70499	.4185	.2235	.7355	49
12	.53288	.84619	.62973	.5880	.1818	.8766	.54756	.83676	.65438	.5282	.1951	.8263	.56208	.82708	.67960	.4714	.2091	.7791	.57643	.81714	.70542	.4176	.2238	.7348	48
13	.53312	.84604	.63014	.5869	.1820	.8757	.54781	.83660	.65480	.5272	.1953	.8255	.56232	.82692	.68002	.4705	.2093	.7783	.57667	.81698	.70586	.4167	.2240	.7341	47
14	.53337	.84588	.63055	.5859	.1822	.8749	.54805	.83644	.65521	.5262	.1955	.8246	.56256	.82675	.68045	.4696	.2095	.7776	.57691	.81681	.70629	.4158	.2243	.7334	46
15	.53361	.84573	.63095	1.5849	.1824	1.8740	.54829	.83629	.65563	1.5252	.1958	1.8238	.56280	.82659	.68087	1.4687	.2098	1.7768	.57714	.81664	.70673	1.4150	.2245	1.7327	45
16	.53386	.84557	.63136	.5839	.1826	.8731	.54854	.83613	.65604	.5234	.1960	.8230	.56304	.82643	.68130	.4678	.2100	.7760	.57738	.81647	.70717	.4141	.2248	.7319	44
17	.53411	.84542	.63177	.5829	.1828	.8723	.54878	.83597	.65646	.5233	.1962	.8222	.56328	.82626	.68173	.4669	.2103	.7753	.57762	.81630	.70760	.4132	.2250	.7312	43
18	.53435	.84526	.63217	.5818	.1831	.8714	.54902	.83581	.65688	.5223	.1964	.8214	.56353	.82610	.68215	.4659	.2105	.7745	.57786	.81614	.70804	.4123	.2253	.7305	42
19	.53460	.84511	.63258	.5808	.1833	.8706	.54926	.83565	.65729	.5214	.1967	.8206	.56377	.82593	.68258	.4650	.2107	.7738	.57809	.81597	.70848	.4115	.2255	.7298	41
20	.53484	.84495	.63299	1.5798	.1835	1.8697	.54951	.83549	.65771	1.5204	.1969	1.8198	.56401	.82577	.68301	1.4641	.2110	1.7730	.57833	.81580	.70891	1.4106	.2258	1.7291	40
21	.53509	.84479	.63339	.5788	.1837	.8688	.54975	.83533	.65813	.5195	.1971	.8190	.56425	.82561	.68343	.4632	.2112	.7723	.57857	.81563	.70935	.4097	.2260	.7284	39
22	.53533	.84464	.63380	.5778	.1839	.8680	.54999	.83517	.65854	.5185	.1974	.8182	.56449	.82544	.68386	.4623	.2115	.7715	.57881	.81546	.70979	.4089	.2263	.7277	38
23	.53558	.84448	.63421	.5768	.1841	.8671	.55024	.83501	.65896	.5175	.1976	.8174	.56473	.82528	.68429	.4614	.2117	.7708	.57904	.81530	.71022	.4080	.2265	.7270	37
24	.53583	.84433	.63462	.5757	.1844	.8663	.55048	.83485	.65938	.5166	.1978	.8166	.56497	.82511	.68471	.4605	.2119	.7700	.57928	.81513	.71066	.4071	.2268	.7263	36
25	.53607	.84417	.63503	1.5747	.1846	1.8654	.55002	.83469	.65980	1.5156	.1980	1.8158	.56521	.82495	.68514	1.4595	.2122	1.7693	.57952	.81496	.71110	1.4063	.2270	1.7256	35
26	.53632	.84402	.63543	.5737	.1848	.8646	.55090	.83453	.66021	.5147	.1983	.8150	.56545	.82478	.68557	.4586	.2124	.7685	.57975	.81479	.71154	.4054	.2273	.7249	34
27	.53656	.84386	.63584	.5727	.1850	.8637	.55121	.83437	.66063	.5137	.1985	.8142	.56569	.82462	.68600	.4577	.2127	.7678	.57999	.81462	.71198	.4045	.2276	.7242	33
28	.53681	.84370	.63625	.5717	.1852	.8629	.55145	.83421	.66105	.5127	.1987	.8134	.56593	.82445	.68642	.4568	.2129	.7670	.58023	.81445	.71241	.4037	.2278	.7234	32
29	.53705	.84355	.63666	.5707	.1855	.8620	.55169	.83405	.66147	.5118	.1990	.8126	.56617	.82429	.68685	.4559	.2132	.7663	.58047	.81428	.71285	.4028	.2281	.7227	31
30	.53730	.84339	.63707	1.5697	.1857	1.8611	.55194	.83388	.66188	1.5108	.1992	1.8118	.56641	.82413	.68728	1.4550	.2134	1.7655	.58070	.81411	.71329	1.4019	.2283	1.7220	30
31	.53754	.84323	.63748	.5687	.1859	.8603	.55218	.83372	.66230	.5099	.1994	.8110	.56664	.82396	.68771	.4541	.2136	.7648	.58094	.81395	.71373	.4011	.2286	.7213	29
32	.53779	.84308	.63789	.5677	.1861	.8595	.55242	.83356	.66272	.5089	.1997	.8102	.56688	.82380	.68814	.4532	.2139	.7640	.58118	.81378	.71417	.4002	.2288	.7206	28
33	.53803	.84292	.63830	.5667	.1863	.8586	.55266	.83340	.66314	.5080	.1999	.8094	.56712	.82363	.68857	.4523	.2141	.7633	.58141	.81361	.71461	.3994	.2291	.7199	27
34	.53828	.84276	.63871	.5657	.1866	.8578	.55291	.83324	.66356	.5070	.2001	.8086	.56736	.82347	.68899	.4514	.2144	.7625	.58165	.81344	.71505	.3985	.2293	.7192	26
35	.53852	.84261	.63912	1.5646	.1868	1.8569	.55315	.83308	.66398	1.5061	.2004	1.8078	.56760	.82330	.68942	1.4505	.2146	1.7618	.58189	.81327	.71549	1.3976	.2296	1.7185	25
36	.53877	.84245	.63953	.5636	.1870	.8561	.55339	.83292	.66440	.5051	.2006	.8070	.56784	.82314	.68985	.4496	.2149	.7610	.58212	.81310	.71593	.3968	.2298	.7178	24
37	.53901	.84229	.63994	.5626	.1872	.8552	.55363	.83276	.66482	.5042	.2008	.8062	.56808	.82297	.69028	.4487	.2151	.7603	.58236	.81293	.71637	.3959	.2301	.7171	23
38	.53926	.84214	.64035	.5616	.1874	.8544	.55388	.83260	.66524	.5032	.2010	.8054	.56832	.82280	.69071	.4478	.2153	.7596	.58259	.81276	.71681	.3951	.2304	.7164	22
39	.53950	.84198	.64076	.5606	.1877	.8535	.55412	.83244	.66566	.5023	.2013	.8047	.56856	.82264	.69114	.4469	.2156	.7588	.58283	.81259	.71725	.3942	.2306	.7157	21
40	.53975	.84182	.64117	1.5596	.1879	1.8527	.55436	.83228	.66608	1.5013	.2015	1.8039	.56880	.82247	.69157	1.4460	.2158	1.7581	.58307	.81242	.71769	1.3933	.2309	1.7151	20
41	.53999	.84167	.64158	.5586	.1881	.8519	.55460	.83211	.66650	.5004	.2017	.8031	.56904	.82231	.69200	.4451	.2161	.7573	.58330	.81225	.71813	.3925	.2311	.7144	19
42	.54024	.84151	.64199	.5577	.1883	.8510	.55484	.83195	.66692	.4994	.2020	.8023	.56928	.82214	.69243	.4442	.2163	.7566	.58354	.81208	.71857	.3916	.2314	.7137	18
43	.54048	.84135	.64240	.5567	.1886	.8502	.55509	.83179	.66734	.4985	.2022	.8015	.56952	.82198	.69286	.4433	.2166	.7559	.58378	.81191	.71901	.3908	.2316	.7130	17
44	.54073	.84120	.64281	.5557	.1888	.8493	.55533	.83163	.66776	.4975	.2024	.8007	.56976	.82181	.69329	.4424	.2168	.7551	.58401	.81174	.71945	.3899	.2319	.7123	16
45	.54097	.84104	.64322	1.5547	.1890	1.8485	.55557	.83147	.66818	1.4966	.2027	1.7999	.57000	.82165	.69372	1.4415	.2171	1.7544	.58425	.81157	.71990	1.3891	.2322	1.7116	15
46	.54122	.84088	.64363	.5537	.1892	.8477	.55581	.83131	.66860	.4957	.2029	.7992	.57023	.82148	.69415	.4406	.2173	.7537	.58448	.81140	.72034	.3882	.2324	.7109	14
47	.54146	.84072	.64404	.5527	.1894	.8468	.55605	.83115	.66902	.4947	.2031	.7984	.57047	.82131	.69459	.4397	.2175	.7529	.58472	.81123	.72078	.3874	.2327	.7102	13
48	.54171	.84057	.64446	.5517	.1897	.8460	.55629	.83098	.66944	.4938	.2034	.7976	.57071	.82115	.69502	.4388	.2178	.7522	.58496	.81106	.72122	.3865	.2329	.7095	12
49	.54195	.84041	.64487	.5507	.1899	.8452	.55654	.83082	.66986	.4928	.2036	.7968	.57095	.82098	.69545	.4379	.2180	.7514	.58519	.81089	.72166	.3857	.2332	.7088	11
50	.54220	.84025	.64528	1.5497	.1901	1.8443	.55678	.83066	.67028	1.4919	.2039	1.7960	.57119	.82082	.69588	1.4370	.2183	1.7507	.58543	.81072	.72211	1.3848	.2335	1.7081	10
51	.54244	.84009	.64569	.5487	.1903	.8435	.55702	.83050	.67071	.4910	.2041	.7953	.57143	.82065	.69631	.4361	.2185	.7500	.58566	.81055	.72255	.3840	.2337	.7075	9
52	.54268	.83993	.64610	.5477	.1906	.8427	.55726	.83034	.67113	.4900	.2043	.7945	.57167	.82048	.69674	.4352	.2188	.7493	.58590	.81038	.72299	.3831	.2340	.7068	8
53	.54293	.83978	.64652	.5467	.1908	.8418	.55750	.83017	.67155	.4891	.2046	.7937	.57191	.82032	.69718	.4343	.2190	.7485	.58614	.81021	.72344	.3823	.2342	.7061	7
54	.54317	.83962	.64693	.5458	.1910	.8410	.55774	.83001	.67197	.4881	.2048	.7929	.57214	.82015	.69761	.4335	.2193	.7478	.58637	.81004	.72388	.3814	.2345	.7054	6
55	.54342	.83946	.64734	1.5448	.1912	1.8402	.55799	.82985	.67239	1.4872	.2050	1.7921	.57238	.81998	.69804	1.4326	.2195	1.7471	.58661	.80987	.72432	1.3806	.2348	1.7047	5
56	.54366	.83930	.64775	.5438	.1915	.8394	.55823	.82969	.67282	.4863	.2053	.7914	.57262	.81982	.69847	.4317	.2198	.7463	.58684	.80970	.72477	.3797	.2350	.7040	4
57	.54391	.83914	.64817	.5428	.1917	.8385	.55847	.82952	.67324	.4853	.2055	.7906	.57286	.81965	.69891	.4308	.2200	.7456	.58708	.80953	.72521	.3789	.2353	.7033	3
58	.54415	.83899	.64858	.5418	.1919	.8377	.55871	.82936	.67366	.4844	.2057	.7898	.57310	.81948	.69934	.4299	.2203	.7449	.58731	.80936	.72565	.3781	.2355	.7027	2
59	.54439	.83883	.64899	.5408	.1921	.8369	.55895	.82920	.67408	.4835	.2060	.7891	.57334	.81932	.69977	.4290	.2205	.7442	.58755	.80919	.72610	.3772	.2358	.7020	1
60	.54464	.83867	.64941	1.5399	.1922	1.8361	.55919	.82904	.67451	1.4826	.2062	1.7883	.57358	.81915	.70021	1.4281	.2208	1.7434	.58778	.80902	.72654	1.3764	.2361	1.7013	0
′	cos	sin	cot	tan	cosec	sec	cos	sin	cot	tan	cosec	sec	cos	sin	cot	tan	cosec	sec	cos	sin	cot	tan	cosec	sec	′
	57°						56°						55°						54°						

786 APPENDIX II GENERAL TABLES

	36°						37°						38°						39°						
′	sin	cos	tan	cot	sec	cosec	sin	cos	tan	cot	sec	cosec	sin	cos	tan	cot	sec	cosec	sin	cos	tan	cot	sec	cosec	′
0	.58778	.80902	.72654	1.3764	1.2361	1.7013	.60181	.79863	.75355	1.3270	1.2521	1.6616	.61566	.78801	.78128	1.2799	1.2690	1.6243	.62932	.77715	.80978	1.2349	1.2867	1.5890	60
1	.58802	.80885	.72699	.3755	.2363	.7006	.60205	.79846	.75401	.3262	.2524	.6610	.61589	.78783	.78175	.2792	.2693	.6237	.62955	.77696	.81026	.2342	.2871	.5884	59
2	.58825	.80867	.72743	.3747	.2366	.6999	.60228	.79828	.75447	.3254	.2527	.6603	.61612	.78765	.78222	.2784	.2696	.6231	.62977	.77678	.81075	.2334	.2874	.5879	58
3	.58849	.80850	.72788	.3738	.2368	.6993	.60251	.79811	.75492	.3246	.2530	.6597	.61635	.78747	.78269	.2776	.2699	.6224	.63000	.77660	.81123	.2327	.2877	.5873	57
4	.58873	.80833	.72832	.3730	.2371	.6986	.60274	.79793	.75538	.3238	.2532	.6591	.61658	.78729	.78316	.2769	.2702	.6218	.63022	.77641	.81171	.2320	.2880	.5867	56
5	.58896	.80816	.72877	1.3722	.2374	1.6979	.60298	.79776	.75584	1.3230	.2535	1.6584	.61681	.78711	.78363	1.2761	.2705	1.6212	.63045	.77623	.81219	1.2312	.2883	1.5862	55
6	.58920	.80799	.72921	.3713	.2376	.6972	.60320	.79758	.75629	.3222	.2538	.6578	.61703	.78693	.78410	.2753	.2707	.6206	.63067	.77605	.81268	.2305	.2886	.5856	54
7	.58943	.80782	.72966	.3705	.2379	.6965	.60344	.79741	.75675	.3214	.2541	.6572	.61726	.78675	.78457	.2746	.2710	.6200	.63090	.77586	.81316	.2297	.2889	.5850	53
8	.58967	.80765	.73010	.3697	.2382	.6959	.60367	.79723	.75721	.3206	.2543	.6565	.61749	.78657	.78504	.2738	.2713	.6194	.63113	.77568	.81364	.2290	.2892	.5854	52
9	.58990	.80747	.73055	.3688	.2384	.6952	.60390	.79706	.75767	.3198	.2546	.6559	.61772	.78640	.78551	.2730	.2716	.6188	.63135	.77549	.81413	.2283	.2895	.5839	51
10	.59014	.80730	.73100	1.3680	.2387	1.6945	.60413	.79688	.75812	1.3190	.2549	1.6552	.61795	.78622	.78598	1.2723	.2719	1.6182	.63158	.77531	.81461	1.2276	.2898	1.5833	50
11	.59037	.80713	.73144	.3672	.2389	.6938	.60437	.79670	.75858	.3182	.2552	.6546	.61818	.78604	.78645	.2715	.2722	.6176	.63180	.77513	.81509	.2268	.2901	.5828	49
12	.59060	.80696	.73189	.3663	.2392	.6932	.60460	.79653	.75904	.3174	.2554	.6540	.61841	.78586	.78692	.2708	.2725	.6170	.63203	.77494	.81558	.2261	.2904	.5822	48
13	.59084	.80679	.73234	.3655	.2395	.6925	.60483	.79635	.75950	.3166	.2557	.6533	.61864	.78568	.78739	.2700	.2728	.6164	.63225	.77476	.81606	.2254	.2907	.5816	47
14	.59107	.80662	.73278	.3647	.2397	.6918	.60506	.79618	.75996	.3159	.2560	.6527	.61886	.78550	.78786	.2692	.2731	.6159	.63248	.77458	.81655	.2247	.2910	.5811	46
15	.59131	.80644	.73323	1.3638	.2400	1.6912	.60529	.79600	.76042	1.3151	.2563	1.6521	.61909	.78532	.78834	1.2685	.2734	1.6153	.63270	.77439	.81703	1.2239	.2913	1.5805	45
16	.59154	.80627	.73368	.3630	.2403	.6905	.60552	.79582	.76088	.3143	.2565	.6514	.61932	.78514	.78881	.2677	.2737	.6147	.63293	.77421	.81752	.2232	.2916	.5799	44
17	.59178	.80610	.73412	.3622	.2405	.6898	.60576	.79565	.76134	.3135	.2568	.6508	.61955	.78496	.78928	.2670	.2739	.6141	.63315	.77402	.81800	.2225	.2919	.5794	43
18	.59201	.80593	.73457	.3613	.2408	.6891	.60599	.79547	.76179	.3127	.2571	.6502	.61978	.78478	.78975	.2662	.2742	.6135	.63338	.77384	.81849	.2218	.2922	.5788	42
19	.59225	.80576	.73502	.3605	.2411	.6885	.60622	.79530	.76225	.3119	.2574	.6496	.62001	.78460	.79022	.2655	.2745	.6129	.63360	.77365	.81898	.2210	.2926	.5783	41
20	.59248	.80558	.73547	1.3597	.2413	1.6878	.60645	.79512	.76271	1.3111	.2577	1.6489	.62023	.78441	.79070	1.2647	.2748	1.6123	.63383	.77347	.81946	1.2203	.2929	1.5777	40
21	.59272	.80541	.73592	.3588	.2416	.6871	.60668	.79494	.76317	.3103	.2579	.6483	.62046	.78423	.79117	.2639	.2751	.6117	.63405	.77329	.81995	.2196	.2932	.5771	39
22	.59295	.80524	.73637	.3580	.2419	.6865	.60691	.79477	.76364	.3095	.2582	.6477	.62069	.78405	.79164	.2632	.2754	.6111	.63428	.77310	.82043	.2189	.2935	.5766	38
23	.59318	.80507	.73681	.3572	.2421	.6858	.60714	.79459	.76410	.3087	.2585	.6470	.62092	.78387	.79212	.2624	.2757	.6105	.63450	.77292	.82092	.2181	.2938	.5760	37
24	.59342	.80489	.73726	.3564	.2424	.6851	.60737	.79441	.76456	.3079	.2588	.6464	.62115	.78369	.79259	.2617	.2760	.6099	.63473	.77273	.82141	.2174	.2941	.5755	36
25	.59365	.80472	.73771	1.3555	.2427	1.6845	.60761	.79424	.76502	1.3071	.2591	1.6458	.62137	.78351	.79306	1.2609	.2763	1.6093	.63495	.77255	.82190	1.2167	.2944	1.5749	35
26	.59389	.80455	.73816	.3547	.2429	.6838	.60784	.79406	.76548	.3064	.2593	.6452	.62160	.78333	.79354	.2602	.2766	.6087	.63518	.77236	.82238	.2160	.2947	.5743	34
27	.59412	.80437	.73861	.3539	.2432	.6831	.60807	.79388	.76594	.3056	.2596	.6445	.62183	.78315	.79401	.2594	.2769	.6081	.63540	.77218	.82287	.2152	.2950	.5738	33
28	.59435	.80420	.73906	.3531	.2435	.6825	.60830	.79371	.76640	.3048	.2599	.6439	.62206	.78297	.79449	.2587	.2772	.6077	.63563	.77199	.82336	.2145	.2953	.5732	32
29	.59459	.80403	.73951	.3522	.2437	.6818	.60853	.79353	.76686	.3040	.2602	.6433	.62229	.78279	.79496	.2579	.2775	.6070	.63585	.77181	.82385	.2138	.2956	.5727	31
30	.59482	.80386	.73996	1.3514	.2440	1.6812	.60876	.79335	.76733	1.3032	.2605	1.6427	.62251	.78261	.79543	1.2572	.2778	1.6064	.63608	.77162	.82434	1.2131	.2960	1.5721	30
31	.59506	.80368	.74041	.3506	.2443	.6805	.60899	.79318	.76779	.3024	.2607	.6420	.62274	.78243	.79591	.2564	.2781	.6058	.63630	.77144	.82482	.2124	.2963	.5716	29
32	.59529	.80351	.74086	.3498	.2445	.6798	.60922	.79300	.76825	.3016	.2610	.6414	.62297	.78224	.79639	.2557	.2784	.6052	.63653	.77125	.82531	.2117	.2966	.5710	28
33	.59552	.80334	.74131	.3489	.2448	.6792	.60945	.79282	.76871	.3009	.2613	.6408	.62320	.78206	.79686	.2549	.2787	.6046	.63675	.77107	.82580	.2109	.2969	.5705	27
34	.59576	.80316	.74176	.3481	.2451	.6785	.60968	.79264	.76918	.3001	.2616	.6402	.62342	.78188	.79734	.2542	.2790	.6040	.63697	.77088	.82629	.2102	.2972	.5699	26
35	.59599	.80299	.74221	1.3473	.2453	1.6779	.60991	.79247	.76964	1.2993	.2619	1.6396	.62365	.78170	.79781	1.2534	.2793	1.6034	.63720	.77070	.82678	1.2095	.2975	1.5694	25
36	.59622	.80282	.74266	.3465	.2456	.6772	.61014	.79229	.77010	.2985	.2622	.6389	.62388	.78152	.79829	.2527	.2795	.6029	.63742	.77051	.82727	.2088	.2978	.5688	24
37	.59646	.80264	.74312	.3457	.2459	.6766	.61037	.79211	.77057	.2977	.2624	.6383	.62411	.78134	.79876	.2519	.2798	.6023	.63765	.77033	.82776	.2081	.2981	.5683	23
38	.59669	.80247	.74357	.3449	.2461	.6759	.61061	.79193	.77103	.2970	.2627	.6377	.62433	.78116	.79924	.2512	.2801	.6017	.63787	.77014	.82825	.2074	.2985	.5677	22
39	.59692	.80230	.74402	.3440	.2464	.6752	.61084	.79176	.77149	.2962	.2630	.6371	.62456	.78097	.79972	.2504	.2804	.6011	.63810	.76996	.82874	.2066	.2988	.5672	21
40	.59716	.80212	.74447	1.3432	.2467	1.6746	.61107	.79158	.77196	1.2954	.2633	1.6365	.62479	.78079	.80020	1.2497	.2807	1.6005	.63832	.76977	.82923	1.2059	.2991	1.5666	20
41	.59739	.80195	.74492	.3424	.2470	.6739	.61130	.79140	.77242	.2946	.2636	.6359	.62501	.78061	.80067	.2489	.2810	.6000	.63854	.76958	.82972	.2052	.2994	.5661	19
42	.59762	.80177	.74538	.3416	.2472	.6733	.61153	.79122	.77289	.2938	.2639	.6352	.62524	.78043	.80115	.2482	.2813	.5994	.63877	.76940	.83022	.2045	.2997	.5655	18
43	.59786	.80160	.74583	.3408	.2475	.6726	.61176	.79104	.77335	.2931	.2641	.6346	.62547	.78025	.80163	.2475	.2816	.5988	.63899	.76921	.83071	.2038	.3000	.5650	17
44	.59809	.80143	.74628	.3400	.2478	.6720	.61199	.79087	.77382	.2923	.2644	.6340	.62570	.78007	.80211	.2467	.2819	.5982	.63921	.76903	.83120	.2031	.3003	.5644	16
45	.59832	.80125	.74673	1.3392	.2480	1.6713	.61222	.79069	.77428	1.2915	.2647	1.6334	.62592	.77988	.80258	1.2460	.2822	1.5976	.63944	.76884	.83169	1.2024	.3006	1.5639	15
46	.59856	.80108	.74019	.3383	.2483	.6707	.61245	.79051	.77475	.2907	.2650	.6328	.62615	.77970	.80306	.2452	.2825	.5971	.63966	.76865	.83218	.2016	.3010	.5633	14
47	.59879	.80090	.74064	.3375	.2486	.6700	.61268	.79033	.77521	.2900	.2653	.6322	.62638	.77952	.80354	.2445	.2828	.5965	.63989	.76847	.83267	.2009	.3013	.5628	13
48	.59902	.80073	.74809	.3367	.2488	.6694	.61290	.79015	.77568	.2892	.2656	.6316	.62660	.77934	.80402	.2437	.2831	.5959	.64011	.76828	.83317	.2002	.3016	.5622	12
49	.59926	.80056	.74855	.3359	.2491	.6687	.61314	.78998	.77614	.2884	.2659	.6309	.62683	.77915	.80450	.2430	.2834	.5953	.64033	.76810	.83366	.1995	.3019	.5617	11
50	.59949	.80038	.74900	1.3351	.2494	1.6681	.61337	.78980	.77661	1.2876	.2661	1.6303	.62706	.77897	.80498	1.2423	.2837	1.5947	.64056	.76791	.83415	1.1988	.3022	1.5611	10
51	.59972	.80021	.74946	.3343	.2497	.6674	.61360	.78962	.77708	.2869	.2664	.6297	.62728	.77879	.80546	.2415	.2840	.5942	.64078	.76772	.83465	.1981	.3025	.5606	9
52	.59995	.80003	.74991	.3335	.2499	.6668	.61383	.78944	.77754	.2861	.2667	.6291	.62751	.77861	.80594	.2408	.2843	.5936	.64100	.76754	.83514	.1974	.3029	.5600	8
53	.60019	.79986	.75037	.3327	.2502	.6661	.61405	.78926	.77801	.2853	.2670	.6285	.62774	.77842	.80642	.2400	.2846	.5930	.64123	.76735	.83563	.1967	.3032	.5595	7
54	.60042	.79968	.75082	.3319	.2505	.6655	.61428	.78908	.77848	.2845	.2673	.6279	.62796	.77824	.80690	.2393	.2849	.5924	.64145	.76716	.83613	.1960	.3035	.5590	6
55	.60065	.79951	.75128	1.3311	.2508	1.6648	.61451	.78890	.77895	1.2838	.2676	1.6273	.62819	.77806	.80738	1.2386	.2852	1.5919	.64160	.76698	.83662	1.1953	.3038	1.5584	5
56	.60088	.79933	.75173	.3303	.2510	.6642	.61474	.78873	.77941	.2830	.2679	.6267	.62841	.77788	.80786	.2378	.2855	.5913	.64189	.76679	.83712	.1946	.3041	.5579	4
57	.60112	.79916	.75219	.3294	.2513	.6636	.61497	.78855	.77988	.2822	.2681	.6261	.62864	.77769	.80834	.2371	.2858	.5907	.64212	.76660	.83761	.1939	.3044	.5573	3
58	.60135	.79898	.75264	.3286	.2516	.6629	.61520	.78837	.78035	.2815	.2684	.6255	.62887	.77751	.80882	.2364	.2861	.5901	.64234	.76642	.83811	.1932	.3048	.5568	2
59	.60158	.79881	.75310	.3278	.2519	.6623	.61543	.78819	.78082	.2807	.2687	.6249	.62909	.77733	.80930	.2356	.2864	.5896	.64256	.76623	.83860	.1924	.3051	.5563	1
60	.60181	.79863	.75355	1.3270	.2521	1.6616	.61566	.78801	.78128	1.2799	.2690	1.6243	62932	.77715	.80978	1.2349	.2867	1.5890	.64279	.76604	.83910	1.1917	.3054	1.5557	0
′	cos	sin	cot	tan	cosec	sec	cos	sin	cot	tan	cosec	sec	cos	sin	cot	tan	cosec	sec	cos	sin	cot	tan	cosec	sec	′
	53°						52°						51°						50°						

	40°						41°						42°						43°						
′	sin	cos	tan	cot	sec	cosec	sin	cos	tan	cot	sec	cosec	sin	cos	tan	cot	sec	cosec	sin	cos	tan	cot	sec	cosec	′
0	.64279	.76604	.83910	1.1917	1.3054	1.5557	.65606	.75471	.86929	1.1504	1.3250	1.5242	.66913	.74314	.90040	1.1106	1.3456	1.4945	.68200	.73135	.93251	1.0724	1.3673	1.4663	60
1	.64301	.76586	.83959	.1910	.3057	.5552	.65628	.75452	.86980	.1497	.3253	.5237	.66935	.74295	.90093	.1100	.3460	.4940	.68221	.73115	.93306	.0717	.3677	.4658	59
2	.64323	.76567	.84009	.1903	.3060	.5546	.65650	.75433	.87031	.1490	.3257	.5232	.66956	.74276	.90146	.1093	.3463	.4935	.68242	.73096	.93360	.0711	.3681	.4654	58
3	.64345	.76548	.84059	.1896	.3064	.5541	.65672	.75414	.87082	.1483	.3260	.5227	.66978	.74256	.90198	.1086	.3467	.4930	.68264	.73076	.93415	.0705	.3684	.4649	57
4	.64368	.76530	.84108	.1889	.3067	.5536	.65694	.75394	.87133	.1477	.3263	.5222	.66999	.74236	.90251	.1080	.3470	.4925	.68285	.73056	.93469	.0699	.3688	.4644	56
5	.64390	.76511	.84158	1.1882	.3070	1.5530	.65716	.75375	.87184	1.1470	.3267	1.5217	.67021	.74217	.90304	1.1074	.3474	1.4921	.68306	.73036	.93524	1.0692	.3692	1.4640	55
6	.64412	.76492	.84208	.1875	.3073	.5525	.65037	.75356	.87235	.1463	.3270	.5212	.67043	.74197	.90357	.1067	.3477	.4916	.68327	.73016	.93578	.0686	.3695	.4635	54
7	.64435	.76473	.84257	.1868	.3076	.5520	.65759	.75337	.87287	.1456	.3274	.5207	.67064	.74178	.90410	.1061	.3481	.4911	.68349	.72996	.93633	.0680	.3699	.4631	53
8	.64457	.76455	.84307	.1861	.3080	.5514	.65781	.75318	.87338	.1450	.3277	.5202	.67086	.74158	.90463	.1054	.3485	.4906	.68370	.72976	.93687	.0674	.3703	.4626	52
9	.64479	.76436	.84357	.1854	.3083	.5509	.65803	.75299	.87389	.1443	.3280	.5197	.67107	.74139	.90515	.1048	.3488	.4901	.68391	.72956	.93742	.0667	.3707	.4622	51
10	.64501	.76417	.84407	1.1847	.3086	1.5503	.65285	.75280	.87441	1.1436	.3284	1.5192	.67129	.74119	.90568	1.1041	.3492	1.4897	.68412	.72937	.93797	1.0661	.3710	1.4617	50
11	.64523	.76398	.84457	.1840	.3089	.5498	.65847	.75261	.87492	.1430	.3287	.5187	.67150	.74100	.90621	.1035	.3495	.4892	.68433	.72917	.93851	.0655	.3714	.4613	49
12	.64546	.76380	.84506	.1833	.3092	.5493	.65869	.75241	.87543	.1423	.3290	.5182	.67172	.74080	.90674	.1028	.3499	.4887	.68455	.72897	.93906	.0649	.3718	.4608	48
13	.64568	.76361	.84556	.1826	.3096	.5487	.65891	.75222	.87595	.1416	.3294	.5177	.67194	.74061	.90727	.1022	.3502	.4882	.68476	.72877	.93961	.0643	.3722	.4604	47
14	.64590	.76342	.84606	.1819	.3099	.5482	.65913	.75203	.87646	.1409	.3297	.5171	.67215	.74041	.90780	.1015	.3506	.4877	.68497	.72857	.94016	.0636	.3725	.4599	46
15	.64612	.76323	.84656	1.1812	.3102	1.5477	.65934	.75184	.87698	1.1403	.3301	1.5166	.67237	.74022	.90834	1.1009	.3509	1.4873	.68518	.72837	.94071	1.0630	.3729	1.4595	45
16	.64635	.76304	.84706	.1805	.3105	.5471	.65956	.75165	.87749	.1396	.3304	.5161	.67258	.74002	.90887	.1003	.3513	.4868	.68539	.72817	.94125	.0624	.3733	.4590	44
17	.64657	.76286	.84056	.1798	.3109	.5466	.65978	.75146	.87801	.1389	.3307	.5156	.67280	.73983	.90940	.0996	.3517	.4863	.68561	.72797	.94180	.0618	.3737	.4586	43
18	.64679	.76267	.84806	.1791	.3112	.5461	.66000	.75126	.87852	.1383	.3311	.5151	.67301	.73963	.90993	.0990	.3520	.4858	.68582	.72777	.94235	.0612	.3740	.4581	42
19	.64701	.76248	.84856	.1785	.3115	.5456	.66022	.75107	.87904	.1376	.3314	.5146	.67323	.73943	.91046	.0983	.3524	.4854	.68603	.72757	.94290	.0605	.3744	.4577	41
20	.64723	.76229	.84906	1.1778	.3118	1.5450	.66044	.75088	.87955	1.1369	.3318	1.5141	.67344	.73924	.91099	1.0977	.3527	1.4849	.68624	.72737	.94345	1.0599	.3748	1.4572	40
21	.64745	.76210	.84956	.1771	.3121	.5445	.66066	.75069	.88007	.1363	.3321	.5136	.67366	.73904	.91153	.0971	.3531	.4844	.68645	.72717	.94400	.0593	.3752	.4568	39
22	.64768	.76191	.85006	.1764	.3125	.5440	.66087	.75049	.88058	.1356	.3324	.5131	.67387	.73885	.91206	.0964	.3534	.4839	.68666	.72697	.94455	.0587	.3756	.4563	38
23	.64790	.76173	.85056	.1757	.3128	.5434	.66109	.75030	.88110	.1349	.3328	.5126	.67409	.73865	.91259	.0958	.3538	.4835	.68688	.72677	.94510	.0581	.3759	.4559	37
24	.64812	.76154	.85107	.1750	.3131	.5429	.66131	.75011	.88162	.1343	.3331	.5121	.67430	.73845	.91312	.0951	.3542	.4830	.68709	.72657	.94565	.0575	.3763	.4554	36
25	.64834	.76135	.85157	1.1743	.3134	1.5424	.66153	.74992	.88213	1.1336	.3335	1.5116	.67452	.73826	.91366	1.0945	.3545	1.4825	.68730	.72637	.94620	1.0568	.3767	1.4550	35
26	.64856	.76116	.85207	.1736	.3138	.5419	.66175	.74973	.88265	.1329	.3338	.5111	.67473	.73806	.91419	.0939	.3549	.4821	.68751	.72617	.94675	.0562	.3771	.4545	34
27	.64878	.76097	.85257	.1729	.3141	.5413	.66197	.74953	.88317	.1323	.3342	.5106	.67495	.73787	.91473	.0932	.3552	.4816	.68772	.72597	.94731	.0556	.3774	.4541	33
28	.64900	.76078	.85307	.1722	.3144	.5408	.66218	.74934	.88369	.1316	.3345	.5101	.67516	.73767	.91526	.0926	.3556	.4811	.68793	.72577	.94786	.0550	.3778	.4536	32
29	.64923	.76059	.85358	.1715	.3148	.5403	.66240	.74915	.88421	.1309	.3348	.5096	.67537	.73747	.91580	.0919	.3560	.4806	.68814	.72557	.94841	.0544	.3782	.4532	31
30	.64945	.76041	.85408	1.1708	.3151	1.5398	.66262	.74895	.88472	1.1303	.3352	1.5092	.67559	.73728	.91633	1.0913	.3563	1.4802	.68835	.72537	.94896	1.0538	.3786	1.4527	30
31	.64967	.76022	.85458	.1702	.3154	.5392	.66284	.74876	.88524	.1296	.3355	.5087	.67580	.73708	.91687	.0907	.3567	.4797	.68856	.72517	.94952	.0532	.3790	.4523	29
32	.64989	.76003	.85509	.1695	.3157	.5387	.66305	.74857	.88576	.1290	.3359	.5082	.67602	.73688	.91740	.0900	.3571	.4792	.68878	.72497	.95007	.0525	.3794	.4518	28
33	.65011	.75984	.85559	.1688	.3161	.5382	.66327	.74838	.88628	.1283	.3362	.5077	.67623	.73669	.91794	.0894	.3574	.4788	.68899	.72477	.95062	.0519	.3797	.4514	27
34	.65033	.75965	.85609	.1681	.3164	.5377	.66349	.74818	.88680	.1276	.3366	.5072	.67645	.73649	.91847	.0888	.3578	.4783	.68920	.72457	.95118	.0513	.3801	.4510	26
35	.65055	.75946	.85660	1.1674	.3167	1.5371	.66371	.74799	.88732	1.1270	.3369	1.5067	.67666	.73629	.91901	1.0881	.3581	1.4778	.68941	.72437	.95173	1.0507	.3805	1.4505	25
36	.65077	.75927	.85710	.1667	.3170	.5366	.66393	.74780	.88784	.1263	.3372	.5062	.67688	.73610	.91955	.0875	.3585	.4774	.68962	.72417	.95229	.0501	.3809	.4501	24
37	.65100	.75908	.85761	.1660	.3174	.5361	.66414	.74760	.88836	.1257	.3376	.5057	.67709	.73590	.92008	.0868	.3589	.4769	.68983	.72397	.95284	.0495	.3813	.4496	23
38	.65121	.75889	.85811	.1653	.3177	.5356	.66436	.74741	.88888	.1250	.3379	.5052	.67730	.73570	.92062	.0862	.3592	.4764	.69004	.72377	.95340	.0489	.3816	.4492	22
39	.65144	.75870	.85862	.1647	.3180	.5351	.66458	.74722	.88940	.1243	.3383	.5047	.67752	.73551	.92116	.0856	.3596	.4760	.69025	.72357	.95395	.0483	.3820	.4487	21
40	.65166	.75851	.85912	1.1640	.3184	1.5345	.66479	.74702	.88992	1.1237	.3386	1.5042	.67773	.73531	.92170	1.0849	.3600	1.4755	.69046	.72337	.95451	1.0476	.3824	1.4483	20
41	.65188	.75832	.85963	.1633	.3187	.5340	.66501	.74683	.89044	.1230	.3390	.5037	.67794	.73511	.92223	.0843	.3603	.4750	.69067	.72317	.95506	.0470	.3828	.4479	19
42	.65210	.75813	.86013	.1626	.3190	.5335	.66523	.74664	.89097	.1224	.3393	.5032	.67816	.73491	.92277	.0837	.3607	.4746	.69088	.72297	.95562	.0464	.3832	.4474	18
43	.65232	.75794	.86064	.1619	.3193	.5330	.66545	.74644	.89149	.1217	.3397	.5027	.67837	.73472	.92331	.0830	.3611	.4741	.69109	.72277	.95618	.0458	.3836	.4470	17
44	.65254	.75775	.86115	.1612	.3197	.5325	.66566	.74625	.89201	.1211	.3400	.5022	.67859	.73452	.92385	.0824	.3614	.4736	.69130	.72256	.95673	.0452	.3839	.4465	16
45	.65276	.75756	.86165	1.1605	.3200	1.5319	.66588	.74606	.89253	1.1204	1.3404	1.5018	.67880	.73432	.92439	1.0818	.3618	1.4732	.69151	.72236	.95729	1.0446	.3843	1.4461	15
46	.65298	.75737	.86216	.1599	.3203	.5314	.66610	.74586	.89306	.1197	.3407	.5013	.67901	.73412	.92493	.0812	.3622	.4727	.69172	.72216	.95785	.0440	.3847	.4457	14
47	.65320	.75718	.86267	.1592	.3207	.5309	.66631	.74567	.89358	.1191	.3411	.5008	.67923	.73393	.92547	.0805	.3625	.4723	.69193	.72196	.95841	.0434	.3851	.4452	13
48	.65342	.75700	.86318	.1585	.3210	.5304	.66653	.74548	.89410	.1184	.3414	.5003	.67944	.73373	.92601	.0799	.3629	.4718	.69214	.72176	.95896	.0428	.3855	.4448	12
49	.65364	.75680	.86368	.1578	.3213	.5299	.66675	.74528	.89463	.1178	.3418	.4998	.67965	.73353	.92655	.0793	.3633	.4713	.69235	.72156	.95952	.0422	.3859	.4443	11
50	.65386	.75661	.86419	1.1571	.3217	1.5294	.66697	.74509	.89515	1.1171	.3421	1.4993	.67987	.73333	.92709	1.0786	.3636	1.4709	.69256	.72136	.96008	1.0416	.3863	1.4439	10
51	.65408	.75642	.86470	.1565	.3220	.5289	.66718	.74489	.89567	.1165	.3425	.4988	.68008	.73314	.92763	.0780	.3640	.4704	.69277	.72115	.96064	.0410	.3867	.4435	9
52	.65430	.75623	.86521	.1558	.3223	.5283	.66740	.74470	.89620	.1158	.3428	.4983	.68029	.73294	.92817	.0774	.3644	.4699	.69298	.72095	.96120	.0404	.3870	.4430	8
53	.65452	.75604	.86572	.1551	.3227	.5278	.66762	.74450	.89672	.1152	.3432	.4979	.68051	.73274	.92871	.0767	.3647	.4695	.69319	.72075	.96176	.0397	.3874	.4426	7
54	.65474	.75585	.86623	.1544	.3230	.5273	.66783	.74431	.89725	.1145	.3435	.4974	.68072	.73254	.92926	.0761	.3651	.4690	.69340	.72055	.96232	.0391	.3878	.4422	6
55	.65496	.75566	.86674	1.1537	.3233	1.5268	.66805	.74412	.89777	1.1139	.3439	1.4969	.68093	.73234	.92980	1.0755	.3655	1.4686	.69361	.72035	.96288	1.0385	.3882	1.4417	5
56	.65518	.75547	.86725	.1531	.3237	.5263	.66826	.74392	.89830	.1132	.3442	.4964	.68115	.73215	.93034	.0749	.3658	.4681	.69382	.72015	.96344	.0379	.3886	.4413	4
57	.65540	.75528	.86775	.1524	.3240	.5258	.66848	.74373	.89882	.1126	.3446	.4959	.68136	.73195	.93088	.0742	.3662	.4676	.69403	.71994	.96400	.0373	.3890	.4408	3
58	.65562	.75509	.86826	.1517	.3243	.5253	.66870	.74353	.89935	.1119	.3449	.4954	.68157	.73175	.93143	.0736	.3666	.4672	.69424	.71974	.96456	.0367	.3894	.4404	2
59	.65584	.75490	.86878	.1510	.3247	.5248	.66891	.74334	.89988	.1113	.3453	.4949	.68178	.73155	.93197	.0730	.3669	.4667	.69445	.71954	.96513	.0361	.3898	.4400	1
60	.65606	.75401	.86929	1.1504	.3250	1.5242	.66913	.74314	.90040	1.1106	.3456	1.4945	.68200	.73135	.93251	1.0724	.3673	1.4663	.69466	.71934	.96569	1.0355	.3902	1.4395	0
′	cos	sin	cot	tan	cosec	sec	cos	sin	cot	tan	cosec	sec	cos	sin	cot	tan	cosec	sec	cos	sin	cot	tan	cosec	sec	′
	49°						48°						47°						46°						

44°

′	sin	cos	tan	cot	sec	cosec	′
0	.69466	.71934	.96569	1.0355	1.3902	1.4395	60
1	.69487	.71914	.96625	.0349	.3905	.4391	59
2	.69508	.71893	.96681	.0343	.3909	.4387	58
3	.69528	.71873	.96738	.0337	.3913	.4382	57
4	.69549	.71853	.96794	.0331	.3917	.4378	56
5	.69570	.71833	.96850	1.0325	.3921	1.4374	55
6	.69591	.71813	.96907	.0319	.3925	.4370	54
7	.69612	.71792	.96963	.0313	.3929	.4365	53
8	.69633	.71772	.97020	.0307	.3933	.4361	52
9	.69654	.71752	.97076	.0301	.3937	.4357	51
10	.69675	.71732	.97133	1.0295	.3941	1.4352	50
11	.69696	.71711	.97189	.0289	.3945	.4348	49
12	.69716	.71691	.97246	.0283	.3949	.4344	48
13	.69737	.71671	.97302	.0277	.3953	.4339	47
14	.69758	.71650	.97359	.0271	.3957	.4335	46
15	.69779	.71630	.97416	1.0265	.3960	1.4331	45
16	.69800	.71610	.97472	.0259	.3964	.4327	44
17	.69821	.71589	.97529	.0253	.3968	.4322	43
18	.69841	.71569	.97586	.0247	.3972	.4318	42
19	.69862	.71549	.97643	.0241	.3976	.4314	41
20	.69883	.71529	.97700	1.0235	.3980	1.4310	40
21	.69904	.71508	.97756	.0229	.3984	.4305	39
22	.69925	.71488	.97813	.0223	.3988	.4301	38
23	.69945	.71468	.97870	.0218	.3992	.4297	37
24	.69966	.71447	.97927	.0212	.3996	.4292	36
25	.69987	.71427	.97984	1.0206	.4000	1.4288	35
26	.70008	.71406	.98041	.0200	.4004	.4284	34
27	.70029	.71386	.98098	.0194	.4008	.4280	33
28	.70049	.71366	.98155	.0188	.4012	.4276	32
29	.70070	.71345	.98212	.0182	.4016	.4271	31
30	.70091	.71325	.98270	1.0176	.4020	1.4267	30
31	.70112	.71305	.98327	.0170	.4024	.4263	29
32	.70132	.71284	.98384	.0164	.4028	.4259	28
33	.70153	.71264	.98441	.0158	.4032	.4254	27
34	.70174	.71243	.98499	.0152	.4036	.4250	26
35	.70194	.71223	.98556	1.0146	.4040	1.4246	25
36	.70215	.71203	.98613	.0141	.4044	.4242	24
37	.70236	.71182	.98671	.0135	.4048	.4238	23
38	.70257	.71162	.98728	.0129	.4052	.4233	22
39	.70277	.71141	.98786	.0123	.4056	.4229	21
40	.70298	.71121	.98843	1.0117	.4060	1.4225	20
41	.70319	.71100	.98901	.0111	.4065	.4221	19
42	.70339	.71080	.98958	.0105	.4069	.4217	18
43	.70360	.71059	.99016	.0099	.4073	.4212	17
44	.70381	.71039	.99073	.0093	.4077	.4208	16
45	.70401	.71018	.99131	1.0088	.4081	1.4204	15
46	.70422	.70998	.99189	.0082	.4085	.4200	14
47	.70443	.70977	.99246	.0076	.4089	.4196	13
48	.70463	.70957	.99304	.0070	.4093	.4192	12
49	.70484	.70936	.99362	.0064	.4097	.4188	11
50	.70505	.70916	.99420	1.0058	.4101	1.4183	10
51	.70525	.70895	.99478	.0052	.4105	.4179	9
52	.70546	.70875	.99536	.0047	.4109	.4175	8
53	.70566	.70854	.99593	.0041	.4113	.4171	7
54	.70587	.70834	.99651	.0035	.4117	.4167	6
55	.70608	.70813	.99709	1.0029	.4122	1.4163	5
56	.70628	.70793	.99767	.0023	.4126	.4159	4
57	.70649	.70772	.99826	.0017	.4130	.4154	3
58	.70669	.70752	.99884	.0012	.4134	.4150	2
59	.70690	.70731	.99942	.0006	.4138	.4146	1
60	.70711	.70711	1.00000	1.0000	.4142	1.4142	0

′	cos	sin	cot	tan	cosec	sec	′

45°

GLOSSARY

Abrasive. A substance such as finely divided aluminum oxide or silicon carbide used for grinding (abrading), smoothing, or polishing.

Acicular. Needlelike; resembling needles or straws dropped at random.

Acute angle. An angle less than 90 degrees.

Alignment. The proper positioning or state of adjustment of parts in relation to each other, especially in line as in axial alignment.

Allotropic. Materials that can exist in several different crystalline forms are said to be allotropic.

Alloy. A combination of two or more substances, specifically metals such as alloy steels or aluminum alloys.

Aluminum oxide. Also alumina (Al_2O_3). Occurs in nature as corundum and is used extensively as an abrasive. Today most aluminum oxide abrasives are manufactured.

Ammonia. A pungent colorless gaseous alkaline compound of nitrogen and hydrogen (NH_3). It is very soluble in water.

Amorphous. Having no definite form or outline. Materials such as glass that have no definite crystalline structure.

Angular. Having one or more angles; measured by an angle; forming an angle.

Angularity. The quality or characteristic of being angular.

Angular measure. The means by which an arc of a circle is divided and measured. This can be in degrees (360 degrees in a full circle), minutes (60 min. in one degree), and seconds (60 sec. in one minute), or in radians. See radian.

Anhydrous. Free from water.

Anneal. A heat treatment in which metals are heated and then cooled very slowly for the purpose of decreasing hardness. Annealing is used to improve machinability and to remove stresses from weldments, forgings, and castings. It is also used to remove stresses resulting from cold work, and to refine and make uniform the microscopic internal structures of metals.

Arbor. A rotating shaft upon which a cutting tool is fastened. Often used as a term for mandrel.

As rolled. When metal bars are hot rolled and allowed to cool in air, they are said to be in the ''as rolled'' or natural condition.

Austenite. A solid solution of iron and carbon or iron carbide in which gamma iron, characterized by a face-centered cubic crystal, is the solvent.

Axial. Having the characteristics of an axis (that is, centerline or center of rotation); situated around and in relation to an axis as in axial alignment.

Axial rake. An angular cutting surface that is rotated about the axial centerline of a cutting tool such as a drill or reamer.

Axis. Centerline or center of rotation of an object or part; the rotational axis of a machine spindle, which extends beyond the spindle and through the workpiece. Machining of the object imparts the machine axis to that area of metal cutting. The line along which a major machine tool component such as a mill table, saddle, or spindle travels.

Backlash. A condition created due to clearance between a thread and nut. The amount of thread turn before a component begins to move.

Beam. The scale on a vernier caliper or height gage that is graduated in true or full sized units.

Bellmouth. A condition in a machined hole where the end is flared out in a bell shape to a dimension larger than the nominal size of the hole.

Bezel. A rim that holds a transparent face of a dial indicator that can be rotated to bring the index mark to zero.

Bimetallic. Made from two different metals.

Blind hole. A hole that does not go completely through an object.

Blotter. A paper disc placed between a grinding wheel and the retaining flange, often marked with wheel type and speed rating.

Bolster plate. A structural part of a press designed to support or reinforce the platen (base surface) on which the workpiece is placed for press work.

Bore. A machined hole, or the process of enlarging a drilled hole to a larger size.

Boring. The process of removing metal from a hole by using a single point tool. The workpiece can rotate with a stationary bar or the bar can rotate on a stationary workpiece to bore a hole.

Brinell hardness. The hardness of a metal or alloy measured by hydraulically pressing a hard ball (usually 10 mm dia.) with a standard load into the specimen. A number is derived by measuring the indentation with a special microscope.

Brittleness. That property of a material that causes it to suddenly break at a given stress without bending or distortion of the edges of the broken surface. Glass, ceramics, and cast iron are somewhat brittle materials.

Broaching. The process of removing unwanted metal by pulling or pushing a tool on which cutting teeth project through or along the surface of a workpiece. The cutting teeth are each progressively longer by a few thousandths of an inch to give each tooth a chip load. One of the most frequent uses of broaching is for producing internal shapes such as keyseats and splines.

Buffing wheel. A disc made up of layers of cloth sewed together. Fine abrasive is applied to the periphery of the cloth wheel to provide a polishing surface as the wheel is rotated at a high speed.

Burnish. To make shiny by rubbing. No surface material is removed by this finishing process. External and internal surfaces are often smoothed with high pressure rolling. Hardened plugs are sometimes forced through bores to finish and size them by burnishing.

Burr. (1) A small rotary file. (2) A thin edge of metal, usually very sharp, left from a machining operation. See Deburr.

Bushing. A hollow cylinder that is used as a spacer, a reducer for a bore size, or for a bearing. Bushings can be made of metals or nonmetals such as plastics or formica.

Button die. A thread cutting die that is round and usually slightly adjustable. It is held in a diestock or holder by means of a cone point setscrew that fits into a detent on the periphery of the die.

Calibration. The adjustment of a measuring instrument such as a micrometer or dial indicator so it will measure accurately.

Cam. A rotating or sliding part with a projection or projecting geometry that imparts motion to another part as it slides or rotates past.

Carburizing compound. A carbonaceous material that introduces carbon into a heated solid ferrous alloy by the process of diffusion.

Cavity. A machined feature, such as a hole, groove, or slot, enclosed on all sides in two dimensions. The space in a casting mold where molten metal will flow to form a cast part.

Celsius. A temperature scale used in the SI metric systems of measurement where the freezing point of water is 0° and the boiling point is 100°. Also called centigrade.

Cementite. Iron carbide, a compound of iron and carbon (Fe_3C) found in steel and cast iron.

Centerline. A reference line on a drawing or part layout from which all dimensions are located.

Chamfer. A bevel cut on a sharp edge of a part to improve resistance to damage and as a safety measure to prevent cuts.

Chasing a thread. In machine terminology, chasing a thread is making successive cuts in the same groove with a single point tool. Also when cleaning or repairing a damaged thread.

Chatter. Vibration of workpiece, machine, tool, or a combination of all three due to looseness or weakness in one or more of these areas. Chatter may be found in either grinding or machine operations and is usually noted as a vibratory sound and seen on the workpiece as wave marks.

Checked. A term used mostly in grinding operations, indicating a surface having many small cracks (checks). The term heat checked or crazed is used in reference to friction clutch surfaces.

Chips. The particles that are removed when materials are cut; also called filings.

Chip trap. A deformed end of a lathe cutting tool that prevents the chip from flowing across and away from the tool.

Circularity. The extent to which an object has the form of a circle. The measured accuracy or roundness of a circular or cylindrical object such as a shaft. A lack of circularity is referred to in shops as out of round, egg-shaped, or having a flat spot.

Circumference. The periphery or outer edge of a circle. Its length is calculated by multiplying π (3.1416) times the diameter of the circle.

Clutch. A component usually found in a mechanical drive that permits a driven component and driving component to be mechanically disconnected and reconnected at will.

Coarseness. A definition of grit size in grinding or spacing of teeth on files and other cutting tools.

Coincident. Two graduations on separate graduated scales being in line with each other, such as the coincident line of a vernier and true scale graduations.

Cold finish. Refers to the surface finish obtained on metal by any of several means of cold working, such as rolling or drawing.

Cold working. Any process such as rolling, forging, or forming a cold metal in which the metal is stressed beyond its yield point. Grains are deformed and elongated in the process, causing the metal to have a higher hardness and lower ductility.

Complementary angles. Two angles whose sum is 90 degrees. Often referred to in machine shop work since most angular machining is done within one quadrant or 90 degrees.

Concave. An internal arc or curve; a dent.

Concentricity. The extent to which an object has a common center or axis. Specifically, in machine work, the extent to which two or more surfaces on a shaft rotate in relation to each other; the amount of runout on a rotating member.

Contour. Machining an uneven but continuous path on a workpiece in two or three dimensions.

Convex. An external arc or curve; a bulge.

Coolant. A cutting fluid used to cool the tool and workpiece, especially in grinding operations; usually water based.

Cosine error. A condition where the axis of a measuring instrument is out of line with the axis of the measurement to be taken, resulting in an error equal to the measuring instrument reading multiplied by the cosine of the misalignment angle.

Coordinate. A method of specifying point locations in a two dimensional plane system defined by two perpendicular axes.

Crest of thread. Outer edge (point or flat) of a thread form.

Critical temperatures. The upper and lower transformation points of iron between which is the transformation range in which ferrite changes to austenite as the temperature rises.

Cutting fluid. A term referring to any of several materials used in cutting metals; cutting oils, soluble or emulsified oils (water based), and sulfurized oils.

Cyanogen $(CN)_2$. A colorless, flammable, poisonous gas with characteristic odor. It forms cyanic and hydrocyanic acids when in contact with water. Cyanogen compounds are often used for case hardening.

Deburr. The removal of a sharp edge or corner caused by a machining process.

Decarburization. The loss of surface carbon from ferrous metals when heated to high temperatures in an atmosphere containing oxygen.

Decibel. A unit for expressing the relative intensity of sounds on a scale from zero (least perceptible sound) to about 130 (the average pain level).

Degrees. The circle is divided into 360 degrees, four 90 degree quadrants. Each degree is divided into 60 minutes and each minute into 60 seconds. Degrees are measured with protractors, optical comparators, and sine bars, to name a few methods. Degrees are also divisions of temperature scales.

Dendrite. A formation that resembles a pine tree in the microstructure of solidifying metals. Each dendrite usually forms a single grain or crystal.

Diagonal. A straight line from corner to corner on a square, rectangle, or any parallelogram.

Diameter. Twice the radius; the length of any straight line

going through the center of a figure or body; specifically, a circle in drafting and layout.

Diametral pitch. The ratio of the number of teeth on gears to the number of inches of pitch diameter.

Die. (1) Cutting tool for producing external threads. (2) A device that is mounted in a press for cutting and forming sheet metal.

Die cast metal. Metal alloys, often called pot metals, that are forced into a die in a molten state by hydraulic pressure. Thousands of identical parts can be produced from a single die or mold by this process of die casting.

Dimension. A measurement in one direction; one of three coordinates — length, width, and depth. Also thickness, radius, and diameter are given as dimensions on drawings.

Discrimination. The level of measurement to which an instrument is capable within a given measuring system. A .001 in. micrometer can be read to within one thousandth of an inch. With a vernier, it can discriminate to one ten-thousandth of an inch.

Distortion. The alteration of the shape of an object that would normally affect its usefulness. Bending, twisting, and elongation are common forms of distortion in metals.

Dovetail. An angular shape used on many types of interlocking slide components, especially on machine tools.

Ductility. The property of a metal to be deformed permanently without rupture while under tension. A metal that can be drawn into a wire is ductile.

Ebonized. Certain cold drawn or rolled bars that have black stained surfaces are said to be ebonized. This is not the same as the black scaly surface of hot rolled steel products.

Eccentricity. A rotating member whose axis of rotation is different or offset from the primary axis of the part or mechanism. Thus, when one turned section of a shaft centers on a different axis than the shaft, it is said to be eccentric or to have "runout." For example, the throws or cranks on an engine crankshaft are eccentric to the main bearing axis.

Edge finder. A tool fastened in a machine spindle that locates the position of the workpiece edge in relation to the spindle axis.

E.D.M. Electro-discharge machining. With this process, a graphite or metal electrode is slowly fed into the workpiece that is immersed in oil. A pulsed electrical charge causes sparks to jump to the workpiece, each tearing out a small particle. In this way, the electrode gradually erodes its way through the workpiece that can be a soft or an extremely hard material such as tungsten carbide.

Elasticity. The property of a material to return to its original shape when stretched or compressed.

Emulsifying oils. An oil containing an emulsifying agent such as detergent so it will mix with water. Oil emulsions are used extensively for coolants in machining operations.

Expansion. The enlargement of an object, usually caused by an increase in temperature. Metals expand when heated and contract when cooled in varying amounts, depending on the coefficient of expansion of the particular metal.

Extruding. A form of metal working in which a metal bar, either cold or heated, is forced through a die that forms a special cross-sectional shape such as an angle or channel. Extrusions

of soft metals such as aluminum and copper are very common.

Face. (1) The side of a metal disc or end of a shaft when turning in a lathe. A facing operation is usually at 90 degrees to the spindle axis of the lathe. (2) The periphery or outer cylindrical surface of a straight grinding wheel.

Fahrenheit. A temperature scale that is calibrated with the freezing point of water at 32° and the boiling point at 212°. The Fahrenheit scale is gradually being replaced with the Celsius scale used with the metric system of measurement.

Ferrite. The microstructure of iron or steel that is mostly pure iron and appears light gray or white when etched and viewed with a microscope.

Ferromagnetic. Metals or other substances that have unusually high magnetic permeability, a saturation point with some residual magnetism, and high hysteresis. Iron and nickel are both ferromagnetic.

Ferrous. Iron, from the Latin word ferrum, meaning iron. An alloy containing a significant amount of iron.

Fillet. A concave junction of two surfaces; an inside corner radius of a shoulder on a shaft; an inside corner weld.

Finishing (surface). The control of roughness by turning, grinding, milling, lapping, superfinishing, or a combination of any of these processes. Surface texture is designated in terms of roughness profile in microinches, waviness, and lay (direction of roughness).

Fixture. A device that holds workpieces and aligns them with the tool or machine axis with repeatable accuracy.

Flammable. Any material that will readily burn or explode when brought into contact with a spark or flame.

Flash. Excess material that is extruded between die halves in die castings or forging dies; also the upset material formed when welding bandsaws.

Flute. The groove in a drill, tap, reamer, or milling cutter.

Floating. Free to move about over a given area; for example, a floating edge finder tip, floating die holder, or floating reamer holder.

Forging. A method of metal working in which the metal is hammered into the desired shape, or is forced into a mold by pressure or hammering, usually after being heated to a more plastic state. Hot forging requires less force to form a given point than does cold forging, which is usually done at room temperature.

Formica. A trademark used to designate several plastic laminated products; especially, a laminate used to make gears.

Forming. A method of working sheet metal into useful shapes by pressing or bending.

FPM or SFM. Surface feet per minute on a moving workpiece or tool.

Friction. Rubbing of one part against another; resistance to relative motion between two parts in contact, usually generating heat.

Galling. Cold welding of two metal surfaces in intimate contact under pressure. Also called seizing, it is more severe and more likely to happen between two similar soft metals, especially when they are clean and dry.

Gib. A part of a slide mechanism used to adjust the clearance between two sliding parts.

Glazing. (1) A work hardened surface on metals resulting from using a dull tool or a too rapid cutting speed. (2) A dull grinding wheel whose surface grains have worn flat causing the workpiece to be overheated and "burned" (discolored).

Graduations. Division marks on a rule, measuring instrument, or machine dial.

Grain. In metals, a single crystal consisting of parallel rows of atoms called a space lattice.

Grain boundary. The outer perimeter of a single grain where it contacts adjacent grains.

Grain growth. Called recrystallization. Metal grains begin to reform to larger and more regular size and shape at certain temperatures, depending to some extent on the amount of prior cold working.

Grit. (1) Any small, hard particles such as sand or grinding compound. Dust from grinding operations settles on machine surfaces as grit, which can damage sliding surfaces. (2) Diamond dust, aluminum oxide, or silicon carbide particles used for grinding wheels is called grit.

Ground and polished (G & P). A finishing process for some steel alloy shafts during their manufacture. The rolled, drawn, or turned shafting is placed on a centerless grinder and precision ground, after which a polishing operation produces a fine finish.

Gullet. The bottom of the space between teeth on saws and circular milling cutters.

Hardenability. The property that determines the depth and distribution of hardness in a ferrous alloy induced by heating and quenching.

Hardening. Metals are hardened by cold working or heat treating. Hardening causes metals to have a higher resistance to penetration and abrasion.

Harmonic chatter. A harmonic frequency is a multiple of the fundamental frequency of sound. Any machine part, such as a boring bar, has a fundamental frequency and will vibrate at that frequency and also at several harmonic or multiple frequencies. Thus, chatter or vibration of a tool may be noted at several different spindle speeds.

Hazard. A situation that is dangerous to any person in the vicinity. Also, a danger to property, such as a fire hazard.

Heat treated. Metal whose structure has been altered or modified by the application of heat.

Helical. The geometry of a helix where a point both rotates and moves parallel to the axis of a cylinder. Examples include a thread, spring, or drill flute.

Helix. The path described by a point rotating about a cylinder while at the same time being moved along the cylinder. The distance of movement compared to each revolution is the lead of the helix.

High pressure lube. A petroleum grease or oil containing graphite or molybdnum disulfide that continues to lubricate even after the grease has been wiped off.

Hog. To remove large amounts of material from a workpiece with deep heavy cuts.

Horizontal. Parallel to the horizon or base line; level.

Hot rolled. Metal flattened and shaped by rolls while at a red heat.

Hub. A thickening near the axis of a wheel, gear, pulley, sprocket, and others that provides a bore in its center to receive a shaft. The hub also provides extra strength to transfer power to or from the shaft by means of a key and keyseat.

Increment. A single step of a number of steps. A succession of regular additions. A minute increase.

Inert gas. A gas, such as argon or helium, that will not readily combine with other elements.

Infeed. The depth a tool is moved into the workpiece.

Interface. The point or area of contact between tool and workpiece; also the contact point or area of two mating parts in an assembly.

Interference fit. Force fit of a shaft and bore, bearings, and housings or shafts. Negative clearance in which the fitted part is very slightly larger than the bore.

Internal stress. Also called residual stress. Stress in metals that is built in by heat treatment or by cold working.

Involute. Geometry found in modern gears that permits mating gear teeth to engage each other with rolling rather than sliding friction.

Iron carbide. Also called cementite (Fe_3C), a compound of iron and carbon, which is quite hard.

Jig. A device that guides a cutting tool and aligns it to the workpiece.

Journal. The part of a rotating shaft or axle that turns in a bearing.

Kerf. The width of a cut produced by a saw.

Key. A removable metal part that, when assembled into keyseats, provides a positive drive for transmitting torque between shaft and hub.

Keyseat. An axially located rectangular groove in a shaft or hub.

Keystock. Square or rectangular cold rolled steel bars used for making and fitting keys in keyseats.

Keyway. Same as keyseat (British terminology).

Knurl. Diamond or straight impressions on a metal surface produced by rolling with pressure. The rolls used are called knurls.

Laminated. Composed of multiple layers of the same or different materials.

Lattice. The space lattice or rows of atoms in a metal crystal.

Lead. The distance a thread or nut advances along a threaded rod in one revolution.

Loading. A grinding wheel whose voids are being filled with metals, causing the cutting action of the wheel to be diminished.

Lobe. The offset or projection on a cam that contacts the part to which motion is to be imparted.

Longitudinal. Lengthwise, as the longitudinal axis of the spindle or machine.

Machinability. The relative ease of machining, which is related to the hardness of the material to be cut.

Magnetic. Having the property of magnetic attraction and permeability.

Malleability. The ability of a metal to deform permanently without rupture when loaded in compression.

Mandrel. A cylindrical bar upon which the workpiece is affixed and subsequently machined between centers. Mandrels, often erroneously called arbors, are used in metal turning and cylindrical grinding operations.

Mar. To scratch or otherwise damage a machined surface.

Martensite. The hardest constituent of steel formed by quenching carbon steel from the austenitized state to room temperature. The microstructure can be seen as acicular or needlelike.

Mechanical properties (of metals). Some mechanical properties of metals are tensile strength, ductility, malleability, elasticity, and plasticity. Mechanical properties can be measured by mechanical testing.

Metal cementation. Introducing a metal or material into the surface of another by heat treatment. Carburizing is one example of metal cementation.

Metallizing. Applying a coating of metal on a surface by spraying molten metal on it. Also called spray weld and metal spray.

Metal spinning. A process in which a thin disc of metal is rapidly turned in a lathe and forced over a wooden form or mandrel to form various conical or cylindrical shapes.

Metrology. The science of weights and measures or measurement.

Microstructure. Structure that is only visible at high magnification.

Mode. A particular way in which something is done or a machine is operated, such as manual or automatic mode on machines.

Mushroom head. (1) An oversize head on a fastener or tool that allows it to be easily pushed with the hand. (2) A deformed striking end of a chisel or punch that should be removed by grinding.

Neutral. In machine work, neither positive nor negative rake is a neutral or zero rake; a neutral fit is neither a clearance nor interference fit.

Nitriding. A surface hardening treatment for ferrous alloys that is obtained by heating an alloy in the presence of disassociated ammonia gas, which releases nitrogen to the steel. The formation of iron nitride causes the hardened surface.

Nitrogenous gas. Ammonia (NH_3) used in nitriding.

Nomenclature. Pertaining to the names of individual parts of machines or tools; a list of machine parts indicating their names.

Nominal. Usually refers to a standard size or quantity as named in standard references.

Nonferrous. Metals other than iron or iron alloys; for example, aluminum, copper, and nickel are nonferrous metals.

Normalizing. A heat treatment consisting of heating to a temperature above the critical range of steel followed by cooling in air. Normalizing produces in steel what is called a normal structure consisting of free ferrite and cementite or free pearlite and cementite, depending on the carbon content.

Nose radius. Refers to the rounding of the point of a lathe cutting tool. A large radius produces a better finish and is stronger than a small one.

Obtuse angle. An angle greater than 90 degrees.

Oxide scale. At a red heat, oxygen readily combines with iron to form a black oxide scale (Fe_3O_4), also called mill scale. At lower temperatures 400 to 650°F (204 to 343°C) various oxide scale colors (straw, yellow, gold, violet, blue, and gray) are produced, each color within a narrow temperature range. These colors are used by some heat treaters to determine temperatures for tempering.

Oxidize. Combine with oxygen; to burn or corrode by oxidation.

Oxy-acetylene. Mixture of oxygen and acetylene gases to produce an extremely hot flame used for heating and welding.

Orthographic drawing. Projections of a single view of an object in which the view is projected along lines perpendicular to both the view and the drawing surface.

Parallax error. An error in measurement caused by reading a measuring device, such as a rule, at an improper angle.

Parallel. The condition in which lines or planes are equidistant from each other.

Parting. Also called cutting off; a lathe operation in which a thin blade tool is fed into a turning workpiece to make a groove that is continued to the center to sever the material.

Pearlite. Alternating layers of cementite and ferrite in carbon steel. The microstructure of pearlite sometimes appears under a microscope like mother-of-pearl, hence the name. It is found in steels that have been slowly cooled.

Pecking. A process used in drilling deep holes to remove chips before they can seize and jam the drill. The drill is fed into the hole a short distance to accumulate some chips in the flutes and then drawn out of the hole, allowing the chips to fly off. This process is repeated until the correct depth of the hole is reached.

Pedestal. A base or floor stand under a machine tool.

Penetrant. A thin liquid that is able to enter small cracks and crevices. Penetrant oils are used to loosen rusted threads; dye penetrants are used to find hidden cracks.

Periphery. The perimeter or external boundary of a surface or body.

Perpendicular. At 90 degrees to the horizontal or base line.

Pin. Straight, tapered, or cotter pins are used as fasteners of machine parts or for light drives.

Pinning. A condition where chips of workpiece material jam in the teeth of a file.

Pinion. The smaller gear of a gear set, especially in bevel gears.

Pitch. In saw teeth, the number per inch; in threads, one divided by the number per inch; the diameter or radius to the centerline of a number of features or feature located on the circumference of a circle, such as pitch circle or pitch diameter.

Pitch diameter. For threads, the pitch diameter is an imaginary circle, which on a perfect thread occurs at the point where the widths of the thread and groove are equal. On gears, it is the diameter of the pitch circle.

Potassium cyanide. A very poisonous crystalline salt (KCN) used in electroplating and for case hardening steel.

Pot metals. Die casting alloys, which can be zinc, lead, or aluminum-based, among others.

Precipitation hardening. A process of hardening an alloy by heat treatment in which a constituent or phase precipitates

from a solid solution at room temperature or at a slightly elevated temperature.

Precision. A relative but higher level of accuracy within certain tolerance limits. Precision gage blocks are accurate within a few millionths of an inch, yet precision lathe work in some shops may be within a few thousandths of an inch tolerance.

Pressure. Generally expressed in units as pounds per square inch (PSI), and is called unit pressure, while force is the total load.

Prototype. A full scale original model on which something is patterned.

Profile. An outline view, also a side or elevation view.

Proportion. An equality of two ratios.

Pulley. A flat-faced wheel used to transmit power by means of a flat belt. Grooved pulleys are called sheaves.

Quench. A rapid cooling of heated metal for the purpose of imparting certain properties, especially hardness. Quenchants are water, oil, fused salts, air, and molten lead.

Quench cracking. Cracking of heated metal during the quenching operation caused by internal stresses.

Quick-change gearbox. A set of gears and selector levers by which the ratio of spindle rotation to lead screw rotation on a lathe can be quickly set. Many ratios in terms of feeds or threads per inch can be selected without the use of change gears.

Quick-change tool post. A lathe toolholding device in which preset cutting tools are clamped in toolholders that can be placed on the tool post or interchanged with others to an accurately repeatable location.

Quill. The nonrotating but retracting and extending portion of a drill press or milling machine containing the bearings and machine spindle.

Radial. Radiating outward from the center.

Radial rake. On cylindrical or circular cutting tools, such as milling cutters or taps, the rake angle that is off the radius is called the radial rake.

Radian. A unit of angular measurement that is equal to the angle at the center of a circle subtended by an arc equal in length to the radius.

Radius. On a circle, a distance equal to one-half the diameter.

Rake. A tool angle that provides a keenness to the cutting edge.

Rapid traverse. A rapid travel arrangement on a machine tool used to quickly bring the workpiece or cutting tool into close proximity before the cut is started.

Recessing. Grooving.

Reciprocating. A movement back and forth along a given axis.

Recrystallize. Metal crystals become flattened and distorted as the metal hardens when it is being cold worked. At a particular temperature range (about 950°F or 510°C for low carbon steel) for each metal, called its recrystallization temperature, the distorted grains begin to reform into regular, larger, softer grains or crystals.

Reference point. On a layout or drawing, there must be a point of reference from which all dimensions originate for a part to avoid an accumulating error. This could be a machined edge, datum, or centerline.

Relief angle. An angle that provides cutting edge clearance for the cutting action.

Resistance. In an electrical circuit, the opposition to current flow.

Resulfurized. Sulfur in steel is normally a contaminant that causes steel to be ``hot short'' (separates while being hot forged) because of iron sulfide inclusions. As much sulfur as possible is therefore removed at the steel mill. Resulfurized steel is free machining because sulfur and manganese (to control the sulfur) are deliberately added to make manganese sulfide (instead of iron sulfide) inclusions that make a sort of lubricant for the chip and do not cause hot shortness.

Right angle. A 90 degree angle.

Ring test. A means of detecting cracks in grinding wheels. The wheel is lightly struck and, if a clear tone is heard, the wheel is not cracked.

Rockwell. A hardness test that uses a penetrator and known weights. Several scales are used to cover the very soft to the very hard materials. The Rockwell ``C'' scale is mostly used for steel.

Root. The bottom of a thread or gear tooth.

Root truncation. The flat at the bottom of a thread groove.

Rotameter. A device used to indicate the flow of gases in terms of cubic feet or inches in a given period of time.

Roughing. In machining operations, the rapid removal of unwanted material on a workpiece, leaving a small amount for finishing, is called roughing. Since coarse feeds are used, the surface is often rough.

RPM. Revolutions per minute.

Runout. An eccentricity of rotation as that of a cylindrical part held in a lathe chuck being off center as it rotates. The amount of runout of a rotating member is often checked with a dial indicator.

Scaling. The tendency of metals to form oxides on their surfaces when held at a high temperature in air is called scaling since the oxides usually form as a loose scale.

Scriber. A sharp pointed tool used for making scratch marks on metal for the purpose of layout.

Sector. A portion of a circle between two rays defining a specific angle.

Seize. A condition where two metal parts are pressed together without the aid of lubrication, resulting in frictional forces tearing metal from each part and causing a mechanical welding (seizing) of the two.

Semiprecision. Using a method of layout, measurement, or machining in which the tolerances are greater than that capable by the industry for convenience or economy.

Serrated. Small grooves, often in a diamond pattern, used mostly for a gripping surface.

Set. The width of saw tooth. The set of saw teeth is wider than the blade width.

Setup. The arrangement by which the machinist fastens the workpiece to a machine table or workholding device and aligns the cutting tool for metal removal. A poor setup is said to be when the workpiece could move from the pressure of the cutting tool, thus damaging the workpiece or tool, or when chatter results from lack of rigidity.

SFPM. Surface feet per minute.

Shallow hardening. Some steels such as plain carbon steel (depending on their mass), when heated and quenched, harden to a depth of less than one-eighth inch. These are shallow hardening steels.

Shank. The part of a tool that is held in a workholding device or in the hand.

Shearing action. A concentration of forces in which the bending moment is virtually zero and the metal tends to tear or be cut along a transversal axis at the point of applied pressure.

Sheaves. Grooved pulleys such as those used for V-belts or cables.

Sherardized. Zinc inoculated steel, a process by which the surface of steel is given a protective coating of zinc. It is not the same as galvanized or zinc-dipped steel. Zinc powder is packed around the steel while it is heated to a relatively low temperature in the sherardizing process.

Shim. A thin piece of material used to take up space between workpiece and workholding device; a piece used to fill space between machinery and foundations in assemblies.

SI. Systéme Internationale. The metric system of weights and measures.

Silicon carbide. A manufactured abrasive. Silicon carbide wheels are used for grinding nonferrous metals, cast iron, and tungsten carbide, but are not normally used for grinding steel.

Sine bar. A small precision bar with a given length (5 or 10 inches) that remains constant at any angle. It is used with precision gage blocks to set up or determine angles within a few seconds of a degree.

Sintering. Holding a compressed metal powder briquette at a temperature just below its melting point until it fuses into a solid mass of metal.

Slot. Groove or depression as in a keyseat slot.

Snagging. Rough grinding to remove unwanted metal from castings and other products.

Soluble oils. Oils that have been emulsified and will combine with water are called soluble oils.

Solution heat treating. See Precipitation hardening.

Solvent. A material, usually liquid, that dissolves another. Dissolved material is the solute.

Spark testing. A means of determining the relative carbon content of plain carbon steels and identifying some other metals by observing the sparks given off while grinding the metal.

Specifications. Requirements and limits for a particular job.

Speeds. Machine speeds are expressed in revolutions per minute; cutting speeds are expressed in surface feet per minute.

Sphericity. A condition of circularity in all possible axes. The quality of being in the shape of a ball. The extent to which a true sphere can be produced with a given process.

Spherodize anneal. A heat treatment for carbon steels that forms the cementite into spheres, making it softer and usually more machinable than by other forms of annealing.

Spiral. A path of a point in a rotating plane that is continuously receding from the center is called a flat spiral. The term spiral is often used, though incorrectly, to describe a helix.

Spline. A shaft on which teeth have been machined parallel to the shaft axis that will engage similar internal teeth in a mating part to prevent turning.

Sprockets. Toothed wheels used with chain for drive or conveyor systems.

Squareness. The extent of accuracy that can be maintained when making a workpiece with a right angle.

Stepped shaft. A shaft having more than one diameter.

Stick-slip. A tendency of some machine parts that slide on ways to bind slightly when pressure to move them is applied, followed by sudden release that often causes the movement to be greater than desired.

Straightedge. A comparison measuring device used to determine flatness. A precision straightedge usually has an accuracy of about plus or minus .0002 inches in a 24 inch length.

Strength. The ability of a metal to resist external forces. This can be tensile, compressive, or shear strength.

Stress. An external force applied to an object.

Stress relief anneal. A heat treatment, usually under the critical range, for the purpose of relieving stresses caused by welding or cold working.

Stroke. A single movement of many movements, as in a forward stroke with a hacksaw.

Surface plate. A cast iron or granite surface having a precision flatness used for precision layout, measurement, and setup.

Symmetrical. Usually bilateral in machinery where two sides of an object are alike but usually as a mirror image.

Synthetic oils. Artificially produced oils that have been given special properties such as resistance to high temperatures. Synthetic water soluble oils or emulsions are replacing water soluble petroleum oils for cutting fluids and coolants.

Tang. The part of a file on which a handle is affixed.

Tapered thread. A thread made on a taper such as a pipe thread.

Tap extractor. A tool that is sometimes effective in removing broken taps.

Tapping. A method of cutting internal threads by means of rotating a tap into a hole that is sufficiently under the nominal tap size to make a full thread.

Telescoping gage. A transfer type tool that assumes the size of the part to be measured by expanding or telescoping. It is then measured with a micrometer.

Temper. (1) The cold worked condition of some nonferrous metals. (2) Also called draw, a method of toughening hardened carbon steel by reheating it.

Temperature. The level of heat energy in a material as measured by a thermometer or thermostat and recorder with any of several temperature scales: Celsius, Fahrenheit, or Kelvin.

Template. A metal, cardboard, or wooden form used to transfer a shape or layout when it must be repeated many times.

Tensile strength. The maximum unit load that can be applied to a material before ultimate failure occurs.

Tension. A stretching or pulling force.

Terminating threads. Methods of ending the thread, such as undercutting, drilled holes, or tool removal.

Test bar. A precision ground bar that is placed between centers on a lathe to test for center alignment using a dial indicator.

Thermal cracking. Checking or cracking caused by heat.

Thread axis. The centerline of the cylinder on which the thread is made.

Thread chaser. A tool used to restore damaged threads.

Thread crest. The top of the thread.

Thread die. A device used to cut external threads.

Thread engagement. The distance a nut or mating part is turned onto the thread is called the thread engagement.

Thread fit. Systems of thread fits for various thread forms range from interference fits to very loose fits; extensive references on thread fits may be found in machinist's handbooks.

Thread lead. The distance a nut travels in one revolution. The pitch and lead are the same on single lead threads but not on multiple lead threads.

Thread pitch. The distance from a point on one thread to a corresponding point on the next thread.

Thread relief. Usually an internal groove that provides a terminating point for the threading tool.

Tolerance. The allowance of acceptable error within which the mechanism will still fit together and be totally functional.

T-nut. A threaded nut in a T shape that is designed to fit into the T-slot on a machine tool table.

Tool geometry. The proper shape of a cutting tool that makes it work effectively for a particular application.

Tooling. Generally any machine tool accessory separate from the machine itself. Tooling includes cutting tools, holders, workholding accessories, jigs, and fixtures.

Toolmaker. An experienced general machinist often involved with high precision work making other tools, die, jigs, and fixtures used to support regular machining and manufacturing.

Torque. A force that tends to produce rotation or torsion. Torque is measured by multiplying the applied force by the distance at which it is acting to the axis of the rotating part.

Toxic fumes. Gases resulting from heating certain materials are toxic, sometimes causing illness (as metal fume fever from zinc fumes) or permanent damage (as from lead or mercury fumes).

Transfer measurement. A step in measurement in which a transfer measuring tool such as a telescoping gage is set to the unknown dimension and subsequently measured with a direct measuring tool such as a micrometer.

Transformation temperature. Same as critical temperature; the point at which ferrite begins to transform to austenite.

Traverse. To move a machine table or part from one point to another, usually crosswise to the major axis of the machine.

Trueing. In machine work, the use of a dial indicator to set up work accurately. In grinding operations, to dress a wheel with a diamond.

Truncation. To remove the point of a triangle (as of a thread), cone, or pyramid.

T-slot. The slot in a machine tool table, shaped like a T, and used to hold T-nuts and studs for various clamping setups or their hold-down requirements.

Tungsten carbide. An extremely hard compound that is formed with cobalt and tungsten carbide powders by briquetting and sintering into tool shapes.

Turning. Machine operations in which the work is rotated against a single point tool.

Vernier. A means of dividing a unit measurement on a graduated scale by means of a short scale made to slide along the divisions of a graduated instrument.

Vibration. An oscillating movement caused by loose bearings or machine supports, off center weighting on rotating elements, bent shafts, or nonrigid machining setups.

Vise. A workholding device. Some types are bench, drill press, and machine vises.

Wedge angle. Angle of keenness; cutting edge.

Wheel dressing. Trueing the grinding surface of an abrasive wheel by means of a dressing tool such as a diamond or Desmond dresser.

Wiggler. A device used to align a machine spindle to a punch mark.

Wrought. Hot or cold worked; forged.

Zero back rake. Also neutral rake; neither positive nor negative; level.

Zero index. Also zero point. The point at which micrometer dials on a machine are set to zero and the cutting tool is located to a given reference, such as workpiece edge.

INDEX